Microbiology in Nursing Practice

*There are not two kinds of science —
practical and applied. There is only
Science and the applications of Science,
and one is dependent on the other, as
the fruit is to the tree.*

Louis Pasteur (1822–1895)

Microbiology
in Nursing Practice

Marion E. Wilson, M.A., Ph.D. Chief Microbiologist, New York
City Department of Health, Bureau of Laboratories. Formerly, Assistant Director of Laboratories
(Microbiology and Serology), St. Luke's Hospital, New York City; Instructor, Department of
Microbiology and Immunology, State University of New York, Downstate Medical Center, Brooklyn,
N.Y.; Science Instructor, School of Nursing, Massachusetts General Hospital, Boston, Mass.

Helen Eckel Mizer, R.N., A.B., M.S. Instructor, Department
of Nursing Education, Western Connecticut State College, Danbury, Conn. Formerly, Science Instructor
(Microbiology), St. Luke's Hospital School of Nursing, New York City; Senior Medical Research
Assistant, Harvard School of Public Health, Boston, Mass.; First Lieutenant, U.S. Army Nurse Corps,
Brooke Army Hospital, Fort Sam Houston, Texas, and 130th Station Hospital, Heidelberg, West Germany;
Staff Nurse, Margaret Hague Maternity Hospital, Jersey City, N.J.

The Macmillan Company

Collier-Macmillan Limited
LONDON

Fourth Printing, 1971

Acknowledgments: The illustration on the cover is an immunofluorescent photomicrograph depicting rabies virus localized in the neurons and on the dendrites of Purkinje cells in mouse cerebellum. It is reproduced with the kind permission of Dr. Harvey R. Fishman, Assistant Director, Bureau of Laboratories, Otisville Branch, New York City Department of Health, and Staff Member, The Public Health Research Institute of the City of New York.

The illustrations of pathogenic cocci that appear on pages 1 and 285 are reprinted with permission of the U.S. Department of Health, Education, and Welfare, National Communicable Disease Center, Atlanta, Georgia. The illustration on page 643 is a photomicrograph of anthrax bacilli in an impression smear of a human lymph node stained by the immunofluorescent technique. It was obtained through the courtesy of Dr. William B. Cherry, Chief of the Bacterial Chemistry Unit, National Communicable Disease Center, U.S. Department of Health, Education, and Welfare, Atlanta, Georgia, and is reproduced with his permission.

Library of Congress catalog card number: 68-15272

THE MACMILLAN COMPANY
866 THIRD AVENUE, NEW YORK, NEW YORK 10022

Collier-Macmillan Canada, Ltd.,
Toronto, Ontario

Printed in the United States of America

Preface

THE TITLE OF this book has been chosen to reflect its single intention: to present the nurse with basic information, relevant to her practice, concerning the principles of microbiology and the nature and epidemiology of microbial diseases. The authors' purpose is to give the nursing student a fundamental background of knowledge that will be most applicable to her later role in the care of infectious patients, and to provide the practicing professional nurse with a continuously useful reference volume dealing with the nursing management and control of microbial diseases.

In teaching nursing students, and in working with clinical instructors and staff nurses, the authors have long been of the conviction that the nurse's microbiologic education should be strongly oriented, from the beginning, toward the epidemiology of infection. Further, the authors believe that the student's knowledge of the morphology and the physiologic behavior of individual microorganisms need not be detailed, but that she should be directed toward an understanding of the clinical events that occur in infection or infectious disease and of the epidemiologic significance of those events. Accordingly, the major emphasis of this book is placed on microbiologic principles as they apply to the nursing care of patients, and the approach is twofold. On the one hand, host-parasite relationships are stressed, because it is essential that the nurse should have a working knowledge of the infectious disease process and of its causative agent in action, so that she may anticipate the clinical course of an infection from onset to outcome to the patient's best advantage. At the same time, the communicability of infection is of vital concern and has been presented from the nursing point of view. In a very real sense the nurse stands between the infectious patient and the uninfected but susceptible patient, and she must be capable of establishing and maintaining effective barriers between them. She must understand the nature and common sources of infection, as well as the pertinent routes of entry to, and transfer from, the body, so that she can play her important epidemiologic role of limiting each case of active infection and preventing its spread to others.

This textbook is divided into two major parts. Part One is intended primarily for classroom use, as the basis for an introductory course in microbiology for the nursing student. Included are the most pertinent facts concerning (a) the nature and behavior of microorganisms (Section I), (b) the interrelationships that operate between microbes and the human host in health and disease (Section II), and (c) the principles of prevention and control of infectious diseases (Section III).

The morphologic and physiologic characteristics of the five classes of microorganisms (bacteria, rickettsiae, viruses, fungi, and the animal parasites) are discussed in Part One (Chap. 2) in rather broad and general terms. The authors have deliberately avoided the inclusion of extensive laboratory information concerning individual microorganisms, preferring to leave to the judgment of classroom instructors the presentation of such further details as they may deem important. For the convenience of instructors, students, and graduate nurses, a classifying summary of all the important pathogenic microorganisms has been placed midway in the book. This summary falls in Chapter 12, which introduces Part Two. It shows the relationships of the important divisions, orders, families, genera, and species of the medically significant organisms, and provides a brief description of the outstanding features of each group as well as some general methods for their laboratory recognition.

Part Two is designed for quick reference by the practicing professional nurse, as well as the nursing student during her clinical experience. The specific infectious diseases of importance to man are presented here, the order of presentation and the format of each discussion emphasizing the application of epidemiologic principles to their management in nursing practice. The diseases are grouped in an order based primarily on currently available information regarding the most probable routes of entry of the microbial agent, secondarily on the nature of their causative agents (fungi, bacteria, rickettsiae, viruses, and parasites) or their routes of exit and transmission. The authors have used this approach in the hope

that the nurse will learn to associate the infectious agent of a given disease with its portals of entry and communicability, so that her practices will be oriented toward the probable nursing requirements of the patient and the simultaneous protection of others from the possibility of infection transfer. Repeated emphasis is placed on the fact that the site of entry of an infecting organism does not always coincide with the route of exit and transmission. In the case of diseases for which the entry site is not certain, or for which alternate routes may exist, discussions and cross-references are placed appropriately to draw attention to the most frequent paths of transfer or those that constitute the greatest public health hazard.

Within this over-all order, individual disease entities are described with respect to their outstanding clinical features, available methods for laboratory confirmation of the diagnosis, and important epidemiologic aspects. The epidemiology of the infectious diseases is related particularly to those measures of control and prevention that must be practiced by the nurse as well as by other members of the medical group concerned with the patient's care. The sequence of discussion is based on practical considerations, paralleling the series of problems confronting the nurse responsible for the management of a case of infectious disease. She must be familiar with the clinical appearance and course of apparent infection and with the usual means by which it is diagnosed. When laboratory studies are to be done, she must be ready to play an informed role in the collection and timing of appropriate specimens. Above all, she must be prepared to apply the principles of asepsis and to carry out precautionary procedures in an effective, pertinent course of action designed to meet the epidemiologic situation.

With these practical necessities in mind, Part Two is arranged in four major sections (IV through VII) that group the infectious diseases according to the entry route through which they are usually acquired — that is, the respiratory tract, the gastrointestinal tract, the intact skin and mucosa, and the parenteral route, respec-

tively. Each section is introduced with a chapter summarizing the epidemiologic patterns of the diseases grouped under the common entry portal. The significance of that portal as a possible route of exit and transfer of infection is also discussed, together with general recommendations for the nursing control of infectious diseases acquired through that point of entry. These chapters (13, 18, 22, and 26) may be of use to clinical instructors and graduate nurses as a review, as well as to science instructors and nursing students. In the ensuing discussions of individual diseases, the authors have attempted to provide the basic information required by the nurse in meeting and understanding the important problems of each type of infection as it may arise. Specific control measures are emphasized, as indicated by the nature of each disease and the possibilities for its transfer and spread. In addition, the authors have stressed some of the problems of cross infections and those of endogenous origin, which so frequently arise in hospitals among patients already handicapped or debilitated by underlying organic disease, surgery, or one or the other extreme of age.

In Part One, each chapter contains a bibliography and a set of questions for study and review. In Part Two, the last chapter of each section is followed by a bibliography pertinent to the entire section, as well as questions designed to assess the student's ability to apply her knowledge of microbiologic principles to specific nursing situations. For the convenience of both the student and the graduate nurse using this book, each of the chapters in Part Two that deals with a number of infectious diseases ends with a summarizing table outlining the salient features of each disease, its diagnosis, and its control or prevention. In addition, the appendixes include several summaries that may be useful as a rapid source of information on the microbial flora of clinical specimens, skin tests and serologic tests of diagnostic value, the tissue localizations and transmission routes of the animal parasites, aseptic nursing precautions, sterilization and disinfection techniques, and the bacteriologic control of sterilizing equipment.

Acknowledgments

The authors are indebted to a host of colleagues, friends, and relatives for their interest, cooperation, and patience throughout the period of preparation of the manuscript. Indeed, without their help and encouragement it would not have been possible for us to undertake or to complete the work. We gratefully acknowledge their many contributions to the strengths of the finished product, while assuming full responsibility, as authors, for its imperfections.

Those who reviewed parts or all of the manuscript and made many constructive suggestions for its revision include the following: Dr. Margaret Heise-Stevens, formerly of the University of Miami, Coral Gables, Florida; Miss Ruth E. Dittmar, R.N., St. Luke's Hospital School of Nursing, New York City; Mrs. Jane Lowther Redmond, R.N., formerly of the same institution; Dr. Charles F. Begg, Department of Laboratories, St. Luke's Hospital Center, New York City; Dr. Lenore Pugh, Corcoran School of Nursing, St. John's Riverside Hospital, Yonkers, New York; Miss Catherine F. Yetman, R.N., formerly of the Massachusetts General Hospital, Boston, Massachusetts, currently nurse-assistant to Dr. Wilbur James Gould, New York City; Miss Virginia P. Wilson, R.N., formerly of the Union Memorial Hospital, Baltimore, Maryland; Dr. Yvonne C. Faur, New York City Department of Health, Bureau of Laboratories; and Mr. Edwin H. Mizer, of the Robert E. Bell School, Chappaqua, New York.

The authors are also indebted to the many people who graciously provided photographs and other illustrations. Throughout the text, the source of each figure is indicated in the legend. For their particular generosity in this respect thanks are due Dr. Kenneth Phifer, Rockville, Maryland; Dr. Kendall K. Kane, St. Luke's Hospital Center, New York City; Dr. Thomas W. M. Cameron, McGill University, Montreal, Canada; Dr. A. E. Bolyn, The National Drug Company, Swiftwater, Pennsylvania; Mr. Coy D. Smith, University of Kentucky College of Medicine, Lexington, Kentucky; Dr. Elaine L.

Updyke, Dr. Max D. Moody, and Dr. William B. Cherry of the National Communicable Disease Center, U.S. Department of Health, Education, and Welfare, Atlanta, Georgia; Dr. Stanley S. Schneierson, The Mount Sinai Hospital, New York City; Dr. Harvey R. Fishman, New York City Department of Health, Bureau of Laboratories; and Dr. Harry E. Morton, chairman of the Committee on Visual Materials of the American Society for Microbiology and member of the faculty of the School of Medicine, University of Pennsylvania, Philadelphia, Pennsylvania. The authors are especially grateful to Dr. Earle H. Spaulding, School of Medicine, Temple University, Philadelphia, Pennsylvania, for permitting them to include his recommendations for the chemical disinfection of medical and surgical materials. The excellent services of Mr. Mario Rosel, of Scott's Studio, Peekskill, New York, are also acknowledged, with thanks for his special help in preparing many of the black-and-white photographic prints. Most of the line drawings are the work of Mr. Otto Schmidt, of Yorktown Heights, New York, whose cooperation and skill are deeply appreciated. It is a privilege to acknowledge each distinguished contributor.

Those whose help was often nonspecific but nonetheless essential must receive our special thanks for their unfailing support of our efforts. They include Miss Evelyn Peck, R.N., assistant director of St. Luke's Hospital Center for Nursing and Related Services, New York City; Mrs. Helen Galgano and Dr. Charles F. Begg, both of the Department of Laboratories, St. Luke's Hospital Center, New York City; Dr. Morris Schaeffer, Dr. Daniel Widelock, Dr. Paul S. May, and Dr. Yvonne C. Faur, all of the New York City Department of Health, Bureau of Laboratories; and Mrs. Katherine Eierdanz, Miss Catherine F. Yetman, R.N., and Miss Barbara Smith Conrad.

Finally, the authors wish to extend appreciative thanks to The Macmillan Company for the many courtesies shown to them during the preparation and production of this book. In particular, thanks are due Miss Joan C. Zulch, medical editor, for her skillful and patient help throughout every phase of the work.

M. E. W.
H. E. M.

Contents

Part Two   The Microbial Diseases and Their Epidemiology

Appendixes

Part One The Basic Principles of Microbiology

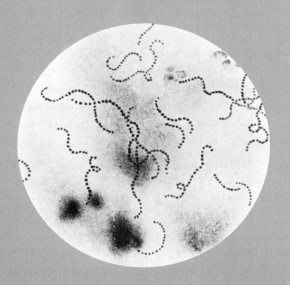

Section I The Character of Microorganisms

1 Introduction: The Background of Microbiology

The discovery that living but invisible organisms are responsible for some of the most devastating of human diseases illumines the recent history of man's progress. This finding was made just a little more than one hundred years ago, but even in so short a time it has led to the development of a new understanding of the mechanisms of health and disease. In this light the field of microbiology has expanded explosively and has become one of the most important biologic sciences upon which modern medical and nursing practice is based.

The name of this science is derived from its concern with the study (*-ology*) of living (*bios*) organisms that are so small (*micro-*) that they can be seen only through the enlarging lenses of a microscope. Because of their size, these minute organisms are often called, collectively, *microorganisms* or *microbes*. Knowledge of their existence dates back some two and one-half centuries, preceding by many years the recognition of their importance in disease. Throughout the long ensuing period, it has become slowly but increasingly apparent not only that the invisible microbial world is enormous, but that it influences our lives in many vitally important ways.

Microorganisms share all segments of the world we live in and are involved together with plants, animals, and human beings in the great biologic cycles of force and counterforce that characterize the ongoing physical life of this planet. Thousands of microbial species are constantly active in our

4

natural environment and many also live in continuous association with us on our body surfaces, as well as on animals and plants. These relationships lead to biologic interplays and interdependencies that are often essential to our welfare, but they may also militate against us if we lose our physiologic balance.

Medical Microbiology

Among the vast numbers of species of microorganisms with which our lives are bound, there are a relative few whose properties and interactions with the human body may lead to the development of disease. These are of concern in the field of *medical* microbiology where tremendous progress has been made in defining the nature and properties of harmful microorganisms as well as the disease processes they induce. Such studies have led to the understanding that *infection* usually represents a balanced relationship between microbes and other living things, whereas *infectious* (or *microbial*) *disease* results from a much more damaging interplay between microorganisms with injurious properties and the infected body's responses to them. It has also become clear that the properties of a particular microbe that are responsible for harmful effects in one individual or species do not necessarily induce injury in another, confirming the recognition of microbial disease as a series of interactions between two living organisms, each exerting opposing forces on the other, with resultant injury to the infected (or "host") organism. This concept provides an important basis for the application of microbiologic principles in medicine and nursing.

The management and control of infectious diseases today require the concerted efforts of people trained in several disciplines: physicians, nurses, pathologists, clinical microbiologists and chemists, and epidemiologists. Successful *treatment* of a microbial disease depends on its prompt and accurate *diagnosis*. This is the physician's area of skill and responsibility, supported by evidence provided by laboratory specialists. The *control* and *prevention* of these diseases are also

essential, however, because they are so frequently communicable from one person to another and can involve large numbers of people in epidemics. Here the epidemiologist applies his special knowledge of microorganisms, of the manner in which they are transferred from man to man (or among animals, and from animals to man), of their capacity for survival in the natural environment, and of their resistance or susceptibility to changing environmental conditions.

The professional nurse, as a member of this team of specialists, has a highly important role to play in each aspect of the management of infectious disease — in the diagnosis, treatment, and control of active infection, and also in its prevention. In a very real sense, the nurse's professional education and training combine the basic elements of each speciality involved, and she applies them continuously in her practice. She must be conversant with the diagnostic signs of infectious disease and with methods of treatment, particularly with regard to the patient's response to antibiotic drugs. She must be able to participate in making the diagnosis, not only through accurate reporting of the patient's symptoms seen from her particularly close point of view, but also by assuring well-timed, careful collection of specimens ordered for laboratory studies and used in the identification of the cause of infection. Using her knowledge of the nature of the microbial agents of infectious disease, the nurse must apply appropriate precautionary measures in her bedside care of every patient so that communicable diseases cannot be spread from one to another, and problems of new infection are not superimposed upon patients who are ill with other conditions.

The *control* of active infectious disease requires a working knowledge of the usefulness and applications of physical and chemical agents that suppress or kill microorganisms, as well as familiarity with the sources of potentially dangerous microbes, the routes by which they spread, and their portals of entry into the human body. The *prevention* of infectious disease hinges on adequate control of these sources and transmission routes. It also frequently depends on specific measures designed to improve individual resis-

tance to infectious microorganisms. Specific resistance is spoken of as *immunity* and plays a vital role in prevention.

While the nurse's responsibilities extend across all the areas of infectious disease management, above all she must be a good epidemiologist, competent in her knowledge of the nature of infectious diseases and of available means for controlling or preventing them. In every field of nursing, whether it be practiced in hospitals, in the public health agency, in medical offices, or in industry, a knowledge of basic principles of microbiology is essential. The necessity for such a background of preparation in the nursing curriculum is further highlighted today by the dramatic ease, speed, and frequency of human travel, on and beyond our planet, that bring distant diseases closer to home, open up new pathways for the communicability of infections, and create new problems in their control.

The Background of Microbiology

In beginning the study of microbiology it should be rewarding to take a brief glance around the broad field of which it is a part and to see in general how it has evolved. As all living organisms are linked together by the interrelated mechanisms of their biologic functions and processes, so those who would study any one group of living things find the field of their scientific interest interlocked and overlapping with many others.

Biologists and Tools

The field of biology embraces all the sciences that inquire into the nature of life — that is, into the structure, character, and behavior of living forms. These inquiries have been going on insistently since the beginning of recorded history. For centuries, botanists, zoologists, chemists, and physiologists have sought to define life in its many forms, at every observable level. Where the search has been hindered for lack of a method for

accurate observation, efforts often have been concentrated on devising better tools or more refined techniques. In general, these efforts have constantly enlarged both our visual and our intellectual range, so that increasingly minute structural features have been visualized, or more subtle details of function have become better understood (see Figs. 1–1 to 1–8). So it was that the world of microscopic life, long imagined but always invisible to the unaided physical eye, finally became apparent, late in the seventeeth century, when a curious eye looked through an enlarging lens at a suspension of material that contained living microbes, swimming and moving about.

The owner of this eye, who applied it to a microscope of his own making and used them both so well that he became the founder of a new science of far-reaching influence, was Antony van Leeuwenhoek. He was a Dutch merchant and businessman with a hobbyist's interest in lens grinding and optics. His skill with lenses was extraordinary, and his interest in the world that they revealed to him was unending. In a long series of letters to the Royal Society of London, written over a period of 50 years, he described his observations of "incredibly small" living creatures abounding in drops of lake water, in scrapings of tartar from his teeth, in fecal suspensions, in pepper infusion, and in other fluids. His lenses gave him magnifications up to about three hundred diameters with which he could see little "animalcules," as he called them. In a letter to the Royal Society dated 1683, and another in 1692, he included drawings that clearly depict forms identifiable as bacteria (cocci and bacilli), spirochetes, and protozoa.

Leeuwenhoek's microscope was not the first to be invented. That achievement had come earlier in his century and spurred his interest in lenses, no doubt, but he preferred to make his own. He had received relatively little schooling and was not a scientist; so he may have been unaware that the existence of microorganisms had been postulated, but unconfirmed previously, by medical men concerned with the causation of diseases that spread by "contagion." His contri-

bution was all the more remarkable in view of his personal simplicity. The objective nature of his reports left no doubt as to the validity of his observations.

Controversies and Delays

Microbiology thus made a tentative beginning, but it was not to become a science, in the disciplined sense of that word, for nearly two hundred years. Although Leeuwenhoek's animalcules were believable and could be confirmed, they were not taken very seriously for a time. One of the reasons for this was that the simple observation of microbial life was difficult to interpret without some means of cultivating microorganisms and studying their properties and behavior. Certainly their relationship to some of the diseases of man, animals, or plants was not immediately recognizable and received little or no attention.

Over the ages there had been no dearth either of strong popular beliefs and superstitions or of highly astute, educated theories concerning the cause of contagious diseases, but these ideas had to be subjected to scientific testing before real progress could be made. It had been recognized from ancient times that diseases can spread from person to person, and many forms of control were devised accordingly, meeting with more or less success according to their basis in pure superstition or clear observation. Efforts to explain the nature of such diseases, and the dreadful epidemic form they so often took, led to some very discerning theories in a number of instances. Fracastorius in the sixteenth century, and Kircher in the seventeenth, both wrote with perceptive conviction and foresight of living but invisible agents as the possible cause of contagions and their spread. At the time, however, neither these nor conflicting ideas could be proved.

Through the centuries the question of the origin of life itself was interwoven with this problem. From the time of the early Greek philosophers the theory that life could be generated from nonliving matter had enjoyed strong support. By

1700 scientific experiments had dispelled belief in the spontaneous generation of animals of visible proportions, but when microorganisms were discovered, many people continued to apply the theory to this form of life. Thus, until the middle of the nineteenth century, Leeuwenhoek's little animalcules remained in the center of a controversy concerning their origin and were often the subjects of poorly designed experiments that led to claims of further proof for the theory of spontaneous generation. For example, flasks of vegetable broth that became cloudy with the growth of microbes after several days of exposure to air were thought to provide such proof. Nothing was known of the presence of bacteria in the air, or of their adherence to dust particles settling from the air into open flasks containing nutrient material. Furthermore, nothing was known of the ability of some bacteria to form heat-resistant spores, so that experiments in which bacterial growth could be demonstrated even in flasks of heated broth were similarly open to misinterpretation.

In spite of the work of several investigators whose well-controlled experiments led to results that refuted the theory of spontaneous generation, the controversy continued until 1860 when Louis Pasteur, a French biochemist and physicist, conducted a series of classic experiments which demonstrated that no growth can occur in flasks of broth properly protected from contamination by air-borne microorganisms. In one type of experiment, he introduced beef bouillon into a long-necked flask and then drew the neck out into a long, sinuous "swan-neck" shape. When he boiled the liquid in the flask, vaporization forced the air out of the opening at the end of the long neck. Upon cooling of the liquid, air was pulled back into the flask but had to pass over condensed moisture in the neck that washed it free of dust and other particles, so that the bouillon remained clear and free of growth. Control flasks were also heated, but immediately afterward the long necks were broken off, and as a result air pulled into the fluid during cooling was not first washed but delivered dust particles with their burden of viable microorganisms di-

Fig. 1–1. Antony van Leeuwenhoek's microscope. A replica of one of the first and simplest microscopes made by Leeuwenhoek around 1673. A single tiny lens is in the peephole in the flat plate. The object to be viewed is placed on the spike and adjusted with screws. The microscope is held up to the eye for viewing. A magnification of approximately 200 to 300× can be obtained. (Courtesy of Armed Forces Institute of Pathology, Washington, D.C.)

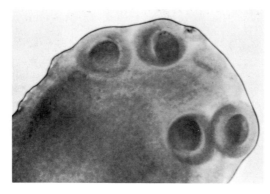

Fig. 1–2. This is the head (scolex) of the beef tapeworm (*Taenia saginata*). It has the dimensions of a very short, small pin and is visible to the eye, but would look like this with one of Leeuwenhoek's lenses (see Fig. 1–1). (Magnification 200×.)

Fig. 1–3. The Holmes microscope. A compound microscope devised by Oliver Wendell Holmes for student use in 1873. A magnification of approximately 400× could be obtained. (Courtesy of Armed Forces Institute of Pathology, Washington, D.C.)

Fig. 1–4. *Endamoeba histolytica,* an amoeba that causes amebic dysentery. (Wet mount. 800×.) Organisms of this size could readily be seen through the Holmes microscope (Fig. 1–3). Further magnification was gained in the photograph above by a photo-enlarging technique.

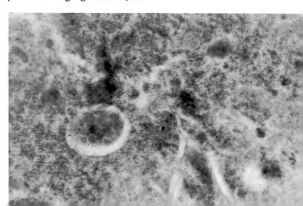

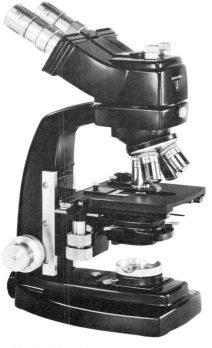

Fig. 1–7. The electron microscope. This microscope enlarges objects with electron beams instead of light rays. Essentially a research tool, it magnifies objects 12,000 to 16,000×. Further enlargement can be made photographically. Many advances in medicine have paralleled the evolution of the microscope. (Reproduced from *Health News*, April, 1962. Courtesy of New York State Health Department, Albany, N.Y.)

Fig. 1–5. A binocular compound microscope. This is the type of precision instrument used by the modern medical microbiologist. With the oil-immersion lens and a 10× ocular, microorganisms can be magnified approximately 1000×. (Courtesy of Bausch & Lomb, Rochester, N.Y.)

Fig. 1–6. This is a bacterium called *Diplococcus pneumoniae* (an agent of pneumonia). The picture was taken through a compound microscope (see Fig. 1–5) at a magnification of 1000×. Compare this picture with Fig. 1–8. (Courtesy of Dr. Kendall K. Kane, St. Luke's Hospital Center, New York, N.Y.)

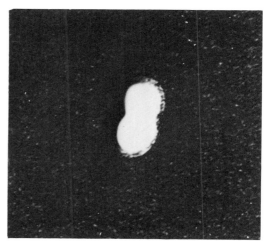

Fig. 1–8. An electron micrograph of *Diplococcus pneumoniae* (36,000×). (Compare with Fig. 1–6.) (Courtesy of The Upjohn Company, Kalamazoo, Mich.)

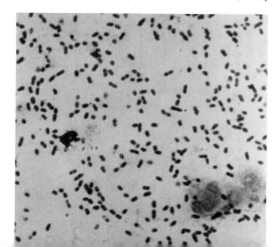

rectly into the nutrient fluid, which soon became cloudy with microbial growth (see Fig. 1–9). In another series of experiments, Pasteur used an idea of earlier workers and introduced a cotton plug into the necks of his flasks. The cotton acted as a filter, effectively straining out dust particles and keeping nutrient fluid in the flask free of microorganisms derived from the air. (Cotton plugs are still commonly used for this purpose, in test tubes or flasks, but screw caps and slip-on metal or plastic closures serve the same purpose

of air exclusion and are easier to prepare and apply.)

When Pasteur presented the results of these experiments, the conclusion that life at every level must be self-reproducing, rather than spontaneous, began to take precedence and the way was cleared for the development and application of scientific methods to study the nature of microscopic organisms and the mechanisms of their self-duplication.

Fig. 1–9. Louis Pasteur and one of his historic experiments. Pasteur sterilized the broth in these flasks by prolonged boiling. The open mouth of each flask was in contact with the air; however, the broth in one of them remained sterile because the curves of its drawn-out, tubelike neck prevented air currents from carrying dust, laden with microorganisms, into the nutrient fluid. Evidence of microbial growth can be seen in the cloudy broth of the flask with the short, broken-off neck. With this simple experiment Pasteur established the validity of the concept that life is self-generating rather than spontaneous: *Omne vivum ex vivo*, that is, "All life from life."
(This picture of Pasteur is one of a series entitled "A History of Medicine in Pictures." It is reproduced by special permission of Parke, Davis & Co., Detroit, Mich., who commissioned the original oil paintings and hold the copyrights. The project was written and directed by George A. Bender; the painter is Robert A. Thom.)

Bacteriology's Golden Age

Pasteur's greatest contributions evolved from his demonstrations of the relationship of certain microorganisms to the spoilage of wines and of others to a disease of silkworms. These were matters of great economic importance to France at the time. The experimental proof that they were of microbial origin led Pasteur to a similar approach in his study of anthrax in sheep and of certain human infections. The successful identification of particular microorganisms as the agents of individual diseases of plants, animals, and human beings then led him to re-examine and reformulate the old "germ theory of disease," which attributed the cause of infection to microbial agents. He brought sound scientific evidence to bear on this point for the first time, however, and this soon came to the attention of the great English surgeon Joseph Lister, who applied the theory in his surgical practice.

Lister speculated that if Pasteur was right about the ubiquitous presence of microorganisms in the air, and if these could fall into a flask of fluid medium that supported their growth, such organisms could also enter open surgical wounds and be responsible for the sepsis and wound deterioration that so often led to surgical deaths in those days. With this idea in mind, Lister began to use a phenolic solution in the operating room, using it for his hands and instruments and spraying it into the air around his patients, with the result that his surgery was attended by a very low fatality rate as compared with that of other surgeons who used no precautions to prevent complications they did not believe in as "infections."

At about the same time during the 1860's, but without prior knowledge of Pasteur's work, a German physician named Robert Koch began to make laboratory discoveries of the organisms responsible for various notable human diseases. Together with his students and associates, Koch developed many of the technical methods of cultivation, staining, and animal experimentation vital to the study of microorganisms and the interpretation of their behavior as agents of disease.

A few years before (in 1840), Jacob Henle, another German scientist, had again outlined the germ theory of disease, stating that its proof would be provided by a series of necessary procedures, which included (1) recognition of the infectious microbe in every case of human disease but not in healthy persons, (2) laboratory isolation of the organism from the patient and its pure cultivation, free of other microbes, (3) demonstration of its capacity to produce disease in healthy laboratory animals, and (4) recovery of the organism in pure laboratory culture from infected animals that had displayed typical disease following their inoculation. Henle had no technical means to prove the validity of these "postulates." It was Koch who developed the techniques necessary to the application of these principles (which have since become known as "Koch's postulates"), and armed with such methods he and his associates provided, in rapid succession, the necessary proof of the microbial origin and nature of such major human diseases as tuberculosis, diphtheria, typhoid fever, cholera, and gonorrhea.

Thus the field of microbiology achieved scientific status. However, the greatest excitement was generated in the area of medical bacteriology and its advances were most important to human welfare. The immortal contributions of Pasteur, Lister, and Koch established the truth of the germ theory and provided the basis for today's progress in the understanding of infectious diseases. The laboratories of Pasteur in France and of Koch in Germany became centers of attraction for students from around the world who came to learn methods and ideas and who made, in their turn, personal contributions that marked the end of the nineteenth century as the "golden age of bacteriology."

The Microbial World Today

In the two and one-half centuries that have elapsed since Leeuwenhoek's first glimpse of bacteria and protozoa, microbiologic investigations have resulted in the accumulation of a vast

body of knowledge that has contributed to man's understanding of the nature of all life and that has lightened immeasureably the burden of human disease. Microbiology has, literally and figuratively, changed the face of the earth, particularly since the time of Pasteur, Lister, and Koch, just a brief hundred years ago.

The microbial world, as we recognize it today, contains a tremendous variety of organisms, exhibiting an amazing diversity of size, structure, and activity. Microorganisms of one type or another are to be found wherever life is possible — in the soil, in water and air, and associated with plants, animal, or human life. Many of their vital functions supporting growth and reproduction, respiration, synthesis, and excretion, and also their responses to environmental stimuli, have been found to have the same basic character as those of more structurally complex forms of life. Indeed, the study of microorganisms has, of late, served more and more frequently to elucidate many fundamental biologic mechanisms operative in higher organisms as well. Biologists working in the fields of genetics, biochemistry, and biophysics have found microorganisms to be useful and profitable tools in their studies of the nature of life processes. Furthermore, it has become ever more obvious that microbial forms of life make an essential contribution to the maintenance of balanced relationships among all living things.

In the field of medical microbiology today, emphasis is placed not only on the relatively small group of microbes that adversely affect human health as the cause of infectious disease, but as importantly on the interplay of factors that affect the ability of the human organism to maintain its balance in a world it shares with so many microbial types. In the nursing profession far more is now required than a familiarity with the microorganisms of medical importance. The fundamental principles of microbiology, as they are currently understood, apply to every phase of nursing practice. The crisis of infection and the threat of epidemic have been minimized for the modern world by the development of specific measures for their treatment, control, and pre-

vention, but the problem of chronic infection continues, and other problems now confront us. On the one hand, vigilance must be kept over the preventable diseases by every effective method currently available, while existing infections must be cared for and controlled as completely as possible. It should also be understood that new problems of infection have arisen from many of the modern methods of medical and surgical treatment that successfully relieve or cure serious diseases that were once considered hopeless. The widespread use of antibiotics has not eliminated infectious microorganisms, but indeed has often made it possible for new types that are resistant to these drugs to emerge. The prolongation of life for patients with debilitating organic diseases creates a population for which the risk of infection is greater and which is also more than normally susceptible to such risk. The development of sophisticated surgical techniques for the treatment of cardiac defects and problems of kidney function, or for the removal of extensive tumors, has provided new challenges for the protection of patients from the added burden of infection that can be acquired during surgery or during the difficult period of postoperative recovery (see Fig. 1–10). For the professional nurse, as for every other member of the medical team, an understanding of the potential of infection, existing or threatened, forms an important basis for most procedures and for the total approach to every patient.

Microbiology in Nursing Practice

In this text a primary effort is made to provide the nurse, both student and graduate, with the most practical and applicable information regarding the microbial diseases, including bacterial, rickettsial, viral, and fungal infections and the diseases caused by the animal parasites.

The emphasis is twofold with regard to the nursing care of the patient ill with an infectious disease. On the one hand, a knowledge of the suspected or diagnosed disease process itself, and

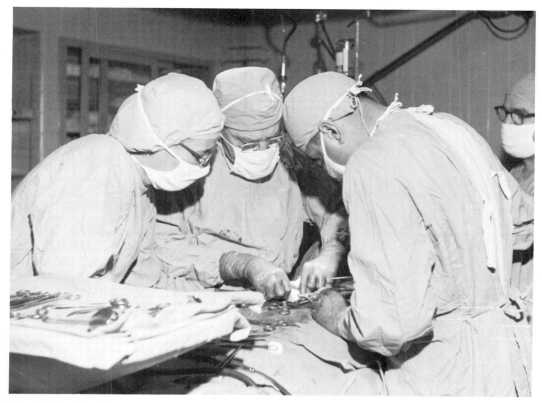

Fig. 1–10. Physicians being assisted by an operating-room nurse during abdominal surgery. All the protective clothing including gowns, masks, gloves, and drapes has been sterilized. The nurse passes sterilized instruments to the physician. (Courtesy of Northern Westchester Hospital, Mt. Kisco, N.Y.)

of its agent, is essential so that its course from onset to outcome can be anticipated to the patient's best advantage. Second, the communicability of the infection is of vital concern. The nurse must understand the common sources of infection, as well as pertinent routes of entry to and transfer from the body, so that she can help to limit each case of active infection, preventing its spread to other patients in a hospital, to other members of a household, or to those occupied in the care of the patient, whether or not they are in direct contact.

The infectious diseases are presented in Part Two of the text, in an order based primarily on currently available information as to the most probable route of entry of the microbial agent and secondarily on routes of exit and transmission, or on the nature of the organisms involved — that is, fungi, bacteria, rickettsiae, viruses, protozoa, or helminths. If the nurse as a student learns to associate the infectious agent of a given disease with its routes of communicability and entry, her techniques as a graduate will be oriented toward the probable nursing requirements of the patient and the simultaneous protection of others (including herself) from the possibility of infection transfer.

Before considering individual diseases, how-

ever, the student must learn some basic facts
about microbial behavior in general, the fundamental relationships that operate between microbe and host in health or disease, and the
general principles of prevention and control as

they apply to most infectious diseases. The
microbial world is outlined in broad terms in the
following chapter, and the succeeding chapters of
Part One describe the basic principles of microbiology.

Questions

1. What role does the nurse play in the diagnosis, treatment, control, and prevention of
   infection?
2. Briefly describe Antony van Leeuwenhoek's contribution to microbiology.
3. Describe Pasteur's experiments that ended the "spontaneous generation" controversies.
4. How did Lister apply Pasteur's work on the "germ theory of disease" to his surgical
   practice? *asiopis*
5. What contributions to the science of microbiology are attributed to Robert Koch? *postulates*
6. What knowledge is necessary in the nursing care of a patient ill with an infectious disease?

References

Pertinent References

Burdon, Kenneth L., and Williams, Robert P.: *Textbook of Microbiology*, 6th ed. The Mac-
millan Co., New York, 1968.
Dubos, René: *The Unseen World*. The Rockefeller Institute Press, New York, 1962.
Mizer, Helen E.: Microbiology in the News, *Nurs. Outlook*, **10**:243, 1962.
Nightingale, Florence: *Notes on Nursing: What It Is, and What It Is Not*. D. Appleton Century,
Co., Inc., New York and London, 1938.
Pelczar, Michael J., and Reid, Roger: *Microbiology*, 2nd ed. McGraw-Hill, New York, 1965.

Popular Literature

Clendening, Logan: *Behind the Doctor*. Garden City Publishing Co., Inc., Garden City, N.Y.,
1933, Chap. 7, "The Microscope"; Chap. 21, "Disease Cells"; Chap. 22, "Germs."
Clendening, Logan: Compiled with notes by: *Source Book of Medical History*. Dover Publi-
cations, Inc., New York, 1960, Chap. 32, "Bacteriology."
DeKruif, Paul: *Microbe Hunters*. Harcourt Brace, New York, 1926, Chap. 1, "Leeuwenhoek,
First of the Microbe Hunters"; Chap. 2, "Spallanzani, Microbes Must Have Parents";
Chap. 3, "Pasteur, Microbes Are a Menace"; Chap. 4, "Koch, the Death Fighter";
Chap. 5, "Pasteur: And the Mad Dog."
Dobell, Clifford: *Antony van Leeuwenhoek and His Little Animals*. Dover Publications, Inc.,
New York, 1960.
Dolan, Edward F., Jr.: *Pasteur and the Invisible Giants*. Dodd, Mead & Co., New York, 1958.
Dubos, R. J.: *Louis Pasteur, Free Lance of Science*. Little, Brown and Co., Boston, 1950.
Haggard, Howard V.: *Devils, Drugs and Doctors*. Blue Ribbons, New York, 1929, Chap. 16,
"Toward a Better Civilization."
Shippen, Katherine: *Men of Medicine*. The Viking Press, New York, 1957, Chap. 13, "Louis
Pasteur Points to His Microbes."
Shippen, Katherine: *Men, Microscopes and Living Things*. Grosset and Dunlap, Tempo Books,
New York, 1963, Chap. 8, "So Many Marvels"; Chap. 9, "You Are Linnaeus."
Shryock, Richard Harrison: *Medicine and Society in America, 1660–1860*. Great Seal Books,
Ithaca, N.Y., 1962.

Sigerist, Henry E.: *The Great Doctors.* Doubleday Anchor Book, Garden City, N.Y., 1958, Chap. 42, "Louis Pasteur."

Styler, Herman: *Plague Fighters.* Chilton Co., Philadelphia and New York, 1960, Chap. 2, "Shadow of Microbes."

Thompson, Morton: *The Cry and the Covenant.* Doubleday & Co., Garden City, N.Y., 1949.

Vallery-Radot: *Louis Pasteur, a Great Life in Brief.* Alfred C. Knopf, New York, 1958.

Walker, Kenneth: *The Story of Medicine.* Arrow Books, Limited, England, 1954, Chap. 7, "17th Century Genius."

Woodham-Smith, Cecil: *Florence Nightingale.* McGraw-Hill, New York, 1951.

Woodham-Smith, Cecil: *The Great Hunger.* Harper and Row, New York, 1962.

2 The Microbial World Defined

Classification of Living Things

The Importance of Classification

Since the time of Aristotle, efforts to classify living organisms have been a continuously important part of their study. Classification, or *taxonomy*, is a science in its own right, for it unifies and summarizes existing knowledge of the interrelationships among living things. It documents their differences as well as their similarities, furnishes clues as to origins and developmental pathways, and provides biologists with a common language through which this knowledge can be communicated precisely. Linnaeus, a Swedish naturalist of the eighteenth century, was the first scientist to bring some semblance of order to the accumulated knowledge of botanists and zoologists by working out a systematic classification of plants and animals. The Linnaean system is still in use today, with some modifications and enlargements. It permits classifications of all living organisms not only by structure, or anatomy, but also by function, metabolism, reproductive processes, and so on.

The Two Great Kingdoms

The living world is first divided into two major groups of organisms: the *plant* and *animal king-*

doms. The next division within a kingdom is a *phylum.* Further subdivisions follow in regular sequence, so that the total identification of an organism involves placing it first in its kingdom, then the phylum, then the *class, order, family, tribe, genus,* and, finally, the *species.* Thus, man, as a human being, belongs to the animal kingdom, of course, and is further classified with the phylum Chordata (subphylum Vertebrata), class Mammalia, order Primates, family Hominidae, genus *Homo,* species *sapiens.* The final scientific name given to an organism consists of the two words that designate the genus and the species, printed in italics, e.g., *Homo sapiens* for man.

Plants and animals are alike in many essential ways. They are composed of cells, which are the fundamental units of structure and function, and there are many similarities in their metabolic processes. Obviously, however, there are important differences between them in cellular composition, methods of growth and reproduction, nutritional sources, and the use they make of nutrient. A fuller discussion of the comparative metabolism of plants and animals will be found in Chapter 3, where some of their basic processes are considered together with those of microscopic forms of life.

Microorganisms belong to one or the other of the two major kingdoms, some being classified with animals, some with plants. Certain microorganisms have remained difficult to classify with precision, however, their known characteristics appearing to occupy a borderline position between animals and plants or to overlap with both, or, in some cases, being insufficiently studied for final classification.

The Animal Kingdom

The first phyletic divisions of the animal kingdom separate it into two large groups, containing the *vertebrate* and the *invertebrate* animals. The earliest distinction that occurs between these two types appears during embryologic development. In the developing *vertebrate* animal, a structure called the notochord materializes, from which the backbone is later derived. Embryologic evidence, together with anatomic and functional distinctions, provides the basis for further subdivisions among the higher vertebrates. External anatomic features taken alone may be misleading, as in the case of the fish and the whale, for instance. These two are both anatomically equipped to live in the water, but they have little else in common, the whale being a mammal and therefore of a higher order and class than the fish.

Some of the factors that determine animal classifications are cellular differentiation, if any; body symmetry and axis orientation (radial or bilateral, round or flat); the number and type of embryonic cell layers; and the type of body cavity and body segmentation. The highest member of the animal kingdom is man, in terms of both structure and function. Although the human body develops from a single cell, formed by the union of two single cells, the cellular subdivisions that subsequently occur result in a highly complex, multicellular animal. As we pass down through the animal kingdom to the *invertebrates*, the animals become structurally more simple, but in function they are still capable of very complex activities at the level of their differentiated organs, tissues, or individual cells. The simplest structural form of animal life is *unicellular*. The single-celled animals are classified in the phylum Protozoa, and among them are some of the microorganisms of medical importance. All the multicellular, higher animals, whose cells are differentiated into tissues with specialized functions, are referred to collectively as *metazoa*, and these occupy the many other phyla of the animal kingdom. Some of the lower metazoans, notably the parasitic worms, also fall into the province of the medical microbiologist.

Protozoa

The animal kingdom began with its microbial segment, the *Protozoa*, which are the oldest persisting forms of animal life. (They were predated in the plant world by bacteria as evidenced by the finding of fossil bacteria estimated to be two

billion years old.[1]) This group of unicellular animals includes the largest of the microorganisms, but together they exhibit a wide range of size and form. Some are just large enough to be seen without the help of the microscope, but others must be magnified nearly 1000 times to be clearly visible (see Table 2–1). Although they are structurally simple, their vital functions — food intake and utilization, excretion, locomotion, reproduction — are quite complex. The Protozoa have in common such fundamental structures as a nucleus with its limiting membrane, cellular cytoplasm in which digestive and excretory processes are performed, and an outer cell membrane. The cell performs as a unit, but it may have specialized structures for particular functions, such as cilia or flagella for self-propulsion, vacuoles for food digestion or water excretion, and a gullet for food intake.

Protozoa are capable of adapting to many different environmental conditions. In some cases this is due to their ability to pass into a *cystic* stage when environmental conditions are unfavorable. The cyst wall is thicker and less permeable than before and therefore protects the cell against drying or other natural injuries. For some protozoans, the cyst may also play a role in reproduction, through nuclear divisions leading to new cell formation. The adult, functioning form is called a *trophozoite*, or a *vegetative* cell. It is largely on the basis of the type of locomotion exhibited by the trophozoite, or of reproductive mechanisms, that the Protozoa are classified into four subphyla: *Sarcodina* (the amoebae); *Ciliophora* (ciliated forms); *Mastigophora* (flagellated forms); and *Sporozoa*. In the first three subphyla named, reproduction occurs largely by asexual processes. Members of the subphylum Sporozoa, however, reproduce typically by alternating asexual multiplication with sexual processes. The sporozoans do not have specialized organs of locomotion, but in some instances their asexual trophozoite forms display an active amoeboid motility. (See Chap. 12, pp. 300–301, for a fuller classification of these organisms.)

The subphylum Sarcodina (class Rhizopodea) includes the group of organisms known as amoebae, which move about by extending and retracting their protoplasm. The protruding extensions are known as *pseudopods*, or false feet. When seen through the microscope, an amoeba has an ever-changing shape. As it extrudes a pseudopod, now in one direction, then another, it has a fluid kind of gliding motion. Within it can be seen a nucleus, particles of ingested food, and vacuoles. The trophozoites of some amoebae are capable of passing into a cyst stage, which not only is protective under adverse conditions but also takes part in the reproductive cycle, which is entirely asexual.

There are many types of free-living amoebae to be found in soil or water. A few species are dependent on higher animal organisms for their life. When they derive their own support at the expense of the other organism, and do damage to the latter, they are considered *parasitic* (see Chap. 5 for a discussion of this type of relationship). A number of species of amoebae may live in the human intestinal tract, where they may cause little or no harm, but there is one species of particular medical importance. The latter is *Endamoeba histolytica* (see Fig. 2–1), the cause of amoebic dysentery in man. This can be a relatively mild or a very severe disease, in which the patient suffers acute distress as a result of eroding damage to the inner wall of the large bowel. Either the trophozoite or cystic stages of the organism, or both, can be identified by microscopic examination of feces, but they must be carefully distinguished from other, less harmful, types of amoebae that may be found in such specimens. These distinctions are based on the details of nuclear morphology (form and structure), some of the cellular components, differences in cyst development, and the shape and appearance of pseudopods in the trophozoite.

The subphylum Ciliophora (class Ciliatea) contains organisms that have a permanently definite shape and a more efficient method of locomotion than that of the amoebae. The rapid motility of

---

[1]Schopf, J. W., Barghoorn, E. S., Maser, M. D., and Gordon, R. O.: Electron Microscopy of Fossil Bacteria Two Billion Years Old, *Science*, **149**:1365–67, 1965.

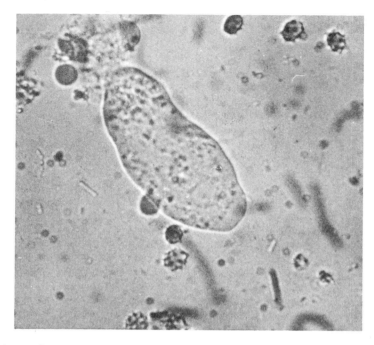

Fig. 2–1. *Endamoeba histolytica,* trophozoite. The organism is in the process of ingesting red blood cells in this preparation. Magnification 2500×.

ciliates is due to fine, threadlike extensions of protoplasm, called *cilia*, which extend through the outer membrane. The cilia cover the outer surface of the cell and move it along by a coordinated, rhythmic beating. Inner structures of the cell provide this coordination of the cilia and also permit the cell to back and turn. These organisms have a mouth and fixed gullet, also lined with cilia to bring in food particles, and an excretory pore. Unlike other protozoans, ciliates are characterized by the possession of two nuclei per cell in the vegetative stage. One is smaller than the other (it is called a *micronucleus*) and is responsible for reproduction; the larger (*macronucleus*) directs ordinary cellular activities. Some types of ciliates can form protective cysts, which also contain two nuclei. Reproduction is usually asexual but may also occur by conjugation (sexual). This is true of the species *Balantidium coli* (see Fig. 2–2), the largest intestinal protozoan of man. It is the relatively rare cause of a chronic, recurrent dysentery.

The subphylum *Mastigophora* (*class Zoomastigophorea*) constitutes a group whose members owe their motility to the presence of long, whiplike ectoplasmic extensions, or flagella, which project from the anterior end. They have a definite shape, usually oval, but some species may be quite elongated, and some may form pseudopods to engulf their food. Others have a mouth and gullet as seen in the ciliates. Some species form cysts, and there are also important types that go through transitional, cyclic stages of development in which the flagellum may be lacking. These re-

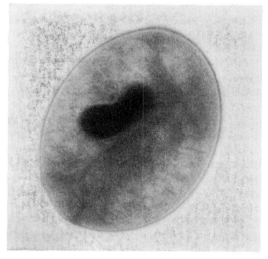

Fig. 2–2. *Balantidium coli.* The large dense area is the macronucleus; the small light spot is the micronucleus. Note the delicate cilia lining the outer membrane. Magnification 2000×.

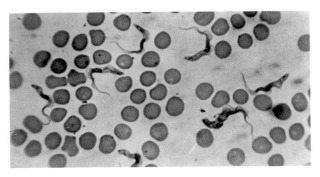

Fig. 2–3. *Trypanósoma gambiense* is a flagellated protozoan that parasitizes human blood and is responsible for the disease called "African sleeping sickness." Note that each organism has a single flagellum at one end, an undulating membrane, and a centrally placed nucleus. Magnification 1000×. The large round objects are human red blood cells. (Courtesy of Dr. Thomas W. M. Cameron, McGill University, Montreal, Canada.)

productive stages are basically of an asexual nature. Flagellated protozoans are frequently found in the intestinal tract of man, or on mucosal surfaces, where they are usually of little or no consequence. Occasionally, species of the genus *Trichomonas* may find an opportunity to multiply in large numbers on the vaginal or perineal surfaces and cause a troublesome irritation. Of much greater medical concern are the few parasitic flagellates that may cause disease following their entry into the blood and tissues, usually through the agency of a biting fly or other insect infected with the organism. African sleeping sickness (trypanosomiasis), which is transmitted by the bite of the tsetse fly, is an example of such a

disease. The flagellated organism that causes it belongs to a genus called *Trypanosoma* (see Fig. 2–3).

The subphylum Sporozoa contains nonmotile organisms that have distinct environmental limitations. They are parasitic in that they can live only in the body tissues or fluids of other, higher organisms. Their life cycle is complex, involving two alternate means of reproduction. Developmental stages of an asexual type of nuclear division occur in a vertebrate host, such as man, while other transitional forms are produced by sexual union and nuclear division, usually in invertebrate insect hosts. The cells resulting from sexual division are called *sporozoites*, hence the name of this group. Blood-sucking insects, notably some species of mosquito, which prey on vertebrates infected with sporozoans, ingest forms of the parasite during the blood meal. Further reproduction in the mosquito leads to the production of sporozoites, which are then injected into the blood of the next animal upon which the mosquito feeds. A reservoir of infection is thus maintained by this cyclic transmission of the organism from one host to another and by its alternate reproductive properties. *Malaria* is an outstanding example of a sporozoan disease of man, which may be caused by one of several species of the genus *Plasmodium* and is transmitted by various types of mosquitoes (see Fig. 2–4).

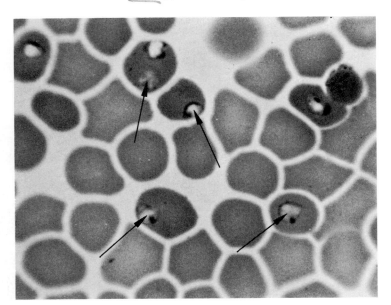

Fig. 2–4. *Plasmodium falciparum* is a protozoan organism (subphylum, Sporozoa) that parasitizes man's red blood cells during part of its complex life cycle. It is one of several *Plasmodium* species that cause malaria in man (see Chap. 27). *Arrows* point to parasitized erythrocytes in a stained smear of human blood. Magnification 2000×.

Metazoa

All the multicellular animals are grouped together as *metazoa*, the term including both vertebrates and invertebrates. The worms, or *helminths*, belong to the invertebrate phyla, including those that cause human and animal diseases. In their fully developed, adult forms, most worms are large enough to be clearly visible to the unaided eye, and therefore they are not microorganisms in the true sense. However, the immature forms of their developmental cycles, that is, their *ova* (eggs) and *larvae* are microscopic in size (see Table 2–1), and it is the recognition of these forms in the excretions or tissues of infected patients that is often necessary to the diagnosis of the disease. Also, the methods used to study these organisms in the laboratory, as well as those applied to the prevention and control of helminthic diseases, are similar in principle to those employed in microbial infections. For these reasons the parasitic worms are of interest and concern to the medical microbiologist. (See Chap. 12, pp. 301–302, for the classification of these organisms.)

The helminths are soft-bodied invertebrate animals whose anatomic structures include differentiated muscle tissue; nervous, excretory, and reproductive systems; and often a simple digestive tract. The size range for the entire group is from nearly microscopic dimensions (the adult pinworm is just barely visible without a magnifying lens) to several feet in length (some adult tapeworms can be measured with a yardstick). There are many thousands of species of worms, most of which live freely and harmlessly in the soil, or in both fresh and salt water. The relatively few species that are parasitic are medically important because they may infest man and animals in some stage of their cyclic type of life. The degree of damage induced in their hosts by their presence may be so slight as to be unnoticeable, or it may be so severe as to threaten life.

There are two major groups of helminths: the *nemathelminths*, or roundworms, and the *platyhelminths*, or flatworms. They differ in anatomic respects as well as in their reproductive methods and life cycles.

The nemathelminths, or roundworms (also often called *nematodes*), are cylindric, with bilateral symmetry. The outer skin, or integument, of roundworms is a tough cuticle that may be smooth, rough, or spiny. Their bodies are not segmented, and they are pointed at both ends. A few members of this group, notably the hookworms, have hooks or cutting plates around the mouth for attachment to the intestinal wall of the animal or human whose body they have entered. Roundworms have a complete digestive tract and excretory system, as well as a nervous system. The sexes are usually separate, male roundworms being smaller than the females and often grossly recognizable as males by the fact that their tails are sharply twisted. The larger female produces eggs constantly, as many as 200,000 a day in some cases. After fertilization larval development begins, the egg being encased in a shell by that time. When the larvae are hatched, they may go through several subsequent stages before the adult form is reached.

The cyclic development of roundworms from adult to adult, through egg and larval forms, varies greatly among species. In the sections of Part Two where helminthic diseases are discussed, the life cycle of each worm is considered in its relation to human infestation (a word commonly used to refer to invasion of the body by helminths), as well as to methods of prevention and control.

Among the important nematodes associated with human disease are *hookworm* and *Ascaris* (see Fig. 2–5), which infect the intestinal tract, the *trichina* worm, whose larvae become lodged and encysted in muscle tissue, and the *filarial worms*, whose adult and larval forms both live in the blood and various tissues. As in the case of the protozoan agent of malaria, blood-sucking insects that ingest the larvae of filarial worms in a meal taken from an infected person play an important role in the transmission and life cycle of the filariae.

The platyhelminths, or flatworms, also have bilateral symmetry and organized tissues differentiated for special functions, that is, simple muscle and nerve tissue, digestive and excretory organs, and reproductive systems. They are ori-

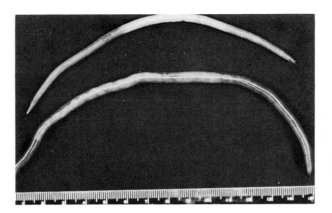

Fig. 2–5. Adult forms of *Ascaris lumbricoides,* a nematode or roundworm. The ruler measures 15 cm.

ented dorsoventrally, hence the term "flat." They vary greatly in shape and size, some being thinly elongated and segmented, others being nonsegmented and thickly ovoid. On the basis of such anatomic differences, and the accompanying differences required in internal structure and function, the flatworms are subdivided into two major groups: the *cestodes*, which are tapeworms, and the *trematodes*, also often called flukes.

The tapeworms have certain highly distinguishing features. Their bodies are flattened, elongated, and composed of individual segments, each of which contains both male and female sex organs. This combination of sexes in one individual is termed *hermaphroditism*. The series of segments begins with a head, or *scolex*, equipped with muscular suckers, and sometimes with a circlet of hooks as well, which permit attachment to the inner wall of the intestine of an animal, or of man. Just below the scolex is an area of growth, called the neck, from which arises a series of maturing segments, or *proglottids*, each containing fully developed sex organs, nervous and excretory systems, but no digestive tract. At the far end of the series, the mature segments become filled with the eggs they produce and are therefore said to be *gravid*. The whole length of tapeworm is called the *strobila*, its full reach varying with the type of worm from three to four proglottids to several hundred (see Fig. 2–6). Eggs are extruded from the segments into the intestines, or the gravid proglottids may break off and be passed from the body in the feces, together with free eggs. Sometimes long chains of proglottids

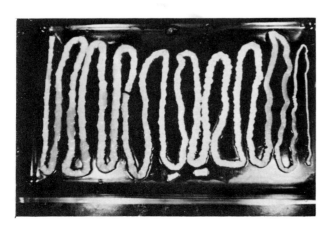

Fig. 2–6. This tapeworm (*Taenia saginata*) is 114 in. long. The entire strobila (fully developed worm) with the scolex (head) was recovered from a case of human infestation. The dish measures 11 in. × 16 in. (See Fig. 1–2, p. 8, for a close-up view of the scolex.)

are passed, providing very visible evidence of infestation. While the scolex and neck remain attached to the bowel wall, however, regeneration of segments continues and the strobila can grow again, even if all proglottids have broken away.

Although tapeworms have no mouth or digestive tract, they derive nourishment from digested food in solution in the intestinal tract of the animal housing them, by absorbing it through their outer walls. When a worm of great length is present, or if the infestation is multiple and more than one adult is developing in the intestinal tract, the infected individual can become gradually debilitated from loss of vital nutrients. Other symptoms of infection are related to irritation of the bowel and to interference with its mechanical functions.

The eggs of tapeworms must pass through stages of larval development before the adult form is re-established. For the most part these intermediate stages require one or more additional animals in which they can develop. For this reason, the latter are spoken of as *intermediate hosts*, while the animal that harbors the adult cestode is called the *final*, or *definitive*, *host*. Most of the tapeworms that infest man live in his intestinal tract, in the adult form. This is true of the so-called beef, pork, and fish tapeworms, and man is therefore one of the definitive hosts for these. In one important case, man may find himself an intermediate host for a small tapeworm that lives harmlessly, in the adult form, in the intestinal tracts of dogs. The larval form of this worm, called *Echinococcus*, derived from eggs passed by the infected dog, penetrates into the

tissues of an intermediate host, such as man, and develops structures called *cysts*, or *hydatids* (fluid-filled sacs). The condition that results is spoken of as hydatid disease.

The trematodes, or flukes, include several species of medical importance. Structurally and functionally, there are two types of flukes: those that are flattened, thickly leaf-shaped, and hermaphroditic; and those that are elongated, round, and bisexual. None of the flukes is segmented but, like the tapeworms, they have only a rudimentary digestive system. All of them have a tough outer cuticle and muscular suckers for attachment to the host. In their often-complicated life cycles, man and other mammalian animals are the definitive hosts for the adult forms, which inhabit and produce eggs in various sites of the body, while consecutive larval stages require one or more aquatic animals to complete their development.

The flukes that cause human disease are commonly referred to according to the site in the body where the adult usually lives and produces its eggs. On this basis they are divided into groups known as blood flukes (the *Schistosomes*), intestinal, liver, and lung flukes. Structurally, the blood flukes fall in the group mentioned above that are elongated, round, and bisexual (see Fig. 2–7). The adults are quite small, comparable in size to the smallest roundworms. They live within blood vessels, the female producing her eggs in the small capillaries of such organs as the large intestine, the liver, or the urinary bladder. All the other flukes have a thickly ovoid shape and are hermaphroditic. The intestinal fluke lives

Fig. 2–7. *Schistosoma mansoni.* A pair of adult schistosomes or blood flukes. The smaller female can be seen lying in a canal-like groove in the ventral surface of the larger male. Magnification 10×.

in the lumen of the upper part of the small bowel, the liver fluke in the bile ducts, and the lung fluke in the lung tissue itself. The eggs produced by flukes at these various sites may often be trapped in the tissues where they cannot develop further, but produce defensive reactions in the host. Many eggs, however, may find an exit route from the body, through the feces, urine, or sputum. If and when they are deposited in water, the ova hatch into larval forms, which then pass through several generations in intermediate aquatic hosts. Human infestation is incurred by the ingestion of the larvae in infected fish, or crustaceans, or water plants (these hosts differ for the several types of flukes), or by the direct penetration of the skin by a larval form swimming freely in infected water. Development of the adult form then proceeds in the final host, and the production of eggs continues the cycle.

The Plant Kingdom

The vast world of plants is divided into several phyla, their classifications being based, as in the animal kingdom, on anatomic structures and developmental and evolutionary relationships. The more primitive plants, which have no vascular system and are without roots, stems, or leaves, are contained in the phylum *Thallophyta*. This group is an enormous one in itself, containing hundreds of thousands of species, ranging from unicellular microorganisms to great ropy seaweeds. The *thallus*, or body, of the multicellular plants in this group may be differentiated into structural parts, but the only true specialization of function is associated with the reproductive structures.

The first major division among the thallophytes separates them into two subphyla: the *algae*, which contain chlorophyll and are relatively independent of other forms of life because they can utilize simple inorganic substances as nutrient (they are said to be *autotrophic*, or self-nourishing because of this), and the *fungi*, which do not have chlorophyll and are dependent on complex organic foods derived from other living things, dead or alive (they are called *heterotrophic*

because of this, meaning their food comes from others). All the microbial forms of medical importance that are classified with plants fall in the latter group.

The Fungi

There are many thousands of species of fungi, distributed universally. They are grouped into two large divisions: the *Eumycotina*, or the true fungi; and the *Protophyta*, which encompass the *Schizomycetes*, or bacteria (see Chap. 12, p. 290).

The True Fungi. There are four classes of true fungi, which include such simple plants as the unicellular yeasts and the multicellular molds and mushrooms. The body of a multicellular fungus is composed of a mat of long, branching, filamentous tubes containing cytoplasm, with nuclei strung out at irregular intervals. The entire mat is referred to as the *mycelium*, and the individual filaments that compose it are called *hyphae*. The hyphae form originally from the elongation of a germinating, reproductive cell, microscopic in size, called a *spore* (see Table 2–1). Some of the yeasts, which are classified with the true fungi, have spores that fail to produce a mycelium and merely pinch off daughter spores at their germinating tips (see Fig. 2–8). These yeasts are, therefore, unicellular.

As more and more mycelium is produced by the growing, branching hyphae, the plant reaches visible proportions. Its eventual size will depend on the continuing availability of nutrient and on other environmental conditions. Most molds do not grow to a height of more than $\frac{1}{4}$ to $\frac{1}{2}$ in., but they extend laterally along the surfaces of, and downward into, the material supporting them. That portion of the plant extending downward and into the medium is called the *vegetative mycelium*, while that which extends above the surface is the *aerial mycelium*. Usually the reproductive structures are found in the aerial portion, and their presence contributes to the powdery or fuzzy look of the mold.

The four classes of true fungi are recognized and classified according to the appearance of the

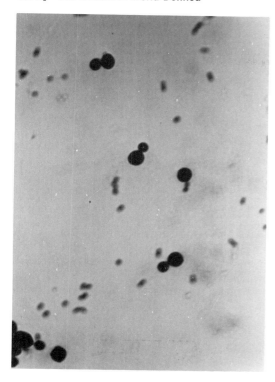

visible growth; the characteristics of microscopic structures, that is, mycelium, hyphae, and spores; and, most importantly, the type of sexual reproduction displayed. Most of the fungi associated with human disease fall into one class, the *Fungi Imperfecti* (Deuteromycetes), so-called because sexual reproduction is unknown, or has remained unrecognized, in this group. The other three classes are the *Phycomycetes*, the *Ascomycetes*, and the *Basidiomycetes*. (Note that the Greek word for fungus, *mykes*, forms the explanatory root of such words as *mycelium; mycosis*, a disease caused by a fungus; *mycotic*, the adjective referring to a disease caused by a fungal agent; and the suffix, *-mycete*.)

The Phycomycetes are characterized by a type of sexual reproduction in which a spore called a *zygote* is formed from the fusion of a pair of cells, each derived from a different plant (see Fig. 2–9). Germination of the zygote leads to the production of a new generation. Asexual spores are also formed by the fungi of this class. The mycelium of any species of Phycomycete characteristically gives rise to certain specialized hyphae that rise aerially and develop at their tips a round, saclike structure, called a *sporangium*. Within this sac, many asexual *sporangiospores* are developed, and when these are released by rupture of the sac, each may germinate to produce new hyphae and a new mycelium.

One of the most familiar members of this class

Fig. 2–8. Photomicrograph of yeast cells in the process of budding. The small bodies are bacteria. Note the difference in the size of these two types of organism. Magnification 1000×. (Courtesy of Dr. Kendall K. Kane, St. Luke's Hospital Center, New York, N.Y.)

Fig. 2–9. Various types of sexual spores of fungi. *A, B,* and *D* are spores of Ascomycetes (*A* is a budding yeast cell, or blastospore; *B* is an ascus containing four sexual spores). *E, G,* and *F* are spores of Basidiomycetes. (Reproduced from Conant, Norman F. *et al.*: *Manual of Clinical Mycology*, 2nd ed. W. B. Saunders Co., Philadelphia, 1954.)

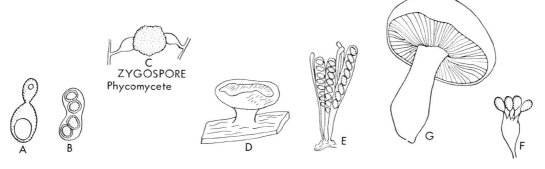

is the common black mold of bread, *Rhizopus nigricans.* Another member of the group is the genus *Mucor,* which is associated occasionally, probably by accidental opportunity, with human disease.

The Ascomycetes comprise the largest class of fungi, which includes the true yeasts as well as some mildews and molds. The characteristic sexual spores of this group occur, always in even numbers (from two to eight), within a sac called an *ascus,* from which they take the name of *ascospore* (see Fig. 2–9). Asexual reproduction is accomplished by spores or by a budding cell often called a *blastospore.* This is the type of cell previously mentioned that pinches off a daughter cell and that is typical of the yeasts. Some yeasts are unicellular; that is, their bodies are formed only by budding cells. Others may produce a filamentous mycelium like that of other fungi.

One of the most familiar members of this class is the widely used baker's yeast. Others are used in brewing beer, or in making wine. There are three genera of yeastlike organisms, known as *Candida, Cryptococcus,* and *Geotrichum,* that are of medical interest. Their classification with the Ascomycetes is not secure because it has been difficult, or impossible, to demonstrate their production of sexual spores, but in other morphologic respects they closely resemble the yeasts. *Candida* and *Geotrichum* species often live harmlessly on human mucosal surfaces, but if circumstances permit their overgrowth, or if they have an opportunity to find their way into deeper tissues, serious infection can result. *Cryptococcus* is associated with serious diseases of the lung, brain, and other vital organs.

The Basidiomycetes include the well-known mushrooms and toadstools, as well as the rusts and smuts that cause disease in some plants. A club-shaped structure called a *basidium* produces the typical sexual spore (*basidiospore*). In the case of the mushrooms, the vegetative mycelium develops underground and pushes upward a compact mass, or button, that develops into the well-known little umbrella-like structure. The basidia develop on the gills underneath the umbrella, producing basidiospores that drop to the ground and give rise to a new plant if the right

conditions persist (see Fig. 2–9). From the medical point of view, this group contains no members capable of causing *infectious* disease in man, although some species of mushroom, or toadstool, contain a substance that is poisonous to man if it is eaten.

The Fungi Imperfecti constitute a large and very mixed group in which a recognizable sexual stage is lacking and whose final classification is uncertain. There are many types of asexual spore production among the members of this group, and this forms an important basis for the identification of each individual plant, together with other microscopic structural details and with its visible appearance (see Figs. 2–10 and 2–11).

All the fungi important in human mycotic diseases, with the possible exception of the three mentioned with the Ascomycetes, are grouped with the Fungi Imperfecti. There are many fungus infections that involve only the superficial tissues, that is, the skin and mucous membranes. The well-known problems of "athlete's foot" and ringworm are examples of such infections. These are usually not serious in the life-threatening sense, but they can be quite troublesome for a number of reasons. Some of them are difficult to cure and therefore are a continuing, often debilitating problem to the patient. Furthermore, some are easily spread from one person to another and present a problem in control, as in the

THALLOSPORES

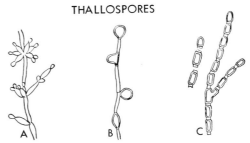

Fig. 2–10. Some types of fungal asexual spores. These varieties are called *thallospores* because they are produced by or within the main body of the plant: *A.* Blastospores (budding cells). *B.* Chlamydospores (thick-walled resting cells). *C.* Arthrospores (segments of fragmenting hyphae). (Reproduced from Conant, Norman F., *et al.: Manual of Clinical Mycology,* 2nd ed. W. B. Saunders Co., Philadelphia, 1954.)

ASEXUAL SPORES

Conidia

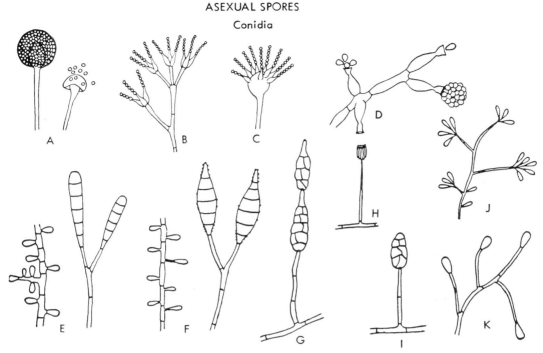

Fig. 2–11. Various fungal asexual spores of the *conidial* type. All are borne on specialized hyphae. (Reproduced from Conant, Norman F., *et al.* : *Manual of Clinical Mycology*, 2nd ed. W. B. Saunders Co., Philadelphia, 1954.)

case of scalp ringworm among schoolchildren. There is also a small group of fungi associated with serious systemic diseases, in which various vital organs, including the brain, may be involved. Among these are diseases such as histoplasmosis, blastomycosis, and coccidioidomycosis for which the mortality rate is high because the tissue involvement may become extensive and treatment is difficult.

On the other hand, the dramatically useful role played by some fungi in many bacterial diseases of man has been continuously extended since the famous ascomycete, *Penicillium*, was first demonstrated to be capable of producing a substance, *penicillin*, that is strongly antagonistic to many bacteria, among them some important agents of human infection (see Fig. 2–12). Since the time of that discovery the search for such antibacterial agents, commonly called *antibiotics*, among fungi

and other organisms has extended around the world and reached stupendous proportions. Untold numbers of fungi, and fungal products, have been studied exhaustively in laboratories every-

Fig. 2–12. *Penicillium notatum* growing in a slide culture. Magnification 400×. (Compare with Fig. 2–11 *B*.)

where in the effort to produce drugs that can be safely used in the treatment of human infectious diseases. A large majority of such products have had to be discarded either because they are toxic in themselves to human beings or because they are relatively inefficient in their action on a range, or *spectrum*, of bacteria. However, a handful of clinically useful, relatively safe antibiotics has emerged from the search and has become an inseparable part of the medical approach to infectious disease. It has also become a part of the daily routine of the diagnostic microbiologist to test these drugs for their efficacy against the bacterial agents of infection isolated from the patient, so that the physician can choose appropriately among them for treatment of the case.

The Schizomycetes, or Bacteria

The classification of bacteria with the fungi (see Chap. 12, p. 290) constitutes a recognition of some of their basic physiologic similarities with the plant world at large and with the chlorophyll-free, heterotrophic fungal plants in particular. They are unicellular fungi, but structurally simpler and considerably smaller than any of the single-celled plant (or animal) cells discussed so far. The highest power of magnification (about $1000\times$) of a good light microscope is required to get a close look at them (see Table 2–1), and even then it is usually necessary to stain them to see their surfaces distinctly. Clear visualization of their internal structures requires the still greater magnifications of the electron microscope (see Chap. 4). Classifications become very difficult, however, at this point, for distinctions between the simple plants and animals are themselves frequently unclear. At the lower levels of organization of living material physiologic and other characteristics are often variable. This applies particularly to bacteria and to other smaller microorganisms that appear to lie at the very edge of organized life.

The use of the term "schizomycete" to classify the bacteria with, but distinct from, the *true* fungi refers to their usual manner of asexual reproduction by simple binary fission, or splitting (*schizo-*).

An individual bacterial cell simply splits in half, forming two new individuals. Further classifications of the many thousands of species of bacteria are based on a number of characteristics, such as their basic shapes (i.e., morphology), the patterns formed as repeated cell divisions occur, and their physiologic capabilities and requirements.

Three basic shapes are displayed among bacteria (see Fig. 2–13, *A–F*): individual cells appear to be either spherical, rodlike, or spiraled. The spherical forms are called *cocci*, the rods are known as *bacilli* (see Fig. 2–13, *D*), and those that have a spiral shape are the *spirilla* (see Fig. 2–13, *E*). The singular form of each of these words is, respectively, *coccus, bacillus, spirillum*. Not only is the shape of an individual cell useful in the recognition of bacteria, but the groupings formed as cell divisions occur and as multiplication proceeds from a few to many cells gathered together are sometimes helpful in their identification. Among the cocci, fission may occur at different planes within the round cell. Cocci that split along one plane only tend to arrange themselves in pairs (*diplo*cocci) (see Fig. 2–13, *A*), or in chains of varying length (*strepto*cocci) (see Fig. 2–13, *B*). When the division occurs alternately in each of two planes, groups of four (tetrads) or cubelike packets of eight are the characteristic result. Haphazard splitting on several planes produces an irregular cluster of cocci, bunched together like grapes (*staphylo*cocci) (see Fig. 2–13, *C*). The patterns formed by bacilli are more limited because they split only across their short axis. They may appear as end-to-end pairs (diplobacilli), or they may line up in chains (streptobacilli). Sometimes, the two new bacilli formed by the split of a parent cell bend away from the point of fission and lie for a time in V, X, or Y patterns. Very short, small bacilli can resemble cocci (the term "coccobacillary" is often used for this), but since they divide on one plane only, they do not form packeted or clustered groups. The spirilla are short spiral forms, with from one to three fixed curves in their rigid bodies. (Those with only one resemble a comma. See Fig. 2–13, *E*.) They also split on their short axis, and when they remain close to each other after division, they may form long, sinuous chains.

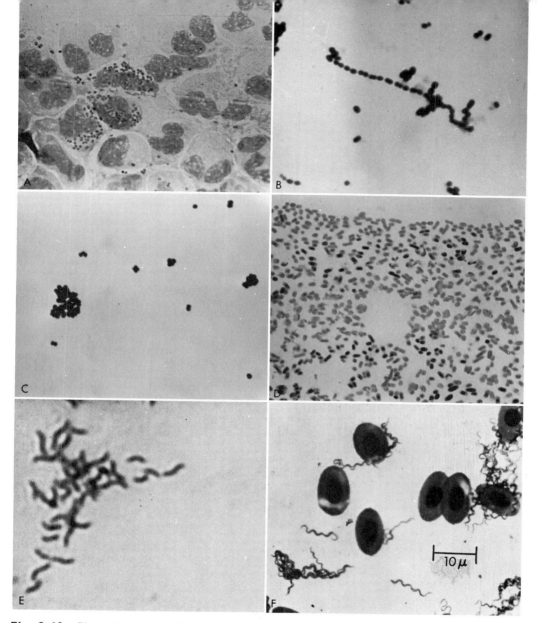

Fig. 2–13. Photomicrographs illustrating the morphologic characteristics of some bacteria. *A*. Cocci (spheres) in pairs, diplococci. (The large objects are white blood cells.) *B*. Cocci in chains, streptococci. *C*. Cocci in irregular clusters, micrococci or staphylococci. *D*. Bacilli, straight rods. (*A*, *B*, *C*, and *D* courtesy of Dr. Kendall K. Kane, St. Luke's Hospital Center, New York, N.Y.) *E*. Curved rods, vibrios. (Courtesy of Dr. Victor Bokkenheuser, St. Luke's Hospital Center, New York, N.Y.) *F*. Spirochetes, flexible spirals. (The large objects are avian blood cells.) (Reproduced from McNeil, E.; Hinshaw, W. R.; and Kissling, R. E.: *J. Bact.*, **57**:191–206, 1949.)

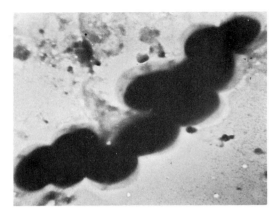

Fig. 2–14. An electron micrograph of pneumo-
cocci with clearly visible capsules. (19,700×.)
(Courtesy of Dr. A. I. Laskin, Squibb Institute for
Medical Research, New Brunswick, N. J.)

There is another group of spiraled organisms
classified with the bacteria, called the *spirochetes*
(see Fig. 2–13, *F*). These are higher forms and
bear more resemblances to the protozoa than to
the fungi. They are much longer and more tightly
coiled than the spirilla, their bodies are flexible,
and they propel themselves by rapid rotation
around their long axes, as well as by undulatory
motions.

The cell wall of true bacteria is rigid, like that
of plants, but permeable to the passage of liquid
nutrient material into the cell and to the outward
passage of substances produced within the cell.
The structure, arrangement, and composition of
the molecules composing cell walls are of integral
importance to the properties and behavior of
bacteria, as many recent studies have shown; indeed, their functions, and their responses to the
world about them, must be mediated through the
components of the wall. In many cases, the
bacterial wall is surrounded by a viscous polysaccharide coating, often referred to as a slime
layer or as a *capsule* (see Fig. 2–14). The production of capsular material may be a function of
the cell wall, or of some component within the
cell, but in any case it is under the direction of
the cell's nuclear apparatus. The capsule can
play a vital role in protecting the cell against its
environment, a matter of great importance in

some bacterial infections in which the defense
mechanisms of the body must deal with capsular
substance.

The motility of bacteria is dependent on the
presence or absence of *flagella* (see Fig. 2–15),
which originate in the cytoplasm of bacterial
cells. Morphologically, they resemble those possessed by some of the protozoa except that they
are structurally much more simple. When they
are present, they provide the cell with the capability for active motion, but only in liquids or on
moistened surfaces. Bacteria cannot move independently through the air, but must be carried
on droplets of moisture or particles of dust. In
general, cocci are not flagellated and therefore
are nonmotile, but most spirilla and many bacilli
are quite active. This was one of the things that
astonished Leeuwenhoek when he saw them, in
drops of liquid magnified with a lens, dashing
about with great speed or moving in graceful
undulations. The flagella of bacteria are too fine
to be seen directly with the light microscope,
even with modern lenses, but they can be demonstrated with special staining techniques. They are
composed of a single strand of a protein molecule,
which repeats itself in a spiral (helical) pattern.
This protein differs from those found in the cell
wall or in other parts of the cell.

During their normal growth cycle, some bacilli
are capable of passing into a resistant stage with
the production of an *endospore* or, more simply

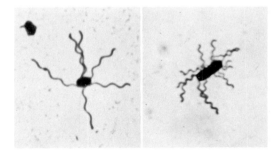

Fig. 2–15. Photomicrographs of the flagellated
organism *Proteus mirabilis.* (2000×.) Note the
straight and wavy flagella. (Reproduced from
Leifson, Einar, *et al.*: Morphological Characteristics
of Flagella of Proteus and Related Bacteria, *J.
Bact.,* **69**:73–82, 1955.)

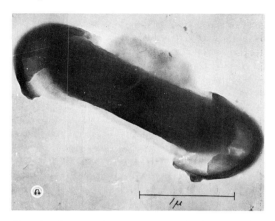

Fig. 2–16. An electron micrograph of a vegetative bacterial cell emerging from a germinating spore. Note that the two halves of the completely severed spore coat still remain as caps on the ends of the bacterium. (Reproduced from Knaysi, Georges; Baker, R. F.; and Hillier, James: A Study, with the High-Voltage Electron Microscope, of the Endospore and Life Cycle of *Bacillus mycoides*, *J. Bact.*, **53**:525–37, 1947. Courtesy of Society of American Bacteriologists and RCA Laboratories.)

called, a *spore* (see Fig. 2–16). The vegetative (actively growing) bacterial cell loses moisture and condenses its contents within a wall thicker than the original one, forming a round or ovoid body. Unlike the spores of fungi, bacterial spores are not a reproductive form. They represent a resting and protective stage, in which the cell can resist such adverse conditions as excessive temperatures, humidity, or drying. The transforming process is called *sporulation*, and when it is later reversed under favorable growth conditions each spore germinates into a single vegetative cell, capable of function and reproduction in the normal manner once more. Spores are capable of surviving for long periods in soil and dust, and they are quite resistant also to effects of boiling or of exposure to live steam. Vegetative bacterial cells, on the other hand, are readily killed in a few minutes in boiling water. These differences are of great importance in the establishment of methods of sterilization (a process that kills all living organisms) and are inherent in the discussions of this subject later in the text.

The internal structures of bacteria include a dense cytoplasm, granules of protein and carbohydrate material, lipoid substances, and functional nuclear material. The new staining and microscopic techniques of the last decade have demonstrated that bacterial nuclei contain chromosomal structures like those of higher plant and animal cells, and that they conduct a mitotic type of division, in cell reproduction, similar to that of other asexual processes. It is also possible, though infrequent, for a sexual type of reproduction to occur when unlike cells fuse and exchange hereditary material (see Chap. 2).

There are thousands of species of bacteria, some (the so-called higher bacteria) showing an obvious relationship with the fungi, others, like the spirochetes, forming a link with the simple animal cells. In between are all the true bacteria, many of which are useful and necessary to human life. The bacteria that cause human disease represent a very small fraction of the whole group to which they belong, but because of their potential in this respect they have great importance for us. Their recognition, and further classification, are based upon the type of characteristics discussed above and on others described in Part Two for individual organisms.

The Smallest Microorganisms

Passing downward in size beyond the range of resolution of the ordinary microscope, we find that there are three general groups of microorganisms of diminishing dimensions and a dwindling display of characteristics associated with independent life processes. The smallest of these approach the size of a single, large molecule (see Table 2–1) and challenge in other ways, as well, our concepts and definitions of cellular life. The largest are almost the size of the smallest bacteria, but they are more primitive in either structure or independent function.

These three groups are the *Mycoplasma* (pleuropneumonia organisms and their relatives), the rickettsiae, and the viruses. All contain members associated with human disease, but the number, variety, and seriousness of these diseases are greatest among the viruses.

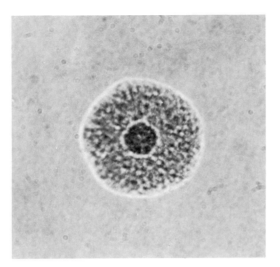

Fig. 2–17. Photomicrograph of a colony of *Mycoplasma hominis*, magnified 150×. (Courtesy of National Institute of Allergy and Infectious Diseases [NIAID], Bethesda, Md.)

The Mycoplasma are classified with the bacteria but differ from them not only in being somewhat smaller, but also in lacking distinctive cell walls (see Fig. 2–17). They have plastic, variable shapes that appear different when they are seen growing in fluid or on solid nutrient substances. They will multiply on nonliving organic material and grow into protoplasmic masses that, by special staining techniques, can be shown to contain unorganized granular structures and chromatin material. In liquid nutrients their forms may resemble rings, bacilli, spirals, and filaments.

Mycoplasma were first demonstrated in a disease of cattle known as pleuropneumonia, from which they first took their name. Other organisms of this type have since been associated with other diseases of animals, and similar, but not identical forms (pleuropneumonia-like organisms, or PPLO) have been recognized in specimens from the respiratory and urinary tracts of humans. Their association with human diseases has been suspected, but definitely established only in the case of the infectious disease called "primary atypical pneumonia."

The rickettsiae resemble the smallest bacteria in size and appearance (see Chap. 12, p. 298 for their classification). They are nonmotile coccobacillary forms, but they require special stains and the highest possible magnification of the light microscope for good visualization (see Table 2–1). The most striking difference they display with reference to bacteria is an absolute dependence on the living cells of a higher animal for their nourishment and multiplication. They can be seen within such cells, living in the cytoplasm surrounding the nucleus (see Fig. 2–18). In the laboratory, they will survive and grow only in animal cells grown in the test tube (tissue culture), or in the developing embryos of chicken eggs, or in insects and experimental animals. They cannot be studied on artificial nutrients, no matter how rich in organic substances, for they lack the ability to convert such material into a form they can utilize, requiring an animal cell to do this for them. This is an example of an extreme

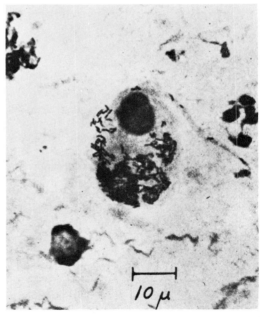

Fig. 2–18. Photomicrograph of the rickettsiae of typhus fever. Note their intracellular position. (Reprinted by permission of the Rockefeller Institute Press; from Plotz, Harry; Smadel, Joseph E.; Anderson, Thomas F.; and Chambers, Leslie A.: *J. Exper. Med.,* **77**:355–58, 1943.)

kind of parasitism (obligate intracellular parasitism), discussed more fully in Chapter 5.

In nature, the rickettsiae occur chiefly as harmless parasites of insects such as lice, ticks, and mites, living in the cells of their intestinal tracts and salivary glands. Sometimes the insect becomes diseased and dies of this infection, but often the relationship continues without damage, and the insect may transmit the rickettsiae to the next generation via its eggs. The situation assumes medical importance when rickettsiae are transmitted to man by the bite of these blood-sucking insects. The microorganisms take up an intracellular life in the human being thus infected, and the result can be a disease of serious proportion, often with a fatal outcome.

There are several kinds of rickettsial diseases that occur in various parts of the world, their geographic distribution depending largely on the nature and habitat of insect and animal hosts, but also on the rickettsial species. Of these, the most widespread damage and suffering in human populations has been caused by the agent of *typhus fever* (not to be confused with typhoid fever), which is transmitted by lice and has a potential for reaching epidemic proportions. Other important rickettsial diseases include Rocky Mountain spotted fever, rickettsialpox, and Q fever. These infections are usually classified according to the method of their transmission, via the insect host, and are arranged accordingly in the appropriate sections of Part Two. The name of *Rickettsia* was assigned to this genus of organisms as a tribute to Dr. Howard T. Ricketts, who discovered an important member of the group, identified it as the cause of Rocky Mountain spotted fever (1909), and died in 1910, at the age of 39, of typhus fever accidentally acquired through his continuing work with the agents of these diseases.

The Viruses.   The viruses are the smallest of all the microorganisms and the most difficult to classify by conventional means (see Chap. 12, p. 299). There is great variety among them, in terms of size, structure, function, and as agents of disease (see Fig. 2–19). Dimensionally, they range from those comparable in size to the rickettsiae, and therefore visible with the proper techniques

with the light microscope, to those of molecular proportions. (See Table 2–1 for the size range of microorganisms and molecules.) In structure, some resemble a tadpole in shape, having a globular "head" with a "tailpiece" (see Fig. 2–20); some are globular; others are multifaceted; some are crystalline upon purification. Like the rickettsiae, they have a strict requirement for the assistance of living cells in propagating themselves, but they are much more widely distributed than the former. There are many viruses that cause diseases of plants, and these do not usually also cause animal or human disease. On the other hand, the viruses of the animal world often are associated with more than one species and can be transmitted in a variety of ways. There are a number of virus diseases that are transmitted between humans, or from animals to humans, only by the bites of insects. In other cases the transmission is direct from person to person, or from animal to man without an intermediary.

In recent years the development of methods for the successful cultivation of animal and human tissues or cells in the test tube has brought about many significant advances in our knowledge of viruses. As it is for the rickettsiae, the developing embryo of the fertilized chicken egg is a convenient and inexpensive cellular medium in which many viruses can grow and multiply and in which they can be produced in large quantities for closer study. These types of culture are often used, also, by the diagnostic virologist for the isolation of viruses from appropriate specimens obtained from patients.

Concurrently with the development of these techniques, sophisticated methods have been devised for measuring, visualizing, and purifying viruses, which have led to better demonstrations of their functions and activities within cells. The problems are further compounded by the fact that some viruses appear to be limited not only to an intracellular life, but to particular types of cells (e.g., nerve, lung, or liver cells) from particular hosts. Such requirements affect not only the natural pattern of disease but also the laboratory methods by which the viruses in question can be studied effectively.

Research into the nature of virus activity

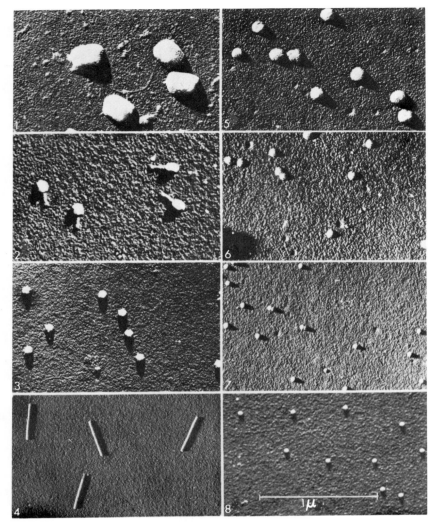

Fig. 2–19. Electron micrographs of eight viruses shown at the same magnification. *1.* Vaccinia virus. *2.* T₂ bacteriophage. *3.* T₃ bacteriophage. *4.* Tobacco mosaic virus. *5.* Influenza virus. *6.* Rabbit papilloma virus. *7.* Bushy stunt virus. *8.* Polio virus. (Reproduced from Stanley, Wendell H.: On the Nature of Viruses, *Mod. Med.,* pp. 79–82, July, 1958. Micrographs by R. C. Williams; virus preparations by staff members of the Virus Laboratory, University of California, Berkeley, Calif.)

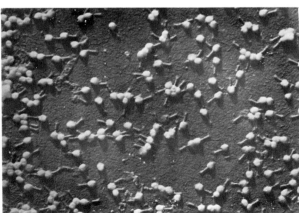

Fig. 2–20. Colon bacillus bacteriophage, type T₄. This electron micrograph was taken at a magnification of 46,000✕. Note the globular head and the tailpiece of these organisms. (Courtesy of Dr. Ralph W. G. Wyckoff, University of Arizona, Tucson, Ariz.)

Table 2–1. The Size Range of Microorganisms and Molecules and Their Microscope Requirements*

Object	Size Range†	Microscope Requirements‡
Largest tapeworm	12 to 75 ft (length)	None
Smallest tapeworm	3 to 6 mm (length)	Magnifying lens or light microscope, low-power objective (2.5× to 10×)
Tapeworm ova	25 to 50μ (diameter) by 50 to 90μ (length)	Light microscope, high dry objective (oil-immersion lens for detail) (40× to 100×)
Largest intestinal roundworm	8 to 12 in. (length)	None
Smallest roundworm	2 to 13 mm (length)	Magnifying lens or light microscope, low-power objective (2.5× to 10×)
Roundworm ova	20 to 40μ (diameter) by 50 to 90μ (length)	Light microscope, high dry objective (oil-immersion lens for detail) (40× to 100×)
Protozoa		
Smallest	2 to 4μ (diameter)	Light microscope, oil-immersion lens (100×)
Largest	80 to 100μ (diameter)	Light microscope, high dry objective (oil-immersion lens for detail) (40× to 100×)
Human red blood cells	7.5μ (average diameter)	Light microscope, high dry objective (oil-immersion lens for detail) (40× to 100×)
Fungus spores	1 to 5μ (diameter) by 5 to 20μ (length)	Light microscope, high dry objective for largest; oil-immersion lens for smallest (40× to 100×)
Bacteria	0.5 to 1.5μ (diameter) by 1 to 6μ (length)	Light microscope, oil-immersion lens (100×)
Rickettsiae	0.3 to 0.5μ (diameter) by 0.3 to 2.0μ (length)	Light microscope, oil-immersion lens (100×); electron microscope for detail
Viruses	10 to 300 mμ (diameter)	Electron microscope
Molecules	1 angstrom to 25 mμ (diameter)	Electron microscope

*See also Figs. 1–1 through 1–8 and Fig. 12–1 for comparisons of microbial sizes.
†Units of measurement:
        mm = millimeter = 1/25.4 in.
          μ = micron = 1/1000 mm or 1/25,400 in.
         mμ = millimicron = 1/1000 μ or 1/25,400,000 in.
    angstrom = 1/10 mμ or 1/10,000 μ or 1/10,000,000 mm or 1/254,000,000 in.
‡Microscope objectives (see Chap. 4 for description of light and electron microscopes):
    Low-power objectives magnify from 2.5 to 10×, depending on the choice of lens.
    High-power objectives magnify 40×.
    High- and low-power objectives are used without immersion oil and are therefore said to be "dry" lenses.
    Oil-immersion objectives magnify 98 to 100× depending on the choice of lens.

within host cells has also been stimulated repeatedly by evidence pointing to the possible involvement of viruses in cancer, as it occurs in humans, animals, and plants. While some animal cancers have been shown to be caused by viruses, and others can be experimentally induced by viral agents, there is no conclusive evidence at present that human cancers are associated with viruses.

Much has been learned, however, about the nature of viruses and the method by which they infect cells. The smallest virus particles appear to represent the final essence of cellular genetic material, wrapped only in a protein coat. The inner substance often has the same composition and type of activity as that of genes, which are the basic nuclear units of higher cells through which hereditary characteristics are transmitted in cell division, or of "messenger" molecules that assure such transmissions. Such a particle is stripped of all other machinery, all independence, and all function except that involved in reproduction and, so to speak, in the direction of cellular future. When such a particle enters an animal cell, the protein coat is discarded at the door and the virus core settles down in the cell's cytoplasm, or, later perhaps, in the nucleus. It then begins to direct the cell's genetic traffic, inducing the cell to produce more virus substance and sidetracking it, in the process, from the continued production of its own hereditary material or the conduct of its everyday affairs. In a very short time a quantity of new virus particles is produced and released from the infected cell, and the process is repeated as new cells are infected, with the consequent formation of more and more virus.

This is the ultimate in parasitism, but the events just described represent one extreme of a range of cell-virus relationships. It is also possible (among bacteria, for instance, that have their own viruses, called bacteriophages) for viruses to lie dormant within a cell, interfering little if at all with host activities and themselves undergoing no duplication. This may continue for long periods of time, during which the virus is said to be *latent*, until conditions change in some way for the host, or the virus, and the latter becomes active. This situation is now known to occur in

human virus infection, for on the one hand viruses often are isolated from entirely healthy individuals, and on the other hand they can be shown to cause repeated problems in infected persons who have long periods of freedom from symptoms between attacks. The common cold sore affords an example of the latter situation, its viral agent being present in many persons, but inactive until some stress, such as fever or sun exposure, changes the situation for the host cell.

Current classifications of viruses place them together with the rickettsiae (both groups being obligate parasites) in the most primitive class of the plant world. The viruses are subdivided further, according to their host requirements, into bacterial viruses and plant and animal viruses.

Among the viruses that cause human disease, several methods of classification exist, none of which is very satisfactory because of the difficulties in documenting viruses in all their capabilities and host cell relationships. The many viruses isolated with increasing frequency from normal individuals, together with those associated with mild, ill-defined clinical infections, are particularly difficult to classify. A system designed to emphasize their affinity for, or isolation from, particular types of tissues in the body cannot be easily maintained, for many viruses can and do reproduce in more than one type of cell or tissue. Thus, poliomyelitis virus is thought of as *neurotropic* because it has an affinity for nerve cells, but it is also classified with a group of viruses called *enteroviruses* because, like these, it can grow in cells of the intestinal lining and apparently does so on its initial entry into the body. Measles virus is spoken of as *dermatotropic* because it affects the epithelial cells of the skin, producing a characteristic rash, but it also multiplies in cells of the lungs and damages them. To make matters worse, there are some viruses that can cause more than one type of clinical disease, depending on where in the body they localize.

In most instances where a one virus–one disease relationship exists, the virus is named for the clinical entity, e.g., yellow fever, hepatitis, measles, and mumps. Viruses are also named, sometimes, according to the geographic area in which the disease, or the virus, was first recog-

nized, e.g., Coxsackie virus, Japanese B virus, West Nile virus; or according to the type of animal, other than man, with which they are importantly associated, e.g., equine encephalitis virus. Clinically they are often also grouped according to an outstanding and fairly constant symptomatic feature. Thus, viruses that characteristically involve the skin and produce a rash (measles, German measles, roseola) are grouped together, as are those that produce pocks on the skin (smallpox, chickenpox, and herpes viruses).

Viruses primarily associated with respiratory diseases (influenza and the adenoviruses) or that require an insect to transmit them from man to man (yellow fever) or from animals to man (equine encephalitis) are similarly classed together.

Obviously, each of these systems encounters the difficulties of serious overlapping or of grouping unrelated viruses or diseases, and obviously, also, this confusion reflects a deficiency of knowledge and information.

Questions

1. What characteristics distinguish the phylum Thallophyta? *plant no vascular systems roots or leaves*
2. What characteristics of protozoa are used to classify these microorganisms? *movements*
3. Name the distinguishing characteristics of each of the four classes of protozoa.
4. Why are the large metazoa included in the study of microbiology?
5. What is the outstanding difference between the platyhelminths and the nematodes?
6. Name the four classes of fungi and briefly describe their method of reproduction.
7. What are the three basic shapes of bacteria? Describe and name each of the arrangements of bacteria.
8. List the special structures of bacteria and their importance.
9. What characteristics do viruses and rickettsiae have in common?
10. How do viruses, rickettsiae, and mycoplasmas differ from bacteria?

References

Pertinent References

Burdon, Kenneth L., and Williams, Robert P.: *Textbook of Microbiology*, 6th ed. The Macmillan Co., New York, 1968.
Dubos, René J.: *The Bacterial Cell.* Harvard University Press, Cambridge, Mass., 1946.
Pelczar, Michael J., and Reid, Roger: *Microbiology*, 2nd ed. McGraw-Hill, New York, 1965.

Periodicals

BACTERIA
Calafiore, Dorothy: Streptococcal Infections, *Nurs. Outlook*, 7:712, Dec., 1959.
Thompson, LaVerne: Staphylococcus Aureus, *Amer. J. Nurs.*, 58:1098, Aug., 1958.
Watanabe, Tsutomu: Infections and Drug Resistance, *Sci. Amer.*, 217:19, Dec., 1967.
Zinder, Norton D.: Transduction in Bacteria, *Sci. Amer.*, 199:38, Nov., 1958.

VIRUSES
Anderson, Robert J.: Viruses and the Public's Health, *Minnesota Med.*, 43:647, Oct., 1960.
Horne, R. W.: The Structure of Viruses, *Sci. Amer.*, 208:48, Jan., 1963.
Jacob, Francois, and Wollman, Elie L.: Viruses and Genes, *Sci. Amer.*, 204:92, June, 1961.
Johnson, Karl M.: Some Newly Discovered Respiratory Disease Viruses, *Amer. J. Nurs.*, 63:67, Nov., 1963.
Melnick, Joseph: Enteroviruses, *Sci. Amer.*, 200:89, Feb., 1959.
Pines, Maya: The Quickening War Against Viruses, *Harper's Magazine*, May, 1964.

Rubin, Harry: A Defective Cancer Virus, *Sci. Amer.*, **210**:46, June, 1964.

Thompson, LaVerne: Viruses, Old and New, *Amer. J. Nurs.*, **59**:349, March, 1959.

The Virus Enemy, *Life*, **60**:56, Feb. 18, 1966.

YEASTS

Rose, Anthony H.: Yeasts, *Sci. Amer.*, **202**:136, Feb., 1960.

PPLO

Morowitz, H. J., and Tourtellotte, M. E.: The Smallest Cells, *Sci. Amer.*, **206**:117, March, 1962.

RICKETTSIAE

Bovarnick, Marianna B.: Rickettsiae, *Sci. Amer.*, **192**:74, Jan., 1955.

Popular Literature

Clark, Paul F.: *Alice in Virusland.* Society American Bacteriologists, University of Wisconsin, Madison, 1938.

Kavaler, Lucy: *Mushrooms, Molds and Miracles.* John Day, New York, 1965.

Smith, Kenneth M.: *Viruses.* Cambridge University Press, Cambridge, England, 1962.

Williams, Greer: *Virus Hunters.* Alfred A. Knopf, New York, 1959.

3 The Behavior of Microorganisms

Comparative Metabolism: Plants, Animals, Microorganisms

The division of the living world into the plant and animal kingdoms emphasizes the differences that exist between plants and animals, but it is important to recognize the many fundamental similarities that unite living things, particularly at the cellular level (see Table 3–1).

The Differences

One of the most obvious anatomic differences between the higher plants and animals is that most plants have no organs for locomotion, and therefore must remain stationary, while animals can move about freely. This relates, in turn, most importantly, to their different methods of obtaining and using nourishment. Plants owe their color to the green light-sensitive pigment chlorophyll, which enables them to utilize the energy of light to convert water and carbon dioxide from the atmosphere into the carbohydrate they need for their own energy. Animals have no such metabolic independence and must obtain their nutrient from other animals or plants, but they are anatomically free to move around in their search for food. Since they must share their environment, plants and animals maintain it for each other by contributing to it, and taking from

39

Table 3–1. Comparison of Some Important Life Activities of Man and Microorganism

Activities of Life	Man	Microorganism (Heterotrophic Bacterium)
1. Absorption of nutrients	Capable of digesting most foods; absorbs soluble nutrient through small intestine; requires proteins, carbohydrates, fats, vitamins, minerals	Cannot digest particulate matter; must have nutrient in soluble form for absorption through cell wall; requires proteins, carbohydrates, fats, vitamins, minerals
2. Conversion of nutrient to energy	Tissue cells enzymatically convert absorbed soluble nutrients to amino acids (from protein), glucose (from carbohydrates), and fatty acids (from fats); oxidative and fermentative processes release energy and provide compounds needed in synthesis of body materials	Cellular enzymes convert absorbed soluble nutrients to amino acids (from protein products), glucose (from carbohydrates), and fatty acids (from fats); oxidative and fermentative processes release energy and provide compounds needed in synthesis of cellular structures
3. Respiration	Atmospheric oxygen taken in, utilized in breakdown of carbohydrates by cellular enzymes to carbon dioxide and water; oxygen exchange complex and varied	Atmospheric oxygen taken in, utilized in breakdown of carbohydrates by cellular enzymes to carbon dioxide and water; oxygen exchange complex and varied
4. Excretion	Metabolic end products (nitrogenous wastes, water, carbon dioxide) are excreted through kidneys, lungs, and skin; bowel excretes unabsorbed food residue and water	Metabolic end products (nitrogenous wastes, water, carbon dioxide) are excreted through cell wall
5. Growth and reproduction	Sexual conjugation required for reproduction; offspring usually single; requires approximately 280 days for gestation, 18 years for complete growth; reproduction and growth limited by adverse conditions	Reproduction usually asexual; sexual conjugations also occur; rapid reproduction and growth produce many offspring within a few hours; can reproduce and grow under much wider range of adverse conditions than can man
6. Response to stimuli	Responds to heat, light, sound, and other physical stimuli; extremes adversely affect many body processes	Responds to heat, light, sound, and other physical stimuli; extremes that affect life processes are usually much greater than those that limit man's vital activities

it, alternate essentials. Thus, in their respiration, animals take oxygen from the air, convert it in their lungs to carbon dioxide, and return the latter to the atmosphere in their exhalations. Plants perform this exchange in reverse, taking up the carbon dioxide and returning the oxygen required by animals.

Another important anatomic distinction relates to the specialization of structures for the intake of food. Plants are very limited in this respect, having only their roots and leaves or, in the case of the thallophytes, no special structure at all. This means that they must have their food in solution so that they can absorb it from their

environment. Animals, of course, are well equipped for the intake, not only of liquid nutrients, but of solid foods, the mouths of most higher forms being further specialized for the mechanical breakup of food particles as well.

The visible rigidity of plants, as opposed to the plasticity of animal shapes, results from the presence of cellulose in the wall of individual plant cells. The hard outer wall encloses and gives support to the plant. It also makes the plant impervious, in large degree, to environmental harm, though this is relative of course. Animal cells, on the other hand, do not contain cellulose (there are a few exceptions to this general rule), do not have a cell wall, and are not rigid. The thin membrane that surrounds them permits many changes in their shape and is semipermeable to its environment, allowing a controlled exchange of materials between the cytoplasm of the cell and the world without. This makes for quicker responses to environmental changes, by animals as opposed to plants, but it also leaves them more vulnerable to harmful and destructive influences.

In nutritional classifications, the terminology used emphasizes other important differences and is applied to microorganisms as well as to higher forms. Thus, organisms that are relatively independent of other forms of life in their nutrition and can therefore be thought of as self-nourishing are called *autotrophic*, while those that derive their food from organic material originally produced by other living things are termed *heterotrophic*. Plants that contain chlorophyll and through its mediations are able to nourish themselves from simple inorganic substances are *autotrophs;* but all animals, as well as the simple colorless plants that lack chlorophyll (that is, the fungi and many bacteria), are *heterotrophs*, requiring organic compounds such as proteins, vitamins, and carbohydrates because they cannot synthesize (manufacture) these vital substances from inorganic molecules. The key element in this distinction is carbon in the form of CO_2, an essential requirement of all living organisms. Autotrophic organisms (plants and some bacteria) can utilize CO_2 as their sole source of carbon, converting it to carbohydrate. The autotrophic bacteria can also synthesize other complex

organic molecules (proteins, vitamins, fats, and carbohydrates) from simple inorganic salts. Heterotrophic organisms (animals and many bacteria, including all those that cause diseases) utilize CO_2 but it does not suffice as their sole source of carbon. The heterotrophs must also have carbon in an organic form such as carbohydrate (see Table 3–2).

Among the heterotrophs, those that can take in their food in solid form and then digest and absorb it are said to be *holozoic*, while those that must absorb their organic nutrient in solution are referred to as *saprophytic*. When a heterotrophic organism of either type lives in or on the body of another living organism from which it derives its nutrient, it is said to be *parasitic*, and the organism that supports it is called its *host*. Some heterotrophs are capable of living saprophytically on dead organic material unassociated with a living host but become parasitic if presented with the opportunity. Those that cannot survive on dead matter but most have a living host are called *obligate parasites*, and those that can live only within the cells of their hosts, rather than in extracellular situations, are known as *obligate intracellular parasites*.

Many of the structural and nutritional differences noted for higher plants and animals often play an observable role in the behavior of microorganisms of both types. The unicellular amoebae are holozoic, as are most other protozoans and the larval and adult stages of metazoans. The

Table 3–2. Comparison of Autotrophic and Heterotrophic Bacteria

Autotrophs	Heterotrophs
1. Utilize CO_2 as sole source of carbon	1. Utilize CO_2 but also require carbon in organic form
2. Synthesize complex proteins, carbohydrates, fats, and vitamins from simple inorganic compounds	2. Require organic compounds for synthesis of proteins, carbohydrates, fats, and vitamins
3. Independent, free-living	3. Dependent, saprophytic or parasitic

agent of amebic dysentery in man, for instance, ingests red blood cells and particles of other disintegrating cells, a fact that contributes to its damaging effects on host tissues. Most of the microbial heterotrophs are saprophytes, however, and the great majority of these are capable of living freely on dead organic material. Also, many of the saprophytes that parasitize higher organisms are not obligate parasites, for they can resume a more independent life outside of their hosts, in soil or water or in the laboratory on artificial nutrient. Among the obligate parasites, only the rickettsiae and viruses are bound to an intracellular life.

In its parasitic existence, the limiting wall or membrane of the organism, the presence or absence of capsular substance, and any special mechanisms it may possess for locomotion are all influencing factors in the organism's ability to survive in the host environment. It will be remembered that bacteria, like the higher plants, have a rigid cell wall, containing a variety of components that not only mediate their nutrition, but also may give rise to specific defensive responses from the host in many cases. Cell walls, or membranes as the case may be, are involved, also, in the differing reactions of microbial cells to stains, to antibiotics, and to chemical solutions, such as disinfectants, that are used to suppress or kill microorganisms.

The Similarities

Many of these distinctions between animals and plants become more and more difficult to make as organisms approach the unicellular level. Indeed, it has become increasingly evident that, at the cellular level at least, all forms of life are governed by the same fundamental biologic laws, although the method of operation of these laws may be influenced by anatomic and chemical differences in plant or animal cells. Modern concepts of hereditary mechanisms, for example, began to take form in the mid-nineteenth century in the work of Gregor Mendel, whose experiments with crossed garden peas led him to propose a theory of genetic law that has since been con-

firmed for many different plants and animals. Some 50 years later, T. H. Morgan's work with fruit flies became an important milestone, because it not only upheld Mendelian theory but led to the definition of genes as the intracellular units of inheritance. Current evidence being provided by microbial geneticists pins down the transmission of hereditary information in all living cells studied, including the viruses, to specific molecules of intracellular nucleic acids.

Similarly, respiratory and metabolic processes in plant and animal cells have certain common components. The raw materials required by different types of cells may differ widely (carbon dioxide, sunlight, and soluble nutrients are needed by green plants; oxygen, sometimes other atmospheric elements, and soluble or insoluble foods must be available for animal cells), but the metabolic methods by which these materials are utilized are often very similar. Organic catalysts, called *enzymes*, are vital components of both types of cells and assist in the utilization of raw materials. Enzymes, which initiate and direct chemical reactions without taking a direct part in them, not only act within cells, but may be excreted by cells into the surrounding environment. Here they may act on solid food particles to make them soluble for absorption through cell walls or in other ways make the environment more supportive to the life of the cell. Enzymes are usually quite limited, that is, *specific*, in the kind of reaction they catalyze. For instance, some are involved only in the digestion of protein components, some act only in specific steps in the breakdown of particular carbohydrates, others on fatty substances, and so forth. With these limitations on their activity, a battery of different enzymes, most if not all of them vital to cellular health and function, is required in the normal metabolism of both multicellular and unicellular organisms.

The metabolic requirements, mechanisms, and activities of microorganisms are as closely related to their enzymatic components as are those of larger forms. Furthermore, many different microbial and higher organisms contain the very same enzymes, or enzyme systems, — a fact that is not surprising when one considers the uniform dis-

tribution of *substrates* (substances on which enzymes act specifically) such as carbohydrates and organic compounds of protein origin.

Yeasts and molds, which are among the highest of the microbial plants, exemplify in their activities some of the metabolic processes and accomplishments of saprophytes. Most of these microorganisms are free-living, and widely distributed in nature (see Fig. 3–1). Many of them produce extracellular enzymes that reduce solid food materials to a soluble form for easy absorption and utilization. The molds are well-known for their ability to grow on bread and to spoil other foods not carefully protected from contamination by mold spores or from their germination.

The yeasts and their metabolic processes have been known and put to good use for many thousands of years. With the help of their enzymes, yeast cells utilize glucose for energy, converting it, under aerobic conditions (in which plenty of oxygen is available), into carbon dioxide and water. If oxygen is not available, these organisms will put a different set of enzymes to work to break down the sugar, producing ethyl alcohol.

The *aerobic* fermentation of glucose by yeasts is utilized in bread-making. In the leavening process, the release of carbon dioxide from the breakdown of the sugar contributes to the rising of the bread. In this connection it is of interest to note that the main energy food for many animal cells, including those of man, is also glucose, which is oxidized through the activity of enzymes in muscle cells to produce carbon dioxide and water and, most importantly, energy. Animals exhale a part of this carbon dioxide from their lungs, thus providing the atmosphere with a constant replenishing source of this gas required in the respiration of plants (see Table 3–3).

The *anaerobic* process by which yeasts convert glucose to alcohol is responsible for the production of wines and other alcoholic beverages (see Fig. 3–2). Strains of the wine-maker's yeast grow naturally, together with other microorganisms, on the skins of grapes, this combination being called the "bloom." In Europe, the vintner still relies on the bloom to produce a natural fermentation of the crushed grapes, which gives the wine its characteristic flavor, or individual bouquet.

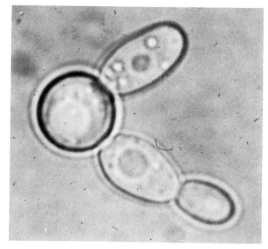

Fig. 3–1. A photomicrograph of a budding yeast cell (*Saccharomyces* species). (Reproduced from Schneierson, S. Stanley: *Atlas of Diagnostic Microbiology*. Abbott Laboratories, North Chicago, Ill., 1965.)

In bad years, when the bloom may be overgrown by extraneous molds, the wine-grower can resort to artificial fermentation, using a laboratory-grown pure culture of yeast. The latter method is usually employed in the production of North American wines. True vintage wines are produced by natural fermentation by the bloom, so that knowledge of the locale and year of the grape harvest is important to their purchase.

The viruses, as obligate intracellular parasites, exemplify the extreme in metabolic simplicity among microorganisms. The largest viruses appear to possess limited enzymatic capacity for a few metabolic processes of their own, but the smaller viruses, as we have seen in Chapter 2, contain only the essentials required for reproduction and even this function must be mediated through the host cell's genetic mechanisms. Virus particles are composed of a core of complex nucleic acids, DNA (deoxyribonucleic acid) or RNA (ribonucleic acid) or both, surrounded by a protein coat. In December, 1967, a group of American scientists headed by Dr. Arthur Kornberg reported that they had artificially synthesized the DNA molecule, which is the active core of the virus particle. Since DNA is the master

Table 3–3. Some Chemical Accomplishments of Microorganisms

A. $C_6H_{12}O_6$ $\xrightarrow[\substack{\text{yeast} \\ \text{enzymes}}]{\text{aerobic}}$ CH_3CH_2OH + CO_2 + H_2O
  Glucose   *Alcohol*   *Carbon*   *Water*
            (ethyl)   *dioxide*

B. $C_6H_{12}O_6$ $\xrightarrow[\substack{\text{yeast} \\ \text{enzymes}}]{\text{anaerobic}}$ CH_3CH_2OH
  Glucose   *Alcohol*
            (ethyl)

C. $C_6H_{12}O_6$ $\xrightarrow[\substack{\text{microbial} \\ \text{enzymes}}]{\text{aerobic}}$ CH_3CH_2OH $\xrightarrow[\substack{\text{Acetobacter} \\ \text{species}}]{\substack{\text{aerobic} \\ \text{enzymes}}}$ CH_3COOH + H_2O
  Glucose   *Alcohol*   *Acetic*   *Water*
            (ethyl)   *acid*

D. $C_6H_{12}O_6$ $\xrightarrow[\substack{\text{bacterial} \\ \text{enzymes}}]{\text{fermentative}}$ CH_3CH_2COOH
  Glucose   *Lactic acid*

E. Organic $\xrightarrow[\substack{\text{bacterial} \\ \text{enzymes}}]{\text{oxidative}}$ NH_3 + O_2 $\xrightarrow[\substack{\text{bacterial} \\ \text{enzymes}}]{\text{oxidative}}$ HNO_2 + H_2O
  nitrogen   *Ammonia*   *Oxygen*   *Nitrite*   *Water*
  sources

    HNO_2 + O_2 $\xrightarrow[\substack{\text{bacterial} \\ \text{enzymes}}]{\text{oxidative}}$ HNO_3 + *Energy*
    Nitrite   *Oxygen*   *Nitrate*

    HNO_3 $\xrightarrow[\substack{\text{bacterial} \\ \text{enzymes}}]{\text{oxidative}}$ N_2 + H_2O
    Nitrate   *Nitrogen*   *Water*

Fig. 3–2. Wine-making. When fermentation by yeast cells has produced alcohol and characteristic flavor, the wine is aged in vaults. (Courtesy of Taylor Wine Company, Inc., Hammondsport, N.Y.)

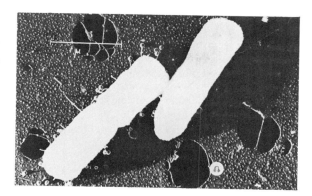

Fig. 3–3. Two cells of *Escherichia coli,* one of which (left) is being invaded by bacteriophage. The polyhedral head structures of the phage are at the opposite end of the tail structures. The bacterial cell on the right has no phage particles attached to it, indicating that it is resistant to this phage. (Reproduced from Anderson, Thomas F.; Wollman, Elie L.; and Jacob, François: Sur les Processus de Conjugaison et de Recombinaison chez *Escherichia coli.* II. Aspects morphologiques en microscopie electronique, *Ann. Inst. Pasteur,* **93**:450–55, 1957.)

chemical of all life and directs the genetic mechanisms of all living things, this brilliant achievement points to the possibility that life can be generated in the laboratory and that genetic inheritance may be directed at will.

The bacteriophages, which are viruses that live within bacterial cells, have structures that appear to be specialized for entry into their host cells, being equipped with a tail and sometimes with a tail-plate having fibrils or spikes. The phage virus attaches its tail to the cell wall of a bacterium and "injects" its own DNA or RNA into the host cell (see Fig. 3–3). Once inside, the virus nucleic acid molecule takes over, as previously described, utilizing the bacterium as a source of energy and propagating mechanisms. Animal viruses do not have a special tail, but the attachment and absorption process occur in a similar way. In the case of the polio virus, and possibly others as well, the evidence indicates that new virus does not accumulate as it is formed within a parasitized cell but leaks out quickly, and death of the animal cell does not occur until virus production has ceased. It has been postulated that the failure to associate specific viruses with human cancers may be due in part to the possibility that virus material, after absorption into the cell, is too minute or too closely similar to components of the host cell, and too closely associated with them, to be detectable by currently available methods.

Not all virus infections lead to adverse effects on the host. The streaking and variegation so admired in tulip blossoms, for example, can be the result of a virus infection that apparently does no harm to the parasitized organism (see Fig. 3–4). The popularity of the streaked tulip once

Fig. 3–4. Streaked tulips. The streaking or "break" of these Darwin tulips is caused by a lily-latent-mosaic virus. Streaked tulips are now propagated genetically; the virus-infected varieties are regarded as sick and poor-growing individuals, and are seldom grown. (Courtesy of Dr. Francis O. Holmes, Rockefeller University, New York, N.Y.)

led to a "tulipomania" in the Netherlands, during the sixteenth and seventeenth centuries, and to a boom in the tulip market, which promptly collapsed when tulip-growers found that the carefully guarded secret of their variegation lay in the mere rubbing together of a nonstreaked and a streaked bulb. This is an excellent example of infection acquired by direct contact, as well as a reminder that, figuratively speaking, and like the tulip, we owe much of the variegation in our lives to microorganisms.

The Metabolic Behavior of Bacteria

Bacteria are classified with the plants, as we have seen, because of their requirement for soluble nutrient. Some bacteria are autotrophic, their synthesizing equipment conferring on them a high degree of independence, but the majority are saprophytic heterotrophs. They are ubiquitously distributed, in soil and water, in the intestinal tracts and on the surface tissues of animals and humans, thriving on nonliving organic substances.

Bacterial Culture

In nature, bacteria obtain the carbohydrate and protein materials, vitamins, and minerals required for all their vital processes from dead or decaying matter or from living, parasitized hosts. To cultivate bacteria in the laboratory, and study these requirements more closely, or identify them through their metabolic behavior, it is necessary to provide the substances essential to their survival, and growth, in appropriate form. A basic medium for bacterial culture contains meat that has been cooked to break down its proteins partially, to soluble, usable forms; some carbohydrate (usually glucose); and a few simple salts. Some pathogenic bacteria (disease-producing) may require additional enrichments, such as the serum proteins or the whole blood of various animal species, special carbohydrates, particular amino acids (constituents of proteins), vitamins, and specific minerals. These special growth fac-

tors usually are required only in very small amounts. The final medium may be used in liquid form, or solidified by the addition of agar, a nonnutritive substance resembling gelatin in its physical properties.

Environmental Requirements

The environmental requirements of bacteria that must be considered and met in the laboratory include such factors as the pH and water content of the medium, atmospheric conditions, temperature, and light.

The pH of the medium, that is, its degree of acidity or alkalinity, is carefully adjusted before use because bacteria can be quite sensitive to minor changes in this balance. Many have a narrow pH range beyond which they cannot survive while others may be capable of growing at extremes of acidity or alkalinity. It is sometimes useful, therefore, to adjust the pH of a culture medium to an extreme point that will permit the isolated growth of an organism having a wide pH range. For example, in a specimen containing a mixture of bacterial species most organisms will fail to grow at an extreme pH, but the medium will support the growth of a pH-indifferent organism if it is present in the mixture.

Water is an essential for the growth of bacteria as is soluble food. It is water that keeps the food in solution so that organisms can absorb it through their cell walls. Removing water from the environment does not necessarily kill the organisms, for many are quite resistant to the effects of drying, but it will suppress active metabolism and growth. For this reason, bacteria can be preserved for long periods by quickly freezing them in suspension and then drying them under vacuum.

Oxygen is required in some form by all living organisms, but not necessarily as the atmospheric form. Bacteria vary in their need for free oxygen, the majority requiring it. These are called *aerobes*, while those that are not dependent on the air for oxygen, but obtain it chemically from the medium in which they are growing, are termed *anaerobes*. Some anaerobic organisms find free oxygen poi-

sonous and are called obligate, or strict, anaerobes. Between the two extreme requirements is a large group of bacteria that can adapt to either atmosphere. Such organisms are referred to as *facultative* anaerobes. Still others may require a reduction in the total amount of free oxygen present in the atmosphere. These are called *microaerophilic*, meaning, literally, that they like only a little air.

The oxygen requirements of bacteria are of great significance in certain practical situations. Among human infections, those induced in wounds by anaerobic organisms, growing in dead tissue devoid of oxygen, can be extremely serious. Deep wounds, or those that close prematurely before new tissue can be formed with its rich oxygen supplies from the blood, offer particularly good opportunities for the growth of anaerobic bacteria. Also, in the canning of foods, it is of great importance to destroy bacteria by appropriate methods before the food is sealed into cans or jars so that anaerobes cannot subsequently grow and produce toxic substances within the container.

Temperature is another critical factor in the growth of bacteria. Some prefer temperatures as low as $10°$ C $(50°$ F), while others will grow only at temperatures of $50°$ to $60°$ C. Most pathogenic bacteria, however, find normal human body temperature ($37°$ C or $98.6°$ F) most suitable for their own physiologic activities. Usually there is a 15-to-20-degree temperature range, with maximum and minimum limits and an optimum area between, required for the growth of particular types of bacteria.

Light is not a requirement for most bacteria, since the majority are not autotrophic and cannot use light for energy. On the contrary, many species are sensitive to the effects of the ultraviolet component of sunlight. Although laboratory cultures are usually kept in the dark, it is sometimes necessary to adjust both light and temperature conditions in order to observe a particular property or product of growth in a given species. For example, some bacterial pigments are often light-sensitive and display changes in properties as light conditions are altered.

In the laboratory, the manipulation of some or all of these environmental factors constitutes a part of the approach to the identification of bacteria and to the study of their metabolic processes. More detailed and pertinent information is obtained, however, from observations of their morphology, their enzyme components and biochemical activities, and some of their many physiologic properties.

The Chemical Accomplishments of Bacteria

The bacteria as a group are tremendously versatile, not only in their utilization of organic substances and the conversion of these in synthetic processes, but in their ability to bring alternate metabolic mechanisms into play in adjustment to the demands of their environment. If the supply of a particular substrate dwindles, or if other environmental changes occur, bacteria can meet these problems, probably by calling into play alternate enzyme systems or by changes in the constituents of their cell walls. This becomes of great practical importance when human infections are treated with drugs such as antibiotics that are antagonistic to certain growth mechanisms in particular species, or when physical and chemical agents, such as heat, disinfectant solutions, or ultraviolet radiation, are used to control the growth of bacteria. Bacteria may survive such measures in such various ways as by changing their method of utilization of a particular substrate, by turning to another kind of available nutrient, or by entering into a resting stage.

In the *natural* world, the metabolic activities of bacteria busily at work maintaining and nourishing themselves on the organic components (carbohydrates and proteins) of animal wastes or dead animals and plants play an indispensable role in the maintenance and nourishment of all life on our planet. The decay and putrefaction of such materials are due in large part to the action of bacterial enzymes that break them down to forms they, and other organisms as well, can absorb and transform into new compounds for their own cellular structures and functions. Without bacteria and other microorganisms to conduct the pro-

cesses of decay, the basic elements of proteins would remain locked up in the bodies of plants and animals as they die; the raw materials needed by higher organisms for energy, structure, and growth would vanish; and life would slowly disappear into death.

In man's *economic* world, the activities of bacteria have been put to a variety of productive uses. Bacteria, like the yeasts, utilize carbohydrates for food by converting them into acids, alcohols, and gases, in aerobic and anaerobic processes directed and controlled by their enzymes. The ability to use a particular carbohydrate, or other organic compound, differs among species of bacteria, depending on whether or not they possess an enzyme specifically capable of acting on that substrate and changing it chemically (see Table 3–3). This in turn directs the choice of a particular strain of organism for the job one may wish to have done. In the making of wines, or other alcoholic beverages such as hard cider, for instance, fermentation of the sugar to alcohol is a job usually assigned to yeasts, as we have seen. If desired, the alcohol may be further degraded into acetic acid, or vinegar, by introducing a culture of bacteria of the *Acetobacter* genus whose oxidative enzymes conduct the transformation. In the dairy industry, the ability of the so-called lactic acid bacteria to ferment lactose is put to use in the production of sour milk and sour cream. The production of many popular foods is made possible by such bacterial conversions (see Fig. 3–5). Other practical uses of bacterial activities include the preparation of animal hides for leather manufacture, of plant fibers used to make fabrics or rope, of tobacco

Fig. 3–5. Cheddar cheese is made by adding a culture of bacteria to a vat of milk. Curds form and are cut into blocks. Here the sliced blocks of curd are being turned over for the first time. This is called "cheddaring." (Courtesy of U.S. Department of Agriculture, Washington, D.C.)

and tea leaves to improve their flavor, and of industrial alcohols and acids. Many industries of basic importance to our economy have developed, and continue to do so, by use of the chemical talents of bacteria and other microorganisms for the production of materials that are essential in our progress and useful in our pleasures.

Conversely, the bacterial profits of the economic world are balanced against the expenditures of ingenuity, effort, and time required to circumvent or control the less desirable features of bacterial activity. The spoilage and decay of useful foods and other valuable materials is costly and has stimulated major research and development in the field of food preservation. Methods designed to prevent the multiplication of putrefactive (decay-producing) bacteria in food must not in themselves be deleterious to flavor, or to nutritional content, and they must, of course, avoid the use of substances that might be toxic on ingestion by human beings. Natural physical methods of preserving foods include dehydration, cold storage, freezing, and radiation; chemical methods employ the antibacterial effects of salting, pickling in vinegar or in high concentrations of sugar, smoke-curing, and so forth. Antibiotics also are used to suppress bacterial growth in some foods, including fish and poultry.

In the world of *medicine* and *public health*, microbial activities are turned to our greatest use and advantage in (1) the production of antibiotics) and (2) the disposal of sewage and wastes.

Antibiotics are substances that are intermediate or end products of microbial metabolism, excreted through their walls into the environment beyond. In the soil, where many microorganisms live together, the waste products of one species may be quite toxic in their effects on another, or in other cases they may be supportive to the growth of neighboring organisms. The term "antibiosis" (against life) applies to the antagonistic effect (see Fig. 3-6). The great names in the discovery and development of antibiotics for medical purposes are Fleming, Florey, and Chain, in England, and Selman Waksman, in the United States, all recipients of Nobel Prizes acknowledging the significance of their work in this field. It

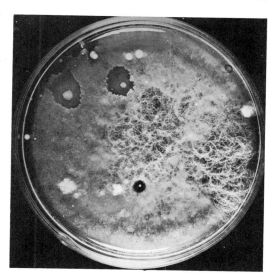

Fig. 3-6. Microbial antagonism. An agar plate was seeded with 1 ml of a 1 : 10,000,000 dilution of soil and incubated at 28° C for five days. A major portion of the plate is covered with growth of *Bacillus mycoides*, but several other types of colonies have also grown. Clear areas around these small colonies are zones of inhibition of the growth of *B. mycoides*. (Courtesy of Dr. Albert Kelner, Brandeis University, Waltham, Mass.)

was Fleming who first observed the antibacterial effects of *Penicillium*, as noted in Chapter 2; Florey and Chain who identified the substance, penicillin, responsible for the effect and opened the door to its medical application; and Waksman who began extensive investigations in the antibiotics field in this country, discovered streptomycin, and stimulated many major research efforts that followed. Antibiotic production has become one of the major concerns of the large pharmaceutical companies, and current research in the laboratory synthesis of antibiotic materials, as previously mentioned, promises important developments for the future.

Sewage and waste disposal exploits to our best advantage the digestive activities of the putrefactive bacteria. One of the common methods for handling sewage is to direct it slowly over beds of gravel and sand so that solid matter will have time to settle out and be acted upon by the

various bacteria in these beds. As the water seeps through, it is cleaned and purified, pathogenic bacteria are removed and die, and the water is made ready again for consumption. Digestion of the settled material by bacteria converts it into a form that can be collected, dried, and used as fertilizer. The purification of water is discussed in more detail in Chapter 11, together with other measures of concern to the public health in the control of infectious diseases.

Bacteria in the intestinal tracts of man and animals also break down food residues by digestive processes. Some of these organisms are capable of synthesizing specific growth factors called vitamins that they require in their own metabolism. This provides a sort of built-in supply of vitamin for the human or animal host, who needs it as well and can absorb it from the intestine. On the other hand, some of the products of bacterial decomposition are toxic to human beings or would be if they were ingested, preformed, in spoiling food. However, when they are formed in the intestinal tract by organisms living there, they are usually not absorbed in more than minute quantities but are eliminated frequently in feces. The small amounts that are absorbed are quickly changed in the liver to nontoxic forms (that is, they are detoxified) and excreted in the urine or bile. If an abnormal condition arises to block intestinal excretion, the decomposition products of continuing bacterial activity can accumulate and be absorbed in larger quantities that may cause harmful effects on the body.

It was pointed out above that the biochemical flexibility of bacteria presents a challenge to the use of antibacterial agents in medicine or in environmental sanitation. This versatility is reflected also in some of the complex interrelationships that exist between bacteria and the cells and tissues of the hosts they may parasitize. The host's ability to resist the effects of their presence in its tissues and the organism's ability to survive in spite of this constitute a competition at the cellular level. The enzymes of host and parasite may compete for the same substrate, and each may produce substances that are antagonistic for the other. In finding alternate metabolic pathways

for utilization of its food, the bacterial cell is often much more versatile than the cells or tissues of the human or animal body, and this of course provides it with a strong capacity for survival.

The products of bacterial cell growth and metabolism that are harmful to humans and animals are usually referred to as *toxins*. When they diffuse out of the bacterial cell into the surrounding medium, they are spoken of as *exotoxins* (diphtheria toxin is an example of this type), but when they are associated with the organism itself, as a part of its chemical structure, they are called *endotoxins*. The important exotoxins, such as those produced by the bacterial agents of tetanus, botulism, and diphtheria, have been isolated and studied extensively. In purified form they are protein in nature and highly lethal to experimental animals. The endotoxins are more difficult to isolate and define chemically. They are complex molecules of protein and carbohydrate, sometimes having a lipid (fatty) component as well. The endotoxins of many different species of bacteria are closely similar, as one might expect if they are a part of the cell's normal structure. Isolated endotoxins are also lethal for animals, but quantitatively much less so than exotoxins.

Bacteria frequently produce pigments that are characteristic enough to assist in species identification. Although disease-producing organisms such as *Staphylococcus aureus* (the species name indicates the pigment color, having a Latin root meaning gold) may manufacture pigments their production and presence does not necessarily contribute to the disease process. By the same token, pigment production does not always imply a dangerous organism. For instance, a common, free-living bacterium that is rarely associated with infection is notable for a bright red pigment (see Fig. 3–7). Called *Serratia marcescens*, it was thought to be miraculous in origin when it was seen growing on the eucharistic bread in medieval cathedrals (which were often damp and dark and offered excellent conditions for microbial growths). As in the case of toxins and other bacterial products, pigments may be intracellularly or extracellularly located. In the former case they become visible as masses of cells accumulate in

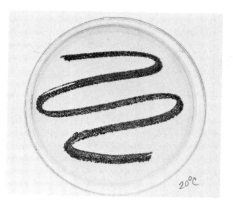

Fig. 3–7. *Serratia marcescens* is noted for its ability to produce a red pigment. In this black-and-white photograph the pigmented streak of growth contrasts sharply with the colorless agar background. (Reproduced from Mizer, Helen E.: Rings Transmit Microorganisms, *Tomorrow's Nurse,* **2**:24, 1961.)

one place and give the colony (as such a mass is called) a distinctive color. When pigments are excreted by the cells, the colonies remain colorless, but the medium around them is stained.

In the world of the *medical microbiologist*, the laboratory identification of bacteria isolated from patients suspected of having infectious diseases is based in large part on the demonstration of their biochemical activities, as well as on their microscopic and colonial features.

Metabolic processes may be recognized in several ways but the most common approach is to identify one or more enzyme activities. This is done by providing the organisms with some particular compound that is a substrate for the enzyme to be identified and observing the nature and extent of any changes that may occur in that compound. Such observations can be made quite simple by incorporating into the test a chemical indicator of a kind that will provide visible evidence that a change has occurred. Thus, if it is important to know whether or not a particular organism possesses an enzyme specifically required for the utilization of lactose, a culture medium is prepared that will support the organism's growth but is free of all sugars other than lactose. If the enzyme for lactose is present, the sugar molecule will be broken down to simpler

compounds that are acidic. The pH of the medium is adjusted so that no acid is present to begin with, and the other ingredients of the medium are balanced so that little or no acid will be formed during growth if the lactose is not fermented. Finally, an indicator is put in that will provide a visible color change if the pH is lowered by the accumulation of acid products. After the organism has grown in the medium for a few hours, a mere glance at the color of the indicator suffices to determine whether or not lactose fermentation has occurred.

It may be necessary to conduct a number of such tests in narrowing the identification of an organism, first as a member of a large family with widely shared characteristics, then to a smaller tribe or genus with more particular properties, and finally to a species with a unique set of metabolic features.

Variation and Genetic Behavior in Bacteria

In the preceding discussion emphasis has been placed on the ability of bacteria to respond to their environment in a number of ways and to display changes in their physiologic characteristics in the process. These variations in response to environmental influences must be distinguished from those that occur by virtue of changes in their nuclear structures and are, therefore, inheritable (*genetic*).

Environmental Influences

Variations induced by environmental influences do not involve the nuclear material of cells. They appear and persist from one generation of cells to another so long as the situation in the environment that provoked them persists. When external conditions change, bacterial behavior does also, and the organisms may revert to their "normal" patterns or display other variations as the new change may require. This is the type of variation most commonly encountered, of course, for the natural environment is itself dynamic as a result

of the competitive responses and interactions that continuously occur among the living things in it.

For the microbiologist the practical implications of this lie in the recognition of variability when organisms are to be identified with accuracy and, on the other hand, in the advantage that may be taken of bacterial properties that will vary if the environment is manipulated. In the diagnostic laboratory, where the first concern is correct identification of the bacteria in patient's specimens, the standardization of culture conditions is of utmost importance. Recognition of the key features of bacterial growth depends on the careful regulation of the composition and pH of culture media and of temperature and oxygen requirements, and on reproduction of these conditions uniformly, each time cultures are prepared. However, if a particular enzyme, property, or product of bacterial growth is to be identified, this will usually require precise changes in the environment, as previously discussed in the case of the demonstration of lactose fermentation. Further advantage can be taken of environmental influences when it is desirable to isolate and purify some product of bacterial metabolism. For example, the provision of a particular nutrient in the culture may encourage the production of much larger quantities than usual of a bacterial toxin to be used in making a vaccine or an antibiotic substance to be studied. Atmospheric conditions and temperature may also be factors in enhancing an organism's ability to produce such materials when better quality or quantity is desired.

Genetic Variations

Genetic variations occur naturally in bacteria as in all living things, and they can also be induced by experimental methods. In either case they occur as a result of changes in the nuclear structures called *genes*, which are the fundamental units of heredity in all cells. More specifically, genes are the structural units of the chromosomes in the nucleus of all cells. Each time a cell divides asexually, its chromosomes and all their component genes are duplicated, so that each of the new cells contains exactly the same number and type of chromosomes as the parent cell. According to current evidence, the chromosomes are composed of molecules of the nucleic acids called DNA (deoxyribonucleic acid) and RNA (ribonucleic acid), strung together in patterns that are definite and repeating for each type of cell. The genes are individual DNA or RNA units making up the whole. These genic structures direct all of the cell's functions, providing it with its total capacity for conducting its vital affairs in its own individual way. The possession of a specific gene, for instance, may lead to the production of a specific enzyme, or a particular kind of protein structure, or some other individual trait, and the total effect of the function of all its genes provides the cell with its total individuality. The duplication of genes in cell division, furthermore, assures the transmission of this total individuality from the parent to each daughter cell; that is, it establishes the heredity of the new generation.

Genes are subject to change, and when this happens, the cellular trait, or traits, for which they are responsible change also. A new characteristic may be added, or an old one lost, and if the alteration in the gene does not result in the death of the cell or render it incapable of further reproduction, the change will be transmitted through succeeding generations of cells as the gene duplicates at each cellular division. *Changes in the characteristics of the cell that are transmissible because of gene alteration are called mutations.* They occur from time to time among all living things as what appear to be "natural" or "spontaneous" events, the cause being unknown for most of them. It is quite possible, however, that specific agents for mutational changes will be identified in the future as geneticists obtain more detailed information concerning the exact nature and function of the genes themselves.

Mutations occur much more frequently among microorganisms than among higher species, simply because multiplication of unicellular organisms is much more rapid than that of multicellular animals or plants and produces tremendously large populations. Mutations are seen very commonly among bacteria, affecting

one or more of their many and varied characteristics, such as their colony types, pigment or toxin production, enzyme production and activity, or their ability to resist the action of antibiotics. In the latter instance, the parent cells of a given strain of bacteria may be susceptible to the action of a particular antibiotic because, let us say, the antibiotic inactivates an enzyme vital to its nutrition. Now suppose that a mutation occurs, for some reason, in the gene responsible for the production of this vital enzyme in one cell of this bacterial population. The altered gene directs the production of an altered enzyme, still highly functional in the cell's nutrition, but indifferent to the presence of the antibiotic that poisoned the enzyme of the parent cell. The progeny of the cell with the mutant gene will all possess the new enzyme, but their numbers will not be noticeable with respect to the entire population of which they are a part. If, at this point, the parent and mutant cells are exposed together to the antibiotic in question, all the susceptible parent cells will die as a result of the exposure, but the mutants, being unaffected by it, will survive and continue to multiply, transmitting their indifferent enzyme continuously from one to another. The end result, therefore, is the emergence of a population *all* of whose members are resistant to the action of the antibiotic. This type of mutation, which can be demonstrated in the laboratory, can occur as well among bacteria that are living in or on the tissues of a human being. Treatment of the individual with an antibiotic would then produce the same result: susceptible mircoorganisms would die, and resistant mutants would survive the antibiotic effect. If the survivors are also capable of resisting the many other factors involved in their relationship with the body's tissues, they will remain alive, ready to multiply if opportunity permits and indifferent to any future encounters with the antibiotic.

Mutations can be induced *experimentally* in bacteria, as in other organisms, by radiation with x-rays, radioactive substances, or ultraviolet light or by the action of chemical agents such as hydrogen peroxide, manganese chloride, or nitrogen mustard.

Two other mechanisms have been demonstrated for inducing genetic changes in bacteria but not as yet in other organisms. One of these is mediated by virus infection of the bacterial cells and is called *transduction;* the other involves a simpler transfer of nuclear material from one cell to another and is called *transformation.*

Transduction

It will be remembered that viruses are composed of the nucleic acids DNA or RNA (or both), but they cannot reproduce themselves except within host cells and with the assistance of the nuclear material of the latter. When new virus material is formed, therefore, it contains nucleic acid molecules (DNA) derived from the host. Bacterial cells infected with bacteriophage DNA may contribute one or more of their own genes to the formation of the new virus particles, which, on liberation, then enter other bacterial cells, transporting this genetic material from the old host to the new. If some of the newly infected cells survive the bacteriophage invasion and are able to continue their own reproduction, the new genetic material acquired by this transport will be perpetuated in succeeding cell divisions. No change in characteristics of the new cells will be noted, of course, if the transport occurred between genetically identical organisms. But if the transduced genes are different from those already possessed by the recipient cells, the latter will display new traits accordingly, together with their usual ones, and so will their progeny.

Transformation

A transfer of DNA from one bacterial cell to another is involved in this type of change also, but no bacteriophage "letter-carrier" takes part as in transduction. In the process referred to as transformation, DNA is liberated from a donor cell by lysis (dissolution of the cell) or by an artificial process of extraction and isolation of the material. When a susceptible recipient cell is exposed to this isolated DNA, it absorbs and

incorporates the new molecule into its own nuclear apparatus. The recipient cell then takes on new characteristics as directed by the transforming DNA, and these are inherited by its progeny. Changes that can be induced in certain bacteria in this manner may involve the nature of their capsular material, their fermentative activities, some morphologic features, or their resistance to antibiotics.

All the environmental or genetic changes in bacteria that have been discussed thus far are observable in the course of their usual asexual type of cellular division. In addition to these, there is now a substantial body of evidence indicating that a *sexual recombination of genes* can occur among bacteria. It has been demonstrated in only limited species of bacteria and is apparently a rare event in any case. The work of Joshua Lederberg with strains of *Escherichia coli*, a common bacterial inhabitant of the intestinal tracts of man and animals, indicates that in potentially fertile strains, some individuals carry a "male" determinant, particle F. This unit directs the transfer of most or all of the genetic material of the cell to another, F-deficient cell (or "female") probably during a brief cellular conjugation. The F factor itself can also be transferred, converting the recipient cell into a "male" type. Succeeding generations of cells, derived only from the recipient cell, display some combined characteristics of both the donor and the recipient cells.

The processes of transduction, transformation, and sexual recombination among bacteria offer partial explanations for their behavior in the natural world and in infectious diseases. Variations in the ability of microorganisms to produce disease are of particular interest to the medical microbiologist. The broad implications of work in this field point to the possibility that the heritable characteristics of living cells may some day be manipulated at will. Suitable changes thus induced in microbial agents of disease might indeed be profitable to mankind.

Questions

1. What roles do enzymes play in metabolic activities?
2. How have yeasts and molds been used to economic advantage? *wine + cheese*
3. What is a bacteriophage? *letter carrier in transduction   Virus – Bacteria virus*
4. Distinguish between the autotrophic and heterotrophic bacteria.
5. What are the growth requirements of bacteria? How are these provided for in the laboratory?
6. Describe briefly the chemical accomplishments of bacteria.
7. Of what significance is pigment production?
8. Why are bacterial mutants important? Describe transduction and transformation.

References

Pertinent References
Burdon, Kenneth L., and Williams, Robert P.: *Textbook of Microbiology*, 6th ed. The Macmillan Co., New York, 1968.
Pelczar, Michael J., and Reid, Roger: *Microbiology*, 2nd ed. McGraw-Hill, New York, 1965.

Periodicals
Amerine, Maynard A.: Wine, *Sci. Amer.*, **211**:46, Aug., 1964.
Braude, A. I.: Bacterial Endotoxins, *Sci. Amer.*, **210**:36, March, 1964.
Chain, Ernest, as told to Ratcliff, J. D.: We Tamed Penicillin, *Reader's Digest*, **86**:89, March, 1965.

Goulian, Mehran; Kornberg, Arthur; and Sinsheimer, Robert L.: Enzymatic Synthesis of DNA, XXIV. Synthesis of Infectious Phage ϕX174 DNA. *Proc. Nat'l. Acad. Sci.*, **58**:2321, Dec., 1967.

McElroy, William D., and Seliger, Howard H.: Biological Luminescence, *Sci. Amer.*, **207**:76, Dec., 1962.

Maramorosch, Karl: The Friendly Viruses, *Sci. Amer.*, **203**:138, Aug., 1960.

Rose, Anthony: Beer, *Sci. Amer.*, **200**:90, June, 1959. New Penicillins, *Sci. Amer.*, **204**:66, March, 1961.

Popular Literature

Epstein, Samuel, and Williams, Beryl: *Miracles from Microbes.* Rutgers University Press, New Brunswick, N.J., 1946.

Maurois, André: *The Life of Sir Alexander Fleming.* E. P. Dutton and Co., New York, 1959.

Roueché, Berton: Something Extraordinary, in *Eleven Blue Men.* Berkeley Publishing Corp., New York, 1953.

Shippen, Katherine: *Men of Medicine.* The Viking Press, New York, 1957.

Styler, Herman: New Hope for Tomorrow, in *Plague Fighters.* Chilton Co., Philadelphia and New York, 1960.

4 The Tools and Techniques of Microbiology

The work of the medical microbiologist is directed to the recognition and study of the microbial agents of infectious disease and to the interrelationships that influence both the microorganism and the human host. In the laboratory, these studies require techniques and tools designed to cope with the miniscule size of microorganisms, the many variations in their physiologic behavior, and the abundance with which species of all types are scattered through our environment. In practical terms, it is a good deal like looking for a needle in a haystack to locate and recognize a particular kind of organism among a welter of others that resemble it closely in size and shape, but when both the needle and the hay are of a size about 100 to 200,000 times *smaller* than the tiniest dot we can see with our own eyes, something better than a magnet is needed!

Modern microscopes have provided the laboratory with the visual wherewithal for a good look at microorganisms, but unfortunately this alone may not be very informative. Within each range of size and shape encountered among microbial cells there may be many different species that are exactly alike in appearance but very different in their properties and behavior. The microbiologist must, therefore, often use additional techniques that can distinguish one organism from another in a number of ways other than their microscopic appearance. These distinctions include staining

properties, physiologic requirements for growth and metabolism, the production of enzymes and other active substances, and responses to physical and chemical agents.

Before our needle, once it is located, can be studied for its own individual properties, however, it must be separated from the interfering haystraws. Since it is not lifeless in this analogy, the isolated needle can be persuaded to reproduce and multiply in accumulating numbers that will become easily visible, en masse, and less awkward to handle. The laboratory refers to this process as the *isolation* of an organism in *pure culture* (see Fig. 4–1). Once accomplished, it permits the study of many features of the organism's growth in a culture environment that can be controlled and manipulated by the investigator, without the pressures of competing microbial cells.

The fundamental methods and the basic equipment of the microbiology laboratory, and the general principles of their use, are the subject of discussion in this chapter.

The Tools

The Compound Light Microscope

The diagnostic microbiology laboratory uses, to their fullest extent, the optical services of a good microscope, usually at the highest and sharpest magnification of which it is capable.

The compound light microscope has two sets of magnifying lenses, placed at opposite ends of a tube that is mounted on a stand so that it can be raised or lowered. The uppermost or viewing lens is called the *ocular*. The other lens, which is nearest the object being magnified, is called the *objective*. Usually there are three objectives on a revolving nosepiece, capable of magnifying the object 10, 45, and 100 times ($10\times$, $45\times$, $100\times$), respectively (see Fig. 4–2). The magnification provided by the objective is further increased by the ocular. If the latter is a $10\times$ lens, which is usual, the combined enlargement provides a total magnification of $100\times$, $450\times$, or $1000\times$.

The close study of organisms as small as bacteria requires the use of the $100\times$ objective,

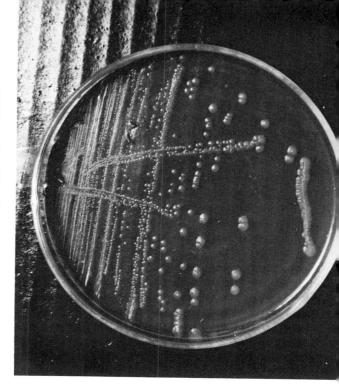

Fig. 4–1. A pure culture of *Corynebacterium diphtheriae* streaked out on an agar plate. (Courtesy of Dr. A. E. Bolyn, The National Drug Company, Swiftwater, Pa.)

which must be immersed in a drop of oil placed on top of the slide holding the object. The oil improves the *resolution* of the objective, that is, its ability to provide sharpness of detail, which is particularly necessary at high magnifications. Resolution and magnification are the two essentials of microscopy, neither being of much value without the other. For the microbiologist, the best possible combination of the two is essential.

The platform that holds the slide being viewed is called a *stage*. Just below the centrally placed opening in the stage is the *substage condenser*, which functions to collect and concentrate the light and to direct it upward through the object on the stage. The object absorbs and bends the light, so that when it passes onward through the objective and ocular it is patterned in the image of the object. The condenser is fitted with an *iris diaphragm* to regulate the amount of light passing into it. Raising or lowering the position of the condenser also changes the amount of light it can collect. Light is reflected from its

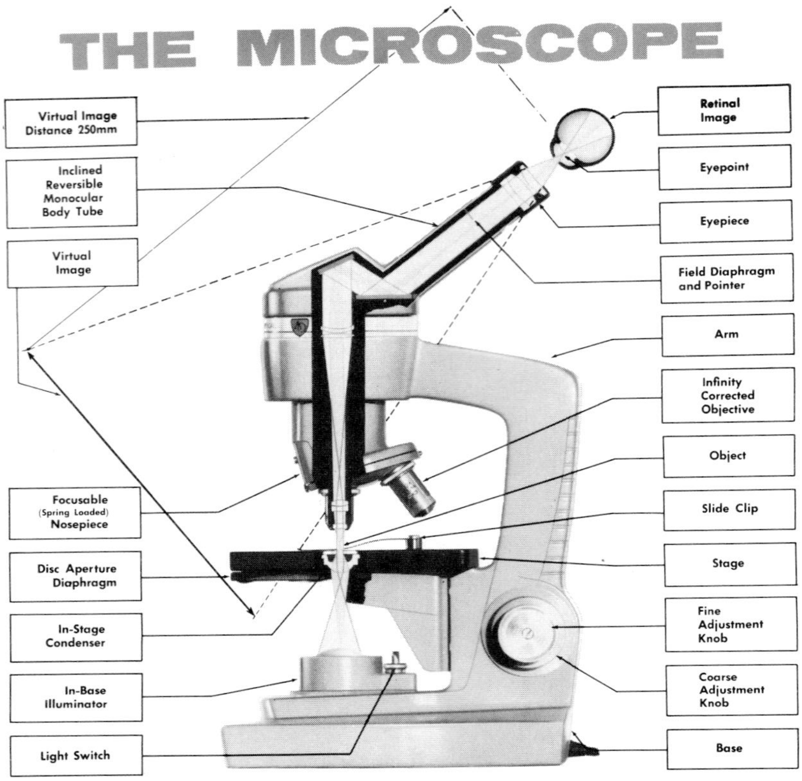

THE MICROSCOPE

Virtual Image Distance 250mm

Inclined Reversible Monocular Body Tube

Virtual Image

Focusable (Spring Loaded) Nosepiece

Disc Aperture Diaphragm

In-Stage Condenser

In-Base Illuminator

Light Switch

Retinal Image

Eyepoint

Eyepiece

Field Diaphragm and Pointer

Arm

Infinity Corrected Objective

Object

Slide Clip

Stage

Fine Adjustment Knob

Coarse Adjustment Knob

Base

Optical and Mechanical Features of Series SIXTY Microscope

Cross section of scanning objective, 4X.

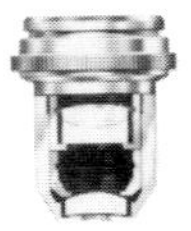

Cross section of low power objective, 10X.

Cross section of "high dry" objective, 43X.

Cross section of oil immersion objective, 97X.

Fig. 4–2. A modern compound microscope with parts labeled for easy identification. The pathway of light is also illustrated. (Courtesy of American Optical Company, Buffalo, N.Y.)

source into the condenser by a *mirror*, attached at the base of the microscope. In general, the higher the magnification desired, the more intense the light must be, but the degree of illumination needed varies also with the density of the object. For this reason, stained material usually requires more light then unstained preparations.

The Electron Microscope

The electron microscope is not ordinarily of use in the diagnostic microbiology laboratory. It is essential, however, if the morphology of viruses is to be studied, and it is a valuable tool in the demonstration of fine cellular details in bacterial cytology (the study of cell structure).

Direct visualization of an object through the compound light microscope is accomplished by visible light rays and magnifying lenses, as we have seen. The resolution of this microscope is finally limited, however, as objects diminish in size, because the latter can no longer absorb and redirect light — they merely scatter it and are seen with less and less clarity in visible light. However, wavelengths shorter than those of visible light can be formed into clear patterns by very small objects, and although these cannot be seen with the eye, they can be registered on a surface that is sensitive to them. If this surface is a photographic plate coated with a material

that responds to the short waves that strike it, one can have a picture of that response and thus see an invisible object.

Operating on this principle, the electron microscope sends a stream of short-wave electrons through a vacuum chamber (to avoid their scatter by air) to strike an object in its path. Instead of absorbing these waves, as a larger object would do with visible light, the object scatters them in a pattern that forms its image. Circular electromagnets attract the scattered electrons still farther outward, thus enlarging the image, which is then focused on a fluorescent screen. Electrons hitting the screen cause visible fluorescence that can be viewed directly and also can be photographed with still further enlargement. The image on the screen is enlarged 10,000 to 20,000 times. When the photograph is developed, it can be stepped up about 10 times more to give a total possible enlargement of 200,000. Thus, through a series of enlarging steps, if initial resolution is good, the invisible can be brought up into the visual range of the human eye (see Fig. 4–3).

Other Laboratory Equipment

The identification of large microorganisms, such as the eggs and larvae of the parasitic worms, may often be accomplished simply by the recognition of pertinent structures under the microscope. However, the identification of the yeasts and fungi, and of the smaller bacteria, frequently requires the use of culture methods as well as microscopy. The conditions required for successful cultivation, and the recognition of identifying characteristics, vary widely with the type of organism to be studied. The equipment of the individual laboratory will be varied also, according to the areas of its interest and concern.

The *medical diagnostic laboratory* must be prepared to find and identify, by microscopic or culture methods or both, microorganisms of many types in specimens from patients suspected of having infectious diseases. Often an individual laboratory, in a small hospital for instance, cannot afford all the equipment, staff, time, or space

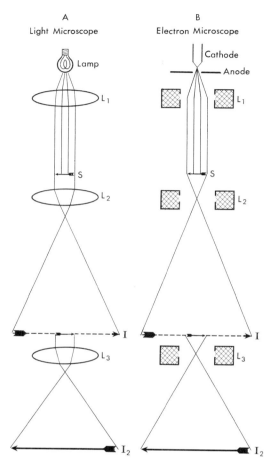

Fig. 4–3. Comparison of the optics of the compound light microscope with that of the RCA electron microscope. The system of glass lenses in the light microscope serves the same function as the system of magnetic fields in the electron microscope. In the diagram, L_1 is the condensing lens, L_2 is the objective lens, and L_3 is the projector lens. S is the object, I is the primary image, and I_2 is the final highly magnified image. (Courtesy of Dr. Thomas F. Anderson, The Institute for Cancer Research, Philadelphia, Pa.)

required for the full range of microbial possibilities in such specimens, but in that case it may use the facilities of a specialized laboratory or the services of city and state health department laboratories. There are certain basic items of equipment, however, that are essential to the

successful operation of every microbiologic laboratory, and these will be described here.

Microbiological glassware is, for the most part, identical to that used in a chemical laboratory, with its assortment of test tubes, flasks, beakers, pipettes, and the like. One of the items specifically designed for microbiologic purposes is the Petri dish (or plate). It is named for its originator, Richard Petri, a German bacteriologist, and has been a standard item since 1887 when he first designed it. It is simply a shallow, covered dish for the convenient, safe handling of solidified culture media, upon which bacteria, and a few other microorganisms, can be grown.

Methods for Preparing Glassware. The two most important provisions that must be made for all microbiologic glassware are *cleanliness* and *sterility*. Every laboratory that handles specimens and cultures containing organisms capable of producing disease must provide for the *sterilization* of all materials and glassware after such use as well as before.

Sterilization means the destruction of all forms of life, and *sterility* is, of course, the condition that results. It can be accomplished by several alternate methods involving the use of physical or chemical agents. The principles and methods of sterilization and other forms of control of microorganisms are discussed fully in Chapter 10. Suffice it to say here that, in general, two methods are used by most laboratories to sterilize clean, dry glassware on the one hand and discarded culture or specimen vessels on the other. Both methods rely on heat as the active agent of microbial destruction.

Dry heat applied in an *oven* is the usual method preferred for the sterilization of clean, dry glassware. The air within a properly insulated modern oven is heated by an electrical element fitted with thermostatic controls. The heated air raises the temperature of all glass or metal surfaces exposed to it, provided the latter are arranged within the oven in a way that permits even distribution and flow of the heated air. The temperature and time of baking are adjusted to assure the death of even the most heat-resistant organisms. Since clean glass vessels and other items prepared for oven sterilization must be closed or covered, often with cotton or paper, to prevent the later exposure of their interior surfaces to extraneous microorganisms from the environment, it is important that care be taken not to allow overheating that would char cotton plugs or paper wraps and destroy their protective value. One hour at 175° to 180° C (347° to 356° F), one and one-half hours at 165° to 170° C (329° to 338° F), or two hours at 160° C (320° F) will accomplish sterilization in the oven. (Note that decreases in time must be compensated by increases in temperature.) Oven sterilization of clean glassware is preferred as a routine because there is no dampening of glassware, cotton, or wraps and because, with proper arrangement of items within the oven, one can be assured that all interior as well as exterior surfaces will be brought to the sterilizing temperature by the heated air.

Moist heat, applied as *steam under pressure* in an *autoclave*, is used in the laboratory for the sterilization of culture media (see Fig. 4–4), discarded cultures, dirty glassware, and many other items that might be damaged by dry heat. The autoclave is an indispensable piece of equipment, not only in the laboratory, but in other hospital areas such as operating rooms and central supply areas, where sterilization of equipment and supplies for surgical procedures and other patient uses is of critical importance. In principle, the autoclave is very much like the well-known kitchen pressure cooker, in a larger version with more complicated controls to assure its efficiency and safe operation. Essentially, the autoclave is a chamber that can be sealed and filled with steam that replaces the cooler air within. Steam under pressure is admitted to the chamber so as to displace all the air through a discharge line. When the last of the cool air has been evacuated, the air discharge valve is closed and more steam is admitted until a pressure of 15 to 20 lb per square inch has been reached within the chamber. At this pressure pure steam has a temperature of 121° C. This is a much lower temperature than that used for oven sterilization, but it is much more efficient because moist heat penetrates more quickly than dry heat and more deeply when it is applied under pressure. (In the kitchen, it will

Fig. 4–4. The supplies in a medical diagnostic microbiology laboratory must be scrupulously clean and sterile. Here a technician removes baskets of sterile media from the autoclave. (Reproduced from *Health News*, April, 1962. Photo by M. Dixson. Courtesy of New York State Health Department, Albany, N.Y.)

be remembered, the advantage of the pressure cooker is that it cooks foods much more quickly and thoroughly than either boiling, which provides moist heat without pressure, or oven-baking.)

Sterilization can be accomplished in the autoclave at 121° to 125° C (250° to 256° F), with 15 to 20 lb of steam pressure, in 15 to 45 minutes, the time depending on the size, contents, and distribution of the load, as will be discussed more fully in Chapter 10.

In addition to the uses mentioned above, the autoclave is also quite satisfactory for the sterilization of clean, empty glassware, provided damp cotton plugs, paper wraps, or other fabrics

used are permitted to dry undisturbed. Microorganisms deposited on wet porous surfaces can make their way through to the interior along the moist channels between fibers. It is also important to arrange empty vessels in the autoclave for sterilization so that the air within them will not be trapped but can be freely replaced by steam, which is always hotter and lighter than air and does not mix with it easily. This means that empty tubes, flasks, bottles and other such vessels must be laid horizontally, with their plugs or caps very loosely in place, so that the heavier, cooler air within them can run out and down, and so that steam can cover their interior surfaces.

Vessels containing liquids such as culture

media or other solutions can be sterilized in an upright position, because these liquids vaporize at autoclave temperatures; the rising vapor displaces the air in the vessel upward and out of the tube or flask, while the pressure of the steam prevents any violent bubbling of the liquid. When the sterilizing period is ended, the steam in the chamber is permitted to escape very slowly, so that the liquid can cool below its boiling point while enough pressure remains to prevent its bubbling over.

All *dirty* glassware from the microbiology laboratory that has been used for the collection of patients' specimens, or for any part of the culture procedures, must, of course, be sterilized before it can be handled further. The autoclave is always used for this purpose, to assure rapid killing of organisms within the depths of liquid materials and to spare glassware from the damage it would suffer if its contents were baked onto its surfaces with dry heat. To prevent this from happening even in the moist heat of the autoclave, it is best to place empty, dirty glassware in buckets and add enough water to cover its surfaces (see Fig. 4–5). After sterilization, glassware must be scrupulously cleaned and freed of chemical impurities that might, even in trace amounts, adversely affect bacterial cultures. Laborious hand-scrubbing of glassware has been largely superseded by modern mechanical methods, using

detergents that readily loosen soil but do not react with glass, so that they rinse away easily. Mechanical dishwashers adapted for laboratory glassware are an integral part of the operations of modern laboratories. These machines also provide a final rinsing with distilled or deionized water that removes inorganic residues. The glassware is then allowed to drain dry, or it is dried with heat.

All *clean* glassware, or other items to be resterilized for use in the laboratory, must be carefully closed or covered in a way that will not permit contamination following sterilization. The covers and tops of glass Petri dishes are assembled, and groups of dishes are either wrapped in paper or placed in metal canisters. Test tubes, flasks, and bottles are fitted with either screw-on caps, light metal covers, or cotton plugs tailored snugly so that the air that will pass through cotton will be efficiently filtered free of dust and bacteria. Pipettes are fitted with a small cotton plug at the mouth end, to protect the user from mischance in drawing up liquid cultures or other contaminated materials. The plug also protects the culture from reverse contamination from the user's mouth. After plugging, pipettes can be wrapped in paper or placed in suitable covered containers so that they can be picked up for use at the plugged end, without touching the delivery tip. Whether these items are ster-

Fig. 4–5. Loading contaminated glassware into a steam sterilizer where all microorganisms are killed before the glassware is washed. (Reproduced from *Health News*, April, 1962. Photo by M. Dixson. Courtesy of New York State Health Department, Albany, N.Y.)

ilized in the oven or the autoclave, the load must be arranged in the chamber so that dry hot air, on the one hand, or pressurized steam, on the other, can reach and sterilize all surfaces.

One other type of sterilizing equipment frequently used in microbiology laboratories is the _filter_. It is used to remove bacteria or larger microorganisms from fluids or solutions that cannot be heat-sterilized. There are several types of filters in common use, but the general principles of their design and use are similar. Filters are made of porous materials (asbestos, diatomaceous earth, sintered glass, cellulose membranes, collodion) of various grades of porosity or pore size. When solutions are filtered through them, particulate matter, including microorganisms, will be retained according to the relative size of particles and pores. Most viruses and rickettsiae are _filterable;_ that is, filters of the finest porosity cannot retain them because of their very small size. In most bacteriologic work, however, this is not of practical importance if the filtered solution does not contain living cells that could support the growth and multiplication of any viruses that might be present. Filtration can be used, therefore, to prepare bacteria-free fluids for various purposes. In the preparation of culture media, for instance, some of the enriching substances used are heat-sensitive and cannot be added to the basal ingredients of the medium prior to autoclaving. Such components as blood serum, vitamin solutions, and certain carbohydrates in solution can be passed separately through filters of suitable porosity. The filtrate can then be added to the culture medium after its sterilization, using sterile pipettes or syringes for the final steps of the addition. In use, the filter is mounted on a flask (both must be sterilized beforehand) fitted with a side-arm. A piece of rubber tubing connects the flask arm to a vacuum. The solution will be pulled through the filter into the flask, but care must be taken not to exert so much force that small bacteria will also be pulled through.

Other major items of equipment for the laboratory are refrigerators and freezers, for the storage of supplies of culture media, blood, serum, completed cultures, and antibiotics; and

Fig. 4–6. An incubator that is maintained at 35° to 37° C provides the proper temperature for optimum growth of many pathogenic organisms. (Courtesy of St. Luke's Hospital Center, New York, N.Y.)

incubators to provide the constant temperatures required by microbial cultures (see Fig. 4–6). Modern incubators have an insulated interior chamber, with a thermostatically controlled heating element to provide constant temperature, and provision for circulation of heat and air, so that uniform conditions prevail for cultures regardless of their position in the chamber. Incubators are generally set for one desired temperature, commonly in the 35°-to-37°-C range since this is optimum for most bacteria that cause disease. If it is frequently necessary to incubate cultures of certain organisms at temperatures above or below this point, it is best to have a separate incubator set for the alternate temperature. Yeasts and fungi, for instance, prefer warm room temperature (28° to 30° C, or 82° to 84° F); other requirements may range upward from 5 to 20 degrees above 37° C.

Fig. 4–7. A diagnostic microbiology laboratory. Note that the laboratory request forms that accompany each specimen are kept near the working area. Daily notations of the progress of the work are made on the laboratory copy of each form. The Bunsen burner is used to sterilize the inoculating loop, the mouths of open test tubes, and flasks. (Courtesy of St. Luke's Hospital Center, New York, N.Y.)

The Techniques

Aseptic Technique

The extensive preparation of glassware and other items, as described above, would be wasted if it were not for the scrupulous care with which the microbiologist subsequently handles his work. He must be meticulous in technique as he handles cultures, to assure his own safety and that of his co-workers from their contents and to protect the cultures themselves from contamination by stray organisms from the environment. With media and glassware sterile at the start, the microbiologist manipulates every tool and culture so that the microbes he is studying cannot contaminate hands, clothing, or any part of the working area or become mixed with extraneous organisms (see Fig. 4–7). His approach is described with the term "aseptic technique," which means that it is designed to prevent or avoid "sepsis." The latter word refers to any condition, such as putrefaction or infection, resulting from the growth of microorganisms, and *asepsis*, accordingly, means the absence of such growth. By learning where, when, and under what circumstances microbes may grow and multiply, one first develops an awareness of their presence (a "seeing eye" for the invisible) and, from this, an aseptic technique to circumvent their possible effects. The phrase

describes a set of *attitudes*, as well as of methods, that is fundamental and essential for all who are concerned with the diagnosis and care of patients with infectious diseases and the protection of others from the transfer of infection.

The Technique of Transfer

The tool most frequently used by the microbiologist for transferring microbes, or the material containing them, from one place of growth to another for examination or further culture is the *inoculating loop* or *needle* (see Fig. 4–7). It consists of a piece of heat-resistant wire, 2 to 3 in. in length, held firmly in a pencil-shaped handle. The wire can be twisted into a small loop at its free end, so that it will hold a drop of liquid, or it can be used as a straight needle. It is heated in the flame of a Bunsen burner, a device that mixes illuminating gas with air to give a narrow cone of very hot flame. Other means of applying a high degree of heat can also be used, such as an electric coil or an artificial gas torch. When the inoculating loop is held to the heat, it will quickly glow, and any organisms on its surfaces will be incinerated. After cooling, the sterile wire can then be used to pick up a small quantity of the material to be studied and to transfer it to a glass slide for examination with the microscope or to a Petri dish or other vessel containing culture medium. The loop must

be carefully flamed again after use to destroy the organisms left on its surfaces. This process of twice flaming is intrinsic to the correct use of the loop.

Whenever a culture tube or bottle is opened for any reason, the exposed lip of the vessel is passed quickly through a hot flame before the sterile loop or any other tool is introduced. While the vessel is open, its cotton plug, screw cap, or other type of closure must be held in the hand with the loop in such a way as to prevent contamination of its undersurface by organisms normally present on the hands and other surfaces. While the vessel is open it is held at an angle so that dust particles in the air, with their possible load of bacteria, cannot drop directly into it. All these applications of aseptic techniques help to ensure the purity of the culture and the safety of the worker.

Other tools commonly used in the transfer of organisms from one vessel to another are sterile pipettes, syringes, and swabs. These are useful if larger quantities are to be transferred. Pouring liquids or fluid culture media into other containers is not an acceptable technique if sterility is to be maintained, for it is difficult to guarantee asepsis as the material flows over the lip of one vessel and into another. It is particularly dangerous to attempt this type of transfer of fluid cultures containing living microorganisms.

Microscopic Examinations

Bacteria and larger organisms can be examined microscopically in the living state, suspended in a fluid, or in dried, stained smears in which the microbes are no longer alive.

Wet Preparations. Microorganisms can be studied in the *living* state for such characteristics as motility, shape, size, and group arrangements. Larger forms, such as yeasts, fungi, protozoans, and helminth ova, when they are in fluid suspensions, or "*wet*" *preparations* as they are often called, can be seen with good resolution with the dry lenses. Internal structures can often be identified, even without staining, but to clarify

these a dye that will be taken up by the cells without distorting them (a "vital" stain) can be used. Weak solutions of methylene blue or of iodine are examples of such stains. Bacteria are too small to be seen with good resolution, even with the oil-immersion lens, in wet preparations, but their motility can be appreciated, as well as their patterns and arrangements (chaining, clustering, packeting, etc.).

There are two ways of making a wet preparation. A drop of the fluid containing the organisms (this may be a liquid culture medium, a specimen such as urine or spinal fluid, or a saline emulsion of organisms from a solid medium) can simply be transferred to a clean glass slide with the inoculating loop and covered with a thin cover glass. If necessary, the edges of the cover glass may be sealed with a rim of Vaseline or petroleum jelly to prevent rapid drying. A longer-lasting mount, with greater depth, can be prepared as a "hanging drop." In this case, the clean, greaseless cover glass is first rimmed lightly with the sealer; then a drop of material for study is placed in the center of the cover. A hollow-ground slide is next inverted so that the concavity is placed directly over the drop on the cover slip. A little gentle pressure seals the slide and cover together, and when the slide is quickly reinverted, the drop is suspended in the concave well of the slide.

In such preparations, motile organisms can be seen moving about, often in characteristic fashion (spinning, undulating, dashing), and in the case of the protozoans, the locomotive structures (flagella, cilia, pseudopods) can often be visualized. Capsules of large organisms, such as yeasts, can also be demonstrated by adding a drop of India ink to the preparation. This provides a dark background, against which the capsule appears as a clear, glassy zone around the organisms, the latter being visible within.

Dried, stained smears permit better resolution of bacteria and of the details of the internal structures in larger organisms. Stained smears examined with the oil-immersion lens can provide a sharp, clear view of even very small bacteria, when they are thinly spread and well-separated. Some part of the cell must retain the color of

the stain that has been used; otherwise so much light will pass through the cell that it cannot be seen distinctly. The aniline dyes react intensely with most bacteria. The composition of the cell, its contents, or its surface determines the staining reaction, which differs with the dye as well as with the type of cell involved. These distinctions provided by staining reactions are often quite helpful in the identification of bacteria.

When the material to be studied microscopically has been smeared thinly on the surface of a clean glass slide, using the inoculating loop or a sterile swab, it must be allowed to *dry completely*, in air. Drying fixes the material to the slide so that it will not wash off during the staining process. When it is dry, the slide may be passed quickly through the Bunsen flame, to "*heat-fix*" the drop still more firmly to the glass. Excessive heating may distort the cells, however, and should be avoided. The process of air-drying, heat-fixing, and staining kills the organisms without affecting their morphology unduly.

The *fixed* smear may be stained either with a single dye that will reveal individual and group morphology or with a combination of stains that distinguishes between kinds of organisms. There are several differential staining methods that can be employed, but the two used most commonly are the *Gram stain* (devised by the Danish physician, Christian Gram, in 1884), and the *acid-fast* or *Ziehl-Neelsen* stain (named for the two men who developed it, in 1892). In both these procedures, staining is accomplished in three essential steps: (1) a dye is applied for a time sufficient to stain all the bacteria uniformly and is then washed away with water; (2) an alcoholic solvent is applied briefly to remove the dye from all organisms that have not reacted to it permanently; and (3) a dye of a different color than the first is applied, then removed with a final rinse. The second dye counterstains those organisms that were decolorized by the alcohol, but it does not change the color of those that reacted with and retained the first stain. Thus, the result is differential for two kinds of organisms, staining with one color or the other.

In the case of the *Gram stain*, the first dye is a solution of crystal violet, which stains some

bacteria a very dark purple. An iodine solution then follows as a mordant, to "fix" the dye firmly to the cells. Bacteria that retain the purple color through the decolorizing and counterstaining steps are called *Gram-positive*. Those that lose the first color and are restained with the pink color of safranin, the counterstain, are called *Gram-negative*. These differences are a reflection of dissimilar chemical composition of the bacterial cell walls. For practical purposes, the Gram stain is an invaluable ally in the early as well as the later stages of identification of unknown bacteria. Very often it is the first step taken in the attempt to make a bacteriologic diagnosis of an infectious disease, the stain being applied directly to a smear of an appropriate specimen (sputum, urine, spinal fluid) obtained from the patient.

The *Ziehl-Neelsen*, or *acid-fast*, stain employs the same principles, with application of a solution of carbol fuchsin in the first step. This dye, when used with a wetting agent or gently heated to its steaming point on the slide, can penetrate the fatty substances that characterize the cell walls of some bacteria, such as the tubercle bacillus (the agent of tuberculosis), and stain the cells a bright pink. When this dye has been washed away, the second step decolorizes organisms that cannot retain the carbol fuchsin when washed with an acid alcohol solution. The counterstain of the third step is methylene blue. Bacteria such as the tubercle bacillus that retain the red stain of the carbol fuchsin are said to be *acid-fast* because they resist the acid action of the alcoholic decolorizer. Bacteria that wash free of the red dye and take the blue counterstain are non-acid-fast. This procedure is very useful for, and commonly applied to, the detection of tubercle bacilli in specimens obtained from patients suspected of having tuberculosis. It is also used, of course, in the identification of these organisms when they have grown in culture.

Special stains for the demonstration of particular bacterial structures, such as capsules, spores, and flagella, none of which stain well with the two methods described above, may sometimes have to be employed.

The detection and examination of *parasitic*

worms, their ova or larvae, in clinical specimens do not ordinarily require the assistance of any but the simplest stains. These organisms are usually studied in wet mounts, to which an iodine solution can be added to provide greater clarity of detail. *Yeasts and fungi* also are large enough to be studied closely in wet preparations under a cover glass, but in this case it may be necessary to mount the material in a solution that will dissolve other kinds of cells present, leaving the fungi intact. This type of preparation is made, for instance, when a scraping of skin or nail is to be examined directly for evidence of fungus infection. Fibrous threads running through such material and protoplasmic extensions of the cells of the skin can be confusing and must not be mistaken for fungi. A solution of potassium hydroxide, or of lactophenol, will disrupt the structures of the fragment of skin or nail being examined and permit any fungi present to stand out clearly. A stain such as cotton blue may also be added to the preparation, if necessary, to clarify some detail.

When intracellular organisms, such as *rickettsiae or viruses* growing in clumps within parasitized cells, are to be stained, the method must differentiate them from the structures of the host cell. When properly stained, aggregates of these submicroscopic organisms can be visualized with the oil-immersion lens of the light microscope, and their location and arrangement within the parasitized cell or its nucleus can be studied.

Methods for the Cultivation of Microorganisms

Microscopic examination of microorganisms provides important and necessary information about their morphology, but can tell us very little about the essential biologic characteristics of the microbes.

To obtain this information it is necessary to observe and study microorganisms in *culture*. Their final identification is then made on the basis of several characteristics considered together, such as morphology and staining reac-

tions, food requirements, the atmospheric conditions (aerobic or anaerobic) that are optimal for growth, and their responses to growth factors or antagonists. Although viruses and rickettsiae require the presence of living cells for their growth in culture and yeasts, molds, and the few protozoan species that are cultivable have their special requirements as well, many of the basic methods for the preparation and handling of cultures of these organisms are very similar to those used to study bacterial properties. Since the parasitic heterotrophic bacteria are of paramount concern in medical microbiology, the methods for their cultivation will receive the major emphasis here.

The Nature and Preparation of Culture Media. It was pointed out in Chapter 3 that in nature parasitic bacteria obtain their nourishment from the host being parasitized, and that their cultivation in the laboratory necessitates the provision of the required nutrients and conditions for growth.

The *composition* of a good culture medium (plural, *media*) requires the rather exact adjustment of a number of ingredients and factors. In general, nutritional media must contain products of partial protein breakdown, since many bacteria cannot digest intact protein materials. Protein components, such as peptides, peptones, and amino acids, are required for the synthesis of bacterial cell protoplasm and for cellular structure. These are commonly provided in the form of partially cooked meat or meat extracts. Bacterial syntheses require energy; therefore carbohydrates such as glucose, lactose, or starch must be provided. Minerals and vitamins may be added in purified form or as components of some natural food. Minerals are often present as their salts in meat digests, and yeast extract is an excellent source of vitamin B_1. Water is always present in large proportion. Other ingredients can be added for special purposes or for bacteria with special growth requirements. A medium can be made *selective* by incorporating one or more ingredients that will inhibit the growth of some organisms while encouraging the multiplication of others. A *differential* medium can be prepared

by including a substance to which different bacteria respond differently, thus making it possible to distinguish between them by their growth characteristics in such a medium. The medium may be used as a liquid broth, or agar may be added to solidify it at temperatures below 45° C (113° F).

Media prepared with meat extracts are usually referred to as *nutrient* agar or broth media, while those prepared with meats that have been slowly cooked, or infused, with enzymes added to digest them partially are called *infusion* broths or agars. In the diagnostic laboratory, where parasitic bacteria must be provided every opportunity to grow in such artificial media, removed from their living hosts, infusion media are often preferred to the extracts because they are more enriched. Blood may also be added to provide further enrichment. For this purpose, whole blood that has been *defibrinated* (the fibrin removed to prevent clotting) is used in a proportion of 5 to 10 per cent by volume. The blood may be of human or animal origin, each having certain advantages. For some bacteria, it may be necessary to liberate the hemoglobin from the blood cells so that they can utilize it. This can be done by heating the blood gently or adding it to a hot medium. In the process the hemoglobin color changes from its customary bright red to a rich brown, so that an agar medium prepared with heated blood is called *chocolate* agar. If an enriched medium without the color or turbidity of blood is desired, other materials can be used, such as human or animal serum, yeast extract, or protein components in extra amounts.

Before the medium is complete and ready for use, it is important to assure the stability of its acid-alkaline balance, or pH. (pH is a mathematical term used to express the degree of acidity or alkalinity a solution may have.) Most bacteria require that the pH of their environment be neutral, or nearly so, that is, neither actively acid nor alkaline. This means that not only must the finished medium be *adjusted* to neutrality, but it must also be *buffered* against major changes in pH that may occur as a result of bacterial growth in the medium later. As bacterial growth products increase in an artificial medium, from which they cannot diffuse away as they might in a natural environment, large shifts in the pH of the medium toward acidity or alkalinity can occur, and since bacteria are sensitive to such changes, the culture may die. For this reason, it is desirable to incorporate substances, known as *buffers*, into the medium. Buffers are compounds capable of reacting with free acids and alkalis and, in so doing, of binding them so that they are no longer in active solution. Continuing buffer action in the culture throughout the period of bacterial growth therefore prevents large pH changes in the medium.

The microbiologist often wants to be sure that a culture remains stable in pH, or he may be testing for the ability of an organism to produce a pH change by utilizing some ingredient of the medium. For these reasons, indicator dyes, which are sensitive to free acid or alkali and assume a different color at various pH values, are frequently added to culture media. A shift in pH as the culture grows will then produce a visible color change to inform the observer of this event. It is necessary to know the color range for each indicator in response to pH changes. By comparing the color of the test with the standard colors for the indicator at each pH value, an estimate of the degree of acidity or alkalinity developing in the test can be made. Finer measurements of pH can be made with electrical instruments when it is necessary to be more exact.

Since bacteria can be exacting in their growth requirements and also quite variable in their behavioral response to environmental changes, the composition and reliability of culture media are vital factors in their study and identification. The ingredients, as well as all glassware and tools used in preparing the medium, must be free of chemical impurities that might produce misleading results, and the finished product must, of course, be free of any extraneous organisms from the general environment. Such organisms would contaminate the medium with their own growth products, compete for nutrient with the species being studied, and make accurate interpretation of results impossible. The *final step*, therefore, in the preparation of culture media is *sterilization*, usually in the autoclave, as described earlier in this chapter, or by filtration if heat-sensitive ingredients are involved. It should also

be pointed out that in the preparation of media there should be no lapses of time between the various steps taken prior to sterilization that would permit contaminating microorganisms to establish themselves and begin their growth. Subsequent sterilization of the media will kill these organisms, but it will not restore changes they may have produced in nutrient ingredients or remove impurities they may have added.

To summarize, then, the basic requirements of an adequate and reliable medium for microbial culture are that it contain the right ingredients, appropriate to its use, in utilizable form and correct quantities; that it be stable with respect to pH; that it be free of chemical and microbial impurities when prepared; and that it be sterilized to prevent further growth of accidental, living contaminants.

Fortunately, much of the time-consuming burden of preparing culture media in the laboratory has been assumed by commercial manufacturers who can supply them ready to use or in dehydrated form. Because of the difficulties inherent in the storage of supplies of prepared media ready to use and the possibilities of their dehydration or deterioration during unpredictable periods when they are not needed, many laboratories prefer to stock dehydrated supplies. These media contain all the ingredients required for a particular purpose, including salts and buffers, so that it is usually necessary only to add a volume of distilled water sufficient to obtain the correct concentration of their contents. The mixture is heated gently to dissolve all components and dispensed in appropriate containers (tubes, flasks, bottles, etc.), which are then closed with cotton plugs or caps and sterilized. These commercial media offer the many advantages of uniformity of composition, ease and convenience of final preparation, and low cost. When they are not readily available, or when special manipulation of ingredients must be made, the laboratory must prepare its own, using fresh materials and exact measurements.

The Use of Culture Media.   Agar media can be used conveniently in several ways. At the time of preparation, an agar medium may be dispensed into a number of test tubes, which, after sterilization, are laid at an angle to cool. When the agar has solidified, as it will do at about 40° C, the medium will have a sloping surface, called a *slant*. When slants are inoculated, the surface is streaked with the inoculating wire, and the latter may also be plunged, or stabbed, to the bottom of the tube through the solid butt of medium below. Most frequently, agar media are *plated* by pouring them into Petri plates. This is always done after the medium has been sterilized, in tubes, flasks, or bottles, and has cooled to about 50° C (or has been melted down again after solidification). The material to be cultured can be placed in the Petri dish or added to the agar before it is poured, if desired. The result, in this case, is the growth of organisms throughout the medium, in its depths as well as on the surface, and the preparation is called a *pour plate*. If the medium is poured before it is inoculated, the material for culture is streaked across its hardened surface with the inoculating loop or a sterile swab. This will result in the growth of organisms across the surface along the lines drawn by the tool, and the preparation is called, in this case, a *streak plate*.

Tubed agar media can also be solidified in an upright position, for inoculation by a *stab* of the wire down through the column. Such a *stab culture* may be useful in demonstrating the characteristic way a particular organism will grow along the path of the wire, depending on whether it is motile and can diffuse outward from the stab through the medium and on its ability to grow at varying depths where oxygen availability becomes a factor. Frequently, the agar concentration of the medium used in this way is less than that required to prepare a solid plate, and the medium is referrred to as *semisolid*.

A medium used in liquid form, without the addition of agar, is usually called a *broth*. It may be prepared in test tubes in small quantities (5 to 10 ml) or in flasks or bottles. Sometimes a wide, shallow layer of broth in small amount in a large flask is desirable. For other purposes a deep column of liquid may be required (oxygenation is again a factor). It is also useful at times to layer a little broth medium over part of a solid agar slant, so that organisms will have a very wet

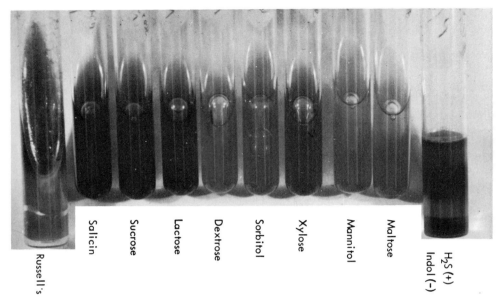

Salicin Sucrose Lactose Dextrose Sorbitol Xylose Mannitol Maltose

Russell's

H₂S (+)
Indol (−)

Fig. 4–8. Fermentation tubes inverted in tubes of broth containing carbohydrates trap any gas that may be formed during microbial utilization of the sugar. Note the bubbles of gas present in the tubes containing dextrose, xylose, maltose, and mannitol. This is one of the methods used to distinguish members of the genus *Salmonella* or *Shigella* from other Gram-negative enteric bacilli.

solid surface for their growth. A particularly frequent use of a tubed carbohydrate broth involves the addition to the tube of a smaller tube, placed in an inverted position (see Fig. 4–8). The inner one is called a *fermentation tube*, its purpose being to trap any bubbles of gas that may be formed if the carbohydrate of the medium is fermented by an organism growing therein. The visible evidence of gas formation joins the array of other information by which the organism is identified.

The Temperature and Atmospheric Conditions of Culture. The choice of temperature for the incubation of clinical specimens in primary culture is generally made on the basis of clinical expectations as to the nature of the pathogenic microorganisms they may contain, and this is also true with respect to the control of atmospheric conditions. Cultures of specimens expected to yield pathogenic bacteria are generally incubated at temperatures in the narrow range

of 35° to 37° C, but when fungous infections are suspected, the temperature of cultures should not exceed 28° C or fall below 22° C. Some pathogenic fungi display two types of growth, one duplicating the morphology seen in the body and requiring incubation at body temperature (37° C); the other developing best at cooler temperatures (22° to 28° C). Occasionally lower or higher temperatures may be indicated by the nature of microorganisms suspected to be the cause of infectious disease, and these requirements can readily be met in the laboratory provided adequate indication is given as to the tentative clinical diagnosis. In such instances the laboratory generally sets up duplicate or triplicate cultures for incubation at different temperatures in order to assure proper conditions for growth of significant organisms and their recognition in culture.

Atmospheric conditions can be similarly adjusted to meet the differing needs of various types of microorganisms. Microaerophilic or

anaerobic organisms can be cultivated in airtight incubators in which the atmosphere is manipulated by evacuation of air and the substitution of nitrogen, carbon dioxide, or other desired gases. Many simpler methods have also been devised over the years. A "candle jar" provides the lowered oxygen tension required by microaerophilic organisms and also supplies added carbon dioxide that enhances the growth of many pathogenic bacteria. This is simply a container that can be closed with an airtight lid after culture plates or tubes have been placed within it together with a lighted candle. When the lid is firmly fixed so that additional air cannot be admitted from the outside atmosphere, the candle burns until all available atmospheric oxygen within the jar has been exhausted by the oxidation of the burning wax. The chemical reaction binds free oxygen with carbon derived from the wax, forming carbon dioxide (CO_2), which is released into the jar's atmosphere, replacing the depleted oxygen supply.

Many techniques have been devised for the complete exclusion of oxygen from culture media in which anaerobes are expected to grow. Among these, two rather simple methods are in common use today. One provides for the addition of a reducing agent (sodium thioglycollate is most satisfactory) to a liquid nutrient medium tubed in a deep column. Anaerobic organisms grow in the depths of the tube, out of reach of atmospheric oxygen dissolved in the surface layers. The advantage of such a medium is that it supports (in its upper layers) the growth of aerobic and microaerophilic organisms as well as that of anaerobes, but a mixed flora growing in liquid media must later be separated on a solid medium. The other method makes it possible to incubate either agar plates or tubed liquid media in an anaerobic atmosphere, using an airtight jar from which air can be evacuated via an outlet in the lid. Hydrogen gas, illuminating gas, nitrogen, or a mixture of nitrogen and carbon dioxide can be used to restore atmospheric pressure within the jar, which is then placed in an incubator providing the desired temperature. Airtight incubators are also available today. These are equipped with temperature controls, as well as

inlet and outlet valves so that the atmosphere of incubation can be manipulated in any desired manner. Use of an anaerobic jar or incubator makes it possible to streak out clinical specimens on agar plates and to identify isolated colonies of anaerobic organisms more quickly than can be done when cultures in fluid media must be replated for separation of mixed growth.

Serologic Identification of Microorganisms. Conclusive identification of microorganisms can often be obtained by serologic methods. These are based on the fact that the protein and certain other constituents of microbial cells are "antigenic" — that is, they stimulate the human or animal body to produce "antibodies" during the time of active infection, when the tissues are exposed to living bacteria or other organisms. The antibodies are often present in the circulating blood as a component of serum. When a sample of blood is taken from an animal or person who has been infected, the serum is separated in the laboratory and tested with the microorganism suspected as the agent of the infection. In the test tube, antibodies react specifically in certain visible ways with the microbial antigens that stimulated their production in the body. This type of reaction is used to confirm the identity of a microorganism when the nature of the antibody in a given serum sample is known, or conversely to determine the presence and nature of antibodies in an "unknown" serum tested with known organisms. The term "serology" refers to such studies of serum for its antibody content. The application of serologic methods comprises an important part of the work of the microbiology laboratory in establishing the diagnosis of infectious diseases, through the identification of organisms isolated from clinical specimens or of antibodies in the patient's serum, or both. The nature of antigens and antibodies and the underlying principles involved in serologic diagnosis are discussed fully in Chapter 6.

The Techniques Taken Together. The work of the diagnostic microbiologist begins with the arrival in the laboratory of a specimen from a patient, with a request from the physician for a

culture. The work, and its results, are influenced, however, before the specimen reaches the laboratory by the method and timing of its collection and transport. If these are inadequate or incorrect, the results may be also, and, even more unfortunately, this source of error may pass unnoticed so that the results are not subjected to proper interpretation. This matter of specimen collection, often performed at the patient's bedside by a nurse or physician rather than by the microbiologist, is of such importance that it will be emphasized many times in this text.

The *nature of the specimen*, and the kind of information desired from it, determine the type of culture procedures that are initiated. As we shall see, many areas of the human body are parasitized by microorganisms that cause no harm, but there are differences in the kinds of organisms found in different areas because environmental conditions for them vary from one section or tissue of the body to another. Thus a particular kind of specimen, such as a sputum or a sample of feces, has its own "normal flora." These organisms will grow out in the media as a *mixed culture*, in which any *pathogenic* (disease-producing) stranger that may be present must be recognized. The suspected pathogen must then be separated from the others and persuaded to grow alone, in *pure culture*, so that its appearance, properties, and behavior can be identified. Furthermore, not only do the organisms normally found in certain specimens vary from those of others, but the kind of pathogenic organism that can be expected in different specimens varies also. For instance, one would not expect to find the diphtheria bacillus in a fecal sample, because it is not likely to survive in the bowel, or the agent of a venereal disease in a sputum culture. On the other hand, certain types of specimens, such as blood, urine, and spinal fluid, are normally sterile in the healthy body and contain microorganisms only by accident or as a result of an infectious process. Therefore, any organism found in such a specimen may be suspect.

For all these reasons, and also because the microbiologist is alert to the unpredictability of living organisms, the *initiation* of culture procedures is carefully guided by the specimen, its source, and the diagnostic possibilities. A battery of different media is inoculated with the specimen, the whole group being chosen to provide a wide range of bacterial requirements — that is, *enrichment* for fastidious organisms, *selective* nutrient to reduce competition and permit the suspected organism to flourish, a *differential* medium to indicate different kinds of organisms growing upon it (see Fig. 4–9), a medium with reduced oxygen for *anaerobes*, and so on. The widest possible screening, consistent with practical limitations on time and space, is provided to cover the widest possible range of intelligent expectation. In addition, stained smear preparations of the specimen may provide evidence of the presence of a particular organism, or some other diagnostic hint may indicate the advisability of further procedures and of the use of one or two special media beyond the routine battery.

Time, as well as appropriate action, is often of the essence in medical microbiology. Specific measures for treating the patient seriously ill with an acute infection may be dependent on

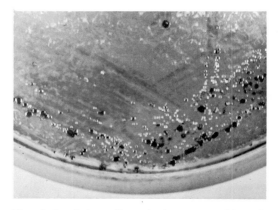

Fig. 4–9. *Salmonella* colonies on a bismuth sulfite agar plate. This medium is said to be selective because it inhibits many coliform organisms but supports the growth of *Salmonella* strains. It also differentiates the *Salmonella* colonies because these take on a characteristic dark-green or black color, often with a metallic sheen, as seen above.

news from the laboratory regarding the nature of microorganisms, if any, being isolated from the patient's specimens and their response in culture to the action of clinically useful antibiotics. Between the time cultures are started and identifications are complete, the laboratory can provide tentative, preliminary information concerning its results to guide those who are caring for the patient. Even incomplete results can be useful to the physician and the nurse in making decisions as to whether or not the patient should be isolated from others or treated in some specific way.

Each day after culture of specimens is started, the microbiologist makes observations of the growth occurring in each of the media inoculated and *plans the next, shortest step* that will narrow identifications to a final decision, as quickly as possible. The work is organized in a logical sequence designed to establish a pattern of facts from a number of clues, both positive and negative, in much the same way as a detective sets out to find evidence and fit it together.

Plated agar media are examined for growth, and particular note is made of its appearance. Bacteria multiplying on agar surfaces form visible areas of massed growth called *colonies*. The colonial growth of different types of bacteria is often quite characteristic in its appearance on the various kinds of agar plated. The surfaces of colonies may be rough or smooth; their edges may be even and entire, filamentous, or eroded; and their elevation from the surface may be convex, peaked, or patterned in some way. In addition, bacterial enzymes, or other products of colonial growth, may react with the surrounding medium in some observable manner. On blood agar, for instance, some types of bacteria may cause destruction, or *lysis*, of the red blood cells adjacent to them, leaving clear, colorless zones around the colonies growing on an otherwise red and turbid medium. Such a reaction is referred to as *hemolysis* (hemo: blood), and the organism is said to be *hemolytic*. Pigment production may be a marked feature of growth, remaining within individual cells to color the whole colony in some cases, in others diffusing away to change the original color of the medium. The utilization of some particular ingredient in a selective or differential medium will also be obvious because of the presence of an indicator reacting visibly to the changes produced.

In the liquid media included in the original set of cultures for a specimen, bacterial growth may appear diffusely homogeneous, or granular; it may occur in layers in a liquid or semisolid column, or the bacteria may tend to remain clustered together in colonizing groups, appearing as small puffballs floating in the medium. Some broth media contain substances that reduce or remove the free oxygen from solution, so that anaerobic organisms can grow in their depths, while aerobic types also find it possible to grow, but only near the surface where atmospheric oxygen is still available. Most bacteria, being facultative, will grow at all levels.

Microscopic examination of stained smears or wet mounts made from the growth in liquid or on solid media provides another guide to further steps toward final identification. Motility, Gram-stain reactions, individual cell morphology, and patterns of arrangement of the bacteria in these cultures lead to decisions as to the next test to make or medium to use. If the original cultures contain more than one type, or species, of bacterium, however, these must be separated and grown singly in pure culture before further efforts can be made to identify them, since their reactions to a test medium may vary and lead to confusion of results.

Separation of bacterial species for pure cultures is best accomplished with plated media, on which colonies tend to be individual and separated if the streaking technique has not allowed them to crowd together. Isolated colonies are picked from the surface with the inoculating loop or straight wire and transferred to another medium where they can grow alone and display such properties as the medium supports or encourages. Broth cultures are streaked out on agar media, of appropriate composition, using the inoculating loop for the transfer and spreading the drop out carefully over the surface to permit the growth of isolated colonies.

The temperature and atmosphere of incubation are chosen for this second set of cultures, or *subcultures* as they are called, according to indications in the original media as to the nature and preferences of the organisms being studied.

The *pure subcultures* of isolated organisms are examined after 18 to 24 hours of incubation, and if they provide sufficient information, final identifications are made. If not, further subcultures may have to be made for tests of additional properties. Carbohydrate media are inspected for evidence of fermentation, provided by the color of a pH-sensitive indicator that can reveal an acid change in the medium and by the presence or absence of gas in the fermentation tube if the test was made in a sugar broth. This type of reaction is particularly useful in identifying Gram-negative bacilli isolated from stool cultures. Many such bacilli are normally found in the bowel and are indistinguishable in their morphology from some of the pathogenic organisms, such as the typhoid bacillus, associated with active infection of the intestinal tract. A key physiologic difference, however, lies in the ability of many of these "normal" organisms to ferment lactose, while the typhoid bacillus cannot. Furthermore, the typhoid bacillus is capable of fermenting some other sugars, such as glucose, but the breakdown is not complete, and while acid end products are formed, no gas is liberated. This fact also helps to distinguish the typhoid organism from some of its close relatives. In addition serologic methods have particular value in the identification of pathogenic Gram-negative bacilli.

Other types of enzyme activity, characteristic for a group or a species, can be demonstrated rather quickly and simply with pure subcultures. Some strains of staphylococci, for instance, produce an enzyme called coagulase because it is capable of coagulating fresh blood plasma. The clotting of the plasma, mixed in a test tube with a loopful of organisms from an agar plate colony, is readily visible after one or two hours of incubation at 37° C. Identification of this property, together with colonial morphology and pigment production, and microscopic appearance, might lead to the report of a "hemolytic *Staphylococcus aureus*, coagulase-positive," an organism commanding respect for its ability to cause serious infections and for the relative ease with which it can be spread from one person to another. Another example of an enzyme easily identified is the urease possessed by certain fecal organisms commonly encountered in cultures of stools, and other specimens as well. As its name implies, this enzyme is capable of breaking down urea, in solution, to ammonia and carbon dioxide. When the organisms are mixed in a urea solution containing a color indicator, the breakdown is recognized by the color response of the dye to the highly alkaline ammonia as it is released.

Many other such tests are available and may be conducted if necessary, but usually the systematic application of a few, designed to reveal key characteristics, is sufficient to make identifications within 24 to 72 hours of the time the culture was originated. During all of this process, the microbiologist keeps careful notes and records of his tests and their results, so that final decisions can be made with clear factual support.

Special Tests and Techniques

In addition to the basic work, described above, of identifying bacteria through the study and recognition of their morphologic and physiologic activities, the microbiology laboratory may be requested to make two other types of determinations: a *quantitative* estimation of the bacteria present in a specimen, and an evaluation of their *response to antibiotics*.

Quantitative Cultures. It is often important to know not only *what* organisms are present in a particular specimen, but also *how many*. This is because the mere presence of an organism in the specimen, even though it may be of a potentially pathogenic variety, does not necessarily mean that it is the cause of the patient's disease. It may simply be an organism normally present in the

area of the body from which the specimen was derived, or a contaminant from the environment, but its occurrence in large numbers offers one type of evidence of its possible significance.

This question is very often of particular interest in the case of urine samples. Specimens of urine for culture are ordinarily not collected directly from the patient's bladder through a sterile catheter but are voided into a sterile bottle. This means that they may contain, in small numbers, organisms normally found on the perineum. If, however, the sample is collected with a clean technique and reaches the laboratory quickly, before any organisms present in it have an opportunity to multiply directly in the urine, as many are capable of doing, a numerical *count* of the bacteria growing out in culture offers a better evaluation of their significance than a mere report of their presence.

A quantitative culture is prepared by placing a measured quantity of the sample on one or more solid media, counting the number of colonies that appear subsequently, and translating the figure arithmetically to express the number of organisms present in 1 ml of sample. For example, if a loop standardized to deliver one one-hundredth of 1 ml of urine (0.01 ml) is used to inoculate the surface of an agar plate, and if this inoculum yields a total of 15 colonies, the count for the specimen would be 15×100, or 1500 colonies in 1 full ml. If the specimen appears, by visual or microscopic examination, to contain very large numbers of organisms that would be difficult to count by direct sampling, measured dilutions may be prepared and the plating done from these. It is usual to make such dilutions in sterile water or saline, in multiples of ten, and to plate out three diluted samples, each in duplicate, so that an average can be obtained. The plating can be done with either a pour plate or a streak plate method, and the size of the inoculum can be adjusted as desired. If larger quantities than the loop can deliver are to be inoculated, a sterile pipette is used to measure the amount sampled.

If a urine is plated in dilutions of 1:10, 1:100, and 1:1000, using a loop to streak out 0.01 ml each time, the *actual* colony count on each plate is multiplied by 100, and then by the dilution factor, to express the result in terms on numbers of colonies per milliliter of urine. The final figures obtained for each dilution should agree closely enough to permit an average, as seen in the following example:

0.01 ml of a 1:10 dilution on plates A and B:

    actual colony count, plate A = 150
    colonies per ml, plate A   = $150 \times 100 \times 10$ = 150,000

    actual colony count, plate B = 142
    colonies per ml, plate B   = $142 \times 100 \times 10$ = 142,000

0.01 ml of a 1:100 dilution on plates C and D:

    actual colony count, plate C = 13
    colonies per ml, plate C   = $13 \times 100 \times 100$ = 130,000

    actual colony count, plate D = 16
    colonies per ml, plate D   = $16 \times 100 \times 100$ = 160,000

0.01 ml of a 1:1000 dilution on plates E and F:

    actual colony count, plate E = 1
    colonies per ml, plate E   = $1 \times 100 \times 1000$ = 100,000

    plate F = no growth

With a count in this range, obviously a larger sample of the 1:1000 dilution would have been required to produce a countable result. A 1-ml sample, for instance, might have yielded 150 colonies per plate, in agreement with the 0.01-ml inoculum from the 1:10 dilution, each indicating the presence of 150,000 colonies per milliliter. However, the results obtained from the four plates representing the two lower dilutions can be used, since they are in good agreement, and the two plates from the 1:1000 dilution ignored because they are out of range. The final report of colonies per milliliter in this sample is 145,500, the average obtained from plates A through D, inclusive.

The bacteriologic and arithmetic reliability of such counts is the responsibility of the microbiologist, who must manipulate dilutions and quantities of inoculum in such a way as to produce plates that have encouraged all organisms present to grow, in numbers per plate that can be counted with accuracy. Plates with too few or too many organisms must be discarded, only those within range being counted. For practical purposes, it is often sufficiently informative for the laboratory to provide a result expressing the approximate range of the count, rather than an exact figure, such as 10,000 to 100,000 organisms per milliliter, or *more than* 100,000 per milliliter, the latter figure being considered, arbitrarily, as the lowest consistent criterion of active infection. It cannot be overemphasized, on the other hand, that the *clinical* reliability and interpretation of a specimen colony count depend with *equal* importance on the adequacy of specimen collection and the speed with which the culture can be initiated, following collection. If a time lapse is unavoidable before the culture can be started, the specimen may be refrigerated in the interim to prevent bacterial multiplication in the sample.

Specimens other than urine can also be set up in quantitative culture if it is difficult to evaluate the significance of organisms present. Even when obtained from healthy persons, some specimens may contain bacteria that are potentially pathogenic. These organisms may have little or no significance in small numbers, but their presence in large quantities may indicate a disturbance of the normal host-parasite balance or their responsibility for infectious disease. Therefore it may be important to perform quantitative cultures, particularly when obvious agents of infectious disease cannot be found. Quantitation is not necessary, of course, for specimens that are normally sterile and in which a significant organism has been demonstrated.

Antibiotic Susceptibility Testing. Antibiotic tests can be performed as soon as individual organisms can be isolated in pure culture from the specimen. For several reasons it is not good practice to test mixed cultures for their response to antibiotics. It may be impossible to determine the response of each organism in a mixture to a particular antibiotic; the mixed species may compete with each other for growth on the medium, adding to the antagonism exerted by the drug on one or the other; or the species present may be mutually supportive so that the antibiotic's effect on one or another is lessened. In any of these cases, results are difficult to interpret and may be quite misleading to the physician. It is usual, therefore, for the laboratory to prepare the specimen, on receipt, for culture and to wait for isolated bacterial growth, which can then be tested. An exception to this general rule may be made if the situation is urgent, and if stained smears of the specimen reveal the presence of only one type of organism or of one that is largely predominant, so that the presence of others will not offer undue interference in the test. However, it is always best to repeat such results, to confirm them, with pure growth of each organism obtained from the culture later.

There are several methods for testing the response of an organism to antibiotic action. Most of these can provide quantitative information concerning the precise quantity of each drug tested that will suppress or kill the organism being tested, under particular laboratory conditions. The technique can also be applied to the serum, urine, or other body fluid of the patient being treated, to determine the amount of effective antibiotic present in such material. These quantitative methods are time-consuming, however, and require personnel and space that are

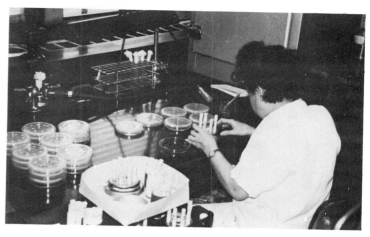

Fig. 4–10. The bacteriologist is placing antibiotic disks on plates that have been streaked with pathogenic bacteria to determine their antibiotic susceptibility. (Courtesy of St. Luke's Hospital Center, New York, N.Y.)

often not available in the diagnostic laboratory. For this reason, most microbiology laboratories perform a simpler, semiquantitative test as a routine procedure and offer more elaborate methods according to their facilities.

The method most frequently used involves placing small paper disks of uniform size and shape, each previously impregnated (by the manufacturer) with an antibiotic in known concentration, on the surface of suitably enriched nutrient agar plates that have been "seeded" with the organism to be tested. Seeding the plate means inoculating it with the organism, using, for this purpose, uniform, close streaking that assures confluent growth evenly distributed across the entire surface of the plate. A number of antibiotic disks containing different drugs, or different concentrations of the same drug, are then placed on the plate, spaced at regular intervals from each other (see Fig. 4–10). Several factors have an important influence on the results and should be considered. The medium must be supportive for the organism but have no effect on the antibiotic itself; the latter must be soluble, so that it can diffuse into the medium from the disk; and growth on the plate must be neither so abundant as to obscure any antibiotic effect nor so scant and spotty as to magnify the antagonistic action of the drug on any disk. If all these conditions are properly met, reasonably reliable results can be obtained after about 18 to 24 hours of incubation under conditions correctly adjusted for the organism being tested.

When the plates are examined, any disk containing a drug with an antagonistic effect on the organism will be seen to be surrounded by a clear area where no growth has occurred, while the rest of the plate shows unimpeded growth. Such an area is called a "zone of inhibition" because the organism has been prevented from growing by the antibiotic that has diffused into the zone around the disk. The organism is then reported to be *susceptible* to the action of that drug. If the antibiotic is not effective in inhibiting the growth of the organism, the latter is said to be *resistant* to that drug. In this case, growth can be seen to extend right to the rim of the disk, surrounding it completely (see Fig. 4–11).

Because time is important, it is often desirable to perform antibiotic testing even before identification of the organism is complete. In that case, identification procedures and antibiotic testing can proceed together, the results being reported simultaneously. Under any circumstances that make interpretation of antibiotic results difficult, however, it is better to take the time required for a proper test, under optimal conditions, than to report a premature, possibly inaccurate result, particularly if the patient's antibiotic therapy (treatment) is to be chosen on this basis.

Other special methods for identifying different kinds of organisms, or demonstrating particular properties, may be employed in the microbiology laboratory when the routine procedures provide inadequate information or results that are inconclusive. For instance, it may be important to study an organism's *pathogenicity* (ability to produce disease), particularly if it has been isolated from a specimen in which one might normally expect to find its nonpathogenic relatives,

Fig. 4–11. An antibiotic susceptibility test. The agar plate was inoculated with a microorganism before the disks impregnated with antibiotics were placed on the surface. The clear areas around the disks are zones of inhibition of microbial growth. This inhibition is caused by antibiotic that has diffused from the disk into the adjacent medium. Each disk that is surrounded by confluent growth and shows no zone of inhibition contains an antibiotic to which the organism is resistant.

if the latter cannot be readily distinguished by other, simpler means. In such a case it may be necessary to use experimental animals to demonstrate the pathogenicity of an organism. One or more animals, of one or more species, may be inoculated, either with the specimen or with a preparation of the pure growth of a suspect organism. The pathogenic character of the strain may then be evaluated, according to the kind of disease it produces, if any, in the inoculated animals, taking note of the fact that animal species, including humans, differ in their responses to the same microorganism. Animal inoculation may become necessary, also, in the case of microorganisms, such as viruses and rickettsiae, that are difficult or impossible to cultivate in the laboratory, but will grow readily in the tissues of the intact experimental animal. One may then evaluate the relationship established between the animal and the microorganism and assess the significance of this in human infections.

In general, the methods applied by the laboratory to the identification of any organism depend on the ease with which it may be recognized by microscopic means alone, by these plus artificial cultivation and demonstration of physiologic properties, or by some other special technique of recognition.

Microscopic examination with the light microscope is usually sufficient for the identification of protozoans and the parasitic worms or their ova and larvae. It is also often adequate for the recognition of yeasts and molds, but in this case cultures may be necessary to distinguish between closely related members of a genus or group, particularly if they are not all pathogenic. For the bacteria, as we have seen, microscopy alone is helpful, but usually not able to provide final identifications reliably. For this, cultural characteristics must be demonstrated and, on occasion, pathogenicity studies in animals may be indicated. The viruses and rickettsiae cannot ordinarily be studied with the light microscope, but they can be visualized and studied with the electron microscope. They can be cultivated in the laboratory only if living animal cells or tissues are provided, in tissue culture rather than artificial medium culture. Otherwise, living experimental animals must be used for their study.

The final determinants for the laboratory in its selection of appropriate methods, and in its success in performing them, are the nature of the medical problems with which it is primarily involved (those of a general hospital differ from those of a specialty or research practice), the funds available for its facilities of space and equipment, and, most important of all, the training and skill of its personnel.

Questions

1. Name the parts of a light microscope and give the function of each.
2. How is the total magnification determined?

3. Describe briefly how an object viewed with an electron microscope is enlarged.
4. Describe briefly the methods used to prepare glassware for laboratory use. Why are they necessary?
5. Why is a wire inoculating loop used to transfer microorganisms in the laboratory? *sterile*
6. Briefly describe the Gram stain. Why is it called a differential stain?
7. Why is the careful preparation of laboratory media important?
8. Why are quantitative cultures done in the laboratory? What preliminary steps are necessary to ensure accurate results?

References

Pertinent References

Ajello, Libero; Georg, Lucille K.; Kaplan, William; and Kaufman, Leo: *Laboratory Manual for Clinical Mycology*. U.S. Dept. HEW, PHS, CDC, Atlanta, Ga., 1966.

Bailey, W. Robert, and Scott, Elvyn G.: *Diagnostic Microbiology*, 2nd ed. C. V. Mosby Co., St. Louis, 1966.

Damon, Samuel R.: *Collection, Handling and Shipment of Diagnostic Specimens*. USPHS, CDC, Atlanta, Ga., 1962.

Gillies, R. R., and Dodds, T. C.: *Bacteriology Illustrated*. The Williams and Wilkins Co., Baltimore, 1965.

Harris, Albert H., and Coleman, Marion B.: *Diagnostic Procedures and Reagents*, 4th ed. Amer. Pub. Hlth. Assoc., Inc., New York, 1963.

Schneierson, S. Stanley: *Atlas of Diagnostic Microbiology*. Abbott Laboratories, North Chicago, Ill., 1965.

Periodicals

Kalter, Seymour, and Hillis, William D.: *Procedures for Routine Laboratory Diagnosis of Virus and Rickettsial Diseases*. School of Aerospace Medicine, USAF Aerospace Medical Center, Brooks Air Force Base, Texas, Nov., 1961.

Laboratory Diagnosis of Microbial Diseases, *Ann. N.Y. Acad. Sci.*, **98**:615, 1962.

McQuay, Russell M.: Good Parasitologic Examinations Depend on Proper Procedures, *Hos. Top.*, **44**:85, Oct., 1966.

Medical Research, *World Health*, **15**:6, Nov., 1962.

Schaeffer, Morris: Diagnosis of Viral and Rickettsial Disease, in *Applied Virology*, edited by M. Sanders and E. H. Linnette. First Annual Symposium in Applied Virology, Boca Rotan, Florida, Dec., 1964. Olympic Press, Sheboygan, Wis., 1965.

——— The Virology Lab — Pitfalls and Potentials, *Hosp. Practice*, Dec., 1966.

Section II The Character of Microbial Diseases

5 The Natural Interrelationships of Man and Microbes

John Donne's famous phrase, "No man is an island unto himself," has wide biologic as well as philosophic meaning, for no living thing can survive as an island, independent of support from other life.

The Science of Ecology

The vital interrelationships of living organisms, sharing a natural world at every level of existence, are the focus of interest in the science of *ecology*. An understanding of these ecologic relationships requires, as well, a continuing study of the environmental factors that influence the survival and welfare of individual or collective species. Ecologic and environmental pressures, functioning together, determine the survival of species and the direction of their evolution. With the evolution of the human species, and its capacity for independent thought and action, a new pressure on the natural world has been added. The steadily increasing size of the human population is, in itself, a pressure, and this coupled with the nature and variety of human activities introduces further complexities into the maintenance of fragile balances.

The kind of life a given geographic area can support depends on what it can offer in the way of food and water, of course, and also on the range of its atmospheric conditions. The influence of temperature, humidity, and altitude on ter-

restrial life is most obvious when one considers the extremes of conditions prevailing in deserts or mountainous regions, polar or tropical areas, coastal land or inland plains. The flora and fauna of such regions differ to an extreme that reflects their ability to utilize available nutrient under the conditions that prevail. Aquatic life is subject, in the same way, to regional variations in temperature, salt concentration, oxygen supply, and many other factors. The life of a freshwater lake or mountain stream is vastly different from that of an ocean, with its high concentration of sodium chloride and other salts, just as the life of a mountain slope differs from that of the valley below. Between the extremes, from the Himalayas to the jungles of Peru, from the Arctic Ocean to the Sargasso Sea, many subtler variations occur in plant and animal populations sensitive to minor differences in regions of the same general type, to artificial factors introduced by man, and to pressure created by shifts in the balance of such populations as they respond differently to environmental changes.

Microbial Ecology

Ultimately, the total amount of energy on tap in any given area that supports an animal and plant population is made available by the microorganisms in the soil and is dependent on them. The decaying, putrefactive, and fermentative processes of microorganisms release vital chemical elements, such as nitrogen, carbon, potassium, and phosphorus, from the organic components of dead material in the area. The released elements are essential to living plants for synthesis and growth, and the plants, in turn, are a source of food for animals. When animals and plants die, the soil microorganisms again break down their complex organic substances, thus perpetuating the cyclic turnover of matter and energy.

The populations of microorganisms residing together in the soil are themselves dependent on the available food material, the temperature, oxygen concentration, and pH of the soil, and the metabolic products of microbial neighbors. As we have seen, these metabolic wastes are sometimes antagonistic (*antibiotic*), sometimes beneficial to adjacent species. When the food or water content of the soil fluctuates, microbes must adjust to the new conditions or be eliminated. As acids, carbon dioxide, and other products of microbial activity accumulate, further adjustments must be made. Some organisms may flourish under the changed conditions, while the activity of others may be diminished until such time as competition lessens, more food or oxygen becomes available, a different pH is reached, or some other factor improves their lot. Marked and lasting shifts in microbial ecology may produce resultant changes for the higher life of the area. Because their growth periods are much longer than those of microorganisms, higher plants and animals may suffer severe and lasting damage if their microscopic chemists, cooks, and purveyors dwindle off, or vanish from the scene. Without the saprophytic bacteria, yeasts, and molds of the soil — the "chefs of the underworld" — to transform the substance of dead organisms into the elements essential for the living, our world would become cluttered with death, and life would cease altogether (see Fig. 5–1).

Ecologic Patterns

The biologic interrelationships of living things, whatever their level of development, are recog-

Fig. 5–1. The available energy (food) in an area limits the amount of life. The annual energy output in the tundra of the Arctic is low and distributed among only a few species; therefore any upset within the population of a particular species has a great effect on others. The arctic fox, hare, weasel, lemming, vole, caribou, and wolf are all important in the carnivore's food chain or energy cycle. Microorganisms aid in the decomposition of the dead animal, and the raw materials are returned to be regenerated. (Reproduced from *What's New*, Oct.–Nov., 1961. Drawing by Edward Kasper. Courtesy of Abbott Laboratories, North Chicago, Ill.)

nized in four general patterns, scaled in terms of the dependencies inherent in their associations. At one end of the scale, there may be complete *independence* between two different kinds of organisms living side by side, but otherwise unassociated with, and indifferent to, each other. The other three patterns each involve a close relationship in which some type of interdependency is displayed between two diverse types of organisms, and these associations are described collectively by the Greek word *symbiosis*, meaning literally "a living together." The dependency may be mutual, in that each organism derives some benefit, trivial or vital, from the other, the pattern being known as *mutualism*. If only one of the two associates is benefited by the relationship, while the other is unaffected by it, the term "commensalism" is used, and the partners are referred to as *commensal* organisms (see Fig. 5–2). In the third type of symbiosis, one organism derives some degree of support from another, at the latter's expense, this being the pattern of *parasitism* (see Fig. 5–3). Previously (see Chap. 3, p. 41) we defined a parasite as an organism that resides in or on the tissues of a living host; an obligate parasite as one that cannot live without such a host; and an obligate intracellular parasite as one that can survive only within living host cells. Now it should be appreciated that a parasite not obligated to a living partner (who pays more or less dearly for the parasite's board and room) can support itself, if need be, on nonliving organic matter, the change often being accomplished with relative ease. As we have seen, many parasitic species of bacteria, yeasts, and molds, when taken from the human body on which they have been dependent, can be cultivated in the laboratory on nonviable nutrient media. The microbiologist's purpose in the laboratory is to grow the organisms of interest in pure culture, so that each may be studied in isolation, without interference from others. There are no pure cultures in nature, however, and the relationships that exist between living organisms are not necessarily static or fixed. Between the two ecologic extremes of a free-living, saprophytic existence and one of obligate parasitism, the gradient conditions of symbiosis among living things may reflect, in part, their diverse abilities to respond, not only to each other, but to changing environmental pressures.

Fig. 5–2. Bacterial satellitism. This blood agar plate was first streaked across its entire surface with a strain of *Hemophilus influenzae*. Immediately afterward, the agar was jabbed at several points with an inoculating needle that had been dipped in a pure culture of *Staphylococcus aureus*. The plate was then incubated at 37° C for 24 hours. The staphylococci grew at the points where they had been inoculated, but *H. influenzae* colonies (the tiny translucent colonies surrounding the dense growth) grew only in the immediate vicinity of the staphylococcal colonies. (Courtesy of Drs. Harry E. Morton and Earl S. Long, University of Pennsylvania School of Medicine, Philadelphia, Pa.)

Man and His Microbes

From the moment of his birth, and throughout his life, the human being lives in the midst of the microbial world, and vice versa. The associations between man and microorganisms of many varieties are continuous and fluctuating, their contacts never-ending. There is a constant traffic of microorganisms entering the human body, in the air inhaled, in the food eaten, on the surfaces of things touched or placed in the mouth; and

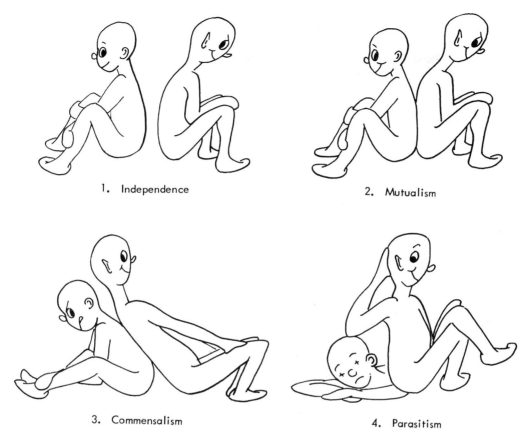

1.   Independence

2.   Mutualism

3.   Commensalism

4.   Parasitism

Fig. 5–3.   Microbiologic relationships.
1. Independence. Many organisms may coexist without exerting influence on each other.
2. Mutualism. A symbiotic relationship that benefits both partners.
3. Commensalism. A relationship in which one partner benefits without harming the other.
4. Parasitism. A parasite flourishes at the host's expense.

leaving it in excretions from the intestinal tract, the mucosal surfaces, and the skin. In normal circumstances, this traffic flows only over the surfaces of the body, that is, the skin and the mucosal linings of the respiratory, alimentary, and genitourinary tracts. Any daring excursions into the deeper tissues beneath these linings are met, with lethal effect, by the healthy body's defensive mechanisms. The skin and mucosal surfaces, however, not only tolerate the presence of microorganisms, but offer many conditions suitable for the growth and multiplication of saprophytes. Dead or dying cells in the outer layers of skin, the secretions of skin and mucosal glands, the food that passes into and along the intestinal tract — all provide excellent organic nutrient (nonviable) for the saprophytic microorganisms that take up residence temporarily or permanently on the body.

In the individual associations of particular species with their human hosts, as well as in the collective relationships of microorganisms with each other, in various parts of the body, the several ecologic patterns we have defined may be

observed. Furthermore, these associations are influenced, just as they are in the world around us, by the environmental conditions of the human body's surfaces (type of nutrient, pH, moisture, darkness, oxygen supply, temperature, and so on), which may differ, markedly or subtly, from one region of the body to another. Other factors may also be involved in this ecology, such as individual or racial differences among humans and the geography and sociology of human populations, as we shall see in later chapters.

Mutualism

Mutualistic relationships exist among microorganisms cohabiting the human body and between these and their host. Bacteria living in the intestinal tract, for instance, receive their primary support from the food materials present there. Some species may be of benefit to each other by digesting or synthesizing substances important to both, according to their alternate capacities. In turn, some of the products synthesized by certain

Fig. 5–4. Antagonism of coliform bacteria against shigellae. The entire surface of an agar plate was inoculated with *Shigella paradysenteriae.* After drying, several points on the surface of the agar were inoculated with different cultures of coliform organisms isolated from human stools. Coliform strains 297 and 311 did not affect the growth of *Sh. paradysenteriae.* Coliform strain 31 exerted a slight antagonism, but strains 534, 438, and 214 produced large zones of inhibition of the growth of this species of *Shigella.* (Reproduced from Halpert, Seymour P.: The Antagonism of Coliform Bacteria Against Shigella, *J. Immun.,* **58**: 153–67, 1948.)

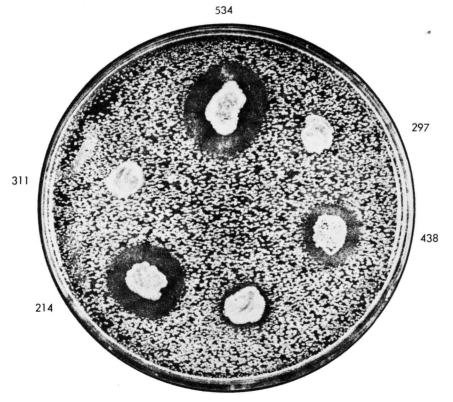

bacterial species are of use to the human host, who can absorb them from the intestine and put them to use. The bacterial production of vitamin K is an example of this kind, the vitamin being essential to man for the synthesis of a component involved in the mechanism of blood clotting.

Conversely, the antagonisms exerted by microorganisms upon each other are of importance to their human host, because they serve to control microbial populations and prevent overgrowths of species that might be harmful in large numbers (see Fig. 5–4). The demonstration of particular mutualisms and antagonisms among organisms holds many implications for man in his efforts to control his environment to his own advantage. The use of antibiotic or chemical substances in the control of infectious diseases, the deliberate introduction into the body of one species of organism that may supplant or control the growth of others, or a specific attack on one member of an interdependent pair to destroy the other indirectly — all these are approaches that may have value in particular situations. There is a growing interest in the relative merits of these methods in the control of insect pests as well as of microorganisms. In this connection, it has been shown that termites, for instance, have a mutualistic relationship with certain flagellated protozoans that live in their intestinal tracts (see Fig. 5–5). When the termite has foraged successfully for a woody meal, the protozoa in its intestine produce enzymes that digest the cellulose fibers, thus benefiting the termite. In return, the protozoa are housed and fed; neither can get along without the other. If the flagellates are eliminated from this association, the termites die within 10 to 20 days; when the flagellates are reinstated, the insects survive. These facts suggest that it may be possible to control the insect by measures designed to eliminate its mutualist companion.

Commensalism

Commensalism is a very common type of association between man and his microbial populations. Organisms that are commensal with man

Fig. 5–5. The termite and its intestinal protozoan partner provide an excellent example of *mutualism*. The protozoa live in the termite's intestinal tract and digest the wood eaten by the insect. Either organism would die of starvation without the other. (Courtesy of U.S. Department of Agriculture, Washington, D.C.)

are supported by him but do not affect his welfare one way or the other. Commensalism differs from parasitism in that the microorganism derives its support from nonliving organic substances on the host's surfaces without offering harmful competition to the living cells and tissues of the body. On the other hand, no benefits are obtained from the relationship by the host, who remains indifferent to it. It is important to remember, however, that such relationships are subject to change with changing conditions and opportunities for the microorganism. Many of

the commensals living harmlessly on the body's surfaces have a capacity for parasitism, if circumstances permit a competitive association with the body's tissues, just as parasitic organisms may adjust to a more independent, saprophytic life.

Parasitism

Parasitism implies some degree of harmful effect induced in the host by an organism that itself benefits from the association. When a parasite actually lives in the tissues of cells of the host, it is called an *endoparasite*, a term that applies to microorganisms. Larger organisms that attach themselves to skin or mucosal surfaces of a human or animal host and take their nourishment from living host tissue or blood beneath the surface lining are called *ectoparasites*. The period of attachment may be quite temporary, as in the case of a mosquito bite, or relatively permanent, as

in the attachment of hookworms to the bowel wall (unless interrupted by drug treatment). (Fig. 5–6.)

The nature, as well as the degree, of harm suffered by the host may be so slight as to be scarcely recognizable, or serious enough to threaten life. In other words, parasitism is distinct from disease, the development of the latter depending on characteristics displayed by both the parasite and the host in their responses to each other. From the point of view of the parasite, a truly successful parasitism results when a state of balance exists in its relationship with the host, so that the latter can furnish the required support while continuing to function within reasonably normal limits.

The host requirements of parasites are sometimes quite specific, sometimes quite broad, with regard both to the species of host that can be parasitized and to the kind of tissue within the body of a given host where they can localize. Thus, the parasites of plants are, in general, not

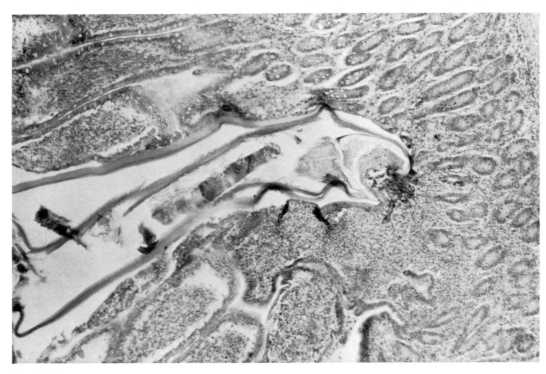

Fig. 5–6. A photomicrograph of a hookworm attached to the intestinal wall.

capable of living in animal tissues, while animals may share their parasites to a wide extent. Man acquires many of his parasitic worms from the animals with which he associates or whose flesh he eats. As we have seen in Chapter 2, some of the helminths have complex cyclic requirements for more than one host, requiring particular tissues in each for their support and development. Cell and tissue specificity is often quite marked among the viruses and rickettsiae also, while bacteria, yeasts, and molds are frequently more versatile in their ability to localize in various host tissues.

Resident and Transient Flora of the Human Body

The commensal organisms living on the skin and mucosal surfaces of the body are referred to, collectively, as the *resident*, or *normal*, flora. The nature and variety of this flora remain relatively constant in particular areas of the body. It undergoes changes with age, from birth onward, and it varies from one site of the body to another with differences in the structure and physiology of surface lining cells. The resident flora may fluctuate also in response to the host's activities, habits, and external environment. Differences between individuals with respect to all these factors, including skin types, may result in characteristic differences, from one individual to another, in the nature, variety, and numbers of resident commensals. However, within the limitations of all such modifications, there appears to be a fixed and well-defined normal flora distributed over the body surfaces, which re-establishes itself whenever it is disturbed. Members of the resident flora, as pointed out previously, also are capable of parasitism on occasion, if the opportunity for it arises, but their potential for inducing active or severe disease is not great as a rule.

Since microorganisms are ubiquitous, and their contacts with the body constant, it is not difficult for new organisms to deposit on body surfaces. However, most of the new acquisitions do not linger permanently. They may be washed away easily from external areas, they may die in competition with resident organisms, they may fail to survive conditions presented by the body itself, or they may simply be ushered out, in a viable state, in the body's excretions. For obvious reasons, organisms that are present on the body temporarily, for a few hours, days, or weeks, but do not become firmly entrenched, are collectively referred to as *transient* flora. Occasionally, under suitable conditions, some transients may hold their place long enough to become resident commensals, or, more importantly, they may establish themselves in a parasitic relationship with the host. In that case, depending on their properties and on the resistance with which they are met, active disease of the host may ensue.

The Skin

The anatomic structures and the physiologic functions of the skin vary from one part of the body to another, and the normal, resident flora of different areas may reflect these modifications. In addition, the constant exposure of the skin to contact with the environment assures the continuous presence, and constant exchange, of transient microorganisms.

The most common resident commensals of the skin are bacterial, and among these various strains of staphylococci often predominate. Often these staphylococci are lumped together under the term *Staphylococcus epidermidis*, but more specific names can be given them, such as *Staphylococcus aureus*, *Staphylococcus albus*, or *Staphylococcus citreus*, depending on their pigmentation. They differ also in their aerobic and anaerobic requirements, hemolytic qualities, and ability to produce coagulation of blood plasma. Other bacteria predominating on the skin include aerobic and anaerobic diphtheroid bacilli (members of the genus *Corynebacterium*); aerobic sporeforming bacilli; streptococci of several types; and Gram-negative bacilli of intestinal origin.

With reference to particular anatomic areas, the resident flora is modified by such features as the presence or absence of hair; folded skin surfaces in close contact, characterized by abundant

secretions of sweat and sebaceous glands; proximity to mucosal surfaces such as those of the mouth, nose, and throat and the anal or genital regions; and the nature and condition of clothing worn habitually. Yeasts and fungi, as well as many bacterial species, are often present in hairy parts of the body, under the nails, and in skin folds (axilla and groin). Intestinal bacteria such as enterococci (fecal streptococci) and Gram-negative enteric bacilli of the coliform type (*Escherichia coli* and *Aerobacter* species) may abound on the skin of the groin and buttocks. Harmless acid-fast bacilli of the *Mycobacterium* genus may be found in areas rich with sebaceous secretions, such as the external ear canal or the inguinal areas. Organisms from the mouth, nose, and throat easily find their way, at least transiently, to the skin of the hands and face. These surfaces, therefore, often predominantly display strains of staphylococci and streptococci, some of which may be transient, some resident. The soles of the feet, being highly cornified, display a rather limited bacterial flora, but the soft folds of skin between toes, with their sweat and sebaceous secretions, provide good conditions for many species of bacteria, yeasts, and molds. The habitual wearing of shoes contributes to these conditions by eliminating the drying effects of air and by maintaining a constantly dark, moist atmosphere in which secretions accumulate. Under such conditions, if no relief is provided for the skin of the feet, it may become macerated and offer further possibilities for the overgrowth of microorganisms, with resultant damage to tissues. Clothing for other parts of the body may produce similar effects, particularly if it is close-fitting, nonabsorbent, or infrequently washed or cleaned.

Such habits, as well as occupational activities, greatly influence the *transient* flora of the individual human host, as well. Transient microorganisms on the skin, being superficially located and held in place by sweat, oil, and grime, can usually be washed away easily with soap and water, aided by mechanical brushing or scrubbing. Therefore, people who subject their hands to frequent washing and keep their bodies and clothing scrupulously clean and free of accumulating secretions or soil display fewer transient

organisms than others less assiduous in such efforts. Nurses, physicians, and all persons concerned with the care of patients who may have infectious diseases or who are unusually subject to the risk of infection must take particular care of their skin and clothing, not only to reduce the risk of personal infection with transient microorganisms but to avoid transferring them through contacts with such patients. Physiologic factors of the skin, such as pH, particular fatty acids present in sebaceous secretions, and substances with some antibacterial effect present in tears, sweat, and mucus secretions, also assist in the elimination of transient organisms.

On the other hand, the reduction of *resident* organisms of the skin by mechanical or physiologic means is not simply or permanently accomplished. Vigorous scrubbing of the hands by physicians and nurses preparing for surgery, for instance, may eliminate transients, as well as superficial resident commensals, but a basic proportion of residents located in deeper layers of the skin remains, no matter how prolonged the period of scrubbing may be. Antibacterial agents applied during the scrub assist in the removal of superficial organisms but are incapable of eliminating the deeper residents. For this reason, surgeons, nurses, and other members of the surgical team wear presterilized rubber gloves on their hands to prevent the possible transferral of their lingering resident organisms to the tissues of the patient undergoing surgery. The gloves, in turn, provided they remain intact and undamaged, protect the hands from recontamination with transient microorganisms. From the moment the scrubbed hand is gloved, however, its diminished resident flora is rapidly replenished from the deeper skin layers, so that by the time a prolonged operative procedure is complete, and the gloves are removed, the flora of the hands may be restored to its usual numbers. It is particularly important, therefore, that meticulous care should be taken in the operating room, not only to avoid contamination of the sterile surfaces of gloved hands by touching unclean surfaces, but to prevent punctures and nicks of the gloves through which viable microorganisms may pass. Another precaution taken by operating-room

personnel to prevent the transfer of resident skin commensals includes the wearing of a sterile cap to cover the hair, a sterile mask for the mouth and nose, and a sterile gown to cover clothing. All instruments, solutions, and coverings used for the patient are sterilized before use and handled in the operating room with strict aseptic technique. The patient's skin, at the operative site, is also carefully prepared beforehand, shaved clean of hair, and scrubbed with a suitable antibacterial agent to reduce the patient's own resident skin flora to the minimum possible numbers.

The Genital Tract

The external genitalia of both sexes display a large variety of resident microorganisms. The normal flora includes saprophytic species of spirochetes, yeasts, and bacteria such as staphylococci, Gram-negative enteric bacilli of the coliform type, fecal streptococci, and lactobacilli. Flagellated protozoans of the genus *Trichomonas* may also reside normally in this region. Along the mucous membranes as they extend inward to the genital organs themselves, the numbers and variety of organisms normally present diminish and disappear. The urethra is usually sterile, in both the male and the female, although the area into which it opens is not. Urine or other secretions collected for culture at the urethral opening may, therefore, be contaminated with organisms normally present on the external genital mucosa and, conversely, under abnormal conditions, such organisms may extend inward along the mucosal surfaces. However, in the female this extension is usually sharply limited by the acidity of the vaginal secretions. Soon after birth the vaginal canal becomes colonized with lactobacilli. These organisms enjoy, and help to maintain, an acid pH, which persists in the vagina for a few weeks after birth. The pH then shifts to neutrality and remains relatively neutral until puberty, the lactobacilli, during this time, being replaced by a mixed group of bacteria. From puberty to menopause, lactobacilli again predominate and contribute to a normally acid vaginal pH. They also serve to discourage the extension of yeasts,

protozoans, and bacteria from the external mucosa into the vaginal canal in any large numbers, although the normal vaginal flora includes other species of organisms, such as anaerobic sporeforming bacilli (of the genus *Clostridium*), aerobic and anaerobic streptococci, and staphylococci. After the menopause, the acidity of the vagina diminishes, lactobacilli dwindle again in numbers, and a mixed flora takes over once more.

If the normal ecology of the vagina is disturbed, as in the antibiotic therapy of an infectious process elsewhere in the body that coincidentally suppresses the vaginal lactobacilli, other organisms such as *Trichomonas*, yeasts, or various bacteria may increase greatly in number, producing a troublesome irritation, or vaginitis.

As the mucosal lining of the female genital tract extends upward into the cervix, it becomes sterile. Normally the cervical mucosa is free of a resident flora and discourages its establishment through its secretions, which contain lysozyme, a substance having antibacterial activity.

The Mouth and Upper Respiratory Tract

The mouth, throat, and nose offer fertile conditions, also, for the survival and growth of many kinds of microorganisms. These areas are colonized during, or soon after, birth by several bacterial species, among which the alpha-hemolytic (or *viridans* type) streptococci, staphylococci, Gram-negative cocci of the genus *Neisseria*, and diphtheroid bacilli predominate. Such organisms are probably passed along from the respiratory mucosa of the mother and all others who may handle and care for the infant. Yeasts also may occur in the mouth, the baby acquiring them from the skin of the mother's breast or from rubber nipples. In the newborn infant's mouth, with its scarcity of bacterial species to maintain control over the growth of yeasts, the latter may multiply rapidly and extensively, damaging the oral mucosa and producing a condition known as "thrush."

At the time the infant's first teeth begin to

erupt, other organisms establish themselves in the gingival tissues. These include anaerobic spirochetes, fusiform bacilli, and lactobacilli. Most of these organisms remain in the mouth for life.

The normal flora of the throat, tonsils, and trachea includes streptococci, staphylococci, *Neisseria* species, members of the genus *Hemophilus*, and diphtheroids. Other organisms may come and go transiently, some of them associated with a high potential for producing local or generalized disease. Bacterial species such as *Diplococcus pneumoniae* (frequently associated with bacterial pneumonia), the diphtheria bacillus, and the meningococcus (a species of *Neisseria* capable of producing severe disease) often enter the body by way of the respiratory tract, localizing first in the throat. The same is true for many viruses associated with infectious disease. The mere presence of such organisms in the throat does not necessarily imply that disease will ensue, however, for they may be quickly suppressed by the resident flora, or by the body's own physiologic mechanisms.

In health, the nose harbors only a few microorganisms, usually staphylococci and diphtheroids, with occasional strains of streptococci. The frequent colonization of the nose by strains of *Staphylococcus aureus* is a matter of concern with respect to the possible spread of staphylococcal infection from the healthy individual to others whose resistance to the organism is low for some reason. The possible transfer of such strains from hospital personnel, including nurses and physicians, to patients who may offer the organism unusual opportunities for entry, localization, and multiplication, with resulting disease, is made more troublesome by the fact that many nasal strains colonizing hospital personnel are resistant to the useful antibiotics.

Very few microorganisms are capable of surviving the passage downward from the trachea to the lower surfaces of the respiratory tract, or of establishing themselves permanently there. The bacterial species normally recoverable from sputum, when it is raised from the bronchioles and bronchi, usually reflect the resident flora of the trachea and tonsillar and pharyngeal surfaces,

since sputum must pass over these to be collected for culture. When infectious disease of the lower respiratory tract exists, however, its agent may be present in the sputum and must be separated, in laboratory cultures, from the normal throat flora also present.

The Intestinal Tract

The intestine of the newborn infant is sterile, but this situation is only momentary. Many species of bacteria and yeasts take up residence in the bowel from the time the infant begins to take nourishment, in a progression that varies with age, eating habits, and different segments of the intestinal tract.

The esophagus contains only transient organisms introduced in food and saliva, the latter harboring species that have found their way on the surfaces of the many items that are taken into the mouth, even of a very young infant. The normal acidity of the stomach prevents the establishment of microorganisms there, but as the pH rises and becomes alkaline in the duodenum and jejunum a more and more abundant resident flora implants, reaching its peak in the large intestine.

In breast-fed babies, the predominant organisms of the small intestine are lactic acid streptococci, while lactobacilli are more numerous in the colon. The flora is more mixed in bottle-fed infants, and as children begin to eat a variety of foods, the character of the intestinal flora approaches that of adults. Throughout life, diet has a continuing influence on the variety and number of microorganisms in the bowel and feces. Basically, however, Gram-negative coliform bacilli (related to the species *Escherichia coli*) are the most abundant residents of the adult large intestine, making up about 75 per cent of the normal flora. Other aerobic organisms present include the fecal streptococci (enterococci), bacilli of the *Proteus* and *Pseudomonas* groups, some lactobacilli, and yeasts. The two most prominent types of anaerobic bacilli are the Gram-negative, nonsporeforming *Bacteroides* species and the

Gram-positive, sporeforming members of the *Clostridium* genus.

Under normal conditions, the ecology of the resident intestinal flora is self-balancing. Competitions and mutualisms, as we have seen, between microorganisms, and between these and their host, serve to maintain the status quo. If the intestinal tract becomes diseased in some way, however, as by tumor, obstruction, or infectious disease, the normal flora may change greatly, in respect both to number and variety of organisms. Antibiotic drugs, particularly if taken orally, can also induce marked shifts in the normal intestinal flora, by suppressing the drug-susceptible organisms of the intestine. Other commensals normally held in check by those that have been suppressed may then thrive to an unusual degree, and this, in turn, may induce an uncomfortable gastrointestinal irritation, or even more severe disorders. Antibiotics are commonly used prior to surgery of the bowel, to reduce its bacterial contents to a minimum by the time of operation. In this situation, to avoid a merely unbalanced flora, in which some organisms are eliminated but others thrive, broad-spectrum antibiotics, or combinations of such drugs, are used so that a wide variety of organisms may be equally affected and suppressed. In a relatively short time — usually about one or two weeks — after such treatment the normal flora restores itself, but its members are largely drug-resistant, being the progeny of resistant survivors that replace the drug-susceptibles. Still later, susceptible strains may again make their appearance in the bowel, being reintroduced in food, milk, and water.

The Conjunctiva

The conjunctiva, the mucous membrane that lines the eyelids and is reflected onto the eyeball, is also a site of bacterial commensalism. The resident flora contains a few varieties of bacteria such as diphtheroid bacilli, *Neisseria* species, white-pigmented staphylococci, streptococci, and some small, microaerophilic, Gram-negative bacilli. The numbers of transient organisms, frequently introduced by hands or handkerchiefs, are kept to a minimum by the washing action of tears, as well as by their antibacterial component of lysozyme. Injury to the normal membrane barrier, caused by frequent or hard rubbing or by foreign bodies, may permit the entry of transient or resident organisms into the tissue beneath, and active disease of the area may then result.

Table 5–1 summarizes the indigenous microbial flora to be found in various areas of the human body.

Infection and Infectious Disease

From the point of view of the host, *infection* can be defined as a state in which the host harbors microorganisms that survive and multiply in or on his tissues. Commensalism, whether it be resident or transient, is included in this definition, and therefore it can be said that the human host lives all of his life in a fluctuating, more or less equilibrated, state of infection. The definition also includes, but does not necessarily imply, *infectious disease*.

The *potential* for infectious disease exists when microorganisms live in a parasitic relationship with their host or shift to this type of association from a commensalistic or saprophytic one. Such a shift is not purposeful on the part of the parasite, of course, but is made possible by the circumstances in which it finds itself and by the nature of its own properties and requirements, as well as those of its host. It has been stated previously that parasitism is distinct from disease, assuming that the latter is a condition marked by active symptons of abnormality and some degree of distress. The extent of the harm caused by a parasite may be clinically unrecognizable, or perfectly obvious through a range of symptoms from mild to severe, but in any case it depends on *the properties and functions of both the parasite and the host*. When the damage is sufficiently marked to become clinically manifest, the term "infectious disease" then applies fully, indicating a noticeable state of abnormality induced by a living organism.

Table 5–1. Microbial Flora Indigenous to the Human Body*

Anatomic Location	Microorganisms	Comments
Skin	Staphylococci (*S. epidermidis, S. aureus*) Streptococci (*Strep. viridans*, non- hemolytic strep, and enterococci) Corynebacteria (diphtheroid bacilli) Gram-negative enteric bacilli (*Escherichia* and *Aerobacter* species) Mycobacteria (acid-fast bacilli) Yeasts and fungi	In addition, exposed skin may harbor many transients, which may remain for hours, days, or weeks; transients are readily removed but reduction in numbers of residents is temporary at best
Eye Conjunctiva	*Staphylococcus epidermidis* Streptococci (*Strep. viridans* and nonhemolytic strep) *Neisseria* species Corynebacteria (diphtheroid bacilli) Microaerophilic Gram-negative bacilli	Washing action of tears and their content of lysozyme help to control microorganisms
Nose and throat	Staphylococci (*S. epidermidis, S. aureus*) Streptococci (*Strep. viridans*, non- hemolytic strep, and enterococci) *Diplococcus pneumoniae* *Neisseria* species Corynebacteria (diphtheroid bacilli) *Hemophilus* species	Action of nasal ciliary cells, swallowing, mucous secretion, and lysozyme of saliva help to control microorganisms
Alimentary tract Mouth	Staphylococci (*S. epidermidis, S. aureus*) Streptococci (*Strep. viridans*, non- hemolytic strep, enterococci) *Lactobacillus* species Fusiform bacilli Spirochetes *Actinomyces* species Yeasts	Swallowing action, lysozyme of saliva, good dental hygiene help to control microorganisms
Esophagus	No indigenous flora	Organisms swallowed with food or saliva remain only temporarily
Stomach	No indigenous flora	Gastric acidity is too high for microbial growth
Intestines (adults)	Gram-negative enteric bacilli (species of *Escherichia, Aerobacter,* *Proteus, Pseudomonas*) Streptococci (enterococci) Anaerobic bacilli (species of *Bacteroides* and *Clostridium*) Yeasts Protozoa	The intestines contain much larger numbers of microorganisms than any other area of the body

Table 5–1. (*Cont.*)

Anatomic Location	Microorganisms	Comments
Genital tract	Staphylococci (*S. epidermidis, S. aureus*) Streptococci (enterococci and non-hemolytic strep, sometimes *Strep. viridans*) Lactobacilli Gram-negative enteric bacilli (species of *Escherichia, Aerobacter, Proteus, Pseudomonas*) Anaerobic bacilli (*Clostridium* species) Mycobacteria (acid-fast bacilli) Spirochetes Yeasts Protozoa (especially *Trichomonas* species)	In the female, lysozyme content of cervical secretions and the acidity of the normal adult vagina control the numbers and variety of microorganisms establishing in this area; lactobacilli predominate between puberty and menopause

*In the bacteriologic culture of specimens obtained from these areas of the body the search for pathogenic organisms, or for commensals that have assumed a pathogenic role, is complicated by the variety of indigenous bacterial species encountered in such specimens.

Microbial Factors in Infectious Disease

The manner in which a disease originates and develops is referred to as its *pathogenesis*, from the Greek words for disease (*pathos*) and origin (*genesis*). Accordingly, the word "pathogenicity" denotes the ability of a microorganism to produce infectious disease. The degree of pathogenicity possessed by a parasitic organism is expressed by the term "virulence," which is a function of two principal attributes: *invasiveness*, or the ability to get into host tissues, survive, multiply, and spread; and *toxigenicity*, or the ability to produce substances that are toxic to host cells and tissues. Pathogenic microorganisms differ in virulence, according to their relative display of such properties.

Host Factors in Infectious Disease

The severity of an infectious disease, and the total degree of damage done, reflect not only the virulence of its pathogenic agent, but also the host's capacity for defense against invasion and toxicity. The host's defense mechanisms function to protect the body from entry by microorganisms and to eliminate or control those that do succeed in entering. The unbroken skin and mucous membranes offer natural barriers to intrusion, and within the body many specific defenses are operative, such as *phagocytosis* (the ingestion of foreign particles, including microorganisms, by white blood cells and certain other tissue cells), the *inflammatory response* (the process by which tissue reacts to injury in order to limit and control it locally), and the *specific immune response* (the ability to resist a particular infectious agent, or its toxic products, by the development of immune substances, or *antibodies*, that react specifically with the agent or its products). Of particular importance to the host, also, is the kind of tissue involved in the infection and the nature of its injury. The vital functions of certain areas of the brain or the action of the heart, for instance, may be seriously handicapped by a small injury, while other organs, such as the lungs, liver, or kidneys, may continue to function with some degree of efficiency even when extensively damaged.

Combinations of Microbial and Host Factors Leading to Disease

Most human infectious diseases result from the introduction of pathogenic *transient* microorganisms into the tissues. On the other hand, members of the *normal flora* of the body, although they are not damaging as commensals, may also be pathogenic if they are introduced into the blood stream or tissues and under these circumstances may produce disease. A number of factors, operating together, determine whether or not infection can be established; whether infectious disease results, or not; and whether the parasite, the host, or both survive the encounter. On the normal skin and mucosal surfaces, the transient pathogen must survive, not only the activities and antagonisms of host cells, but also the activities and antagonisms of commensal organisms already present, and compete with the latter for nutrient. On the other hand, the normal resistance of the host may be overcome in several ways: the virulent qualities of an infecting pathogen may be exceptional, or it may arrive in unusual numbers; an unnatural route of entry may be opened up, as in the case of surgical or accidental trauma to the skin or mucosa; or the host's defensive mechanisms may have been diminished by pre-existing circumstances, such as organic disease,

fatigue or other stress, or the extremes of age. Under such circumstances, the host's own commensals, as well as transient pathogens, may be afforded a better opportunity to establish themselves within the tissues, and the possibility of the development of active disease is enhanced. In the ensuing struggle for survival, the total interplay of forces between an infecting microbe and the host may lead to a complete victory of one over the other in a relatively short time (*acute* infection), or to a prolonged relationship (*chronic* infection), precariously balanced between them. The symptoms displayed by the host vary accordingly from none at all (subclinical infection) to those of a sudden, acute process or a slow, insidious one. Between the extremes, there are many variations in the severity, as well as the duration, of symptoms. The *patterns* of symptoms, and the *course* of the illness, are often characteristic for particular infectious diseases, depending on the properties of the individual pathogenic organism.

The Frequency of Infection Versus Infectious Disease

We have seen that microorganisms are widely distributed in nature, and that many species may

Fig. 5–7. For a given type of infection, the number of people with recognizable *disease* represents the visible part of the iceberg, above the surface, while the much greater number who are transiently or permanently infected by the particular agent involved, but who display no *symptoms* of illness, can be compared to the great invisible mass of ice in the sea below. (Courtesy of U.S. Department of the Navy, Alexandria, Va.)

infect human beings from the moment of their birth, without producing clinically apparent infectious disease. When the distribution of a particular pathogenic species, capable of inducing disease, is studied, the same situation is seen to exist in many instances, i.e., large numbers of normal, healthy people may be found to harbor the organism in question (such as poliomyelitis virus, respiratory viruses, strains of staphylococci and streptococci), greatly outnumbering those who are made ill by it. This wide prevalence of infection in the human population, together with the relative infrequency of clinically active infectious disease, presents a picture whose contours resemble those of an iceberg. The insidious feature of an iceberg is the large mass that floats unseen beneath the surface of the sea, the visible ice giving little indication of the shape or extent of the mass below (see Fig. 5–7). For a given type of infection, the number of people with recognizable *disease* represents the visible part of the iceberg, above the surface, while the much greater number who are transiently or permanently infected by the particular agent involved, but who display *no symptoms* of illness, can be compared to the great invisible mass of ice in the sea below.

The properties and mechanisms of infectious organisms on the one hand, and of the human host on the other, that take part together in producing this picture are discussed in detail in the following two chapters.

Questions

1. Define ecology.
2. Define and give examples of the following terms: "parasitism," "commensalism," "symbiosis."
3. What is the difference between resident and transient flora?
4. Define pathogenicity, virulence, invasiveness, toxigenicity.

References

Pertinent References

Buchsbaum, Ralph, and Buchsbaum, Mildred: *Basic Ecology.* Boxwood, Pittsburgh, Pa., 1957.

Carson, Rachel: *Silent Spring.* Houghton Mifflin Co., Boston, 1962.

Dowdeswell, W. H.: Ecology and Its Background, and Special Animal Relationships, in *Animal Ecology.* Harper Torch Books, The Science Library, 1961.

Periodicals

Limbaugh, Conrad: Cleaning Symbiosis, *Sci. Amer.,* **205**:42, Aug., 1961.

Pruitt, William O., Jr.: The World of the Arctic Wolf, *What's New,* Abbott Laboratories, Oct.–Nov., 1961.

Wilson, Marion E.; Frick, Hugh; and Bass, Phyllis: Betadine, pHisohex, and 3, 4', 5-Tribromosalicylanilide as Surgeon's Skin Germicides, *Bact. Proc.,* Amer. Soc. Micro., 1965.

Yoeli, Meir: Animal Infections and Human Disease, *Sci. Amer.,* **212**:161, May, 1960.

Popular Literature

Fiennes, Richard: What is Disease?, Population Numbers and Disease, The Evolution of Parasitism, Parasites and Disease, Infection and Infectious Disease, in *Man, Nature and Disease.* Signet, The New American Library, New York and Toronto, 1964.

Nicol, Hugh: A Saltspoonful of Soil, in *Microbes and Us.* Penguin Books, Ltd. Harmondsworth, Middlesex, 1955.

6 The Infectious Microbe Versus the Host

In this chapter we shall consider the factors of importance in the establishment of infection and the production of infectious disease. Since the process of infection begins at the moment, and at the site, of entry of the host by an infectious microbe, we must be particularly concerned with the *means of entry* to the human host that are available to microorganisms. They are discussed in the first part of this chapter. *The properties and activities of microorganisms* associated with their pathogenicity and virulence, that is, their ability to enter and entrench themselves in human tissues and to produce disease, are described in the second half of the chapter.

Entry Routes

General Considerations

Entry of the human body by microorganisms is effected by one of four major avenues: (1) they may enter with inhaled air into the *respiratory tract;* (2) they may be ingested with material taken into the mouth and *gastrointestinal tract;* (3) they may themselves infect or penetrate the *skin or superficial mucous membranes* and be limited to these tissues or spread from there to deeper sites; and (4) they may be deposited *directly into tissues* beneath the skin and mucosa when these barriers are penetrated or traumatized

(injured) by some other agent. The latter avenue may be referred to as the *parenteral route*, implying direct access to the body tissues by such means as puncture and injection (by a biting or blood-sucking insect vector or an artificial vector such as a hypodermic needle), by more extensive trauma (caused by accident or surgery or the bites of animals), or by extension from mucosal surfaces (respiratory, alimentary, or genital).

Establishment of Infection. The entry route does not necessarily determine the site, or sites, in which the infective organism will ultimately establish itself and multiply. The areas in which the parasite may gain a foothold are dictated by its own properties, together with the biochemical environment afforded by host tissues, as well as the existence of unusual circumstances or opportunities that may increase the host's vulnerability. Once having entered, however, the pathogen may then induce damage in one, or both, of two general ways: (1) it may *localize at or near the site of entry* and damage the surrounding tissues mechanically or physiologically, or (2) the organism itself, or its toxigenic products, or both, may *disseminate through the body*, producing injury to tissues far removed from the entry point. Dissemination of the parasite may be accomplished by its own ability to spread through the tissues, by virtue of its *invasive* qualities, or it may be carried in lymphatic channels or the blood stream and thus be distributed widely. Toxigenic substances are also disseminated by way of the blood and lymph flow from a local site of microbial growth where they are produced. The general possibilities for localization along the entry route, or for dissemination therefrom, will be considered for each of the four avenues of entry.

Since the point of entry marks the beginning of infection and also affords one of the last opportunities for its prevention, it is important for those who are involved with the care of infectious patients to understand its possibilities. Furthermore, the ultimate sites of localization of a parasite usually determine the portals through which it may leave the body, at the beginning of its route of transmission to another

individual. Nursing procedures designed to limit the spread of infection from one person to another, or to prevent its occurrence, are predicated on a knowledge of the particular routes of entry and exit that may be taken by pathogenic microorganisms, in particular or in general.

The Respiratory Tract

From the point of view of the human host, the respiratory tract appears to offer the easiest, and the most frequently traveled, access route for infectious microorganisms. It is also the most difficult one to control effectively. Infections acquired by this route have a wide distribution throughout the world, wherever people have face-to-face contacts.

Microorganisms are taken into the nose or mouth by the inhalation of droplets of moisture containing them. Such droplets are sprayed into the air by the talking, coughing, or sneezing of other persons whose oral, nasal, and pharyngeal secretions contain many of the commensal or parasitic organisms which they happen to harbor. The quantity of droplets reaching the air, and the distance to which they are scattered, depend on the force and frequency with which people talk, cough, or sneeze. (Oral secretions are also deposited on the surfaces of items that people so frequently take into their mouths, such as fingers, pencils, cigarettes, eating utensils, or children's toys. They may then find their way into another mouth by the transfer of such items, the microorganisms thereon being ingested rather than inhaled.)

The larger droplets of mucous spray settle rapidly from the air and are not likely to be inhaled. Fine droplets, however, lose their moisture quickly by evaporation and linger in the air, with their burden of microbes, ready for inhalation by another individual. When microorganisms enter the nose or mouth, several possibilities await them. They may lose the competition for nutrient with other organisms already present in the upper respiratory tract; they may die from the antagonistic effects of substances secreted by other microorganisms; they may be

destroyed by the activities and secretions of host cells; or they may survive these hazards, only to be confronted later with other host defenses. Many of them will be caught in and moved along with the mucus secreted by cells lining the upper respiratory tract. The ciliated epithelial cells keep the mucus moving and draining into the throat, where it is either swallowed or expectorated, or into the nose, from which it can be blown out. Microorganisms that are carried into the gastrointestinal tract from the mouth and throat may be killed by the acidity of the gastric secretions or by the competition they encounter farther along from the intestinal commensals.

The organisms present in inhaled air are thus subjected to *filtration, mechanical removal,* or *rerouting,* before the air is carried down into the deeper reaches of the respiratory tract. Only a relative few reach the lungs or penetrate the lining surfaces to deeper tissues, where other defensive mechanisms await them. Inhaled, pathogenic microorganisms that do survive and establish a foothold may then *localize* in either the upper or lower respiratory tract; or they, or their toxic products, or both, may *disseminate* and cause damage to tissues elsewhere.

Localization in the Respiratory Tract. The most familiar example of an inhalation infection localized in the *upper* respiratory tract is the common cold. Several viral agents have been associated with this mild disease. The localization of the virus within the mucosal cells of the pharynx and nasopharynx and its interference with their normal functions result in the characteristic nasal irritation, sore throat, and the profuse watery discharge that replaces normal mucus secretion. *Bacterial* pathogens that commonly localize and exert damaging effects in the upper respiratory tract include the coagulase-positive staphylococci, the hemolytic streptococci, pneumococci, and members of the *Hemophilus* genus. Frequently, also, members of the normal intestinal flora, such as coliform bacilli or fecal streptococci, may find their way to the throat and can exert pathogenic effects in this new location. Such organisms as these, multiplying in excess

and producing toxic secretions, may damage the epithelial cells or the lymphatic tissue of this region, producing a pharyngitis, tonsillitis, or laryngitis, or a combination of these symptoms.

It should be remembered that, aside from their arrival into the area as transient pathogens in inhaled air, many of these bacterial species, or their close relatives, live commensally in the normal nose and throat. If the pharyngeal membranes are injured, however, by a virus infection, or by excessive dryness, or some other contributory factor that interferes with their normal functions and secretion of mucus, one or more of these commensals may be given the opportunity to multiply excessively. They may then add to the pre-existing damage as their metabolic products increase in concentration. In such a situation the offending commensals are often called "secondary invaders," or "opportunists."

In the lower respiratory tract, infectious diseases acquired by inhalation include such notable examples as influenza, psittacosis, and other pneumonias of *viral* origin; tuberculosis and the pneumonias caused by *bacterial* pathogens, such as the pneumococcus, streptococci, staphylococci, or the plague bacillus (pneumonic plague); and fungus diseases such as histoplasmosis, coccidioidomycosis, blastomycosis, and candidiasis. Pulmonary disease may also be caused by members of the other major groups of microorganisms, that is, the rickettsiae, protozoa, and helminths, but, with the exception of the rickettsial agent of Q fever, the entry route in these cases is not by way of the upper respiratory tract, through droplet inhalation.

As air carrying infectious droplets passes from the upper to the lower respiratory tract, microorganisms are filtered out by the mechanisms described above, so that, as a rule, few remain in the air that finally reaches the alveolar spaces of the lungs. Depending on the organism, and its particular environmental requirements, localization may occur at different points along the way. A virus producing symptoms of a cold in the upper respiratory passages may pass downward from its original focal point and infect cells of the bronchial linings, while the influenza virus probably does not find a suitable locale until it

reaches the smaller branches of the bronchial tree. Psittacosis virus apparently must reach the alveolar spaces in fairly large numbers to be infective. Pathogenic bacteria such as the tubercle bacillus and the Gram-positive cocci also differ in their capabilities for localization. The tubercle bacillus may reach the lungs and localize there, but it can also penetrate the tissues of the upper respiratory tract, localize in lymphoid tissue, and be carried from there in lymphatic channels or in the blood stream. The pathogenic cocci may reach the lungs directly, localizing en route in the bronchial passages or in the alveolar walls of the lung beds. They may then spread peripherally though the adjacent lung tissues. Like the psittacosis virus, spores of pathogenic fungi, such as *Histoplasma* and *Coccidioides* species, must reach the depths of the lungs in fair numbers, and in finely disseminated particles, to establish primary pulmonary disease. Fine dust from the soil, in areas where these organisms are prevalent in animals or birds, appears to be more infective than the larger droplets of mucous secretions from infected persons. This is probably due to the fact that the infectious particles are more numerous and concentrated in such dust, which also remains air-borne for longer periods than moist droplets.

Dissemination of Microorganisms or Their Toxins from the Respiratory Tract. Following their entry into the body by inhalation, infective organisms can have serious effects in tissues far removed from the respiratory portal. As described in the opening part of this chapter, this may happen if (a) the pathogen itself penetrates directly, or is carried to, other parts of the body, or (b) toxigenic substances, secreted by the organism multiplying in a site of localization within the respiratory tract, are distributed through the body by the blood or lymph.

a. *Penetration and spread* of an infectious organism through the body are well exemplified by the meningococcus (*Neisseria meningitidis*), the bacterial agent of a severe systemic infection. This organism commonly finds a respiratory entry and localizes in the nasopharynx. It may reside there as a harmless transient or commensal, or it may produce a local infection that is usually not remarkable, its symptoms being like those of a cold and sore throat. However, it can reach the blood stream directly from this site, be circulated through the body, and relocalize in vital areas such as the brain and the adrenal glands. Multiple lesions may be produced also in the skin, joints, eyes, ears, and lungs, the symptoms and signs of the disease depending on the site of such localizations. In the brain, for instance, the characteristic injury is to the *meninges*, the inner membranous coverings of the brain and spinal cord, which become greatly inflamed. Inflammation of this tissue, whatever the cause, is called *meningitis*, hence the name *meningococcus* for the organism, although it is not the only infectious agent capable of producing meningeal injury.

There are many other systemic infections whose agents find a primary point of entry and localization somewhere in the respiratory tract and are later disseminated to other tissues. This is the situation, for instance, with the viral agents of poliomyelitis and infectious hepatitis, both of which may localize initially in the throat, then in the bowel, and be carried to other vital tissues. It may occur also in tuberculosis, as we have seen, in pulmonary anthrax, and in the fungus diseases of the lungs. As in the case of meningococcal infection, the disease effects are produced by the disseminated organism itself and by most tissue reaction to it, with symptoms referable to the location of various foci of infection.

b. *The dissemination of toxigenic substances* produced by microorganisms, from a point of localized growth and multiplication in the respiratory tract, can also result in serious systemic disease. When microbial toxins circulate in the blood and cause damage to tissues, the condition is spoken of, clinically, as a *toxemia*, the word meaning "toxins in the blood." (When organisms themselves are present in the blood, words such as "bacteremia," "viremia," or, more specifically, "staphylococcemia," "streptococcemia," and so on, would apply.)

Diphtheria and scarlet fever are well-known examples of diseases originating as local infections in the upper respiratory tract, but charac-

terized also by the serious effects of toxemia. In both these instances, the infective organism localizes, grows, and multiplies near its entry point in the pharynx. An acute sore throat results from the particular type of damage each organism causes to the mucous membranes, or to the underlying tissues, but, even more importantly, each secretes a characteristic *exotoxin* that is distributed widely in the body by the blood stream. These and other bacterial exotoxins (such as those associated with tetanus and botulism) have distinctively individual properties, which affect different cells and tissues in different ways. (See Chap. 3, p. 50.) The diphtheria toxin induces a particular kind of damage to heart muscle and nerve tissue, as well as other organs, probably by interfering with the action of respiratory enzymes in the cells of these tissues. The streptococcal toxin associated with scarlet fever affects the epithelial cells of the skin, producing the typical scarlatinal rash.

The important infectious diseases acquired through the respiratory route of entry are discussed in more individual detail in Part Two, Section IV.

The Gastrointestinal Tract

Another major route of entry to the human body for microorganisms is the gastrointestinal tract, which may offer admission to members of any of the microbial groups. Entry may be effected with the many items and materials that are taken into the mouth, but of course the most common sources of infection by this route are food, water, milk, and fingers.

It has been pointed out previously that many of the microorganisms introduced through the mouth and swallowed do not survive their journey through the intestinal tract, but succumb to conditions provided by the host or by microbial competitors. Some are eliminated in the mouth by the lysozyme activity of saliva; others are killed by the stomach's acidity. In the small intestine, the activity of digestive enzymes, capable of breaking down protein material, may destroy

the surface proteins of bacterial cell walls. The possibilities for infectious disease arise, as they do in the respiratory tract, when pathogenic microorganisms manage to survive all this and either *localize in the bowel*, producing damage at this site; penetrate the intestinal wall and *disseminate;* or *produce substances toxic* for human cells from their site in the bowel.

Localization in the Gastrointestinal Tract. The best known infections of the bowel itself are caused by protozoa, helminths, and some species of bacteria. Localization of such organisms occurs in either the small or large bowel, the site usually being characteristic for the microbe in question. Mucosal cells may be damaged and eroded, with consequent invasion of deeper tissues in some cases. Symptoms often include nausea and vomiting, diarrhea, intestinal spasm with accompanying pain, and, in some cases, sloughing of the mucosal lining with bleeding into the bowel. Among the *protozoa* that may infect the bowel, many of them as commensals, the one that is associated with serious human disease is *Endamoeba histolytica*, the agent of amoebic dysentery. *Helminth* infections (or infestations, as they are often called) of the bowel are caused by the common roundworms (pinworm, hookworm, *Ascaris*) and the tapeworms. Intestinal diseases of *bacterial* origin include gastroenteritis induced by strains of the genus *Salmonella;* bacillary dysentery caused by bacilli of the *Shigella* genus (often called shigellosis); a diarrhea of infants and young children associated with pathogenic strains of *Escherichia coli* (these are close relatives of the normal commensal strains of this species); and cholera, a severe disease of the bowel caused by a small curved rod known as *Vibrio comma.*

Yeast and fungus infections of the bowel are harmless for the most part. These organisms are usually transient rather than resident in the bowel and are relatively incapable of invading intestinal or other tissue from this entry site. One group worth mentioning here, however, are the yeastlike members of the genus *Candida* (*Monilia*), which may infect and damage the mucosal surfaces of the mouth and throat as well as the

lower bowel. *Candida* species are the agents of the troublesome infection of the mouths of newborn infants, known as thrush. (See Chap. 5, p. 93.) When they are resident in the bowel, these organisms may opportunistically cause intestinal irritation if host resistance, or microbial competition, or both are lowered for some reason. In the latter instance, antibiotic therapy, which reduces or eliminates bacterial members of the normal flora of the bowel, may permit the secondary overgrowth of *Candida*, with resultant local damage.

Dissemination of Microorganisms from the Gastrointestinal Tract. Typhoid and paratyphoid fevers afford excellent examples of *bacterial* diseases whose agents enter the body through the alimentary canal, usually in contaminated water or food, but which penetrate the intestinal lining directly. They localize first in the lymphoid tissue of the bowel wall and are disseminated from there by lymphatic channels and the blood stream to other organs, notably the liver, gallbladder, and kidneys. The typical symptoms of typhoid and associated fevers are produced by this systemic invasion, not by localization in the bowel.

Endamoeba histolytica may also erode its way into the bowel wall, enter the portal circulation, and be carried to the liver, where it induces abscess formation. From this site, it can extend directly through the diaphragm into the lungs, or it may be carried from such sites to establish itself in other parts of the body, including the brain.

In some *helminthic infections*, adult worms living in the intestinal tract produce eggs or larvae capable of penetrating the intestinal lining. They are picked up in the blood stream and distributed widely. When they have been deposited in human tissues, these larval forms cannot complete their development into mature adults. Some of them die as a result of host reactivity to their presence and later become calcified, but others remain alive in the tissues for long periods of time (see Fig. 6–1). The best-known example of a roundworm infection of this type is *trichinosis*, acquired by ingestion of larval forms of the worm *Trichinella spiralis* in infected pork tissue, inadequately cooked. The serious nature of this disease is related to larval invasion of muscle tissue.

The agents of two very important *virus* diseases also commonly localize in the bowel, as well as

Fig. 6–1. Calcified cysts of *Trichinella spiralis* in human muscle (300×). (Courtesy of Dr. Kenneth Phifer, Rockville, Md.)

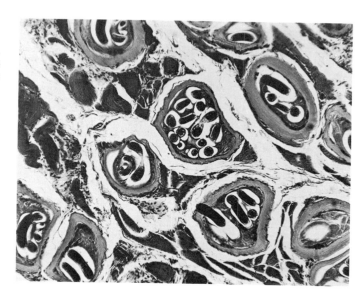

in the upper respiratory tract (as mentioned earlier in this chapter), but produce disease by invasion of other tissues. These are the polio-myelitis virus, which invokes its most serious effects when distributed to cells of the central nervous system, and the virus of infectious hepa-titis, which invades and damages liver cells. A number of other "enteroviruses," so-called be-cause of their enteric, or intestinal, localization, may induce an acute, but brief, gastroenteritis, or they may be disseminated to other tissues and cause more serious injury.

The Toxins of Intestinal Pathogens. Most of the bacterial enteric pathogens produce disease of the intestinal tract itself by virtue of their content of *endotoxins.* (See Chap. 3, p. 50.) Since these toxic substances are a part of the structure of the bacterial cells, or their walls, they are not liber-ated into the environment until the cell dis-integrates. Therefore their injurious effects are concentrated in those areas where the bacterial cells themselves are localized, multiplying rapidly, and dying in a quick turnover of generations. They are not disseminated to any great extent to other parts of the body from areas of bacterial localization in the intestinal tract, such as exist in the case of cholera, *Salmonella* enteritis, and many types of shigellosis. However, when endo-toxic organisms, such as *Salmonella typhosa* (the typhoid bacillus) or *Salmonella paratyphi,* them-selves penetrate to other tissues, or are distrib-uted, the endotoxic effect accompanies them and is operative wherever they may be located in the body tissues.

In one notable instance of infection of the intestinal tract, the primary disease effect is due to the secretion of an *exotoxin,* but here again the toxin remains localized in the bowel with the organism and is not absorbed from the intestinal tract. One member of the *Shigella* group, *Shigella dysenteriae,* the agent of bacillary dysentery, produces an exotoxin whose effects on the mu-cosal lining cells, particularly those of the large bowel, are primarily responsible for the symptoms of pain, often bleeding, and severe watery diar-rhea. There are several other types of *Shigella*

species whose effects on the bowel are primarily endotoxic.

Bacterial Food Poisoning. The term "bacterial food poisoning," used so frequently, refers to one of three types of disease induced by the ingestion of food contaminated with bacteria or their toxic products.

The first type is an intestinal infection, already mentioned, caused by members of the genus *Salmonella.* When these organisms are ingested with food or water that they have actively con-taminated, they may survive and continue to multiply in the bowel. The enteritis that results is produced by their endotoxins, but the orga-nisms are often eliminated quickly, and their effects are therefore acute, but short-lived. In some cases, however, they may continue to reside in the bowel without producing symptoms, thus constituting a continuing threat of trans-ferred infection to the contacts of the infected individual. In some instances, following an initial enteritis, these *Salmonella* species may penetrate the intestinal mucosa, invade the enteric lym-phoid tissue, and disseminate to other organs such as the liver and gallbladder, producing fever and systemic symptoms of the paratyphoid type.

The second type of food poisoning is not an infection, but results from the ingestion of food in which an exotoxin-producing *Staphylococcus* species has been multiplying. The *enterotoxin,* as this exotoxin is called, is thus preformed in the food and upon ingestion rather promptly pro-duces an acute irritation of the bowel, manifest by nausea and vomiting, and often diarrhea as well. The symptoms subside, and do not recur, as soon as the last of the toxin has been eliminated and its effects have receded.

The third type of bacterial food poisoning also involves a preformed bacterial exotoxin, pro-duced in food before it is eaten by the anaerobic soil organism *Clostridium botulinum.* When this organism is present in canned or vacuum-packed foods, having survived the cooking or canning process by passing into a heat-resistant spore stage, it may multiply under the conditions of anaerobiasis provided in the sealed container. In

doing so, it secretes a substance that happens to have extreme toxicity for certain human cells. Unlike the staphylococcal enterotoxin, the *botulinum* exotoxin is absorbed from the bowel, after its ingestion, and exerts powerful, far-reaching, often fatal effects. The organism that produced it, however, although it may be ingested also with the contaminated food, does not reach the tissues at all, nor does it produce toxins or exert any effect, of itself, in the bowel. The exotoxin is a neuromuscular poison; that is, it affects motor nerves in such a way that the nerve impulse cannot be transmitted to muscle, and the muscle, therefore, cannot contract. The resulting paralysis of muscles of the intestinal tract, of the eyes, sometimes skeletal muscle, but, most importantly, muscles of the respiratory tract is usually severe, and death may ensue from respiratory paralysis.

The Skin and Superficial Mucous Membranes

The skin and external mucosa offer still another possible portal of entry for microorganisms, but the variety of microbes that find their way into the body by these paths is normally more limited than in the two routes discussed above. We have already seen that the surfaces of the skin and the superficial membranes have a large commensal flora, varying with the anatomic area and, for the genital mucosa, with sex and age. Obviously, then, these surfaces are normally impervious and indifferent to the many microorganisms with which they come in contact, and many of the latter are easily washed away or mechanically removed. Breaks in the surface of the skin or mucosa, although they may be minor, or some unusual capability on the part of an infecting organism apparently is required before microorganisms can enter to cause infectious disease, either locally or at some distant point.

Localization in the Surface Tissues. Infectious disease of the skin or mucous membranes, as a result of direct contact with, or entry by, the

pathogenic microorganism, may be caused by *yeasts and fungi* (*Candida* species, ringworm, "athlete's foot"), by *bacteria* (notably staphylococci or streptococci), by a few *viruses* (such as those of herpes infection, or of warty growths), or by the larval forms of *helminths* (the "ground itch" induced by hookworm larvae and the "swimmer's itch" caused by larvae of *Schistosoma*).

Differences in the type of skin lesion produced by various kinds of microorganisms are related, in part, to the capacities, preferences, and opportunities of the organism to localize in particular anatomic areas or in certain layers of the epidermis or dermis and, in part, to the kind of reaction they elicit from the host. Thus, the so-called "superficial" fungi infect only the outermost layers of skin or its appendages, as a rule, some characteristically involving the hairy skin (ringworm of the scalp); others the smooth skin surfaces, skin folds (between fingers or toes, axilla or groin), or the nails or their supporting skin tissue. Similarly the herpes virus of the "cold sore" shows a preference for particular cells, notably those of the oral mucocutaneous border. Often the host reaction is minimal to such superficial infections as these, but if the organism involves deeper layers or structures of the dermis, more vigorous defenses will be brought to bear by the normal, healthy skin. Helminthic larvae entering the skin from contaminated soil or water and wriggling about in the lower layers of the epidermis, unable to penetrate further, elicit a good deal of response from host cells whose job it is to deal with foreign intruders. (These are the *phagocytes*, the cells of the blood and tissues that ingest foreign particulate matter, living or dead.) Organisms as large as larvae are not easily inactivated, however, so that the reaction around them tends to be rather diffuse until they die and can be walled off.

Bacterial infections of the skin, on the other hand, generally involve structures in the deeper layers of the dermis and elicit considerably more response from the host as well as more effective reaction. Bacteria are generally not capable of penetrating the intact skin, but they may enter

hair follicles or the openings of sweat and sebaceous glands. The secretions of these glands discourage the establishment of microorganisms, for
they have an acid pH and contain antimicrobial
substances, such as fatty acids and lysozyme.
When bacteria do establish themselves in these
sites, by virtue of their own invasive properties
or some local abnormality in the skin or its functions, the cells of the dermis, assisted by cells and
substances marshaled to the area by the blood
stream, make every effort to localize the infection, and prevent its spread. Thus, the typical
lesion of a staphylococcal infection of the skin
is a "pimple" or "boil," a small abscess cir-
cumscribed and limited by a defensive wall of
material laid down around it by the host. The
pus that forms in an abscess contains many
phagocytes, which ingest the bacteria, while the
tissue formed around the area keeps them localized. This type of host response, together with
other mechanisms of resistance, is described more
fully in Chapter 7.

**Dissemination of Infection Through or from a
Superficial Entry Point.** Some of the organisms
mentioned above, particularly streptococci and
staphylococci, may produce substances that
enable them to resist localization by the tissues
and to spread through the skin, often involving
wide areas. This is the case, for instance, in
erysipelas, a streptococcal infection of the skin
characterized by a diffuse and rapidly spreading
involvement of dermal tissues, with an accumulation of fluid (edema) but little pus formation. In
impetigo, a staphylococcal infection often associated with streptococci as well, superficial blisters
form on the involved skin, break easily, and
liberate infected fluid, which spreads to involve
adjacent areas. The invasive quality of such infections presents the further risk of extension to
deeper tissues also. The organisms may enter
lymphatic or blood vessels within the area of the
skin lesions to be distributed through the body
and to induce severe damage to more vital tissues.

The venereal diseases constitute the most
important, and frequent, group of systemic
infections acquired by direct contact with the
infectious agents which enter through superficial

mucous membranes. These are diseases associated
with sexual intercourse, the causative organism
being transmitted directly from an infected to an
uninfected individual. The genital mucous membranes offer the usual route of entry to the pathogens, but the mucosal surfaces themselves are not
necessarily, or seriously, involved in the consequences. There are five principal human diseases of this type, caused by microorganisms
from three different major groups. Syphilis, the
most serious of the venereal diseases, is caused by
a spirochete, *Treponema pallidum*. Three of these
infections have bacterial agents: gonorrhea
(caused by the gonococcus, *Neisseria gonorrhoeae*); chancroid, or soft chancre (due to
Ducrey's bacillus, a member of the *Hemophilus*
group); and granuloma inguinale (caused by
Calymmatobacterium granulomatis, another bacillus). The fifth disease of the group, lymphogranuloma venereum, has a viral agent. The
nature of the systemic disease induced and its
symptoms are quite different in each case and
depend upon the tissues infected by the organism
following its penetration and spread from the
site of entry. These diseases are discussed in
Part Two, Section VI.

The Parenteral Route

Finally, we must consider the possibility of
entry of infection directly into the deeper tissues
of the body, or into the blood stream, by (1) penetration of, or (2) deep injury to, the skin and
mucosal barriers.

1. Penetration to Deep Tissues. Without significant injury to, or infection of, the skin or
mucosa, penetration may be accomplished in one
of three general ways: (a) direct entry of the
organism itself into the blood capillaries or
lymphatic vessels of the skin, without localization
in the dermis; (b) injection of the organism by a
biting or blood-sucking insect; and (c) injection
of organisms by a contaminated needle, syringe,
or solution.

a. *Direct entry of an organism* to the parenteral
tissues, as an active rather than a passive ac-

complishment, is relatively rare. It has been pointed out that intact skin and mucous membranes present a very strong barrier to microorganisms, and there are few that are capable of penetrating it to reach tissues beyond. Injured or infected skin may permit such access, of course, as we have seen. In the case of the microorganisms associated with venereal disease, penetration to the tissues beyond the superficial mucosa probably occurs through minor breaks or abrasions. The health of the skin and surface membranes and their careful protection when the risk of infection is high, as in the handling of infectious material from sick patients, the introduction of catheters over delicate membranes, or the laboratory manipulation of cultures, are of very great importance.

The best examples of organisms with an active capability for penetration of human skin are found among the helminth larvae, notably the hookworms and *Schistosoma* (the blood flukes). Some species of these worms, parasitic for animals other than man, are unable to find their way beyond the skin, as mentioned previously. The human parasites, however, are more successful. Infective hookworm larvae on the surface of moist soil or *Schistosoma* larvae swimming freely in water following their emergence from their intermediate snail hosts attach to the surface of the skin, wriggle through, and are picked up in the blood stream from the capillary beds in the lower layers of the skin. From there they find their way to tissues in which further development into the adult form may occur.

b. *Injection of an organism by a biting or blood-sucking insect* is the access route for a rather large number of human diseases. The entire group of parasites that may gain entry in this fashion includes members of each of the major classes of microorganisms, with the exception of the yeasts and fungi. For some of these organisms, man is only an accidental and occasional host; but for others he is the only susceptible species, and perpetuation of the parasite depends on both man and the vector.

As an *accidental* host, man is occasionally infected by certain species of rickettsiae that infest ticks or mites and ordinarily are passed around

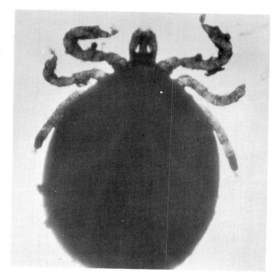

Fig. 6–2. A wood tick. Many species of this arthropod are natural hosts for rickettsiae. Man becomes an accidental host for the microorganism if he is bitten by an infected tick.

only among the wild rodents and other small animals that these insects themselves parasitize. Man, if he happens to be around, is also attractive to ticks and mites, and through their bites he may become infected with their rickettsiae (see Fig. 6–2). Two diseases acquired in this way are Rocky Mountain spotted fever and the Oriental infection known as tsutsugamushi. On the other hand, diseases such as malaria and yellow fever are *primarily human infections*, kept going in the human population by mosquito vectors, which transmit them from one person to another. Of course mosquitoes bite animals other than man, and in the case of the malarial parasite there are species that infect birds, rodents, and a few other animals, but these, like the human malarial species, are usually infective only for one kind of animal (see Fig. 6–3). Between these two extremes there are a number of diseases vectored by a variety of insects (mosquitoes, biting flies, "true bugs," lice, ticks, and mites), whose microbial agents find suitable reservoirs in several animal species as well as man.

The microbial agents of diseases transmitted to

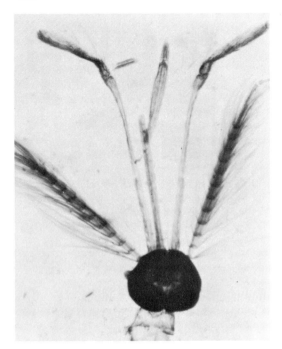

Fig. 6–3. The head of an *Anopheles* mosquito. Part of the life cycle of *Plasmodium vivax* takes place in the midgut of this insect, which in turn bites man and releases the parasite into man's blood stream.

man by biting insects, which assure their entry into parenteral tissues, include *protozoa* (such as the organisms responsible for malaria, the trypanosomes of "African sleeping sickness," and species of *Leishmania*); *roundworms* of the group known as filaria; a few *bacteria* (such as the plague bacillus and *Bartonella*); the *rickettsiae* of typhus fever, rickettsialpox, and others mentioned above; and a number of *viruses* (such as yellow fever, dengue fever, and Eastern and Western equine encephalitis viruses). In addition, the relapsing fevers caused by *spirochetes* of the genus *Borrelia* are vectored from man to man by body lice (as in the case of typhus fever) or from infected animals to man by ticks.

Many of these diseases occur naturally only in tropical or semitropical areas of the world, primarily because of climatic restrictions on the insect vector, or the function it fills for the

microbe, or both. However, geographic boundaries no longer prevent the mixing of human populations as they once did, so that the recognition and treatment of these diseases may be important in any area to which people have traveled or migrated after becoming infected in their native region. Also, the prevention and control of such diseases have become an ever more pressing concern, not only for the sake of individuals or armies, in peace or war, who travel into these areas, but in the interest of assuring the welfare of human populations struggling to reach civilized standards of health and function.

c. *The injection of organisms by a contaminated needle, syringe, or solution* is an ever-present possibility wherever these items are used. Pathogenic, or merely "opportunistic," organisms may be introduced in this way into parenteral tissues, or into the blood stream itself, sometimes with disastrous results. In some instances, because this constitutes an unnatural route of entry for a particular type of organism, it may not be able to survive and establish itself. Also, some microorganisms appear to be totally incapable of pathogenicity, or, in other cases, they may be successfully eliminated by the host's defenses. On the other hand, the host may overreact to the presence of the organism, or its protein constituents, and develop symptoms of what is called *hypersensitivity*. It is equally possible that infection may be established at the site of injection, or in any other area suitable for the growth of the organism to which it has been disseminated.

Constant maintenance of the strictest techniques of sterilization and asepsis offers the only assurance that infection will not be acquired by this route.

2. Deep Injury to the Skin and Mucosal Barriers. Trauma to the skin or the mucous membranes, whether it results from accident or the bite of an animal or as a necessary risk of surgery, opens up many possibilities of entry by microorganisms of all types.

During *surgery*, these possibilities are strictly limited, or eliminated altogether for many organisms, by the sterilization of instruments, linens, and clothing and by the aseptic techniques

of the operating room. Commensals of normally low pathogenicity from the skin or mucosal surfaces may take advantage of the surgical situation, however, and enter to infect the wound or more distant tissues. Surgical entry of the bowel, or its perforation in areas ulcerated by infection or other causes, creates the risk of exposing the peritoneal cavity, normally sterile, to microorganisms usually confined to the intestinal tract, and peritonitis may result. Similarly, major or minor wounds in the mouth resulting from tooth extraction, or other oral surgery, may admit normal mouth flora to deeper tissues or to the blood stream, with consequent risk of systemic infection.

The bite of an animal introduces into human tissues microorganisms from the animal's mouth that may be normal residents in the latter but pathogenic for human cells. They may also be highly pathogenic for the animal, who bites because he is ill and thus transmits his infection to the person bitten. Among microorganisms that can be transmitted to human beings in this way the one with the most serious potential is the rabies virus. Rabies in man is uniformly fatal, although its development may be prevented, following the bite of a rabid animal, by injections of a related but nonvirulent virus that stimulates the body to produce antibodies against the rabies virus. The latter is thus inactivated, and the threat of disease avoided, if antibody is formed before the virus enters the cells of the brain where it causes irreversible effects. (The development of this method of prevention of rabies was another of the contributions of Pasteur, one hundred years ago.) Rabies is often associated with dogs, but it should be pointed out that dogs themselves often acquire it from the bites of smaller wild animals that they hunt. These, together with bats, appear to constitute the reservoir.

Other accidental wounds, such as lacerations, gunshot wounds, or crushing of tissue, may also introduce a variety of microorganisms into deep tissues, not only from the body's surfaces, but from those of the penetrating or crushing objects. The risk of infectious disease is always increased in such instances, not only because the barriers are broken, but because the tissues are handicapped, with respect to their antimicrobial defenses, by the injury. Organisms may thus have a much better opportunity to survive, multiply, and penetrate deeper before the tissue has a chance to heal and defend itself. Furthermore, normal blood supply to the injured tissue may be cut off, or seriously reduced, if blood vessels are damaged or compressed by tissue reaction. This means that substances normally carried in the blood to an area of injury to take part in its defense and healing are prevented from reaching it in adequate concentration. This would include antibiotics administered to assist in combating infection. For these reasons, the prompt surgical cleaning of such wounds, with removal of foreign objects, dead tissue, blood clots, and so on, is of first and foremost importance in the prevention of infection and the promotion of healing.

The Toxins of Wound Pathogens.   Organisms of particular importance with respect to their production of powerful exotoxins should be noted here as possible contaminants of deep traumatic wounds. These are anaerobic, sporeforming bacilli, members of the genus *Clostridium*. These organisms were mentioned previously in Chapter 5 as frequent members of the normal intestinal flora. They are also present in the intestinal tracts of many animals, including dogs, horses, and cattle, and therefore they are widely distributed in the soil. Because they are able to form resistant spores, they may survive for very long periods in this stage and be found in dust, as well as soil, indoors, as well as outdoors. Consequently, they are often present on the surfaces of objects with which wounds are inflicted accidentally, such as rusty nails, sharp sticks, animal claws, knives, and bullets. *Clostridium* spores are also frequently to be found on the skin or bed linen of sick patients, a fact of some importance to the patient with a surgical or accidental wound, if the wound permits the conditions necessary for their growth within its traumatized tissue.

To germinate from the spore stage into vegetative bacilli capable of active growth and multiplication, clostridial species require anaerobic

conditions. Further, they are saprophytic organisms, which thrive best on dead organic matter. Wounds that contain dead traumatized tissue and whose supply of blood, and therefore of oxygen, is inadequate offer excellent conditions for the growth of clostridia that might otherwise merely contaminate a wound without being capable of multiplying. The damage they induce is a consequence of their production, during active growth stages only, of toxins which may exert their effects locally in the wound or be disseminated.

Local clostridial toxicity is exemplified by the clinical condition known as gas gangrene. The species of most importance in this very serious infection is *Clostridium perfringens* (once named the "Welch" bacillus, or *Cl. welchii*). Several exotoxins are produced by this organism as it grows anaerobically within injured tissue. These substances have a disintegrating effect on adjacent living host cells, so that additional areas of dead tissue are provided for the growth of the organism, more toxins are produced, and the infection spreads, often with great rapidity, threatening large areas and even life itself. This is an example of infection spreading locally by virtue of the effects of exotoxin within the area.

Disseminated clostridial toxicity is exemplified by the disease known as *tetanus*, or "lockjaw," caused by the species *Clostridium tetani*. In this case, also, the germination of tetanus spores within a contaminated wound that provides anaerobic conditions and the subsequent multiplication of the organisms lead to exotoxin production. However, neither the toxin nor the organism exerts much local effect, this species being incapable of tissue invasion. The serious consequences of tetanus arise from the absorption of the exotoxin from the local area and its extension along peripheral motor nerve trunks to the spinal cord. It is a *neurotoxin*, which acts only on nerve tissue, interfering with the normal transmission of nerve impulse to muscle. Severe muscle spasm results in anatomic regions reflecting the point of origin of toxin formation and its advance along nerve trunks. The typical convulsive contractions of voluntary muscles may become quite generalized. When the muscles of the face, jaw, and neck become "locked" in contraction, the mouth cannot be opened, and swallowing is difficult or impossible, hence the term "lockjaw." Involvement of the muscles of respiration may have fatal consequences.

The possibilities of the growth of clostridial contaminants in traumatic wounds, with elaboration of exotoxins by the multiplying organisms, offer another urgent reason for prompt surgical removal of dead tissue, the restoration of an adequate blood supply, and aeration of the wound. Other specific measures to combat such infections, and their accompanying toxicities, are discussed for the clostridial diseases in Part Two, Section VII.

The Microbial Properties of Pathogenicity and Virulence

At this point it is obvious that the production of infectious disease in man does not depend solely on the opportunity for entry of the human body by microorganisms. If this were true, illness would be the rule, rather than the exception that it is. The biologic resistance of the human host and the artificial defenses that it applies provide a partial explanation for the fact that infection is more common than infectious disease. The other half of the explanation lies in the fact that the great majority of the microorganisms with which man is surrounded, or to which he is exposed, have few or none of the properties associated with pathogenicity and virulence.

Pathogenicity

In the preceding chapter it was stated that the *pathogenicity* of an organism is related to its ability to produce disease, and that its *virulence* in this regard is a matter of degree. We have seen also that following their entry into the body pathogenic microorganisms display their virulence in terms of two general qualities: their *invasiveness*, or ability to survive, multiply, and spread in the tissues; and their *toxigenicity*, or

their production of substances, during their growth in the body or in food prior to its ingestion, that are injurious to human cells and tissues. Among the relatively small group of microbes that are pathogenic for man, the properties that add up to virulence are not always fully understood, but a number of factors appear to make a definite contribution to the pathogenesis of some infectious diseases.

Virulence

The measurement of virulence is commonly expressed in terms of the numbers of a particular organism that are required to kill a given species of experimental animal (or its cells in tissue culture), under well-defined experimental conditions. Factors that must be defined in this measurement are related to controlled, or acknowledged, variations in both the host and the pathogen. The host, or its isolated cells in the culture tube, must be susceptible to the organism in question. The intact animal must be infected with the organism via an entry route that permits the latter to establish itself and induce disease (the route of administration may be intravenous, intramuscular, intraperitoneal, intracerebral, etc., depending on the organism and the susceptibility of the host in question). The numbers of organisms introduced, and the period of time they then require to induce disease, or death, or both, must also be defined. Virulence is then expressed in quantitative terms for the organism: as the *minimum lethal dose* (MLD), or the smallest number of organisms inducing disease and death of a particular susceptible host, or its cells, in a specified time period; or the *50 per cent lethal dose* (LD_{50}), which allows for variations in host resistance and states the numbers of organisms required to kill 50 per cent of all the infected animals or cell cultures within a certain time, when a large number are inoculated for the test of virulence. These terms reflect both the invasiveness and the toxigenicity of a pathogenic organism under controlled conditions and help to explain differences in virulence as they are observed under natural conditions. Thus, the nat-

ural occurrence of infectious disease in an individual human host may be the result of entry of large numbers of relatively *avirulent* organisms, or small numbers of a *virulent* one. In either case, the route of entry and the particular opportunities it may offer the entrant also reflect the properties of an organism that enable it to establish itself under the existing circumstances.

Invasiveness

Specific explanations of the invasive character of virulent organisms have been found in some instances. In general, they relate to the ability of an organism, once it has gained access to the body of a suitable host, to (1) grow and multiply, (2) protect itself against the defenses of the host, and (3) penetrate and spread through the tissues.

1. Factors Involved in Growth and Multiplication Within the Host. All the properties of an organism that contribute to its production of disease depend first of all on its ability to utilize available nutrient within the host's tissues and to grow and multiply there. If the nutrients vital to its growth processes are not present, or not in available form or sufficient quantity, the invading organism cannot grow and therefore appears to be avirulent. Sometimes the failure to grow reflects the presence or absence of oxygen at the entry site (depending on the organism's aerobic or anaerobic requirements); the prevailing pH of the area; the degree of competition offered for a particular growth factor (such as a vitamin or a certain mineral) by the host's own cells or by commensal organisms resident in the area of entry; or the host's deficiency with respect to the particular nutrient requirements of the microorganism. On the other hand, the successful utilization of available nutrient by the invading organism may deprive host cells of growth factors vital to their own health, so that tissue injury may be the result of such starvation, whether or not other microbial properties are involved.

2. Factors That Protect Microorganisms from Host Defenses. Phagocytosis is one of the im-

portant processes, as we have seen, by which the body deals with foreign particles or microbes that find their way into tissues. The invasiveness of some bacterial pathogens appears to be related to their ability to resist phagocytosis or to destroy the phagocytes themselves.

The ability to resist the action of phagocytes is due in some cases to the nature of surface components present on the bacterial cells. Many species of bacterial are encapsulated by viscous polysaccharide material (e.g., strains of pneumococci) or possess surface proteins (streptococci) or polypeptides (anthrax bacilli). Such components of the cell either prevent their ingestion by phagocytes or enable them to survive it. In the latter case, the cells may multiply within the phagocyte and thus kill it. The products of bacterial growth may be protective in other instances. For example, the familiar *coagulase* associated with some strains of staphylococci is an extracellular enzyme secreted by the organism under optimal conditions for its growth. It induces clotting of the plasma that exudes from the blood capillaries into an area of tissue injury. When staphylococci are themselves producing this injury, and the infected area in which they are growing contains coagulase they have produced, they become surrounded by a fibrinous clot as plasma seeps in and is coagulated. The organisms are thus walled away from the action of phagocytes, as well as from other host defenses.

The ability to kill phagocytes, aside from the effects microorganisms may have following their ingestion, is associated with the production of a substance that is toxic for leukocytes and is called, therefore, *leukocidin*. Leukocytes are white blood cells, some of which are highly phagocytic. These cells enter an injured area from adjacent capillaries, but they may be inactivated and killed by leukocidin secreted into the tissue by organisms, such as actively growing streptococci and staphylococci.

In some instances, phagocytes may fail to recognize an invading organism as foreign because it contains substances identical to those of host cells. Such an organism would not be eliminated rapidly and would have a better opportunity for growth than another subjected to immediate phagocytic attack.

3. Factors That Contribute to the Penetration and Spread of Microorganisms. A number of the extracellular products of bacterial growth have been associated with specific kinds of damage to host tissue and consequent spread of the offending organism. Like the staphylococcal coagulase, mentioned above, several of these products are enzymes, for which the substrates are components of the host tissue. Some of these enzymes are listed below.

Collagenase, an enzyme that disintegrates the proteins of collagen tissue.

Mucinase, an enzyme that digests the mucin produced by many mucosal lining cells.

Hyaluronidase, an enzyme capable of breaking down hyaluronic acid, the gel-like matrix of connective tissue.

Lecithinase, an enzyme destructive for lecithin, a component of many human cells including red blood cells.

Kinase, an activator of an enzyme present in plasma. When activated, the enzyme, called fibrinolysin, is capable of dissolving fibrin clots.

Hemolysins, substances capable of destroying red blood cells. Some hemolysins, such as lecithinase, are enzymes; others are not.

The production of one or more of such substances by a microorganism multiplying within host tissues creates additional injury to the latter, disrupting their normal architecture, interfering with their defensive activities, and promoting the spread of the organism to adjacent tissue. Blood and lymph vessels within the injured area may be eroded in the process, so that organisms can enter, or be carried into, the blood and lymph streams to be distributed to other parts of the body. The flow of blood into the infected region, on the other hand, is often reduced or cut off during the course of such events, so that the concentration of both nutrient and defensive substances brought by the blood is further diminished.

Perhaps the clearest example of a cycle of destruction to tissue set up by the enzymes of an invading organism is seen in the case of gas gangrene, caused by *Clostridium perfringens*, as noted earlier in this chapter. In this case, the anaerobic bacilli get their start in traumatized tissue to which the supply of blood and oxygen

is low. As they multiply, they produce their exotoxins, which in this case are enzymes with collagenase and lecithinase activity. These substances break down healthy tissue on the margins of the injured area, enlarging the damage, releasing more nutrient for the organisms from host cells, and extending the zone of reduced blood supply. Such a process can expand rapidly, since continuing growth of the organisms means continuing production of enzymes that contribute to the injury and ensure further bacterial multiplication, with more enzyme secretion.

The spread of streptococci through the tissues is often associated with their production of hyaluronidase. These organisms, as well as strains of pathogenic staphylococci, also secrete a kinase, known appropriately as streptokinase or staphylokinase, as the case may be. In addition, many strains of streptococci and staphylococci are hemolytic, and this property, too, is associated with their virulence, although its contribution to the pathogenesis of the diseases they may induce is not always clear. Mucinase is a product of the growth of influenza virus in mucosal cells of the respiratory tract and probably contributes to the spread of this organism from its entry site by altering the surface characteristics of mucin.

Toxigenicity

Many of the substances mentioned above are not directly toxic in themselves, their effect being to promote the infectious process itself. The endo- and exotoxins of bacterial pathogens, however, produce chemical injury to the host, often in a specific way to particular cells and tissues.

Endotoxins, as components of the bacterial cell, are not released into the surrounding area until after the death of the cell. The cell walls of many Gram-negative bacteria, particularly, contain substances that are toxic in the same way when released into the tissues on disintegration of the organisms. Most of the damage occurs locally, but if steady, or large, quantities are being released, some may be distributed and produce systemic reactions. In *Salmonella* and *Shigella* infections of the intestinal tract, endotoxin is injurious to the mucosal cells of the bowel, usually none being absorbed into the body. In systemic *Salmonella* infection, such as typhoid or paratyphoid fever, the endotoxic effect is seen primarily in those tissues to which the organisms have penetrated, such as the lymphoid tissue of the intestinal wall, the liver, spleen, gallbladder, bone marrow, or kidneys. Dissemination of endotoxin may produce damage elsewhere, however, notably in the lining cells of blood vessels, resulting in thrombosis (the formation of blood clots) or hemorrhage. Many of the symptoms of these diseases, including the characteristic fever, are referable to the release of endotoxin. Meningococcus infections are also noted for the complications induced by endotoxin effects. Blood vessel walls are frequently involved also, but in this case the meningococci themselves may be localized there. Small capillary hemorrhages in the skin characteristically occur in meningococcemia, and if material is obtained from these by gentle scraping with a sterile scalpel, the organism can be demonstrated directly by stained smear and culture. The treatment of Gram-negative infections is often complicated by the fact that antibiotics may produce the sudden death of large numbers of organisms, thus abruptly releasing excess endotoxin, with a corresponding flare of symptoms and added stress for the patient.

Exotoxins, as we have seen, are substances, usually protein in nature, produced and secreted by bacteria during their growth. Only a few bacterial pathogens secrete exotoxins, and these toxins differ from each other chemically as well as in their biologic effects, each producing a specific type of injury to particular cells and tissues (see Table 6–1). The important toxin-producing bacteria have all been mentioned in connection with their usual entry routes into the human body and the manner in which their toxins induce disease. They are summarized here briefly with reference to the diseases with which they are associated.

Bacterial Food Poisoning. Two of the three types of bacterial food poisoning are caused by toxins, preformed in food in which bacteria had been growing prior to its ingestion. (1) The toxin

Table 6–1. Comparison of Endotoxins and Exotoxins Produced by Bacteria

Endotoxins	Exotoxins
1. Toxins are components of bacterial cells	1. Toxins are secreted into surrounding medium
2. Stimulate production of antibodies that may or may not have protective value	2. Stimulate production of antibodies (antitoxin) with high protective value
3. Antitoxins not available commercially	3. Antitoxins available commercially
4. Produce nonspecific symptoms such as fever, weakness, generalized aches (more severe in some diseases), regardless of microbial source	4. Produce specific symptoms so that each disease is recognizable
5. Endotoxic diseases: typhoid fever, bacillary dysentery, gonococcal arthritis, undulant fever, tularemia	5. Exotoxic diseases: gas gangrene, tetanus, botulism, diphtheria, scarlet fever

of *Clostridium botulinum* is a neurotoxin that is absorbed from the intestines to exert its effects on the central nervous system in the disease known as *botulism*. (2) The enterotoxin of *staphylococci* is not absorbed after its ingestion but acts on the lining cells of the stomach and intestine. In either case, entry and multiplication of the organism in the body are not required to produce disease.

Diphtheria and Tetanus. In each of these two cases, the organism in question usually remains localized at or near its entry site, producing toxin that is absorbed and disseminated in the body. (1) Tetanus toxin is a neurotoxin, which acts on peripheral motor nerves and the spinal cord. (2) Diphtheria toxin acts on the cells of many organs, particularly the heart, liver, kidneys, and adrenal glands. The tetanus bacillus is itself noninvasive, producing little or no damage to tissue at the site of its localization. The diphtheria bacillus produces a characteristic lesion in the upper respiratory tract, damaging the surface epithelium and interfering with its blood supply, but it is not markedly invasive and does not spread to other tissues.

Gas Gangrene. *Clostridium perfringens* and a few other clostridial species as contaminants of injured tissue multiply and spread rapidly through such tissue, producing toxins that exert their effect locally, promoting invasion by damaging more tissue in which the organism can grow

anaerobically. Lecithinase and collagenase production, in particular, make this advance possible. These and other toxins produced by the organisms are also disseminated through the body and can produce injurious effects elsewhere. The bacteria themselves, however, cannot grow in healthy tissue and remain in the injured area.

Scarlet Fever. Strains of *streptococci* entering and localizing in the upper respiratory tract produce an exotoxin that is absorbed and disseminated and produces damage in other areas, notably to cells of the skin. Many streptococcal strains are also highly invasive, however, owing to their production of hyaluronidase and streptokinase, to the nature of their surface proteins, and to less well-defined factors. They infect the surface epithelium of the upper respiratory tract and from there invade regional lymphoid tissue. The infection may extend upward into the sinuses, laterally through the eustachian tube to the inner ear and mastoid, or downward into the lower respiratory tract. In this case, virulence may be attributed to both invasiveness and toxigenicity.

Other Factors Contributing to Infectious Disease

In addition to the chemical injuries that may be caused by the products and secretions of

microorganisms, a good deal of *mechanical* damage may be done. As foreign bodies their presence in the tissues is irritating and may be mechanically disruptive. A mass of worms in the intestinal tract, for instance, may cause intestinal obstruction. The presence of helminth larvae in other organs, such as the liver, bone, or muscle, may disrupt normal architecture and thus interfere with the function of those tissues. They may also block the flow of blood through a vessel and thus diminish the supply of blood to adjacent tissues. These physical effects are often aggravated, furthermore, by the nature of the host's reaction to a foreign body. The supply of blood to an injured area usually is increased, and both cells and fluid from the blood exude into the tissue, causing swelling. This increases the pressure and further disrupts the functions of the tissue. As the reaction proceeds, fibrinous tissue is laid down around the area (see Fig. 6–4). When the infection subsides, the damaged region may be filled in with fibrinous scar tissue, it may be further solidified with deposits of calcium, or it may be completely cleared and returned to normal.

Another form of injury that may result from the host's own reactions to an invading organism is known as *hypersensitivity*. If the host becomes overreactive to a microorganism, or to its products, the tissue at the site of the reaction is often damaged by the process. Hypersensitivity is developed through the same mechanism that leads to immunity in most cases. It is discussed in Chapter 7, together with other host responses to infection (see Table 6–2).

Unanswered Questions Concerning Microbial Disease

Many explanations have yet to be found for the pathogenesis of some infectious diseases. Virulence has been defined as a combination of invasiveness and toxigenicity; yet neither of these is synonymous with the production of disease. For instance, some organisms (such as certain viruses) may be widely invasive of the human body without producing apparent ill effects;

Fig. 6–4. An adult trematode, or fluke (*Clonorchis sinensis*), established within a bile duct (10×). Its presence there is injurious to the architecture and function of the duct. The host's inflammatory reaction and the fibrosis that occurs later also narrow or obstruct the duct. (Courtesy of Dr. Kenneth Phifer, Rockville, Md.)

others may fail to cause illness in spite of their close resemblance to species that do so (such as intestinal strains of *Escherichia coli*, some of which cause severe infant diarrhea); and still others display strict host specificity with regard to virulence (as in the case of the strain of tubercle bacillus that is virulent for man and the guinea pig but does not produce significant disease in the rabbit).

The evaluation of an organism as the virulent agent of a given disease often rests, even today, on the conditions or "postulates" originally outlined by Robert Koch in the late 1800's. These require the repeated isolation of the organism from cases of the clinical disease having similar or identical symptoms; its repeated recognition in pure laboratory culture; its ability to produce the characteristic disease in a suitable experimental animal; and its reisolation from the infected animal. These conditions satisfactorily established the microbial agents of many infectious diseases, particularly those caused by bac-

Table 6–2. The Microbe Versus the Host

Infection Versus Infectious Disease	Mechanisms of Pathogenesis (Microbial)

I. Parasitism
   A. Obligatory
   B. Facultative
 	
II. Commensalism
   A. Resident ("normal") flora
   B. Transient flora
 	
III. Mutualism
 	
IV. Independence
	I. Routes of entry
	   A. Respiratory tract (droplets and droplet nuclei)
	   B. Gastrointestinal tract (milk, water, food, fingers, fomites)
	   C. Intact skin and mucosa
	   D. Parenteral entry
	     1. Trauma
	       a. Accidental
	       b. Surgical
	
	     2. Injection
	       a. Accidental (syringe and needle)
	       b. Insect vectors
	
	II. Microbial activities
	   A. Local multiplication at entry site
	     1. Mechanical damage
	     2. Metabolic competition
	     3. Chemical damage
	     4. Allergenic stimuli, hypersensitivity of host
	   B. Penetration and multiplication at distant sites; factors 1, 2, 3, and 4 as above
	   C. Virulence factors
	     1. Exotoxins (e.g., diphtheria)
	     2. Endotoxins (e.g., O antigens)
	     3. Enzymes (e.g., lecithinase, coagulase, kinase, hyaluronidase)
	     4. Other products of microbial metabolism serving as analogues or antagonists to human cell physiologic processes

teria and higher organisms, but they are difficult to apply to viruses, and they do not explain virulence, as such, or host specificity.

It may be that, like infection, virulence is an expression of the combined properties of the host, or a host species, and the pathogen. Infection is a dynamic state in which two organisms continuously oppose each other. In a simple analogy, it might be said that the relationship between a parasitic microorganism and the host that harbors it is rather like a seesaw, the position of the board depending on the weight each opponent can bring to bear on the other (see Fig. 6–5). It depends, also, on the balance point, and whether its placement allows either adversary an advantage over the other. Thus, a normal,

healthy individual balanced against an organism of low virulence may easily hold his own, but a person whose resistance has been lowered for some reason might have less success with the same organism. In the same way, virulent microbial species may induce more or less serious disease, depending on the host's ability to control the situation. Their failure to do so at all in a certain type of host may reflect the weight of biochemical properties brought to bear by one type of host as compared with another.

We have considered some of the factors that add weight to the parasite's position on the board; now let us turn our attention to the human host and the power with which he can balance or tip the board in his own favor.

Fig. 6–5. The balance between the microbe and the host is an ever-changing one. The virulence of the organism is pitted against the resistance of the host. What factors tip the seesaw in favor of the host? In favor of the organisms?

Questions

1. List the routes through which microorganisms gain entry to the human body.
2. Give examples of diseases that may be acquired through each entry route.
3. Describe briefly the three types of bacterial food poisoning.
4. What factors determine the differences in types of skin lesion in various diseases?
5. What group of diseases constitute the most important and frequent group of systemic infections acquired by direct contact with infectious agents through superficial mucous membranes? List examples.
6. How do organisms enter the body parenterally?
7. What organisms may contaminate deep traumatic wounds? Why are these important?
8. List the extracellular products of bacterial growth that contribute to penetration and spread of the microorganisms.
9. Compare endotoxins and exotoxins.

References

Pertinent References

Dubos, René: *Biochemical Determinants of Microbial Disease.* Harvard University Press, Cambridge, Mass., 1954.

Dubos, René J., and Hirsch, James G. (eds.): *Bacterial and Mycotic Infections of Man,* 4th ed. J. B. Lippincott, Philadelphia, 1965.

Faust, Ernest C., Beaver, P. C., and Jung, R. C.: *Animal Agents and Vectors of Human Disease,* 2nd ed. Lea and Febiger, Philadelphia, 1964.

Faust, Ernest, and Russell, Paul Farr: *Craig & Faust's Clinical Parasitology,* 7th ed. Lea and Febiger, Philadelphia, 1965.

Horsfall, Frank L., Jr., and Tamm, Igor (eds.): *Viral and Rickettsial Infections in Man,* 4th ed. J. B. Lippincott, Philadelphia, 1965.

Popular Literature

Baron, A. L.: *Man Against Germs.* E. P. Dutton and Co., New York, 1957.

Burgess, Perry: *Who Walk Alone.* Henry Holt and Co., New York, 1940.

Hailey, Arthur: *The Final Diagnosis.* Doubleday and Co., Inc., Garden City, N.Y., 1959.

Hoehling, A. A.: *The Great Epidemic.* Little, Brown and Co., Boston, 1961.

Leasor, James: *The Plague and the Fire.* McGraw-Hill, New York, 1961.

Sigerest, Henry: *Civilization and Disease.* Cornell University Press, Ithaca, N.Y., 1943.

Trevor, Elleston: *Pillars of Midnight.* William Morrow Co., New York, 1958.

Zinsser, Hans: *Rats, Lice and History.* Little, Brown and Co., Boston, 1935.

7 The Host Versus the Microbe

To maintain its position and balance in a world in which many antagonizing or inimical biologic forces are constantly brought to bear upon it, the human body has had to develop many defensive mechanisms. It has probably done so fairly continuously from the time of its earliest evolution, as have other living organisms. The problems created by the inroads of parasitic microorganisms of one type or another that infect human cells and tissues have, in particular, necessitated the development of protective processes. Some of these are *nonspecifically* directed against *any* foreign substance or particle that may find its way into the body, while others are *specifically* elicited by definite, individual kinds of substances that often are components of microorganisms or of their products. Most of these responses of the body, if they are adequate and successful, contribute to health and well-being, but self-damage can be induced if the body becomes overreactive, or *hypersensitive*, to specific substances. The resistance of the body to infection may also be affected by environmental factors, directly or indirectly.

In this chapter we will consider the most important of the reactions displayed by the human host in response to infection, grouping them in the three categories mentioned, according to their nonspecific, specific, or hypersensitive character.

121

Nonspecific Resistance to Infection

In previous chapters we have seen that the mere entry and invasion of human tissues by microbes does not necessarily lead to infectious disease, and that the latter is most likely to occur if the invading organisms have virulent properties or enter by an appropriate route in overwhelming numbers. The *general* resistance offered by the healthy body to most microorganisms is nonspecific in two connections: it does not operate against any one organism only, but is effective against microbes in general; and in many particulars it operates as well against nonliving foreign bodies, functioning also to inactivate chemical substances that do not necessarily originate in living organisms. *Environmental* conditions may also nonspecifically influence the body's general resistance to all types of infection.

Host Factors in Nonspecific Resistance

The most important, and also the best defined, host factors involved in nonspecific resistance are associated with the functions of (1) the skin and mucous membranes, (2) the cellular and fluid elements of the blood, (3) the cells of the reticuloendothelial system (RES), (4) the lymphatic system, and (5) the inflammatory response. Other factors, less well defined as to the mechanism of their contribution to resistance, will also be mentioned and discussed briefly.

1. The Skin and Mucous Membranes. These structures offer the first barrier to microorganisms coming into contact with the body. We know that many avirulent organisms normally may survive on these surfaces as saprophytes, deriving their nourishment from secretions or waste products of epithelial and adjacent tissues, without creating damage or arousing noticeable opposition. If the skin and mucous membranes are intact, entry to deeper tissues is impossible for most microbes. All of the reasons for this have not been clarified, but it can be partially explained on a *mechanical*

basis, partly by the *physiologic* properties of these tissues, and partly by the properties of *phagocytes and plasma components* constantly supplied to them by the blood stream.

Mechanically speaking, the architecture of the skin and mucous membranes is such that a continuous sheath of closely connected, or bridged, cells covers all exposed surfaces, supported beneath by dense connective tissue. In addition, the outermost surface of the skin is layered over with *keratin*, a protein substance that is not only tough and dense, but waterproof. At the opening of the respiratory tract, the nasal hairs prevent entry of large particles into the nose. Mucous secretions, together with the surface activity of the ciliated epithelial cells of the nasal membrane, trap and remove most of the particles that do enter by that route, as previously described. In the mouth, the salivary gland secretions provide a mechanical flushing action, while the movements of the tongue and the reflexes of swallowing ensure that most ingested particles will be carried to the stomach.

The *physiologic defenses* of these tissues include the secretions of the skin, notably those of the sebaceous glands and of the sweat glands, which have an antimicrobial effect. The fatty acids of the sebaceous gland secretions may function to prevent fungi, as well as bacteria, from localizing on the skin or the scalp. The acid and salt concentration of sweat may provide a similar protection. Another important substance, which is present in high concentration in nasal mucous, in tears, to a lesser extent in saliva and in skin secretions, is an enzyme called *lysozyme*. This enzyme has the ability to break down some carbohydrates, including a polysaccharide found in the cell walls of many bacteria. The activity of lysozyme in tears, combined with their flushing action, helps to keep the conjunctival surfaces free of colonizing organisms. Lysozyme is found in many secretions and cells of the body, including the leukocytes. *In the stomach*, the acidity of gastric secretions kills great numbers of microorganisms that are swallowed, but it does not destroy them all. For instance, tubercle bacilli are not greatly affected by gastric acidity, and some other organisms, such as poliomyelitis virus or

bacteria of the *Salmonella* and *Shigella* groups, can survive it as well. *In the small and large bowel*, the action of the body's digestive enzymes, together with microbial competition from the commensal flora of those regions, keeps the numbers of surviving newcomers in check under normal circumstances. The final removal of many microorganisms occurs with the passage of fecal material from the body. *In the genitourinary tract*, there is a similar process of mechanical bathing of the surface tissues with fluids whose direction of flow, pH, salt concentration, or other chemical composition effectively discourages the localization of any but commensalistic micro-organisms, under healthy conditions.

When the skin or mucous membranes are damaged or diseased, their ability to withstand infection, or to prevent the penetration of micro-organisms to other tissues, is compromised. Even minor wounds and abrasions open up routes of entry for microbes and should be protected when the risk of entry is great. Moisture is a factor important to the integrity of surface structures, healthy skin being relatively dry, mucous membranes normally moist. Skin becomes macerated in the continuing presence of excessive moisture, such as may accumulate under tight, dense, or wet dressings. The risk of infection by organisms trapped and multiplying in such moisture is increased, while at the same time damage to the skin's structures decreases its effective resistance to infection. Conversely, excessive dryness of mucosal surfaces, particularly those of the respiratory tract, also predisposes to infection. The malfunction of important structures, such as may result from the occlusion of glandular ducts to the surface (those of lacrimal, salivary, sebaceous, or sweat glands), offers still another opportunity to microorganisms to cross the surface barriers.

When for any reason microbes have succeeded in penetrating the skin or mucosa, other body defenses are then called into action. Primary among these are essential components of the blood stream, which nourishes every tissue.

2. The Role of the Blood in Nonspecific Resistance. The blood is a vital and dynamic factor in the body's resistance to infection. Not only does it constantly supply oxygen and nutrient to all tissues, but it carries away the waste products of cellular metabolism that would become toxic if they were to accumulate. If circulation is diminished or cut off from any area, tissue injury or death (necrosis) may result, and the involved area becomes more susceptible to the activities of any microorganisms that may enter it. A wound in which dead tissue is present, or in which hemorrhage has resulted in the formation of a hematoma (a mass composed of clotted blood), provides excellent conditions for the growth of bacteria, should they find their way into it.

Blood is comprised of a fluid portion, called *plasma*, and of *cellular* constituents. Both have important functions in responding to foreign substances, including microbes and their products.

Plasma. Some of the components of plasma provide it with important defensive properties. Outstanding among such properties are those associated with *antibodies*, which are discussed more fully in the next section of this chapter as a part of the mechanism of specific resistance to infection. It should be pointed out here, however, that antibodies are produced by certain cells of the tissues and the blood in specific response to particular foreign substances and become widely distributed in body fluids, including the blood plasma. Infectious microorganisms, their components, or their products usually stimulate antibody production, so that the concentration of antibodies in plasma characteristically rises during the course of an infection. Other plasma components, conversely, play a nonspecific role in infection, in that they occur normally in plasma, their concentration is not increased in response to infection, and their activities are not directed against any particular organism but against infectious agents in general. These non-specific substances may participate, however, in the reactions that occur between antibodies and microorganisms, supplementing the antibody effect or bringing it to completion.

One such nonspecific constituent of plasma is *complement*, so-called because it makes an important contribution to (that is, it complements) the effect of antibodies in some of their reactions.

Complement is a complex of proteins normally present in plasma. Acting alone it has no destructive effect on foreign cells. If these cells, microbial or other, have stimulated the body to produce antibodies, however, the latter combine specifically with them. Complement then also attaches to the combination of cell and antibody and brings about the destruction, or lysis, of the cell. Complement activity requires the presence also of *calcium* and *magnesium*, both of which are normally present in the blood in ionized form.

Another normal plasma protein, called *properdin*, has been described as having antimicrobial properties when complement and magnesium ions are present. The identity and role of properdin as a nonspecific plasma factor have not been clearly established, however. It is capable of destroying some bacteria, as well as certain protozoa, viruses, and abnormal red blood cells. Also, the amount of properdin present in the blood correlates directly with resistance to infection, in that high levels are associated with protection against certain infections, while low levels coincide with generally lowered resistance. It may develop, therefore, that the properdin effect is a specific one, related to low levels of antibodies reacting with specific organisms in the presence of complement.

Cellular Constituents of Blood. The cellular constituents of the blood of importance in nonspecific resistance to infection are those white blood cells, or *leukocytes*, that have phagocytic

activity. In actuality, all the leukocytes of the blood are capable of phagocytosis, but the polymorphonuclear neutrophils (neutral-staining cells whose nuclei have many varied shapes) are the most efficient, as well as the most numerous and responsive in infection. These cells circulate normally in the blood stream and therefore are constantly available at any point of entry of foreign material into any tissue to which there is an adequate blood supply. The presence of a foreign substance, especially if it is a living microorganism, provides a chemical stimulus that attracts phagocytes to the scene. This attraction is spoken of as *chemotaxis*. The polymorphonuclear cells are able to respond rapidly because they have an independent, amoeboid type of motility. They can migrate out of the blood capillaries, when attracted by a chemotactic stimulus, make their way to its source, and begin the attempt to eliminate the foreign object by, quite literally, devouring it. (The Greek word meaning to eat is *phagein*.) Moving as amoebae do, these phagocytes surround particulate matter, engulf it, and digest it if they can (see Fig. 7–1). They possess a number of digestive enzymes, including lysozyme, which can hydrolyze (break apart) polysaccharide and protein molecules. Such molecules are, as we know, important constituents of microorganisms or of their cell walls.

Probably most of the microbes that manage to penetrate the body's outer barriers and reach the tissues find themselves thus suddenly imprisoned. Probably also, for most, swift destruction ensues;

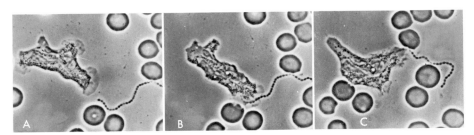

Fig. 7–1. Phagocytosis. *A.* A polymorphonuclear cell approaches a long chain of cocci. *B.* Thirty seconds later phagocytosis is in progress. *C.* After another sixty-five seconds the phagocytic cell is still in good condition and phagocytosis is proceeding. (Reproduced from Wilson, Armine T.: The Leukotoxic Action of Streptococci, *J. Exp. Med.,* **105**:463–84, 1957. Courtesy of Rockefeller Press and Dr. Grove D. Wiley, Alfred I. DuPont Institute, Wilmington, Del.)

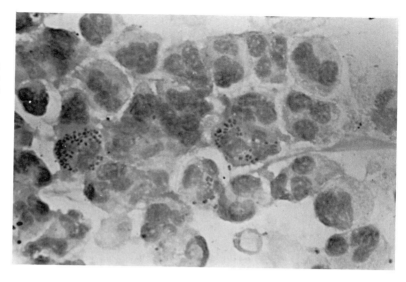

Fig. 7–2. Gonococci (*Neisseria gonorrhoeae*) are characteristically found within phagocytic white blood cells in smears of genital exudates from infected persons. (Courtesy of Dr. Kendall K. Kane, St. Luke's Hospital Center, New York, N.Y.)

but some, like Jonah in the belly of the whale, may survive and escape. The virulence of some pathogenic bacteria, such as tubercle bacilli, meningococci, or typhoid bacilli, is associated with their ability not only to survive but to multiply within phagocytes. In the process they may kill the leukocytes, but first they may be carried within these cells through the blood stream to other tissue sites, far from the point at which they were picked up. When such organisms emerge from the cells they have destroyed, they may localize in the new site, if conditions there are conducive to their growth; they may be picked up again by other phagocytes; or they may be met by more specific defenses.

In the tissues, the process of phagocytosis usually occurs in the presence of plasma that has also exuded from the capillaries at the site of entry of an intruding organism or substance (see Fig. 7–2). Phagocytosis is greatly enhanced by the nonspecific components of plasma, together with any specific antibodies it may contain for particular microorganisms that may have entered. Antibodies, which are large protein molecules, combine specifically with surface constituents of microorganisms to which they are responsive, forming a sticky coat on their surfaces. In this condition, flagellated organisms become immobilized, microbial activities conducted at or in the cell wall are slowed down, and the microbes can no longer take in or put out soluble materials in a normal manner — they are, in a word, stuck. Thus inactivated, microorganisms are more ap-

petizingly prepared for the phagocytic feast and more easily ingested, and digested, by the phagocytes. The antibodies that have performed this helpful catering service are called *opsonins*, a literal use of the Greek word meaning "to prepare food for." The enhancement of phagocytosis via antibody combination and coating is termed the "opsonic effect."

When antibody is not available, phagocytosis is facilitated by the presence of fibrin, which serves as a sort of trap to pin down microorganisms. The same effect may operate on rough or irregular surfaces, formed sometimes by the polymorphonuclear leukocytes themselves which have gathered on and adhered to the walls of small blood vessels or the alveoli of the lungs, as they sometimes do in infection. Bacteria passing by in the blood stream, or in inhaled air, are caught on irregular edges, and "surface phagocytosis" then occurs.

3. The Reticuloendothelial System (RES). The polymorphonuclear leukocytes of the blood are not the only cells of the body with a phagocytic capacity. The term "reticuloendothelial system" refers to phagocytic cells that occur and are fixed in a variety of tissues in the body, such as lymphoid tissue, spleen, bone marrow, the lungs, the central nervous system, connective tissue, the linings of blood vessels, and other strategic locations. In some of these situations they have been given particular names:

In the lungs, the phagocytic cells fixed in the

alveolar linings are called *dust cells* because they take up particles of dust from the inhaled air, as well as microorganisms.

In the central nervous system they are called *microglia*.

The phagocytic cells lining the blood vessels of the liver are called *Kupffer's cells.*

In connective tissue the cells are called *resting-wandering cells* because, like the blood leukocytes, they have amoeboid activity and are capable of wandering about, responding to chemotactic stimuli. These wandering cells are larger than the white blood cells and are mononuclear in type. For this reason they are often referred to, also, as *macrophages.*

Whatever their location, the principal function of the RES cells is the engulfment and removal of foreign, or useless, particles, living or dead. They have a great capacity for clearing a local scene, not only of microorganisms and other unwanted intruders, but also of the body's own cellular debris, including dead or dying leukocytes, red blood cells, and the fragments of other disintegrating cells. When the battle of infection is over, so to speak, it is the macrophages and the fixed RES cells that clean up the rubble and help to restore order, so that tissues can function normally once more.

4. The Lymphatic System. This system of tissues also has a significant role to play in the nonspecific resistance of the body to infection. Lymphoid tissue is scattered throughout the body, but the nodes of the upper respiratory tract and the cervical region, the gastrointestinal system, the genitourinary tract, and the inguinal area are strategically located to pick up microorganisms that first get past the main entry barriers. Here, most of them are filtered out by the phagocytes that line the numerous branching channels within the node. Some may escape to the efferent lymph vessel, but may be filtered out in the next or succeeding nodes. The lymphatic vessels themselves can be penetrated readily by bacteria and other particles, but such foreign bodies are quickly drained via afferent lymphatics to a node in the area and filtered out of the lymph stream there.

Altogether then, the phagocytes of the blood, the RES, and the lymphatic system offer a highly efficient nonspecific defense against microorganisms, functioning continuously to maintain the safety and the sterility of body tissues (see Fig. 7–3). When organisms are involved whose virulent properties include the capacity to multiply inside the phagocytes and destroy them, then other defense mechanisms are needed more urgently, and sometimes the disease becomes persistent, even progressive. In the case of diseases such as gonorrhea, tuberculosis, and brucellosis, infection is primarily intracellular, phagocytes being chiefly involved. Tissues constantly engaged with microbial encounters at a major entry point such as the upper respiratory tract may also become, and remain, chronically infected. In this way, the effective function of tonsils and adenoids may not only be reduced, but these tissues may then constitute a possible source of infection to other areas via their efferent lymphatics. Under these circumstances, surgical removal of tonsillar and adenoidal tissue is often recommended by physicians, after duly considering the consequences of losing any protective value they may yet afford.

The lymphatic tissues of the body are also highly important in the production of antibody, as discussed in the section of this chapter dealing with specific resistance to infection.

5. The Inflammatory Response. The normal body response to infection or tissue injury is called *inflammation.* It constitutes a marshaling of nonspecific defense mechanisms, most of which have been discussed individually.

The inflammatory response appears to be designed to localize foreign substances, bodies, or particles, including living organisms, at the site of their entry, to prevent or deal with their penetration into other areas, and to assist in the subsequent restoration of injured tissues to normal function. It is important to remember that the reaction can be elicited by nonliving matter, or chemical injury, and does not necessarily signify infection.

As the inflammatory response begins at the site of injury, the walls of small blood vessels in the

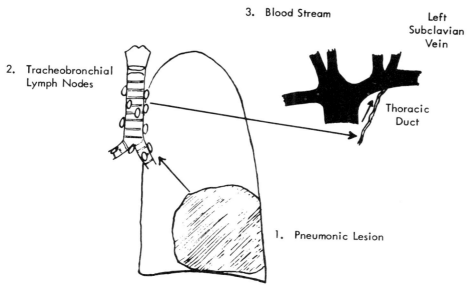

3. Blood Stream

Left Subclavian Vein

2. Tracheobronchial Lymph Nodes

Thoracic Duct

1. Pneumonic Lesion

Fig. 7–3. Anatomic sites of cellular defense in acute bacterial pneumonia. Within the pneumonic lesion (*1*), bacterial multiplication may exceed the capacity of the local defenses for bacterial destruction. Bacteria escaping from local resistance mechanisms are carried through the lymphatic system to the thoracic-bronchial lymph nodes (*2*) where many are filtered out and phagocytized. Those that successfully run this gamut are carried along in the lymphatic stream to the point where the thoracic duct empties into the blood stream at the left subclavian vein (*3*). The neutrophils, lymphocytes, and monocytes of the circulating blood continue the phagocytic attack on the bacterial invaders. (Adapted from Wood, W. Barry: Studies on the Mechanism of Recovery in Bacterial Pneumonia, *J. Exp. Med.*, **84**:355–402, 1946.)

vicinity become more permeable, so that plasma and cells pass through them more readily. Dilatation of the local blood vessels also occurs, markedly increasing the total supply of blood to the affected tissues. The leukocytes of the blood and the tissue macrophages migrate to the scene, congregating quickly. Sometimes the larger phagocytes of the tissues fuse together (as in tuberculosis and some systemic fungus diseases) to form giant cells, sharing their many nuclei. Even if they cannot destroy ingested organisms, these fused cells assist in walling them off and segregating them from adjacent tissue. Segregation proceeds most efficiently, however, through the continuing formation of fibrous connective tissue, the resulting fibrosis providing a relatively

firm wall around the site of infection or injury. Within the zone of active inflammation, plasma components exert their effects, cellular efforts continue, and the battle wages on, its outcome depending on the host's vigor weighed in the balance with the nature and extent of the injury (see Fig. 7–4). Many microorganisms die under these conditions, but some, such as tubercle bacilli, fungus spores, and helminth larvae, may remain viable though quiescent for very long periods of time.

The collection of fluid and cells that forms within the area of injury is called the *inflammatory exudate*. This material may vary a good deal in consistency and character. When it is thick and yellow with large numbers of leukocytes, it is

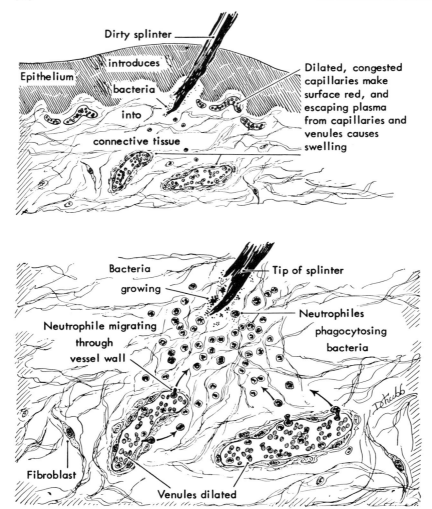

Dirty splinter

Epithelium

introduces

bacteria

into

connective tissue

Dilated, congested capillaries make surface red, and escaping plasma from capillaries and venules causes swelling

Bacteria growing

Tip of splinter

Neutrophile migrating through vessel wall

Neutrophiles phagocytosing bacteria

Fibroblast

Venules dilated

Fig. 7–4. Injury to human tissues is characteristically met by an inflammatory response. Here a splinter has become lodged in the skin. Small blood vessels in the area become dilated and congested with cells. Amoeboid, phagocytic neutrophils migrate from these vessels toward the site of injury. They surround and attempt to ingest both the splinter and the bacteria it has introduced into the subcutaneous tissue. Plasma escaping from the swollen blood vessels causes swelling. Redness of the local skin area results from the dilatation of these vessels. (Reproduced from Ham, Arthur W.: *Histology*, 5th ed. J. B. Lippincott Co., Philadelphia, 1965.)

called a *purulent*, or *suppurative*, exudate (more commonly, *pus*), and the agent that elicits this type of response (usually a microorganism) is said to be pus-producing, or *pyogenic*. When the exudate contains more plasma than cells and is therefore thin, it is called a *serous* exudate. If it contains sufficient fibrinogen (another of the normal components of plasma involved in blood clotting) to form a fibrin clot, it is referred to as a *fibrinous* exudate.

The physical symptoms that accompany this sequence of events vary with the battle arena. If it occurs superficially in skin or mucous membranes, the inflammatory reaction usually becomes quickly manifest with the local development of redness, heat, tenderness, and swelling, as the blood supply to the area increases and as exudate accumulates, pressing on the adjacent nerve supply. Individual tissue cells are compressed as the spaces between them fill up. As the area becomes walled off with fibrinous clots and a fringe of connective tissue, it grows more tense and hard to the touch. An *abscess* is forming, reddened on its periphery by excessive blood supply, yellowing at the center where the cellular exudate is heaviest. Eventually it may rupture spontaneously through the surface (*suppurate*), or it may be opened surgically to drain its contents. Abscess formation in the deeper tissues and organs of the body follows much the same course, provoking symptoms of tenderness (depending on nerve supply) or tissue dysfunction (depending on the degree of swelling and architectural disturbance). A deep abscess may also rupture and disseminate its contents to adjacent tissues or, circumstances permitting, it may be approached and drained surgically. On the other hand, the inflammatory reaction may proceed quite effectively, without any interruption, to its own conclusion. Most successfully, inflammation ends with complete solution of the problem before permanent tissue damage is done; the exudate is absorbed, cellular debris is completely phagocytized, fibrinous deposits are removed, and the area returns to a state of normal appearance and function. Lesser degrees of success may involve permanent disfigurement of the involved tissue by its partial or total replacement with fibrous scar tissue (sometimes calcified), or an intermediate state of affairs in which a viable but subdued organism is held in check by a chronic inflammation. In the latter case, the outcome is measured in terms of the host's ability to react defensively over a long period of time, on the one hand, and, on the other, the capacity of an infectious microorganism to survive the host's strengths and to revive its own when the opportunity presents. This is often the situation in chronic infectious diseases that may become arrested or remain slowly progressive, such as tuberculosis and brucellosis.

The inflammatory reaction is, of course, a most vital defense, providing early response to, and warning of, infection and a prompt effort at localization and prevention of spread. Even when the success of the process is not complete, the evidence is strong that it prevents the survival and further growth of many invading infectious organisms. The mechanics of this accomplishment are related, most obviously, to the antibacterial properties of plasma and phagocytes; to a general increase in the leukocytes of the circulating blood (leukocytosis); to a rising concentration of metabolic products of both host and microbial cells within a walled-off area; and to a rise in local temperature, all injurious to microbial cells. The price paid by the host may be minimal or large, depending on the degree of mechanical injury induced locally by exudate and swelling and of chemical injury caused by the accumulated toxic products of disintegrating cells and microorganisms. Such toxic substances may be carried through the body, in the blood stream, to exert damaging effects on tissues distant from the original site. A secondary fall in the leukocytes of the peripheral blood may occur as a consequence of the production and dissemination of injurious materials during the course of the inflammatory reaction. In general, however, this host response is of primary defensive value.

6. Other Nonspecific Factors Associated with Resistance. A number of biologic as well as environmental factors, less well defined in their effects than those described above, appear to influence the human host's ability to resist infection. Age and hormonal and genetic constitution are fundamentally involved, and these in turn are influenced by external factors, such as nutrition, stress, and physical environment.

Age is a determining factor with respect to susceptibility and resistance to infection for several reasons. The changing incidence of infectious diseases from childhood to adulthood and old age is largely due to the operation of immune mechanisms, as we shall see later, and

to the ability of the host to produce effective antibody. The latter function changes progressively from birth and throughout life, in a definite relationship to age. As age progresses, structural, metabolic, and functional changes that occur in the host's tissues and cells undoubtedly affect their ability to maintain a balance with microorganisms as they are encountered, though such factors have been difficult to document. Profound shifts in hormone production and balance that occur at puberty, during pregnancy, or at menopause also influence the health of tissues and, therefore, their resistance.

Hormones also appear to influence susceptibility to infection independently of age. This is true not only of the hormones of the reproductive system, but particularly of hormones of the pancreas, thyroid, adrenal, and pituitary glands as well. Thus, the deficiency of pancreatic hormone (insulin) that occurs in diabetes seems to lower resistance, for diabetic patients are commonly confronted with complicating infections, such as tuberculosis and fungous diseases or troublesome urinary tract infections. The production of thyroid and adrenal hormones in amounts above or below normal may likewise lead to changes in susceptibility or in the infectious process itself. The regulatory role of pituitary hormone on thyroid and adrenal output and in control of reproductive organ activity implies at least an indirect effect of this secretion on the response to infection. The most clearly demonstrable of these hormone effects is that of excessive adrenal hormone in suppressing the inflammatory reaction and the production of antibody. This is a serious consideration in the use of adrenal hormone therapy for certain organic diseases, for with suppression of two of the body's essential defensive mechanisms susceptibility to infection is markedly increased. Furthermore, if the efficiency of the inflammatory reaction is decreased, pre-existing infection, such as tuberculosis, may no longer be well-contained but may become generalized.

Genetic and *racial* factors are often correlated with the incidence of infection in certain types of individuals or among groups. For individuals the explanation sometimes lies in inherited abnormalities, usually physiologic, involving one or more

of the nonspecific defense mechanisms. Among races of people, such differences as hormone production, metabolic factors, and environmental or nutritional factors may affect nonspecific resistance to infection, but the evidence is not clear. The specific, immune basis for genetic and racial responses to infection is discussed in the next section of this chapter.

The *nutritional* status of the host contributes to his ability to resist infectious disease in several ways. Nutritional deficiencies lead to an increased risk of infection in many instances. The reason for this is that the malnourished individual cannot maintain his tissues in a state of normal, healthy function. This may mean, in turn, that his body cannot produce an adequate quantity or quality of some of the substances involved in defense, such as plasma proteins (complement, antibody), hormones, and external secretions. Good nutrition alone may not spare the host from infection with virulent organisms, of course, but it may reduce the opportunities for microorganisms of low pathogenicity to initiate infectious problems. On the other hand, there is a certain amount of evidence that some organisms prefer the cells of a well-nourished host, since these provide growth factors essential to the microbe. The yeastlike fungus *Cryptococcus*, for instance, requires thiamin (one of the vitamins of the B complex) for the production of its capsule. When the organism is fully encapsulated, it is better able to resist phagocytosis and it is therefore more virulent than when the capsule is not produced. It has been suggested, on this basis, that a thiamin deficiency induced in patients suffering from cryptococcosis might be useful therapeutically. Obligate intracellular parasites probably also require host cells in a good nutritional state to serve their own metabolic interests. In general, however, dietary deficiencies lead to a decreased resistance to infection by diminishing the normal functions of the body.

Stress, whether physical or emotional, frequently results in a lowering of resistance to infection. The adrenal gland responds to stress with an increased output of hormone and, as pointed out earlier, this results in suppression both of antibody formation and of the inflamma-

tory reaction. In addition, stress may produce such effects as an increased blood pressure, with resultant changes in blood vessels that diminish the blood supply to some tissues. Such a combination of factors may well afford additional opportunities for infection by microorganisms normally held in check by the body's defenses, particularly if the conditions of stress are prolonged.

Climate, and other factors of the physical environment, also affect the nonspecific mechanisms of resistance, particularly in individuals subjected to sudden marked changes to which they have not adapted. Very cold climates where the humidity is low, for example, are irritating to the unaccustomed respiratory mucosa and may reduce its efficiency in resisting the localization of microorganisms, even those of low pathogenicity. In warm, moist climates the health of the skin is more difficult to maintain. It may become macerated by perspiration, especially on the feet and in the axillary or inguinal folds, and is more susceptible, in this condition, to fungous and secondary bacterial infections. Warm areas of low humidity and normal to high atmospheric pressure, on the other hand, offer benefits to patients with respiratory diseases, such as tuberculosis, because the lungs are better aerated and have a better blood supply under these conditions than in chilly sections where humidity runs high and barometric pressure low.

Specific Resistance to Infection: The Principles of Immunity

The Immune State

Immunity can be defined as a state of *specific, relative resistance* to infection, each of the three italicized words contributing precisely to its meaning. The words "relative resistance" describe all that we have observed up to this point of the shifting, uneasy relationship that the host maintains with parasitic microorganisms. This leaves us short of the full concept of immunity, however, until the word "specific" is added, which now implies that whatever degree of rela-

tive resistance may exist, it is directed against a particular type of microorganism. It is this specificity of resistance that is the important characteristic of immunity. The basis for it will be described and defined in the following discussion.

Immunity may occur as a *natural* phenomenon, existing even though there has been no previous contact between the host and the infectious agent. Much more is known, however, about immunity that is *acquired*, through biologic or artificial contacts with microorganisms. In either case, it confers on the individual host possessing it the ability to resist, with more or less success depending on the completeness of his immune state, the establishment of infection, or of infectious disease, by a *specified* organism.

Natural Immunity

Species Immunity. The human host has a natural resistance to many microorganisms that cause diseases in other species. To state the case more fully, a given microorganism may be pathogenic for one or more species of animals or plants, but not for others. There are, for instance, almost no infectious diseases of plants to which man is susceptible, and vice versa. Similarly, many of the infections that occur in lower animals are not seen in human beings, the reverse being true as well. A specific example has been cited previously in the case of the response of the rabbit, rats, and birds to strains of the tubercle bacillus that cause human tuberculosis. Avian tuberculosis, on the other hand, is caused by a strain of this organism that almost never infects man. Another example would be the natural immunity of many laboratory animals to poliomyelitis virus. In this case, although the virus can be adapted to grow in the tissues of some other animals, it produces symptoms most like those of the human disease only in monkeys or other primates closely related to man.

The basis of species immunity is obscure. Physiologic differences, the biochemical constitution and function of individual tissues, anatomic structures, and nutritional and environmental limitations may play a part, individually or

collectively, in creating barriers for microorganisms in one species as opposed to another. Many of these factors have their roots in the genetic, inheritable constitution of the species. It may be that these immunities are built in to the inheritable characteristics that distinguish and maintain each species.

Racial Immunity. Within the human species certain races and families are more resistant to some infectious diseases than are other persons. Specific racial resistances are even more difficult to explain than species immunity, since the anatomic and physiologic differences observable between races within a species are minor, often quite subtle, as compared with the wide variations that mark off one species from another.

Nonetheless, both the incidence and the severity of some infectious diseases, such as smallpox, tuberculosis, and certain systemic fungous diseases, have varied markedly among peoples of the world. From the time of their first contact with such diseases, and with repeated exposures for long years of history, Negroes, American Indians, and some other dark-skinned races have found them devastating in impact and outcome. Smallpox and tuberculosis have made deep inroads on the white races also, but a racial capacity to resist and survive these diseases is far more evident among the latter groups.

The explanation may have several facets: these groups are subject to different stresses of environmental and nutritional origin; their biochemical heredity may be as disparate as their ethnic histories; the history of exposure is longer by centuries for white "Caucasians" than for the other groups. The latter fact, particularly, suggests that racial immunity, if it has a genetic basis, is a manifestation of biologic adaptation, occurring over a long period of time. When susceptible populations are decimated by disease, and the resistant survivors are capable of reproducing, the biologic characters of resistance are transmitted to succeeding generations and become more and more firmly established in later populations. Ethnic considerations (in the case of human beings) continue, throughout, to guide and determine the nature of successive matings,

so that as inheritable constitutional factors of resistance are passed along, they become numerically more prevalent within the racial framework of the population. On the other side of the coin, the parasite involved must make adjustments of its own, if it is to survive within this population. Parasites capable of survival within resistant host races must also possess permanent, inheritable characteristics reflecting their selection from previous microbial generations more susceptible to host defenses. In this case, succeeding microbial generations must be able to maintain themselves within a resistant host population, but as time goes by the damage produced by infection is less severe among the genetically resistant hosts.

The biochemical definition of the inheritable factors that may account for racial and family immunity remains to be provided in most cases. It may be as subtle as the hereditary supply and function of a particular red cell enzyme, a deficiency of which is known to bring about a change in the hemoglobin molecule, which in turn leads to an increased resistance to one of the malarial parasites. In other cases, interlocking tissue components and functions may be involved.

Individual Immunity. Still unaccountable, also, is the fact that populations highly susceptible to a particular microorganism may contain individuals who are strongly resistant to it, even though no previous contact with the organism can be demonstrated. Such *individual immunity* is a kind of biologic variation, very common among living things. It may be based in part on nonspecifically protective mechanisms, such as good nutrition and hormonal and metabolic health, but these do not account for the specificity of resistance displayed by an individual toward a specified organism, particularly if susceptibility to that organism is the rule in the population around him.

It may be deduced, from all of this, that natural immunity fits into the definition of specific, relative resistance for reasons as yet unknown. It is not necessarily dependent on prior or repeated contacts between microorganism and host or on the operation of nonspecific mechanisms of defense, but both these factors may be influential in

this type of resistance. The strongest explanations appear to link this type of immunity with biochemical characteristics, of both parasite and host, that are genetic in origin, but not yet precisely defined.

Acquired Immunity

The immunity that results from the production and activity of *antibodies* (see p. 123 of this chapter) in the host defending itself specifically against intruding foreign substances, including those contained in or produced by microorganisms, is referred to as *acquired*. This term is used because the acquisition of antibodies explains the resistance conferred by this type of immunity. Foreign substances capable of inducing antibody formation in the host are spoken of as *antigens*. Antibodies and antigens react together in ways that are detectable primarily through resulting changes in the antigen itself. These changes often lessen the threat presented by the antigen to the host, so that the host's resistance to the antigen is thereby increased, and he becomes immune to it in some degree.

Antibodies may be acquired either *actively* or *passively*. The term "active, acquired immunity" implies that the host has produced his own antibodies in response to the presence of an antigen in his body. The antigen may be encountered in a natural manner, or it may be introduced in an artificial way designed deliberately to induce the host to produce antibodies against it. *Passive, acquired immunity* means protection of the host by antibodies he did not produce himself, but acquired from another host, either naturally (as by placental transfer from mother to child) or artificially, by injection. The host from whom the antibody is derived must, of course, have had an active immunity, acquired naturally or artificially.

Immunity to Infection.   Before we consider the biologic nature of antigens, antibodies, and their interactions, let us think about immunity to infection in practical terms, applying the definitions given above.

Everyone is familiar with the characteristic course of an infectious disease, from the time it begins, often with rather vague symptoms, through the stage of fever and acute illness, to the day the fever subsides and convalescence begins. It is also common knowledge that in many cases the individual who has recovered from such an attack is not likely to experience that same disease again, at least not for some time or in as severe a form. He is said to be *immune*, having *acquired* this state of security through a *natural* process of illness and recovery. His disease was caused by a microorganism that entered his body and damaged his tissues through some pathogenic property, as we know. Being a foreign substance, the microorganism acted also as an *antigen*, stimulating the body to produce *antibodies*. During this time the symptoms of disease were probably at their height, but from the time antibody production was in full swing, if other nonspecific resistance mechanisms had done their work well meantime, the symptoms began to decline. This is because antibodies, once formed, will react with the antigen that stimulated their production. An infectious organism, acting as an antigen, may then be inactivated by the antibody, so that it is no longer capable of damaging the tissues sufficiently to cause symptoms of disease. The antibody that was formed in response to this organism will persist for some time, but more importantly, the cells that produced it will "recognize" the same foreign material the next time it is encountered, forming additional antibody even more quickly. Thus, if the individual should become infected again with the same organism, lingering antibody together with a promptly produced new supply may interact with the antigen before it has an opportunity to entrench in the tissues or damage them, and disease will not ensue.

It is also well known that a number of infectious diseases can be prevented by the administration of *vaccines*. A vaccine is a preparation that contains the infectious agent of a particular disease, or some product of that agent (such as a toxin) responsible for the damage to tissues, treated in some way so that it can be administered safely. Given orally or injected into the tissues it will not produce disease, but the antigen or antigens it

contains will induce the body to form antibodies. The vaccinated individual will then have an immunity to the microorganism in question. If he should become infected with it in a natural way at some later time, his antibody mechanism will provide specific protection against it. In this case, the individual has acquired his immune state through an *artificial* process, the effect being the same as that resulting from an attack of the disease in question, without the discomfort or risk.

In both these instances, *active immunization* results from the presence in the tissues of a specified microorganism, or its products, and its *direct stimulation of antibody formation* by certain cells of the body. Active immunity due to antibody production may thus be acquired through the introduction of an antigen into the body in a natural or in an artificial process.

The individual human or animal host who has actively produced antibodies in response to an episode of an infectious disease or to a vaccine may now become a source of supply of such antibodies for other individuals who have not had an opportunity to produce them themselves. Antibodies may be readily transferred from one individual to another, or from an animal to a human being, because, as we have seen, they are usually present in the plasma of the circulating blood. A quantity of blood may be drawn from an immune individual, the cellular portion of the sample separated off, and the remaining fluid portion, or *serum* as it is now called, injected into the nonimmune person. The antibodies contained in the injected serum will now provide their recipient with some immunity against the specific antigens that stimulated their formation in the original host. This, of course, is *passive immunity*, acquired in an *artificial* manner. It will not be long-lasting for the recipient, because passively transferred antibodies are slowly destroyed and disappear from the body in a few weeks. Passive antibodies may serve to tide an individual over a short period, for instance immediately following an exposure to a disease to which he is not immune, or through the early acute stages of an infection before his own antibodies are actively formed in adequate concentration. The protective effect is

immediate, but not persistent. The individual must then consider the advisability of active immunization against the infectious agent involved, so that his own antibodies may provide specific, active resistance in the future. If he has had an active infection and recovered from it, probably no further immunization is indicated, but if he was merely exposed and escaped the disease through passive protection, artificial active immunization with a vaccine is desirable, if it is available.

Passive immunity is also acquired by humans and other mammals through the *natural* transfer of maternal antibody via the placenta during embryonic development in the uterus. The newborn child may thus be protected during the early weeks and months of its life against those infections to which its mother was immune at the time of pregnancy. By the time these passive antibodies have disappeared, the child's own antibody-forming mechanisms usually have matured sufficiently to begin their function, and he is ready for active immunization with vaccines.

Antigens.   An antigen is most easily defined as any substance, usually foreign to the host and protein in nature, that upon introduction into the tissues of an animal host stimulates the production of antibodies by that host. It should be noted that an antigen must be introduced into the tissues where it can come in contact with the antibody-producing cells. Some antigens could not survive ingestion, for example, for they would be broken down in the digestive tract to a form that is no longer capable of inducing antibody production if and when it is absorbed into the tissues: that is, it is no longer *antigenic*.

The chemical nature or structure of the antigen must be foreign to the host or to the antibody-forming mechanism, because the body does not as a rule produce antibodies against constituents of its own cells or tissues. We have seen many of the other ways in which the host deals with foreign substances: by phagocytosis, inflammation, and fibrosis. It also has mechanisms for excreting foreign chemical substances, after inactivating them, if the molecule is small enough. To be antigenic, a molecule must of course be

retained in the tissues where it can make contact freely with the appropriate cells. Antigenic molecules are, therefore, usually too large to go into solution but are held, instead, in colloidal suspension, and if the antibody response is to be effective it must begin before the antigen is walled off by nonspecific reactions. Many of the substances whose molecules are sufficiently large to be antigenic (molecular weight must be at least 10,000) are protein in character, but some polysaccharides also act as antigens. Some molecules may be too small to have this property but become antigenic if they are linked with protein. Lipids are antigenic only when they are combined with proteins or polysaccharides, or both. A molecule that is not antigenic of itself, but becomes so after linkage with a protein or polysaccharide, is called an *incomplete antigen*, or *haptene*.

The chemical structure of the antigen is important to the specificity of its interaction with antibody, as we shall see. The numbers and physical location on the molecule of acid radicals, ring structures, and other groupings affect the antigenicity of the molecule, that is, its effectiveness in stimulating the formation of antibody and in reacting specifically with it subsequently.

Microbial Antigens. The basic constituents of all living protoplasm are proteins, carbohydrates, and lipids; yet each species is chemically unique. We have also observed that races and individuals within a species differ in physiologic function, probably because of biochemical dissimilarities. This is not surprising in view of the complexity of protoplasmic components. Proteins, in particular, afford unlimited variety because their constituent units, the amino acids, may interlock in as many variations of combination as do letters of the alphabet. The "letters" of different proteins may be the same, but the "words" formed by letter combinations are distinct. Thus the distinctive proteins of one species are quite unique from, and foreign to, those of another. Since foreign proteins behave antigenically upon their introduction into the tissues of animal hosts, this means that the protein components of any dissimilar species can provoke an antibody response in human tissues should they reach them. Obviously, this does not and cannot happen often in nature, except in the case of microbial proteins, which can find their way into the appropriate situation with relative ease.

Many of the constituents of bacteria and other microorganisms are either of protein nature or are linked to protein, and therefore are antigenic. The bacterial cell has been described as a mosaic of antigens in three dimensions. Furthermore, many of the substances produced by microorganisms as metabolic by-products are antigenic. A given organism may, therefore, contain or produce many antigens that, being protein and highly variable in structure, differ one from another and accordingly can induce the response of different antibodies. In a bacterial cell, for instance, the constituents of several structures, or their products, may be distinctive as antigens. These would include:

> The antigens of the cell body (soma) itself. These are called *somatic* or "O" antigens. In some bacteria they are the endotoxins of the cell. Some cellular antigens occur only on the surface of the cell and are called *surface* antigens.
>
> *Capsular* antigens in species that form a capsule.
>
> *Flagellar* antigens (also called "H" antigens) in motile species.
>
> *Exotoxins* and other protein substances secreted by some species.

The different antibodies that are produced in response to such characteristic antigens in the infected patient often provide diagnostic proof of an infectious disease. For instance, typhoid fever is caused by a flagellated bacillus with a characteristic surface antigen. Identification of the antibodies forming in the patient's serum during the course of the disease will reveal that they were specifically invoked by the "H" antigen of the typhoid bacillus, its "O" antigens, and a surface antigen designated "Vi" to associate it with *vi*rulence. Antibodies are given the same name as that of the antigen to which they respond. In this example, therefore, the convalescent patient's serum would contain typhoid O, H, and Vi antibodies.

Antibodies. The definition of an antibody, like its name, is the converse of that given for an antigen: it is a specialized protein substance produced by an animal host in response to the presence of a foreign antigen in its tissues, and it is capable of reacting specifically with that antigen.

Antibody Formation. The best evidence indicates that antibodies are produced by cells of the reticuloendothelial system, notably plasma cells and lymphocytes. These cells are distributed widely throughout the body, but the tissues that appear to be most actively involved in antibody production are the bone marrow and lymphoid tissue. Much of the phagocytic cell production of the body originates in these tissues also. Plasma cells, like many other cells of the RE system, remain fixed in the tissue of their origin, while lymphocytes are found not only in lymphoid tissue and bone marrow, but in the circulating blood as well. The strategic scattering of these cells in the body thus assures their early encounter with foreign substances that may have entered. Phagocytic action on such material, including microbial cells, assists in dispersing the antigens it may contain, so that the latter may be taken up by the cells that form antibody.

The actual mechanism of antibody formation is not clear, but apparently the antigen stimulates the host cell to synthesize a specialized protein. It is a type of protein, called *gamma globulin*, that is closely related to the normal globulins of the blood plasma. Antibody globulin, or immunoglobulin as it is sometimes called, is released from the cells as they produce it and is disseminated widely through the body. It can be found in the blood plasma and in many tissues as well.

Antigen-Antibody Specificity. The antibody molecule is fashioned with a surface structure that is reciprocal, or converse, in a physical sense, to that of the antigen molecule. When antigen and antibody combine, therefore, their surfaces dovetail, like two pieces of a jigsaw puzzle or a lock and its key. This complementary arrangement of their molecular groupings provides the

basis of the specificity that operates in immune reactions.

We have observed previously that large molecules, especially proteins, may be almost endlessly varied in the arrangement of their component units. Different elements and groups may be combined at various points, or in unique arrangements, on their surfaces. Linkage of a protein molecule with a polysaccharide, lipid, or other incomplete antigen also changes its surface characteristics. The reciprocal structure of the antibody molecule, with respect to its antigen, accounts for the fact that differences in antigens are "recognized" by their respective antibodies and that only specific combinations occur between them. The term *homologous* is used to designate either member of a specific pair. An antigen other than the homologous one that induced the formation of a particular antibody is spoken of as being *heterologous* to that antibody, or vice versa. Homologous immune reactions are thus highly specific and can be extremely sensitive to even subtle molecular differences. Such reactions occurring in the test tube sometimes afford the only means by which protein materials can be demonstrated to differ one from another. The immunity acquired by human and animal hosts to infectious agents is similarly exact, the different antigens of various microbial species inducing the formation of specifically different antibodies. Conversely, of course, species similarities are reflected by overlapping antigen-antibody reactions.

The Interactions of Antigens and Antibodies. The results of antigen-antibody reactions are often observable, or can be made so, whether they occur in the test tube (*in vitro*) or in the body (*in vivo*). Most of our knowledge of the nature of antigens, antibodies, and their interactions is derived, of course, from observations of their behavior in the test tube.

In Vitro Reactions. Laboratory studies utilize blood plasma, or serum, from human and animal sources as a source of antibody, and antigens from a variety of sources, including microorga-

nisms. When an antibody combines with its specific antigen, the reaction may have one of several observable results, depending on the nature and condition of the antigen, as well as on the presence of other nonspecific factors. Consequently, antibodies are often described according to the type of reaction that occurs.

Agglutinins are antibodies that cause a visible *agglutination* of the antigen. This type of reaction occurs if the antigen is within, or adherent to the surface of, a large particle (such as a microbial cell, a red blood cell, a latex particle). When antibody combines with an antigen associated with a particle, it forms a coating over the whole surface, making it sticky and causing adjacent particles to clump together. Saline in physiologic concentration must also be present to encourage the adherence of the coated particles. As larger and larger clumps are formed, they settle out of solution. The solution becomes clearer as more particles are removed and the agglutinating clumps become visible, microscopically or, in some cases, macroscopically.

Precipitins are antibodies that cause a visible *precipitation* of the antigen. The reaction occurs in the same way as that just described, but in this case the antigen molecule must be in free solution, unassociated with any cell or particle. Soluble antigens that have been extracted from their parent cells become coated with combining antibody, and in the presence of saline, the complexes formed become visible as a fine precipitate settling out of solution.

Complement-fixing antibodies are those that combine first with their antigen, as usual, to form a complex to which complement will then adhere. Complement, it will be remembered, is a normal constituent of blood plasma. It is sensitive to heat and can be readily removed from, or added to, the plasma or serum in the test tube. If it is added to a tube in which antigen and antibody have combined, it will adhere, or be "fixed," to the surface of the complex. If the antigen involved is associated with a cell, such as a microorganism or a red blood cell, this action of complement on the complex may result in *lysis* of the cell. The antibody in that case is often called a *lysin*

(bacteriolysin, streptolysin, hemolysin). When this occurs the result becomes visible as a clearing of a suspension that had previously been turbid with the intact cells. If the antigen is not associated with cellular particles, or if the latter are not lysed, it may still combine with antibody, with the consequent fixation of complement, but the reaction in this case will not be visible. When this happens, fixation of the complement can be tested for by adding to the test tube a second antigen-antibody complex that will provide a visible result if complement is available. If the complement has been fixed by the first combination, none will remain for the second complex and no change will be seen in the latter. If the second complex does lyse visibly, it means that complement was not fixed to begin with, which in turn signifies that no antigen-antibody combination occurred in the tube before complement was added.

Opsonins are antibodies that combine with the surface antigens of microorganisms or other cells and thus enhance their susceptibility to phagocytosis. This process also is facilitated by the presence of complement. It can be demonstrated in the test tube using phagocytes obtained from the blood or from a purulent exudate. When bacteria are coated with specific antibody, exposed to the phagocytes, and viewed microscopically, they are seen to be taken up much more rapidly and completely than those in a control preparation containing no antibody.

Antitoxins are antibodies that are induced by toxins and combine with them. Toxins, when separated from the microbial cells that produce them, are soluble antigens. When they combine with antitoxin in the test tube, therefore, the result is a precipitation, or flocculation, of the complex. The combination of antitoxin with toxin also results in inactivation, or *neutralization*, of the toxin, a result that can be demonstrated by injecting the complex into an experimental animal. The neutralizing effect of antibodies is discussed under in vivo reactions.

Other antibody effects that may be seen in vitro include the inhibition of growth of homologous microorganisms in culture or visible changes in

the appearance of organisms. Motile bacteria or spirochetes, for instance, become immobilized in the presence of homologous antibody. Also, antibodies directed against the capsular antigens of some bacteria can be demonstrated to cause an apparent swelling of the capsule of the intact bacteria when placed in contact with them. Actually, this is a form of *precipitation* reaction, in which the soluble antigen of the capsule is precipitated in combination with antibody. This increases the surface tension and the density of the capsule so that it becomes more visible and appears "swollen."

The fluorescent antibody technique provides another useful and interesting means of visualizing the interactions of antibodies with particulate antigens such as microbial cells. This method involves the preliminary treatment of antiserum with a fluorescent dye that conjugates firmly with the antibody globulin. The antibody is thus "labeled," and when it combines with its specific antigen, the site of combination can be visualized if the preparation is examined microscopically using ultraviolet light for illumination. As the ultraviolet rays pass through the specimen, the dye-conjugated antibody fluoresces brightly on the surfaces of cells it has coated. The use of fluorescein-labeled antibody makes it possible to locate microorganisms quickly and identify them in smears from clinical specimens or in tissue sections. Intracellular viruses can also be visualized by this method when they are coated with specific antibody tagged with a fluorescing dye. The technical problems encountered in the conjugation of serum with fluorescent dyes are expensive and time-consuming. Furthermore, it is often impractical to test a given specimen with a battery of specific antiserums each containing a different labeled antibody. To solve this problem, an indirect method of fluorescent staining can be used. Human serum is first injected into a rabbit (or other animal), which responds by producing antibodies directed against human globulin. Serum from the animal is then conjugated with fluorescent dye, providing a labeled antihuman antibody. In the meantime, the preparation to be examined for microbial antigens is exposed to unlabeled human antiserum. If a specific anti-

body-antigen combination occurs, the microbial cells become coated with human globulin, but the reaction is not visible. Now the fluorescent-labeled anti-human-globulin antibody from the immunized animal is added to the preparation. It combines with the human globulin coating the cells, providing a new outer layer that now will fluoresce in ultraviolet light. The indirect method makes it possible to use a number of ordinary, unlabeled human antiserums in screening smears for the localization of antigens. They can then be treated with one labeled antihuman globulin, which points out those cells that are coated with specific human antibody, the latter combining with the second antibody specifically. These techniques are illustrated diagrammatically in Fig. 7–5.

Serologic Reactions. The interactions of antigens and antibodies in vitro are spoken of as *serologic reactions*, and the study of serum for its antibody content is called *serology*. These reactions are used routinely to identify antigens or antibodies when one of these reactants is known. The serology laboratory commonly works with the serums of patients thought to have infectious disease, testing them with known microbial antigens. The microbiology laboratory, conversely, tests unknown microbial isolates with serums of known antibody content, confirming their identity after microscopic and culture techniques have established their morphologic and biochemical characteristics. Serologic techniques can be performed in a quantitative manner to provide information as to the relative amounts of antigen or antibody present in a given system. This is done by using one of the two reagents in a constant quantity and diluting the other until it fails to produce further reaction. When a patient's serum is being tested with a particular microbial antigen, for example, the serum is diluted in a serial fashion. A row of tubes containing the saline diluent in even amounts is set up; a measured amount of serum is placed in the first tube and mixed well. Then a measured aliquot of this dilution is placed in the second tube and mixed, this process being repeated down the line so that a graded series of dilutions is obtained. The anti-

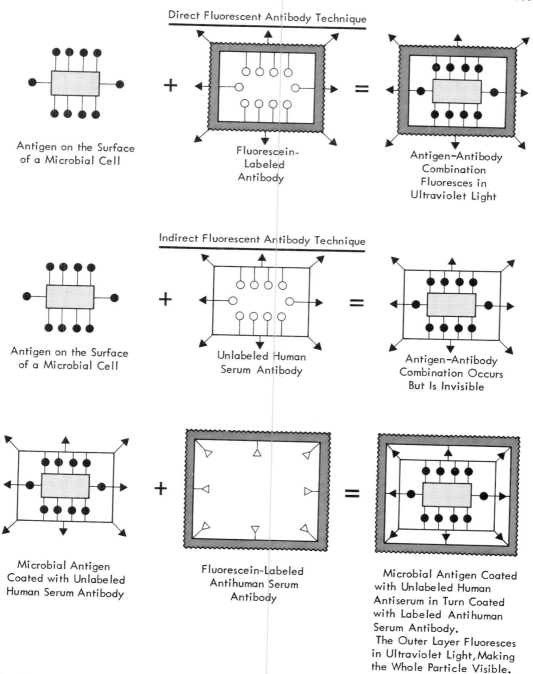

Fig. 7–5. A diagrammatic illustration of fluorescent antibody techniques.

gen is then added to each tube in a constant volume from one to the next. When the tubes are examined for evidence of antigen-antibody combination, the last dilution of serum that shows reactivity is reported, using the dilution figure: that is, 1:10, 1:100, 1:1200, or whatever the case may be. This figure is spoken of as the *titer of the serum* and provides an estimate of the level of antibody present in a unit volume. When two serums are compared for reactivity with a given antigen, the one that can be diluted furthest and still remain reactive is said to have the higher titer.

When serologic diagnosis of infectious disease is attempted by demonstrating the presence of specific antibodies in the patient's serum, it is very frequently necessary to test two samples of serum, one obtained from the patient soon after the onset of his symptoms, the other taken ten days to two weeks later. The reason for this is that antibody production increases during the course of active infection, being first stimulated as the microbial agent begins to grow and multiply in the body, then rising steadily in response to continuing antigenic stimulus. A patient in the early acute stage of illness may have no detectable serum antibodies against the causative microorganism, or the serum titer may be low, in the range of 1:20 or 1:40. Such a level of antibody has little significance, because it might merely reflect a previous vaccination with the microbial antigen or a titer lingering from some previous attack of the infection and does not necessarily indicate the nature of the current disease. If the test is repeated in a week or two, however, and the titer is found to have risen by at least a fourfold increase (1:80 or 1:160 as compared with the examples above), this provides serologic evidence of current active response to the microorganism in question. This type of serologic information is often very valuable, both in diagnosing the present disease and in estimating the past experience of the patient with a given microbial (or other) antigen.

It should be emphasized again that the separate names given to antibodies in reality denote the type of reaction involved, and that the latter is now known to be associated primarily with the nature and condition of the antigen. In other words, the antibody responsible for agglutination of a particulate antigen may cause a precipitation of that antigen if it is in solution or combine with it to fix complement if the latter is present. These descriptive terms remain in common use, however. When patient's serum is to be studied diagnostically for its antibody content, particular laboratory tests are ordered to confirm the clinical or bacteriologic evidence of the nature of the patient's infectious disease. These tests are often called by names that reflect the nature of the antibody sought or of the reaction that will be seen according to the technique of the test. Thus, such terms as "febrile agglutinins," "heterophil antibody," "sheep cell agglutination," "latex agglutination," and "complement-fixation studies" are common. The student will become familiar with the full meaning of this terminology when its application to the diagnosis of individual diseases is described in Part Two. Many of the common laboratory methods used to detect or to study antigens and antibodies can also be found in Appendix II.

In Vivo Reactions.   Any or all of these various types of reactions demonstrated in the test tube may also occur in the body when antibodies combine with antigens in the tissues. Microorganisms that are agglutinated or lysed by antibody, with the assistance of complement, in vivo are thereby inactivated and prevented from exerting further direct damage. They are also more readily phagocytosed in this condition, as we have seen. Exotoxins and other harmful microbial secretions are similarly neutralized by the antitoxins produced in response to their antigenic effect. Viruses may also be neutralized by antibody if enough is present in the circulating blood to combine with such agents before they have localized within body cells. These in vivo effects of antibodies have given rise to still another term for them. When such effects can be demonstrated in man or in experimental animals they are said to be due to *neutralizing*, or *protective*, *antibodies*.

Neutralization of an infectious or toxic agent by antibody can be demonstrated in laboratory animals in one of three ways:

1. A virulent microorganism (or its isolated

toxin) can be killed or inactivated in the test tube by *physical* or *chemical* means, without destroying its antigenic properties. The inactivated agent is then injected into the tissues of an animal to stimulate the production of specific antibodies. When this *actively immunized* animal is later injected with doses of the living, virulent organism in question, or with unmodified toxin, it will survive this "challenge," while nonimmune control animals will succumb to the challenge dose. A specific protective effect of antibody has operated in the immune animal.

2. The serum of animals or humans who have a pre-existing immunity (acquired naturally or artificially) to a given microorganism or its toxin can be injected into another animal. This *passively immunized* animal is then injected with a dose of the living, virulent organism in question, or its toxin. Homologous antibodies present in the injected serum protect the animal from disease, but nonimmune control animals do not survive the challenge with active antigen (see Fig. 7–6). The effect of passively acquired antibody is only temporary, however, because, as mentioned previously, it is destroyed in the recipient's body within a few weeks. For this reason the challenge dose must be given close to the time when the dose of antiserum (immune serum) is given.

3. A toxic or infectious agent can be exposed to specific antiserum in the test tube, where antigen-antibody combination will occur. Neutralization of the antigen by the antibody can then be demonstrated by injecting the complex into a nonimmune animal. This animal will show no evidence of disease or toxicity, while a nonimmune control animal receiving unneutralized antigen alone will succumb to its effects.

Skin tests frequently provide a useful, diagnostic demonstration of antigen-antibody reactions in vivo. The skin of human beings or of animals can often be used as a testing site when it is desirable to know whether or not (1) a particular antibody or (2) a specified antigen is present in the body.

1. Antibody detection is the purpose of most skin tests. Since antibody not only circulates in the blood but localizes as well in many tissues of the body, its presence in the skin may be tested for by the *intracutaneous* injection of homologous antigen. The results must be interpreted in the light of the fact that an antigen-antibody combination occurring suddenly and rapidly at a localized point in the body may, *of itself*, be damaging to the cells of the immediate area. (This is discussed more fully in the last section of this chapter, under hypersensitivity.) When such damage occurs in the skin it can be seen as an area of local injury (reddening, swelling, and tension) at the site of injection of the antigen. Two interpretations of the occurrence of injury (that is, of a *positive* skin test) are possible, depending on the nature and condition of the antigen given. (a) If

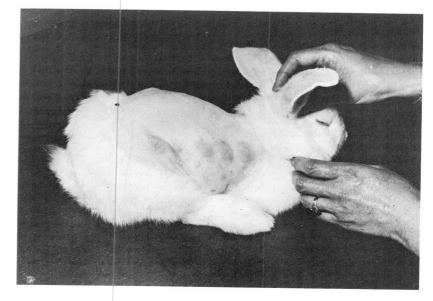

Fig. 7–6. Rabbits can be used to determine the virulence of *Corynebacterium diphtheriae* (that is, its capacity for toxin production). A suspected strain is injected into each of two rabbits, one of which was previously injected with antitoxin. The rabbit pictured above did not receive the antitoxin and developed an inflammatory lesion at the sites of the injection of virulent *C. diphtheriae*. The rabbit that was protected with a previous dose of antitoxin showed no reaction at the site of inoculation. (Courtesy of Dr. A. E. Bolyn, The National Drug Company, Swiftwater, Pa.)

the antigen alone, in the absence of antibody, is not capable of damaging skin, a positive skin test indicates that antibody is present in sufficient quantity to induce the injury through its reaction with antigen. An immune (or more properly, *hypersensitive*) state has been demonstrated. This type of reaction may be elicited by the skin test antigens used to detect tuberculosis and many fungous or parasitic diseases. (b) If the antigen alone, in the absence of antibody, is injurious to skin, as many microbial exotoxins are, the quantity of antigen present in a standard dose is adjusted so that when it combines with a matching amount of antibody in the skin no damage will be caused by the formation of the *complex*. Thus, a *negative* skin test will result in this case if a minimal amount of antibody is present, while a *positive* test indicates damage done by the toxin alone, unneutralized by antibody. This is the basis of the well-known Schick test, which utilizes diphtheria toxin as the antigen in testing for diphtheria antitoxin immunity, and of the Dick test, in which a streptococcocal toxin is used (see below).

2. Antigen detection in the skin by the injection of antibody is, in general, not practicable because antigen localization or concentration at any point selected for testing cannot be predicted as a rule. One notable exception exists, however, in the case of scarlet fever. In this disease, an exotoxin, called *scarlatinal toxin*, is produced by the causative organism (a streptococcus) from its vantage point of growth in the throat. The toxin is disseminated through the body, reaching skin tissues as well as many others. In the skin the injury it inflicts on the cells becomes evident as the typical scarlatinal rash develops. The rash and the disease can be specifically diagnosed with a skin test that employs the homologous antitoxin. Immune serum, containing scarlatinal antitoxin, is injected intracutaneously at the center of an area where the rash is most evident. The resultant combination of antibody with the toxin neutralizes the latter, and the rash fades, or blanches, at the injection site within a few hours. This test is sometimes referred to as the *Schultz-Charlton reaction*, being named for the men who developed it. It should be noted that the Dick test, men-

tioned above, employs the scarlatinal toxin for the opposite purpose of detecting antibody and determining immunity.

Immunity in Virus Infections. A type of protective substance, which is not an antibody, is produced within human and animal cells in response to virus infection. This substance is called *interferon*, a term derived from the fact that its activity results in an interference with the ability of one virus to infect cells already occupied by another.

The phenomenon of virus interference has been recognized for many years but it is only recently that it has been accounted for by the isolation of a protein substance, from virus-infected cells, that protects virus-free cells from infection with the homologous or heterologous viruses. Interferon is produced by cells only in response to virus infection. When the interferons prepared in the cells of various animal species are compared, they are found to show some of the same species differences observed for hormones, enzymes, and antibodies. In any one species, however, the same interferon is produced regardless of the virus used to produce infection. Its protective effects are greatest when tested with cells of the animal species from which it was derived, but it can also protect the cells of closely related species, such as monkeys and man.

In all these respects, interferon activity is quite different from that of antibody. Specific antibody production does occur, of course, in virus infections, but it cannot account for interference with a second virus that bears no antigenic relationship to the first one (see Fig. 7–7). The status of interferon in human virus infections is not yet entirely clear, but it may have great importance in preventing the multiplication of viruses within host cells. Because viruses are obligate intracellular parasites, the antibody-producing mechanism may not be triggered by their presence in cells of other tissues. In such case, the production of interferon by infected cells might afford the only protection possible against future infections.

On the other hand, protective antibody production does occur in many virus diseases. The

antibody-producing cells may encounter viruses in the blood stream, on their way to cellular locations, or in extracellular fluids on their release from cells they have infected and destroyed. Thus, immunity to virus infections may be provided either by interferon alone or by interferon activity at cell surfaces, coupled with specific antibody inactivation of viruses free in the blood or elsewhere.

Active Acquired Immunity. Active immunity, acquired *naturally* through infection, may develop whether or not the infection results in clinically recognizable disease or remains subclinical. In either case, antibody formation continues for as long as antigenic stimulation persists, but some destruction and removal of antibody also occur normally, at a slow rate, so that there is a maximum peak for antibody levels in the blood. This peak may be maintained over the period of time the antigen remains in the body, then slowly decline when the antigen has disappeared. The decline may be quite rapid in some cases, occurring in a matter of days, but in other instances (such as diphtheria or smallpox) antibody is detectable in cells or serum for many weeks, months, or years after the original infection.

The antibody-producing mechanism becomes sensitive to the particular antigen that set it off, so that re-entry of the antigen at some later time results in a more prompt and rapid production of antibody. This phenomenon is referred to as the *anamnestic* (remembering) response. Thus, repeated subclinical infections with a specific organism commonly encountered, such as the poliomyelitis virus, may result in continuous antibody formation at a level sufficient to prevent the disease from ever occurring.

On the other hand, the first attack by a virulent organism may find the body unprepared and unable to avoid disease. Initial production of antibody is not immediate, and protective levels are not reached for at least 10 to 14 days, during which time acute symptoms of illness may be manifest. In the days before the discovery of antibiotics, this period was often critical for the patient (as, indeed, it still may be), until anti-

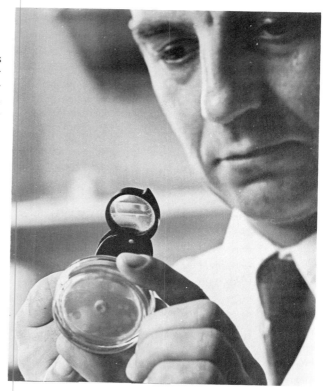

Fig. 7–7. Interferon is a substance produced by living mammalian cells in response to virus infection. This substance interferes with, and inhibits, virus reproduction. Here, a microbiologist examines a Petri dish in which mammalian cells were first cultivated and then infected with a virus. All the cells were killed by the virus except those in the center, which were protected by interferon. (WHO photo by Spooner.)

bodies joined the defense to help turn the tide, sometimes very dramatically, and convalescence began. Antibodies are usually at their peak level at the time recovery becomes complete, then fall away slowly.

In certain chronic, progressive infectious diseases no durable, protective immunity develops, although the body becomes relatively resistant to superimposed, second infections with the same organism. This is true in the case of tuberculosis and in syphilis, for example. Recovery from, or arrest of, diseases of this type rests with the body's nonspecific defenses, some of the effects of hypersensitivity, and, of course, chemotherapeutic measures.

Active Artificial Immunization. Many infectious diseases now can be prevented by immunizing techniques employing an infectious agent or its products treated or administered in such a way that they will not cause clinical illness (see p. 133, this chapter). Some of the most commonly used immunizing agents and methods are discussed briefly below.

1. KILLED VACCINES. This term is used for injectable preparations containing microorganisms grown in laboratory culture (or in experimental animals, chick embryos, tissue culture, etc.), separated from the growth medium, and killed by heat or a chemical agent. Formalin and phenol are the most useful disinfectants for this purpose. Vaccines are usually injected subcutaneously, less often by intracutaneous or intramuscular routes. As a rule multiple injections are required to produce durable protection, two or three being spaced over a few weeks' time and one or more "booster" shots (for the anamnestic effect) being given at yearly intervals. The Salk poliomyelitis vaccine, typhus fever, and typhoid fever vaccines are examples of killed preparations of organisms given in this manner.

2. LIVING, ATTENUATED VACCINES. Virulent microorganisms can be treated by a method that deprives them of their pathogenic properties without killing them or inactivating their antigens. An originally virulent organism in this condition is said to be *attenuated*. The most successful methods for attenuation included drying (Pasteur's original rabies vaccine contained dried, attenuated virus); continued, prolonged passages of the organism through artificial culture media to induce mutations; and cultivation and passage

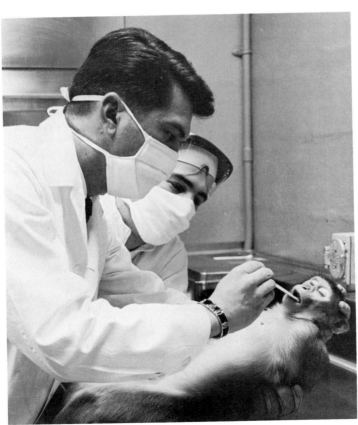

Fig. 7–8. Animals are used to test the safety and efficacy of vaccines prepared for human use. Here a monkey is being examined for abnormalities by a veterinarian. If he finds it to be a normal, healthy animal, it will be added to a group of monkeys to be tested with oral poliomyelitis vaccine. (Courtesy of Lederle Laboratories, Division of American Cyanamid Company, Pearl River, N.Y.)

of the organism through hosts other than man. A combination of alternate passages through an animal host and artificial media is also successful in some cases. Occasionally advantage can be taken of the close relationship of strains of organisms causing disease in man or an animal host, but not both. The agent of bovine tuberculosis, for instance, causes a serious infection in cattle. It is antigenically very similar to the human tubercle bacillus, and it is also capable of inducing human disease. However, a strain of the bovine bacillus has been attenuated by many years of culture on artificial media in the laboratory and is used as a vaccine against human tuberculosis (BCG). It does not stimulate protective antibody production, but it contributes to the resistance conferred by hypersensitivity. A similar antigenic relationship exists between the viruses of cowpox and smallpox, so that the former, which is relatively avirulent for man, can be used as an effective attenuated immunizing agent for human beings. (This was originally Edward Jenner's discovery and great contribution, in the early nineteenth century. It also constitutes the origin of the word vaccine, coined by Jenner from *vacca*, the Latin word for cow.) The oral poliomyelitis vaccines developed by Cox and by Sabin are other notable examples of living, attenuated immunizing agents. With the exception of the rabies vaccine, which must be given in multiple doses over a period of days, these vaccines usually provide a lasting immunity after a single dose (see Fig. 7–8). Repeated smallpox vaccination every three to five years is recommended, however.

3. LIVING, VIRULENT MICROORGANISMS. These may be used for immunization if they are given in doses sufficiently small to avoid producing disease before antibodies are formed or if they are administered by a route unfavorable to the establishment of infection. Specific antiserum may also be given in a combined dose with the organism to provide partial protection against its effects until active antibody is formed. With the development of safer methods this type of immunization is no longer used frequently.

4. TOXOIDS.   These are nontoxic but antigenic substances derived from toxins. Microbial exotoxins, such as those of the diphtheria and the tetanus bacilli, can be prepared in this way, having first been separated from the bacterial cells that produce them. The toxin present in the filtrate of a liquid culture is first treated with heat or formalin to destroy its toxicity, but not its antigenicity. It may then be precipitated with alum to provide an injectable preparation that is slowly absorbed from the tissues, thus assuring a prolonged antigenic effect. Toxoids are usually given intramuscularly in two or three initial dose separated by four to six weeks, followed by an annual booster.

5. FRACTIONS OF MICROBIAL CELLS. These may be obtained by chemical or physical disintegration of a microorganism to be used for immunization. Such materials include the endotoxins (somatic antigens) of some of the Gramnegative bacilli and the capsular antigens of organisms such as the pneumococcus. These agents are, in general, less effective than those described above in their capacity to induce a solid or a protective immunity.

Passive Acquired Immunity. Passive immunity is acquired *naturally* through the placental transfer of maternal antibodies to the blood of the developing fetus in utero, as described earlier in this chapter (see p. 134). The congenital immunity acquired by infants depends, of course, on the infections their mothers have had or have been immunized against as well as on the level and protective qualities of the antibodies involved. The mother's antibodies are also contained in her milk, particularly the colostrum, and these reinforce the breast-fed child's immunity. As maternal antibody declines, the child becomes more susceptible to infection, but by this time (at the age of four to six months), his own antibody mechanism becomes functional. His exposure to common microorganisms at this stage is likely to lead to solid immunity against them, and he can be given further protection against dangerous pathogens by active immunization with vaccines and toxoids.

Artifically acquired passive immunity can be useful in providing temporary protection to a susceptible individual who has been exposed to a

particularly hazardous infection. The source of antibodies is immune serum from a person or animal who has been actively immunized by infection or by an artificial method. Most commonly, a "pool" of serum from a number of individuals of the same species is obtained, the gamma globulin content is separated out by "fractionation" of the serum, and this "purified" antibody is administered. The concentration of serum by this method assures a high level of antibody in a small volume per dose. Furthermore, pooled gamma globulins of human origin may contain antibodies to a number of common human diseases, such as poliomyelitis, infectious hepatitis, measles, and others.

It must be emphasized that the use of passive antibodies in the prevention of disease constitutes an emergency measure only, since the immunity provided does not persist beyond two to three weeks. Susceptible persons who have been exposed, or who face the immediate risk of exposure, to a disease that might have serious consequences for them are suitable candidates for passive immunization. Such persons might include the very old, or the very young, whose immune and nonspecific resistance mechanisms are inadequate. In some instances passive immunization of all contacts of a serious infection, such as infectious hepatitis, is advisable if natural active immunity is not widespread because an effective vaccine is not available or the disease is not frequent. Passive immunization may prevent the development of individual disease altogether or permit only a mild, attenuated infection to ensue. In the latter case, an active, effective immunity usually follows, as a result of direct antigen stimulation of antibody production. Whenever effective vaccines or other immunizing agents are available, however, active immunization should be provided because it assures better and more durable protection. Another reason for the advisability of active immunization is that the use of animal serums in human beings exposes the latter to foreign proteins whose antigenic activity may lead to a hypersensitive state of the body tissues as a result of the production of antibodies to the foreign serum. The "serum sickness" that can ensue from consequent antigen-

antibody combinations can be quite devastating to the tissues. Even if no untoward reaction follows an initial serum dose, another administration of serum from the same animal at the time of a later emergency may produce a violent, immediate reaction, sometimes with fatal consequences. These events are discussed more fully in the last section of this chapter with other problems of hypersensitivity.

With respect to the treatment of infectious disease, immune serum is of limited usefulness in this era of antibiotic therapy. It is helpful in the treatment of certain infections characterized by microbial exotoxin production, however. In diseases such as diphtheria and clostridial gangrene or tetanus, antibiotic attack on the organism is essential in eliminating it from its site of growth and multiplication, but of no effect in counteracting the activity of exotoxin already produced. In this situation, or in botulism, the immediate administration of antitoxin is indicated, to neutralize toxin before it can attach to tissue cells. Speed is of the essence in such cases, because even antitoxin cannot prevent the damage to cells that toxin has reached and adhered to or entered. Before the advent of antibiotics, immune serum was a valuable part of the treatment of such infectious diseases as pneumococcal pneumonia and bacterial meningitis, but antibiotics or chemotherapy is now used almost exclusively of serum. Passively acquired antibodies are helpful in virus infections only if they are given before the virus has had an opportunity to reach and infect the cells. Intracellular viruses, as we have seen, lie beyond the reach of antibodies in the circulating blood.

Hypersensitivity

In the preceding discussion, three different types of immune response to antigenic stimulus were mentioned: (1) the gradual production of antibodies in the nonimmune individual in response to an antigen encountered once or in repeated small dose (as in several subclinical infections with the same organism or multiple doses of vaccine); (2) the more rapid production of

antibodies in the immune individual in response to an antigen encountered at some previous time (this anamnestic or booster effect is utilized frequently in active, artificial immunization schedules); and (3) the tissue injury that may result in the immune individual in response to an antigen previously encountered. The slight sensitivity shown to an antigen newly experienced in the first case and the increased sensitivity of renewed contact in the second elicit a protective effect, without untoward effects. In the third situation, however, the individual appears to become overly reactive to the antigen in question, and his response is described as being *hypersensitive*. He is also said to display an *altered reactivity*, or *allergy*, toward specific antigens; that is, he reacts to them differently than he did at some earlier time or than most other people (or members of the same species) do.

The Characteristics of Hypersensitivity

The chief distinction between hypersensitive and immune reactions is the cellular injury induced by the former, as compared with the protective effects of the latter. The basic mechanisms of specific antigen-antibody interactions operate in both, but the injury that occurs in allergic reactions is apparently associated with the *site* of antibody activity.

The *antibodies* involved in hypersensitivity may sometimes, but not always, be demonstrable in the circulating blood. Of greater importance is the fact that they can frequently be demonstrated to be intimately associated with tissue cells, fixed or attached to their surfaces. The cells are said to be *sensitized* by antibody, in this regard, for they are then subject to injury when the sensitizing antibody is again confronted by its antigen at this site and combines with it at the place of its attachment.

The *antigens* that induce hypersensitivity are called *allergens*. They fall into three major categories as to their chemical nature: (1) some are foreign proteins and act as complete antigens, (2) some are compounds of large molecular

weight and size, nonprotein in nature, but possessing some antigenicity, and (3) some are compounds of small molecular size and weight that act as haptenes (that is, they are incomplete antigens until combined with protein). Allergens of the first two types include such agents as the protein components of plants, foods, or microbial cells, or polypeptide and lipid constituents of these. The third type of substances that are allergenic, but not antigenic, includes many drugs, such as penicillin and some other antibiotics, quinine and its derivatives, many cosmetic products, and the constituents of some plants such as poison ivy, poison sumac, or poison oak (see Fig. 7–9).

When incomplete antigens enter or come in contact with the body, they may combine with some one of the host's proteins to become antigenic, or they may act in such a way as to cause the production of a substance that is antigenic, that is, a "secondary" antigen. Some incomplete antigens are known as *contact allergens* because they may induce hypersensitivity simply by contact with the skin or mucosal surfaces, including the mucosa of the respiratory and gastrointestinal tracts. Inhaled pollens, certain foods, cosmetics, soaps, and poison ivy are common examples of this type.

Microbial antigens may be allergenic for some individuals. Bacterial allergies may include a hypersensitive response even to commensalistic organisms of little or no pathogenicity residing normally on mucosal surfaces. The damage caused by hypersensitivity to bacteria, or their products, may lead to chronic inflammations, particularly of the upper respiratory mucosa in the sinus passages, the eustachian canal, and the middle ear.

The development and extent of allergic reactions differ widely among individuals. In any one person, they depend primarily on his genetic faculty for sensitization by antibody and then on the nature and frequency of his contacts with allergens. The initial dose of an anitgen to which the individual later becomes sensitive is known as the *sensitizing dose*, and the later dose to which he responds with tissue damage is called the *eliciting dose*. When the cellular injury is severe,

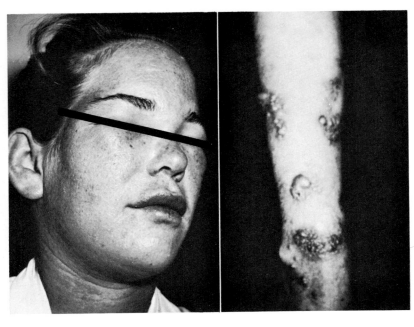

Fig. 7–9. *(Left)* This patient has an acute dermatitis caused by an allergic reaction to poison oak. The clinical lesion *(right)* of poison oak dermatitis is acute and bullous and displays a linear pattern. (Courtesy of Dr. William L. Epstein, University of California Medical Center, San Francisco, Calif.)

the latter is sometimes called the *shocking dose,* indicating that cells and tissues have been at least momentarily stunned. The time that elapses between the eliciting dose and the appearance of hypersensitive symptoms may be quite short or relatively prolonged. This provides the basis for classification of these reactions as the *immediate* type, or the *delayed* type, of hypersensitivity.

The Immediate Type of Hypersensitivity

Immediate reactions appear within a few seconds or minutes of the eliciting dose of antigen. The clinical symptoms may be localized or systemic in their extent, depending on the site or sites of the reaction and the rate at which it proceeds. The nature and degree of injury vary under different circumstances, but in general the following physiologic changes are involved: (1) There is a release of *histamine* from certain cells of connective tissue. This leads to (2) contraction of smooth-muscle cells and (3) an increased muscle spasm occurs particularly in the bronchioles and the small arteries, causing them to constrict. As blood vessel walls become more permeable, plasma and cells accumulate in the surrounding tissues producing edema. There is a corresponding drop in the numbers of leukocytes in the circulating blood. Damage to blood vessels may also result in their dilatation, which, in turn, may lead to a drop in blood pressure. If this is severe, shock may ensue. (4) Release of heparin reduces the coagulability of the blood. (5) The plasma level of complement declines, possibly because the complement has been fixed to antigen-antibody complexes formed in the tissues.

The prominent role of histamine in these reactions can be demonstrated by its capacity to induce many of the symptoms of hypersensitivity when injected into experimental animals. Furthermore, drugs known as antihistamines, which block the effects of histamine, can prevent or alleviate some of the symptoms.

Immediate reactions are usually associated with the presence of antibody in the circulating blood as well as in close association with tissue cells.

Immediate Systemic Reactions. The physiologic changes described above may be intense and widespread in the body, depending in part on the nature of the allergen and in part on the route and timing of the eliciting dose with respect to the

sensitizing dose. The two most important types of systemic reaction resulting from immediate hypersensitivity are *anaphylactic shock* and *serum sickness.*

Anaphylaxis is a term coined to imply an effect opposite to that meant by *prophylaxis,* which signifies the prevention of disease. The extreme of injury that can be produced by hypersensitive immune mechanisms is *anaphylactic shock,* which stands in marked contrast to the prophylactic, or protective, effect usually associated with immunity. It occurs as a result of immediate and simultaneous physiologic changes induced by the eliciting (or shocking) dose of antigen at many sites in the body. To achieve such an effect, the antigen must be introduced by a parenteral route (that is, directly into the tissues) in a fairly concentrated dose. Intramuscular, intravenous, or intracardiac injections may be required, depending on the purity and concentration of the antigen and the degree to which the tissues have become sensitized since the sensitizing dose of antigen was given (or encountered). The allergens involved may be either complete antigens, such as the foreign proteins of the serum of another animal species, or, for man at least, incomplete antigens, such as penicillin and some other antibiotics. The symptoms induced by the shocking dose of such materials in sensitive human beings include sudden difficulty of respiration due to bronchiospasm and to edema of the larynx; facial edema; a rapidly increased heart rate due to arterial constrictions, then a fall in blood pressure with vasodilation and shock. A generalized urticarial reaction may occur as well. This is characterized by the development of giant "hives" at the site of injection of the antigen and also over large areas of skin, resulting from small vessel dilatation and the swelling of tissue in the area. Intense reactions such as these can result in death within minutes or a few hours, depending on the degree of shock and the individual's capacity to withstand the total effects. They can be produced in human beings, for instance, by the injection of animal serums meant to provide a passive immunization to cover an emergency (such as exposure to infection) or by antibiotic injections given for much the same reason. When

anaphylaxis occurs in such situations it indicates that the patient had, on some previous occasion, encountered and become sensitive to the specific antigen involved. The patient may recover from an anaphylactic episode if the shocking dose, the degree of his sensitization, the strength of his constitution, or all these factors permit. Before the administration of potentially shocking agents, the patient can be tested for possible sensitization, as described at the end of this section.

Serum sickness is a systemic type of hypersensitivity that can sometimes be induced by an *initial* dose of sensitizing antigen, but more usually results from a *second eliciting* dose given some time later. The type of antigen most frequently involved is animal serum given prophylactically to provide immediate passive immunity. Horse serum is commonly implicated simply because antiserum can be obtained in large quantities from artificially immunized horses. Tetanus antitoxin, for example, is prepared in this way and may be given immediately after an accident occurs in which tetanus infection and intoxication are threatened. The threat may be especially great if the individual is not actively immune to tetanus toxin. In addition to its antitoxin content, the serum contains horse protein antigens; and because they are foreign to human tissues they induce antibody formation. After the initial dose of serum, antihorse antibodies begin to reach a significant level in the blood and tissues in about 8 to 12 days. If the original antigen (horse serum) has been eliminated from the body by this time, no untoward reactions will take place. If sufficient antigen remains, the antibody reacting with it will produce symptoms beginning at the time antibody level is reaching its height. More frequently, symptoms are provoked by a second dose of serum from the same animal species, on some later occasion in life. In this case, the speed with which symptoms develop depends on current antibody level and the degree of tissue sensitization. If the latter is intense and generalized, anaphylactic shock may result, as described. The symptoms of serum sickness are rather similar in many ways, but less severe. They include sudden fever; hives; edema of the face, hands, and feet; lymphoid reactions

with swelling of many nodes; and often an intense reaction at the site of serum injection. Edema of the laryngeal and other upper respiratory tissues can be a severe threat to normal respiration. The illness continues until all the antigen has been inactivated or eliminated.

Serum sickness may result from the administration of antigens other than those associated with animal serums if the hypersensitivity mechanism is invoked. The incomplete antigens of penicillin and other drugs, mentioned in connection with anaphylactic reactions, may induce serum sickness in hypersensitive individuals. For this reason, the use of a particular antibiotic in the treatment of infectious disease may be contraindicated. The patient's history of possible reactions to drugs should be carefully considered before they are administered. Evidence of hypersensitivity can also be obtained in some cases by skin testing, to be described.

Localized tissue reactions of the immediate hypersensitive type are seen in a great variety of allergies. These include the well-known problems of asthma, hay fever, hives, and other skin rashes. In these instances the cellular injury induced by antigen contact with antibody-sensitized tissue is limited in scope. While these diseases can incapacitate, or even debilitate, patients suffering from them, they are not systemic in their effects. While the antigen-antibody mechanism constitutes the basis of allergic symptoms, other factors such as emotional stress, hormonal changes, and physical reaction to environmental stimuli may influence the response markedly. The capacity for hypersensitivity probably has a genetic basis, as evidenced by the distribution of allergic disorders in families. Actual sensitization of the individual, however, depends on his contacts with particular antigens and the opportunities afforded for antibody development.

Hypersensitive reactions of the immediate type are also thought to play a role in a group of human disorders known as "autoimmune" diseases. In certain situations the human host may become hypersensitive to his own tissues; that is, he produces antibody to some antigenic constituents of his own body. This may come about in one of several ways. (1) Some tissues of the

body are relatively isolated from the antibody-producing cells of the blood and lymph. Thus, under normal circumstances proteins of the crystalline lens of the eye, the thyroid gland, or brain tissue are not encountered by the antibody mechanism. The introduction of such proteins into the circulating blood, through some disease process or by experimentation, may result in the production of specific antiorgan antibodies by cells that react to them as foreign antigens. This is the basis, for example, of a type of chronic *thyroiditis* induced by antibodies against the patient's own thyroid tissue. (2) Antibody formed in response to a specific antigen may cross-react with a different antigen if both large antigen molecules have one or more important constituents in common, "recognizable" by the antibody in its reaction with each of them. Thus, an antibody produced in response to a foreign protein, such as a streptococcal antigen, might also react with a tissue protein of similar molecular structure. This may be the basis of some of the hypersensitive characteristics of diseases such as *rheumatic fever* and *glomerulonephritis* occurring as sequelae to streptococcal infection. (3) Incomplete antigens may attach to the surface of host cells or combine with host protein to alter its antigenic specificity. Antibody production may thus be stimulated by the altered protein, and subsequent antigen-antibody reaction causes injury to the cell. Certain blood disorders, such as "*autoimmune hemolytic anemia*," may be caused by the action of antibodies on antigens of the red blood cells or other elements of the blood, including platelets. In the "*collagen*" diseases (rheumatoid arthritis, lupus erythematosus, and others) an autoimmune destruction of the nuclei of certain types of normal human cells occurs. In some cases the sensitization has been attributed to the administration of certain drugs (quinidine, sulfonamides) and to their subsequent behavior as haptenes. (4) A genetic defect may operate in such a way as to bring about antibody production against some normal human protein. This type of effect also appears to have influence in the patient with *rheumatoid arthritis* whose serum contains a factor that reacts with a normal human globulin, in a specific manner.

The Delayed Type of Hypersensitivity

Delayed hypersensitivity requires from 24 to 48 hours to develop. Reactions of this type continue much longer than those of the immediate type. The responsible antibodies cannot be demonstrated in the circulating blood, but they are associated with tissue cells. Their reaction with antigen does not lead to histamine release; therefore the type of cellular damage induced is quite different from that of anaphylaxis or serum sickness.

Microbial allergies are characteristically of the delayed type. Hypersensitivity is a frequent complication of infections and may sometimes be a major feature of an infectious disease. In many instances, the organism involved may be relatively inert within tissues that have immobilized it or have few toxic properties; yet the disease it induces is of long duration, persistent, and chronic because of hypersensitization. Infestation of the tissues by parasitic worms; fungous infections, particularly those of the skin; viral and bacterial diseases — all may have an allergic component. Any type of tissue may be involved, depending on the localization of antigen-antibody reactions.

Contact allergies of the skin induced by many chemical agents also display the delayed type of hypersensitivity. The symptoms of dermatitis associated with allergy may be those of a minor skin eruption, or they may become quite severe if the functions of deep layers of the skin are involved over wide areas. Allergenic chemicals are numerous and include such widely different agents as metals, soaps, cosmetics, plant substances, disinfectant compounds, and drugs.

Further differences between the immediate and delayed types of hypersensitivity are displayed by the responses to skin tests with different antigens.

Skin Tests in Hypersensitivity. The intracutaneous injection of a small dose of an antigen often serves to reveal a hypersensitive state and to identify it as immediate or delayed in type.

Immediate skin reactions develop within minutes after the superficial injection of an allergen when antibody reacting with it causes the release of histamine. A local erythema (reddening) first appears at the site, caused by the dilation of capillaries; a wheal develops because of the edema resulting from increased permeability of the blood vessels; and the erythema flares out widely as small arteries dilate in the vicinity. All these reactions reflect the same mechanism that operates in anaphylaxis; they disappear usually within 30 minutes to an hour.

As a rule, the anaphylactic skin reaction can be obtained in individuals who have already developed this kind of hypersensitivity before the antigen involved is applied. Because of the risk of fatal anaphylaxis resulting from the parenteral use of foreign proteins, particularly animal antiserums and drugs with an allergenic potential, *these agents should never be used without first attempting to demonstrate hypersensitivity by means of a skin test.*

Delayed skin reactions require 24 to 48 hours to develop. Usually no immediate reaction occurs at the time of intracutaneous injection of the antigen. After some hours redness and edema appear, and increasing induration (hardening) of the area develops. Vasodilation and infiltration of the site with plasma and leukocytes account for these events. The cellular infiltrate often becomes quite dense, containing both polymorphonuclear and mononuclear cells. Tissue necrosis may occur in the indurated area when the reaction is severe. As the reaction subsides, redness and swelling disappear within a day or so, but the induration may persist for weeks.

This type of skin test result is typical when microbial antigens are used to demonstrate the hypersensitivity of infection and thus provides a diagnostic clue as to the nature of an infectious disease or its stage of development. A positive skin test alone, however, is not necessarily indicative of *currently active* infection, but only of the fact that infection (clinical or subclinical) with the agent has occurred *at some time prior to the test.* It may be of assistance in the diagnosis of a large number of diseases, whether of bacterial origin (tuberculosis, brucellosis), viral (lymphogranuloma venereum), fungal (histoplasmosis, blastomycosis), or helminthic (trichi-

nosis). The antigen employed in most instances is a cell-free extract of the organism, containing one or more of its allergenic constituents.

Tuberculin tests typify the use of such materials for the demonstration of delayed hypersensitivity. Filtrates of broth cultures of the tubercle bacillus may be concentrated and used in this form (Old Tuberculin, or OT) or they may be purified by precipitating the protein antigen out of the culture medium (purified protein derivative, or PPD). The material may be applied merely to the surface of the skin, using an adherent patch to maintain contact with the area for two or three days. OT or PPD is also given intracutaneously, in small highly diluted doses to avoid severe reaction. If the test is negative at this dilution, it may be repeated once or twice more, using progressively more concentrated doses, until a negative response is assured or a positive result is obtained. Positive reactors may require other diagnostic tests, however, such as x-rays or bacteriologic cultures, to determine whether or not their hypersensitivity reflects current, active infection. The test area is examined in 24 hours,

Table 7–1. The Host Versus the Microbe

Nonspecific Mechanisms of Resistance	Mechanisms of Specific, Relative Resistance

I. Skin and mucosal surfaces
  A. Architecture
    1. Nasal hairs
    2. Ciliated epithelial cells
  B. Secretions
    1. Lysozyme
    2. Mucus
    3. Saliva
	I. Inherited
	    (genetic or "natural" immunity)
	  A. Species differences
	  B. Racial factors
	  C. Familial factors
	  D. Over-all history of host-microbe encounters

II. Blood
  A. Mechanical action
  B. Chemical functions
  C. Components
    1. Plasma
 	
      Complement ⎫
      Properdin ⎬ (nonspecific)
 	
      Antibody ⎫
      Opsonins ⎬ (specific)
 	
    2. Leukocytes
      Phagocytosis (nonspecific)
      Antibody formation (specific)
	II. Acquired
	  A. Active, acquired immunity
	    1. Natural (via infection or disease)
	    2. Artificial (via immunizations with vaccines, toxoids)
	  B. Passive, acquired immunity
	    1. Natural (congenital transfer from mother to child)
	    2. Artificial
	      a. Antiserum
	      b. Gamma globulin

III. Lymphatic system
  A. Mechanical filtration
  B. Antibody formation	

IV. Inflammatory reaction
  A. Mechanical effect
  B. Chemical effect	

V. Normal activity of hormones	

VI. Environmental factors
  A. Host nutrition
  B. Stress
  C. Climate	

and again at 48 and 72 hours to assure accuracy of interpretation.

It must be re-emphasized that the interpretation of this type of skin test is distinct from that given to tests for the presence of *protective* antibody. The Schick test for diphtheria antitoxin, as described earlier, is adjusted to *prevent* a skin reaction in the presence of antibody, while tests for hypersensitivity produce a skin lesion only if *sensitizing* antibody has been formed.

Skin testing is also commonly used to detect allergies to foods, pollens and other inhalants, or other sensitizing agents. An antigenic extract of the material in question can be applied to the skin either in a small scratch made with a dull instrument or by intradermal injection. Some materials may produce an immediate wheal and flare; others may give a delayed positive result; therefore negative test sites should be read daily for two or three days. When the cause of a food, inhalant, or contact allergy can be identified in this way, the patient can sometimes be offered relief of his symptoms by avoidance of the allergen, if this is possible, or by desensitizing techniques.

Desensitization is attempted by giving repeated doses of very small quantities of the specific allergen to encourage the antibody-forming cells to release an antibody that will circulate freely in the blood plasma rather than attach to cells. The method achieves some success because circulating antibody blocks the formation of antigen-antibody complexes at cellular sites. The new blocking antibody that circulates can remove antigen that is also free, but it does not attach itself to tissue cells to cause further sensitization. The method does not work well in the case of allergies

characterized by the delayed type of hypersensitivity, in which circulating antibodies are not ordinarily produced. It does provide some relief for individuals suffering from allergies in which immediate reactions occur, presumably because the blocking antibody in the blood combines with allergen before it can react with antibody attached to cells.

It should be remembered that injectable preparations of antigens, or antibodies, are almost never "pure" in the sense that they are free of other substances that may have antigenic activity. Foreign proteins derived from a culture medium in a vaccine preparation, or from animal tissues, can also induce antibody production and activity of the hypersensitive type. In addition to the immediate systemic reactivity described for anaphylaxis or serum sickness, these materials, when injected repeatedly into a particular skin site, can induce a localized tissue sensitivity (Arthus reaction). In such case each injection is followed by a more and more intense local reaction, which may terminate in a hemorrhagic necrosis of tissue in this area. It is advisable, therefore, when a series of desensitizing injections are being given, to vary the site of injection of each new dose.

The nonspecific relief of hypersensitivities rests with the use of antihistaminic drugs, when these are appropriate in the immediate type of reaction, and with adrenal hormones that may either counteract histamine effects, suppress antibody formation, or reduce the intensity of inflammatory cell responses.

Table 7–1 summarizes the many mechanisms of resistance that operate in the infected human host.

Questions

1. Briefly describe nonspecific host mechanisms of resistance to infection.
2. What is immunity? How is it acquired?
3. Define the following terms: "antigen," "antibody," "haptene."
4. Briefly describe the antigen-antibody interaction.

5. What substances are used as antigens in active artificial immunization?
6. What is the chief distinction between hypersensitivity and immunity?
7. What is an allergen? What is a sensitizing dose? An eliciting dose?
8. Describe the immediate type of sensitivity.
9. What is anaphylaxis?
10. Describe the delayed type of hypersensitivity.
11. Why are skin tests important?

References

Pertinent References

Davis, Bernard, Dulbecco, Renato, Eisen, Herman N., Ginsberg, Harry S., and Wood, W. Barry, Jr.: *Microbiology.* Harper & Row, New York, 1967.

Dubos, René: *Biochemical Determinants of Microbial Disease.* Harvard University Press, Cambridge, Mass., 1954.

Dubos, René: *Mirage of Health.* Anchor Books, Garden City, N.Y., 1959.

Dubos, René J., and Hirsch, James G. (eds.): *Bacterial and Mycotic Infections of Man,* 4th ed. J. B. Lippincott, Philadelphia, 1965.

Faust, Ernest C., Beaver, P. C., and Jung, R. C.: *Animal Agents and Vectors of Human Disease,* 2nd ed. Lea & Febiger, Philadelphia, 1964.

Faust, Ernest C., and Russell, Paul Farr: *Craig and Faust's Parasitology,* 7th ed. Lea & Febiger, Philadelphia, 1964.

Horsfall, Frank L., Jr., and Tamm, Igor (eds.): *Viral and Rickettsial Infections of Man.* J. B. Lippincott, Philadelphia, 1965.

Periodicals

Acker, Robert, and Hartsell, S. E.: Fleming's Lysozyme, *Sci. Amer.,* **203**:132, June, 1960.

Ager, Ernest A.: Current Concepts in Immunization, *Amer. J. Nurs.,* **66**:2004, Sept., 1966.

Burnet, MacFarlane: The Mechanism of Immunity, *Sci. Amer.,* **204**:58, Jan., 1961.

Crowle, Alfred J.: Delayed Hypersensitivity, *Sci. Amer.,* **202**:129, April, 1960.

Epstein, William L.: To Prevent Poison Ivy and Oak Dermatitis, *Amer. J. Nurs.,* **63**:113, May, 1963.

Isaacs, Alick: Interferon, *Sci. Amer.,* **204**:51, May, 1961.

Johnson, Kenneth J.: Allergen Injections, *Amer. J. Nurs.,* **65**:121, July, 1965.

McLean, James A.: Hay Fever, *Amer. J. Nurs.,* **61**:85, July, 1961.

Mayerson, H. S.: The Lymphatic System, *Sci. Amer.,* **208**:80, June, 1963.

Merrill, John P.: The Transplantation of the Kidney, *Sci. Amer.,* **201**:57, Oct., 1959.

Nossal, G. J. V.: How Cells Make Antibodies, *Sci. Amer.,* **211**:106, Dec., 1964.

Selye, Hans: The Stress Syndrome, *Amer. J. Nurs.,* **65**:97, March, 1965.

Spiers, Robert S.: How Cells Attack Antigens, *Sci. Amer.,* **210**:59, Feb., 1964.

Wood, W. B., Jr.: The Pathogenesis of Fever, *Triangle,* **512**:101, July, 1961.

———: Tissue Compatability, *The Sciences,* **5**:1, May, 1966.

Popular Literature

Camac, C. N. B., collected by: Vaccination Against Smallpox, in *Classics of Medicine and Surgery.* Dover Publications, Inc., New York, 1959.

Clendening, Logan: A New Idea in the World of Prevention; Preventing Plague and Pestilence, in *Behind the Doctor.* Garden City Publishing Co., Inc., Garden City, N.Y., 1933.

Clendening, Logan, compiled with notes by: Smallpox, in *Source of Medical History.* Dover Publications, Inc., New York, 1960.

DeKruif, Paul: Metchnikoff, The Nice Phagocytes, in *Microbe Hunters*. Harcourt Brace, New York, 1926.

Drew, John: *Man, Microbe and Malady*. Penguin Books, Harmondsworth, Middlesex, 1950.

Greer, Gordon G.: Staying Healthy While Traveling Abroad, *Better Homes and Gardens*, **43**:167, April, 1965.

Roueché, Berton: Leaves of Three, in *A Man Named Hoffman*. Little, Brown & Co., Boston, 1965.

Williams, Greer: *Virus Hunters*. Alfred A. Knopf, New York, 1959.

8 The Diagnosis of Infectious Diseases

The prompt, accurate diagnosis of clinical disease is the primary responsibility of the physician. His early recognition and treatment of infectious disease are often of urgent importance not only to the individual patient, but to all others who have been, or will be, exposed to the infection. The family and community contacts of the patient with a communicable disease must be considered and protected from risk insofar as possible. If the patient is admitted to a hospital, appropriate safeguards must be provided to prevent the cross-infection of other patients, whose normal defenses may be lowered because of pre-existing illness, and of members of the hospital staff. Since the route and ease of transmission vary with the nature and the stage of the infectious disease, diagnostic accuracy may be doubly important. The hospital's nursing service and its laboratory facilities can offer immediate assistance to the physician, so that diagnosis and treatment of the patient may proceed without delay, and suitable precautions may be established from the beginning for the protection of others.

To play her essential role well, the nurse must be alert to the symptomatology of infections and their communicability. She must also understand the circumstances in which the laboratory's potential diagnostic value can best be realized in a given clinical situation. The nurse's background of theoretic and practical instruction in the nature

of infectious diseases should provide her with a concept of the rather rhythmic patterns of host-parasite relationships and the correspondingly patterned steps which all concerned must take toward diagnosis and therapy for the patient and prevention and control of infection for others. In this chapter we shall review some of the broad rhythms of infection, its clinical recognition, and its laboratory diagnosis.

Clinical Stages of Infectious Disease

Clinical infections are often described as being either *acute* or *chronic*, depending on the rise and fall of symptoms displayed by the host in response to an *active* parasite. In general, acute infections are characterized by a rising pitch of symptoms that continue for as long as the microorganism or its products are actively capable of inflicting damage, then subside and disappear as host defenses become effective. Chronic situations arise when a pathogenic organism is able to survive the host's defenses and to maintain some level of damaging activity over a longer period of time. In either case, infection proceeds in a series of stages reflected by host responses.

The Stages of Acute Infectious Disease

Human responses to acute infection fall into four periods with respect to the activities of the infectious agent and the symptoms produced thereby. These are the *incubation period*, the *prodromal period*, the *acute stage* of active disease, and the *convalescent stage* of recovery. The nature and variety of events that occur within these periods are often quite characteristic for a particular disease; that is, the symptoms themselves may be diagnostic of the infectious disease. The distinctive symptomatology of many specific infectious diseases is described in Part Two of this text. We shall consider here only the general features of these stages of acute infection, emphasizing those that are common to many or all clinically distinct diseases.

The Incubation Period. At their first encounter, host and parasite appraise each other, so to speak, in the light of their respective capabilities and requirements. The parasite requires adequate living quarters and a little time to establish itself therein. The host meets the intrusion according to his capacity for both nonspecific and specific resistance and to the parasite's effect on his cellular functions. There are no outward signs of infection during this period when the "incubating" parasite is attempting to establish itself and to begin active growth and multiplication. If it fails in this, the only permanent record of its attempt may be kept in the immune accounts of the host whose antibody-producing cells have stored away the memory of the encounter. If the organism survives and multiplies, however, the symptomless incubation period comes to an end at the time the effects of the parasite's activities begin to embarrass host cells and tissues. The length of this period varies with the organism and the many factors that may influence the host's resistance to it. It may be very short (two to three days) for some virulent bacteria or quite long for certain relatively avirulent viruses and fungi (weeks or months), but the average incubation time for most agents of acute infections lies in the range of 10 to 21 days.

The Prodromal Period. In its Greek origin the word "prodromal" means "running before." Its medical use refers to a brief period, usually of no more than one or two days' duration, in which the earliest symptoms of trouble appear preceding the development of acute illness. The patient feels mildly uneasy or indisposed. He may have a "scratchy" sore throat, some headache, or gastrointestinal discomfort, but often he is unable to point out the source of this *malaise*. This *gradual onset* of symptoms is frequently characteristic of infectious disease, but does not always occur. It provides the earliest evidence that may be available of the activities of a pathogenic microorganism, or its products, in host tissues. In some cases it may reflect the general dissemination of the organism through the body from its portal of entry; in others it may coincide with injury developing at the site

of localization of the parasite, for example in the throat or in the gastrointestinal tract. On the other hand, some acute infections have an abrupt onset, illness developing with little or no advance warning.

The Acute Stage of Infectious Disease. This is the period during which host-parasite interactions reach full intensity, producing symptoms of illness corresponding to the degree and the site of resultant injury. The inflammatory response of the host is in full swing, and his immune mechanisms come into play. If this is the host's first encounter with the invading organism, his antibody-producing cells will require time for their response to its antigens, as we know, so that active antibody formation cannot be expected to be protective in the early days of acute illness. An anamnestic antibody response, however, to a pathogen previously encountered, naturally or artificially, may help to shorten the period of acute symptoms or alleviate them. On the other hand, the presence of preformed or developing hypersensitive antibodies is likely to contribute to tissue injury, thus heightening to some degree the symptoms of this period. More usually, however, hypersensitive reactions mark the later stages of chronic infections.

Fever is perhaps the most characteristic and least variable of the symptoms of infection. It is a nonspecific type of response to tissue injury, possibly a defensive mechanism, associated also with many noninfectious diseases, such as malignancies, disorders of the endocrine or central nervous systems, autoimmune hypersensitivities, and others. Fever is apparently induced by mechanical or chemical injury to the centers of temperature regulation in the brain, but the mechanism is not clear. Substances that induce fever (that is, produce a *febrile* reaction) are called *pyrogens*. The endotoxins of certain bacteria are pyrogenic, as are some constituents of leukocytes themselves. It is possible that injury to leukocytes by bacterial pyrogens, during the inflammatory response, results in the liberation of a cellular pyrogenic chemical that stimulates the thermoregulators in the brain.

The pattern of fever seen from day to day in the acute stage of infection may reflect the nature of the disease, its progress, or the manner in which it spreads in the body. In some acute bacterial infections, fever may rise to a peak, continue with little fluctuation while infection persists, then subside as the organism is subdued or eliminated. In other instances, the patient's temperature may fluctuate markedly every few hours, rising and falling between two points. This type of pattern is often seen when "showers" of organisms are released periodically into the blood stream from some localized site in which they are multiplying. The sudden release of numbers of organisms into the blood induces a febrile reaction; therefore, the periodicity and height of the fever peaks may reflect the frequency and the intensity of such releases. When organisms are present in the blood stream, this fact is denoted by attaching the suffix "-emia" to a word descriptive of the microbe involved. Thus, we speak of *bacteremia*, *viremia*, or, more specifically, streptococcemia, staphylococcemia, and so on. Normally, microorganisms that find their way into the blood are easily removed, but in fulminating infections they may disseminate rapidly by this route from an original focus of multiplication to localize in many other sites. This situation is referred to as *septicemia*, meaning sepsis or infection of the blood.

Febrile reactions are also influenced by the age and general condition of the patient. Children, for example, are notorious for their frightening ability to develop sudden high fevers for reasons that may be either quite insignificant or extremely serious. Very old people may also display this kind of unstable temperature control. Patients in shock may have no fever or even a depressed body temperature. It should be pointed out, also, that fever is accompanied by a rise in pulse and respiration rates, as well as general metabolic activity. It often induces restlessness, irritability, loss of appetite, headache, or diffuse pains. Some pathogenic microorganisms may find the host's increased body temperature and metabolic activities antagonistic to their own growth requirements, but fever is not necessarily a defensive mechanism in this sense.

Rash is another frequent characteristic of the acute phase of infectious disease. In some infections, the morphology, or appearance, of the

rash and its distribution on the body may be highly typical and diagnostic, as in the case of scarlet fever, measles, chickenpox, or smallpox. The lesions that appear in the skin (and often in the upper respiratory and oral mucosa as well) are produced differently in various diseases. The cells of the skin may be one of several sites of localization of the organism itself, as in the "pox" diseases; they may be injured by the effects of a circulating toxin, as in scarlet fever; or they may be involved in the host's hypersensitive response to microbial antigens. *Petechial* lesions (from an Italian word meaning "flea bite") appear in the skin when the walls of its small blood vessels rupture, spilling blood into surrounding tissue. If septicemia exists, these petechiae may contain many microorganisms, as in the case of systemic meningococcal infection in which meningococcemia occurs. The rupture of small vessels may occur when their lining cells are injured by microbial constituents or actually infected by microorganisms. The latter occurs in rickettsial infections, such as typhus fever, which are characterized by the appearance of petechial hemorrhages in the skin, often over large areas of the body. The rash of an infection may be very fleeting in its appearance, or it may be pronounced and persistent. When cells of the skin within a particular area die as a result of infection, the local inflammatory reaction may clear the site of cellular debris, leaving no trace. If the damage has been more severe, inflammation may continue to fibrosis and scar formation. This is the case in smallpox, the healed skin lesions remaining as permanent scars, or pocks.

The symptoms of many acute infections are referable to the original or extending sites of localization of the infectious agent. *Nausea, vomiting,* and *diarrhea* are frequent hallmarks of gastrointestinal infection, together with the pain of intestinal spasm. The symptoms of different kinds of intestinal infections may be quite similar; but the time and nature of their onset, their duration and fluctuations, may furnish important clues as to their possible bacterial, viral, or helminthic etiology. Infections of the respiratory tract are also difficult to distinguish by symptomatology, because a cough, sore throat, a catarrhal discharge, and other symptoms of this type are common to many. In a few instances the morphology of a lesion may be characteristic or suggestive; a streptococcal sore throat is typically edematous and red, or "beefy"; in diphtheria a tough pseudomembrane may be formed over the pharynx or the larynx; a purulent exudate is often seen in staphylococcal throat lesions; some virus infections produce small, clear blisters, or vesicles, on the reddened wall of the pharynx. Similarly, the visualization by x-ray of lesions in the lower respiratory tract may be diagnostically useful by revealing their size, shape, density, and distribution. Abscess formation and other manifestations of the inflammatory process, wherever they occur, produce symptoms referable to the local tissue injury. Inflammatory infections of the brain or other central nervous system tissue may be associated with such symptoms as drowsiness, mental confusion, stiffness of the neck, a spastic or flaccid paralysis of involved muscle groups, or other neurologic signs of motor nerve damage.

The Convalescent Stage of Infectious Disease. The patient's survival and recovery from the acute phase of his disease depend on the extent and nature of the damage done, on the strength of his own resistance mechanisms, and on the adequacy of his medical support. When it is possible to offer not only general supportive help, but also specific therapy aimed directly at elimination of the infectious microorganism, the total burden of the disease may be lightened. The acute stage is shortened, the degree of damage done or threatened is less, and the strain on constitutional reserves is lifted.

The convalescent phase begins with the decline of fever, often accompanied by a feeling of weakness but infinite improvement. It is at this point that antibody production has usually reached a peak, and if the level is sufficiently high as well as protective, it contributes significantly to the final inactivation or destruction of the infecting organism. The persistence of antibody may then provide the individual with a long-lasting immunity, in some cases. It should be noted, also, that prompt, successful antibiotic therapy may not only abort the disease but also lower the level of antibody production by eliminating the antigenic stimulus at an early stage.

The speed and completeness of recovery in any case are determined by the nature of any injury induced, its extent and permanence or reversibility.

The Stages of Chronic Infectious Disease

A persistent, chronic relationship between a host and a given parasite may remain unnoticeable, if the latter exerts no pressures the host cannot readily encompass. More usually, chronicity of infection is characterized by a rise and fall of symptoms referable to the activities of the parasite, or its products, and the host's responses to them. These responses often involve the reactions of hypersensitivity, as described previously.

The symptoms may be similar and acute each time the parasite enters an ascendant phase; they may be of diminished character (subacute) if the host's defenses are more effective; or they may change in quality altogether, and increase in intensity, if new tissues become involved in extending infection or in hypersensitive responses. Syphilis affords an excellent example of the latter situation. It is a long and slowly progressive disease whose direction is marked off into three stages, each with a different symptomatology. Tuberculosis is also a chronic disease that may be slowly or rapidly progressive. In both these instances, hypersensitive changes contribute to the tissue injury and are reflected in the permutation of symptoms as time passes. Nonetheless, the pattern of chronic infections reflects the seesaw equilibrium between the two antagonists, just as it does in acute infections, although the level of reaction is different.

The Laboratory Diagnosis of Infectious Disease

The laboratory has two essential functions with regard to clinically significant infections: (1) it can establish or confirm the etiology either by isolating and identifying the agent or by providing proof of specific antibody response in the patient; and (2) when the responsible microorganism can be cultivated in isolation, the laboratory can provide information as to its antibiotic susceptibility in vitro. In this regard it can also assist in the evaluation of antibiotic therapy by testing the patient's serum for its level of antibiotic activity.

Specimens for Microbiologic Diagnosis

The laboratory diagnosis of infectious disease begins with the *proper collection of the right specimen at the optimum time*. For this reason an adequate liaison is essential between the laboratory, the physician, and the nursing service (when the patient is hospitalized). The laboratory depends on the physician for information concerning the possible nature of the infection so that it can apply the most appropriate methods to the isolation of the pathogen. The physician, in turn, may find the laboratory's advice useful with respect to the selection and timing of the specimen. The hospital nurse's role is frequently the essential one of assuring the collection of the desired material at the right time, in a specified manner, and its prompt transportation to the laboratory. She must also be alert to the laboratory's dependence on full identification of the specimen, as to patient, type of material, time of collection, and the nature of the studies desired. The *individual* nursing floor in a hospital may have many such specimens to prepare in a day; the laboratory receives these and as many more, perhaps, from *each* nursing floor or outpatient clinic in the same day (see Fig. 8–1). The patient ill with an infectious disease must depend on physician, nurse, and laboratory to collaborate effectively in the selection, timing, collection, and subsequent handling of his specimen so that prompt, accurate diagnosis and treatment may be assured. Neighboring hospitalized patients must depend on this same group to provide them security from cross-infection, particularly during the interval that may elapse between correct diagnosis and appropriate treatment of the infectious case.

The many kinds of specimens that may be sent to the laboratory for the isolation and identification of significant pathogens include blood, urine, feces, sputum, and pus from draining wounds most commonly, because they are most readily obtained. Infectious microorganisms may be found, however, in a variety of tissues and body fluids from which specimens may have to be taken by surgery, needle aspiration (bone marrow, cerebrospinal fluid, pleural or peritoneal exudates), or intubation (bile drainage). The search for the suspected agent of a given infection may have to take several directions before it is found, but often the clinical signs of localization direct the selection of the most appropriate type of specimen. Blood samples are frequently rewarding, particularly when the patient is febrile but does not immediately present symptoms of localizing infection. Specimens of blood repeatedly drawn over the course of a "spike" of fever may contain the organism being "showered" into the blood stream from some local area of multiplication.

Knowledge of the usual clinical course of a given infection, together with careful observation of the presenting signs of the individual case, guides the selection of appropriate specimens for the laboratory. The timing of their collection must be geared, by the same token, to the rise of symptoms, rather than their fall, if the responsible pathogen is to be recovered in a viable, active state, not significantly affected by host defenses. It is essential, also, that specimens for laboratory culture be taken before antibiotic therapy is initiated. Antibiotics may not only affect the viability of microorganisms in the tissues; they may also remain active in the specimen to interfere with the growth, or change the metabolic characteristics, of organisms sought by in vitro techniques. In view of these considerations, the *right* specimen appears to be one dictated by the nature and localization of the patient's symptoms, while its *optimum timing* corresponds with their development. In acute infectious diseases, blood samples drawn during the prodromal period may yield microorganisms being disseminated silently from an original point of entry, but the stage of acute illness is most

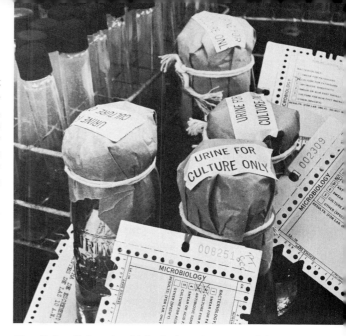

Fig. 8–1. If the microbiologist is to be successful in his search for microorganisms of pathogenic significance in patients' specimens, he must receive appropriate clinical material collected in suitable containers. Specimens and their accompanying request slips must be labeled correctly and fully. (Courtesy of St. Luke's Hospital Center, New York, N.Y.)

likely to reveal organisms not only in the blood but in specimens representing an area of tissue localization (a swab from the throat or an excised lesion, sputum, feces, aspirated spinal fluid, pus from an abscess, and so on). Similarly, throughout the course of a chronic infection specimens collected from involved tissues at the height of recurring symptoms offer the laboratory the best opportunity for isolation and identification of the responsible agent.

The *proper collection* of specimens involves not merely their sterile or aseptic transfer into sterile containers, but such equally important factors as a *quantity* adequate for the necessary studies; *material representative of infection* rather than of the commensal, contaminating flora of the region; and *prompt examination* by the laboratory. The volume of the specimen obtained for testing is often critical. For example, small numbers of significant organisms may not be detected unless a large specimen sample is available for concentration. A generous volume is also necessary

when several culture methods and tests must be performed on the same specimen. When cultures are to be made of material that can be expected to contain commensalistic organisms, it is essential to collect the specimen so that the source of infectious organisms is also represented. Thus, a draining abscess should not be sampled at its surface, where the normal flora of the skin may be predominant, but from its deep interior, where the pathogenic agent can be found. In respiratory infections a sputum sample or a throat swab should be chosen according to localization of lesions, and the inclusion of saliva in the sample should be avoided in either case. The interval between collection and examination of the specimen must be as brief as possible to assure the survival of fastidious pathogens, despite the presence of hardier, antagonistic organisms or other components of the specimen which may be deleterious to them (phagocytic action may continue in a sample of pus, urine may be too acid or alkaline, antibiotic residues may be active).

It should also be carefully noted that clinical specimens are selected and sent to the laboratory for culture because it is hoped or expected that they may contain viable pathogenic agents of infectious disease. For this reason, every such specimen must be considered as itself a potential source of the disease for all who handle it. Careless manipulation of the specimen when it is placed in its container may contaminate the hands of the physician or the nurse, the outer surfaces of the vessel, or the request slip accompanying it. The messenger who transports the container is then also subjected to the risk of contaminated hands or clothing, as are the laboratory personnel who subsequently work with the specimen. Each of these people, in turn, may have many continuing contacts with others — patients, other personnel, friends and family at home — all of whom may form a communicating chain for the transfer of an infection. It is essential therefore that every specimen be handled with thoughtful care, placed in a container of adequate size to retain it without spilling, and fitted with a tight closure. If adjacent surfaces are contaminated by the specimen during its

collection, they should be promptly and carefully disinfected with an effective germicidal agent, kept conveniently at hand for this purpose, before those surfaces are touched again. In the microbiology laboratory, all the techniques and equipment used in the handling of specimens and cultures are designed to reduce the risk of cross-infection to a minimum, both within the laboratory and beyond it. The same principles of aseptic care must be applied at the patient's bedside and throughout the hospital.

The Functions of the Microbiology Laboratory

The clinical appearance of some infectious diseases may be so well related to their etiology as to give the physician a reasonably firm basis for diagnosis and the selection of antibiotic therapy. More often, however, the symptoms of infection do not clearly indicate the nature of the organism producing them, but may point to a few alternate choices. In either case, the laboratory isolation and identification of the infectious agent or an immunologic confirmation of the clinical diagnosis or both are desirable. When the etiology of a given disease can be established by the laboratory, the therapeutic approach is more secure.

The isolation and identification of a pathogenic microorganism frequently begin with the microscopic examination of stained or unstained preparations of the appropriate specimen. An immediate report of the findings in stained smears or wet mounts of the material may be very useful to the physician at this point, even if no organisms can be seen or if those that are visualized cannot be completely identified (see Fig. 8–2). Preliminary microscopic work can be valuable also in guiding the microbiologist as to the direction to be taken in selecting the optimum cultural method, or other procedure, for a conclusive identification of the organism sought. When smears reveal nothing of significance, clinical information as to the possible nature of the infection becomes particularly important in the planning of cultures, since there is no one

method that can assure the isolation of every pathogenic microorganism.

The general techniques of preparing cultures and pursuing the identification of isolated organisms have been described in Chapter 4. Recommended procedures for the laboratory diagnosis of individual infectious diseases are discussed and tabulated in Part Two. Pertinent tables may also be found in Appendixes I, II, and III.

Demonstration of specific antibody response in the patient may be obtained by the study of the patient's serum in the serology laboratory or by the application of appropriate skin-testing antigens. The term "serology" is commonly reserved for the study of serum for its antibody content only, as opposed to its chemical analysis. As discussed in the preceding chapter, a number of serologic methods can be applied to the recognition of antibody in vitro. Agglutination, precipitation, and complement-fixation tests may be chosen, depending on the nature of the antibody suspected and on the type of antigen available. Neutralization and protective tests are frequently used as well, particularly in viral infections.

Correct timing of the collection of blood samples is often particularly critical in serologic work, because immunologic diagnosis often requires the demonstration of a *rising* level of antibody as infectious disease proceeds from the acute to the convalescent phase. The presence of antibody in a single serum sample may reflect *either* current infection or some previous exposure to the specific antigen, but an increasing quantity of the antibody in serum specimens drawn as the disease progresses provides strong evidence that the antigen is now involved in the infectious process. Since antibody formation can be slow, particularly on first exposure, it is important that blood samples be spaced in such a way as to reflect the change in the patient's symptoms, without allowing too much or too little time to elapse, so that corresponding antibody changes can be demonstrated definitively.

The discussion of diseases in Part Two provides information on each as to the availability of a reliable serologic method of diagnosis, the nature

of the test, and its timing. The use of appropriate skin testing antigens is also described, and the interpretation of skin reactivity is indicated.

Antibiotic susceptibility testing may provide information of clinical value when the organism tested has been isolated in pure culture and appears to bear an etiologic relationship to the patient's disease. If the physician has instituted chemotherapy before the laboratory's report is received, the result may confirm his choice of drugs or lead him to modify it. If the patient's condition permits, therapy may be delayed until the results of culture and antibiotic testing can determine the drug of choice. During the course of treatment, the laboratory can also perform tests on the patient's serum to determine whether the drug and the dosage being given are adequate. The serum is tested against the infectious agent, previously isolated, and reported for its ability to inhibit the growth of the organism. The extent to which the serum can be diluted and still display bactericidal activity is a measure of its content of adequate antibiotic.

Fig. 8–2. A specimen has been submitted to the microbiology laboratory for smear and culture for tubercle bacilli. The smear showed the presence of acid-fast bacilli, and the report of this finding is ready for the physician. Since several weeks may be required to grow and identify the organism in culture, the early smear report is of great value in this instance and will be weighed with other evidence required for the correct diagnosis and treatment of the patient. (Courtesy of St. Luke's Hospital Center, New York, N.Y.)

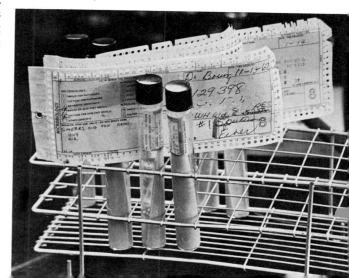

The techniques of antibiotic susceptibility testing are described in Chapter 4, together with some of the factors that may influence the results and their interpretation.

Questions

1. List the clinical stages of acute infectious disease.
2. Define pyrogen, bacteremia, viremia, septicemia.
3. What two essential functions does the laboratory have in regard to clinically significant infections?
4. What are the nurse's responsibilities in the collection of microbial specimens?

References

Pertinent References

Bailey, Robert W., and Scott, Elvyn G.: *Diagnostic Microbiology*, 2nd ed. C. V. Mosby Co., St. Louis, 1966.

Conant, Norman F., Smith, D. T., Baker, R. D., Callaway, J. L., and Martin, D. S.: *Manual of Clinical Mycology*, 2nd ed. W. B. Saunders, Philadelphia, 1954.

Dubos, René J.: *Bacterial and Mycotic Infections in Man*, 4th ed. Lippincott, Philadelphia, 1965.

Faust, Ernest, and Russell, Paul Farr: *Craig and Faust's Clinical Parasitology*, 7th ed. Lea and Febiger, Philadelphia, 1965.

Gillies, R. R., and Dodds, T. C.: *Bacteriology Illustrated*. Williams & Wilkins Co., Baltimore, 1965.

Harris, Albert H., and Coleman, Marion B.: *Diagnostic Procedures and Reagents*, 4th ed. Amer. Pub. Hlth. Assoc., Inc., New York, 1963.

Horsfall, Frank L., Jr., and Tamm, Igor: *Viral and Rickettsial Infections in Man*, 4th ed. J. B. Lippincott, Philadelphia, 1965.

Jawetz, Ernest, J. L. Melnick, and Adelberg, E. A.: *Review of Medical Microbiology*, 7th ed. Lange Medical Publications, Los Altos, Calif., 1966.

Schneierson, S. Stanley: *Atlas of Diagnostic Microbiology*. Abbott Laboratories, North Chicago, Ill., 1965.

Smith, D. T., and Conant, N. F.: *Zinsser's Microbiology*, 12th ed. Appleton, New York, 1960.

Periodicals

Dlouhy, A., Erickson, S. M., Jedlicka, B., Imburgia, F., Ipavec, J., and Kiewlich, S.: What Patients Want to Know About Their Diagnostic Tests, *Nurs. Outlook*, 11: 265, April, 1963.

Mizer, Helen E.: The Tapeworm and the Noodle, *Amer. J. Nurs.* 63: 102, July, 1963.

Mohammed, Mary R. B.: Urinalysis, *Amer. J. Nurs.*, 64: 87, June, 1964.

Section III Epidemiology and Infection Control

9 The Sources, Routes, and Patterns of Infectious Diseases

Epidemiology

The science of *epidemiology* is concerned with the definition of the many factors contributed by the *agents* of disease, the reactive *host*, and the *environment* that *together* determine the occurrence of disease in a given population over a stated course of time. In its original sense the word applied to the study of *epidemics*, that is, of infectious communicable diseases that fell upon large numbers of people simultaneously or in rapid succession. The Greek words *epi* (upon) and *demos* (people) combine to provide this earlier concept of the study of mass outbreaks occurring as distinct episodes. Later, when the microbial agents of many infectious diseases were recognized, it became apparent that they do not always produce disease in epidemic patterns but may be implicated also in occasional, *sporadic* cases. Furthermore, an epidemic outbreak may be limited to very small numbers of people, its size depending in part on the state of resistance to the parasite in question existing at the time in that particular population. It is now apparent, also, that a specific parasite may have a widespread, persistent distribution in a given

Probe
The IT

Washington

The House Judiciary Committee published yesterday voluminous documentation on the tangled web known as "the ITT affair."

But no document substantiated conclusively an allegation that the Nixon administration's settlement of an antitrust suit against the International Telephone and Telegraph Corp. was in re-

She Died of A Splinter

San Diego

Arline Devine, 54, was moving a few pieces of lumber June 29 and ignored the splinter in her finger.

By July 5 she had muscle spasms and the beginnings of lockjaw. Mrs. Devine died this week of lockjaw, the San Diego county coroner's office said yesterday.

Associated Press

7-20-74

host population, as indicated by numerous sub-clinical infections, while the cases of clinical illness attributable to the organism are few, but relatively uniform in number from one time to another. When this is the case, the disease is said to be *endemic*, or "in the people."

The modern concept of epidemiology embraces the entire biography of a disease with respect to its patterns of incidence as these are influenced by the parasite (or other agent), the host populations affected, and environmental factors (see Fig. 9–1). The term is often extended to the study of any condition or circumstance that is viewed in the light of the many interlocking influences that determine its occurrence, distribution, and effect on man's welfare and health. Thus, one may speak of the epidemiology of a particular infection (such as diphtheria or smallpox), or of a noninfectious disease (such as diabetes or arthritis), or of defined social conditions and experiences (such as alcoholism, narcotic addiction, poverty), and so on.

In preceding chapters, emphasis has been placed on the major contributions of the parasite, on the one hand, and of the host, on the other, to the causation and course of individual infectious disease. In this section, we shall discuss some of the influences exerted on host and microorganism by their natural, shared environment, examining the intersecting role of the latter in the epidemiology of infection. The environmental sources and transmission routes of infection may afford a given parasite large, or limited, opportunities for survival and host transfer (that is, they affect its *communicability*). These same factors may also influence the patterns and severity of disease as it occurs in human and other host groups. With knowledge of the epidemiologic basis of infectious disease, we can then consider how it can best be prevented or controlled, by measures designed either to destroy the parasite, to control its environmental existence and distribution, or to improve the resistance of the host, or by any feasible combination of these approaches. Epidemiologic principles form the basis for all methods of controlling infection and they are applicable in handling a single case of communicable disease, or in large-scale problems of public health protection.

The Communicability of Infection

Many microorganisms are capable of survival under a very wide range of environmental and host conditions because of their versatile metabolic mechanisms. This is particularly true of the fungi and the bacteria, which as a group display a marked capacity for a saprophytic life as well as for parasitism. Among the other major classes of organisms with which we are concerned, the parasitic worms on the one hand and the viruses on the other occupy opposite extremes on a scale that measures the ability of structurally simple forms to live, respectively, freely as saprophytes or dependently as obligate parasites. It is obvious, however, that the ubiquitous distribution of microorganisms and their capacity for survival in a variety of situations cannot alone account for the incidence of infectious diseases, else the latter would be overwhelmingly high among human beings and animal hosts. We have seen that the incidence of *disease* versus *infection* can be explained partly by the fact that only a relatively few microorganisms possess the qualities of pathogenicity required to induce host tissue injury and partly by the opposing fact of host resistance mechanisms.

The question then arises: how can we account for the *distribution* of infection and infectious disease, attributable to a given organism of reasonably well-defined pathogenic quality, among human or other host populations possessing the same, or similar, defensive properties? In other words, why are some diseases more *communicable* than others among human or animal populations, or both; and why do some have little epidemiologic importance in terms of their impact on a particular population species? The answer is again twofold: it depends in part on the available *sources* of infection from which disease may arise and in part on the ease and direction of the transferral, or *transmission*, of pathogenic microorganisms from such sources to susceptible hosts.

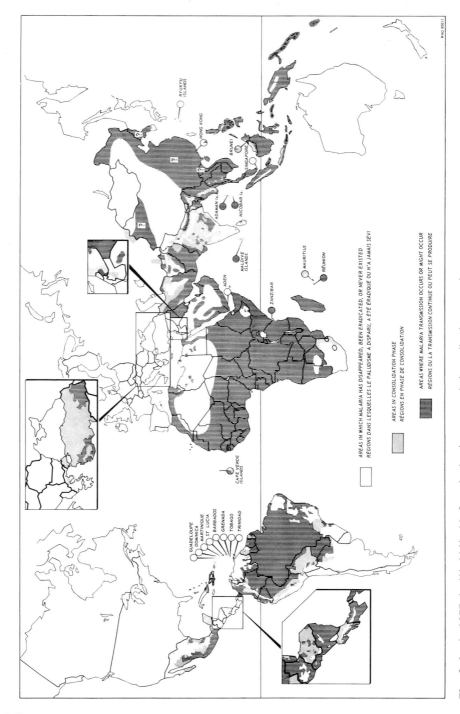

Fig. 9–1. In 1955 the World Health Organization began a malaria eradication campaign that continues to be one of the greatest ventures in public health the world has ever seen. This map provides an epidemiologic assessment of the status of malaria as of June, 1967. (Courtesy of World Health Organization, Geneva, Switzerland.)

The Sources of Infection

Microorganisms are not sentient; they simply reproduce and multiply wherever and whenever conditions, and their own capacities, permit them to do so. If the focus of their activities happens to lie within the body of another living organism that succumbs to the total effect of their presence, the end of the line may be reached, not only for the goose that laid the golden egg, but also for the insentient parasite, unless the latter is by some means transferred to another milieu in which it can continue to live and multiply. The site of colonization of a living host by the parasite determines whether or not transmission is possible and, if so, the ease with which it may be passed along, by a direct or indirect route, to other hosts. An organism localized in deep tissues and organs, without access to the body's excretions and secretions, may not have a portal of exit from the body under normal circumstances or be an epidemiologic threat to others unless some intermediary agent is able to effect a transfer to another host. A biting or blood-sucking insect, for instance, may effectively carry certain microorganisms from the blood stream or tissues of one host to those of another and maintain them in transit. Exudates from the mouth and upper respiratory tract, or discharges from the intestinal and genitourinary tracts, offer the simplest means of escape for many microorganisms that infect the human or other animal host. The total concept of communicability of infection depends, therefore, on the continuing survival of microorganisms from a source of multiplication through their transit to another host.

A local environment, medium, or milieu that supports the survival and multiplication of pathogenic microorganisms is spoken of as a *reservoir of infection.* An infected, though not necessarily clinically diseased, human, animal, or insect host may constitute a *living* reservoir. There are also many environmental media (soil, air, food and milk, water) that may serve as *inanimate* reservoirs of infection. In the full epidemiologic sense, a reservoir can be said to exist when an animate or inanimate medium provides a pathogenic microorganism with adequate conditions for its maintenance over a prolonged period of time and *also* provides opportunities for its transmission to a new, susceptible host.

Living Reservoirs of Infection. The chief reservoir of many important human infections is *man* himself. Very many people, whether or not they display symptoms of clinical disease, harbor pathogenic organisms and transmit them, directly or indirectly, to others. The most obvious of the human sources of infection are, of course, those people who are recognizably ill with a disease that is communicable. This source is also the most readily controlled, when promptly and accurately diagnosed, for the sick individual can be confined at home or in the hospital. The potential reservoir he represents is then restricted so that transmission of the pathogen is limited or impossible, while treatment of the patient is aimed at destruction of the parasite.

The largest continuing human reservoir, and the most difficult one to recognize or control, is comprised of the large number of people who are subclinically infected with one or more pathogenic agents of communicable disease. Infected individuals with only mild symptoms of illness, or none at all, circulate freely in the community, often communicating their infections as they go. This is true, also, of people who are in the incubation or prodromal period of a developing clinical illness who may transmit their disease to others before their own becomes apparent. The infected person who displays no symptoms and develops no illness referable to the parasite he harbors is often spoken of as a "carrier." It must be remembered, however, that the term "carrier" is epidemiologically applicable only if the infection being carried is transmissible to other persons. This is true also for all clinical or subclinical infections. As pointed out above, the availability to the parasite of a portal of exit and a route of transmission is as necessary to its communicability as a site of survival and multiplication.

When an acute infection subsides, the causative pathogen may remain alive, though subdued,

during the patient's convalescence, for weeks, months, or even years after his recovery. The convalescent may thus become a carrier and remain so for as long as he harbors the viable, transmissible parasite. The epidemiologic control of carriers of important communicable diseases is directed primarily at preventing the formation of environmental reservoirs, such as the contamination, by infected persons, of food and water supplies that could involve large numbers of other people.

Man is the reservoir for many of the diseases that afflict him, but not for all. In many instances he may be involved along with other animals, or with insects, as well as the inanimate media of his environment, in the harboring and transferral of infection. When a pathogenic organism is capable of survival in a wide variety of situations, can maintain itself outside of living tissues as well as within those of differing species, and is transmissible from one to another, it may have multiple reservoirs in nature.

Animal reservoirs of infection are a frequent threat to human health in all parts of the world. The infectious diseases of animals that can be transmitted to man are called *zoonoses* (from the Greek words *zoon* for animal, *nosos* for disease). The pathogenic agents of the zoonoses are included in every major group of microorganisms: fungi, bacteria, viruses and rickettsiae, protozoa, and helminths. Human beings may acquire these infections through direct handling of animals and their products, by eating meat or other products from diseased animals, or through the bite of insects that prey on both animals and man. There are a few zoonoses for which infected human beings also serve as reservoirs, capable of transferring their infection directly to other people (as in the case of many *Salmonella* and streptococcal infections) or indirectly through another host or vector (for instance the systemic protozoan diseases, leishmaniasis and trypanosomiasis, transmitted between human beings and animals by biting insects). For the most part, however, man is an accidental, or tangential, victim of the majority of the zoonoses. The infected human individual does not constitute a reservoir for such infections as rabies, anthrax, brucellosis, or trichinosis, because he has no role in their transfer to other hosts.

In a later section of this chapter dealing with sources of infection, the important infectious diseases of man are grouped according to their reservoirs. The zoonoses that infected human beings can and do transfer to others are included in group 4; those that are not kept going in nature by man are listed in group 5. The student will observe that man is the primary source of those infectious diseases that trouble him most frequently.

The *insects* commonly involved in the transfer of infectious agents from one reservoir to another belong in the invertebrate phylum *Arthropoda* (literally, jointed feet, from the Greek words *arthron* for joint and *pod* for foot). There are several classes of arthropods but only two, the *Insecta* and the *Arachnida*, contain members that are important as *vectors* of infection. The class Insecta includes the flies, mosquitoes, fleas, lice, and the true bugs; the Arachnida include ticks and mites (see Figs. 9–2 to 9–7). Most of these arthropod vectors are parasitic themselves, preying on vertebrate animals as a source of blood, a rich protein nutrient from the insect's point of view. An enormous variety of animals — wild birds and domestic poultry, rodents and small game, wild and domestic animals — offer the parasitic insects a source of support. When a biting or blood-sucking insect preys on an infected host, it may pick up infectious microorganisms in its blood meal and later deposit them on or inoculate them into the skin or mucous membranes of another individual of the same or a different species. Thus a number of unrelated animal species may be linked together in the epidemiology of an infectious disease through the activities of an insect vector.

Often the parasitic arthropod becomes a true host to the pathogenic microorganism; that is, the insect is itself infected, affording the microorganism another site of multiplication or of development. There are some instances in which a microbial parasite actually requires an arthropod host to support it through developmental changes that are essential to the maintenance of its life cycle. This is the case, for example, with

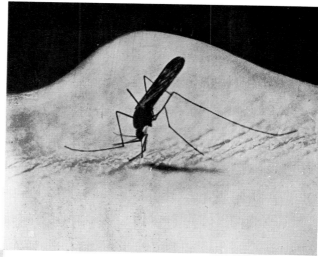

Fig. 9–2. The *mosquito vector* of the malarial parasite. (Reproduced from Herms, William B., and James, Maurice T.: *Medical Entomology*, 5th ed. The Macmillan Co., New York, 1961.)

Fig. 9–3. (*Left*) The *tsetse fly*, vector of the agent of African sleeping sickness. (Reproduced from Herms, William B., and James, Maurice T.: *Medical Entomology*, 5th ed. The Macmillan Co., New York, 1961.)

Fig. 9–4. (*Right*) Two adult *fleas*, an egg, and the larval forms of the insect. This type of arthropod can transmit the plague bacillus from rats to man. (Reproduced from Herms, William B., and James, Maurice T.: *Medical Entomology*, 5th ed. The Macmillan Co., New York, 1961.)

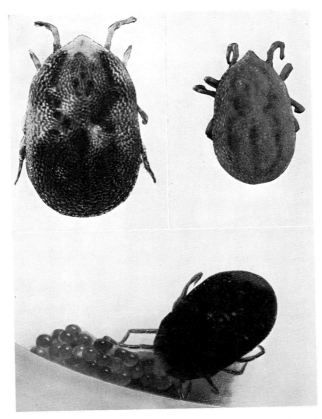

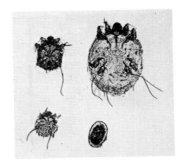

Fig. 9–6. An adult *mite* (the largest of the forms shown) and three developmental stages. This type of insect is involved in the transmission of scrub typhus, a rickettsial disease of the Far East. (Reproduced from Herms, William B., and James, Maurice T.: *Medical Entomology,* 5th ed. The Macmillan Co., New York, 1961.)

Fig. 9–5. One variety of *tick* involved in the transmission of infectious disease. (Note the female depositing eggs, center bottom.) (Reproduced from Herms, William B., and James, Maurice T.: *Medical Entomology*, 5th ed. The Macmillan Co., New York, 1961.)

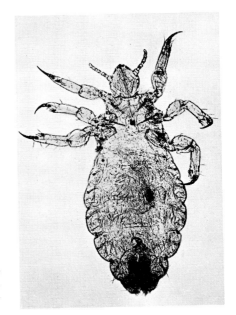

Fig. 9–7. (*Right*) The human body *louse*, vector of *epidemic typhus fever,* a rickettsial disease. (Reproduced from Herms, William B., and James, Maurice T.: *Medical Entomology,* 5th ed. The Macmillan Co., New York, 1961.)

the malarial parasite, which undergoes a sexual stage of development in its mosquito host. Certain helminthic parasites, such as the fish tapeworm and the filarial roundworms, also pass through a portion of their life cycles in an arthropod host. Some pathogenic species of bacteria, viruses, and rickettsiae maintain themselves within their insect hosts throughout the latter's lifetime. The insect itself is not necessarily diseased by this parasitism, and in some instances it may even transmit infecting microbes, through its eggs, to its own succeeding generations. Whether or not the insect dies as a result of its infection, remains unaffected, or transmits it to its progeny, the parasitic type of arthropod vector can be considered a *reservoir* of infection, in the true sense, when it maintains and transfers the microbial agents of infectious disease to man, animals, or both. Insects that serve as host and reservoir for infectious agents are often referrred to as *biologic vectors* to distinguish them from those that function merely as *mechanical carriers* of microorganisms from one reservoir to another.

There are a number of nonparasitic arthropods that have been incriminated as mechanical, or passive, vectors of infection. Chief among these are houseflies and cockroaches, but only the former have been indicted by conclusive evidence that they can, and do, transfer infectious microbial pathogens to human beings. These insects are saprophytic in their nutrient habits; flies, in particular, are notorious for feeding on, and breeding in, organic wastes, such as human and animal excrement and garbage of all kinds. Unlike their parasitic, biting relatives, houseflies do not feed directly on human beings or animals, but they do visit intimately with them and they are capable of transmitting their microorganisms back and forth in a passive transport. Flies may ingest microbial parasites, and although they do not support them for long, they may later deposit them by defecation or regurgitation on any surface they light upon. They also carry microorganisms around on their hairy legs, depositing them in an invisible trail (see Fig. 9–8). The communicability of infections carried in such a mechanical way then depends on a number of

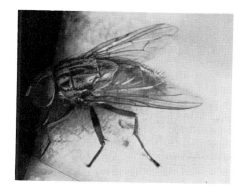

Fig. 9–8.   The *housefly,* a nonparasitic insect that may serve as a mechanical vector of infectious disease. (Reproduced from Herms, William B., and James, Maurice T.: *Medical Entomology,* 5th ed. The Macmillan Co., New York, 1961.)

other factors, such as the density of flies and of infectious microorganisms in reservoirs available to the passive vector; the speed of transfer of a fastidious pathogen to a new source of support; the point of entry to, and the susceptibility of, a new exposed host. In other words, nonparasitic insects do not constitute true reservoirs of infection, but they serve as mechanical transmitting vehicles for microbial agents, contributing to the further spread of infectious disease only when other conditions also permit.

Inanimate Reservoirs of Infection.   In his earliest days man envisioned his life on this planet as dependent on four elements: "earth, air, fire, and water." If we apply a broad interpretation to the word "fire" so that it includes our modern concepts of nutrients as physiologic fuels, we can see that all living things coexisting with man on our planet share the wealth of these vital elements, and that most of them contribute to that wealth and replenish it throughout their continuing existence. In previous sections of this text (see Chaps. 2, 3, and 5) a broad picture has been painted of the ecology of living organisms and, in particular, of the nutrient requirements and metabolic behavior of microorganisms that permit their ubiquitous distribution through every segment of man's world. At this point, let us

consider how the inanimate, basic elements essential to life — *earth*, *air*, *food*, and *water* — may be reservoirs for pathogenic microorganisms and thus play a part in the epidemiology of infectious disease.

The *soil of the earth* teems with microorganisms, most of which are totally without pathogenicity for man. In general, the only *natural inhabitants* of the soil that may be pathogenic for man are *fungi* and the anaerobic bacterial sporeformer, *Clostridium botulinum*. The spores of *fungi* are capable of long-term survival on dry surfaces, but the vegetation and reproduction of these simple plants require moist, nutrient soil. The great majority of fungi are saprophytic, but there are a few species of yeasts and molds with a low-grade capacity for parasitism. These may cause infections in man through his direct contacts with the soil, which constitutes their primary reservoir, or with dried earth blown about as dust. The virulent and invasive properties of the pathogenic fungi are not great, so that when they do come in contact with the tissues of the human body the infection that results is characteristically chronic and persistent, rather than acute. The resistance of the human host to fungous infections varies greatly, also, so that contact with the reservoir and the ease of transmission do not alone assure disease, by any means. The fungous diseases are frequently referred to as *mycoses*. *Systemic* mycoses, or fungous infections of deep tissues and organs, include such diseases as coccidioidomycosis, blastomycosis, histoplasmosis, cryptococcosis, and a few others. These diseases may be chronic and threatening if the organisms survive and multiply slowly in the body, inducing progressive tissue destruction through increasing host reactivity to them. It must be noted that the agents of the *superficial* mycoses (that is, the fungous diseases of skin, hair, or nails, commonly referred to as *ringworm* infections) have a primary reservoir in infected man or animals and are transmitted from these living sources rather than from the soil.

Clostridium botulinum, a sporeforming anaerobic bacterial species responsible for the acute type of food poisoning called *botulism*, also has a primary reservoir in the soil. The organism can be isolated from the feces of domestic animals that graze on soil containing it in abundance, and from the intestinal tract of fish, but it is very rarely found as a commensal in the human intestine. As described in Chapter 6, botulism results from the ingestion of foods in which the vegetative form of these bacilli have been multiplying and producing exotoxin. Most human cases are acquired from eating unheated canned, smoked, salted, or spiced foods in which the spores of *Cl. botulinum* have survived and subsequently have had an opportunity to germinate and multiply under anaerobic conditions.

The soil may also serve as a *secondary* reservoir for some types of organisms whose *primary source* is the intestinal tract of human beings or animals or both. However, this is true only for those pathogenic agents that are capable of surviving — if not multiplying — in the soil through any period that may elapse before they can enter a new host. The intestinal viruses (such as poliomyelitis virus), for instance, cannot remain alive for long outside of viable host cells; consequently, their transfer from contaminated soil by mechanical vectors or by direct means must be very rapid, as there are no durable inanimate reservoirs for them. On the other hand, the sporeforming bacteria of the intestinal tract, protozoans, and the eggs or larvae of intestinal helminths can and do survive in soil, retaining their infectivity long enough to be communicable from a secondary soil reservoir. The aerobic sporeforming bacteria of the genus *Bacillus* fall into a number of species, one of which, *B. anthracis*, is highly pathogenic for man and his domestic animals. The anthrax bacillus, as it is also called, probably does not multiply continuously in soil, for the latter does not provide optimum conditions for its growth, but it forms spores under these conditions. Anthrax spores are very resistant to environmental stresses, remain viable for long periods of time in soil or in the hides, wool, and hair of infected animals, and germinate into vegetative, reproductive bacillary forms on ingestion or inhalation by a new host. The spores of the anaerobic intestinal bacteria of the *Clostridium* genus are similarly

capable of a long survival in soil or dust. Some of the intestinal protozoa can live and reproduce in the soil, at least for short periods, in areas that are sufficiently moist, nutrient, and moderately acid. The protozoan agent of amebic dysentery, *Endamoeba histolytica*, however, does not survive well in soil, although it may find a secondary reservoir in water and food supplies. The eggs of several species of roundworms, and of some tapeworms, find their way to the soil from their primary reservoir in the intestines of infected human beings or animals. The eggs of some species, such as hookworm, may hatch in the soil and go through a period of larval development there, the larvae being infective for new hosts.

In the sense that soil generally does not support the actual multiplication of many pathogenic organisms, but merely offers conditions that permit their survival or some developmental changes, it is a *limited*, rather than a true, reservoir. The route of transmission of pathogenic bacteria, protozoa, and helminths from the soil to a human host may be direct, as in the case of the fungi, or quite indirect by way of other animal hosts, as we shall see in the next section of this chapter.

Air in its pure state does not supply nutrients for any living organisms, though it is vital to their respiratory processes, affording the means for an exchange of gaseous elements essential to their metabolic cycles. Pure air is a gaseous medium in which are mixed reasonably constant quantities of oxygen and nitrogen, a variable content of carbon dioxide and vaporized water, and minute amounts of other gases not utilized by metabolizing organisms. In practical terms, however, air is never pure, for it is constantly being contaminated by dust from the soil, by various volatile products of human activities (such as those carried by smoke), and by respiratory secretions forcibly expelled from the mouth, nose, and throat of human beings. These secretions, in particular, afford the air a certain proteinaceous content that can support the survival of microorganisms for varying periods, depending on the latters' capacities and requirements. They also carry with them, into the air, a burden of microorganisms uprooted from their

localizing sites in the human respiratory mucosa.

In the course of normal social communications, human beings talk, laugh, clear their throats, and thus gently expel their respiratory secretions into the air surrounding them. When their respiratory tracts are irritated by infection, or by other agents, they may cough and sneeze, spraying the air over greater distances with large quantities of finely scattered mucus and its content of commensalistic or potentially pathogenic microorganisms. This mucous spray takes the form of *droplets* of various size, containing protein, and heavy with moisture. These droplets may initially travel a few inches or 2 or 3 ft, depending on the force with which they are expelled, and make direct contact with other individuals nearby. When left free in the air, the heavier droplets settle out quickly, contaminating objects and surfaces on which they happen to fall. The lighter ones hang in the air for a longer time, gradually losing their moisture by evaporation and becoming lighter still, until they are mere *droplet nuclei* of flaked, dry protein, usually with microorganisms still clinging to or held within them. Many pathogenic microorganisms contained within such droplets or droplet nuclei are capable of surviving long enough in air, or on the surfaces they settle upon, to remain infectious for other individuals. Particles of contaminated soil, contributed to the air as dust, also add to its content of microorganisms, some of them potentially pathogenic, perhaps, for the human beings who inhale them. Microorganisms cannot actually multiply in air, but they can remain alive while they are protected from total drying within droplets, droplet nuclei, and dust particles, and they may even be supported by the moisture and protein content of droplets. Pathogenic agents may be widely disseminated upon air currents, or they may be transmitted by other mechanical means, to new susceptible hosts.

For all these reasons, air, like contaminated soil, is a *limited*, *secondary* reservoir of infection. It is also a vehicle of transmission for many different types of microorgansims, most of which enter and exit from the human respiratory tract. Pathogenic microorganisms may be discharged from the human or animal body by other routes,

however, notably from the intestinal and genitourinary tracts, or from open wounds. Discharges from such sources contain protein and other microbial nutrient, moisture, and often many potentially infectious organisms. Such material may contaminate the soil or any of the myriad objects with which man surrounds himself, including his clothing. As it dries, its protein particles become less sticky and readily flake off from the surfaces to which they have adhered. They can be floated into the air when disturbed, or picked up on moist hands, carrying with them any microorganisms that have survived the drying process. The air thus becomes an intermediate source of many infectious diseases of man, including the fungal, bacterial, and viral diseases of the respiratory tract, as well as others whose agents have a ready point of discharge from the body. The limiting factors in air-borne infection include the capacity of microorganisms to survive in drying material; the speed and direction with which microbial pathogens may be carried by air to new, susceptible hosts; the interceding activities of mechanical vectors, such as insects or contaminated hands, which may transfer infection from a place of air deposit to a suitable entry point into a new host; the numbers and virulent properties of the microorganisms in question; and the degree of resistance that exists in exposed host populations. These factors are considered in more detail in a later section of this chapter dealing with the transmission of air-borne infectiosn.

Food for human and animal consumption is, of course, also a source of nutrient for many microbial forms of life. Raw food is probably always contaminated, by microorganisms from the soil or from human hands, but this does not necessarily constitute a threat to health for two reasons: (1) because the average contaminant from such sources lacks pathogenicity for man, and (2) because microorganisms are normally not given an opportunity to multiply actively in food that is eaten fresh, or is adequately preserved, before and after cooking. When food is protected from the effects of microbial growth and spoilage by refrigeration or freezing; by adequate canning or other preserving methods for fruits and vegetables; by smoking, salting, or drying methods for meats and fish; or by pasteurization for milk; or when it is served fresh and sparkling from *clean*, uncontaminated, uninfected sources, it may be eaten without fear of infection, whether or not it is cooked.

Unfortunately, food is all too frequently a primary or secondary reservoir for a variety of serious infections. Foods such as meat, fish, shellfish, and milk that are obtained from *infected animal sources* are a *primary* reservoir for some notable helminthic, bacterial, and viral diseases that may be readily acquired by persons who eat these foods raw or imperfectly cooked or treated. The *contamination* of originally clean food by pathogenic microorganisms can create dangerous *secondary* reservoirs of infectious disease, or production centers for poisonous bacterial toxins, particularly if such contaminated food is improperly preserved, handled, or prepared so that microbial multiplication occurs before it is eaten.

Foods derived from infected animals or their products afford a direct route of transmission from the animal to the human host's intestinal tract. The human infection that results is not necessarily limited to or even primarily localized in the intestinal tract, however, as discussed in Chapter 6. Whatever the localization, if the pathogenic agent finds a portal of exit from the body, the infected human case may also be a reservoir for the infection, capable of transmitting it to other persons. Human beings may also infect their animal neighbors, particularly if the infectious organism is carried in feces, sewage-polluted water and food being the source of infection.

Diseases that may be acquired from the ingestion of infected meat, fish, poultry, eggs, or milk and are also maintained by an infected human reservoir fall chiefly into two groups: those of (1) *helminthic* or of (2) *bacterial* origin (see Group 4, pp. 183–84).

1. The *helminthic* diseases include those caused by pork, cattle, and fish tapeworms, ingested as larval forms encysted in the muscles of these animals, and the trematode (or fluke) infestations acquired by eating fish, crustaceans, or water plants infected with larvae. Although the patho-

genic agents and the clinical symptomatology of these diseases differ in many respects, their epidemiology is similar with regard to sources and routes of infection. Man and animals both play a part in maintaining these helminths in nature, disseminating eggs into the environment. Their geographic distribution is limited by environmental influences on the cyclic developmental stages of the parasite and its hosts. The social and gastronomic habits of the human host also have their effect. In acquiring these infections, human beings are often the victims of their taste for raw food, or of their carelessness in selecting it properly or cooking it thoroughly. Cooks and housewives may find these diseases an occupational hazard if they are given to checking the taste of food before it is completely cooked.

2. The *bacterial* diseases of this group acquired from infected food include bovine tuberculosis, salmonellosis, and a number of streptococcal infections. The vast majority of cases of human *tuberculosis* are caused by a human strain of the tubercle bacillus, for which man is the only important reservoir. The bovine variety of the organism is capable, however, of causing tuberculosis in man as well as cattle, human infection being acquired from the meat or milk of infected cows. The lesions of the bovine type of disease in human disease usually do not involve the lung but may occur in many other tissues of the body, including the skin, lymph nodes, bones, and central nervous system. The disease is not so readily communicable from these localizations as from pulmonary lesions, but man and diseased cattle may both continue the infection. Human cases of bovine tuberculosis have become rare in the United States and other countries where adequate government inspection and control of meats, herds, and milk have been in effect, but the disease remains a problem in some parts of the world. *Salmonella* infections are widespread among animals, rodents, poultry, and other birds. They are also entrenched in many human populations. Their transfer among these reservoirs often occurs through the contamination of food supplies, but it should be remembered that animal meat and products, notably eggs, can be directly infectious. Fresh or dried eggs are a frequent

source of *Salmonella* outbreaks, particularly when they are only lightly cooked or eaten raw, as in eggnogs. The frequent use of eggs as a valuable nutrient for patients and convalescing invalids may expose to infection individuals who are particularly susceptible. For this reason it is especially important for hospitals and nursing homes to choose their suppliers of eggs from infection-free poultry farms and, when in doubt, to serve cooked eggs only. *Streptococcal* strains that can produce human disease may originate in domestic animals such as cattle and horses, although, as in the case of tuberculosis, the majority of streptococcal diseases are of human origin. Streptococcal skin and throat infections may be acquired through the handling of animals or the ingestion of infected milk, or, conversely, the infected human individual may transmit his disease to animals. The dairy farmer who has a streptococcal infection, or is a carrier, may infect his cows, the most common problem being the production of udder infections. The subsequent distribution of milk from such sources may lead to an epidemic spread of streptococcal disease, such as septic sore throat or scarlet fever. The special problems of milk as a reservoir of infection are considered at the end of this section on food.

There are a few diseases that man acquires from infected animal food sources but does not transmit to others. For these man is not a reservoir, but an accidental victim of infection (see p. 184). *Trichinosis*, for example, is a roundworm disease of many wild animals, rodents, and swine. It is a systemic disease, induced by the encystment of larvae in muscles and organs. Man acquires it by eating the flesh of infested animals (domestic pork, wild game animals), ingesting larvae that have survived inadequate cooking. The human disease is also systemic and provides the end of the line for the parasite that has no transferring portal in this case. A few bacterial diseases, such as *brucellosis* and *tularemia*, also belong in this group of zoonoses that may be transmitted to, but not by, human beings. The reservoirs for brucellosis are domestic animals, such as cattle, swine, sheep, goats, and horses. Human infections may be air-borne, from the

dust of stables and pastures; they may be acquired through direct contacts with infected animals; or they may be transmitted through the milk, cheese, and other dairy products derived from infected animals and distributed to people who would otherwise have no contact with the disease. Tularemia is a natural infection of many wild animals and some domestics. It is particularly frequent in rabbits. Several arthropod reservoirs also exist for this organism, commonly the wood tick, and in some areas a biting fly or a mosquito. The disease is transmitted by these insects, but it may also be acquired through the handling of infected animals or by the ingestion of game meat (especially rabbit) that has not been fully cooked. In this country the human disease occurs most frequently during the fall season for rabbit hunting, but it is also associated with other human activities, such as camping and lumbering.

The *contamination* of food by infectious, pathogenic microorganisms entrenched in human and animal populations may occur in a number of relatively simple ways. It may be quite *direct*, from the infected intestine (via feces), skin, throat, or other superficial area to human hands, food, or milk; it may also be *indirectly* mediated by fecal pollution of water supplies from which fish and shellfish are harvested or in which other foods are bathed; or it may be accomplished indirectly through the activities of *mechanical vectors*, such as the housefly, trafficking from feces to food. Food is at its best as a reservoir of infection when it permits active growth and multiplication of the contaminating pathogen. This occurs when it is fully or partially cooked or exposed for long periods to warm temperatures, so that its proteins and other complex nutrients are denatured to forms readily utilized by microorganisms. The addition of milk and egg proteins, as in the preparation of many salads and custards, further enhances the qualities of food as a medium for microbial growth. In addition to its nutrient content of protein, carbohydrate, and fat, minerals, and vitamins, the pH of food is usually adjusted to human tastes at near neutrality, so that in the end it is just as suitable for microbial

nutrition and metabolism as it is for man. Food that is contaminated at some stage during its preparation and is subsequently left for a substantial period of hours at comfortable temperatures that neither kill the organisms (as thorough cooking will do) nor arrest their multiplication (as refrigeration or freezing may do) provides a rich culture medium for many microorganisms, including pathogenic types. Since food contamination may occur unpredictably, silently, and invisibly, the handling of food should always provide barriers to the multiplication of pathogenic organisms it may contain. The best protection that can be afforded against the growth of contaminants that have already found their way into foods lies in immediate thorough cooking or prompt refrigeration, since microbial pathogens do not thrive at temperature extremes.

When contaminating pathogenic microorganisms are given an opportunity to multiply in foods before they are eaten, the stage is set for bacterial "food poisoning," and one of two possible effects may ensue, depending on the nature of the organism involved. (1) An active infection may result from the ingestion of the organisms, or (2) symptoms of toxicity may follow the ingestion of bacterial toxins preformed in food during the period of active microbial growth, prior to the meal.

1. A number of important active infections of man, for which he is the only *living* reservoir, are acquired from secondary food reservoirs directly or indirectly contaminated by infected persons. Some of these diseases are localized in the intestinal tract and are transmitted from that route, notably shigellosis, salmonellosis, cholera, and amebiasis. Others, such as typhoid or paratyphoid fevers or viral hepatitis, have systemic localizations and effects, but the organisms may nonetheless be transmitted via liver and gallbladder secretions to the intestinal tract or to the kidneys and be shed in the feces or urine. When the pulmonary or upper respiratory tracts are involved in these infections, as they sometimes are, transmission may occur through sputum and mucous contamination of hands or other objects involved in food preparation and service. As

pointed out earlier in this chapter, the symptomatic human case of infectious disease, promptly diagnosed and removed from the active scene, may represent a controlled reservoir. The asymptomatic carrier of such infections, however, can unknowingly continue to create secondary reservoirs in food, milk, and water supplies from which disease may spread ever more widely. This is particularly true in the case of typhoid fever and other *Salmonella* infections, as well as in mild, aborted, or incubating cases of viral hepatitis. These diseases are spread not only by the contamination of prepared foods by foodhandlers, but even more widely by food exposed to sewage-polluted water. Fish and shellfish, such as oysters and clams, harvested from polluted water or vegetables washed in contaminated water are often eaten raw or incompletely cooked. Infected foods, or those contaminated with pathogenic organisms permitted to multiply, may, however, still be safe to eat *if they are cooked sufficiently before the meal* to destroy their microbial content.

2. Bacterial toxins produced by staphylococci, streptococci, or *Clostridium* species (especially *Cl. botulinum*) actively growing in foods prior to their ingestion produce illness referable to their effects on cells of the intestinal mucosa or, if they are absorbed, on cells of other tissues. Staphylococci and streptococci are most commonly introduced into food by handlers. *Clostridium* species, including *Cl. botulinum*, are soil inhabitants, whose spores may be present on most fresh vegetables. The spores are not pathogenic, but they are quite heat-resistant, and for this reason may survive light cooking processes that often precede the canning of foods (especially in home canning). Within the anaerobic, sealed can, surviving spores can germinate to vegetative bacterial forms, which in turn produce botulinum toxin as they metabolize. The toxin is relatively sensitive to heat, so that if food containing it is boiled for 15 minutes it may be eaten safely. Unfortunately, canned vegetables, fish, and other foods taken from the can often are cooked very briefly, or not at all, so that the problem of the prevention of botulism poisoning lies with the killing of spores during the canning process. Staphylococcal enterotoxin is more resistant to heat than botulinum toxin and can be destroyed only by prolonged heating.

Bacterial food poisoning is also discussed in Chapter 6, and in Part Two, Section V, according to specific causative agents.

Milk is a special food, rich in protein, carbohydrate, fat, and other nutrients, offering particular opportunities for the multiplication and spread of contaminating, pathogenic microorganisms. It is a liquid medium, of nearly neutral pH, much enjoyed by many organisms. Although milk is sterile when produced by the healthy lactating animal, it passes through mammary ducts that have a normal commensalistic flora. From that point it is further directed over surfaces and into containers that may be contaminated with bacteria and other microbes of wide variety. For these reasons, milk, whatever its source or subsequent handling, can be expected to contain a mixed microbial flora of environmental origin, most of which have no pathogenic import. The most common bacterial species that contaminate milk, and grow well therein, belong to the genera of *Streptococcus, Lactobacillus,* and *Micrococcus.* Species of these groups abound in milk, but cause no more damage, usually, than souring when storage temperature and time permits their overgrowth. The potential threat offered by milk lies in the similar opportunity it may afford pathogenic contaminants to multiply under suitable conditions of temperature and time.

Milk-borne diseases originate either from infected animals or from the hands and methods of milk-handlers. The important diseases of animals transmitted to human beings through their milk are tuberculosis and brucellosis. Less frequently encountered are such infections as Q fever, a respiratory disease of rickettsial origin, and foot-and-mouth disease, a viral disease that can devastate cattle herds but to which man is, fortunately, largely resistant. Human streptococcal infections may originate from animal sources, or from the cross-infection of animal milks by infected handlers, as previously described.

Human diseases most commonly transferred

through milk contaminated by handlers or their methods include not only streptococcal infections but also diphtheria, both transmitted by respiratory or skin contacts, via contaminated air, equipment, or hands. Infections transmitted and acquired by the gastrointestinal routes are also frequently traced to secondary milk reservoirs. Important diseases of this type include bacillary dysentery, or shigellosis; intestinal *Salmonella* infections; and systemic salmonelloses such as typhoid or paratyphoid fever.

Water as obtained from natural sources is, like air, seldom pure. Whether it comes to us from ground sources (springs and wells), from surface accumulations (rivers, lakes, reservoirs), or directly from the rain and snow that maintain these supplies, water always contains organic and inorganic material, suspended or dissolved. Rain washes down particulate matter suspended in the air, as well as volatile chemicals from the atmosphere, many of which go into solution in rain water. Surface and ground pools of water are not only fed by rain, but are also exposed to soil. Consequently, water may normally contain many varieties of microorganisms derived from air or soil, as well as the supporting chemical substrates they need to maintain themselves and to multiply in this milieu. Water may be purified of its microbial or chemical contents by several methods, as discussed in Chapters 10 and 11. Such purification is indicated whenever there is a chance that water has been contaminated by pathogenic organisms or harmful chemicals, or when it has been polluted with materials that give it obviously unpleasant characteristics of odor, taste, or appearance.

Man himself is responsible for the most frequent and hazardous pollution, or contamination, of water supplies. The normal microbial flora of water, as derived from the soil or from air, does not include species pathogenic for man, but rather this flora is composed of many heterotrophic saprophytes and autotrophic varieties of microorganisms. Man contributes a dangerous contamination to water when he permits it to be polluted with his sewage. The water drained from kitchen sinks, laundry tubs, bathtubs, and toilets not only contains high concentrations of soaps and detergents, but teems with microorganisms of pathogenic as well as nonpathogenic varieties, many of which are capable of survival and multiplication in impure water. The possibility of disease transmission arises when sewage contaminates water or food supplies intended for human consumption, especially if subsequent purification, heating, or sterilization is not accomplished. The diseases most commonly transferred in this way, from a water reservoir directly, or via food supplies bathed in contaminated water, are those of enteric origin. Microbial pathogens excreted in feces from an intestinal colonization, or from a lesion draining to the intestinal tract from the liver or gallbladder, include the bacterial agents of typhoid and paratyphoid fever, shigellosis, and cholera; the viruses responsible for poliomyelitis and infectious hepatitis; the protozoan agent of amebic dysentery; and a number of species of helminth ova. Among the latter, those cestode (tapeworm) and trematode (fluke) eggs that hatch in water and complete their life cycles in aquatic animals should be emphasized whenever water is considered as a possible reservoir and transmitting agent of disease. Fish tapeworm, *Schistosoma*, and other flukes are maintained through the transmission of eggs to water and their further development in aquatic hosts. The distribution of such infections depends on environmental influences affecting both host and organism and is often limited geographically, while bacterial, viral, and protozoan pathogens may find favorable conditions for parasitic or saprophytic survival in a wider range of aquatic environments.

Pathogenic organisms excreted in urine may also survive in water and be transferred through this type of intermediate reservoir. The systemic *Salmonella* infections, such as typhoid and paratyphoid fever, may be transferred through urine. The same is true for the hemorrhagic jaundice caused by spirochetes of the *Leptospira* genus and for *Schistosoma* infections of the bladder.

For many pathogenic microorganisms, water is a limited reservoir in that it cannot support their continuing multiplication. Fish and shellfish foods that become infected with water-borne parasitic organisms, bacterial, viral, or hel-

minthic, may of course continue the chain of disease. Water itself, however, does not remain infectious indefinitely unless it is continuously supplied with the organic nutrient required by pathogenic organisms capable of saprophytic existence or is constantly recontaminated.

Endogenous Sources of Infection.   The adjective term "endogenous" means that something is originating, growing, or proceeding from *within*. In biologic usage, "within" may refer to an entire living organism, such as the human body, or to a tissue segment, or to an individual cell. An infectious microorganism growing within individual cells or tissues of the body may be tolerated and well contained by a regional set of circumstances, yet raise havoc if it gains access to other types of cells or tissues functioning under other conditions in different parts of the body. For instance, a *Salmonella* infection restricted to the intestinal tract may be inapparent, because it is well tolerated by the lining cells of the bowel, or it may produce symptoms reflecting its local toxic effects within the intestine. Should circumstances arise that permit the dissemination of *Salmonella* organisms to body tissues beyond the intestinal tract, the localization of infection in new sites produces a new and different symptomatology. One might say that a systemic disease, distinct in many ways from the original, has been acquired in this case, from an *endogenous* source, rather than from an outside, or *exogenous*, reservoir, although the latter may have been the first locus of infection.

It is equally important to remember that microorganisms that live a commensalistic or saprophytic kind of life on the skin or mucosal linings may induce destructive reactions in systemic tissues to which they are foreign. Coliform bacilli, streptococci, and staphylococci, for example, derived from endogenous sources within the intestinal tract or the skin, where they may reside unnoticed, can be injurious to other tissues to which they are introduced. Accidental trauma, erosions of the skin or bowel by ulcerative conditions or tumors, and surgical procedures offer the most common means of transfer of microorganisms from endogenous sources, usually by

way of the lymph or blood stream, to parenteral tissues where their successful localization may result in infectious disease. Pulmonary, hepatic, or renal infections can arise in this way, as well as endocarditis or osteomyelitis. Since the organisms involved seldom have well-marked properties of virulence, these infections may be subacute and slow to progress, depending also on the nature, function, and reactivity of the infected tissue. (See Chaps. 5 and 6.)

Recognition and firm identification of endogenous sources of infection are often quite difficult. The bacteriologic recovery of organisms normal to the skin and mucosa in specimens of blood, sputum, urine, or pus from wounds frequently raises the question as to whether such a culture result simply reflects contamination of the specimen with saprophytic flora or actually identifies an active infectious agent. Repeated cultures, or quantitative culture techniques that demonstrate numbers of organisms well in excess of normal findings, may clarify such a situation. Thus, a culture of blood should normally be sterile. If a blood culture yields an organism of a type frequently found on normal skin, such as a *Staphylococcus* or *Streptococcus* strain, its interpretation is subject to the question of contamination of the specimen during or after its collection. In such a case, *repeated* isolation of the same organism from a series of blood cultures, timed if possible to coincide with the patient's clinical symptoms of a suspected bacteremia or septicemia, greatly increases the significance of the result. On the other hand, specimens of sputum, or of voided urine, can normally be expected to contain small numbers of commensalistic bacteria. Recognition of an ordinarily nonpathogenic organism as a significant agent of respiratory or genitourinary infection may require repeated *quantitative* demonstration of its presence in such specimens in abnormally excessive numbers. It is particularly important in such cases that specimens be collected with scrupulous attention to aseptic technique and submitted promptly to the laboratory for examination and culture. If the physician is to make an adequate correlation of laboratory information with clinical symptomatology, he must first be assured that

the specimens tested were truly representative of the patient's suspected infection in their timing and selection, and that each of the techniques involved in their collection, transport, and laboratory culture was performed appropriately and accurately. Without such assurance, culture results may be open to misinterpretation that can lead to errors in the diagnosis and treatment of the patient.

Diseases and Reservoirs. In nature multiple reservoirs are available to pathogenic organisms that are capable of survival in a wide variety of situations. The limitations on their distribution are determined in large part by their ability to maintain themselves outside of living tissues, or within those of differing species. On the following pages many of the common communicable diseases of man or animals are arranged in groups according to their major reservoirs. This grouping illustrates and re-emphasizes the concept that a reservoir of infection must offer the infectious agent in question suitable opportunities for transfer to new hosts, as well as an appropriate milieu for its growth and multiplication.

The Reservoirs of Infectious Disease

Group 1. Man is the only reservoir.

Diseases:

Viral :   Measles, mumps, influenza, poliomyelitis, chickenpox, smallpox, lymphogranuloma venereum, trachoma.

Bacterial :   Gonorrhea, syphilis.

Fungal :   Candidiasis, actinomycosis (the agents are endogenous commensals of human oral mucosa).

Note: The causative microorganisms of these diseases have not established themselves in animal species other than man. Furthermore, they generally do not survive long enough outside of living tissues to form durable environmental reservoirs.

Transmission: Direct from man to man, or by way of prompt contact with objects, air-borne droplets, or ingested materials (food, milk, water) that have been *freshly* contaminated.

Group 2. Man is the only living reservoir.
Secondary reservoirs exist in the inanimate environment.

Diseases:

Viral :   Infectious hepatitis.

Bacterial :   Typhoid fever, shigellosis, cholera, whooping cough, diphtheria, tuberculosis (human), staphylococcal and streptococcal infections (of human origin).

Protozoan :   Amebiasis.

Helminthic :   Hookworm disease, ascariasis, enterobiasis.

Note: The agents of these diseases are in general not well supported by animal species other than human beings. However, they can survive, sometimes multiply, or continue a developmental stage in soil, water, or food contaminated by an infected person.

Transmission:	Direct from man to man, or indirect from environmental reservoirs: *Food* harvested from contaminated water (oysters, clams) or soil (garden vegetables) and eaten raw or insufficiently cooked. *Water* for drinking, washing, cleaning, or swimming. *Soil* contacts with skin (hookworm). *Surfaces* (some of the organisms involved in this group are capable of survival in minimal supplies of nutrient, spread thinly over the inanimate surfaces of floors, walls, mops, sponges, or any soiled object; they may also survive in dried dust).

Group 3. Man and one or more species of arthropods are the reservoirs.

Diseases:	
Viral:	Yellow fever (mosquito).
Rickettsial:	Epidemic typhus fever (louse).
Protozoan:	Malaria (mosquito).
Note:	The infectious agents of this group are biologically maintained both by man and by biting or blood-sucking insects.
Transmission:	Arthropod to man, man to arthropod. Direct man-to-man transmission does not occur.

Group 4. Man and one or more species of animals are the reservoirs. Arthropods involved as biologic or mechanical vectors for some. Secondary environmental reservoirs may exist for some.

Diseases:	
Fungal:	The superficial mycoses: ringworm of hair, skin, nails.
Bacterial:	Salmonellosis, staphylococcal and streptococcal infections (of animal origin), tuberculosis (bovine), pneumonic plague, clostridial diseases (tetanus, gas gangrene), listeriosis.
Protozoan:	Leishmaniasis, trypanosomiasis.
Helminthic:	Filariasis (tissue nematode), taeniasis (intestinal tapeworms), schistosomiasis and other trematode diseases.
Note:	These are the zoonoses transmissible from animals to man, by varying routes as shown below.

Transmission:	
Superficial mycoses:	Direct from animal to man or animal. Direct from man to man.
Salmonellosis Streptococcal infection Staphylococcal infection Tuberculosis (bovine) Listeriosis	Direct from animal to man or animal; direct from man to man or animal; indirectly from environment, especially food, milk, or water.

Group 4. (Cont.)

Pneumonic plague:	Rat to rat flea to man; direct from man to man via respiratory droplets.
Clostridial diseases:	These are included here because the normal intestinal tract of man and animals is the reservoir. Transmission is endogenous or indirect from fecally contaminated soil.
Leishmaniasis Trypanosomiasis Filariasis	Arthropod to man or animals; direct man-to-man transmission does not occur.
Taeniasis:	Human ingestion of infected beef or pork.
Trematode diseases:	Reservoirs are human, animal, and aquatic hosts (snails and water plants). Transmission is indirect through water or marine plants containing larval forms.

Group 5. Various animal or arthropod species, or both, are the reservoirs.
(Man may be an accidental victim of these infections, but he is *not* a reservoir for them, since they are rarely, if ever, transmitted from infected human beings to others of any species).

Diseases:

Viral:	Psittacosis, equine encephalitis, rabies.
Rickettsial:	Scrub typhus, murine typhus, Rocky Mountain spotted fever, Q fever.
Bacterial:	Anthrax, brucellosis, tularemia, bubonic plague, leptospirosis, relapsing fever.
Helminthic:	Echinococcosis, trichinosis.
Note:	Man does not play a role in the maintenance and transfer of these diseases in nature.

Transmission:

Psittacosis:	Direct contact with infected birds, or indirect through air-borne dust. Man-to-man transmission direct but rare.
Equine encephalitis:	Horses to mosquito to man. Direct man-to-man transmission does not occur.
Rabies:	Bite of a rabid dog or other animal. Direct man-to-man transmission possible but not demonstrated.
Rickettsial diseases (except Q fever):	Animal to arthropod (ticks, mites, fleas) to man. Direct man-to-man transmission does not occur.
Q fever:	Indirect from animals to man via air-borne dust from areas contaminated by infective animal tissues (placental tissue, birth fluids) or through ingestion of raw milk. Direct transmission from animals to man possible. Direct transmission from man to man does not occur.
Anthrax Brucellosis Tularemia Leptospirosis	Direct or indirect from animals to man. Dust from infective hides or tissues (anthrax); raw milk (brucellosis), ingestion of infective meat (tularemia), contaminated swimming water (leptospirosis) the usual transmittal agents.

Bubonic plague:	Rat to rat flea to man. Direct man-to-man transmission does not occur except in cases of bubonic plague terminating with plague pneumonia.
Relapsing fever:	Lice and ticks transmit to man. Direct transmission does not occur from man to man.
Echinococcosis	Human ingestion of infective ovum derived from intestinal infection of an animal, usually dogs.
Trichinosis	Human ingestion of pork containing encysted larvae. These parasites are maintained in nature by carnivorous and grazing animals. The human disease is characterized by the invasion of deep tissues by larval forms of the parasites. The infected human host offers them no means to transfer to another host.

Group 6. Soil is the primary reservoir.
Animals (including birds and fish) may be secondary reservoirs.

Diseases:	
Bacterial:	Botulism.
Fungal:	The systemic mycoses: coccidioidomycosis, cryptococcosis, histoplasmosis, blastomycosis, nocardiosis, sporotrichosis.
Note:	The agents of these diseases live and propagate in the soil, which provides a direct or indirect source of infection for man as well as for animal species, including birds (fungi) and fish (*Clostridium botulinum*). Infected (but not necessarily diseased) animals probably contribute these organisms to the soil via their excreta.
Transmission:	Usually by contact with contaminated soil: through skin contact, especially via minor breaks; through inhalation of air-borne dust; or, in the case of botulism, through spore-contaminated foods in which spores have germinated and the vegetative bacteria have produced exotoxin.
	Direct transmission from man to man does not occur in most cases. Direct transmission from animals to man unlikely except for botulism acquired from eating inadequately processed fish. Birds may indirectly spread some fungal agents over wide areas (see Fig. 9–9). In the case of fungal diseases, draining lesions or infective sputum may contaminate the environment, with possible subsequent transmission through skin lesions or dust inhalation.

The Routes of Transfer of Infection

The communicability of infection depends not only on the nature and accessibility of reservoirs, but also on the routes and mechanisms available to the infectious agent for its transmission to new hosts. We have seen that there are four major avenues through which infecting microorganisms may enter the human body: the respiratory tract, the gastrointestinal tract, the skin and mucosal surfaces, and the parenteral route. (See Chap. 6.)

These same avenues may also serve as exit routes, depending on the site of localization of the organisms in the infected body and the availability of a transporting mechanism. *Respiratory* and *gastrointestinal* discharges are expelled from the body with ease and continuing frequency. They may spread infection far and wide through droplet contamination of the air; through contamination of surfaces, hands, and handled objects; and through the establishment of secondary reservoirs of microbial growth in water,

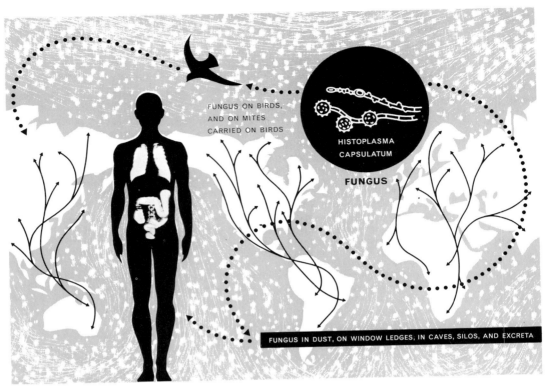

FUNGUS ON BIRDS,
AND ON MITES
CARRIED ON BIRDS

HISTOPLASMA
CAPSULATUM

FUNGUS

FUNGUS IN DUST, ON WINDOW LEDGES, IN CAVES, SILOS, AND EXCRETA

Fig. 9–9. The fungus agent of histoplasmosis may be carried to all parts of the world by birds. (Adapted from *What's New,* Summer, 1962. Courtesy of Abbott Laboratories, North Chicago, Ill.)

milk, or food supplies. Infectious discharges from exposed lesions of the *skin and mucosa* may also be widely disseminated by hands and other mechanical vectors, or by person-to-person contacts. *Parenteral (deep) tissue* infections, not exposed to the surface, cannot be transmitted unless their microbial agents find their way into the body's discharges or into an insect host as it takes a meal.

The transfer of an infectious microorganism from its exit point from one host to its portal of entry into another may be quite direct and immediate, or it may be delayed and sometimes extremely devious. Intermediate, inanimate reservoirs may link the travel routes of the organism between living hosts, sometimes at close range, but in some instances over great physical distances. Some of the parasitic protozoa and helminths display complex developmental cycles

that require their transfer in sequence from one type of host or reservoir to another. The mechanisms for spread of infection among living hosts depend in part on the nature of the infectious agent, as we have seen, and in part on the nature of the reservoir providing the source of infection.

Transmission Routes from Living Reservoirs. There are two basic modes of transmission of infectious agents from infected human, animal, or insect hosts to susceptible human beings: (1) transfer may be made by *direct contact* with an infected, living host, or (2) it may follow upon *indirect contact* with infectious material derived from a diseased host.

1. Direct Contact. This type of transfer involves close, or frequent, physical encounters between susceptible and infected hosts, the infectious

agent being transmitted directly to an appropriate site of entry to a new host.

Infected *human* hosts may transfer their microbes to other persons through their many physical contacts: hand-shaking, kissing, sexual intercourse, or other personal and tactual associations. Droplet transmission may also be quite direct among people in close proximity. Infectious respiratory droplets may be projected to a distance of 2 or 3 ft during talking, coughing, or sneezing to make immediate contact with the faces of others. The most usual exit and entry sites for infections spread among and by human beings in direct association are the respiratory, oral, and genital mucosa. The venereal diseases are spread almost exclusively by sexual contact. The bacterial agent of gonorrhea may infect the conjunctival mucosa of a newborn infant at the time of its delivery by an infected mother whose vaginal discharge contains the organism. Syphilitic mothers may also transmit their disease to the developing fetus, in utero. Children sometimes acquire venereal diseases from infected adults through fondling and kissing. Other genitourinary diseases, gastrointestinal infections, as well as respiratory infections, may also be spread by contaminated hands, either those of the infected individual or those of persons in close contact with him. Surface infections from suppurating wounds, pimples, or boils are readily transferrable by hands as well. Hand to mouth, or hand to skin, then constitutes the usual transfer route. Direct skin transfer usually requires some injury or break in the barrier tissue if an infectious agent is to make effective entry at such a site.

Nurses and physicians who care for infectious patients, particularly those whose diseases are directly transmissible, must take every precaution to protect others, as well as themselves, from contact spread of infection. Medical personnel may carry infectious organisms, in a nearly direct route, on their hands, on their clothing, or even on their faces, from one patient to another. One of the first to recognize this simple truth was a Viennese obstetrician, Ignaz Semmelweis, who demonstrated, in the 1840's, that maternal mortality rates attributable to sepsis were higher on obstetric wards attended by physicians in frock coats, with unwashed hands (fresh from the autopsy room), then among patients whose attendants scrupulously scrubbed their hands before examining or delivering an expectant mother. In the United States at much the same time, Oliver Wendell Holmes had also reached the conclusion that childbed fever (puerperal fever) is infectious, and he emphasized its contagious nature of spread. Today the cardinal principles of good medical and nursing care of all patients include aseptic techniques designed to prevent the spread of infection. These techniques are of particular importance to patients whose susceptibility to infection is high: surgical and obstetric patients; the very old or the very young; and those with underlying, debilitating disorders that undermine the normal resistance mechanisms. Methods for the prevention and control of infectious diseases are discussed in Chapters 10 and 11.

The viral and bacterial diseases of man included in group 1, above, are all transmissible by direct contact with infected human beings. The diseases of group 2 are also directly transmissible from man to man (with the exception of hookworm infection, which is derived from an intermediate soil reservoir), but these infections have a greater potential for indirect transfer, as well, than do those of group 1. In group 4, the fungal and bacterial infections can be transmitted directly from person to person, but the protozoan and helminthic infections of this group, like the diseases of group 3, require another host species for their transmission and cannot be transferred by contact with infected human beings.

Infected *animals* may also transfer their infections to susceptible human hosts who come into direct contact with them. Animal-breeders, farmers, dairymen, butchers, hide- and leather-workers, poultry-raisers, pet-lovers, and, be it noted, meat-eaters — all are subject to exposure to a number of animal infections that are transmissible by a direct route. The most frequent transfers occur by the hand-to-mouth route; by ingestion of infected meat or animal products, such as milk or cheese; by direct inhalation of contaminated air-borne excretions; or through

abraded skin or mucosal surfaces. Many of the diseases of groups 4 and 5 are transmissible to man by direct contact with infected animals or their products, while a few involve an intermediary arthropod host that, in turn, effects the transfer.

Direct contact with *insect vectors* that are biologic hosts and reservoirs for a number of infectious microorganisms may result in the parenteral introduction of infection into human tissues or blood. The insect-borne diseases are not directly transmissible between human or animal hosts, their agents being dependent on the contacts, transport, and support of their arthropod hosts for their continuation in nature and for their access to other host species. The diseases of group 3 are maintained primarily by the direct transfers of their agents between human and arthropod host species. The protozoan infections of group 4, some of the viral and rickettsial diseases of group 5, and bubonic plague constitute further examples of diseases transferable to man only by direct contact with arthropod hosts.

2. Indirect Contact.   Human infections may be acquired from other infected hosts even without immediate intimate contact. Microorganisms that can survive on surfaces contaminated by sick persons, animals, or infected insects may later find an entry route into susceptible human hosts who touch or handle such items. Clothing, bedding, surgical dressings, instruments, bedpans, paper or linen handkerchiefs, toys, eating utensils, food, drinking glasses, or their contents — all may provide a bridge of indirect contact between infected hosts and new susceptibles. Insect vectors, acting either as hosts or as mechanical carriers, can play an indirect role in the spread of disease by depositing infectious material on food, skin, clothing, or other contact surfaces.

Routine provision for the nursing care of hospitalized patients includes the sterilization of many items that could be an indirect source of infection on contact. Items such as water carafes, glasses, dishes, bedding, bedpans, and thermometers are either disinfected or sterilized after their use to assure that neither acute nor clinically inapparent infections will be transferred by these means. Disposable materials, to be used once and thrown away, greatly relieve the labor of some hospital nursing routines, but care must be taken that such items are disposed of in a manner that will not permit infection to continue or flourish. Incineration is generally the method of choice, since this disposes of microbial contaminants as well as the object in question.

The usual route of entry for infections acquired by indirect contact is oral, following a hand-to-mouth transfer of infective matter from a contaminated surface. Occasionally, entry may occur through the skin or mucosa, particularly if a local injury or lesion permits. Many of the diseases cited in groups 1, 2, 4, and 5 can be transmitted to man in an indirect fashion, the limiting factors being the accessibility of infectious microorganisms to normal exit routes; the density in which they are deposited on contact surfaces; their ability to survive in restricted nutrient outside of host tissues; and the effects of time, drying, sunlight, or other stresses on their vital processes.

Transmission Routes from Inanimate Reservoirs.
We have seen that most inanimate media (soil, air, food, milk, water) serve as secondary reservoirs for those infectious microorganisms they can support, providing the latter with an interim means of survival and transport between living, primary reservoirs. The saprophytic fungal agents of the systemic mycotic diseases of man and the bacterial species *Clostridium botulinum* (group 6, above) alone have a primary reservoir in inanimate sources, such as soil or decaying vegetable matter. The fungi are transmitted to human beings through direct skin contact with the soil, or indirectly through the inhalation of contaminated dust; botulism, through the ingestion of contaminated food in which exotoxin has been preformed.

The route of transmission to susceptible human hosts of pathogenic organisms surviving less permanently in inanimate media depends on the nature of man's exposure to, or use of, these

secondary reservoirs. Infectious water, food, or milk may reach the gastrointestinal tract by an obviously direct route, or by a less apparent, indirect path, via contaminated objects or skin. Water that is used for washing clothes or utensils, for bathing or swimming, or for irrigating crops may carry infection directly to the intestinal tract. It may also contaminate food, objects that will be handled, clothing, or skin. Some of the helminthic parasites that undergo a phase of their normal development in water or wet soil are capable of direct penetration of normal human skin (the larvae of hookworms and *Schistosoma* species), while other kinds of pathogenic organisms contaminating these media can enter the body only through injured skin or the alimentary mucosa. Air containing infectious droplets or particles of dust commonly finds a direct route of entry to the respiratory tract, but it may also deposit its burden on surfaces from which a hand-to-mouth transfer can occur later.

Biologic products, including serum, plasma, soluble nutrients (e.g., dextrose or vitamin solutions), drugs, or vaccines may also become contaminated with microorganisms capable of surviving and multiplying in them. When such contaminated materials are injected parenterally into the human body, very serious infections may arise from this direct introduction of microorganisms into the tissues or blood stream, even though the agents involved may display little or no ability to establish themselves by entry through more readily available portals.

Inanimate reservoirs, or intermediary objects contaminated by them, thus may serve as vehicles for the transport of infectious agents and their introduction into the body by any of the usual entry routes. Water, food, or milk supplies for public consumption offer the greatest possibilities for widespread dissemination of infectious disease if they contain multiplying pathogenic microorganisms. Infectious air-borne droplets or dust particles may also reach large numbers of people, particularly if they are concentrated in closed areas. The patterns of epidemics attributable to these sources are discussed in the last section of this chapter.

The diseases most frequently disseminated from inanimate reservoirs are those of group 2 and the bacterial infections of group 4. Most of the infectious agents involved are capable of prolonged survival outside of the body or of active multiplication in inanimate nutrient media. (Table 9–1 summarizes the transmission routes.)

Table 9–1. Transmission Routes

From Living Reservoirs		From Inanimate Reservoirs	
Direct	Indirect	Direct	Indirect
Contact with living host	Contact with infectious material derived from diseased host, i.e., sputum, feces, exudate from wound, animal tissues	Infected water, food, milk	Via contaminated objects
Hands and face		Biologic products	Inanimate objects, clothing, bedding (usual route is oral following hand-to-mouth transfer of infectious material from contaminated surface)
Kissing		Soil	
Hand-shaking			
Droplet transmission during talking, sneezing			
Sexual intercourse			
Genital, oral, respiratory mucosa			
Insect vectors			
Animal contacts			

The Routes of Transfer of Animal Parasites. We have seen that the communicability of a microbial disease depends on the reservoirs for continuing multiplication of the etiologic parasite and the pathways available for its transfer from one source to another. It is apparent, also, that the very survival of a parasitic species depends on this same chain of circumstances. Reservoirs for its growth and multiplication must be available, and when these are animate hosts, the parasite (that is, some members of its population) must be capable of entry, establishment, escape, and transfer, in a cyclic pattern.

During the course of these events, parasitic organisms themselves pass through cyclic, developmental stages of growth, maturation, and reproduction. The full circle of changes involved (in structure or physiology) is referred to as a *life cycle*. In the case of the more primitive microorganisms, that is, bacteria, rickettsiae, viruses, and even the structurally more complex fungi, these developmental cycles occur in fairly rapid, repeated succession within the body of each infected host (or on inanimate media, when this is possible). Since the developmental stages of microorganisms are brief and their multiplication is continuous, the transfer of new infection is not critically dependent on the age, condition, or form of the microbe at the time. In the case of the higher organisms with which we are concerned a different situation exists, however. The parasitic protozoa and helminths have more complex life cycles, during which they may undergo profound morphologic changes, some of which may be strictly dependent on the availability of particular reservoirs. Survival of the parasite then becomes a matter of completion of its cycle, and the direction of transfer of infection to new hosts is dependent, to varying degree, on the developmental stage and its requirements. Furthermore, except in the case of the intestinal protozoans, which can multiply in the bowel indefinitely, animal parasites cannot complete their life cycles in one host or reservoir, so that infections of this type are not characterized by the continuous multiplication of their agents.

The animal parasites vary widely in the complexity of their life cycles, but they display, basically, four types of patterns with respect to their host requirements. These are discussed briefly below and illustrated in the accompanying figures and tables. Individual parasitic diseases, their reservoirs and transmission routes, are discussed in appropriate sections of Part Two. The morphology of these organisms and of their developmental stages is described in Chapter 2.

The Life Cycles of Parasitic Protozoans and Helminths. The human or animal hosts of these organisms may be parasitized either by their adult, reproductive forms or by their intermediate, immature forms, sometimes by both. The host in which the adult parasite lives and reproduces is called the *definitive*, or *final*, host, while the host in which immature stages of development of the parasite occur is defined as the *intermediate* host. More than one type of intermediate host may be required, in sequence, to complete the life cycles of some parasitic worms. *Alternate hosts* are those that each, individually, can support both the adult and intermediate forms of a parasite but, only by alternating, together make possible the completion of the organism's life cycle. On the basis of definitive, intermediate, or alternate host requirements, four types of life cycles can be distinguished among animal parasites.

Type 1. The cycle is maintained by definitive hosts only. Intermediate and (or) alternate hosts are not required, although many of the parasites in this group must have a period of intermediate development in soil. All the *intestinal* roundworms (nematodes) and the *intestinal* protozoa display this simple type of host-host or host-soil-host cycle.

A. *Host-to-host transfer* is possible for the intestinal protozoans, and for one of the roundworms: *Enterobius vermicularis*, or *pinworm*.

Among the protozoans, *Endamoeba histolytica*, the agent of amebic dysentery and of systemic amebiasis, is the only one of consistent medical importance. The vegetative *trophozoites* invade the mucosal tissue of the large intestine (they may also be carried to other tissues and organs in the body where they induce abscess formation).

The ameboid trophozoites may be passed from the body in feces, but they do not survive long outside of the body, and if they are ingested directly they usually are killed by the acidity of the gastric juice or by the action of bile in the upper intestine. The most infective form of this parasite is the *cyst*, which is more resistant to chemical and physical agents than the trophozoite. The cyst is also a reproductive form; with its four nuclei it can give rise, by mitosis, to eight amoebae. The patient with an active clinical infection may pass both cysts and trophozoites. Most amebic infections are clinically inapparent, but "carriers" pass cysts and can be dangerous sources of infection until they are recognized. Amebic cysts can survive in water and food and on cloth or other objects that have been subject to fecal contamination. When ingested, following their direct or indirect transfer, they pass without injury through the stomach and small bowel to the large intestine, where they "excyst," each forming eight trophozoites.

Enterobius vermicularis is the smallest of the roundworms, having the dimensions of a small straight pin — hence its nickname. The adult worms live in the human intestine and copulate there. The gravid female then migrates downward through the large bowel to the anus, where she deposits fertilized ova. Her presence and activities on the perianal skin may cause an intense pruritus. Scratching transfers the ova to hands and fingernails, which pass them, in turn, to inanimate objects or to mouths (see Fig. 9–10). The ova also survive well on contaminated clothing or bedding. When shaken from these, they may remain viable in dust for some time. When ingested, each pinworm ovum develops into an adult in the intestine, and the cycle is renewed.

B. *Host-to-soil-to-host* transfer is the route for all the other parasitic roundworms. Among them we see three kinds of variation in the basic pattern of the cycle.

Trichuris trichiura, commonly called the *whipworm*, lives as an adult in the intestinal tract. Its ova are shed in feces, but they must reach soil, and they must have several weeks there for further development. They become infective when the

larval form developing within each egg is well differentiated. Fingers, clothes, toys, or other objects contaminated with infective soil are the usual transferring vehicles. When the eggs are swallowed, they develop into adults in the lower intestine.

Ascaris lumbricoides, the largest of the roundworms (8 to 12 in. in length), resembles *Trichuris* in the cycle of maturation of eggs passed in feces to the soil and subsequently transferred to the mouth. When infective eggs are swallowed, however, the larvae are hatched in the upper intestine, penetrate its wall, and are carried by the

Fig. 9–10. The life cycle of *Enterobius vermicularis* (the pinworm) illustrates the type of cycle that is maintained by definitive hosts only (*type 1*). Children are the most frequent victims of this roundworm infestation. When they scratch themselves to relieve the anal itching, their fingers and nails pick up many pinworm ova from the perianal skin. The ova are readily transferred from contaminated hands to everything and everyone they touch. These eggs are infective, and when introduced into the mouth and swallowed by the original or another host, they hatch in the intestinal tract and a new infestation begins.

blood stream to the lungs. Here they wriggle through the alveolar walls and up the air passages of the bronchial tree, into the trachea, the larynx, and finally past the epiglottis into the mouth. They are swallowed again, and when they reach the intestine once more, after all this peregrina-

tion, they finally develop into adult, egg-producing worms. The migrations of *Ascaris* larvae into the lungs (and sometimes into other organs, via the blood stream) cause far more serious disturbances than does the intestinal infestation. Insofar as the cycle is concerned, however, the

Fig. 9–11. The eggs or larvae of most of the parasitic roundworms require a period of maturation in the soil before they become infective for another definitive host, although their cycles do not require intermediate or alternate hosts (*type 1*). This illustration shows how the soil becomes contaminated by the unsanitary disposal of feces from persons infested with roundworms, or by the use of "nightsoil" as a fertilizer.

The hookworms (*Necator americanus and Ancylostoma duodenale*) live in the human intestinal tract and deposit eggs that are passed in the feces. The ova hatch in the soil and develop into infective larvae. When people walk barefooted in such soil or work in contaminated fields, their unprotected hands or feet may come in direct contact with hookworm larvae. The larvae penetrate the skin, and the cycle is continued as a new infestation gets under way.

The eggs of *Trichuris* and *Ascaris* species may reach the soil in the same manner. After a period of maturation, the eggs reach an infective stage. New human infestations begin when the mature eggs are carried to the mouth by unwashed hands that are dirtied with contaminated soil.

transfer route is from feces to soil to mouth, the infective form being the ovum containing a differentiated larva.

Hookworm species (*Necator, Ancylostoma,* and their close relatives *Strongyloides*) display another variation. The hookworm females produce their ova in the intestinal tract. The ova are passed in the feces, but they must reach warm, moist soil for further development. Under the right conditions, the larvae hatch after a day or two in the soil. They develop into active, attenuated, threadlike forms (filariform larvae) that are capable of penetrating human skin directly, usually through the soft areas between the toes and around the ankles of barefooted victims. Once into the dermis, the larvae are carried by the blood stream through the body to the lungs. As described above for *Ascaris,* the hookworm larvae make their way up the bronchi to the pharynx and are swallowed. Final maturation of the larvae occurs in the intestinal tract, and the cycle continues with the production of eggs by new adults. *Strongyloides* species follow a closely similar path, but the ova of this worm hatch into larvae in the intestinal tract. Sometimes these larvae develop within the intestine into a stage that can penetrate the wall and migrate in the blood stream to the lungs or elsewhere, resulting in a new intestinal infection or in systemic lesions, or both. Usually, the larvae pass into the soil, where they develop into infective forms that can penetrate skin. This worm may also live freely in the soil, developing into adult forms that may later produce larvae infective for man (see Fig. 9–11).

Type 2. The cycle is maintained by alternate hosts. Adult and larval forms develop in each host supporting this type of parasite, but each new host represents a dead end for the invading organism unless an alternate host comes along. The tissue-invading roundworm, *Trichinella spiralis,* the agent of trichinosis, is the only outstanding example of this type of worm that is parasitic for man. The natural reservoirs for the trichina worm are the pig and the rat, man being an accidental victim (see Fig. 9–12). The adult worm develops in the intestinal tract, where it

Fig. 9–12. This drawing illustrates the life cycle of an animal parasite that is maintained by *alternate* hosts (*type 2*). *Trichinella spiralis* is a tissue-invading roundworm that can be perpetuated only if the flesh of one infested mammal is consumed by another. The pig fattened on uncooked garbage that contains infected meat scraps is the main reservoir of infection for man. The rat feeding alongside the pig is the reservoir for the latter. Man may be the victim of his own eating habits in this case. If he eats infected pork that has not been thoroughly cooked, he develops trichinosis, but for the parasite the cycle has come to an end.

produces larvae. The larvae migrate, enter the blood stream, and localize in skeletal muscle tissue. Their own activities in muscle, together with the body's defensive reactions, cause their

encystment, and they remain a permanent fixture of the involved muscle, so to speak. The muscle tissue must be ingested by another animal, while the encysted larvae remain viable, if the parasite's cycle is to continue.

For man, the infective stage of trichina is encountered in pork flesh. If it is eaten without adequate cooking or curing, viable larvae excyst as the meat is partially digested in the stomach, and adults develop in the upper small intestine. Human epidemics of trichina infection are not the result of man-to-man transfer of the parasite. They occur when numbers of people are exposed to the same infected meat.

In nature, rats acquire trichinosis from ingestion of infected pork flesh (in slaughterhouses or on pig farms). Pigs pick it up again, sometimes from eating rats, but more usually from garbage scraps containing uncooked infected animal flesh.

Type 3. The cycle is maintained sequentially in insect and animal (or human) hosts. Definitive and intermediate hosts in alternate sequence keep the parasites of this group going in nature. Human beings and animals are the intermediate hosts for the *protozoans* that parasitize their tissues, the biting or blood-sucking insects that transfer these parasites being their definitive hosts (see Fig. 9–13). There are also some *nematodes*, of the group known as *filarial* worms, that are transferred to human tissues by insects. In this case, however, the host roles are reversed. Humans and animals support the adult and first intermediate stages of filarial worms, while insect hosts not only transport these parasites, but afford them the conditions and time necessary for the development of a second intermediate form.

The blood- and tissue-infecting protozoans of man include species of *Plasmodium* (malaria), *Leishmania* (kala-azar, oriental sore, espundia), and *Trypanosoma* (African sleeping sickness, Chagas' disease). These organisms, and the diseases they cause, can be of overwhelming importance in those areas of the world in which

Fig. 9–13. Some animal parasites are maintained in alternate sequence by biting or blood-sucking insect hosts and by animal (or human) hosts (*type 3*). The illustration above shows how malaria, for example, is transmitted by the *Anopheles* mosquito from one infected human being to another. The malaria parasite (*Plasmodium* species) requires both man and the mosquito to complete its complex life cycle.

their insect vectors flourish. They are brought closer to our own country each day by our involvement in wars in tropical countries and by the rapidity of modern transportation. The public threat of such diseases, however, exists only in those areas in which the definitive insect host can survive, or to which it can adapt, for these parasites are not directly transmissible from man to man.

Since protozoans are unicellular organisms, the recognition of "adult" and "immature" forms rests on different criteria than those applied to the structurally complex worms. Protozoa are capable of reproduction by the asexual mechanism known as mitosis, but they are also dependent on "sexual" recombinations and meiotic divisions for species continuation. Those that are involved in the blood and tissue infections of man reproduce asexually in the human body, displaying several developmental stages, all of the mitotic or asexual type. The blood-sucking mosquitoes and biting flies that prey on man for their blood meals pick up these parasites and provide conditions required for their continuing reproduction by sexual, or meiotic, divisions. For this reason, man is defined as the intermediate host, insects as the definitive hosts, for protozoan parasites of this type. Transferral of these agents of human disease always involves the biologic function, as well as the mechanical intervention, of insects.

The filarial nematodes live in human tissues as adult worms, producing larval forms that circulate in the blood. The larvae, often called *microfilariae*, are ingested by blood-sucking insect hosts that support their development through continuing intermediate stages. When infected insect hosts (mosquitoes and flies) prey again on human beings, they inject infective larval forms into their new human hosts. The route of transfer again involves insects, but this time they serve as intermediate hosts, transmitting immature forms that evolve to maturity in the human, or definitive, host.

Type 4. The cycle is maintained by one definitive host and one or more intermediate hosts. Definitive and intermediate hosts in alternate sequence also maintain the parasites of this group, but insects are not involved. The flatworms, or cestodes, display this type of complex life cycle. The group includes the intestinal tapeworms, one important tissue-invading tapeworm, and the flukes, or trematodes.

The intestinal tapeworms of man live as adults in the human bowel. Man is the definitive host for these organisms, which include *Taenia saginata* (the beef tapeworm), *Taenia solium* (the pork tapeworm), and *Diphyllobothrium latum* (the fish tapeworm). The eggs produced by these worms are discharged in feces into soil or water, and ingested by another animal. The ova hatch, in the intestinal tract of the second animal, into larval forms that penetrate the animal's bowel to invade and encyst in its tissues. In the case of the fish tapeworm, the egg is first eaten by a fresh-water arthropod, which is in turn ingested by a fish. The cycle is continued for the intestinal tapeworms by man and other animals who eat the infected flesh of intermediate hosts. Viable larvae in raw or inadequately cooked beef, pork, or fish develop into adult tapeworms in the intestinal tracts of man and other animals that eat such flesh (see Fig. 9–14).

The tissue-invading tapeworm, *Echinococcus granulosus*, has a natural reservoir in dogs, which serve as definitive hosts, and ruminant domestic animals (sheep, cattle), and pigs, the intermediate hosts. The adult worm inhabits the dog's intestinal tract, where it causes no disturbance. The eggs are discharged in the dog's feces and are ingested by an intermediate host, ordinarily a domestic animal grazing on contaminated grass or rubble. Ingested eggs hatch in the intestinal tract of intermediate hosts, penetrate the bowel, and develop into immature larval forms within various organs, notably the liver. In the natural course of events, dogs complete the cycle by ingesting the larval forms in the flesh of slaughtered animals or those they have killed. Man becomes an accidental victim of this infection through his association with infected dogs. The ova discharged in dog feces can be transferred to man by contaminated hands or food (see Fig. 9–15). As an intermediate host, man suffers the same larval invasion of tissues as experienced by other animals, but human infection represents

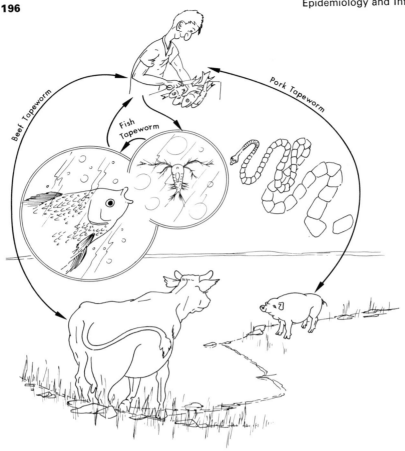

Fig. 9–14. This drawing illustrates the life cycles of those animal parasites that require one or more intermediate hosts as well as a definitive host (*type 4*). Parasitic arthropods are not involved in these cycles. This group includes the pork tapeworm (*Taenia solium*), the beef tapeworm (*Taenia saginata*), and the fish tapeworm (*Diphyllobothrium latum*).

Man is the definitive host for these parasites and excretes their ova in his feces. Cattle and pigs are the intermediate hosts for *T. saginata* and *T. solium*, respectively. These animals become infested when they feed or drink in areas where the soil or water has been contaminated with human feces containing *Taenia* eggs. "Water fleas" (copepods) and fish are the intermediate hosts for *D. latum*, acquiring the infection when their fresh-water habitat is contaminated with human feces containing the tapeworm ova. When man eats the raw or partially cooked flesh of infested cattle, pigs, or fish, he maintains the parasite's life cycle.

Control of these parasites lies in the sanitary disposal of feces, in government inspection of animal meats, and in the adequate cooking of meat or fish.

the end of the line for the parasite's cycle of development. It is often fatal for the human victim, as well, because echinococcal cysts (frequently called hydatid cysts) contain developing larvae and increasing quantities of fluid that produce pressure damage to tissues in which they are lodged.

The flukes also enter man's tissues as larval

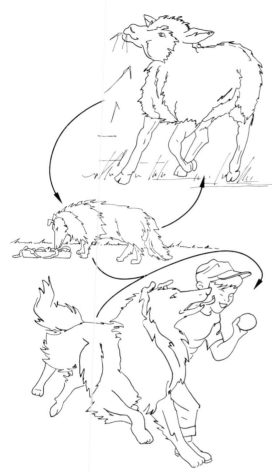

Fig. 9–15. *Echinococcus granulosus* is a tapeworm with a life cycle of the same type as that shown in Figure 9–14 (*type 4*). In this case, however, dogs and other canines are the definitive hosts, while sheep, cattle, pigs, and sometimes man are the intermediate hosts.

The infestation in dogs is intestinal. They acquire it by eating the raw flesh or viscera of slaughtered sheep or other animals whose tissues are infested with the larval form of the parasite. In the dog's intestinal tract, the adult worm produces eggs that are discharged in the feces, and other animals or human beings (especially children) become infected by ingesting the eggs from this source. Man and other intermediate hosts suffer a larval invasion of parenteral tissues. As in the case of trichinosis (see Fig. 9–12), human infestation represents the end of the parasite's cycle.

forms, but they develop there into adults that produce ova, so that man is a definitive host in this case. There are several varieties of parasitic trematodes whose distribution throughout the world is dependent on the ecology of their intermediate hosts (snails and water plants) as well as on the social and gastronomic habits of their human hosts. Adult flukes have different predilections for human tissues. The *Schistosoma* species are called *blood* flukes because the adults live and copulate in blood vessels, but the ova penetrate to surrounding tissues. The liver flukes, *Clonorchis* and *Fasciola*, lodge in the biliary ducts of the liver; intestinal (*Fasciolopsis*) and lung (*Paragonimus*) flukes, similarly, have specific localizations. At these various sites of lodgment, adult flukes produce ova that find their way out of the body via feces, urine, or sputum. They must reach water rather promptly if further development is to occur. The larval forms that hatch from the eggs in water are motile and can swim about, but they must find a suitable species of snail to continue their intermediate stages of maturation. They reproduce asexually within the snail, producing new forms that emerge to the water again. These motile larvae may be infective for man, capable of penetrating his skin when he swims, bathes, or wades in infected water (see Fig. 9–16). The larval forms of some flukes may encyst on water plants or be ingested by fish, crabs, and other crustaceans that are subsequently eaten by man, either raw or only partially cooked. Whether the larvae enter the body through the skin or the alimentary tract, they penetrate to small blood vessels, and are carried through the body, localizing finally in tissues where they can best develop into adults, to continue the cycle.

The *control* of diseases caused by animal parasites is based on a knowledge of their life cycles, so that their routes of transfer can be interrupted. Parasites of type 1 are best controlled by the proper disposal of human feces to prevent water or soil contamination. Control of those of type 2 calls for the protection of farm animals from infected food, the destruction of rodents, and public education on the necessity for the proper preparation of meat, especially pork, for the table. The destruction of insects, control of

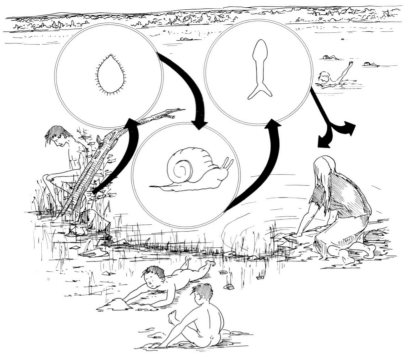

Fig. 9–16. The trematodes have a life cycle that requires a definitive host and also one or more intermediate hosts. Man is a definitive host for these parasites. The adult forms live in his tissues and produce eggs that may be discharged from the body in either feces or urine, depending on the site of infestation. If human excreta containing these ova are deposited in water inhabited by a suitable snail host, the latter supports the intermediate larval development of the parasite. (Type 4.)

   The perpetuation of the life cycle of *Schistosoma* species is depicted above. Man swims, bathes, launders, and plays in water that he has also contaminated with urine or feces containing *Schistosoma* ova. The eggs hatch into free-swimming miracidia in the water, enter snails, and emerge again a few weeks later as motile, infective larvae (cercariae). When the larvae swimming about in the water come in contact with human skin, they penetrate it and reach the subcutaneous tissue where they may enter small blood vessels and be carried through the body to some site in which they can develop into adults.

their breeding, and personal protection from insect bites are indicated in the case of the parasites having arthropod vectors. Tapeworm and fluke diseases are controlled by the protection of animals, sanitary measures that prevent the fecal contamination of water, and education of the public in personal hygiene and adequate preparation of food. The recognition and treatment of human and animal cases of parasitic diseases

may remove some of the sources of infection, but inapparent infections often remain as continuing reservoirs. (See also Appendix IV.)

The Patterns of Infectious Diseases

   Epidemiology is the study of the natural occurrence of diseases within a community. In the

communicable disease field, it is the province of the epidemiologist (usually a physician-specialist), the public health nurse, and the microbiologist working together to discover the sources and routes of infection, to recognize the patterns of disease spread, and to apply methods for the prevention and control of clinical infection. The major sources and routes of transfer of infectious organisms have been described in the preceding sections of this chapter. Let us now consider the manner in which infectious diseases appear, and wane, in human communities, before turning our attention to preventive methods, which are discussed in the next two chapters (10 and 11).

The occurrence of infectious diseases in human populations is characterized by patterns that are either epidemic, endemic, or sporadic. As we have seen, these terms reflect the *numbers* of persons who are clinically ill during a given period of time, as well as those who have inapparent infections, the *frequency* with which overt illness occurs, and the *rate of its spread* through a population. The factors that influence these three features of community disease (numbers, frequency, spread) are numerous, but they can be considered in three major categories: (1) the degree of effective resistance in the host population, with respect to a particular microbial agent of disease; (2) the sources, transmissibility, and incubation period of the infectious microorganism; and (3) the physical and social conditions of the human environment.

When the number of cases of communicable disease occurring within a stated time period (a week, a month, a year) exceeds expectations based on previous experience in similar periods, the situation is termed an *epidemic*. The extent of the epidemic is determined by the ratio of susceptible versus resistant individuals in the population, and this in turn is influenced by the familiarity of the community with the disease. If the disease is a new one, or if the agent is a new strain of a mutating pathogen, its introduction may result in a large epidemic because the population can be expected to contain a high proportion of susceptible people. Epidemics may also result when a disease is reintroduced to a community that has not experienced it for one or more generations. As the number of susceptibles declines during the course of an epidemic, spread of the disease becomes difficult and finally ceases, unless new susceptibles are continuously introduced. Conversely, as the proportion of immune individuals rises transmission is steadily reduced, even among the nonresistant. For this reason, artificial active immunization of large numbers of people is often an effective block to the epidemic spread of infection.

On the other hand, even small numbers of cases of infectious disease may constitute an epidemic, when they are seen in communities that are normally free of the disease in question. Small outbreaks may reflect a limited source of infection, or of restricted opportunity for exposure of susceptibles, or they may be the forerunners of larger events to come.

The frequency of epidemic disease often reflects the rise, duration, and waning of immunity in a population. Many of the viral diseases of childhood, such as measles and mumps, provide a lifelong immunity. They are seen primarily in young children, rather than in immune adult groups. They often occur in epidemic patterns, following two- to four-year cycles, as succeeding groups of susceptibles are born into a community or enter it from outside. Cyclic epidemics of influenza, on the other hand, may occur among people of all ages who are introduced to new strains, or to old ones for which their immunity has waned. By contrast, diseases such as the common cold are seen in fairly high, uniform incidence, particularly in winter seasons, because specific resistance to cold viruses is never significantly effective or long-lasting.

The rate at which an infectious disease spreads through a susceptible population is primarily a function of the sources, transmissibility, and incubation period of the agent in question. The respiratory diseases that are spread from person to person on an air-borne route travel with great speed, particularly when people are exposed to each other in closed areas, such as theaters, schools, barracks, and other communal places. The shorter the incubation period required for manifest disease, the more explosive the epidemic will appear, as in the case of influenza, strepto-

coccal sore throat, or scarlet fever. Similarly, food-, water-, and milk-borne outbreaks may appear explosively, because large numbers of people may be exposed to the same source of infection simultaneously, or within a short period of time. Diseases such as *Salmonella* food poisoning, amebic dysentery, staphylococcal and streptococcal infections, carried in milk, food, or water, all have short incubation periods. They can appear in a population within a matter of hours following ingestion of contaminated material. On the other hand, diseases such as infectious hepatitis, the systemic fungal diseases, or parasitic infestations take more time to develop than those mentioned above. When these occur in epidemic patterns among people exposed to a common source (those sharing a meal containing virus-infected shellfish or trichina-infected pork, for example, or those working in an area where dust inhalation involves the common risk of fungous infection), the slow development of overt disease may make it difficult to relate individual cases to their point of origin. Arthropod-borne infections may also appear in epidemic distribution when seasonal breeding increases the numbers of insect vectors that have access to an animal reservoir of infection. Outbreaks of equine encephalitis in the United States, for example, are usually associated with a spring or summer increase in the density of mosquito populations.

Diseases become *endemic* in populations with which infectious agents have established some balance. Clinically inapparent infections become the rule in such communities. Sporadic cases of disease occur from time to time, but epidemics do not occur while the equilibrium lasts. The balance can be disturbed by sudden changes in the proportion of susceptible persons, as when armies enter an area of endemic disease or by

environmental stresses that involve large numbers of people, such as those reduced by war to poverty and hunger. The ability of an infectious agent to establish the equilibrium of endemicity in a human or animal population depends on the availability of suitable reservoirs and transmission routes and on the responses of susceptible individuals to infection.

The physical and social conditions of the human environment may influence enormously the patterns and incidence of infectious disease. Low-income groups experience the constant stresses of poor nutrition, crowded and unsanitary living conditions, and the social habits of ignorance. Exposure of such populations to a new and highly virulent infectious agent may have disastrous consequences, of epidemic proportions. On the other hand, persistent, low-grade infections are the rule in poor communities, these endemic diseases contributing to a decreased resistance to any new diseases that may be introduced. Social customs, particularly in the matter of food and drink, sanitary standards, and even the political stability of a society — all can play a role in the nature and incidence of communicable diseases. We have also seen (Chap. 5) how large an influence the physical environment exerts on man's interrelationships with microorganisms. Climate, weather, and geography determine the ecology of human, animal, plant, and microbial populations. For microorganisms such factors may establish the availability of reservoirs and vectors, of vital importance to their continuation in nature. For human beings, the total environment presents the constant challenge of necessity to discover the means of prevention or control of infectious disease, at its source or along the route of transmission.

Questions

1. Define epidemiology. 199
2. Why are some diseases more communicable than others among human or animal populations?
3. Define reservoir of infection. Give examples of inanimate and living reservoirs.
4. What are endogenous sources of infection? Give examples.

5. List six major reservoirs of infection. Give examples of diseases in each group.
6. Name the routes of transfer of infection.
7. Describe briefly the four types of life cycles among animal parasites. Give examples in each group.

References

Pertinent References

Gordon, John (ed.): *Control of Communicable Diseases in Man*, 10th ed. American Public Health Association, New York, 1965.

Hilleboe, Herman, and Larrimore, Granville W.: *Preventive Medicine*, 2nd ed. W. B. Saunders, Philadelphia, 1965.

Periodicals

Bird-Borne Diseases in Man, *What's New*, **228**:27, Summer, 1962, Abbott Laboratories, North Chicago, Ill.

Chagas, Agnes W.: A General Survey of World Health Problems, *Amer. Assoc. Industr. Nurs.* **9**:10, Oct., 1961.

Dauer, Carl C.: 1960 Summary of Disease Outbreaks and a 10 Year Resume, *Public Health Rep.*, **76**:915, Oct., 1961.

Devlin, John C.: Pigeons Blamed in Two Deaths Here, *The New York Times*, Oct. 1, 1963.

Dubos, René J.: Health and Disease, *J.A.M.A.*, **174**:5, Oct. 1, 1960.

Editorial: Modern Concepts of Epidemiology, *J. Chronic Dis.*, **2**:593, Nov., 1955.

Galton, Mildred M., and Steele, James H.: Laboratory and Epidemiological Aspects of Food-Borne Diseases, *J. Milk & Food Tech.*, **24**:104, 1961.

Geister, Janet: The Flu Epidemic, *Nurs. Outlook*, **5**:583, Oct., 1957.

Greenberg, Bernard: Flies and Disease, *Sci. Amer.*, **213**:92, Jan., 1965.

Gregg, Michael B.: Communicable Disease Trends in the United States, *Amer. J. Nurs.*, **68**:88, Jan., 1968.

Lester, Mary: Every Nurse an Epidemiologist, *Amer. J. Nurs.*, **57**:1683, Nov., 1957.

Miller, Adah, and MacDonald, Ellen: Staphylococcal Infections — A Community Problem, *Nurs. Outlook*, **7**:584, Oct., 1959.

Riley, Richard E.: Airborne Infections, *Amer. J. Nurs.*, **60**:1246, Sept., 1960.

Shortel, Hazel, and Hunt, M. Estelle: Epidemiology: A Joint Activity of the Private Physician and the Public Health Nurse, *Nurs. Outlook*, **1**:468, Aug., 1953.

Sullivan, Walter: Hepatitis Traced to an Oysterman, *The New York Times*, Nov. 19, 1961.

Winchester, James H.: Food Poisoning and How to Avoid It, *Reader's Digest*, **86**:161, May, 1965.

Popular Literature

Atkinson, D. T.: Crede and the Fight Against Venereal Blindness, Semmelweis and the Conquest of Childbed Fever, Walter Reed and W. C. Gorgas and the Control of Yellow Fever and Malaria, in *Magic, Myth and Medicine*. A Premier Book, New York, 1958.

Clendening, Logan: Humanitarian Medicine and Sanitation, in *Behind the Doctor*. Garden City Publishing Co., Inc., New York, 1933.

Clendening, Logan, compiled with notes by: Preventive Medicine, in *Source Book of Medical History*. Dover Publications, Inc. New York, 1960.

DeKruif, Paul: Theobold Smith, Ticks and Texas Fever, Bruce, Trail of the Tsetse, Ross vs. Grassi, Malaria, Walter Reed, in the Interest of Science and for Humanity, in *Microbe Hunters*. Harcourt Brace, New York, 1926.

Roueché, Berton: *Eleven Blue Men.* Berkley Medallion Books, New York, 1955.

Roueché, Berton (ed.): Snow on Cholera and the Broad Street Pump, in *Curiosities in Medicine.* Little Brown and Company, Boston, 1964.

Shippen, Katherine: The Mystery of Malaria, in *Men of Medicine.* The Viking Press, New York, 1957.

Styler, Herman: A Vicious Female, On the Trail of Typhoid Mary, in *Plague Fighters.* Chilton Co., Philadelphia and New York, 1960.

Walker, Kenneth: Medieval Epidemics, in *The Story of Medicine.* Arrow Books, Ltd., Tiptree, Essex, England, 1954.

Williams, Harley: Control of Tropical Disease, in *Masters of Medicine.* Pan Books, London, 1954.

Winslow, Charles Edward A.: Three Pioneer Epidemiologists, Concept of the Carrier, Insect Host, Modes of Infection, in *The Conquest of Epidemic Disease.* Princeton University Press, Princeton, N.J., 1943.

10 The Prevention and Control of Infectious Diseases

General Principles

The continuing expansion of our scientific knowledge of the causes and sources of infectious diseases has been accompanied by the steady development of improved methods either for preventing diseases or for treating and controlling them when they arise. The prevention or control of infection requires methods that can effectively accomplish one or more of the following results: (1) the destruction or control of the microbial agents of disease; (2) the elimination or control of the sources, routes, or agents of transmission of infection; and (3) the partial or full protection of the human host from the serious effects of disease through improvement of his resistance, specific treatment of his infections, or both.

The successful application of such approaches, singly or in combination as they have been developed for the attack on specific microorganisms, has virtually eliminated some diseases in certain areas and greatly reduced the importance of others. Smallpox and diphtheria, for example, now occur as only occasional cases in the United States and other countries where large-scale immunization and other control measures can be carefully maintained. Improved sanitary standards and the more recent development of effective vaccines for poliomyelitis have similarly

reduced the incidence and broken the pattern of spread of this disease. In other instances where prevention has not been possible, much control has been gained over the sources or transmitting agents of infection, as in the case of the insect-borne diseases caused by protozoa (malaria), viruses (yellow fever, encephalitis), and rickettsiae (epidemic typhus fever). It is also possible to control some infectious diseases by averting their severe consequences. Viral diseases such as hepatitis, measles, or mumps can be aborted or prevented if exposure of nonimmune persons is recognized and followed by prompt administration of gamma globulin to provide passive protective antibody. Specific chemotherapy administered immediately upon the appearance of diagnostic symptoms is now usually quite effective for controlling the formerly serious diseases caused by pneumococcal and streptococcal infections. Among the venereal diseases, gonorrhea and syphilis, though they remain uncontrolled at their source, can be successfully cured by early, adequate chemotherapy. A significant measure of control is obtained over diseases that can be aborted by either immunologic or therapeutic means, for not only is the individual case resolved, but the opportunities are removed for

further spread of virulent infection from a sick patient.

In the following sections of this chapter, attention will be given to the principles involved in each of the three important approaches outlined above for the prevention and control of infectious diseases. The emphasis here will be on the problems of individual infection. Application of the principles to the protection of the public health are discussed in Chapter 11.

Definitions

Discussion of the measures used to destroy or suppress microorganisms, or to break the chain of their transmission from one host to another, requires the use of technical terms whose meanings should be clear to all who use them. The student should review them before continuing to study the principles of control and should refer to them frequently in subsequent reading of the text to become thoroughly familiar with their proper use. They are arranged in two major groups: those referring to the destruction or suppression of *microorganisms*, and those applying to the control of *infectious diseases*.

I. Terms Indicating the Destruction or Suppression of Microorganisms

A. Destruction

Sterilization: The *complete* destruction of all forms of microbial life. Sterility is an absolute term; there can be no gradations or degrees of meaning in its proper use. Phrases such as "partial sterility," or "almost sterile" have no meaning, for they imply that some, a few, or even one microorganism may be left alive, in which case sterilization has not been accomplished.

Asepsis: This term means literally "without infection" or without the causative agents of infectious disease. It is a condition resulting from techniques that prevent or avoid the introduction of living microorganisms. In use it generally implies the *intention* of providing a sterile situation by methods that set up protective barriers and exclude microorganisms from passing through them. In practice, it is often more difficult to guarantee the *exclusion* of viable organisms with aseptic techniques than it is to *sterilize* the area and its contents

and to prove sterility (e.g., by introducing living test organisms and demonstrating that they are destroyed).

This term is frequently modified with the adjectives "surgical" or "medical." The phrase *surgical asepsis* refers to the use of techniques designed to exclude *all* microorganisms from surgical procedures, since *any* microbe might produce infection if introduced into tissues by surgery. *Medical asepsis* refers to techniques that exclude the agents of naturally communicable disease (as opposed to those of surgical infection), but does not imply that all *other* microorganisms have been eliminated.

Disinfection: A process that destroys *pathogenic* microorganisms. Disinfectants are chemical or physical agents used to kill infectious agents that may contaminate inanimate objects.

Concurrent disinfection means the immediate application of disinfectant techniques to infectious discharges from an infected patient or to objects soiled by such discharges.

Terminal disinfection means the final application of disinfectant techniques to all of the surfaces and objects within an area that has been, but is no longer, occupied by an infectious patient.

Antisepsis: The chemical disinfection of skin surfaces or other living tissues. The same chemical agents may sometimes be used as disinfectants or as antiseptics, provided they can be tolerated by living cells. Antiseptics are applied in the preparation of both the patient's and the surgeon's skin prior to surgery.

-cide: A noun suffix derived from a Latin word meaning "to kill." The adjectival suffix is "-cidal."

Germicide: An agent that kills germs.

Bactericide: A specific term applied to an agent that kills bacteria. The suffix can be used to denote the destructive properties of an agent for other particular kinds of organisms or their stages: thus, a *sporicide* kills bacterial spores, a *fungicide* kills fungi, a *virucide* kills viruses, and so on. Disinfectants, antiseptics, and some antibiotics are bactericidal, though not necessarily for all species of bacteria.

B. Suppression

-stasis: A noun suffix derived from a Greek word meaning "to halt." The adjectival suffix is "-static."

Bacteriostasis: A condition in which bacterial growth is arrested. Bacteriostatic agents are substances (e.g., some dyes, drugs, antibiotics) that halt the multiplication of bacteria but do not kill them. When the agent is removed the organisms can resume active growth. Fungistatic

and virustatic agents operate in the same way on fungi and viruses, respectively.

Antibiotic: Literally, against life.

Antibacterial: Literally, against bacteria.

Antimicrobial: Literally, against microbes.
                    These terms are commonly used to refer to drugs or other agents that suppress or inhibit growth.

Sanitization: A process that *removes* pathogenic microorganisms from inanimate objects. The term implies that organisms have been reduced to a safe number by a cleaning action. It cannot be used to mean that sterilization or complete disinfection has been achieved.

Cleaning: A process that removes soil or other extraneous material from surfaces. It may result in the simultaneous removal of many microorganisms, but the term never implies sterility or even disinfection.

II. Terms Used in the Management of Infectious Diseases

Contamination: The presence of microorganisms on animate or inanimate surfaces or in water, food, or milk. In medical use, the term implies the possibility that infectious agents may be present.

Infection: A state in which a living host harbors microorganisms that have entered, survived, and multiplied in his tissues. The result may or may not be clinically apparent; therefore, the term is not synonymous with infectious disease (see Chap. 5). The word should be used to refer only to living hosts or their tissues, not to the presence of infectious agents on or in inanimate matter. In the latter situation the term "contamination" is proper.

Infectious disease: A state of evident disease in man or animals resulting from infection.

Communicable disease: An infectious disease arising through the transmission of a specific infectious agent, or its toxic products, from an animate or inanimate reservoir, directly or indirectly, to a susceptible host. It should be noted that not every infectious disease is communicable between hosts of the same species.

Isolation: "The separation for the period of communicability of infected persons from other persons, in such places and under such conditions as will prevent the direct or indirect conveyance of the infectious

agent from infected persons to persons who are susceptible or who may spread the agent to others. This applies also to animals."*

Quarantine:

"(1) *Complete quarantine* is the limitation of freedom of movement of such well persons or domestic animals as have been exposed to a communicable disease, for a period of time equal to the longest incubation period of the disease, in such manner as to prevent effective contact with those not so exposed.

"(2) *Modified quarantine* is a selective, partial limitation of freedom of movement of persons or domestic animals, commonly on the basis of known or presumed differences in susceptibility, but sometimes because of danger of disease transmission. It may be designed to meet particular situations; examples are exclusion of children from school or exemption of immune persons from provisions required of susceptible persons, such as contacts acting as food handlers, or restriction of military populations to the post or to quarters.

"(3) *Personal surveillance* is the practice of close medical or other supervision of contacts in order to promote prompt recognition of infection or illness but without restricting their movements.

"(4) *Segregation* is the separation for special consideration, control, or observation of some part of a group of persons or of domestic animals from the others, to facilitate the control of a communicable disease. Removal of susceptible children to homes of immune persons, or the establishment of a sanitary boundary to protect uninfected from infected portions of a population are examples."*

Communicable period:

"The time or times during which the infectious agent may be transferred directly or indirectly from an infected person to another person, from an infected animal to man, or from an infected man to animal, including arthropods.

"In diseases such as diphtheria and scarlet fever, in which mucous membranes are involved from the first entry of the pathogen, the period of communicability is from the date of first exposure to a source of infection, until the infecting microorganism is no longer disseminated from the involved mucous membranes; i.e., from before the prodromata until the termination of the carrier state, if such develops.

"In diseases such as tuberculosis, syphilis, and gonorrhea, the communicable state may be at any time over a long and sometimes intermittent period when unhealed lesions of the disease permit the discharge of infectious agents from the surface of the skin or through any of the body orifices. In certain diseases communicability does

* As defined by the Committee on Communicable Disease Control, American Public Health Association, in *Control of Communicable Diseases in Man*, 10th ed., published by the A.P.H.A., 1965.

not occur during the early incubation period or after full recovery, e.g., measles and chickenpox.

"In diseases transmitted by arthropods, such as malaria and yellow fever, the periods of communicability are those during which the infectious agent occurs in the blood or other tissues of the infected person in infective form and in sufficient numbers for vector infection. A period of communicability is also to be distinguished for the arthropod vector, namely that time during which the agent is present in the tissues of the arthropod in such form (infective state) as to be capable of transmitting infection."*

Control of Infectious Microorganisms

To the microbiologist, a dead microbial cell is one that has permanently and irreversibly lost its ability to reproduce, as tested by available techniques for the demonstration of its growth, in vitro or in vivo. Assuming that such techniques are always adequate in providing optimal media and other growth conditions in which viable organisms may multiply, the basic information they provide permits the following generalizations:

1. Microorganisms can be irreversibly "killed," or reversibly inhibited, by a number of physical agents as well as by chemical methods.

2. The various microbial groups differ greatly in their response to sterilizing or inhibiting agents. The cells of a particular bacterial species may also vary in this respect, young growing cells being more susceptible than older resting ones, while the spores formed by some bacterial species are very much more resistant to antimicrobial agents than are their vegetative forms.

3. Sterilization is always a function of time, regardless of the agent employed or the microorganism involved, since the changes leading to the death of cells occur gradually, and not all the organisms die simultaneously, even in homogeneous cultures.

4. The rate of sterilization is also dependent on the nature, concentration, or intensity of the sterilizing agent, as it is on the nature and numerical density of microorganisms present.

Ibid.

5. The choice of a method of sterilization, disinfection, or inhibition, in a given situation, must take into account a number of other factors that may limit the success or practicality of the procedure. Some of these factors are: the nature and function of the material to be processed (fabrics, rubber, glassware, etc.); conditions that may affect the activity of the antimicrobial agent; and the influence of extraneous factors on the response of microorganisms to the agent (the presence of proteins, lipids, salts, the pH, etc.).

In the following discussion, the more useful of the physical and chemical agents employed for sterilization, disinfection, or microbial inhibition will be described, together with the reasons for, and the limitations on, their use.

The Antimicrobial Activity of Physical Agents

Heat. The application of heat is the simplest, most reliable, and least expensive means of assuring sterilization of materials that are themselves not damaged by it. It is a rapid process to which all living protoplasm is susceptible.

Mode of Action. The efficiency of heat as a sterilizing agent is a function of two primary factors operating together: the intensity of the heat applied, i.e., *temperature*, and the *time* for which a given temperature is maintained. When these two factors are specified, the effect of heat on various species of microorganisms may be compared. The lowest temperature that kills all the organisms in a standardized pure culture

within a specified time period is the "thermal death point" of that species, while the time required to sterilize the culture at a stated temperature is its "thermal death time."

The effects and consequently the practical applications of heat are further dependent on whether it is *moist* or *dry*. Most of the proteins of microbial cells are enzymes that function only within a narrow temperature range. In the intact cell they are held in a fine suspension. When heat is applied in the presence of moisture, the structure of the cellular proteins is altered, they are coagulated (as the white of an egg is coagulated when it is boiled), and their enzymatic function is destroyed. On the other hand, protein structure is much more stable to heat in the dry state. When the temperature of dry heat is raised, cell proteins do not coagulate, but they and other components of the microbial cell are oxidized. At low temperatures dry-heat oxidation is very

much slower than protein coagulation in the presence of moisture (see Fig. 10–1). Moist-heat sterilization is more efficient, therefore, because it can be accomplished more rapidly and at lower temperatures than dry-heat methods. It is also far less injurious to many materials that would themselves be oxidized by the high temperatures required for sterilization by dry-heat methods.

The Uses of Moist Heat. The thermal death point for most pathogenic microorganisms lies between 50° and 70° C, with ten minutes' exposure. However, the heat-resistant spores of some species of pathogenic bacteria can survive at 100° C for many minutes, while those of certain saprophytic species can resist up to 24 hours of boiling. The choice of a moist-heat method of sterilization depends, therefore, on the nature of the job to be done and the temperature that can be produced by the method.

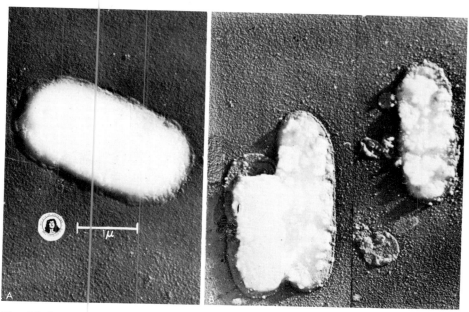

Fig. 10–1. The effect of moist heat on *Escherichia coli. A.* An electron micrograph of a typical cell of *E. coli* from a one-hour broth culture. There is little shrinkage of the cytoplasm away from the cell wall. *B.* Three cells of *E. coli* that have been heated at 50° C in saline for ten minutes. The coagulated cytoplasm is granular and has shrunken away from the cell wall. (Reproduced from Heden, Carl-Göran, and Wyckoff, Ralph, W. G.: The Electron Micrography of Heated Bacteria, *J. Bact.,* **58**:153–60, 1949.)

Fig. 10–2. A modern pasteurizer. The proper handling of milk *before* and *after* pasteurization also reduces the possibility of disease being transmitted by milk. (Courtesy of The Borden Company, New York, N.Y.)

Pasteurization is a process that utilizes the minimum degree of moist heat that can be expected to kill nonsporing pathogenic bacteria in milk or other potable liquids within a time period that will not spoil the flavor or quality of the beverage. The method was first devised by Pasteur, who found that the spoilage of wine could be prevented by heating it to 60° C for a time sufficient to kill fermentative and oxidative organisms that cause souring. Pasteurization of milk before its consumption has resulted in an effective control of a number of important milk-borne diseases, notably, tuberculosis, brucellosis, salmonellosis, and streptococcal diseases of bovine origin. The technique consists of raising the temperature of milk to 62.9° C (145° F) for 30 minutes, or to a somewhat higher temperature (71.6° C or 161° F) for a much shorter period (15 seconds), then cooling it rapidly to avoid flavor loss (see Fig. 10–2). This temperature-time relationship is based on the thermal death point of the rickettsial agent of Q fever, one of the most heat-resistant of the vegetative microorganisms that may contaminate milk. The non-pathogenic, heat-resistant bacteria that occur naturally in milk are not killed by pasteurization. These include the streptococci and lactobacilli that cause milk to sour rapidly at room temperature, or more slowly at refrigerator temperatures.

Boiling water provides a very simple means of disinfection under many circumstances. The temperature of boiling water, and of the steam it

evolves, is 100° C. Since this is well above the thermal death point of vegetative bacteria, fungi, and most viruses, boiling for 10 to 30 minutes will kill all except the heat-resistant spores and viruses. Contaminated materials may be *disinfected* in this way, after their use, provided there is no reason to suspect the presence of pathogenic spores or viruses. However, it is essential that detergent agents be added to the water when dirty items are boiled to prevent the coagulation of extraneous protein matter (blood, mucus, pus), for bacteria trapped within large coagulated particles are protected from the killing effects of the surrounding temperature and moisture. Clean instruments, syringes, needles, and other metal or glass items may be *disinfected* by complete immersion in boiling water for not less than 30 minutes. If such materials are to be used for patient care, they must be carefully protected from air contamination following removal from the water. Since the method cannot be guaranteed to produce sterility, its safe use is dependent on an adequate understanding of its limitations and the demands of a particular situation. When sterilization is essential, safer methods must be used in the preparation of equipment.

Hot water, at temperatures from 60° C to boiling, accomplishes sanitization, and at least partial disinfection, particularly if it is applied with force and agitation in washing and rinsing items to be cleaned. Modern laundry and dishwashing equipment provides far better conditions for disinfection than manual washing of clothing, bedding, or dishes. The action of detergent soaps added to wash water also plays a large role in the mechanical removal of microorganisms, as well in their inhibition or destruction at elevated temperatures.

Steam under pressure is the most reliable form of moist heat for sterilization. The temperature of freely flowing steam is 100° C. It is sometimes used in this form as a sanitizing or disinfecting agent, as in the steam-flushing of bedpans in the hospital or of animal cages in the laboratory. Steam becomes a sterilizing medium when its temperature is increased by subjecting it to increasing positive pressure. It was Pasteur, again, who introduced this practical method for the laboratory sterilization of media and glassware. Since that time, the steam pressure sterilizer, or *autoclave* as it is often called, has become essential, not only to the routine operations of the microbiologic laboratory, but to the safety of many hospital practices as well (see Fig. 10-3).

A steam pressure sterilizer is essentially a chamber that permits, in sequence, first, the entry of flowing, saturated steam and the exit of displaced air; then closure of the air outlet so that the continued admission of steam produces a rising pressure. As the pressure increases, the temperature of steam rises proportionately to a degree that can be balanced with reasonably short time periods to accomplish sterilization. Temperature and time are the essential sterilizing factors; increasing pressure provides the means for raising the temperature of steam, thus shortening the time required. Table 10-1 illustrates the influence of pressure on the temper-

Table 10-1. Pressure-Temperature-Time Relationships in Steam Pressure Sterilization

Steam Pressure	Temperature		Time
Pounds per Square Inch (Above Atmospheric Pressure)	Centigrade	Fahrenheit	(Minutes Required to Kill *Exposed* Heat-Resistant Spores)
0	100°	212°	——
10	115.5°	240°	15–60
15	121.5°	250°	12–15
20	126.5°	260°	5–12
30	134°	270°	3–5

Fig. 10–3. A load of carefully packed and arranged articles is being pushed into the high-vacuum sterilizer. The articles are placed on end so that steam can circulate and permeate the packaged contents. (Courtesy of AMSCO, American Sterilizer Company, Erie, Pa.)

ature of steam and on the time needed to ensure destruction of heat-resistant organisms (exposed without consideration to limiting factors in autoclaving supplies or materials).

The factor of first importance in successful autoclaving is the complete elimination of air from the sterilizing chamber. Air is cooler, dryer, and heavier than steam, and although an air-steam mixture can be brought to any desired pressure, the mixture will have a lower temperature than that of pure steam at the same pressure. The temperatures stated in Table 10–1 above are accurate only for saturated steam unmixed with air.

When steam saturated with moisture enters the autoclave chamber, it quickly condenses on the cold surfaces within. This condensation of steam releases a large amount of latent heat (about 540° per cubic foot) and at the same time wets materials exposed to it. The rapid release of heat and moisture has a penetrative effect that quickly raises the temperature of inner, as well as outer, surfaces of items within the sterilizer to that of the surrounding steam. Vessels or containers having hollow air spaces must be covered loosely, however, or placed in horizontal positions (if they do not contain liquid material) to permit air displacement and steam condensation. At the end of the sterilizing period, steam is slowly released from the chamber. When the pressure within the autoclave has returned to normal, a drying period is required for fabrics, clean glassware, and other items that must be free of condensed moisture before use.

Time is a factor equal in importance to that of temperature in accomplishing steam pressure sterilization. Since it takes a few minutes for steam pressure to rise within a closed chamber, the timing of an autoclave procedure cannot begin until a sterilizing temperature has been reached. The time required to sterilize a particular item or group of materials placed together in a full loading of the autoclave chamber varies with the nature of the load. Steam penetration of thick, bulky, porous articles such as linen packs for the operating room takes longer than steam condensation on the exposed, impenetrable surfaces of metal or glass instruments, which are quickly raised to sterilizing temperatures. Microorganisms buried within the depths of porous materials are not reached so rapidly as those lying on exposed surfaces. For these reasons, the timing of autoclave procedures must be judged for each load, with critical care.

Materials and items that must be sterilized vary in their own susceptibility to heat. Nonporous materials such as glass or metal withstand it very well, but cloth, rubber, cellophane, and plastic may be damaged by it. Time and temperature adjustments of heat sterilization must be made with this in mind, as well. Furthermore, the steam penetrability of covering materials must be borne in mind when the autoclave is used for sterilization. Rubber and some plastic surfaces can be successfully sterilized without deterioration under steam pressure, but they can never be used as covering for other items to be sterilized because they are impenetrable to steam.

The requirements and limitations of steam pressure sterilization may be summarized as follows:

Fig. 10–4. A loading cart properly loaded before sterilization. The packs have been placed on their sides in loose contact with each other. If two layers of packs are used, the upper layer is perpendicular or at right angles to the lower layer. This arrangement permits the downward flow of air between the packs and its replacement by steam entering from the top and back of the chamber. (Courtesy of AMSCO, American Sterilizer Company, Erie, Pa.)

1. The temperature of the steam chamber must reach a sterilizing level. This is possible only if all air originally present has drained out through the discharge outlet.

2. Items to be sterilized must be packaged and arranged within the autoclave to permit full steam penetration to the depths of each package, as shown in Figure 10–4. (Instruments or other objects to be used promptly after sterilization may be autoclaved without covering, provided they are not exposed to undue risk of air contamination upon removal from the sterilizer.)

3. The timing of the autoclave procedure must be based on the period during which sterilizing

temperature is available and on the nature of the materials in the load. It is dangerous to underestimate time, but it is inefficient and wasteful to prolong it unnecessarily or to the point of injury to valuable materials.

Modern autoclaves are equipped with regulating devices for the control of air discharge, pressure, temperature, and timing, which reduce the work of the operator to a minimum. Like all mechanical equipment designed by human effort to meet a need, however, they require continuing intelligent monitoring. Autoclaves and automobiles, for instance, have one vital thing in common: their misuse or abuse can lead to injury or death of the unwary or of the innocent. The safeguards surrounding the use of automobiles are often far better observed than those for autoclaves, however, because the causes and effects of automobile accidents are more immediately and shockingly obvious. For this reason, the law requires that those who drive must be licensed through a practical demonstration of proficiency, that manufacturers must meet basic standards, and that owners must keep their cars in good operating condition. In any case, no responsible person who drives an automobile would dream of leaving its care and maintenance to the salesman from whom it was purchased. The safe operation of an autoclave is similarly the responsibility of the person who uses it, *on each occasion*, the more so because its efficiency involves the welfare of others, *upon every use*. Yet all too frequently this responsibility is neither recognized nor assumed. In modern hospitals, the final responsibility for the safety of sterilization procedures employed on or for nursing units falls on nursing personnel, whose obligation it is to understand thoroughly the uses, operation, and limitations of the equipment at their command. The manufacturers of sterilizing equipment fulfill their obligations in guaranteeing its performance under proper conditions and in describing these explicitly. It is incumbent on those who operate sterilizers, or who delegate this duty to others under supervision, to use them correctly, or to teach others how to do so.

The final criterion of the safety of steam pressure sterilization is the bacteriologic demonstra-

tion of its efficiency in killing heat-resistant organisms. The microbiologic laboratory can provide suitable materials for conducting such tests (usually a preparation of living, heat-stable spores), and it can also perform the necessary culture work, but the actual use of the test material is more critically managed by those who consistently operate the autoclave for particular purposes (one driver cannot take a test for another who would like to have a license!). When properly designed and executed, bacteriologic tests can provide information regarding the mechanical efficiency of the autoclave; the adequacy of techniques for the packaging of individual, typical items; and the proficiency of the operator in arranging the total load and regulating conditions to permit full steam penetration throughout the chamber. These are particular problems, best understood by those who are responsible for them and deal with them daily. The collaborative advice of the laboratory should be called upon, but the direction and use of controls are the concern of those responsible for the end result.

Further information on the hospital use of steam pressure sterilization, and on methods for determining its adequacy, can be found in Appendixes VI and VIII.

The Uses of Dry Heat. Sterilization by dry heat has an oxidative effect, not only on microorganisms but also on the materials they contaminate and from which they must be removed. If the latter are expendable, or resistant to fiery temperatures, burning them completely, or flaming their surfaces, will sterilize them easily and quickly.

Incineration is an effective technique for the disposal of many contaminated objects that cannot be used again, *provided* the temperature within the incinerator is kept sufficiently intense to ensure the prompt ashing of materials at the rate they are fed into it. Overloading of a dry-heat incinerator may result in the "lumping" of partially burned material, inadequately heated, with condensation of its moisture content, coagulation of protein material, and consequent protection

of microorganisms trapped within. Incinerating chambers must be of a size adequate to the maximum load introduced, and they must be capable of maintaining temperatures that will burn their largest loads promptly and completely, or sterilization cannot be guaranteed. Various hospital practices in this respect are open to serious question: the design of such equipment is frequently inadequate to the need; its use is turned over to untrained personnel; the results of "incineration" are taken on faith, without observational or other grounds for judging their efficacy.

Flaming the surface of a heat-resistant object may be effective in its sterilization if the heat of the flame is sufficiently intense to bring about the immediate vaporization of any moisture present and the prompt oxidation of exposed microorganisms. The microbiologist commonly uses the flame of a Bunsen burner to sterilize his wire inoculating loop or needle. The heat of such a burner will sterilize metal surfaces within seconds, provided they are not covered with moist proteinaceous materials that coagulate before their microbial content can be oxidized. Such materials tend to "clump" in suddenly applied heat and to spatter from the flame, carrying organisms that may still be viable. For this reason, laboratory burners not only should be capable of immediate incinerating temperatures, but also should be equipped with heat-conductive shields to catch spatter and oxidize it completely, so that the air, the workbench, or the worker will not be sprayed with potentially infectious material. The hospital use of alcohol lamps for flaming is to be discouraged, as is the practice of alcohol-dipping followed by flaming. In neither case is it likely that a sterilizing temperature can be reached by the relatively cool flame of burning alcohol, unless the time is prolonged to the point of damage to the flamed object (forceps, scalpel, or other metal instrument). The oxidative effect of dry heat on metal surfaces produces discoloration and, more importantly, dulls the edges of sharp instruments.

Hot-air baking in an insulated, thermostatically controlled oven is an effective method for steri-

Fig. 10–5. A hot-air sterilizer is used for sterilizing powders, oils, Vaseline, hypodermic needles, and glassware. Materials such as oils and Vaseline resist penetration and permeation by moist steam. (Courtesy of AMSCO, American Sterilizer Company, Erie, Pa.)

lizing materials that can withstand high temperatures (see Fig. 10–5). Since dry heat does not penetrate well, sterilization requires higher temperatures for longer periods with dry heat then with moist heat. The time allowed for the hot-air method depends, as always, on the temperature used. Both these factors may be destructive, however, to some materials, notably fabrics, paper wraps, and synthetic materials. Rubber and plastic goods are quickly destroyed by dry heat, but glass and metal withstand it very well. Some materials, such as powders, waxes, oils, glycerin, and petroleum jelly, are not penetrable by moist

heat, or would be damaged by moisture, and for these hot-air sterilization is a necessity.

The limitations imposed by both time and temperature must be considered in selecting a baking method for particular items. Temperatures *below* 160° C require periods in excess of two hours, and are therefore impractical, while a temperature of 180° C or more may cause charring of many items. Therefore, the range between these two temperatures is usually chosen, depending on the nature of the oven load, and timing is adjusted to the temperature selected. At 160° to 165° C sterilization is accomplished in two hours; at 170° to 175° C, in one hour, *provided* all parts or surfaces of every item in the oven are evenly heated to these temperatures. Oils, waxes, and jellies are not easily penetrated by moderate heat; yet they can be damaged by intense temperatures. To meet these limitations, such materials should be prepared in small units, of shallow depth, and baked for two hours at 160° C. Clean, dry glassware, metal items, syringes, and hypodermic needles are readily brought to the sterilizing temperature of the hot air surrounding their inner and outer surfaces; such materials can be baked for one hour at 170° C without injury.

The even distribution of heat in a sterilizing oven is an essential factor. It is the air within the oven, heated to the desired temperature and circulating freely, that is the sterilizing agent. The heat of the air is transferred to objects exposed to it as rapidly or slowly as their own heat-conductive properties permit. The temperature of the air is maintained by a constant source of heat (gas or electricity) and kept within the desired range by the action of a thermostat. The oven must, of course, be sealed against any exchange of air with the outside atmosphere, when heating begins. When the load is arranged, each item must be placed in such a way as to ensure its full exposure to the heated air, without blocking air circulation over other objects. Items that are wrapped or placed in containers to maintain their sterility on removal from the oven must be prepared with due consideration of the necessity for complete heat transfer, so that their

interior and exterior temperatures will reach the desired degree.

Cold. The metabolic activities of microorganisms are slowed at decreasing temperatures to the point of complete inhibition of their growth under freezing conditions. Cold is, therefore, an antimicrobial, or bacteriostatic, agent, but it does not usually have a sterilizing, disinfecting, or bactericidal effect. Reduced temperatures are frequently used in the laboratory to preserve cultures of microorganisms for long periods of time. Freezing and drying under vacuum, for example, stop the growth and reproduction of bacteria, but they can remain viable in this condition for years.

In the natural world, cold inhibits and sometimes even kills some of the microorganisms of water and soil, but it does not sterilize these reservoirs. As a matter of fact, ice from contaminated water, or ice that has later become contaminated, has frequently been incriminated as a source of spread of infection when it has been used to chill drinking water, other beverages, or food. Under the inhibition of cold temperatures, microorganisms do not grow, or do so very slowly, but when normal temperatures are restored their growth proceeds once again (as when infectious organisms are swallowed with iced water).

On the other hand, refrigeration and freezing are time-honored, effective methods for the preservation of foods from microbial spoilage. The quality and flavor of foods are not greatly affected by storage in the cold, but the growth of spoilage organisms is very slow at normal refrigerator temperatures (0° to 8° C), or inhibited altogether at freezer temperatures (−5° to −25° C). Frozen foods must be kept in the freezer until they are to be prepared for the table. It is unwise to refreeze food that has thawed, because microbial growth may produce metabolic products or induce changes in the food that will not be affected by refreezing but could be unpleasant or harmful at the next thawing.

Drying. Many microorganisms are inhibited but not killed by drying. In the absence of moisture,

a microbial cell is not capable of growth and reproduction but it may remain viable for years in the dried state, resuming growth when moisture and nutrient are restored. This fact is applied in the laboratory to the preservation of cultures, as mentioned above, by drying them under vacuum from the frozen state. (Freeze-drying is also used to preserve serum and other blood products.)

Drying is one of the oldest methods known for the preservation of foods of all kinds. Fruits, vegetables, and meats can all be kept free of microbial activity by desiccation, though of course their flavor and quality undergo a marked change. The nutrient value of food is somewhat reduced by drying (vitamin content is not retained, for example) but this is not a problem in normal diets containing adequate supplements of fresh foods. Some foods are eaten in the dried state (raisins, prunes), but many can be reconstituted with water and reassume their normal flavor and consistency (dried potato flakes restored as mashed potatoes).

In the hospital situation it is most important to remember the survival capacity of dried microorganisms. Bacterial spores have an extraordinary resistance to drying, but vegetative bacteria, viruses, fungi, protozoa, and helminth ova may withstand it also, though to a lesser degree. Dust, clothing, bedding, dressings, and other items may contain the dried remnants of urine, feces, sputum, or pus contamination, with infectious microorganisms still present and viable. Incautious shaking of soiled fabrics, sweeping, dry-mopping, or dry-dusting all contribute to the wide dissemination of microorganisms, many of which may be infectious, especially in the hospital environment.

Ultraviolet Radiation. Sunlight contains light rays of varying wavelengths (measured in Angstrom units, Å). In the visible light spectrum, the longest rays (7500 Å) are at the red end of the scale, the shortest (4000 Å) at the violet end. The invisible part of the spectrum contains rays that are longer than those of the visible reds (*infrared*) and others that are shorter than the violets (*ultraviolet*). The ultraviolet spectrum

extends from 4000 Å downward in length to about 2000 Å, and the lower end of this scale (2800 to 2500 Å) has a strongly destructive effect on many microorganisms, particularly bacteria.

Ultraviolet rays must be absorbed to be effective. They do not pass through ordinary transparent glass or through opaque substances. In bacterial cells, ultraviolet rays are absorbed by nuclear proteins. The chemical effects on the genetic mechanisms of cells may induce mutations or death.

In the natural world the ultraviolet component of sunlight probably affects many organisms that are exposed directly to it. However, the use of sunlight as a sterilizing or disinfecting agent is not very reliable, since the short rays will not penetrate surfaces but can kill only those organisms that are most superficially exposed.

Ultraviolet radiation produced by mercury vapor lamps is widely used as a sterilizing agent, however. Such lamps are used to help in the control of air-borne infection when placed in confined areas of public use (elevators, schoolrooms, barracks) or in critical hospital areas (operating rooms, nurseries, infectious disease wards). In the laboratory they are used to kill suspensions of microorganisms that are to be prepared as vaccines and also for the decontamination of working areas. In the commercial preparation of sterile biologicals or of foods and their containers, ultraviolet radiation can reduce or eliminate the possibilities for microbial contamination. The effectiveness of ultraviolet lamps is limited by the life of the radiation source, whose output should be measured after every thousand hours of use. These lamps may continue to glow visibly after their short-ray output has become ineffective, so that reliance on them in this condition may be dangerous. Their placement is also a matter of important strategy, if circulating air or surfaces are to be effectively sterilized. People using ultraviolet lamps directly on their work must protect their eyes from any exposure to radiation.

Ionizing Radiations.   Some types of radiation, of shorter wavelength and greater energy than ultraviolet rays, have a lethal effect on many types of cells (tissue cells, bacteria, viruses, and other microorganisms) because they cause ionization of molecules that lie in their path. X-rays, gamma and beta rays from radioactive materials, and high-speed electrons emitted in a beam from an electron "accelerator" — all are destructive in sufficient dosage. This type of radiation is not practical for use in ordinary sterilization procedures, however, because it is extremely expensive and also can be extremely injurious to human tissues. It has limited microbiologic applications in the sterilization of expensive surgical materials that are heat-sensitive; in the treatment of chronic, progressive infections; in the sterilization of tissues to be used for transplantation; and in preventing food spoilage.

Sonic Disruption.   Sound waves that exceed the limit of audibility for human ears, at frequencies of 100,000 per second or higher, have some remarkable effects on materials in solution or suspension. In coursing through liquid media they induce the very rapid formation and collapse of submicroscopic bubbles, which in turn creates a negative pressure, or suction effect, on any particles in suspension in the liquid. Protein materials are coagulated by this action, bacteria are disintegrated, and other types of particles are broken up and dispersed.

Sonic disruption is sometimes used as a method for releasing some of the components of bacterial cells. These cellular constituents can then be extracted for study by simple procedures that do not induce the structural changes often imposed by chemical methods. A more practical application of sound wave action is offered for hospital use by the manufacturers of ultrasonic cleaning equipment. This type of apparatus is expensive and bulky, but it provides a safe and effective method for sterilizing and cleaning delicate instruments, and other sensitive items, without damage (see Fig. 10–6). Ultrasonic baths permit a very simple utilization of a sophisticated principle and mechanism, but their size, cost, and practicality for the sterilization of large items remain as the chief limiting factors. Furthermore, they can be used only for the decontamination of used instruments, not to sterilize them for use.

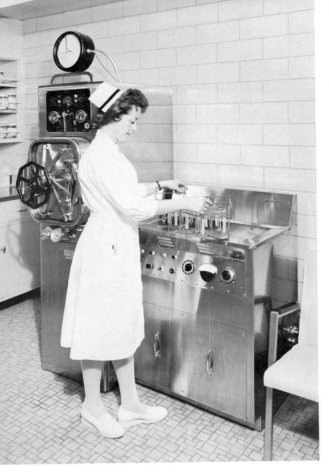

Fig. 10–6. Surgical instruments are cleaned by this ultrasonic machine, thus eliminating the hazard of hand-cleaning contaminated instruments before their sterilization. (Courtesy of Detrex Chemical Industries, Inc., Detroit, Mich.)

Items emerging from an ultrasonic bath must be washed free of liquid, solvent, and dispersed particles of soil and be resterilized before they can be used.

Filtration. Filters whose average pore size is smaller than that of undesirable microorganisms can be used to free liquid or gaseous media of such particles. The finest filters currently available (thin plastic films, sintered glass) do not necessarily yield *sterile* filtrates, for they cannot withhold the small viruses, but they do remove bacteria and other particles of diameters greater than 1.2 to 1.5 μ. Unglazed porcelain, glass and plastic are particularly effective for filtering liquids because they withhold bacteria and larger microorganisms without absorbing fluid (serum, broth culture media, etc.). Asbestos filters and diatomaceous earth are finely porous, but also quite absorptive.

Coarser materials such as cotton, gauze, and paper can effectively filter bacteria from air when used correctly. Cotton plugs can prevent the passage of bacteria in and out of test tubes, pipettes, needle hubs, or other airways, if they are sufficiently deep and dry, made of nonabsorbent cotton, and not charred or moistened by heat-sterilization techniques. Plugs must be thick enough to occlude the opening of the vessel but not fitted so tightly as to prevent the passage of sterilizing hot air or steam through them during sterilization. Paper, gauze, and fabric can be used to wrap items or packs of equipment to be heat-sterilized because these materials will subsequently act as bacterial filters when the packages are exposed to air, hands, shelf storage, etc. Fabrics and paper are not effective as filters, however, if they are moist or if their physical structure is damaged by overheating. Moisture-filled pores may be considered as filters-in-reverse, for they promote the passage of bacteria and other particles along their wet surfaces, to the interior, with a kind of capillary attraction. This is why a drying period is an essential part of the process of steam pressure sterilization of wrapped equipment (see p. 212, this chapter).

Gauze and paper face masks used in surgical procedures, or in other situations requiring asepsis, represent another application of the principles of air filtration. They are designed to prevent the outward passage of microorganisms into a sterile area from the mouth, nose, and throat of the person wearing the mask, or to protect the wearer from the inhalation of infectious organisms from a contaminated atmosphere. In either case, they are effective only for the period during which they remain relatively unsaturated with exhaled moisture. After that, they are not only useless as filters, but dangerously capable of shedding contaminated droplets of moisture in either direction. The practice of wearing a face mask loosely suspended around the neck, as surgical personnel in hospitals so often do, is

baffling. Since the mask is not decorative by design or accident, and its function is highly specific but limited in application, one can only conclude that those who wear it around the neck have no belief in its purpose, or in its potential as a disseminator of microorganisms.

Modern forced-air ventilation systems also employ filtration devices to purify the air of dust. Hospital or laboratory areas where infection is of critical concern can be ventilated with equipment designed to filter out particles of submicroscopic size. It must be emphasized, however, that the efficacy of such equipment is strictly limited by the extent to which it is monitored. Filters must be changed when they become clogged with dust and moisture, or their function is reversed and their action dangerous. It has frequently been observed, without far-reaching effect, that the best machine, however intelligently designed and constructed, cannot teach its operator how to use it.

The Antimicrobial Activity of Chemical Agents

Pasteur's studies of the chemical activities of microorganisms, and of the effects upon them of antagonistic chemical substances, were translated by his contemporary, the great English surgeon Joseph Lister, into the first practical application of the germ theory of disease to the prevention and control of surgical infection. Lister theorized that if microorganisms from the air could fall into unprotected flasks of broth and multiply therein, as Pasteur had shown (see Chap. 1), they could also contaminate open surgical wounds and perhaps be responsible for the "sepsis" that so frequently complicated surgery in those days. Accordingly he began to practice some techniques designed to be "aseptic": he immersed his instruments in 2.5 per cent carbolic acid to free them of microorganisms before surgery, he sprayed the air around the operating table with a dilute solution of carbolic acid, and he washed his hands in a similar solution before operating. The result was that his patients no longer died of

postoperative infection at the high rate seen on wards unprotected by this kind of effort.

It took some time for the medical world to accept the germ theory of infection or the value of Lister's preventive techniques. By the end of the nineteenth century, however, the use of antimicrobial chemicals in both the treatment and the prevention of infectious diseases had gathered a momentum that still continues today. *Chemotherapy*, or the use of chemical substances to inhibit or destroy microorganisms *in the body*, is discussed in the final section of this chapter, which deals with the control of active infectious disease. The principles of *chemical disinfection* as applied to the control of *environmental* sources of infection are reviewed here, and some of the useful chemical disinfectants are described.

The Principles of Chemical Disinfection.   Disinfection has been defined as a process that destroys *pathogenic* microorganisms. It is a chemical process involving interactions between disinfectant agents and various constituents of microbial cells. The result may be inhibitory to the further growth of the cells while they remain in contact with the chemical agent, but reversible upon its removal. When this is the case, the agent is said to be *static* in its effect, i.e., bacteriostatic, fungistatic, etc. If the reaction produces irreversible changes in vital cellular components, however, the result is lethal, or *cidal*, and the cells are unable to grow again even when the agent is removed. To meet the definition, therefore, a chemical disinfectant must be capable of germicidal action, that is, of producing irreversible destructive changes in pathogenic microbial species, and *it must be used in such a way as to ensure this effect*.

Like all chemical reactions, those that take place in disinfection are influenced by the *nature* and *concentration* of the reactants, and by *time*. A number of other factors may also influence the result, notably the physical and chemical properties of contaminating substances that may be present (organic soil, inorganic salt), as well as pH and temperature. The presence of extraneous organic and inorganic materials at the site of reaction between microbial cells and a disinfectant

may prevent the desired result either by chemical inactivation of the disinfectant or by physical protection of the microorganisms. Many chemical agents are lethal to pathogenic organisms under controlled conditions arranged in a test tube, but under actual conditions of use in the hospital environment their efficacy may be quite limited by the circumstances of the practical situation. It is essential, therefore, that those who apply chemical disinfection to the control of infectious disease understand both its principles and its limitations.

Microorganisms Versus Disinfectants. The major classes of microorganisms, as well as certain forms or stages of individual species or groups, are not uniformly susceptible to chemical disinfection. Among the animal parasites, protozoa and the immature, microscopic stages (ova and larvae) of parasitic helminths are susceptible to germicide action. The vegetative forms of fungi are also readily killed by good disinfectants, but their resting spores (chlamydospores) are quite resistant. Similarly, the vegetative forms of most bacterial species succumb within a short exposure period to active disinfectants. The tubercle bacillus is more resistant, but of all microbial forms, bacterial spores display the greatest degree of resistance to chemical, as well as physical, agents of disinfection. Many viruses can be killed as easily as vegetative bacteria, and by the same germicides, but the hepatitis viruses are very much more resistant.

The resistance of bacterial and fungal spores to chemical action is related to their thick and relatively impervious walls and to the fact that their condensed protoplasmic contents contain very little moisture for chemical reactivity. Tubercle bacilli are rich in lipids, and their waxy cell walls are resistant to water (hydrophobic). For this reason, they are not readily penetrated by germicides in aqueous solutions, but are more easily destroyed by those carried in lipid solvents or by hydrophilic "wetting" agents. The wetting action of detergent germicides is described on pages 227 to 228. Among viruses, those that have some lipid content, such as influenza and herpes viruses, are more susceptible to some of the detergent germicides than are lipid-free viruses, such as the enteroviruses, including poliomyelitis. The latter are destroyed by formalin and by alcohol. The resistance of hepatitis virus is neither well understood nor well defined, for the reason that this microorganism has not been cultivated and studied outside of the human body, in tissue cultures or in experimental animals. Because its destruction by chemical agents has not been defined, and because it appears to be considerably more resistant to them than most other viruses, milder disinfection procedures should not be attempted when sterilizing methods are feasible for the destruction of hepatitis virus.

Since microorganisms differ in their response to disinfectants, the choice of the latter for a particular situation must be based in part on the type of microbial contamination to be dealt with. The disinfection of mouth thermometers, for instance, must assure the destruction of all pathogenic vegetative forms of bacteria, including the tubercle bacillus, which might be present in saliva or sputum. When the destruction of bacterial spores must be assured, as in the case of instruments to be used for surgery or dressings removed from a *Clostridium*-infected wound, heat sterilization is a necessity, for disinfection procedures cannot guarantee the killing of all spores under practical circumstances. Chemical sterilization with strong germicides such as formalin is possible with a long exposure period (three hours or more) and is feasible for items that are not of critical surgical importance, provided they are not themselves damaged by the germicide (see pp. 230 to 231). When active hepatitis infection is suspected or recognized, all objects or materials that can be heat sterilized should be either autoclaved or incinerated. Other precautions and disinfection procedures are indicated for this disease in Part Two, Chapter 20.

It must be emphasized that the effectiveness claimed for a disinfectant in killing vegetative bacterial species (such as strains of *Staphylococcus* or *Salmonella*) may have no bearing on its ability to destroy fungal or bacterial spores, tubercle bacilli, or some viruses. It should also be recognized that while most classes of microorganisms can be killed within a 10-to-15-minute period by

many of the available disinfectants, this may be true only for *optimal*, rather than *average*, conditions, as we shall see in more detail.

Disinfectants Versus Microorganisms. The chemical nature of a disinfectant determines its mode of action and its efficacy against different kinds of organisms. Some chemical agents coagulate the microbial cell protein, the effect being rapid and irreversible. The average disinfectant has a less powerful action, however, and denatures cellular proteins by more subtle, slower processes. Oxidation of protein enzymes by halogen compounds (see pp. 229 to 230), changes in the function of cellular membranes by the protein affinities of quaternary ammonium compounds (see pp. 228 to 229), and lysis of cells or leakage of their contents induced by phenolic compounds or their detergent carriers (see pp. 227 to 229) are examples of processes by which disinfection action is accomplished.

Unfortunately, the activity of chemical disinfectants is not specific for the protein components of microbial cells but is destructive to some degree for living protoplasm in general. The stronger and most rapidly effective antimicrobial compounds are limited in their usefulness, therefore, by the fact that human tissues may be damaged by them also. Strong germicides may be used under prescribed conditions for the disinfection, or the chemical sterilization, of small objects, or of materials in small quantities, but compounds with less toxic or irritating properties for human cells are indicated when large-scale disinfection is necessary, as in hospital housekeeping or in surgical asepsis. This limitation on the activity of chemical disinfectants requires the consideration of time as a factor in their use. The weaker or more subtle the action of a germicide, the kinder it will be to human tissues, but the longer it will take to effect the desired antimicrobial action.

Other limitations on the use of chemical agents as disinfectants include the concentration at which they can be used without damaging environmental materials unduly, the concentration of microbial cells and their components that must be inactivated, and the effect on germicide or microbial reactant of extraneous factors, such as temperature, pH, and chemical contamination.

Microbial Concentration. The number of microorganisms present in material to be chemically treated has a direct influence on the adequacy of any chosen concentration of disinfectant applied. The greater the concentration of microbial cells, and their chemical components, the larger must be the germicidal concentration, or the longer the time allowed for the chemical to accomplish its purpose.

This principle is illustrated in Table 10–2. In this example, a given chemical agent (preparation X) is shown to be capable of killing the tubercle bacilli left on a *washed* thermometer, when the agent is used in a 3 per cent dilution for 15 minutes. However, when tests are conducted on *unwashed* thermometers carrying a much larger number of tubercle bacilli, the organisms are killed by germicide X only if (1) the time of exposure to the 3 per cent dilution is prolonged, *or* (2) the concentration is doubled for the 15-minute exposure period. This table also compares the activity of Preparation X with that of another germicide, preparation Y, the latter being more rapidly tuberculocidal in lower concentration.

In the practical application of disinfection techniques, it is always necessary to observe this principle by providing thorough physical cleansing for all items and surfaces before they are treated with germicide. When the density of microbial contamination is reduced, more efficient use of germicides can be made in shorter time periods.

Germicide Concentration. As we have seen in Table 10–2, the effectiveness of a chemical disinfectant can be heightened by increasing its concentration. In general, the time required for disinfection is shortened as germicide concentration is increased. There are two important limitations to this principle, however. (1) The activity of germicides in aqueous solutions is dependent on the presence of a certain amount of water. Decreasing the "water of reactivity" below a critical point by raising the concentration of germicide may destroy some of the disinfectant efficiency of

the solution. Ethyl alcohol solutions offer the best example of this point. Concentrations of ethanol from 10 to 80 per cent are increasingly bactericidal, the most efficient action being obtained in the 60 to 80 per cent range. Ethanol solutions of 80 to 100 per cent volume concentration are little more efficient, however, than a 40 per cent solution. (2) Strong disinfectant solutions are in most instances corrosive to metals, fabrics, and plastics, and to the skin or mucous membranes of those who handle them. On the other hand, these agents may have little or no effective antimicrobial activity, within reasonable time periods, at dilutions that are not damaging.

Table 10–2. Influence of Microbial Numbers, Germicide Concentration, and Time on the Tuberculocidal Effects of Two Germicides

Germicide Concentration	Test Object: Dried Thermometer	No. of TBC per Thermometer	Time of Exposure (Min)	Culture Result (Wk)*
Preparation X				
3%	Washed	10	5	+ (6)
3%	Washed	10	15	− (8)
3%	Washed	10	30	− (8)
3%	Washed	10	60	− (8)
3%	Unwashed	10,000	5	+ (4)
3%	Unwashed	10,000	15	+ (4)
3%	Unwashed	10,000	30	+ (5)
3%	Unwashed	10,000	60	− (8)
6%	Washed	10	5	− (8)
6%	Washed	10	15	− (8)
6%	Washed	10	30	− (8)
6%	Washed	10	60	− (8)
6%	Unwashed	10,000	5	+ (6)
6%	Unwashed	10,000	15	− (8)
6%	Unwashed	10,000	30	− (8)
6%	Unwashed	10,000	60	− (8)
Preparation Y				
2%	Washed	10	5	− (8)
2%	Washed	10	15	− (8)
2%	Washed	10	30	− (8)
2%	Washed	10	60	− (8)
2%	Unwashed	10,000	5	+ (5)
2%	Unwashed	10,000	15	+ (6)
2%	Unwashed	10,000	30	− (8)
2%	Unwashed	10,000	60	− (8)
4%	Washed	10	5	− (8)
4%	Washed	10	15	− (8)
4%	Washed	10	30	− (8)
4%	Washed	10	60	− (8)
4%	Unwashed	10,000	5	− (8)
4%	Unwashed	10,000	15	− (8)
4%	Unwashed	10,000	30	− (8)
4%	Unwashed	10,000	60	− (8)

* The numbers in this column represent the weeks of incubation required to obtain the recorded result. + = positive culture. − = culture negative after 8 weeks of incubation.

The concentration of choice for a given disinfectant is the one that displays the most rapid activity in the destruction of those microorganisms against which it is directed, without simultaneous damage to the objects or materials exposed to it.

Inactivation of Disinfectants. Germicides may be inactivated by the presence of organic or inorganic contaminants on items or surfaces to be disinfected. The active portions of some disinfectant molecules, for example, may combine with human proteins of blood, mucus, or pus. In this bound condition they are no longer free to react with microbial constituents. Plant fibers and fabrics (cotton, gauze, etc.) may also absorb and inactivate certain disinfectants (see pp. 228 to 229). This factor should be considered in choosing a disinfectant and its concentration for a particular purpose, because some agents are more readily bound than others, by virtue of their chemical structure. The use of strong concentrations of some disinfectants, if they are compatible with the materials to be treated, may assure an excess of free, active molecules despite extensive protein contamination.

Inorganic compounds such as salts, metals, acids or alkalis can also interfere with disinfectant activity by affecting the pH of reaction, or by combining with the germicide as proteins do. Volatilization may reduce the available concentration of some disinfectants, particularly those with an alcoholic solvent or base or those that depend on the activity of a halogen, such as chlorine or iodine. Temperature is not an important factor in hospital disinfection, for most germicides are effective at temperatures ranging from just above to slightly below room temperature. In the laboratory, however, the use of chemical agents to kill microorganisms in vaccine production must be surrounded with careful temperature controls to ensure adequate cidal activity. Increasing the temperature to 56° C or up to the boiling point enhances microbial destruction, but it may also denature the antigenic proteins of the cells. The reactivity of a germicide is also increased with rising temperature, provided the heat sensitivity of the compound is not exceeded.

Other Factors Influencing Disinfection. The presence of protein contamination on items to be disinfected may serve not only to inactivate the germicide but also to protect microorganisms from exposure. This is particularly true in the case of strong disinfectant solutions that bring about coagulation of protein. Viable microorganisms may be trapped in the depths of coagulated particles of protein and remain inaccessible to the action of the surrounding chemical solution. Strong disinfectants that coagulate protein should not be used in situations where such protein contamination cannot be avoided, as in the chemical disinfection of feces or sputum.

This protective effect of protein offers another major reason for careful scrubbing and cleaning of objects to be chemically disinfected. Situations sometimes arise, however, particularly in hospitals, when it may be considered unsafe to wash items grossly contaminated with infectious organisms. Surgical instruments covered with pus from infected wounds and heat-sensitive equipment similarly contaminated constitute such problems. In the former instance, the use of washer-sterilizer equipment or of prolonged boiling with detergent disinfectants is recommended. With either method, protein coagulation is prevented by detergent action while heat sterilization proceeds. Instruments so treated must be carefully cleaned and lubricated before being sterilized again for another use. Heat-sensitive items that cannot be safely washed before disinfection may be soaked for long periods in strong germicide solution, preferably in the presence of detergent if the latter is not incompatible with the disinfectant. The increasing availability of disposable equipment offers another solution to the problem in many instances.

The nature of the material to be disinfected may influence the choice of disinfectants and techniques in still another way. The physical properties of objects and surfaces to be chemically disinfected must be considered, for they influence the speed and ease with which effective results can be achieved. Hard, smooth surfaces are relatively easy to disinfect, but porous materials are not readily penetrated by many germicides. Grooved or hinged instruments and needles, catheters, or irrigation tubing of small bore offer

particular difficulties, for their inner as well as outer surfaces must be in contact with the disinfectant. The choice of germicide and its concentration must balance its capacities against the type of material it is expected to disinfect, and the technique of application must be designed to ensure its complete efficacy under each individual set of circumstances.

Antisepsis. The chemical disinfection of skin and other living tissue surfaces is usually referred to as *antisepsis*. The term "degermation" is currently preferable because it recognizes that the sterilization of skin is impossible, and that even disinfection can be accomplished only very temporarily at the uppermost layers.

Many of the useful chemical disinfectants are too irritating to skin and mucous membranes to permit their use as antiseptics. At best, the maximum concentrations of safe antiseptics are weak with respect to their antimicrobial activity, as compared with disinfectants that can be applied to inanimate surfaces. When applied to the skin, antiseptics reduce the numbers of surface organisms markedly and rapidly, but they do not penetrate readily to the deeper layers, into hair follicles or glandular crypts. The mechanical action of scrubbing, followed by the flushing effect of running water, is an important factor in the removal of many microorganisms with surface debris and in degerming the deeper layers of some of their resident flora.

Soaps, alcohol, alcohol-and-iodine combinations, hexachlorophene, and iodophor preparations are among the most widely used antiseptics in surgical practice. Each of these has its relative merits and limitations, which should be appreciated by those who use them. For speed of initial degermation, alcohol, alcohol and iodine in combination, and iodophor compounds are among the most effective antiseptics. Hexachlorophene has an advantage in that it is not inactivated by soaps, as are many germicides (including Zephiran and other quaternary ammonium compounds), and when it is used continuously it accumulates in an active residue on skin because it is not readily soluble in water. On the other hand, hexachlorophene is slow in its killing effect on microorganisms, and none of these antiseptics can long prevent the restoration of at least the resident flora on gloved hands during lengthy surgical procedures.

A final word of caution must be added regarding the storage and handling of antiseptics. As pointed out above, these compounds are selected for antisepsis because they are relatively mild in their effects on the cells of the skin and mucous membranes, but for this reason their use-concentrations are not strongly antimicrobial. Antiseptic solutions, ready for use in the operating room as surgical scrub agents or in the preoperative preparation of patients' skin, may become contaminated with microorganisms resistant to their chemical action and capable of growth and multiplication in their presence. This may sometimes happen even with the stronger disinfectants as well. Disinfectant or antiseptic solutions that are actively supporting the growth of microorganisms become a reservoir of possible infection, a particularly dangerous situation when they are specifically, though innocently, applied in surgical or other hospital situations where asepsis is essential. *The assumption that the antimicrobial nature of disinfectants and antiseptics automatically guarantees their sterility is not warranted.* Working solutions, as well as the stock materials from which they are prepared for final use, should be handled and stored under aseptic conditions.

Destruction Versus Inhibition. The static or cidal effects of disinfectants on microorganisms are another important issue in their choice and use. In many instances, the actual conditions for use of a chemical agent may lead to mere *inhibition* of growth — another dangerous result if *destruction* is planned or assumed. Microbiologic methods are required for the final demonstration of disinfectant action in each situation. With proper techniques, such methods can demonstrate whether or not the use-conditions for a disinfectant (its concentration, time of exposure, the presence of extraneous protein) are sufficient not only to prevent the growth of pathogenic microorganisms *while they are in contact with the*

disinfecting agent, but to destroy them so that they cannot subsequently grow and multiply *if and when the agent is removed*. Furthermore, when microbiologic proof of disinfection is sought, the bacteriologist must take care not to misinterpret the effects of disinfectant carried over into culture media from treated items or surfaces. Traces of disinfectant in culture media may continue to be bacteriostatic. For this reason, a negative culture result should not be reported as proof of a bactericidal effect unless the technique of culture confirms the inactivation of lingering disinfectant or the removal of the microorganisms from its sphere of action.

The Evaluation and Selection of Germicides. Unfortunately, adequate laboratory demonstration of the efficacy of disinfectant agents or techniques is not often available in hospitals, or even practical under their circumstances. Accordingly, hospital personnel are usually dependent on their fund of basic information in coping with the claims of many manufacturers and in choosing disinfectants for various purposes. There is a great deal of reliable information currently available on this subject, however. The bibliography for this chapter cites some of the recent reviews that should be of value to those charged with the intelligent selection and use of chemical disinfectants. It must be added that, once the choice is made, it is important to follow the manufacturer's instructions carefully and completely, for otherwise proper analysis of any problems that may arise later is virtually impossible.

In this connection, two final points should be remembered in evaluating descriptive literature concerning germicides and in choosing one for a specific purpose:

1. Comparison of the activity of a disinfectant with that of phenol is frequently offered as evidence of value, but this is not always pertinent. Pure phenol (carbolic acid) is an efficient bactericidal agent, limited in use by its toxicity for skin and other tissues. In high concentrations it coagulates protein; in low concentrations it inactivates microbial enzymes by altering surface tension. When used as a comparative standard

for judging the activity of other disinfectant compounds, its killing action for a particular organism is determined, under controlled conditions, at a stated concentration and time exposure. The values for concentration and time required to kill the same organism, under the same conditions, are then measured for the disinfectant being tested. If the latter requires a greater concentration or a longer time than phenol, its efficiency is judged to be less than that of phenol. The arithmetic ratio of its activity with respect to phenol, that is, its *phenol coefficient*, will be expressed in a figure *less than one*. If the tested disinfectant kills the organism in question in a lower concentration or a shorter time period than the standard phenol preparation, it will be given a phenol coefficient *greater than one*.

This is interesting laboratory information, but it provides no clues as to the numerous other factors that may govern the activity of the test disinfectant under the conditions of its actual use. If it is a compound unrelated to phenol in chemical structure and activity, test-tube comparisons with a phenol standard have no practical meaning and leave the following questions unanswered: Does the tested disinfectant combine easily with protein of any or all kinds and so lose its antimicrobial activity? Is it affected by pH changes, or does it react with salts, minerals, or other frequently encountered chemical contaminants? Is it a lipid solvent, or is it repelled by waxes, whether they occur in microbial cells or on floor and furniture surfaces? Does it have a different mode of action at high and low levels of concentration, as does the phenol standard? What proof exists that it can disinfect a thermometer carrying tubercle bacilli as well as a bedpan contaminated with *Salmonella*? Is it capable of penetrating porous materials, or should its use be restricted to hard-surfaced items? Will it corrode metal, fabric, or skin? The answers to questions such as these are much more important than consideration of phenol coefficient in evaluating the range of action of a disinfectant.

2. The ideal, all-purpose chemical disinfectant *has yet to be discovered*. Therefore, the selection of any germicide must be based on the use to

which it will be put when this is weighed against its properties and expense. As many of the following desirable qualities as are pertinent to the needs of a given situation should be sought when choosing a disinfectant:

a. It should be able to kill all pathogenic microorganisms, including the most resistant types known or suspected to be of concern. If it cannot do this, its spectrum of antimicrobial activity should be clearly defined.

b. It should be capable of killing microorganisms rapidly, at a concentration that is not destructive to materials that must be treated. Its use-dilutions and the time required for their action should be clearly stated for each of its applications and purposes. Its destructive properties, if any, should be described with reference to the kinds of materials affected.

c. Whether or not it is used for skin degermation, it should not be toxic for human tissues. Its physiologic toxicities should be stated with reference to the specifications of the Federal Insecticide, Fungicide and Rodenticide Act.

d. It should be impervious to the inactivating effect of soaps, waxes, proteins, or other chemical contaminants; if not, its limitations in this respect should be clear.

e. It should be stable to pH and temperature changes within reasonable, defined limits.

f. It should be readily soluble in water and stable in solution. If more expensive solvents must be used, their effects and price must be considered.

g. It should be stable for a reasonable period of shelf storage. It is important that the effects of time on its potency be defined, since hospital stocks are frequently purchased in large quantity.

h. It should be simple and uncomplicated to handle and apply effectively, so that even unskilled personnel can use it correctly.

i. It should be easily manufactured at low cost. If this cannot be done, the value of the disinfectant must be judged in the light of the importance and difficulty of the job to be done and the availability of alternate methods.

Some Useful Chemical Disinfectants. *Alcohols* of low molecular weight, which are soluble in water,

may be bactericidal under proper conditions of use. Methyl alcohol, the lightweight of this family of organic compounds, is not a good disinfectant, but ethyl and propyl alcohols have antimicrobial activity in the presence of water. In *absolute* concentrations, 100 per cent pure, alcohols have little or no effect on microorganisms, but in the presence of water, *in 50 to 80 per cent dilutions*, ethyl, propyl, and isopropyl alcohols are lethal (cidal) for the tubercle bacillus and for the vegetative forms of other bacteria. At these concentrations, alcohols act as protein coagulants, when they are able to penetrate microbial cell membranes. They cannot penetrate bacterial spore walls, and they also appear to be ineffective against some viruses, including those of the hepatitis group.

The moisture present in materials to be treated with alcohol must be considered when decisions are made about the dilution to be used. Dry surfaces may be wiped or washed with 50 to 70 per cent alcoholic solutions, but wet materials may require a higher concentration, since they will dilute the disinfectant further. The bactericidal effect of alcohol is lost below a 50 per cent concentration, although bacteriostasis may be accomplished at dilutions as high as 1 per cent. It is important to remember that chemically inhibited organisms may flourish once again when the bacteriostatic agent is removed or evaporates. Alcohols are more volatile than water, and therefore alcoholic solutions become weaker on standing in open containers that permit evaporation. Their bactericidal activity is slowly lost under such conditions, and they become merely bacteriostatic. If misused, alcoholic disinfectants are capable of spreading viable microorganisms over surfaces to be cleaned, and as the alcohol volatilizes, the bacteria freed from its action may grow and multiply.

Alcohols are good lipid solvents and are frequently used to cleanse and disinfect skin surfaces, clearing the latter of oil, debris, and microorganisms. Other disinfectant compounds are sometimes dissolved in alcohol, rather than in water, the resulting *tincture* having added disinfectant properties as well as better grease solvency. (Tincture of iodine and tincture of

Zephiran are two well-known examples of such formulation.) Alcoholic solutions are drying to normal skin, however, since they remove oil, thus damaging one of the natural skin barriers. When used on traumatized tissues, they may add further injury by coagulating cellular proteins. The use of alcohols and tinctures as antiseptics is limited for these reasons, but they have valuable applications in the degermation of normal skin surfaces (in preparation for venipuncture or minor surgery) and of small, hard-surfaced objects such as thermometers. Because they are expensive, volatile, and difficult to control in standing solution, alcohols are not frequently used for the disinfection of large surface areas.

Phenols have been popular disinfectants since Lister first used carbolic acid in his operating room. Phenol itself is still commonly used as a standard in measuring the antibacterial potency of other substances, as described earlier. Because it is irritating and corrosive for skin, however, it is seldom used today as an antiseptic or disinfectant, but some of its derivatives have a safer application. Most of the phenolics currently employed contain a phenol molecule, chemically altered to reduce its toxicity or to increase its antibacterial activity, in combination with a soap or detergent. The latter serves to disperse protein, lipoid, and other organic matter, reducing the possibility that such material may bind and inactivate the disinfectant.

The best known of the phenolic derivatives combined with soaps or detergents are the *cresols* and the *bis-phenols*. Probably the most familiar members of the *cresol* group are Tricresol, Lysol, Staphene, Osyl, and Amphyl, these being proprietary names for different formulations of altered phenols useful as *environmental disinfectants*. The *bis-phenols* are so called because the chemical alteration involves the linkage of two phenol molecules. Hexachlorophene is such a compound. The combination of hexachlorophene and some other bis-phenols with soap or detergent provides compounds that are relatively nontoxic for skin but retain good antibacterial activity. Commonly used proprietary preparations of this type include *pHiso*Hex and Dial soap. The practical considerations that limit our

concepts of skin antisepsis, or skin degermation, were pointed out previously (see p. 224). The action of soaps and detergents combined with antimicrobial agents is described more fully below.

The phenols coagulate protein and are effective in killing the vegetative cells of bacteria. When combined with detergents they are also good tuberculocides, virucides, and fungicides. They are not sporicidal under ordinary conditions of use as surface disinfectants, for they can kill spores only in heated solutions applied for prolonged periods of time. When combined with soaps or detergents, the phenolics are not very soluble in water, but they remain actively disinfectant in aqueous concentrations as low as 1 to 5 per cent. This combination of qualities makes them inexpensive to use, but, more importantly, confers residual bactericidal or bacteriostatic effects when their solutions are left to dry on treated surfaces (walls, floors, furniture, skin). As water evaporates from phenolic films, the disinfectant molecule remains active for a time, deterring bacterial growth. These disinfectants can also be used successfully to treat discarded cultures, sputum, feces, and heavily contaminated objects because of their low affinity for organic matter and their antibacterial activity, even in high dilution.

Surface-active agents (detergents and soaps) have the property of decreasing the tension that exists between molecules that lie on the surfaces of liquid suspensions or solutions. Liquids that have a high surface tension (oils, for example) are not easily penetrated by other materials, nor do they spread into them. They tend, rather, to separate from surrounding substances because of the strong attracting force that holds their surface molecules together. When the surface force of liquids is low, they spread, or "run," more easily. They are said to be "wet" because they flow across, and penetrate into, adjacent surfaces and materials as pure water does. Liquids with low surface tension are also more "miscible"; that is, they mix with other fluids and can *be* mixed. Surface-active agents accumulate at the interfaces of liquids (that is, at their adjacent surfaces), lowering the surface tension of molecules on both sides of the interface, so that they can run to-

gether. The liquids become more miscible, one with the other, and the agent is said to have a "wetting" action. The antibacterial action of soaps and detergents is partly due to their ability to lower the surface tension of liquid interfaces. The membranes of bacterial cells themselves constitute interfaces between the protein-lipid complexes of the cells and their walls and the moist, aqueous surroundings in which they usually lie. When surface-active agents come in contact with microbial interfaces, they remove the molecular barriers that hold cells and surrounding liquid media apart; they form a bridge, so to speak, between the interior contents of cells and the external milieu. Sometimes the bridging compound is itself denaturing for microbial cell contents and induces cellular injury or death. If not, disinfectant chemicals can be mixed with surface-active agents that will effect their entry into cells by lowering surface tension.

Soaps are surface-active agents, capable of improving the miscibility of oils with water. For this reason they are very useful cleansing agents for skin and clothing. Soaps also have a lethal action on a few fastidious pathogenic bacteria, notably streptococci, pneumococci, and *Hemophilus* species, but they have no chemical effects on most skin microorganisms. The efficacy of soaps as skin antiseptics, or as disinfectants for inanimate objects, lies primarily in their ability to change the surface characteristics of greasy substances, so that they are more easily penetrated and removed by water. The physical scrubbing that usually accompanies the application of soaps also accounts for any "disinfection" they appear to accomplish. When disinfectant chemicals are *added* to soaps (as in the case of such proprietaries as Lifebuoy, Dial, Praise, and certain liquid soaps, which contain phenolic disinfectants or other compounds), their antibacterial efficacy is increased. The combination of soaps with disinfectants must be carefully gauged, however, to avoid neutralizing the antibacterial portion of combining chemical molecules. For this reason, the *sequential* use of soaps and disinfectants should be carefully considered, for even traces of soap left on skin or other objects may bind disinfectants subsequently applied and thus neutralize, or inactivate, their chemical effects on microorganisms.

Detergents are natural or synthetic soaps with a high degree of surface activity. Depending on their chemical structure, they may or may not ionize in water solution. Those that do *not* ionize (neutral detergents) have no usefulness as disinfectants, although they may be good cleansers. Those that *do* form ions in aqueous solution have bactericidal activity, probably because their charged ions concentrate on bacterial cell membranes and disrupt their normal functions. *Anionic* detergents are those that form negatively charged ions (anions). These include the natural soaps (the sodium or potassium salts of fatty acids) and bile salts. *Cationic* detergents form positively charged ions (cations). This group includes the most effective bactericidal and bacteriostatic detergent compounds, notably the *quaternary ammonium compounds*, or "quats." The most familiar proprietary name in this group is Zephiran. This compound, like its many relatives (Phemerol, Ceepryn), is an extremely useful disinfectant within strict limitations of application. It is relatively nontoxic and active in low concentrations, highly soluble in water, low in cost. For these reasons it can be used for skin antisepsis, or for the disinfection of instruments and of *chemically clean* surfaces. In aqueous solution it is not a good tuberculocide, fungicide, or virucide, but when dissolved in alcohol (i.e., as a tincture) it is more effective as such. The most severe limitation on the use of quats is their affinity for proteins of both animal and plant origin and for soaps. Thus even trace contamination of surfaces with organic material or soap may "bind" and inactivate a quat disinfectant, rendering it useless as an antimicrobial agent. Similarly, the quaternary detergents are easily bound by plant proteins, such as those of gauze and cotton fibers. They should not be used, therefore, as disinfectant soaks for cotton pads or gauze squares intended for the preparation of skin for venipuncture or for the most minor surgery. Aqueous solutions of quaternary detergents, contaminated by soaps or protein materials, not only lose their antibacterial properties; they may become reservoirs for bacterial growth and multiplication. Tinctures are

less dangerous in this respect, so long as their alcoholic concentration remains at effective levels, but their expense limits their general use.

Oxidizing agents inactivate microorganisms and other types of cells by effecting an oxygen (or positive ion) exchange on some of the free radical groups of their protein molecules. This oxidizing effect may be lethal to cells if it inactivates vital intracellular protein enzymes. Chemical compounds that release oxygen readily may have bactericidal effects. Those most commonly used as antiseptics are hydrogen peroxide, sodium perborate, and potassium permanganate. Peroxide and perborate are sometimes used as wound irrigants, to reduce or control local infection, to oxidize and clear away tissue debris, and to prevent anaerobic bacterial growth in traumatized tissue by oxygenation of the area. Potassium permanganate solutions (in high dilution) are used as urethral antiseptics, and also for the treatment of superficial fungous infections of the skin. At safe concentrations, these compounds are not markedly efficient as bactericides and their use in antisepsis is therefore quite limited.

The most powerful oxidizing agents, and the most useful in antisepsis or disinfection, are the *halogens* and their derivatives. Iodine, chlorine, bromine, and fluorine all have bactericidal properties, probably because they combine irreversibly with protein enzymes, inhibiting their activity. The halogens are also toxic for human tissues and cells, however, and this puts limiting conditions on their use. In the free state, halogen vapors or gases are poisonous if inhaled. In water, these elements ionize freely, forming strongly active, anionic solutions that are rapidly bactericidal.

Iodine is an effective antiseptic for normal skin and for superficial wounds. It is also very useful in environmental disinfection, for it is active against many vegetative bacterial species, including the tubercle bacillus, as well as fungi and some viruses. It is not an effective sporicide in the use-concentrations that must be employed to avoid toxicity. Pure iodine is not readily soluble in water, but it dissolves more easily in solutions of sodium or potassium iodide. The release of free iodine from the iodine-iodide complex of these solutions accomplishes disinfection. A 3.5 per cent tincture of iodine in alcohol containing potassium iodide is a very effective skin antiseptic. Tinctures may also be used for disinfecting thermometers and small instruments, provided volatilization of these solutions is prevented. Tinctures used on the skin may be damaging if the iodine concentration has increased because of alcohol evaporation. This factor, as well as the staining effects of iodine, has tended to discourage the use of tinctures on skin. Both these limitations can be controlled rather easily, however, and are counterbalanced by the rapidly effective action of iodine tinctures as compared with other antiseptics. The preparation of small areas of skin for minor procedures, such as venipuncture, with iodine-alcohol solutions carefully formulated and applied can produce safe results quickly. When large areas of skin must be treated, however, the irritating effects of iodine and alcohol outweigh the advantages. In this case, less toxic iodine preparations or other types of antiseptic agents are used, but more time must be allowed for their action, and mechanical scrubbing becomes more important.

Iodine forms loosely bound complexes with organic molecules. In aqueous solution or suspension, the bound iodine carried by such a complex slowly dissociates and is freed. The carrier molecule is called an *iodophor*. Such compounds retain the useful properties of inorganic iodine solutions, but they are less toxic to the skin. The iodophors commonly used for environmental disinfection contain iodine combined with a nonionic detergent (some of the proprietary names include Wescodyne, Ioclide, and Hi-Sine). Used in a concentration of 75 ppm of available iodine, the iodophors may be applied to the general disinfection of floors, walls, and furniture. A concentration of 450 ppm has tuberculocidal activity. Formulations of iodine with polymeric molecules, such as polyvinylpyrrolidone, are used for skin degermation. Betadine and Isodine are examples of this type of iodophor. The iodophors have a wide range of antimicrobial activity. They should be used in fresh solution, for iodine slowly dissipates from dilutions that are allowed to stand. Fortunately, however, this change is easy to recognize as the original deep-brown iodine color of these

solutions fades to yellow with the loss of iodine. Fabrics and skin are not permanently stained by iodophors, for the color can be washed away, but plastic materials treated with them remain discolored. The chief limitation on the iodophor detergents is their reactivity with protein and other organic matter. In combining with such material they lose disinfectant activity. It is important, therefore, that surfaces to be treated with iodophors be free of extraneous contamination.

Chlorine in gaseous or liquid form is a useful and inexpensive bactericidal agent for the disinfection of water and sewage. There are a number of compounds of chlorine that in aqueous solution release it readily as free or available chlorine. Chlorine itself then combines with water to form hypochlorous acid, a potent oxidizing and bleaching agent with a rapid bactericidal action. A few parts per million of available chlorine in drinking water, or swimming pools, are disinfectant. Larger concentrations are required in sewage, because some of the chlorine also combines with organic substances and is then no longer free to react with bacterial cell proteins.

The most commonly used inorganic compounds of chlorine are hypochlorites of potassium, sodium (e.g., Clorox), or calcium (chlorinated lime). Sodium or potassium hypochlorite in aqueous solution (where it forms hypochlorous acid) can be used to disinfect small objects and surfaces. It is a convenient disinfectant for the sickroom at home, but is seldom used for this purpose in hospitals because, like most other chlorine compounds, it is bleaching, corrosive, and malodorous. Chlorinated lime is prepared by exposing freshly slaked lime to chlorine gas. The resulting compound is unstable and quickly frees the chlorine if exposed to air. It must be kept in tightly sealed containers and be freshly prepared for each use. Solutions of 0.5 to 5 per cent chlorinated lime are used for the disinfection of dairies, barns, abattoirs, and similar installations. Inorganic chlorine compounds are also used in the sanitization of dishes or laundry and in skin antisepsis. Calcium hypochlorites are useful as sanitizers, while sodium hypochlorite is kinder to skin. The latter is sometimes used (Dakin's solution) as a wound irrigant. Organic compounds of chlorine known as chloramines are still less irritating to tissues and are now preferred to Dakin's when this type of treatment must be used. Many other methods for treating wounds are now in use.

Bromine and fluorine have very limited application in disinfection or antisepsis because they are toxic in useful concentrations. Within recent years, however, bromine combinations with certain organic compounds (notably the salicylanilides) have proved to be effective in some environmental uses, such as the treatment of fabrics with a laundry rinse. Their use for the skin has been limited to mild, nontoxic concentrations in hand soaps (Praise), but their formulation for possible use in surgical scrub soaps is under study.

The ions of heavy metals, notably mercury and silver, are readily taken up by the proteins of living cells, including microorganisms. The effect is highly injurious to the activity of enzyme protein and may lead to rapid death of the cell. This broad-spectrum toxicity means that mercury and silver salts have only limited bactericidal applications. The inorganic salts of these metals, e.g., mercuric oxide, mercuric iodide, and silver nitrate, are used in low concentrations as antiseptics. The mercuric compounds are frequently incorporated in ointments for use in the treatment of minor skin infections. Silver nitrate is used in aqueous solution, its best-known application being in the prevention of gonorrheal infection of the eyes of newborn babies. Organic compounds of mercury, such as Merthiolate and Mercurochrome, are also used topically, sometimes for the treatment of superficial infection, sometimes for the degermation of skin prior to surgery. Merthiolate may also be added to microbial vaccines as a preservative. Bichloride of mercury was widely used for many years in operating rooms as an instrument soak and a hand-washing solution, but it has been displaced by less poisonous agents that do not corrode metals or combine so readily with proteins.

Formalin is a 37 per cent aqueous solution of formaldehyde gas. It is one of the few useful chemical disinfectants having sporicidal activity under feasible conditions of use. When in contact

with proteins and nucleic acids, formaldehyde has an affinity for certain chemical groups that occur commonly on these molecules. Its own molecule is capable of combining at two sites, so that its reactivity results in the formation of linkages between protein molecules. As a consequence cells and tissues exposed to formalin become "fixed," and their vital proteins are inactivated. Its lethal effects on microorganisms have two important applications: (1) as an environmental disinfectant, and (2) to inactivate microbial preparations that are to be used as antigens (vaccines) for active immunization.

As an environmental disinfectant, formalin comes close to being a sterilizing agent under proper conditions. Its activity is greatly increased if it is heated or, more practically, if it is used in alcoholic solution. Proprietary solutions (such as Bard-Parker Germicide) utilize it in this form, with small quantities of alkali and other components added to the formula. Such a solution can be used as a soak for small instruments and transfer forceps, killing spores on their surfaces in three hours at room temperature. Formalin must be freshly prepared, however, or kept in tightly covered vessels, for its formaldehyde content vaporizes readily, and solutions become inactive. Also, such containers should be emptied, washed, and sterilized at least once weekly to make certain that resistant organisms do not gain a foothold in a weakening solution.

In the preparation of microbial antigens, formalin is capable of killing microorganisms, or inactivating their toxic properties, without interfering with the antigenic portion of their molecules. Upon injection, such antigens should be capable of stimulating antibody production without risk of infection or toxicity. In antigen preparation a high dilution of formalin is employed for an exposure period of several hours.

The limitations on the use of formalin are centered in its reactivity with normal cell proteins. It is irritating for skin, injuring it on prolonged exposure, and formaldehyde vapor is similarly damaging to the membranes of the nose and throat. Its odor is unpleasant and penetrating. These qualities limit its usefulness as an environmental disinfectant. It is not toxic, however,

under the conditions of its use in vaccines, for in these preparations it is bound to microbial protein and is incapable of further independent action.

Aerosol disinfection of the air and surfaces within a closed room has been a popular, if not totally effective, idea for a number of years. Aerosols are liquid disinfectant solutions, or emulsions, sprayed into the air as finely atomized mists. A family of alcohols known as the *glycols* has frequently been used for this purpose, either for their own disinfectant action or as diluents for other disinfectants. To obtain a maximum killing effect, the aerial concentration of the disinfectant must be high enough to ensure its condensation on all droplet nuclei present or its continuing effective activity on surfaces when it settles out of air suspension. Under practical conditions of use, the disinfectant action of aerosols is limited by the critical effect of humidity on their condensation and by the size, weight, and settling rate of their dispersed molecules. If they remain suspended in the air for sufficient time, condensing in active concentrations on droplet nuclei, they may reduce the number of bacteria per cubic millileter of room air quite significantly. If they contain too much or too little moisture of condensation, or if they settle out too rapidly, they may not accomplish their purpose. However, the settling of aerosols on room surfaces may carry down out of the air particles, droplets, and even some droplet nuclei containing viable microorganisms. Subsequent cleaning and rinsing of these surfaces with liquid disinfectants may then remove the deposited organisms. Aerosols cannot be expected to penetrate deeply into porous materials such as the fabrics of curtains, draperies, bedspreads, blankets, or mattresses. All these items except mattresses can be disinfected by adequate laundering procedures. Mattresses can be covered with impervious materials, such as plastic or rubber, which can be wiped or washed with liquid disinfectant, or they can be disinfected by gas applied under pressure in a large chamber, as described below.

Gas disinfection, or *fumigation*, as it is often called, involves the use of the fumes or vapors of volatile or gaseous chemical agents to kill patho-

genic microorganisms. Gases such as formaldehyde, sulfur dioxide, and beta-propriolactone, when released into closed rooms or chambers in adequate concentrations for sufficient time (several hours), kill most forms of microbial life. There are many limitations on such practices, however, notably the toxicity of these gases for human tissues, their inability to penetrate deeply into porous materials unless they are applied under pressure, and the difficulties inherent in dispensing them in high, active concentration. The fumigation of rooms or instrument cabinets with such agents has been largely abandoned for these reasons, and also because fumigants have been superseded by useful, nontoxic liquid disinfectants that can be applied to most surfaces with greater ease and efficiency. The terminal disinfection of rooms vacated by infectious patients is discussed in a later section of this chapter.

Gas sterilization can be accomplished within a closed chamber, very similar to an autoclave, filled with a gas under pressure. *Ethylene oxide* is a gas suitable for this purpose because it is lethal for all varieties of microorganisms, it is penetrative when under increased pressure, and it does not permanently combine with items or materials exposed to it but dissipates slowly when these are removed from the sterilizer. It is a flammable, explosive gas, however, and for this reason it is used in a mixture with carbon dioxide. In this condition it requires three to four hours under pressure to penetrate shallow layers of materials and to sterilize all surfaces within a chamber load. An equal period of time should be allowed following sterilization for ethylene oxide to dissipate from the treated materials. The total time required for the use of this gas, its toxicity, flammability, and the expense of the equipment needed are limitations to be weighed against its efficacy as a sterilizing agent for sensitive materials. Its use is generally reserved for objects that would be damaged by more efficient methods of heat sterilization or chemical disinfection. Lensed instruments, plastic items, catheters made of synthetic materials, Lucite and plastic components of heart-lung pumps, artificial heart valves and vessel segments, mattresses and other bedding, and many similar articles can be safely sterilized with ethylene oxide, this being the method of choice despite its expense (see Fig. 10–7).

Other chemical agents that are used for a variety of limited bactericidal or bacteriostatic purposes include the organic *solvents*, organic *acids*, aniline *dyes*, and mineral *salts*.

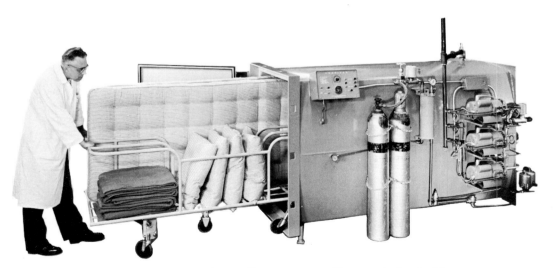

Fig. 10–7. Ethylene oxide can be used to sterilize mattresses, pillows, and other bedding used for patients with known or suspected infectious disease. (Courtesy of AMSCO, American Sterilizer Company, Erie, Pa.)

Organic solvents, such as ether, acetone, chloroform, benzene, and toluene, all have some antimicrobial activity, as do the alcohols previously considered. Most of these compounds, however, are not soluble in water, unlike the alcohols, and they do not have a rapid killing effect on microorganisms. They are most frequently used for their bacteriostatic and fungistatic qualities, as preservatives for protein and other solutions. Certain types of clinical specimens can be preserved with a solvent if they are to be stored, mailed, or shipped, or otherwise delayed in reaching the laboratory for analysis. It must be remembered, however, that the use of such preservatives often makes it impossible to test a specimen submitted for laboratory *culture*, for pathogenic organisms that may be present usually will not survive prolonged exposure to solvents. On the other hand, when *chemical* analyses are to be made, for example on the total volume of urine collected over a 24-hour period, a solvent such as toluene can be added to the collecting bottle to prevent bacterial overgrowth during the time successive urine passages are being collected. *Glycerol*, a heavy, viscous alcohol, is also an excellent preservative, when used in concentrations above 50 per cent. It is used to prevent bacterial growth in specimens of stool, surgical tissues, and other specimens when these are to be sent to distant laboratories. Glycerol-preserved specimens can be used for virus culture work but they are not satisfactory for bacterial cultures, as a rule. Specimens for culture are best preserved by freezing, especially if there is to be a long delay. They can be shipped in the frozen state, packed in dry ice in insulated containers. Glycerol is also used as a preservative in the preparation of vaccines and other injectable materials, for it is not injurious to tissues.

Organic acids are often used in the preservation of foods, to prevent the growth of bacteria and molds. Vinegar, which is dilute acetic acid, is well known for this use. Benzoic and proprionic acids, or their salts, are also commonly added to foods as preservatives. Boric acid solutions are sometimes used for their mild antiseptic action as irrigants for wounds or for eyes.

Aniline dyes are sometimes applied as antiseptics for skin or mucosal infections. They are inhibitory for certain bacteria, particularly Gram-positive species, and for some yeasts and molds. Gentian violet, used in the laboratory to stain bacteria, was once widely applied in the treatment of superficial fungous infections and of vaginal infections caused by yeasts or Gram-positive bacteria. This dye has also been used as an antihelminthic agent in the treatment of intestinal roundworm infestations (e.g., pinworm). The use of dyes creates troublesome problems for the patient, however, and they have been largely replaced by newer methods of chemotherapy.

Mineral salts in concentrations rising from 1 or 2 per cent become increasingly inhibitory for bacteria and other microorganisms. This is the reason salting is an effective method for the preservation of food. In the laboratory, the toxic effect of sodium chloride in 5 to 6 per cent concentration is quite marked for some fastidious organisms but less so for others. This fact can be applied to the cultural differentiation of strains of streptococci, for example, or to the isolation of staphylococci, which are salt-resistant, from specimens containing a mixed, generally sensitive flora.

Table 10–3 summarizes some of the useful chemical disinfectants, their applications, advantages, and limitations.

Control of Environmental Sources of Infection

In nursing practice, the application of the principles of sterilization and disinfection is directed at the provision of a safe environment for all patients and for all personnel involved in their care. Safety from infection is of particularly critical importance in hospitals, where it is also most difficult to guarantee.

As we have seen, people are the reservoir of those infectious diseases transmitted readily from man to man, and people are the major source of infection in hospitals. Patients admitted with active infection; patients with active but masked, undiagnosed communicable disease admitted for treatment of other conditions; patients who develop infections after they enter the hospital, having been exposed before or after admission;

Table 10–3. Chemical Disinfectants*

Group	Proprietary Products	Use — Dilution	Recommended Usage	Special Advantages	Limitations
Alcohol Ethyl, C_2H_5OH Isopropyl, $CH_3CHOHCH_3$		70–90%	Thermometers (add 0.2–1% iodine) Instrument disinfection Disinfection of hands Skin preparation Spot disinfection	Rapidly bactericidal Kills tubercle bacillus	Not sporicidal Will corrode metals unless reducing agent is added, e.g., 0.2% sodium nitrite Dries skin (1:200 cetyl alcohol may be added as an emollient) Bleaches rubber tile
Chlorines Hypochlorites	Clorox Purex Other household and laundry bleaches Dry bleach such as Purex	Strongest concentration recommended by manufacturer Mix to thin paste	Floors Plumbing fixtures Fabrics that will not be damaged by bleaching Spot disinfection Spot disinfection (spilled sputum or excreta)	Kills tubercle bacillus unless highly diluted	Corrodes metals Bleaches colored fabrics Discolors some synthetic fabrics No residual effects
Hydrochlorous acid derivatives, HClO	Warexin	1.5% aqueous solution	Same as hypochlorites Dishes (not silverware)	Limited effect in killing tubercle bacillus	Must be freshly prepared Unstable in presence of hard water

O	Steroxide		...ensed instruments Rubber goods Thermolabile plastics Books, papers	Complete sterilization; sporicidal if contamination is not heavy	Requires long period for effective disinfection Costly
Formaldehyde					
HCHO		Gas	Used in special cabinets	Safe for instruments with delicate parts or cement	Toxic to skin and mucous membranes Odorous
	Bard-Parker Formaldehyde Germicide	Use full strength	Transfer forceps Instrument container	Vaporcidal disinfecting feature Most actively germicidal solution available; sporicidal Noncorrosive properties	
Iodine					
Tincture		0.5-2%	Preoperative skin preparation Thermometers (see Alcohol)		Stains Irritating to tissues
Iodophors	Wescodyne (detergent iodine combination)	Solution 75 ppm (90 ml — 3 oz to 5 gal of water) 450 ppm to kill tubercle bacillus Higher concentrations recommended for unclean and porous surfaces	Disinfection of thermometers, utensils, rubber goods, dishes	Cleaning and disinfecting Nonstaining Color diminishes as germicidal activity diminishes Residual antibacterial effect (tested with *Staphylococcus*)	Somewhat unstable Inactivated by hard water May corrode metals

* Proprietary products are listed as examples only; many similar products are available under other brand names. Unless otherwise noted, the disinfecting time is ten minutes.

Table 10–3. (*Cont.*)

Group	Proprietary Products	Use — Dilution	Recommended Usage	Special Advantages	Limitations
Iodine (Cont.)		Tincture 10% Wescodyne in 50% ethyl alcohol	Rapid disinfection (1–5 minutes) Single presurgical scrub Spot disinfection	Kills tubercle bacillus	Drying to skin
	Betadine	See specific recommendations for product	Skin preparation		
	Many other products designed for specific purposes in eating places or dairies may be suitable for use. A few are: Iobac Klenzade Micro-Klene Virac	See specific recommendations for product			
Phenolics Saponated solution of Creosol OH		2% for 30 minutes 5% if hard water is used	Disinfection of equipment, linen, excreta, and other organic matter	Active in presence of organic matter	Must be mixed with soft water Slow-acting Has odor
Synthetics	Amphyl	0.5–1% (also available as spray)	Instrument disinfection and storage	Not inactivated by soap or hard water	
	Lysol	1%	Laundry rinse for blankets and	Residual effect if allowed to dry	Lysol has some odor

Agent	Trade Names	Concentration	Use	Advantages	Disadvantages
	Tergisyl Armisol	2%	Exclusively environmental; Mechanical cleansing, floors, walls, ceilings, furniture	High detergency; Active in presence of heavy organic matter; Residual effect	

Spot disinfection

Agent	Trade Names	Concentration	Use	Advantages	Disadvantages
Bacteriostatic Soap Additives					
Hexachlorophene (G-11)	Bar soap Dial Gamophen; Liquid detergents Septisol 2% pHisoHex 3% Hex-O-San Surofene; Hand creams Septisol antiseptic skin cream	As recommended by manufacturer	Inhibits growth of bacteria on skin if used exclusively and frequently; Hand-washing; Preoperative skin preparation; Presurgical scrub; Hand cream to alleviate dryness and maintain antibacterial action	Not inactivated by soap; Prolonged action; Continues action of cleansing agent	Not sporicidal and does not kill tubercle bacillus; Slow action
Tetrachlorosalicyl-anilide	Bar soap Coleo		Same as hexachlorophene (G-11)		

Hexachlorophene (G-11) structure: two trichlorophenol rings (each bearing Cl, Cl, Cl and OH) joined by a CH_2 bridge.

Table 10–3. (Cont.)

Group	Proprietary Products	Use—Dilution	Recommended Usage	Special Advantages	Limitations
Quaternary Ammonium Compounds $$\left[R-N \begin{smallmatrix} R_1 \\ R_2 \\ R_3 \end{smallmatrix} \right]^{+} Cl^{-}$$ Cationic	Zephiran and many other proprietary products	1:1000 aqueous solution; Available as towelettes	Cleansing and disinfection of instruments, utensils, rubber goods; Storage of instruments except: those with lenses fastened by cement, lacquered catheters, synthetic rubber goods, and aluminum instruments; Preoperative skin preparation	Bland	No effect on tubercle bacillus; Virucidal activity limited; Must be diluted with distilled water; Inactivated by soap
	Tincture of Zephiran	1:1000	Thermometers	Kills tubercle bacillus	
	Roccal	1:1250–1:5000	Sanitation and disinfection		Does not kill tubercle bacillus
$$\left[O = \overset{O}{\underset{O}{S}} - O - N \begin{smallmatrix} R_1 \\ R_2 \\ R_3 \end{smallmatrix} \right]^{-} Na^{+}$$ Anionic			Laundry disinfectant		Inactive in presence of soap

Adapted by special permission from *Safer Ways in Nursing: To Protect Against Airborne Infections*, Nursing Advisory Service of the National Tuberculosis Association and the National League for Nursing, National Tuberculosis Association, 1962.

and patients who are asymptomatic carriers, and disseminators, of pathogenic microorganisms — all of these are concentrated in hospitals, together with personnel who also contribute their normal and pathogenic flora to the environment. The control of infection in hospitals must include, therefore, not only the treatment of communicable disease and the prophylactic care of exposed contacts, as we shall discuss in the last section of this chapter, but any or all of the physical and chemical methods previously described that can prevent the transmission of microorganisms directly from person to person, or indirectly through environmental reservoirs.

With regard to infection control, the minimum goal that must be met by hospitals is a state of *scrupulous cleanliness*. This is the responsibility of many in the hospital organization, but it begins with the administrator and it includes the housekeeping and maintenance departments, as well as nursing administration. Each area of the hospital, from its garbage disposal facility to the operating room, should be subjected to rigorous, daily cleaning techniques designed to remove organic wastes, to prevent moisture accumulations in which microorganisms can thrive, and to preclude the survival and transmission of microbial pathogens from obvious or probable reservoirs. The cleaning equipment itself should be chosen, handled, and applied with a knowledge of the microbiologic needs of hospitals. Dusting cloths, mops, brooms, and dry vacuum cleaners can themselves contribute to the spread of microorganisms when they are used without regard for the principles of disinfection.

With a basic state of cleanliness existing throughout the hospital, *aseptic conditions* can then be established and maintained with relative ease wherever they are indicated. Medical asepsis has been defined as a condition excluding the infectious agents of communicable disease, while surgical asepsis implies the exclusion of all microorganisms (see pp. 204–205). More often than not, asepsis is a *goal*, rather than a realized condition, because it is dependent on the coordination of many techniques, applied by a number of different personnel (physicians, nurses, housekeepers, maintenance personnel, even patients' visitors,

on occasion), and not all these techniques can be fully effective under all circumstances. When they are well combined and conscientiously applied, however, they can be very effective in providing the safe environment patients have a right to expect in modern hospitals.

Medical Asepsis

Medical asepsis includes all the fundamental concepts of good housekeeping (dust removal, scrubbing, laundering, disinfecting) with some additional techniques applied to the special conditions created by infectious illness. Some of these techniques are taught as a part of the general public education concerning the communicability of infection: the personal hygiene of careful hand-washing and bathing; the sanitary handling of food and dishes; proper methods for cooking or refrigerating foods; hygienic attitudes toward body functions and excretions (toilet habits, covering the mouth and nose when coughing or sneezing, the adequate disposal of facial tissues and handkerchiefs). More specialized methods are added to these by nurses and physicians directly involved in the care of sick patients. These include all the precautionary measures taken to prevent the *direct* transmission of infection from person to person or the *indirect* transfer of pathogens by way of instruments, equipment, or any inanimate objects present in the sickroom.

Surgical Asepsis

Surgical asepsis adds the last links to this chain of techniques designed to eliminate the danger of transferring infection. The aseptic techniques that surround surgical procedures must provide the best guarantees that *all* microorganisms have been eliminated from any scene of action intimately involving the body's deep tissues. When injections are given, superficial wounds are sutured, or deep surgery is performed, the body's primary defensive mechanisms are bypassed, and entry is made into tissues whose susceptibility to infection is increased by the injury induced by the procedure.

Surgical asepsis is intended to prevent the introduction of any contaminating microorganisms. The area of the patient's skin to be entered is thoroughly cleansed and scrubbed with antiseptic, and if the procedure is to be extensive, surrounding areas are covered with sterile cloth drapes, so that a sterile field is established at the site of surgery. The surgeon and all personnel involved similarly prepare their own skin, scrubbing hands and forearms, and then with sterile rubber gloves, gowns, caps, and masks they cover all areas from which microorganisms might be shed onto the operative field. Instruments, dressings, and sutures are all sterilized for use in surgery, and any equipment that cannot be presterilized is treated with an appropriate disinfection technique. The operating room itself and its walls, floors, and equipment are cleaned and disinfected before use, and every pattern of activity within the room is designed to maintain the aseptic atmosphere. The ventilation of operating rooms should be such that, with doors closed, fresh, filtered air is delivered, circulated, and exhausted continuously.

Once asepsis has been adequately established in a closed, properly ventilated operating room, the number of microorganisms present in the air or on surfaces is reduced to the barest possible minimum. From that point on, as surgery proceeds, microbial contamination of the atmosphere progressively increases, its principal source being the people present in the room. The degree to which such contamination rises, and its potential danger to the patient, depend largely on the technique and skill of the attending personnel in controlling their own activities so that the major sources of their microorganisms (nose and throat, hands, uncovered skin and hair) are under continuous, effective restraint. Close guards are kept against breaks in technique: damaged gloves are discarded and replaced by a fresh, sterile pair; saturated masks are exchanged for fresh ones; backup supplies of sterile instruments, solutions, and other essential items are kept at hand.

It should be emphasized, however, that surgical asepsis is a concept to be applied not only in operating rooms, but in any situation requiring close protection of the patient when the risk of infection is high. It should be maintained, with respect to surgical wounds, for the first few postoperative days, or until tissues are sufficiently healed to manage their own defenses. It is applied in delivery rooms to prevent sepsis of injured mucous membranes and in nurseries to protect susceptible newborns from any risk of infection. Wherever it is established, surgical asepsis represents a crowning touch to a basic structure of techniques that begin with sanitary cleanliness and end by disinfecting and sterilizing the environment to the fullest extent possible. (See Fig. 1-10.)

Application of Aseptic Techniques in Hospitals

Infection control measures as they are practiced in hospitals fall into two major categories: (1) those designed to prevent the *direct* transmission of infectious microorganisms from one person to another, and (2) those that prevent the *indirect* transmission of infection through possible environmental reservoirs.

Barriers to the Direct Transmission of Communicable Diseases. In general, all the precautions involved in the nursing care of hospitalized patients are centered in the knowledge that many infectious diseases are transmitted directly from persons with either active or subclinical infections. The first step in control is the isolation of infectious persons; the second is to prevent the transmission of infection from any source by hospital personnel, either to other patients or among themselves.

Isolation of the Infectious Patient. Whenever possible, patients with communicable diseases should be cared for in private rooms properly equipped for their needs as well as for nursing purposes. (Infants and premature babies can be cared for in individual incubator-isolators, or "isolettes.") A private bath should be available, and individual supplies and equipment for the care of the patient should be provided from the time of his admission until his discharge. When

necessary, freshly cleaned or sterilized equipment should be on hand as replacements. If a basin facility with running hot and cold water is not available, a hand-washing basin must be provided within the room, together with an effective antiseptic for skin care. When it is not possible to provide an individual room, every effort must be made to provide physical separation of the infectious patient occupying a shared room or ward. This arrangement is not to be recommended, however, for even with the best precautionary procedures the spread of respiratory or enteric infections through shared facilities is very difficult to prevent.

Concurrent disinfection techniques are practiced throughout the course of the patient's hospital stay, or until such time as the physician considers him to be no longer infectious. These techniques are designed to assure the immediate destruction of pathogenic microorganisms in the infectious discharges of the patient or on objects soiled by such material. Nondisposable items are first disinfected, with a minimum of handling, then cleaned thoroughly or resterilized. If the patient's infection involves sporeforming bacterial pathogens, contaminated articles to be re-used must be sterilized by steam under pressure. Disposable items may be incinerated, or autoclaved if this is more convenient.

Terminal disinfection is carried out after the patient has been discharged from the room. All equipment in the room is either sterilized or carefully disinfected, with particular attention to blankets, mattress, and pillows. All items that can be laundered, including window curtains or drapes (these have no place in an isolation room), are disinfected by good laundry techniques. Plastic covers on pillows and mattresses can be scrubbed with liquid germicide; otherwise ethylene oxide sterilization is recommended for these items. Furniture and floors are washed clean and then treated with an appropriate liquid disinfectant. The walls should also be washed, particularly if the infection was one of serious nature transmitted by air or droplet spread. The room should be well aired, or an aerosol disinfectant may be applied with a "fogging" technique, provided the latter is not used as a substitute for thorough cleaning procedures.

Isolation of the Susceptible Patient. Modern medicine has developed many new medical and surgical techniques for the treatment of patients with severe organic disease. Open-heart surgery, artificial heart and kidney machines, and organ transplants offer new hope for the management of hitherto incurable conditions. However, these procedures frequently involve the patient in long and difficult periods of surgery or continuous treatment, during which he is, or becomes, increasingly susceptible to infection. Furthermore, the complications of infection, should it occur in these patients, can be extremely serious and threatening both to the success of the treatment and even to life itself. Other patients under severe stress offer similar problems of unusual susceptibility to infection: patients with extensive burns, premature babies, and people debilitated by age or by conditions that reduce their normal defenses to a marked degree may be candidates for isolation, with nursing precautions applied *in reverse* to protect them from infection from outside sources. Concurrent disinfection is not necessary in such instances, but surgical asepsis is maintained in the room throughout the critical period of the patient's care.

The Surgical Patient. The preparation of the patient scheduled for surgery is centered on the adequate disinfection of the skin area to be incised. The hair is first removed, and solvents (soap or alcohol) are used to cleanse the area of skin oils and to mechanically remove most of the superficial microorganisms. The final application of an effective antiseptic further reduces the microbial flora of the region so that when it is entered surgically the risk of endogenous infection derived from the patient's skin is reduced as far as possible. Patients being prepared for abdominal surgery are sometimes treated for a few days beforehand with a combination of antibiotics intended to "sterilize" the bowel contents or to reduce the normal intestinal flora to a very low level temporarily. This procedure is also de-

signed to decrease the risk of infection to surrounding tissues of the peritoneum when the bowel must be opened, particularly if prolonged surgery is anticipated or if the patient's defenses are unusually low.

The surgical patient who presents no evidence of overt infection before or after surgery does not require isolation, although the wound itself is isolated, so to speak, by good dressing technique, until normal healing occurs. On the other hand, when an infective lesion is incised in the operating room, particular precautions must be taken for the concurrent and terminal disinfection of the surgical room and all its equipment. The infective postoperative patient must be managed in such a way that he offers no threat of infection transfer to other patients with unhealed surgical wounds. If his infection is severe, and particularly if it involves sporeforming bacterial pathogens, he should be isolated with full precautions. Under less dangerous circumstances, techniques may be adapted to the needs of the situation. In any case, very careful dressing techniques are indicated, with immediate destruction of contaminated dressings. Sterile gloves are sometimes indicated when infected wounds are handled, or dressings may be changed with sterile transfer forceps, one for dirty use and one for clean (see Fig. 10–8). "Occlusive" dressings are sometimes applied to infected wounds as a topical isolation of infectious drainage. This technique employs a water-proof lamina over the dressing and adherent to the patient's skin around the full circumference of the area.

Personnel Techniques. Physicians and nurses who care for patients, and others (including their visitors) who come in contact with them, are sometimes responsible for continuing the chain of transmission of infection. The most obvious and frequent transportation offered to pathogenic microorganisms is by way of *unwashed hands*, but clothing and hair may also serve. It should also be remembered that medical personnel with their own infections (colds, sore throats, infectious skin lesions) can transfer these readily to patients, whose resistance to them may well be lowered by their illness. The basic techniques that can prevent this transmission in large measure are relatively simple, but they should be *conscientiously observed by all concerned* and *consistently practiced.*

Hand-washing is a vital and essential factor in the prevention of disease transmission. Adequate hand-washing facilities should be available in all areas of the hospital for personnel and patients alike. Good antiseptic soaps or detergents should be kept stocked at all hand basins, and these materials themselves must be kept in clean containers, changed frequently. Brush-scrubbing of the hands should be avoided, except in surgery, by those who must wash frequently, because it is irritating.

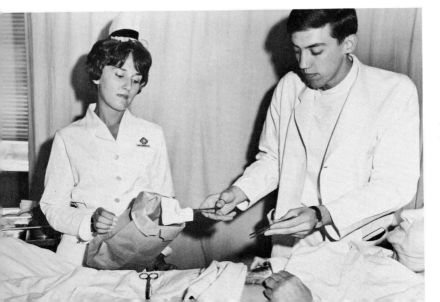

Fig. 10–8. A nurse assists the physician while changing dressings. The soiled dressings, removed with forceps, are carefully placed into disposable paper bags. The nurse remains "clean" so that she can give the physician sterile and clean articles from the dressing cart. (Courtesy of St. Luke's Hospital Center, New York, N.Y.)

The principles of antisepsis must be built in to hand-washing procedures if they are to be effective. The hands always carry a burden of their own normal flora, together with contamination from other sources, unless they have just been washed. They should be freshly washed, therefore, when patients or their equipment is to be handled. When infectious patients are cared for, particularly those in isolation, hand-washing is an essential part of concurrent disinfection and should always be done just before leaving the room. Hand contacts with furniture, telephones, elevator buttons, and doorknobs may also transfer infection, so that frequent washing is again the best defense.

Hand-washing should be thorough each time, with attention to the back as well as the palms, the wrists, and each side of the fingers. Soap or detergent should be rubbed on carefully, the hands being held down from the elbow so that contaminated water will not run up the arm. Rinsing should be complete, preferably under running water. Paper towels for drying are preferable to cloth, particularly in the sickroom, unless the latter are used only once, for a wet used towel may also trap viable microorganisms.

The fingernails should be kept short and scrupulously clean. Rings and wrist watches should not be worn by those caring for infectious patients.

Gown Technique. The use of gowns is indicated under most isolation conditions, whether the patient is infectious or is being cared for with "reverse precautions." A clean gown that is ample in size and can be fastened securely protects the clothing and arms from contamination with infectious microorganisms. A fresh one should be available for each person who enters the sickroom, on each occasion. When gowns are discarded after each use, there is no risk of transferring microorganisms from a previous contact with the patient. Gowns are meant to be protective. If they are to fill this purpose, they should be properly fastened, and they should not be worn if they are wet or soiled. Moist areas on the gown may involve the clothing beneath

and form a capillary bridge for the transfer of microorganisms.

Masks. The use of masks is generally not indicated outside the operating room, where it is necessary to protect surgically injured tissues from contamination with respiratory organisms. The patient in isolation with a communicable respiratory disease should be masked if he must be taken from the room for treatment in some other part of the hospital. Personnel masking may also be protective for short periods of close contact with the patient. The limitations of the mask, as previously described, should be understood, however. They should be worn correctly and discarded promptly after each use. When a used mask has been touched or handled in any way, the hands should be washed thoroughly. Used masks should be laundered and autoclaved between uses.

Personal Hygiene. The nurse, because of her close association with sick people, must be particularly aware of her own personal hygiene, to protect her own health as well as to avoid transmitting infection to others. Her clothing, hair, and skin should be kept clean and in good condition. One of the major reasons for a nursing uniform and the traditional white duty shoes is that this kind of clothing is easy to clean. Furthermore, when it is soiled this fact is immediately recognized and remedied. The practice of wearing this clothing outside of the hospital is a poor one, because the nurse should come to the patient's bedside in clothes as freshly clean as possible.

The personal care of skin and hair should include the use of effective soaps or shampoos, together with nongreasy lubricants that help to avoid excessive drying. The hair should be shampooed frequently, particularly when the nurse is caring for an infectious patient. The coiffure should be simple, so that it does not require frequent arrangement with hands that may be contaminated. If hair is long or unruly, it should be controlled by a hairnet.

Above all, the habit of thorough, frequent hand-washing should be developed early and con-

tinued throughout nursing service. It should be a part of personal as well as professional life to guard the hands against contamination with potentially pathogenic microorganisms, derived from one's own body or from others.

Infections Among Personnel. All medical personnel should have physical examinations at regular intervals. This is of particular importance for physicians, nurses, and dietary personnel who should be examined for evidence of active infections of the respiratory and intestinal tracts or the skin. When indicated, they should be isolated and treated as any other patient would be, with due concern for the relative advantages of home or hospital care with respect to the specific infection. When personnel infections are not severe and can be treated on an ambulatory basis, the individuals involved should either be removed from duty altogether or be placed on duty in hospital areas where patient contacts are impossible or unimportant, until the infection has been cured or all danger of its transmission has passed.

Aseptic Techniques as Barriers to Indirect Transmission Routes. The entire physical environment of the hospital must be considered in the planning and maintenance of effective procedures for infection control. Increasing emphasis is currently being placed on the architectural design of new hospitals with respect to access and transfer routes of infection from physical or human sources. In the meantime, many existing hospitals have fundamental faults of design that create unnecessary difficulties in the control of traffic patterns, the routing of essential hospital services (garbage and waste removal, the flow of clean and dirty laundry, food service), the provision of adequate isolation facilities for infectious patients, or the protection of areas, such as the operating rooms and intensive-care units, in which infection control is of critical importance. In each hospital organization, those responsible for the provision of an aseptic atmosphere must consider the indigenous problems and devise the most effective methods to cope with them at every level. Infection control committees, composed of

representatives from administration, the medical and nursing staffs, housekeeping and maintenance departments, and the laboratory, can establish standard policy and procedures for every hospital unit, based on sound principles of asepsis specifically applied to the local situation. When the efforts of all concerned are not concerted, many problems are compounded, and in the end the hospital's patients pay the price of unnecessary infection or of unwarranted expenses associated with inefficient control methods.

The principles of asepsis should form the foundation of procedures applied by *every* hospital department. The problems of ventilation, air-cooling, and heating are the province of the engineering and maintenance department, which should be aware of the necessity for providing clean, filtered air, particularly to critical areas. Air filters, and refrigerant solutions used for air-cooling, can themselves become reservoirs of multiplying organisms disseminated through hospital ventilators, unless they are properly maintained. When modern ventilation equipment is not available, effective compromise methods for the control of contaminated air flow can be applied by informed personnel. Sanitary maintenance of the hospital, its floors, walls, furniture, and nontechnical equipment, is generally the responsibility of the housekeeping department, whose manager should be expert on the subject of chemical disinfection, as should the laundry manager. The compatibility of soaps, detergents, and disinfectants and their effective combination in assuring asepsis are a matter of fundamental concern in these areas. Knowledge of the capacity of microorganisms to establish reservoirs in organic wastes (on mops, in spilled garbage, in dirty laundry rooms) is fundamental to hospital safety (see Figs. 10–9 to 10–12). The dietary department, of course, is also intimately involved in the application of aseptic principles to the preservation, preparation, and service of food to hospital patients. The sanitizing of kitchen equipment and the use of appropriate methods for food preparation are incumbent upon the dietitian. The continuing health of food-handlers, as well as all other personnel, and their freedom from

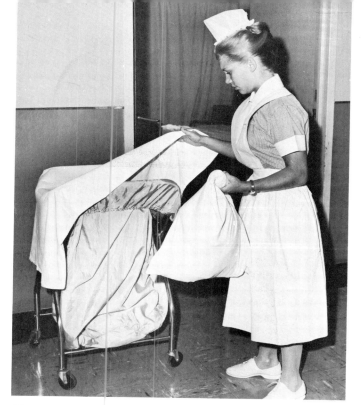

Fig. 10–9. A laundry cart containing soiled linen is kept covered with a sheet to prevent the transmission of microorganisms by air currents. (Courtesy of St. Luke's Hospital Center, New York, N.Y.)

Fig. 10–10. Soiled linen is carefully bagged before it is placed in a laundry chute. This helps to prevent the transmission of microorganisms to other floors by way of the air currents within the chute. It also protects the laundry workers who pick up the dirty laundry at the central collecting point. (Courtesy of St. Luke's Hospital Center, New York, N.Y.)

Fig. 10–11. This hospital laundry can wash, dry, and iron 700 lb of linen in one hour. Careful processing of soiled and clean linen at all stages is important in the control of hospital infection. (Courtesy of Northern Westchester Hospital, Mt. Kisco, N.Y.)

infection are the responsibility of the hospital's health service physician, with assistance from the microbiology laboratory.

In the medical and surgical care of patients, physicians and nurses working together must constantly and consistently apply a procedural knowledge of asepsis. Patients being treated for noncommunicable diseases must not be exposed to the risks of complicating infections, while those who must be isolated for infection should be cared for without neglect of the special emotional as well as physical needs created by the circumstances of isolation. Nurses and physicians are the technical practitioners of asepsis, in the routine situation, in the more demanding circumstances of treating infectious disease in isolation or of preventing it in operating rooms, intensive-care units, nurseries, and other areas where pa-

Fig. 10–12. The collection of waste materials in plastic bags prevents the transmission of micro-organisms through the air. Gloves protect the worker's hands. (Courtesy of St. Luke's Hospital Center, New York, N.Y.)

tients are unusually susceptible to infection risk. The special knowledge of medical personnel is accompanied by special responsibility in these situations.

The function of the microbiology laboratory in infection control is one of consultation and the provision of surveillance methods to determine the efficacy of aseptic procedures. Laboratory tests, properly designed and applied, can demonstrate whether or not hospital practices accomplish the desired result. In-use testing can be applied to equipment, solutions, floors, and furniture, or even to the concept of a technique. In many situations, it can provide the final information needed concerning the value of preventive measures. The laboratory should also be prepared to combine its diagnostic function with surveillance methods so that outbreaks of particular infections, if they occur, can be quickly recognized and traced to their source. In the latter regard, the assistance of epidemiologic experts from city or state health departments is available and should be utilized.

The hospital administrator heads this complex organization of specialists who are together responsible for the safe care of patients in hospitals. The coordination of policies established by medical and governing boards and the maintenance of an orderly framework for the implementation of these policies are administrative functions. The network of infection-control policy, as established by hospital committees, must be held together and kept in functional order by enlightened administrative systems fully cognizant of its central importance to safety.

Control of Active Infectious Disease

When confronted with a case of active infectious disease, the physician must first decide (on the basis of clinical or laboratory diagnosis, or both) whether or not its transmissibility warrants isolating the patient from effective contact with others. If it appears to be one of those diseases that is transmissible directly from person to person or indirectly through inanimate, environmental reservoirs (see groups 1, 2, and 4, Chap. 9,

pp. 182 to 183), the patient should be isolated either at home or in the hospital. Isolation is not indicated in the case of those infections that are not transmitted directly among human hosts (groups 3, 5, and 6, Chap 9, pp. 183 to 185), although in some instances it may be necessary to screen the patient from contacts with insects or animals that might transfer and perpetuate the disease.

Once the diagnosis is made, control of the active disease is centered on the treatment and cure of the patient and, if necessary, the prophylactic (preventive) treatment of his susceptible contacts. Chemotherapeutic methods (that is, the use of specific or supportive chemical agents in therapy) are instituted promptly for the patient. In a few instances, immunotherapy may also be indicated, as in the use of antitoxins (passive immunization) in early tetanus or diphtheria. On the other hand, when it is necessary to protect the contacts of a patient ill with a communicable disease, immune prophylaxis is more often appropriate than preventive treatment with drugs.

Treatment of the Patient

Chemotherapy. The use of chemical agents, applied externally or internally, in the treatment of human disease, is probably as old as man himself. The scientific approach to the chemotherapy of infectious diseases, however, came only after their etiology was discovered in the late nineteenth century. Paul Ehrlich's work in the early years of the twentieth century laid the foundation for the systematic chemotherapeutic approach to microbial diseases. His experiments with arsenical drugs (number 606 in a series of compounds tested was the most successful and famous) in the treatment of syphilis led to his recognition of the selective activity of drugs on microorganisms as opposed to the host cells with which they are associated in disease. He also encountered the development of resistance to drugs by microbial cells and explored means for countering this with combinations of compounds acting in different ways on microbial components. The next important impetus to the chemotherapy of infection

came in the 1930's with the discovery that a family of simple organic compounds known as sulfonamides possessed antimicrobial usefulness, and in 1940 with the demonstration that penicillin, an antibacterial substance produced by the mold *Penicillium*, also had practical value as a therapeutic agent.

The dramatic success of penicillin in the treatment of infection led to the development of many other useful drugs derived from molds and other microorganisms. The term "antibiotic" was applied to those substances, synthesized by microbes, that have an inhibitory or destructive action on other microorganisms. The word was meant to distinguish such agents from natural or synthesized chemical compounds, such as the sulfonamides, used as antimicrobial drugs. In recent years, however, since the discovery of a successful method for the chemical synthesis of penicillin and for chemically altering its molecule to make it more effective against some organisms, the term has lost some of its original distinction, though we still use it.

Although enormous numbers of antibiotics have been discovered in the last two decades (most of them are produced by fungi and other soil organisms), only a relative few have proved to be safe and useful in chemotherapy. Many are too damaging to host cells in effective antimicrobial concentrations, while others are too limited in their action on microorganisms. As in the case of other classes of drugs, the criteria for the selection of antimicrobial agents to be used in chemotherapy are (1) low toxicity for host cells and tissues; (2) lack of allergenic properties giving rise to host hypersensitivity; (3) a broad spectrum of activity against many different types of microorganisms; (4) a cidal rather than a static action on microorganisms; and (5) antimicrobial effects to which microorganisms do not display easy adaptation with the development of resistance. Not all these properties are displayed by every useful antibiotic, but the best possible combination is sought in the purification and preparation of such agents, which must meet minimum regulatory standards.

The mode of action of antimicrobial drugs is a chemical interference (often rather delicate) with

the function or synthesis of vital cell components. The toxicity of a particular drug for host cells as well as microbial cells depends in part on whether or not they share the same kind of molecule affected by the drug or whether this molecule has the same importance of function in both cell types. For instance, some drugs act by interfering with the cellular synthesis of nucleic acids common to animal as well as bacterial cells. Such agents are not selective in their activity (actinomycins are an example) and are too toxic to host cells to be useful in chemotherapy.

Antibiotics may act by inhibiting one or more of the steps involved in the synthesis of cytoplasmic or cell wall protein. In some instances the drug may interfere in the process because it is structurally similar to, but not identical with, compounds used by the cell in synthesis or enzyme function. Substitution of the drug (which is called an analogue in such a case) for the normal compound may lead to failures in cellular function. Penicillin, for example, inhibits the formation of bacterial cell wall proteins, probably because it serves as an analogue for certain amino acids normally involved in synthesis of cell wall peptides and proteins. Human and other animal cells do not have cell walls and do not synthesize proteins of the type found in bacterial cell walls. This may be one of the important reasons for the fact that penicillin has very little toxicity for host cells. The difference in composition of the walls of Gram-positive and Gram-negative bacteria may also account for the greater toxicity of penicillin for the former than for the latter.

The sulfonamides also act as analogues for a vitamin (para-aminobenzoic acid, or PABA) which many microorganisms require for the synthesis of an enzyme involved in the formation of nuclear proteins. The substitution of a sulfonamide for the vitamin interferes with the construction, by the cell, of a properly functional enzyme and therefore prevents further growth (see Fig. 10–13). Bacterial cells that do not require PABA for their growth are not inhibited by the sulfonamide compounds. This is also the reason these drugs are not toxic for human cells.

Some important antimicrobial agents are listed in Table 10–4 according to their use in certain

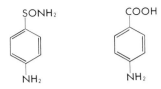

Fig. 10–13. Chemical formulae for sulfanilamide (*left*) and para-aminobenzoic acid (PABA, *right*). Note the close similarity of structure that makes it possible for the drug to substitute for the vitamin in bacterial syntheses, thus interfering with further normal growth of the bacterial cells.

specific infections. Sulphetrone, used in the treatment of leprosy, and the sulfonamides, which are effective against some important Gram-negative organisms (*Neisseria meningitidis, Shigella* and *Brucella* species), are synthetic compounds. Other examples of this type of chemotherapeutic drug are the synthetic derivatives of quinine (Atabrine, primaquine) used in the treatment of malaria; antimony compounds (Fuadin, Neostibosan) used for some helminthic infections; and various compounds of arsenic (Carbarsone, glycobiarsol, neoarsphenamine) effective for amebiasis and some of the spirochetal infections.

Most of the chemical agents used in the treatment of bacterial diseases are antibiotic in origin. By the same token, the antibiotics are generally far more effective in their action on pathogenic bacteria and spirochetes than they are on other classes of microorganisms, with the exception of some rickettsiae and the large viruses of the psittacosis-lymphogranuloma-trachoma group.

The new synthetic penicillin drugs are interesting and important because they enlarge the clinical usefulness of this antibiotic. Penicillin and its earlier derivative, penicillin G, are themselves destroyed by the action of an enzyme produced by many staphylococci and coliform bacilli. This enzyme is called *penicillinase.* It acts by splitting the penicillin molecule and thus rendering it inactive. Penicillinase production is responsible for much of the resistance to this drug seen among many bacterial strains, as opposed to the genetic mutant resistance that arises to other drugs (see p. 53). Some of the synthetic penicillin molecules (oxacillin, methicillin, and cloxacillin), however,

are not destroyed by penicillinase, because they have a slightly different chemical structure (see Fig. 10–14). They can be used effectively, therefore, to treat infections caused by penicillinase-producing staphylococci and other organisms. Ampicillin is another new penicillin that is destroyed by penicillinase activity, but it has a broader spectrum of activity against Gram-negative bacteria than the original antibiotic.

A number of useful antibiotics are produced by microorganisms belonging to the genus *Streptomyces* (a member of the group of "higher" bacteria). Drugs such as streptomycin, chloramphenicol, and the tetracyclines are synthesized by various *Streptomyces* species. The chemical formulae for these are shown in Fig. 10–15.

Problems in Chemotherapy. Depending on the drug and the necessity for speed of action, antimicrobial agents are administered either orally or systemically, by intramuscular or intravenous

injection. In a few instances they may also be useful in topical application to skin lesions or burns, or as irrigants for superficial wounds. Once introduced into the body, antimicrobial drugs interact with host tissues and cells as well as with the pathogenic microorganisms they encounter there. In addition, antibiotics and other drugs may affect the normal flora of the skin and mucous membranes, inducing changes in these organisms as well. The major problems that may complicate the chemotherapeutic approach to infection are discussed briefly below.

Drug toxicity for the host may seriously interfere with the drug's value in therapy. Some drugs, such as penicillin, have few toxic effects and may be given in concentrations and quantities larger than the effective antimicrobial level required without inducing tissue damage. Others, however, must be carefully adjusted in dosage, because their effective concentrations are not much different from their toxic concentrations, allowing

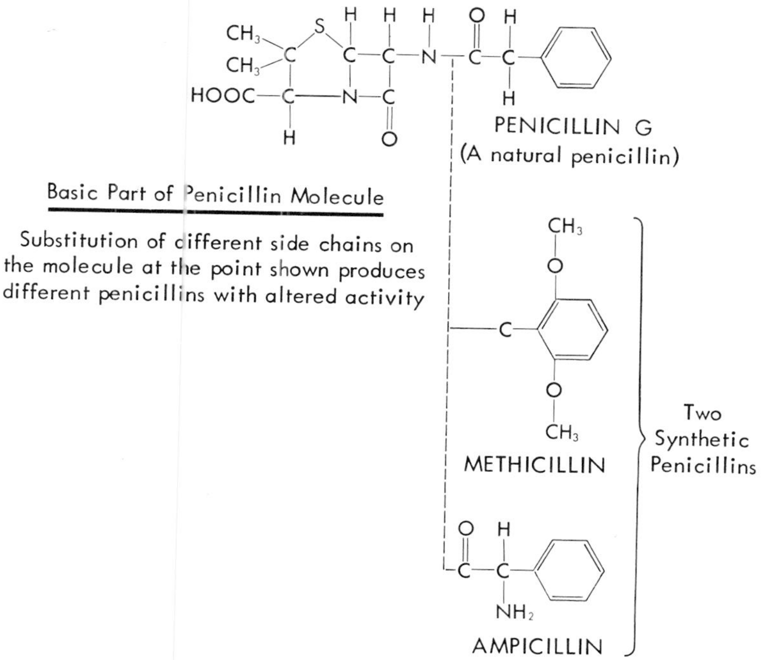

Basic Part of Penicillin Molecule

Substitution of different side chains on the molecule at the point shown produces different penicillins with altered activity

PENICILLIN G
(A natural penicillin)

METHICILLIN

AMPICILLIN

Two Synthetic Penicillins

Fig. 10–14.   Some derivatives of penicillin.

Table 10-4. Choice of Anti-infective Agents

Organism	Gram Reaction	Drug of First Choice	Drug of Second Choice	Disease
Actinomyces	+	Penicillin plus sulfonamides	Tetracyclines	Actinomycosis of skin and lungs
Aerobacter aerogenes	−	Kanamycin	Chloramphenicol	Urinary tract infections
Bacillus anthracis	+	Penicillin	Erythromycin	Anthrax
Bacteroides	−	Tetracyclines	Penicillin	Wound infections
Borrelia recurrentis	−	Tetracyclines	Penicillin	Relapsing fever
Brucella	−	Tetracyclines plus streptomycin	Streptomycin plus sulfonamides	Undulant fever
Clostridia	+	Penicillin	Tetracyclines, erythromycin, sulfonamides, chloramphenicol	Gas gangrene (*Cl. welchii*), tetanus (*Cl. tetani*)
Corynebacterium diphtheriae	+	Penicillin	Erythromycin, tetracyclines, chloramphenicol	Diphtheria
Diplococcus pneumoniae	+	Penicillin	Erythromycin, ampicillin	Pneumonia
Donovania granulomatis	−	Tetracyclines	Chloramphenicol, streptomycin	Granuloma inguinale
Erysipelothrix	+	Penicillin	Tetracyclines, erythromycin	Erysipeloid
Escherichia coli	−	Ampicillin	Tetracyclines, kanamycin, chloramphenicol	Infantile diarrhea; urinary tract infections
Hemophilus influenzae	−	Ampicillin	Chloramphenicol	Secondary pneumonia, meningitis
Hemophilus ducreyi	−			Chancroid
Klebsiella pneumoniae	−	Cephalothin	Ampicillin, tetracyclines plus streptomycin	Pneumonia
Leptospira icterohaemorrhagiae		Tetracyclines	Penicillin	Leptospirosis
(1) *Lymphogranuloma venereum*, (2) psittacosis, and (3) trachoma agents		Tetracyclines or sulfonamides	Erythromycin, chloramphenicol	1. Venereal disease 2. Pneumonia 3. Severe eye disease
Mycobacterium leprae	+	Sulphetrone or		Leprosy, Hansen's disease

Organism		Drug of first choice	Alternative drugs	Principal diseases
Mycoplasma (Eaton agent)		Tetracyclines	Erythromycin	Primary atypical pneumonia
Neisseria gonorrhoeae	−	Penicillin	Chloramphenicol, tetracyclines, erythromycin	Gonorrhea
N. meningitidis	−	Penicillin, ampicillin	Tetracyclines	Meningococcal meningitis
Pasteurella pestis }	−	Streptomycin plus tetracyclines	Chloramphenicol, tetracyclines plus sulfonamides	Bubonic plague, pneumonic plague
F. tularensis }	−			Tularemia
Proteus mirabilis	−	Penicillin, ampicillin	Kanamycin	Urinary tract infections
P. vulgaris	−	Kanamycin	Chloramphenicol	Urinary tract infections
Pseudomonas aeruginosa	−	Polymyxins	Tetracyclines, chloramphenicol	Wound and urinary tract infections, meningitis
Rickettsia		Chloramphenicol	Tetracyclines	Rickettsial fevers, typhus fevers
Salmonella	−	Chloramphenicol	Ampicillin	Enteric infections
S. typhosa	−	Chloramphenicol	Ampicillin	Typhoid fever
Shigella	−	Sulfonamides or tetracyclines	Chloramphenicol	Shigellosis
Spirillum minus	−	Penicillin	Tetracyclines	Rat bite fever
Staphylococcus	+	Penicillin, methicillin, Cloxacillin	Cephalothin, vancomycin, erythromycin	Furuncles, abscesses, bacteremia, pneumonia, meningitis, osteomyelitis
Streptococcus	+	Penicillin	Erythromycin	Streptococcal sore throat, scarlet fever, puerperal fever, erysipelas
Str. faecalis	+	Penicillin plus streptomycin or kanamycin	Ampicillin plus streptomycin	Subacute endocarditis
Treponema pallidum		Penicillin	Erythromycin, chloramphenicol, tetracyclines	Syphilis
T. pertenue		Penicillin		Yaws

Adapted from *Review of Medical Microbiology*, 8th ed., by Ernest Jawetz, Joseph L. Melnick, and Edward Adelberg. Lange Publications, Los Altos, Calif., 1968.

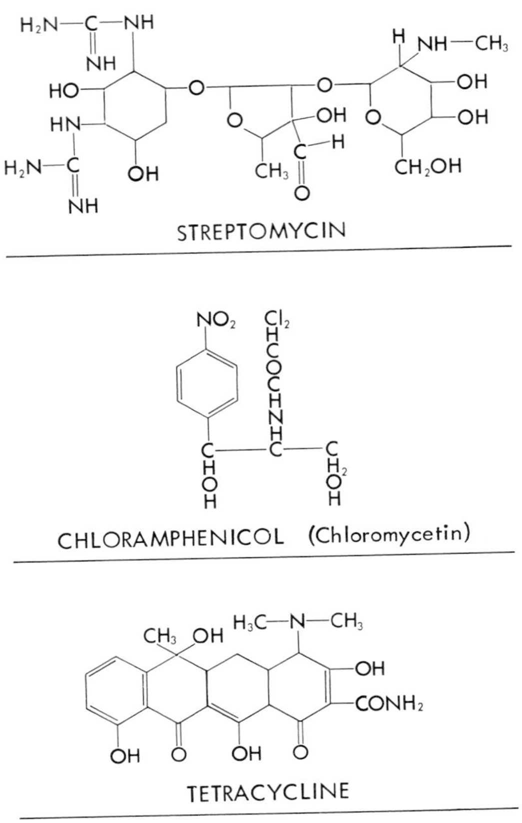

STREPTOMYCIN

CHLORAMPHENICOL   (Chloromycetin)

TETRACYCLINE

Fig. 10–15. Antibiotics produced by *Streptomyces* species.

little leeway. Different antimicrobial drugs may have characteristic toxicities for certain human tissues: the tetracyclines and other broad-spectrum antibiotics given orally may be irritating to the intestinal mucosa, though this may be partly due to their effect on normal intestinal bacteria; streptomycin can induce injury to the eighth cranial nerve resulting in partial or complete deafness; chloramphenicol in prolonged, high dosage may induce an anemia, reversible on drug withdrawal; polymyxin may produce temporary symptoms related to a central nervous system effect (drowsiness, euphoria, ataxia), or it may damage kidneys whose function is already impaired by infection; the sulfonamides may also

cause renal injury, because they are insoluble and tend to precipitate out when they are excreted through the kidney. For these reasons, antibiotic and other chemotherapeutic drugs should be issued only by a physician's order, prescribed with discriminating care, and taken only under his supervision.

Drug allergies, or *hypersensitivities*, may be frequent complications with antimicrobial compounds that have some antigenic properties. For example, the streptomycins, novobiocin, vancomycin, and penicillin not infrequently produce allergic skin rashes, in contrast to the possible side effects of nonantigenic drugs such as chloramphenicol and bacitracin which are toxic rather than allergenic. Allergic effects are the result of previous sensitization of the patient with the drug, the timing and severity of the reaction depending on the route of administration of a repeated dose, the extent of the hypersensitive mechanism, and the tissues involved by it (see Chap. 7, pp. 147 to 153). Penicillin exemplifies a drug with very low toxicity but a frightening allergenic potential for hypersensitized individuals. Reactions among the latter range from skin rashes (manifested as a phase of the serum-sickness type of immediate response) to anaphylaxis, which may be fatal. These hypersensitivities that occur among some individuals afford another important reason for caution in the use of antimicrobial therapy. The treatment of insignificant infections with antibiotics should be discouraged, particularly if the value of the drug's effect on the specific infectious agent being treated has not been established by laboratory procedures involving the identification of the organism, as a minimum requirement, and the demonstration of its susceptibility to the drug as a confirming test of relevance.

The development of microbial resistance to drugs presents another problem in chemotherapy. The genetic basis for the appearance of antibiotic-resistant mutants in susceptible bacterial populations was discussed previously. (See Chap. 3, pp. 52–53.) The continuous use of drugs, particularly in closed environments such as hospitals, tends to suppress susceptible microorganisms and encourage the survival of resistant strains, so that

the latter become prevalent. This situation is further encouraged by the close personal contacts constantly occurring between hospital patients and personnel who exchange their resistant strains directly or indirectly through the immediate environment. This is the reason for the increase and persistence of drug-resistant strains of staphylococci and many species of Gram-negative enteric bacilli indigenous to the human body. When bacterial strains of this kind cause serious infection, the problem of finding adequate means of chemotherapy is proportionately severe. It is sometimes possible to cure or suppress a drug-resistant infection by using high concentrations of an appropriate drug for long periods of time, *provided* the drug is not unduly toxic at the dosage level given. In some instances, however, bacterial susceptibility is not influenced by the concentration of antibiotic.

Combined therapy is sometimes useful in preventing the emergence of resistance in a bacterial strain. Two antibiotics in combination may be antagonistic to each other in their effects on a particular microorganism, or they may be unaffected by combination, so that the effect on the organism in question is either less than, or no greater than, that seen when each of the drugs is used alone. On the other hand, a combination of two antibiotics that act by different mechanisms on the causative organism of the infection to be treated, and that do not interfere with each other, may prevent or delay the appearance of resistant mutants by their *synergistic* action.

Changes in the normal flora of the body frequently occur as a result of antibiotic therapy. The interbalance maintained among the microorganisms of the skin and mucous membranes by their own competitive activities may be seriously disturbed if one or more species of drug-susceptible microorganisms of the normal flora are suppressed during the course of antibiotic treatment of an infection. Under these circumstances, drug-resistant organisms may multiply to an extent that becomes injurious, and a new and different infection may begin. These secondary, complicating infections of antibiotic treatment, or *superinfections* as they are also called, occur most frequently on the mucosal surfaces of the mouth

and throat, the intestinal tract, and the genitourinary system, but they may extend to systemic tissues as well. Strains of yeast (notably *Candida albicans*), staphylococci, and enteric bacteria are most usually involved and are particularly difficult to treat because of their drug resistance. Antimycotic drugs, such as mycostatin, are frequently administered together with the antibiotic of choice when the primary infection is treated, to prevent the overgrowth of yeast if the normal balance is upset during therapy.

The Role of the Microbiology Laboratory in Chemotherapy.   The development of new antibiotics is a major concern of many pharmaceutic and government laboratories. Soil samples from all over the world are analyzed for their content of fungi or other microorganisms that display an inhibitory effect on test organisms. When marked antibiotic effects are seen, the responsible organism is isolated, studied for its growth needs, cultured in larger quantities, and separated from its antimicrobial product by filtration. The filtrates are then purified by chemical methods and studied for their pharmacologic and toxic properties. The antibiotic activity of these preparations is studied for a wide range of microorganisms of medical significance, and the economics of preparing them on a mass scale are reviewed. If the results of these preliminary studies are promising, careful clinical studies are conducted on a strictly controlled basis to determine the therapeutic range of values of the new drug. It may be released to the market only if it meets many rigid standards set by the Food and Drug Commission, which also dictates conditions and controls for its continuing manufacture. Ongoing research in this field is concerned with improvements in the many facets of antibiotic screening and production, and particularly with methods for enhancing the activity and spectrum of antimicrobial drugs.

The diagnostic microbiology laboratory can be of very pertinent assistance to the clinician in selecting effective chemotherapeutic drugs for treatment of infectious disease. This begins with the isolation and identification of the significant organism, which is then tested in pure culture for its response to a number of antibiotics in varying

concentrations. If the results of treatment with a chosen drug are not satisfactory to the physician, the laboratory may test the original organism again by more exacting methods to find a more useful drug or a more effective concentration of the first one. It may also test fresh specimens from the patient to determine whether the infectious agent has become drug-resistant or whether a superinfection has arisen.

The routine method (see Chap. 4, p. 76) employed in most diagnostic laboratories for antibiotic susceptibility testing employs filter paper _disks_ that have been saturated with a selected concentration of antibiotic and dried. The surface of a suitable agar medium, contained in a Petri dish, is swabbed evenly with a suspension of the organism to be tested, so that the bacterial growth will occur in a confluent pattern over the entire plate. A series of six to eight disks, each containing a different antibiotic or a different concentration of the same one, is then placed on the seeded surface. Usually two or three plates are prepared for each organism, so that it can be tested with several antibiotics, each in a low and a high concentration. The disks are colored, shaped, or surface-marked in some distinctive way so that each drug and concentration can be readily identified. Following a suitable period of incubation under conditions appropriate to the organism, the plates are examined for evidence of susceptibility or resistance. Bactericidal or bacteriostatic drugs will inhibit the growth of the organism in an area surrounding the disk. The size of this area is proportionate to the diffusion of the antibiotic, in an effective concentration, into the adjacent medium. The visible evidence of inhibition is a clear zone of unchanged medium around the disk where the organism has failed to grow, this zone being an island in a sea of growth elsewhere on the plate (see Fig. 4–11, p. 78). Resistance to a drug is evident if growth extends to the disk or if a secondary film of growth or new colonies appear in an originally inhibited zone.

The tube dilution method measures the response of the test organism to increasing concentrations of an antibiotic with greater quantitative precision. The antibiotic is diluted serially in tubes of a liquid medium suitable for the growth of the

organism. The same amount of the organism (contained in a liquid suspension) is added to each tube in the series. Following suitable incubation, the tubes are read for evidence of growth, observed as turbidity of the medium. Clear tubes without growth are interpreted as containing inhibitory concentrations of antibiotics. The lowest concentration of antibiotic that completely inhibits growth is reported as the "minimum inhibitory concentration," or _MIC_ (see Fig. 10–16). The question of whether this or higher concentrations of the drug are bacteriostatic or bactericidal can be answered by removing the organism from the influence of the antibiotic in the tube and testing its ability to grow again. This is done by plating a measured loopful of the broth from clear tubes onto an agar medium and counting the colonies that grow from each loopful representing a particular tube. Tubes that yield

Fig. 10–16. An antibiotic assay using the tube dilution method. The same concentration of organisms is present in each tube, but the concentration of antibiotic is increased from tube to tube, beginning with the second tube from the left and reading from left to right. The first tube on the left contains no antibiotic and serves as a control that demonstrates the organisms to be in good condition and capable of rapid growth. Tubes 2 and 3 contain insufficient antibiotic to inhibit the organism, which has grown to the same extent as in the control. In the other tubes, however, the organism has been completely inhibited by the antibiotic concentrations used, and no visible growth has occurred. Tube 4 contains the least amount of antibiotic required to inhibit the organism, and this quantity is reported as the "minimum inhibitory concentration," or the "MIC."

no growth contain a bactericidal concentration of antibiotic: that is, the organism was destroyed. Tubes that yield moderate to large numbers of colonies contain doses of antibiotic that are merely bacteriostatic: that is, such doses inhibit growth while they are in contact with the organism but do not destroy its capacity to multiply if it escapes from the action of the drug. The clinical significance of this kind of laboratory reporting is that it indicates the levels of antibiotic concentrations that must be maintained in the patient's tissues to obtain a therapeutic response. This laboratory prediction is modified, of course, by the toxicity of the drug, the patient's total response to it, and the condition or protected location of the organism in the tissues.

The tube dilution method can also be adapted to test the patient's serum, or other body fluids, for their content of effective antibiotic during therapy. In this case, serum or fluid instead of antibiotic is serially diluted in tubes of broth medium. A standard inoculum of organism is added, and after incubation the tubes are read as described above. The highest dilution of serum that is effectively bacteriostatic or bactericidal is reported to the physician. This information permits him to judge whether he is maintaining effective levels of the antibiotic in the patient's blood by his choice of dosage or route of administration of the drug.

The Surgical Treatment of Infection. When an infectious process is well localized by the inflammatory response of tissues and encapsulated to some degree by fibrotic reaction as in abscess formation, the chemotherapeutic approach may not be helpful without the physical relief of surgery. This is because the cellular barriers thrown up against the causative microorganism may also preclude penetration of the area by an antibiotic in concentrations that are effectively bactericidal, or even bacteriostatic. Under these circumstances surgical excision of the lesion may be indicated, if it lies in an accessible region of the body and does not offer severe anatomic or functional problems to the surrounding tissues. Superficial abscesses occurring in the dermal layers are very simple to open and drain, but those that lie in

deep tissues and organs, such as the lung, liver, spleen, kidney, or brain, may offer many intricate difficulties to surgical removal. Factors determining the feasibility of surgery include the location of the lesion, the degree of encapsulation that appears to surround it, the nature of the invading organism, and the possibility or the established fact of its progression to other tissues. When these and other medical considerations permit, excision of the lesion may afford the most immediate solution to the problem, with antibiotics used as a "cover" to prevent new localizations of organisms scattered by surgical manipulation.

Immunotherapy of Infectious Disease. Prior to the advent of antibiotics, antisera were frequently used in the treatment of certain acute infections, notably pneumococcal pneumonia, the several bacterial meningitides, and diphtheria. During the last two decades, chemotherapeutic methods have superseded those of passive immunization, the former having all the advantages of speed, inclusive antimicrobial action, and economy. The available supply of effective antibiotics has reduced the morbidity and mortality rates attributed to acute bacterial infections to very low levels, while the incidence of such diseases is suppressed by techniques of active immunization on a large scale in many parts of the world (see Chaps. 7 and 11). Passive immunization in the therapy of active infectious disease is now largely limited to those few situations in which bacterial infection is accompanied by the production of highly injurious or lethal toxins. These include diphtheria and the clostridial diseases such as tetanus, gas gangrene, and botulism. Ingested toxin in botulism, or toxin produced by bacteria growing in the tissues in the other instances cited, is not affected by antibiotic drugs. In these situations specific antitoxin given promptly on diagnosis of developing infection or toxemia (see Chap. 7, pp. 145–46) prevents irreparable toxin damage to tissues. The concurrent administration of antibiotics inhibits the further growth — and toxin production — of the invading organisms of gas gangrene, tetanus, and diphtheria.

Passive immunization is not an appropriate therapeutic measure in chronic bacterial infec-

tions because the role of protective antibody is limited. Gamma globulin, as a source of passive antibody against some viruses, such as measles, mumps, or hepatitis, is more useful as a preventive agent than a therapeutic one. During the incubation period of these diseases the virus is not localized within cells and may be neutralized by antibody in the blood stream and tissue fluids. By the time the symptoms of active disease begin, however, the intracellular location of virus puts it out of reach of antibody, so that no therapeutic effect can be obtained.

Treatment of the Patient's Contacts: Prophylaxis

Chemoprophylaxis. In general, the use of antimicrobial drugs is not indicated as a means of preventing the spread of infection among the contacts of an active case. Such a procedure tends to encourage the emergence of resistance among microorganisms that are responsive to such drugs, and it has no effect at all on the viruses and other groups of organisms that are indifferent to drug action.

There are two notable exceptions to this general rule, however. The first is in the case of *Neisseria* infections, that is, gonococcal or meningococcal diseases. Gonococcal infection (gonorrhea) is venereal in its spread and highly communicable by this route. Meningococci are easily transmissible by droplet spread from the upper respiratory tract. Severe meningococcal disease (either meningitis or systemic infection) can reach epidemic proportions in susceptible populations. Because the consequences of these diseases are serious when unchecked, and because both of these species of *Neisseria* are readily susceptible to antimicrobial drugs, the chemoprophylaxis of the contacts of known infectious cases is an important means of control. Gonorrheal cases and their veneral contacts alike are treated with penicillin. Newborn babies are also susceptible contacts of mothers who may have gonorrheal infection. The prophylactic measure in this case is treatment of the eyes of babies at birth with silver nitrate solu-

tion to prevent conjunctival infection with *N. gonorrhoeae*. Meningococci are susceptible both to penicillin and to the sulfonamides. Penicillin is generally preferred for the therapy of active infection, while sulfadiazine is used in prophylaxis. There are several reasons for this: sulfadiazine is effective and inexpensive in an oral dose; it is simple to administer to large numbers of people if necessary; and it does not influence normal respiratory or intestinal flora, or encourage resistant strains, to the same extent as penicillin.

The *second* exception in chemoprophylaxis is in the use of drugs to suppress or prevent *malarial* infection. In this instance, the infectious source is not the case of human disease but a mosquito reservoir. In areas of the world where infective mosquito vectors abound, human exposure is frequent and sometimes unavoidable. A family of drugs related to or derived from quinine (chloroquine, amodiaquine, primaquine) is effective both in treating malaria and in preventing or aborting its development in the exposed individual.

Immunoprophylaxis. For many infectious diseases the most effective means of control is mass active immunization of the population. Even when this has been accomplished, however, sporadic cases of these diseases may occur from time to time (poliomyelitis, smallpox, diphtheria, pertussis) and require immediate consideration of the immunity of exposed contacts. Renewed active immunization with vaccines may be indicated to boost lagging immunity or to protect new susceptible members of the community. When exposure to tetanus infection threatens a nonimmune individual, passive immunization with antitoxin may be necessary to prevent disease, but active immunization with toxoid should then follow. (See Chap. 7, p. 146.)

The use of human gamma globulin as a source of antibodies is indicated following the exposure of susceptible individuals for whom the risk of certain diseases is great. This might be true if the disease is frequently accompanied by serious consequences (poliomyelitis, hepatitis, mumps in adults) and active immunity has waned, or if no active artificial immunization is available. The

prophylactic use of gamma globulin may also be advisable for individuals to whom any infectious disease might represent unusual risk, such as the very young, the very old, or others whose resistance is seriously compromised by medical or surgical problems.

Questions

1. Define sterilization, asepsis, disinfection, antisepsis, germicide, bactericide, bacteriostasis, antibiotic, sanitization.
2. Define contamination, infection, infectious disease, communicable disease, communicable period.
3. Describe the action of heat on microorganisms.
4. Briefly describe pasteurization.
5. Why is boiling water not a reliable sterilizing agent?
6. What is the temperature in the autoclave when a load is being sterilized? How is the temperature reached and maintained?
7. What factors are necessary to ensure sterilization of articles in an autoclave?
8. Give examples of dry heat.
9. What other methods are used to control microorganisms?
10. How do chemicals kill vegetative organisms?
11. What qualities should be sought when choosing a disinfectant?
12. List several chemical disinfectants.
13. List several barriers used to control direct transmission of infectious diseases in hospitals.
14. List several personnel techniques that aid in the control of infection.
15. What is the mode of action of antimicrobial drugs?
16. What are the problems in the use of chemotherapy?
17. What is the role of the diagnostic microbiology laboratory in chemotherapy?
18. How is immunotherapy used in the treatment of infectious diseases?

References

Pertinent References

Becton Dickinson Lectures on Sterilization, Seton Hall College of Medicine and Dentistry, N.J., 1957–1959.

Colbeck, J. C.: *Control of Infections in Hospitals.* Hospital Monograph Series #12 *American Hospital Association*, Chicago, 1962.

Control of Infectious Diseases in General Hospitals. American Public Health Association, New York, 1967.

Davis, Bernard D.: Principles of Sterilization, in Dubos, René J. (ed.): *Bacterial and Mycotic Infections of Man*, 3rd ed. J. B. Lippincott, Philadelphia, 1958.

Gordon, John (ed.): *Control of Communicable Disease in Man*, 10th ed. American Public Health Association, New York, 1965.

Harmer, Bertha, and Henderson, Virginia: *Textbook of the Principles and Practice of Nursing*, 5th ed. The Macmillan Co., New York, 1960.

Jawetz, Ernest, Melnick, J. L., and Adelberg, E. A.: *Review of Medical Microbiology*, 8th ed. Lange Medical Publications, Los Altos, Calif., 1968.

McCulloch, Ernest C.: *Disinfection and Sterilization.* Lea and Febiger, Philadelphia, 1945.

Perkins, John, Jr.: *Principles and Methods of Sterilization.* Charles C Thomas, Springfield, Ill., 1956.

Reddish, G. G.: *Antiseptics, Disinfectants, Fungicides and Chemical and Physical Sterilization*, 2nd ed. Lea & Febiger, Philadelphia, 1957.

Riley, Richard L.: *Airborne Infection, Transmission and Control*. The Macmillan Co., New York, 1962.

Sykes, G.: *Disinfection and Sterilization*. D. Van Nostrand Co., Inc., Princeton, N.J., 1958.

Walters, Carl: *The Antiseptic Treatment of Wounds*. The Macmillan Co., New York, 1948.

Periodicals

ANA Statement on the Responsibility of the Professional Nurse in the Prevention and Control of Infection, *Amer. J. Nurs.* **60**:657, May, 1960.

Au, William Y.: Broadspectrum Antibiotics, *Amer. J. Nurs.*, **64**:105, Oct., 1964.

Benson, Margaret E.: Handwashing, An Important Part of Medical Asepsis, *Amer. J. Nurs.*, **57**:1530, Sept., 1957.

Cavanaugh, Max: Housekeeping and the Operating Room, *Amer. J. Nurs.*, **60**:686, May, 1960.

Cohen, Lawrence, and Cluff, Leighton E.: The Sulfonamides, *Amer. J. Nurs.*, **61**:54, June, 1961.

Criteria for the Selection of Germicides, Committee on Antimicrobial Agents, *Amer. J. Public Health*, **51**:1054, July, 1961.

Cuyton, H. Gerald, Buchanan, Lee M., and Lense, Frederick T.: Evaluation of Respiratory Protection of Contagion Masks, *Applied Microbiol.*, **4**:141, 1956.

Dunbar, Edward S.: Control of Microorganisms on Blankets, *Hosp. Manage.*, **92**:44, Aug., 1961.

Editorial: Attacking Infections, *Amer. J. Nurs.*, **59**:1705, Dec., 1959.

Foster, Marion: A Positive Approach to Medical Asepsis, *Amer. J. Nurs.*, **62**:76, April, 1962.

Gendreau, P., Barbour, N., Baratta, R., Johnson, L., List M., and Lovenzen, S.: Questioning a Procedure, *Amer. J. Nurs.*, **63**:126, Oct., 1963.

Hall, James W.: Drug Therapy in Infectious Diseases, *Amer. J. Nurs.*, **61**:56, Feb., 1961.

Hall, Lawrence B., Snow, D. L., Skaliy, P., and Ettinger, H.: Environmental Health Needs for Hospitals and Medical Centers, *Amer. J. Public Health*, **51**:535, April, 1961.

Hamil, Evelyn R.: The Role of the Nurse in the Control of Staphylococcal Infections in Hospitals, *Calif. Health*, **17**:2, July 15, 1959.

Heavey, J. F., Martin, Edgar, and Schaeffer, Eimer C.: Effective Method for Controlling Contamination in Laundry Chutes, *Hosp. Top.*, **43**:39, Nov., 1965.

Hurst, Valerie, *et al.*: Hospital Laundry and Refuse Chutes as Sources of Staphylococcal Cross Infections, *J.A.M.A.*, **167**:1223, July, 1958.

Koren, H.: Responsibilities and Activities of a Practicing Hospital Sanitarian, *J. Environ. Health*, **28**:368, March–April, 1966.

Kundsin, R. B., and Walter, C. W.: In Use Testing of Bactericidal Agents, *Applied Microbiol.*, **9**:167, 1961.

Medical Department, Bristol Laboratories, New York: Staphcillin, *Amer. J. Nurs.*, **61**:58, 1961.

Nahmias, Andre J.: Infections Associated with Hospitals, *Nurs. Outlook*, **11**:450, June, 1963.

Perkins, J. J.: Destruction of Microbial Life, *Canad. Nurse*, **54**:229, March, 1958.

Price, P. B.: The Bacteriology of the Normal Skin, *J. Infect. Dis.* **63**:301, 1938.

Price, P. B.: Hand Scrubs and Skin Preparations, *Hosp. Top.*, **38**:61, 1960.

Riley, Richard: Protective Measures — Reasonable or Ritualistic, *Nurs. Outlook*, **7**:38, Jan., 1959.

Rockwell, Virginia T.: Surgical Hand Scrubbing, *Amer. J. Nurs.*, **63**:75, June, 1963.

Sister, Mary Florence: Nursing Administration's Role in the Problem of Hospital Infection, *Nurs. Outlook*, **7**:644, Nov., 1959.

Smednik, P., and Kurtagh, C.: Basic Principles of Isolation Technic Remain the Same, *Amer. J. Nurs.*, **56**:575, May, 1956.

Sommermeyer, Lucille, and Frobisher, Martin, Jr.: Laboratory Studies on Disinfection of Oral Thermometers, *Nurs. Res.*, **1**:32, Oct., 1952.

Sommermeyer, Lucille, and Frobisher, Martin, Jr.: Laboratory Studies on Disinfection of Rectal Thermometers, *Nurs. Res.*, **2**:85, Oct., 1953.

Spaulding, E. H.: Principles and Application of Chemical Disinfection, *AORN Journ.*, **1**:36, 1963.

Spaulding, E. H.: Chemical Disinfection in the Hospital, *J. Hosp. Res.*, **3**:7, Jan., 1965.

Spaulding, E. H., Emmons, E. K., and Guzara, M. L.: Ethylene Oxide Sterilization, *Amer. J. Nurs.*, **58**:1530, Nov., 1958.

Streeter, Shirley, Dunn, Helen, and Lepper, Mark: Hospital Infection — A Necessary Risk? *Amer. J. Nurs.*, **67**:526, March, 1967.

Thompson, LaVerne: Evaluating Disinfectants, *Amer. J. Nurs.*, **62**:82, Jan., 1962.

Tyler, Virginia: Gas Sterilization, *Amer. J. Nurs.*, **60**:1596, Nov., 1960.

Wilson, Marion E.; Frick, Hugh; and Bass, Phyllis: Betadine, pHisohex, and 3, 4′, 5-Tribromosalicylanilide as Surgeon's Skin Germicides, *Bact. Proc.*, Amer. Soc. Micro., 1965.

Pamphlets

Guide to Control of Infections in Hospitals. New York State Department of Health.

Curley, H. P.: *Preventive Procedures for Combating Cross Infections.* Research Department of the Hospital Bureau, Inc., New York, 1961.

A Guide to Chemical Disinfection and Sterilization for Hospitals and Related Care Facilities. Michigan Department of Health, May, 1963.

The Manual: Symposia on Professional Hospital Techniques and Procedures, **15**:1, The American Sterilizer Company, Erie, Pa., 1959.

Kelsey, J. C.: Sterilizing Methods in the Hospital, in *Institutionally Acquired Infections.* U.S.P.H.S., U. S. Department of HEW, Washington, D. C., 1963.

Safer Ways in Nursing To Protect Against Airborne Infections. National Tuberculosis Association, 1962.

Popular Literature

Atkinson, D. T.: Joseph Lister and Antiseptic Surgery, in *Magic, Myth and Medicine.* A Premier Book, New York, 1958.

Camac, C. N. B.: Antisepsis, in *Classics of Medicine and Surgery.* Dover Publications, Inc., New York, 1959.

Clendening, Logan: Aseptic Surgery, in *Behind the Doctor.* Garden City Publishing Co., Garden City, N. Y., 1933.

Clendening, Logan: Joseph Lister on the Antiseptic Principle of the Practice of Surgery, in *Source Book of Medical History.* Dover Publications, Inc., New York, 1960.

Haggard, Howard V.: A Gentleman with Clean Hands May Carry the Disease, in *Devils, Drugs and Doctors.* Blue Ribbons, New York, 1929.

Morris, Robert J.: *Fifty Years a Surgeon.* Dutton, New York, 1935.

Shippen, Katherine: Lister and His Antiseptic Method, in *Men of Medicine.* The Viking Press, New York, 1957.

Sigerist, Henry E.: Ignaz Phillip Semmelweis, in *The Great Doctors.* Doubleday Anchor Books, Garden City, N. Y., 1958.

Thorwald, Jurgen: *The Century of the Surgeon.* Pantheon Books, New York, 1956.

Walker, Kenneth: The Mastery of Wound Infections, in *The Story of Medicine.* Arrow Books, Limited, Essex, England, 1954.

Williams, Harley: The Beginnings and Growth of Modern Surgery, in *Masters of Medicine.* Pan Books, London, 1954.

Young, Agatha: The Control of Infection, in *The Men Who Made Surgery.* Hillman Books, Bartholomer House, Inc., New York, 1961.

11 Communicable Disease Control in the Community

Public Health Agencies and Services

The organization of federal, state, and city health departments that exists in the United States today had a slow and difficult history prior to the beginning of this century. Until that time, the structure, authority, and functional services of government-directed health agencies were often insecure, partly because medical authority was itself uncertain about the direction or value of methods to be applied on a public scale, and partly for lack of political or financial support. A new impetus was felt at the turn of the century, however. It was related, in large part, to the new light being shed from the laboratories of Pasteur in France, and of Koch in Germany, on the nature and transmission of infectious diseases. Young American medical graduates who traveled to Europe for their postgraduate training in the 1890's and 1900's came home with the news of some revolutionary answers to old problems of epidemics and their possible control. Since that time, governments around the world have recognized their increasing responsibilities in applying the controls demonstrated by medical research to be effective against many diseases and in offering many other supportive health services as well.

In the United States today, health facilities are offered by government at every level. Since 1953, most of the federal agencies involved in public health affairs have been coordinated within the

Department of Health, Education, and Welfare (DHEW), this organization having cabinet status. The United States Public Health Service, whose origins go back to the year 1798 when the Marine Hospital Service was founded for the medical care of American Navy men, now functions under DHEW administration. It conducts research in the field of preventive medicine, provides hospital facilities for servicemen, and gives financial as well as other practical assistance to state and local health departments.

The state health departments in the United States are autonomous in their authority over health regulations and services within their own geographic areas. Many cities also assume local municipal responsibility for health problems. The New York City Department of Health is one of the oldest of such organizations. It was established in 1866 and became the scene of action of some of the most vigorous and successful battles fought in the United States against such public health problems as diphtheria, smallpox, cholera, and venereal disease. It was the work of local community health departments in the cities and towns that first led to the development of public health services and administration in this country. The U.S.P.H.S. now functions as an advisory leader in this field, offering assistance to the states when emergencies or special problems arise or new programs are to be developed. For example, the current federal legislation that provides for the medical care of the aging (Medicare) requires that independent (privately-owned) clinical laboratories serving these patients must meet certain standards. The state health departments have the responsibility for assuring that these standards are met by independent laboratories within their jurisdiction. With the guidance and support of the U.S.P.H.S. the states are developing programs for the evaluation of the competency of clinical laboratories and for the improvement of standards, where this is indicated, in diagnostic microbiology, clinical chemistry, and the other laboratory sciences.

There are a number of health organizations that operate on an international level in the protection of the public health, the most important of these being the World Health Organiza-

tion, with headquarters in Switzerland. The services of the World Health Organization, supported by many of the nations of the world, include the distribution of technical information and assistance, the standardization of drugs, and the development of international regulations important to the control of epidemic diseases. In the many countries where they have worked, WHO experts have helped those governments to develop programs for the control or eradication of diseases such as malaria, yaws, and trachoma. In the past, the high incidence of debilitating infections has been an important factor in retarding human progress in many parts of the world. With the achievement of increasing control over the epidemic spread of severe infections, and over the endemic incidence of others, improved standards of public health have contributed greatly to the advancing development of the world's resources.

In the United States the development of preventive medicine and public health has been furthered also by the outstanding efforts of some privately endowed voluntary organizations, such as the Commonwealth, Ford, and Rockefeller Foundations. Through the provision of research facilities, money, and technical assistance, the great foundations have been influential in promoting medical progress in every part of the world. Other voluntary health agencies, large and small, have been an integral part of this advance. The American Red Cross, the Catholic Sisters of Charity, the National Tuberculosis Association, and the American Public Health Association are only a few examples of the many voluntary organizations that now function on a national scale but had their beginnings in local communities struggling with individual health problems. It was at this level also that public health nursing first emerged as a community service.

The first formal training course in nursing in this country was given at the New York Hospital in 1798, and the first visiting nurse service was provided a few years later, in 1813, in Charleston, South Carolina. An epidemic of yellow fever in that city spurred the Ladies' Benevolent Society to organize a nursing service for the home care of the sick. By 1862, the year Florence Night-

ingale had established a district nursing association in England, the Civil War in the United States had created an urgent need for the medical and nursing care of sick and wounded soldiers. The Women's Central Relief Association, later incorporated into the Sanitary Commission, was organized to provide nursing, and Miss Nightingale herself was an advisor to this group. The Catholic Sisters of Charity also gave invaluable service as volunteer nurses during that war, moving onto the battlefields in the wake of the fighting to find and minister to the wounded. The eventual establishment of public health nursing as a professional practice dates from the late 1800's in New York. The first strong foundations were established by the work of the New York City Mission in providing trained nurses to care for the sick in their own homes, the establishment of the Henry Street District Nursing Service by Lillian Wald and Mary Brewster (Miss Wald is considered the founder of public health nursing in this country), and the sponsorship of community nursing projects by the New York City Department of Health. Public health nursing as we know it today is an essential function of local, state, and federal health services, with an international role to play as well.

Medical research in public health problems continues to explore for better answers to well-known diseases and to find still more effective methods for their control. Governmental health agencies not only participate in this research, but are responsible for applying regulatory controls, as these are developed, and for monitoring their adequacy. Public controls of communicable disease are directed, in essence, toward the surveillance and protection of the two great sources of infection: environmental and living reservoirs.

Public Health Controls of Environmental Reservoirs of Infection

The major environmental reservoirs of infectious disease in the public domain are water supplies, sewage, and food, including milk. The sanitary standards and regulations that have been developed during this century for control of the purity of water and food resources have effectively curbed these sources of infection, however, and, as a result, the incidence and epidemic patterns of many communicable diseases, once so prevalent and devastating, have been significantly reduced.

Water and Sewage Sanitation

The principal water-borne diseases are typhoid fever and other salmonelloses, cholera, and bacillary and amebic dysentery. Viruses excreted in feces, notably the infectious hepatitis agent and the enteroviruses, including poliomyelitis, may also be spread through contaminated water, together with certain helminth ova. Water as a source of infection was discussed in Chapter 9 (pp. 180–81), where it was pointed out that fecal contamination of water supplies by man and animals constitutes the major infectious hazard and the main necessity for water purification.

In the days before the development of methods to safeguard public water supplies, epidemics of water-borne intestinal disease occurred frequently. Usually they were of short duration, beginning explosively among people sharing a contaminated water supply. Pathogenic organisms do not live long in water, or multiply there. Therefore, epidemics of water-borne infection are usually characterized by the rapid appearance of large numbers of cases (the number depending on the extent to which a water supply is shared) and an almost equally precipitous fall in incidence. On the other hand, the continuous, undetected contamination of water from infectious sewage was sometimes the cause of prolonged epidemics. An epidemic of cholera that occurred in a London parish in the year 1854 provides a dramatic example of water-borne infectious disease. During a ten-day period in the autumn of that year, more than 500 people fell ill of cholera and died of the disease. There was a great deal of cholera elsewhere in the city at that time, but these cases were concentrated in one neighborhood. As the epidemic continued, two men named John Snow and John York began a study of the

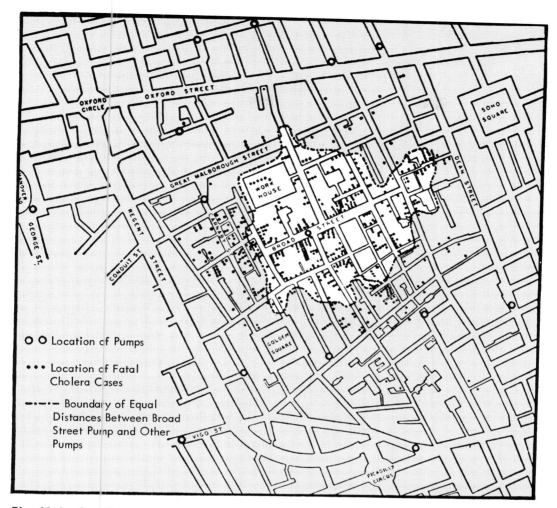

Fig. 11–1. Snow's Broad Street pump. This is one of the earliest examples of disease mapping. By marking on a map each new case of cholera, Dr. John Snow in 1854 was able to prove that the Broad Street pump was a central point in the London cholera epidemic. This map-making also established that cholera was a water-borne disease. (Reproduced from *Spectrum.* Courtesy of Chas. Pfizer & Co., Inc., Brooklyn, N.Y.)

area and were able to prove, by epidemiologic methods only (the bacteriologic nature of the disease was not understood at that time), that the outbreak stemmed from the water of a particular well, known as the Broad Street well. It was also discovered that sewage from the cesspool of a house on Broad Street was the source of pollution of the well, and that there had been a case of undiagnosed intestinal disorder in that house shortly before the cholera outbreak began. Snow

traced many of the cases to the use of water from the Broad Street well and also explained the failure of the disease to involve people who lived in the same neighborhood but did not drink from the polluted well (see Fig. 11–1).

The incidence of cholera, typhoid fever, and other intestinal infections rarely reaches epidemic proportions today in those countries or communities that have established firm sanitary standards for the protection of water and the

disposal of sewage. These diseases persist in endemic form, however, in many parts of the world. Asymptomatic carriers of intestinal pathogens persist in all populations and are a possible source of new epidemics at times when there is a break in sanitation methods or systems. Such breaks may be minor, involving one well or one city apartment house, but when major disasters disrupt the functions of an entire city or a large area, the danger of major epidemics becomes immediate. Storms and floods often pose this problem, as does the damage of war.

Sources of Public Water Supplies. Community water supplies are usually obtained today from surface water, dammed in reservoirs that collect it from brooks, streams, and rivers. These are fed by rainfall directly, or by the runoff of excess rain from the ground. Water runs over large areas to its accumulation point in reservoirs and is subject to pollution along much of its course, so that it must be purified before delivery to the community. Local governments are increasingly careful to restrict the industrial use or population of the territory involving their watersheds. However, neighboring communities frequently create problems for each other in the pollution of shared water supplies. An "upstream" town, for ex-

ample, may secure clean water from its river as it passes and use the same river, at a lower point, for sewage disposal. Other towns, located downstream from this point, are then subject to the hazards of water contamination. Chemical pollution of rivers by industrial wastes may similarly affect many communities sharing a common water supply. The need for firmer state and local government controls on the sources of water pollution is now being widely recognized.

Ground water accumulations from rain and snow can be tapped by well-digging for individual home use. The safety of well water depends on the degree of its protection from surface contamination or from the sewage disposal system employed. Wells must be deep enough to assure good filtration of water seeping from the surface. The location of outdoor latrines, septic tanks in which sewage is collected, or ducts that run sewage off to a distant collection point should be planned with regard to the protection of wells and their water sources from any possible contaminated drainage.

Water Purification. To prepare it for consumption, water is pumped from reservoirs or rivers into purification plants (see Fig. 11–2). It is first screened for large debris, such as leaves, twigs,

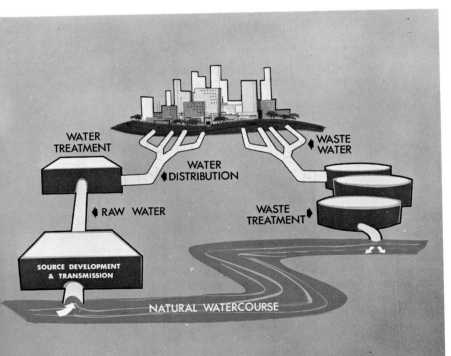

Fig. 11–2. The necessity for sewage treatment is illustrated above. With their growing need for more clean water, cities and towns are finding it necessary to use the water into which raw sewage and wastes have been drained. Waste water and sewage properly treated can be emptied into a natural watercourse without danger to the natural flora and fauna, and the clean water can be used for human consumption. (Courtesy of Communicable Disease Center, U.S. Public Health Service, Atlanta, Ga.)

or dead fish, then pumped into storage reservoirs where it is subjected to the following processes:

1. *Aeration* increases the oxygen content of the water and speeds the oxidative utilization of organic material by bacteria. It also displaces other dissolved gases that may contribute unpleasant odors and tastes to polluted water.

2. *Coagulation* of many soluble chemical contaminants is accomplished by adding compounds such as aluminum sulfate. Colloidal complexes are flocculated as a result and eventually settle out of solution.

3. *Sedimentation* of coagulated or insoluble materials removes the remaining coarse contamination.

4. *Filtration* removes the fine particles, including bacteria. Water seeping down through filter beds passes first through slow sand filters, closely packed, then through looser rapid sand filters into coarse gravel beds. Below the gravel, successive layers of pebbles, larger rocks, and tile continue the filtration, delivering relatively pure water into collecting tanks. The upper sand layers of a filtration system accomplish most of the purification. About 98 percent of the bacteria and most of the suspended solids are trapped there. Oxidative processes remove organic matter, and many bacteria are destroyed by the activities of protozoa. Approximately six million gallons of water are filtered per day through an acre of sand bed, a rather slow process. The filters must be cleaned from time to time by scraping off the top inch of sand and replacing it.

5. *Chlorination* is the final step in water purification. The bactericidal action of chlorine (see Chap. 10, p. 230), in a concentration of 2 ppm, assures the disinfection of filtered water and its safety along the piped route to the consumer. Chlorinated lime or sodium hypochlorite may be used as sources of chlorine, but the gaseous form is least expensive and therefore the usual choice.

Sewage Disposal.   Raw sewage, with its teeming content of potentially pathogenic intestinal microorganisms, is the most dangerous threat to water supplies. It may have disastrous consequences for the fish and wildlife dependent on natural water supplies, as well as for human beings.

Sewage disposal on a community scale involves its collection into a treatment center. Bulky trash is screened out, and the sewage is then stirred and agitated to permit aeration. Large particles are broken up and bacterial decomposition of organic material is promoted. As solid matter settles out (see Fig. 11–3), the "activated" sludge that collects contains harmless products of decomposition, which may be reduced in volume, dried, and sold for fertilizer. The liquid component drawn off from the sludge is treated with chlorine and can be pumped off into a river or the ocean as harmless effluent (see Fig. 11–2).

In a septic tank, sewage is decomposed largely by the anaerobic activities of bacteria, while chemical methods are used for the small collecting tanks in airplanes and trains.

Bacteriologic Standards for Water.   Health department laboratories maintain a constant surveillance of community water supplies, testing them for chemical as well as bacteriologic purity. The "potable" character of water (that is, its suitability for drinking) is judged by its freedom from odor, taste, color, and harmful chemicals. It should be relatively free of nitrate and other decomposition products of organic matter.

The bacteriologic examination of water includes the enumeration of bacterial colonies growing out on agar plates, in a standard plate count (see Chap. 4, p. 74, for quantitative culture techniques), and tests for the presence of coliform bacteria. The latter provide an index of fecal pollution. Potable water should have a low total count of bacteria (0 to 10 per milliliter of water) and be free of coliform organisms.

A *presumptive test* for coliforms is made by inoculating a test sample of water into tubes of lactose broth containing an inverted tube to trap gas. After 24 hours of incubation, the tubes are examined for the presence of gas as an indication of lactose fermentation. Coliform bacteria ferment lactose rapidly, in the concentration of lactose provided in this test, while other organisms that utilize this sugar require 48 hours or

Fig. 11–3. A primary settling tank for sewage. Before being routed into this tank, sewage is first screened to remove large objects such as sticks. It is then passed through a chamber where smaller particles, such as grit, gravel, or sand, are removed. In the settling tank, organic matter slowly settles out. This sediment is taken off as sludge, treated in holding tanks, and finally dried for use as a fertilizer. The dried material is bacteriologically safe, but it is not recommended for cultivating plant foods that will later be eaten without cooking. (Reproduced from *Health News*, Oct., 1960. Courtesy of the New York State Department of Health, Albany, N.Y.)

more to do so. The presence of gas is merely presumptive of coliforms, however, and the test must be confirmed.

The *confirmed test* is done by plating an inoculum from gas-positive lactose tubes onto eosin-methylene-blue (EMB) agar, or Endo's medium. These agar media also contain lactose, together with dyes that inhibit nonenteric organisms and that change color to indicate when colonies growing on the surface have utilized the lactose. Coliform colonies have a characteristic deep purple color on EMB, and their surfaces take on a metallic luster. The appearance of such colonies is a confirmation of the presumptive test.

The *completed test* requires final identification of the characteristic colonies on the agar plates. Isolated colonies are selected for inoculation into other media that identify the biochemical properties of the coliform group. Stained smears of

the organisms complete the proof, if these reveal Gram-negative, nonsporing bacilli.

When tests for coliform bacteria reveal unacceptable levels of contamination, appropriate checks are made for the possible sources of pollution or for failures in the purification system, with corrective action as indicated.

Public Health Standards. Governmental responsibility for safe standards of community sanitation lies with the public health services at local, state, and national levels. Their authority is provided by laws or statutes specifying the protection of water supplies, the adequate disposal of sewage, housing sanitation, the inspection of food, and other matters to be discussed. Federal legislation controls the interstate waterways and their use, with primary responsibility left to the individual states concerned. In 1948 the Water Pollution

Control Act established the federal authority, and in 1961 and 1966 amendments to this act designated the Department of Health, Education, and Welfare as the major water resource agency of the government. The amendments extended federal authority to all navigable waters, including coastal waters; authorized federal enforcement procedures in cases of intrastate pollution; and permitted federal action against municipalities in violation of the law.

Drinking water standards were first defined by the U.S. Public Health Service, and these recommendations are used by many states as a guide for maintaining potable water supplies and adequate sewage disposal.*

Food Sanitation

Food may serve as either a primary or a secondary reservoir of infectious disease. Infected fish and meat, eggs, or milk from infected animals may be primary sources of many different diseases, while the secondary infection of food by handlers or as a result of unsanitary conditions during its preparation may be responsible for bacterial food poisoning. (See pp. 176–80.) Controls on the sanitation and safety of foods are based on the sources and nature of specific kinds of infection; in some cases they must also be selected with regard for the properties of particular foods. The basic requirements of food sanitation are discussed below; they are followed by some examples of specific control measures.

Basic Control Measures. Strict cleanliness is important in all the stages of food preparation, but this must be coupled with adequate refrigeration to prevent spoilage bacteria or pathogens from growing. This is particularly important for foods that have been partially or fully cooked, and for frozen foods. Cooked foods provide better culture media for bacteria than many uncooked foods. Frozen foods are not sterilized by

the freezing process, and when they thaw the rupture of cells and fibers may make them more subject to bacterial growth. The proper cooking of food is necessary to ensure its safety from infectious organisms (or their toxins) that it may contain, while refrigeration provides protection against the growth of contaminants as well.

Public health regulations require the inspection of food processing plants, abattoirs, restaurants, dairies, and all other establishments involved in food preparation for the adequacy of basic sanitation, including refrigeration methods. In addition, health service agencies at all levels conduct a continuous campaign designed to educate the general public, as well as those responsible for food production, in the sanitary principles involved. The importance of adequate cooking receives further emphasis in the control of microorganisms or toxins that cannot be easily detected, or otherwise controlled, before they reach the consumer.

Meat Inspection. Government controls on the safety of meat include its inspection for bacterial spoilage or other deterioration before it is distributed for retail sale (see Fig. 11–4). More importantly, certain primary infections of meat can be detected by visual inspection for tissue lesions. This is particularly true for encysted tapeworm larvae in beef or pork muscle, which can be seen, and sometimes felt, as small, white, hard nodules in the tissue. Unfortunately, fish tapeworms are not so easily detected, nor are the larval encystments of the roundworm *Trichinella*, which may infest pigs. Trichinosis remains prevalent in the United States and other countries for three essential reasons: pigs are fed on garbage containing uncooked meat that perpetuates the cycle of the parasite; pork infestation cannot be detected by inspection; and people accidentally or deliberately eat rare meat or pork products that have not been fully cured or cooked. The only effective methods to control trichinosis lie in the hands of those who raise and feed pigs and those who prepare pork for the table.

---

* *Standard Methods for the Examination of Water and Waste Water*, 12th ed. American Public Health Association, New York, 1965.

Fig. 11–4. The internal temperature of hams is being checked by a government meat inspector. Pork products customarily eaten with little or no cooking require especially careful inspection. (Courtesy of U.S. Department of Agriculture, Washington, D.C.)

Some of the bacterial infections of animals that provide important food supplies can be controlled at their source. Tuberculosis in cattle, for example, is controlled by frequent tuberculin testing of herds and the destruction of positive reactors. Brucellosis can be prevented by the early vaccination of young calves or heifers. On the other hand, *Salmonella* infections in animals are virtually impossible to eliminate because this family of organisms is distributed ubiquitously among all animals, wild or domestic. Animals that are sick with infectious disease can be eliminated, but those with asymptomatic infections may be a source of human disease through their meat or even through products such as eggs and milk. The only effective controls that can be applied involve the destruction of the organisms by adequate cooking or, in the case of milk, by the heat of pasteurization.

The Control of Milk-Borne Diseases. The important diseases that are transmissible by milk are tuberculosis, brucellosis, and a number of streptococcal infections, as discussed in Chapter 9 (pp. 179–80). In the United States, restraints have been maintained on these infections by three essential measures: (1) by controlling the

source of disease in cattle through inspection, elimination of infected animals, and vaccination when appropriate, (2) by controlling the handler as a secondary source of infection, and (3) by controlling the milk by pasteurization and sanitary bottling methods. The first two of these are discussed in the last section of this chapter dealing with the various control measures applicable to living reservoirs of infection.

Pasteurization is a final and very effective precautionary measure for the assurance that milk supplies are safe for public consumption. It is a heat-disinfection procedure that destroys the vegetative forms of all pathogenic microorganisms, with the possible exception of hepatitis virus. It does not destroy spores, but these have no importance in milk, nor do they cause disease in man via the alimentary route. In pasteurization, consideration must be given to those properties of milk that are adversely affected by heat. Milk proteins begin to coagulate at temperatures between 80° and 100° C, its sugars are hydrolyzed, and its taste is correspondingly affected. At temperatures below 60° C, either disinfection is not accomplished at all or the time required is too long to be practical. For these reasons, the two methods most com-

monly used for the pasteurization of milk are: (1) heating to 62.9° C (145° F) for 30 minutes, or (2) heating to 71.6° C (161° F) for a minimum of 15 seconds. The latter method is successful only if the numbers of organisms present in the milk have been held to a minimum, prior to pasteurization, by scrupulous sanitary methods throughout the dairy. These include the scrub-grooming of cows, the sterilization of all equipment, and the delivery of milk by sterile milking machines into a closed presterilized system. The final step in the pasteurization process is rapid cooling, to prevent deterioration of milk components.

The bottling of milk in presterilized glass, plastic, or waxed cardboard containers keeps its content of nonpathogenic organisms at a low level, but this result can be maintained only if milk is kept under constant refrigeration thereafter. The species of *Lactobacillus* and *Streptococcus* that form the normal flora of milk are reduced in number but not eliminated by pasteurization. Their subsequent multiplication results in the formation of lactic acid from the degradation of milk sugars, and this is responsible for milk souring. Pasteurization and subsequent refrigeration together delay this process.

Bacteriologic standards for milk are determined by laboratory methods that (1) count the total numbers of organisms surviving per milliliter of milk, (2) test for the presence of coliform bacteria or for specific pathogens if these are suspected, and (3) determine the adequacy of pasteurization by testing for the heat-sensitive enzyme phosphatase, normally present in raw milk (its absence from pasteurized milk indicates that heating conditions were sufficient for enzyme inactivation). Milk is rated as *grade A* if the total bacterial count does not exceed 30,000 per milliliter after pasteurization. *Grade B* milk has counts in the 30,000 to 50,000 per milliliter range, while *grade C* has high counts, in excess of 50,000, and should not be used except in cooking. *Certified milk* is produced under conditions of extremely careful controls over the health of cattle and handlers and on the sanitary conditions of milk collection. It is the purest milk that can be produced, with counts not exceeding 10,000 per milliliter. Public health regulations permit the sale of unpasteurized certified milk in many areas, but in general only pasteurized milk may be marketed for public consumption. It should be noted, also, that the degree of bacteriologic purity obtainable for water cannot be reached for milk, even under the best circumstances.

Public Health Controls of the Living Reservoirs of Infection

The cardinal principles involved in the prevention and control of infectious disease have been discussed in several contexts throughout previous sections of this text. They are summarized briefly here, together with a description of their broad applications to the protection of the public health.

Probably the most important factor in the prevention of infectious disease in man, and also in animals, is the development of *active immunity*. This may occur naturally following a bout with a pathogenic microorganism, but the protective effect may vary in extent and duration. *Artificial active immunization* through the administration of available vaccines is, therefore, a tool of primary value in the prevention of many human and animal infections, or at least of their more dangerous consequences.

Equally important, though somewhat less effective on a public scale, have been the development and dissemination of knowledge concerning the nature and sources of infection and the means of its transmission. This had led to the establishment of reliable methods (when properly applied) for the protection of the public health (1) under ordinary circumstances (sanitation; control of asymptomatic carriers in sensitive areas such as food-handling; and controls on the other living reservoirs of potential importance, that is, animals and arthropods), and (2) under the abnormal circumstances created by the presence in the community of overt infectious disease (isolation of the sick, prophylaxis for the exposed susceptibles, and epidemiologic controls on the sources of the disease).

The Prevention and Control of Human Infectious Disease

Artificial Active Immunization. The use of vaccines for the specific protection of human beings against disease dates back to the year 1796 when Dr. Edward Jenner first experimented, in England, with the idea that people could be protected from the effects of a serious disease by injection with material derived from others suffering from a related but less severe infection. The world scoffed, but when the idea worked, the first milestone in the effective control of smallpox was noted. This disease had been a terrible epidemic scourge of mankind for centuries: transmitted readily by person-to-person contact, it had decimated military and civilian populations alike, lost and won wars, and sometimes threatened the survival of afflicted communities. (In Jenner's day, about 30 percent of children born in England died of smallpox before reaching maturity, and on the American continent many Indian populations were virtually wiped out by the inroads of this disease introduced by European settlers.)

Jenner's success with the use of fluid collected from the less dangerous lesions of cowpox as a preventive agent for smallpox eventually led to a study of the basic principle involved and to a more controlled application of the principle in the prevention of this and many other infectious diseases (see Chap. 7). Today the threat of smallpox in epidemic proportions is controlled by the continuous and repeated use of vaccine to maintain a protective level of immunity in most of the world's populations. The virus remains endemic in its exclusively human reservoir, but the continuing availability of effective vaccine offered on a mass scale by public health services has controlled its epidemic appearance in most areas of the world. In the same way, control has been achieved also for such diseases as tetanus and diphtheria toxemias, yellow fever, pertussis, typhus and typhoid fevers, and, more recently, poliomyelitis. It should be noted that, in each of these instances, the *endemicity* of infection has not been eliminated, for the human population is large and influenced by many varying conditions, but the *epidemic* dimensions of these

diseases are no longer so frightening. The maintenance of immunity by vaccines applied on a large scale, as a general principle, or on a selective scale in special circumstances of exposure has made this possible.

Many research efforts continue in the field of vaccine development, both for the improvement of antigenicity in vaccines currently used and for the evolution of methods to produce new ones. A number of viral disease agents continue to be a challenge, either because they have not been successfully cultivated outside of the human body (e.g., infectious hepatitis) or because virus grown in substrates suitable for vaccine production does not possess a useful degree of antigenicity (e.g., trachoma). In recent years, influenza vaccines have been widely used, and mumps vaccines are also now available, but in both these instances the protection provided by immunization is short-lived. The prevalence and variety of influenza viruses in the population and the frequent emergence of antigenic variants raise problems in the continuous production of new influenza vaccines that are effective, at best, for a few months to a year only. In the case of mumps vaccine, immunity does not persist for more than two years, so that its use is limited to the protection of adults for whom mumps is a damaging disease. The durable immunity that follows mumps infection in childhood is more protective, and still preferable to vaccination in this instance. On the other hand, the measles vaccines that have been developed in the past decade promise to bring this disease under control at last. These vaccines have been tried under controlled conditions for many millions of children around the world and have thus far been demonstrated to induce an apparently solid immunity.

As vaccines become available, the remaining question of importance to immunization programs is, "Who should be immunized and when?" The most general answer to this is that everyone who is susceptible, and who is likely to be exposed, should be protected against diseases that pose a threat to individual or public health.

Immunization in childhood is indicated against those infectious agents that have a wide distribution and are readily transmissible. Current

immunization programs for children include routine protection against smallpox, diphtheria, pertussis, tetanus, and poliomyelitis. Measles vaccine will probably also be added to this list on a broader basis in the near future. Immunization schedules are based on the capacity of individual vaccines to induce a solid immunity after one or more injections. Combined vaccines containing several different organisms or antigens simplify the procedure, but the length of the series of injections required then depends on the antigenicity of each of the individual components. It is important to remember, also, that artificial immunization does not confer lifelong protection, and that booster doses are necessary to maintain the effect, the interval depending, again, on the characteristics of each vaccine preparation currently available.

Travelers may be exposed to diseases not known or frequently encountered in their own regions, or to which they are not immune for other reasons (e.g., neglect of vaccination). Not only is their own health threatened in this event, but the public health may be compromised by a transmissible infection spread by a traveler along his entire route. In this age of rapid and frequent travel by many people of the world, the necessity for maintaining controls on the international transmission routes of infectious disease is greater than ever before. The public health services of each country work to protect their own people, and through the international cooperation of governments supporting the World Health Organization this protection extends across national borders. The International Sanitary Regulations of the WHO have standardized the requirements for international travel with respect to the infectious problems indigenous to each country, so that travelers can be informed of the immunizations required or recommended for entry into various countries, or for re-entry into their own.

Smallpox vaccination is required for entry into most countries. Evidence of successful vaccination within three years must be presented at the time of arrival. The United States requires a current certificate of vaccination for all persons entering from other countries, including Americans returning from travel. The exceptions to this rule

include travelers from Canada, Bermuda, the Bahamas, and a few other countries where smallpox is well controlled and is not endemic.

Yellow fever and cholera immunizations are also frequently required by many countries, including our own, for travelers coming from or passing through areas in which these diseases are present. Yellow fever remains endemic in parts of Central and South America and in Africa. Persons arriving from yellow-fever-infected countries into an area where mosquito vectors may be receptive to the virus, and transmit it, must present evidence of yellow fever vaccination received within six years. Without a valid certificate, such persons are quarantined for six to nine days and examined for symptoms of developing infection. If the traveler in this situation is vaccinated against yellow fever at the time of his arrival, or shortly before, a 10-to-12-day waiting period is required before the certificate of immunization is considered valid.

Cholera is endemic in many countries of the Near and Far East, including Vietnam. Immunization against this disease is not durable, so that travelers coming from infected areas into countries where it is not prevalent, such as the United States, must have evidence of vaccination within six months.

Other immunizations that are not necessarily required for travel are nonetheless strongly recommended by the U.S. Public Health Service. These include typhoid fever, poliomyelitis, and tetanus vaccination under all circumstances of foreign travel; typhus immunization for persons entering areas where epidemic louse-borne or murine typhus remains endemic; and diphtheria antitoxin for all nonimmune children under the age of 15. Plague immunization is recommended if the country to be visited has recently experienced the disease, or if the traveler anticipates exposure to it in an endemic region. Table 11–1 summarizes the immunization requirements for foreign travel.

Military personnel are immunized routinely against many of the diseases cited above, notably smallpox, diphtheria, tetanus, and typhoid fever. Poliomyelitis and influenza vaccines are also given when indicated. When personnel are assigned to regions of the world outside of the

Table 11-1. Immunization for Foreign Travel*

Disease	Required	Recommended	Comments
Smallpox	On return to U.S. a valid smallpox vaccination certificate is required (except from Canada, Bermuda, and Bahamas)		Smallpox vaccination certificate is valid for 3 years, from 8 days after date of successful primary vaccination or date of revaccination
Yellow fever	If traveling through or coming from a country infected with yellow fever (especially much of Africa, parts of South and Central America)		One yellow fever vaccine inoculation is required; the certificate is valid from 6–10 days following inoculation for 6 years
Cholera	If traveling through or coming from an area where the disease has occurred recently		Two injections of vaccine at 7–10-day intervals; cholera vaccination certificate is valid for six months beginning 6 days after first injection
Typhoid and paratyphoid fever		For personal and public health protection when traveling in a foreign country	Three injections of typhoid vaccine at 7–28-day intervals; annual booster is necessary while in infected area
Tetanus		For the traveler's protection in the event he is involved in an accident	Two to three doses of vaccine at intervals of 3–6 weeks, depending on vaccine used; booster is given annually or at time of accident
Plague		Indicated if entering a country where plague is endemic	Start immunization two weeks before travel date; a booster is given at 4–6-month intervals if remaining in endemic area
Epidemic typhus fever		Indicated for foreign travel to endemic areas	Two injections of vaccine, at 7–10-day intervals for louse-borne typhus; booster is given annually if remaining in infected area
Poliomyelitis		Usually given when traveling to infected area with poor sanitation	Series of four injections and a booster if entering areas where sanitation is poor
Diphtheria		Indicated for children and young adults	Schick test will determine immunity of previously inoculated persons

* Data from Publication No. 384, U.S.P.H.S. 1961. The information for each vaccination certificate required for the trip must be completed and signed by the vaccinating physician. Smallpox and cholera vaccination certificates must have official stamps approved by the health administration of the country in which the vaccination was performed.

United States, new immunizations are scheduled according to the geographic need. Military and other persons currently involved in the Vietnam conflict, for example, must be continuously protected against cholera. Yellow fever is not endemic in that country, but it is considered a "receptive" area with regard to its mosquito vectors, so that immunization is an effective safeguard against establishment of the disease in possible vectors. Malaria, amebiasis, and numerous helminthic diseases are serious problems in Vietnam, but immunization against these infections is not possible, their control unfortunately depending on less specific and often less effective methods.

The great epidemic diseases historically associated with war — smallpox, viral hepatitis, plague, typhus, diphtheria — have been brought under control by the development of vaccines and immunization programs, so that armies no longer must fight these microbial enemies. Also, wounded soldiers are far less subject to the risks of threatening wound infections. Tetanus is under immunologic control, while other complications, such as clostridial gas gangrene and staphylococcal and streptococcal infections can be successfully and promptly controlled by modern surgical and chemotherapeutic methods.

Medical personnel in hospitals and clinics are also important candidates for controlled immunization programs. Physicians and nurses, bacteriologists and other laboratory personnel, aides, orderlies, and all others who come into close and frequent contact with patients, should be fully immunized against those diseases for which effective vaccines are available and which they may encounter in their work. This immunity should be carefully maintained, furthermore, by a regular schedule of booster doses. The basic program should include smallpox, diphtheria, pertussis, tetanus, and poliomyelitis vaccines, with others as indicated by the regional and seasonal needs. When the special risk of tuberculosis is incurred through patient contacts, or laboratory work, BCG vaccine is recommended for personnel negative to the tuberculin skin test (see Chap. 14).

Protection of the Normal Environment. Even under ordinary circumstances, unthreatened to any serious extent by active infectious disease, maintaining safety requires constant vigilance and — as we have seen — the continuous application of sanitary principles to many human activities. In addition to the many public and personal controls that are essential to the hygiene of the environment, surveillance and control of the living reservoirs of infection are necessary to the prevention of disease. The principles of control of animal infections and of the arthropods involved in the transfer of infection to man and animals will be discussed later in this chapter. It must be emphasized here, however, that man himself is a dangerous reservoir of infection, and never more so than when he goes unrecognized. The normal appearance of a healthy carrier of pathogenic organisms, or of a person in the asymptomatic period when he is incubating an infectious disease, challenges epidemiologic detection.

The disease being incubated declares itself soon enough, and until it does there is little that can be done, on a practical scale, to recognize it. Under limited circumstances, as in closed populations (in barracks, schools, prisons, or even immigration offices), the suspicion of infection may be confirmed by bacteriologic and immunologic methods. Diphtheria bacilli or meningococci, for example, may be recognized in throat smears and cultures, or enteric pathogens in stool specimens; but in the absence of symptoms of active infection, such findings do not distinguish immune or resistant carriers from susceptible individuals who are incubating a disease. In the case of diphtheria, skin tests for toxin immunity are significant when correlated with the presence of the bacillus in the throat. Throat-positive individuals who display a negative (immune) reaction to the Schick test are identified as carriers, while those with positive skin reactions should be treated promptly with a suitable antibiotic, or antitoxin, or both. In many other infections, however, measurements of immunity may be quite inconclusive, and the interpretation of positive cultures must await further observation of the patient. When serious

risk of individual or epidemic disease is involved, prophylactic treatment by immunologic or pharmaceutic methods is usually instituted. When detection methods are not practical, the early recognition of developing symptoms provides the best hope for the prompt application of effective and appropriate controls for the patient and his contacts.

When the *carrier* of a specific infection has been identified as such, he may be placed under suitable control. When his carrier state represents a threat to others, he may be treated with antimicrobial drugs in an effort to eliminate the infection, or he may be removed from areas and activities in which transmission of the microorganism is most likely. Carriers of the typhoid bacillus or pathogenic strains of *Staphylococcus*, for example, should not be permitted to prepare food for others or to come in close contact with medical or surgical patients. It is sometimes very difficult to eliminate such infections by chemotherapy and the carrier state remains a difficult problem in many instances. In the typhoid carrier, the organism may be sequestered in deep tissues, such as the kidney or gallbladder, and it may continue to appear in urine or feces. Drug treatment may not succeed in such cases, and while surgical removal of the gallbladder may effect a cure if that organ is the sole site of colonization, the carrier state may persist in some individuals for long periods. Diphtheria carriers are treated by the administration of both penicillin and antitoxin, but here too, permanent cure is not always achieved. Mass prophylactic immunization of children against diphtheria, however, has apparently reduced the carrier rate and has also decreased the significance of carriers by creating an immune population. *Staphylococcus* carriers perhaps represent the most difficult problem of all, particularly when they are found among hospital personnel. Staphylococcal cross-infections acquired by hospital patients can be troublesome and serious, particularly in nurseries and other critical patient areas. The strains are difficult, if not impossible, to eliminate from some carriers, although a patient and systematic attack from several directions may succeed. A combination of bactericidal antibiotic therapy,

maintained at an active level for a sufficient period of time, the administration of staphylococcal toxoid, and the consistent use of disinfectant soaps for skin care may sometimes succeed. The discouraging feature of the staphylococcal carrier state, however, is that the normal flora of the skin and mucous membranes frequently includes antibiotic-resistant strains whose persistence is favored by the use of antimicrobial drugs. Their use is generally avoided, therefore, except in situations of urgency involving, for example, the need for the hospital services of skilled or key personnel who may be persistent carriers of pathogenic staphylococci. On the other hand, the strategic job placement of hospital personnel carriers with more general skills, and their careful instruction in appropriate controls of personal hygiene, can provide a reasonable solution to the double problem of patient protection and personnel employment.

Food-handlers are epidemiologically very important in the control of several important infectious diseases, as we have seen. Health department sanitary codes generally have some very specific requirements regarding the pre-employment examination of food-handlers and their frequent surveillance. Routine pre-employment tests include a complete physical examination for evidence of communicable disease; a chest x-ray to rule out tuberculosis; serologic tests for syphilis; and a stool examination and culture to screen for the typhoid bacillus or any other *Salmonella* species, *Shigella* bacilli, pathogenic amoebae, or helminth ova or larvae. These examinations must be repeated at regular intervals after employment.

The control of food-borne diseases depends in large measure on adequate supervision of food-handlers and their methods. Any symptoms of illness should be reported and treated promptly, with temporary removal from the job if indicated. Sanitary toilet and washbasin facilities must be provided for kitchen personnel, with continuing education and emphasis on the necessity for careful hand-washing. Other matters of personal hygiene should also be stressed, such as the cleanliness of hair, skin, and clothing; short, clean fingernails; and handkerchief protection of

coughs and sneezes. Cuts and breaks in the skin of the hands should be covered with waterproof dressings when food is being handled, and the hands, arms, and face should be examined frequently for the appearance of infected pimples, boils, rashes, or other infectious lesions.

The registration of typhoid carriers is still required by health departments, although this problem has decreased with the declining incidence of endemic typhoid fever in the United States. The typhoid carrier, when detected, is specifically prohibited from participation in food-handling, and also from the care of children or of the sick. Every medical effort is made to clear the carrier of his infection, but until satisfactory results of treatment can be demonstrated, he is kept under surveillance with respect to his possible threat to the public health.

Communicable Disease Control. Definitions of the terms "communicable disease," "isolation," "quarantine," and "communicable period" were stated on pages 206 and 207, Chapter 10. A brief study of these definitions provides in essence a review of our current knowledge of the principles operating in the transfer of infection.

Communicable diseases are not always directly transmissible between hosts of the same species, as we know. Their control depends, therefore, on knowledge of their sources and routes of transfer. Because we possess much more specific information on these matters today than was available one hundred years ago when the infectious nature of many diseases was first being discovered, the rules of control read very differently nowadays. Isolation and quarantine were once words that involved entire communities in the dreaded procedures of social imprisonment. Alarming notices were tacked on the doors of the quarantined; the distress of physical segregation was added to the suffering of illness and death; the stench of fumigation and strong chemicals blended with the odors of sick and unsanitary cities — but the results were effective when methods happened to match the requirements of the situation, despite ignorance of the latter. Today, isolation and quarantine are methods quietly applied in selective situations,

primarily to prevent epidemics rather than to cope with them after the fact.

Isolation of the patient sick with a communicable disease remains an important controlling factor in some instances. The control of epidemic smallpox depends on it, for example, at least until the immunity of the patient's susceptible contacts can be reinforced by booster immunizations or the communicable period of his disease has been successfully weathered (about two or three weeks). Isolation is a necessity, also, in the case of infectious hepatitis, primarily because it is not yet possible to provide artificial immunization against this disease, which is apparently communicable by two easy routes: respiratory and intestinal. On the other hand, we have learned that isolation has little apparent effect in controlling a number of other infections, such as poliomyelitis and the viral pneumonias. The requirement of isolation is left for the most part, today, to the independent judgment of physicians or of hospital infection control committees, to be applied or modified to suit the demands of a local situation. The advice of official health services is always available in these matters, however.

Quarantine is still applied to the control of susceptible individuals exposed to certain communicable diseases, on the grounds that infection may be spread among other nonimmune persons, or to animal and insect hosts, during the incubation period. The necessity for quarantine as a tool in disease control has diminished today, however, because of the effective mass use of available vaccines and a corresponding reduction in the number of persons remaining susceptible to the diseases controlled by this method. More adequate controls on animal diseases and their human contacts also have changed the situation, as have systematic attacks on the arthropod vectors of some infectious diseases. Nonetheless, gaps in our understanding and approach are still apparent, and quarantine remains a useful method of assuring that infectious disease will not be spread during the symptomatically unrecognizable period of incubation. It is applied selectively: to travelers who are careless of the risk to themselves and others when they fail to

obtain appropriate artificial immunization in advance of possible exposure, or who remain uninformed on this subject; to schoolchildren and others (such as military personnel) who are members of closed groups composed of large numbers of susceptibles; and, in a reverse manner, to the protection of critically susceptible patients in hospitals. In the latter situation, physical boundaries are established to avoid any infection of vulnerable patients from human or environmental sources.

In the United States the Public Health Service is responsible for the control of communicable diseases that might be disseminated through international trade and travel. This agency maintains quarantine stations at all ports, sea and air, where foreign commerce enters the country. All ships and planes, American or foreign, arriving from ports in other countries, are required to obtain health clearance from these quarantine stations. U.S. health officials board each vessel, inspect passengers and crew for any obvious signs of communicable disease, and provide clearance or impose quarantine as indicated. Radio contacts with ships or planes entering debarkation ports usually provide advance warning of overt illness aboard. These precautions are designed to prevent the importation of such diseases as smallpox, cholera, yellow fever, plague, typhus, or anthrax. Vessels arriving from countries where such diseases are prevalent or endemic are fumigated after passengers and crew have disembarked. They are also treated with insecticides to kill any insect vectors surviving the voyage. (Such a procedure might have prevented some of the devastating epidemics of yellow fever experienced by our eastern port cities during the early part of the last century when shipping from the West Indies and South American first became intensely profitable.)

When necessary, quarantine is imposed on individuals without valid certificates of vaccination who have been exposed to the communicable diseases of other countries. Passengers who arrive obviously ill with symptoms suggesting any of the diseases mentioned above are quarantined in hospitals where they can be promptly treated. Quarantine restrictions are strictly enforced, under penalty of fine, and can be lifted only by the responsible health agency.

Case finding and reporting within the community are other important aspects of the preventive epidemiologic work of health departments. All local and state health boards require that physicians, hospitals, and similar institutions report certain diseases of a communicable nature. Some endemic diseases, such as measles and chickenpox, are characterized by seasonal increases and cyclic epidemics every three to four years. Health agencies want to be forewarned of these rising incidence rates. Other diseases are reported so that the source of infection can be traced, with a view to preventing further transmission. Most such reports can be submitted by mail, but in the case of acute diseases accompanied by the threat of epidemic, the local health department should be immediately notified by telephone. Immediate reports should be made when cases of smallpox, yellow fever, cholera, plague, rabies, anthrax, poliomyelitis, or psittacosis are suspected.

Health departments also require that new cases of tuberculosis or venereal disease be reported. In view of the ease of transmission of such infections, it is important that all contacts of new cases be investigated to ensure early diagnosis and treatment of developing disease. Public health nurses often play an important part in case finding and in encouraging exposed, susceptible people to seek medical advice or treatment.

Methods of prophylaxis for susceptible persons exposed to communicable diseases are discussed in Chapter 10 (pp. 256–57). Chemoprophylactic and immunologic measures may both be useful on a large scale in the prevention of epidemics. Venereal disease is commonly approached, for example, by the prophylactic expedient of administering penicillin to probable contacts (*before* the fact). Mass immunization procedures with vaccines are sometimes appropriate when diseases such as smallpox enter a community unrecognized and involve large numbers of contacts. On the other hand, passive immunization on a large scale with gamma globulin, as previously applied in epidemics of poliomyelitis, for example, is seldom necessary or appropriate

today. This is because large segments of the population have a natural or artificial active immunity to the diseases of epidemic significance. It is important to re-emphasize, however, that with the wane of certain pathogenic microorganisms from an immunized population, this natural stimulus to continuous antibody production declines, so that it becomes correspondingly more important to maintain active immunity by artificial means. Community immunization programs must recognize the necessity for continuing campaigns to hold a basic level of protective immunity with booster dose schedules for the useful vaccines.

The Prevention and Control of Infectious Disease in Animals

The principles involved in the control of infectious disease are the same in their application to animals as to man. The basic premise in either case is that the best way to control disease is to prevent it, using three major approaches: immunization whenever possible, sanitary protection of the environment, and protection of the healthy from exposure to the sick (isolation of communicable infection, quarantine and prophylaxis of those exposed, control of the sources of the disease).

Control of the Diseases of Domestic Animals. In some instances, successful control of domestic animal infection is achieved by methods that cannot be used for humans. The "isolation of infection," for example, sometimes means the destruction of infected, sick, or dying animals and the use of vigorous methods for the disinfection of carcasses. Quarantine may be applied to an entire herd of animals, without selecting those actually infected. Prophylactic antibiotics are used primarily to prevent the *chance* of infection in normal animals or fowl, as well as to protect exposed individuals (cf., Chap. 10, p. 256). Controlling the sources of animal diseases means not only the elimination of infected or sick members of a herd or flock, but control of the insect vectors that perpetuate many of these infections

and also the protection of animals from infectious human beings. The chain of transmission of many infections (see especially those of Group 4, Chap. 9, pp. 183–84) links man and animals by their direct contacts, and later through the human consumption of animal products, notably milk, eggs, and meat.

Immunologic methods applied to animals include active and passive immunizations and the use of skin testing to detect infection or measure immunity. The sanitation and disinfection of animal quarters, and of equipment used for the preparation of animal food products, are often of critical importance in preventing infection and in controlling its spread.

The important zoonoses of domestic animals that are readily transmissible to man, for whom they have serious consequences, are tuberculosis, brucellosis, anthrax, taeniasis, trichinosis, and echinococcosis. The three bacterial diseases mentioned have been more successfully controlled at their animal source than have the helminthic infestations.

Tuberculosis in cattle is controlled by a rigorous routine of tuberculin testing and the destruction of positive skin reactors. Further control of the transmission of bovine tuberculosis to man has been achieved by the routine pasteurization of milk.

Brucellosis is a disease of cattle, goats, and pigs. The infection is transmitted to man most frequently through raw milk and milk products and by contact with infected animals or their tissues. This disease is an occupational hazard to those who work with animals or meats (farmers, butchers, veterinarians) but it can also involve the milk-drinking public. Control has been achieved for the latter group by milk pasteurization. Methods to control the animal reservoir include the elimination of animals with infection demonstrated by serologic tests, immunization of young animals, and improved environmental sanitation.

Anthrax is a disease of cattle, sheep, horses, and goats, transmissible to man by contact or by the air-borne route. The infectious bacterial agent is an aerobic, sporeforming bacillus. When the vegetative bacilli are exposed to air, in animal

excreta or in carcasses, they rapidly form spores that are capable of survival for many years and may be widely disseminated in soil or dust. Inhalation of such dust from the contaminated wool, hair, or hides of once-infected animals is one of the most frequent avenues of human anthrax infection. Control of the disease can be achieved by mass immunization of animals with anthrax vaccine, isolation of sick animals, and proper handling and disposal of infectious carcasses to prevent contamination of the soil.

Taeniasis, or intestinal tapeworm infestation, is acquired by man through ingestion of beef or pork tissues containing encysted larval forms. The adult forms of these tapeworms live in man's intestinal tract, producing ova that are shed in feces. The domestic animal host becomes infected from grazing or rooting on ground polluted with human feces containing the ova, but for the animal the infestation is systemic rather than intestinal. Control of this type of disease depends on recognizing infected animal meat by careful inspection for encysted larvae and breaking the chain of transmission from man to animals. The sanitary disposal of feces and sewage and the protection of animal feeding grounds would eliminate these infections when combined with fully adequate methods for the inspection and cooking of meats. (See Fig. 9–14.)

Trichinosis is maintained by man, hogs, and rodents as the principal alternate hosts. The infestation is systemic in each host, involving the encystment of larvae in striated muscle. The cysts are not visible on inspection of pork, so that control depends on the thorough cooking or "curing" of all pork products. The protection of hogs from the sources of their infection is also essential to control. This includes the elimination of raw garbage feeding (containing infectious scraps of pork) and the extermination of rats and mice on the premises. It should be pointed out here that some wild animals (bears, foxes, opossums, raccoons) are also hosts to this parasite. Game hunters and others who eat such meat also run the risk of acquiring trichinosis unless adequate cooking is assured. (See Fig. 9–12.)

Echinococcosis is prevalent in some parts of the world in sheep, cattle, and pig reservoirs of the systemic larval infection. Dogs and wild carnivores maintain the cycle of the parasite in nature, by eating infected flesh from which the adult worm develops in an intestinal infestation. Eggs from this source are shed in the feces of dogs and may be ingested by man as well as by grazing animals. Control of the human disease centers largely on preventing dogs from playing their role in transmission. This includes strict personal hygiene on the part of persons who associate with dogs, particularly in endemic areas; deworming of dogs; adequate disposal of discarded flesh of infected, slaughtered animals so that dogs cannot find access to this source; and public education concerning the nature and transmission of this disease. (See Fig. 9–15.)

The immunization of dogs is an essential control on a number of the infectious diseases that may afflict them, such as distemper, canine hepatitis, leptospirosis, and rabies. Of these, the latter is also extremely dangerous to man. The natural reservoir of the rabies virus is in a number of wild animal species (foxes, wolves, raccoons, skunks, and bats, to mention a few) and in dogs. Transmission among animals or to man is usually accomplished by the bite of a rabid animal. Rabies control depends on the elimination of its source in sick animals and on the protection of healthy dogs by immunization with rabies vaccine. The immunization of human beings is not recommended unless there is evidence of exposure to rabies.

When the suspicion of rabies exists, biting dogs must be quarantined for a week to ten days and observed for symptoms of disease (see Figs. 11–5 and 11–6). They must be destroyed if rabies is proven, and efforts must be made to find other animals possibly exposed. These also must be quarantined (for three months) and vaccinated, or, if necessary, destroyed. Stray dogs should be eliminated, and others should be immunized, with booster doses at regular intervals (every one to three years, depending on the vaccine). Domestic dogs should not be permitted to run freely, particularly in areas with endemic foci of rabies among wild animals.

Rabies control in wild animals is under the supervision of federal and state fish and wildlife

Fig. 11–5. A public health agency compound for quarantined dogs.

agencies. Hunting, trapping, and baiting methods are used to find and dispose of sick animals and to bring epidemics under control.

Rodent Control.   Rats and mice are reservoirs for a number of infectious diseases that affect man. Chief among these are bubonic plague and murine typhus, both of which are transmitted by fleas to rodents or to man. The public health control of plague and other diseases associated with rodents includes a continuing program for the extermination of rats by poisoning techniques and by rat-proofing of buildings. Rat-infested ships arriving in port are fumigated with hydrocyanic gas, while their docking lines are shielded to prevent the escape of rats by this route.

Shellfish Control.   Shellfish harvested from sewage-polluted waters may be infectious reservoirs of enteric diseases, notably typhoid fever and other salmonelloses, and infectious hepatitis. Sanitary regulations for the shellfish industry are

Fig. 11–6. Dogs in quarantine and under observation for rabies.

provided and enforced by local and state health departments, with the cooperation of the U.S. Public Health Service.

The Control of Arthropod Vectors of Infectious Disease

Diseases that are transmitted solely by arthropod vectors may be controlled to the extent that it is possible to eliminate the insect reservoir or prevent its human contacts. The principal members of this group of diseases are yellow fever, epidemic typhus, and malaria. (See Group 3, Chap. 9, p. 183.) Since man and the insect host are the only reservoirs for these diseases, significant control can be achieved by insect eradication programs, coupled with immunization or chemoprophylaxis as indicated.

On the other hand, diseases transmitted by arthropods from several animal reservoirs are much more difficult to control. Complete eradication of the vector would be required to eliminate these diseases, because there is no other practical way to protect man against contact with the many species of wild or domestic animals involved in the maintenance of these infections. The widely based arthropod-borne infections include virus encephalitis, many of the rickettsial diseases, leishmaniasis and trypanosomiasis (both protozoan), filariasis (the tissue roundworm), and bubonic plague. Man is not a part of the reservoir in the first two examples, which are maintained in a number of animal hosts, as are the other diseases mentioned. Arthropod control and the protection of human beings from insect contacts are important, but other means of prevention must also be found.

Those diseases in which insects serve only as mechanical vectors do not depend on this means of transmission alone. Flies and other nonparasitic insects are often incriminated in the transmission of such diseases as poliomyelitis, salmonellosis, and other bacterial infections, but these diseases may be transmitted by many other routes as well. Insect control in this case, therefore, would not lead to the elimination of these diseases, although it may help to reduce their incidence.

Control of Insect Breeding.   The most effective methods of eradicating insect species are those that prevent breeding, the techniques depending on the insect. Mosquitoes are among the most important vectors of infectious diseases and the most usual targets of insect eradication programs. They breed in stagnant water: in swamps, still pools, unused rain barrels, or any forgotten vessel that collects and holds water for long periods. Mosquitoes can be eradicated or well controlled only if all these areas are found and drained or treated. Oily films spread on the surface of water prevent larvae from getting oxygen, or insecticides may be used, but draining and filling are most effective.

The sanitary disposal of garbage and sewage and the protection of manure or compost remove some of the breeding places of flies. These and other insects, such as lice, bedbugs, and mites, that breed in and around human dwellings are best controlled by strict sanitation and effective personal hygiene, reinforced by the use of chemical insecticides.

The Use of Insecticides.   A number of chemical compounds kill insects on contact. These are used in sprays directed at insects but are not effective in large-scale control unless they knock out significant numbers. Residual insecticides are more effective in eradication because they can be applied to many surfaces where insects light or crawl. Insecticidal activity is maintained on these surfaces for many weeks or months. DDT is an insecticide of the residual type commonly used in mosquito control. It is also effective in killing lice. It can be used as a dust for clothing and skin, one of the methods effective in the control of the louse vector of epidemic typhus, or as a spray for the inner and outer walls of houses where mosquitoes rest. In the control of malaria and other mosquito-borne diseases, entire communities are usually included in spraying programs (see Fig. 11–7). Other insecticides of this type include chlordane and dieldrin. All these compounds are hydrocarbons to which insects may develop resistance. When this happens, other types of chemicals, such as the organophosphates (malathion), may be used as residual insecticides.

A number of useful insect repellents have been

Fig. 11–7. Mosquitoes usually rest on inside walls after taking a blood meal. In malaria eradication campaigns, the interior as well as the exterior walls of houses are sprayed with a residual insecticide that remains active on these surfaces for several months. The control of mosquitoes helps to break the life cycle of the malaria parasite and to prevent further transmission of this disease. (WHO photo by Philip Boucas.)

developed in recent years. These do not kill insects but they keep them away from skin or clothing for some hours. Repellents sprayed on bedding and window curtains are useful in this way. Citronella is a well-known example of a repellent, but newer compounds such as dimethyl phthalate are much more effective. Materials of this type have an important use in areas where insect-borne infections are endemic. Armies engaged in jungle-fighting, for example, find them helpful, together with the application of residual insecticides to living quarters when this is feasible.

Protection of Human Beings from Insects. Control of insect-borne diseases for which man is a reservoir includes the careful screening of known infectious cases from the pertinent vector. All possible precautions must be taken during the infective period of yellow fever or malaria to screen patients from mosquitoes, for example. In the case of epidemic typhus, patients must be deloused and prevented from acquiring further infestation from others.

The prevention of arthropod-borne infection depends on adequate protection of human beings from the vectors involved. The screening of sleeping and living quarters against mosquitoes and the use of insecticide sprays in these areas at night are important methods in some instances. Personal hygiene and the cleanliness of clothing or bedding are effective in the control of lice and

other ectoparasites. Protective clothing is indicated when exposure to insects such as ticks or mites is anticipated, and frequent careful examination of the body should be made follow-

ing such exposure. Above all, knowledge of the important vectors of infectious diseases should be sought by all who find themselves newly exposed to the risk of infection.

Questions

1. What are the major environmental reservoirs of infectious disease in the public domain?
2. Briefly describe water purification methods.
3. Describe the tests for the bacteriologic examination of water.
4. List public health methods used to control disease and reservoirs of infection.

References

Pertinent References

Anderson, Gaylord W., Arnstein, Margaret G., and Lester, Mary: *Communicable Disease Control*, 4th ed. The Macmillan Co., New York, 1962.

Faust, Ernest Carroll, and Russell, Paul Farr: *Craig and Faust's Clinical Parasitology*, 7th ed. Lea & Febiger, Philadelphia, 1964.

Goerke-Stebbins: *Mustard's Introduction to Public Health*, 5th ed. The Macmillan Co., New York, 1968.

Gordon, John (ed.): *Control of Communicable Diseases in Man*, 10th ed. American Public Health Association, New York, 1965.

Imhoff, Karl, and Fair, Gordon Maskew: *Sewage Treatment*. John Wiley and Sons, Inc., New York, 1940.

Smillie, Wilson G.: *Public Health, Its Promise for the Future*. The Macmillan Co. New York, 1955.

Standard Methods for the Examination of Water and Wastewater, American Public Health Association, New York, 1965.

Pamphlets

Immunization Information for International Travel. U.S. Dept. HEW, Washington, D.C., Public Health Service Publication No. 384, 1961.

Pictorial Keys to Some Arthropods and Mammals of Public Health Importance. U.S. Dept. HEW, Public Health Service, Communicable Disease Center, Atlanta, Ga., 1964.

Pratt, Harry D., Littig, K. S., and Marshall, C. W.: *Introduction to Arthropods of Public Health Importance*. U.S. Dept. HEW, Washington, D.C., Public Health Service. Publication No. 772, 1960.

Pratt, Harry D., and Littig, Kent S.: *Insecticides for the Control of Insects of Public Health Importance*. U.S. Dept. HEW, Public Health Service Publication No. 772, Part II, 1962.

Periodicals

Barnett, S. A.: Rats, *Sci. Amer.*, **216**:78, Jan., 1967.

Buchbinder, Leon: Current Status of Food Poisoning Control, *Public Health Rep.*, **76**:515, June, 1961.

Febles, Francisco, Jr.: Schistosomiasis, A World Health Problem, *Amer. J. Nurs.*, **64**:118, Feb., 1964.

Galton, Margaret M., Steele, James H.: Laboratory and Epidemiological Aspects of Food-borne Diseases, *J. Milk & Food Tech.*, **24**:104, 1961.

Haberer, John C.: Sewage and Waste Disposal, *Health News*, **37**:14, Sept., 1960.

Heubner, Robert J.: The Growing Importance of Virology in Public Health, *Health News*, **37**: 5, Sept., 1960.

Olmstead, Roger O.: A Cleaner City Through Teamwork, *The American City*, Sept., 1961.

Roueché, Berton: In the Bughouse, Annals of Medicine, *The New Yorker*, Nov. 27, 1965.

Shepard, Charles C.: Leprosy: A World Health Problem, *Amer. J. Nurs.* **63**: 112, March, 1963.

The World Health Organization's Program to Rid the World of Malaria, *Amer. J. Nurs.*, **59**:1402, Oct., 1959.

Popular Literature

Clendening, Logan: Epidemic Diseases by Sydenham, in *Source Book of Medical History*. Dover Publications, Inc., New York, 1960.

Haggard, Howard V.: Civilization and Medicine, in *Devils, Drugs and Doctors*. Blue Ribbons, New York, 1929.

Roueché, Berton: Back to Venice, in *A Man Named Hoffman*. Little Brown and Co., Boston, 1965.

Shippen, Katherine: Can We Eradicate T.B.? in *Men of Medicine*. The Viking Press, New York, 1957.

Sigerist, Henry E. Disease and Social Life, in *Civilization and Disease*. Cornell University Press, Ithaca, N.Y., 1943.

Styler, Herman: *Plague Fighters*. Chilton Co. Philadelphia and New York, 1960.

Walker, Kenneth: Public Health, in *The Story of Medicine*. Arrow Books, Limited, Essex, England, 1954.

Current Legislation

Public Law 89-234, Oct. 2, 1965. Amendment to the Federal Water Pollution Control Act, 1965.

Public Law 89-753, Nov. 3, 1966. Clean Water Restoration Act, 1966.

Part Two The Microbial Diseases and Their Epidemiology

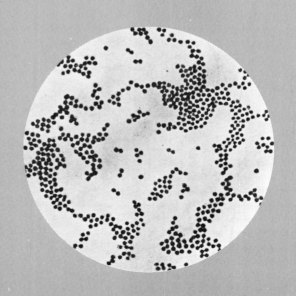

12 Introduction to the Microbial Diseases of Man: The Infectious Agents

The preceding sections of this text have dealt with basic concepts concerning the nature of microbial diseases. The respective contributions of pathogenic microorganisms and the human host to the pathogenesis of infectious disease have been discussed, and the epidemiologic principles involved in the treatment, control, and prevention of injurious infection have been reviewed.

In Part Two the specific infectious diseases of importance to man are presented in a manner designed to emphasize the application of epidemiologic principles to their management when they are encountered in nursing practice. Each disease is discussed briefly with respect to its outstanding clinical features, available methods for laboratory confirmation of the diagnosis, and the most important aspects of its epidemiology as these relate to control measures that can and should be practiced by the nurse as well as by other members of the medical group concerned with the patient's care. The sequence of approach taken in this text is based on practical considerations and it attempts to parallel the series of problems the nurse must face when she is confronted with a case of infectious disease. She must learn to recognize its clinical appearance and to understand what is happening within the body in various stages of the infection; she should know whether or not the laboratory can assist in the diagnosis and, if so, what specimens are of value and how or when they should be collected. Most

important, she must be prepared to take immediate, appropriate steps to control the infection if this is necessary or indicated by the circumstances. Some infectious diseases are easily spread by several routes of transmission and entry; others are self-limited but nonetheless capable of wide dissemination among the patient's contacts; some are particularly restricted by the developmental and physiologic requirements of the infectious microorganism as well as by the opportunities it may have for entry to or exit from the human body; and still others may be acquired by some fortuitous means but are not transmissible under ordinary circumstances. Measures for controlling the further spread of infection must be pertinent to the demands of each specific situation, and they must be based not only on some knowledge of the infectious microorganism and its paths of transferral, but also on the probability of exposure of susceptible human hosts. Diseases encountered in the private home, or in rural situations, sometimes have a very different epidemiologic potential from those occurring in crowded urban districts or in hospitals.

With these considerations in mind, the discussions of specific infectious diseases have been grouped primarily on the basis of the most common route of entry to the human host available to the microbial agent in each case. They are arranged in four sections (IV through VII) dealing, respectively, with entry through the respiratory tract, the gastrointestinal route, the intact skin and mucosal surfaces, and parenteral routes. Repeated emphasis is placed on the fact that the site of entry of an infecting organism does not always constitute the focus of developing infection, nor is it necessarily associated with the route of exit and transmission that may subsequently be available to the microorganism in question. In the case of diseases for which the entry site is not certain, or for which alternate routes commonly exist, descriptive discussion is placed in a section and chapter emphasizing the most probable or usual route, or that which may involve the greatest public health problem. Appropriate cross references are provided to draw attention to alternate possibilities.

Within each section or chapter, secondary groupings of diseases are made according to the nature of their causative agents (*viz.*, bacteria, rickettsiae, viruses, and others) or their portal of exit from the human body and subsequent transmission routes. The implications of these epidemiologic patterns are summarized in a chapter introducing each section. Student and graduate nurses alike are referred to these chapters (13, 18, 22, and 26), which also provide general recommendations for the nursing control of infectious diseases acquired through recognized entry portals. Within the ensuing discussions of individual disease entities, specific control measures are emphasized, as determined by the nature of each infection and the possibilities for its spread. Details of some accepted technical methods for disinfection, sterilization, and other procedures useful in infection control can be found in Appendixes V, VI, and VII, together with summary tables indicating the type of laboratory procedures that are available and valuable in confirming or establishing the diagnosis of the important infectious diseases (Appendixes I to IV, inclusive).

The Infectious Agents

The causative agents of microbial diseases fall into five major groups: the fungi, bacteria, rickettsiae, viruses, and animal parasites. The characteristics of these organisms and their general classifications were described in Chapter 2 and should be reviewed by the student before beginning the study of the clinical diseases they may induce. To assist in that review, and to provide a convenient point of reference for the nurse familiarizing herself with the microorganisms associated with infectious disease, the following pages of this chapter summarize the important features of each group and show the classifying relationships of the important pathogenic species. Figure 12–1 diagrammatically illustrates the size of an average bacterium (*Serratia marcescens*) as compared with red blood cells and with rickettsiae and viruses.

	Diameter or Width x Length in mμ	
Red Blood Cells	7500	Ten Times the Diameter of Larger Circle Below
Serratia marcescens	750	
Rickettsia	475	
Vaccinia	210 x 260	
Influenza	85*	
T2 E. Coli Bacteriophage	65 x 95	
Tobacco Mosaic Virus	15 x 300	
Poliomyelitis	27*	
Hemocyanin Molecule (Busycon)	22	
Japanese B Encephalitis	18	

*Diameter obtained from frozen-dried specimens

Fig. 12–1.   In the diagram above one may compare the size of a red blood cell with those of an average bacterium (*Serratia marcescens*), rickettsiae, some viruses, and a protein molecule. (See Table 2–1.) (Reproduced from Dubos, René: *The Unseen World.* Rockefeller Institute Press, New York, 1962.)

Table 12–1. The Major Divisions, Classes, and Orders of Microorganisms Within the Plant Kingdom

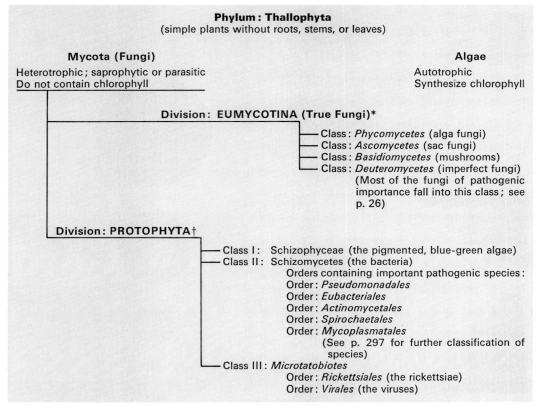

Phylum: Thallophyta
(simple plants without roots, stems, or leaves)

Mycota (Fungi)   **Algae**
Heterotrophic; saprophytic or parasitic   Autotrophic
Do not contain chlorophyll   Synthesize chlorophyll

Division: EUMYCOTINA (True Fungi)*

Class: *Phycomycetes* (alga fungi)
Class: *Ascomycetes* (sac fungi)
Class: *Basidiomycetes* (mushrooms)
Class: *Deuteromycetes* (imperfect fungi)
(Most of the fungi of pathogenic importance fall into this class; see p. 26)

Division: PROTOPHYTA†

Class I: Schizophyceae (the pigmented, blue-green algae)
Class II: Schizomycetes (the bacteria)
Orders containing important pathogenic species:
Order: *Pseudomonadales*
Order: *Eubacteriales*
Order: *Actinomycetales*
Order: *Spirochaetales*
Order: *Mycoplasmatales*
(See p. 297 for further classification of species)
Class III: *Microtatobiotes*
Order: *Rickettsiales* (the rickettsiae)
Order: *Virales* (the viruses)

* Adapted from Medical Mycology, by Norman F. Conant, in *Bacterial and Mycotic Infections of Man*, edited by Dubos and Hirsch, 4th ed., p. 825, J. B. Lippincott Co., Philadelphia, 1965.
† Adapted from *Bergey's Manual of Determinative Bacteriology*, by R. S. Breed, E. G. D. Murray, and N. R. Smith, 7th ed. Williams & Wilkins Co., Baltimore, 1957.

Table 12–2. Important Pathogenic Fungi (Eumycotina)

Organisms	Morphologic Features	Diseases
Yeasts or Yeastlike	Yeasty soft colonies	
Cryptococcus neoformans	Encapsulated budding cells	Pneumonia, meningitis, other tissue infections
Candida albicans	Budding cells, pseudomycelium, and chlamydospores	Skin and mucosal infections, sometimes systemic
Geotrichum candidum	Budding cells, fragmenting mycelium	Oral, respiratory, or intestinal infections

TABLE 12–2. (Cont.)

Systemic Fungi

Histoplasma capsulatum	*In tissues,* intracellular and yeast-like *In culture at 37° C,* a yeast *In culture at room temperature,* a mold with characteristic chlamydospores	Histoplasmosis is primarily a disease of the lungs; may progress through the reticuloendothelial system
Coccidioides immitis	*In tissues,* produces spherules filled with endospores *In culture,* a cottony mold with fragmenting mycelium	Coccidioidomycosis is usually a respiratory disease; may become disseminated and progressive
Blastomyces dermatitidis (North American)	*In tissues,* a large, thick-walled budding yeast *In culture at 37° C,* a yeast *In culture at room temperature* a mold	North American blastomycosis is an infection that may involve lungs, skin, or bones
Blastomyces brasiliensis (South American)	*In tissues,* a large yeast showing multiple budding *In culture at 37° C,* a multiple budding yeast *In culture at room temperature,* a mold	South American blastomycosis is an infection of the skin and mucocutaneous membranes; lymph nodes and other systemic tissues may be involved as well
Sporotrichum schenckii	*In tissues,* a small Gram-positive, spindle-shaped yeast *In culture at 37° C,* a yeast *In culture at room temperature,* a mold with characteristic spores	Sporotrichosis is a local infection of injured skin, subcutaneous tissues, and regional lymph nodes

Superficial Fungi

Microsporum species *Trichophyton* species *Epidermophyton floccosum*	These fungi grow in cultures incubated at room temperature as molds, distinguished by the morphology of their reproductive spores	Ringworm of the scalp, body, feet, or nails

The Laboratory Identification of Fungi. The fungi may be isolated from a variety of clinical specimens representing the localization of the infecting organism (sputum, spinal fluid, pus aspirated from lymph nodes or other soft-tissue lesions, skin scrapings, etc.). They can often be seen in wet mounts of such specimens. Stains are usually not required for such preparations, but potassium hydroxide solutions are used to clear away tissue cells and debris, making the fungi more prominently visible. These are multicellular, differentiated organisms whose microscopic structures vary greatly in size and shape, but all can be readily seen with the light microscope. They are identified by the characteristics of their reproductive spores, and sometimes by mycelial features as well. The fungi grow slowly in culture, producing large colonies with various characteristics also useful in identification. Some are "diphasic," or "dimorphic," growing as yeasts at 37° C (body temperature) and as molds at room temperature. In addition to mycologic methods, the fungous diseases can sometimes be diagnosed by identification of the patient's circulating antibodies or by skin tests with fungal antigens.

Table 12–3 provides an abbreviated key to the bacteria of pathogenic importance. The Schizomycete class contains a total of ten orders, but only five contain organisms associated with infectious disease. The key shows the major identifying features of these five orders and the families, genera, and species of the bacterial pathogens. The classification and names of organism are taken from *Bergey's Manual of Determinative Bacteriology,* but the descriptive terminology is the responsibility of the authors of this text.

Table 12–3. Division: Protophyta, Class II. SCHIZOMYCETES (The Bacteria)

(Unicellular plants, average size 0.5 μ by 2 μ, but some are ultramicroscopic, and some very long and filamentous. Multiplication by cell fission. Nuclear material not organized in single structure, cell walls usually rigid.)

Medically Important Orders, Families, Genera, and Species

Order: PSEUDOMONADALES	Family: PSEUDOMONADACEAE	
Straight, curved, or rigid bacilli; Gram-negative, motile		—*Pseudomonas aeruginosa* (Produces pyocyanin, a blue-green pigment; associated with burn and wound infections)
	Family: SPIRILLACEAE	
		—*Vibrio comma* (*cholerae*) (The agent of cholera)
		—*Spirillum minus* (Associated with one type of rat bite fever)

Order: EUBACTERIALES	Family: ENTEROBACTERIACEAE	
Unicellular: Spherical — cocci Straight — rods Saprophytes and parasites Gram-positive or -negative Motile and nonmotile	Gram-negative bacilli Motile or nonmotile Differentiated by carbohydrate fermentations and by antigenic properties Some are commensalistic inhabitants of the intestinal tract; some of these may have pathogenic potential for extraintestinal tissues Some are pathogenic parasites, acquired through the alimentary route	—*Escherichia coli* (Normal intestinal tract of adults; epidemic diarrhea of infants; urinary tract and wound infections; infections of the debilitated) —*Aerobacter aerogenes* (Urinary tract and wound infections; infections often associated with debility) —*Klebsiella pneumoniae* (Friedlander's bacillus; closely related to *A. aerogenes;* associated with lobar pneumonia and other respiratory infections) —*Paracolobactrum* species (Sometimes associated with gastroenteritis —*Serratia marcescens* (A saprophyte sometimes seen in urinary tract infections) —*Proteus* species (Normal intestinal tract of adults; often associated with urinary tract and wound infections, and with diarrhea of infants) —*Salmonella typhosa* (The agent of typhoid fever) —*Salmonella paratyphi* (A) —*Salmonella schottmuelleri* (B) (Agents of paratyphoid fever)

Table 12– 3. (Cont.)

	—*Salmonella typhimurium* —*Salmonella enteritidis* (These and many other species cause gastroenteritis and sometimes enteric fevers) —*Shigella dysenteriae* (The agent of bacillary dysentery) —*Shigella boydii, Sh. flexneri,* and *Sh. sonnei* are also associated with dysentery

Family: BRUCELLACEAE

Small, delicate Gram-negative rods; some are microaerophilic; most require enriched culture media	—*Pasteurella pestis* (The agent of plague) —*Francisella tularensis** (The agent of tularemia) —*Bordetella pertussis* (The agent of whooping cough) —*Brucella* species (The agents of brucellosis, acquired by man from domestic animals) —*Hemophilus influenzae* (Normal respiratory tract; important cause of meningitis in infants) —*Hemophilus ducreyi* (The agent of chancroid, a venereal disease) —*Hemophilus* species (Associated with mucosal infections: conjunctivitis, vaginitis, others) —*Moraxella* species (Associated with conjunctivitis) —*Calymmatobacterium granulomatis* (*Donovania granulomatis*) (The agent of granuloma inguinale, a venereal disease)

Family: BACTEROIDACEAE

Anaerobic Gram-negative rods; often pleomorphic; require enriched media for growth	—*Bacteroides* species (Normal intestinal tract; associated with wound infections) —*Fusobacterium fusiforme* (Normal oral mucosa, and associated with "Vincent's angina" or trench mouth) —*Streptobacillus moniliformis* (Associated with one type of rat bite fever; also "Haverhill fever")

* Projected classification of *Pasteurella tularensis*: see Pasteurella and Francisella, by K. F. Meyer, in *Bacterial and Mycotic Infections of Man*, edited by Dubos and Hirsch, 4th ed., pp. 659–97. J. B. Lippincott Co., Philadelphia, 1965.

Table 12–3. (*Cont.*)

Family: MICROCOCCACEAE

Gram-positive cocci, arranged in clusters or packets; aerobic or facultatively anaerobic; saprophytic or parasitic; identified by hemolysin and coagulase production	—*Staphylococcus aureus* (Associated with skin abscesses, impetigo, wound infections, pneumonia and other systemic infections, and with food poisoning) —*Staphylococcus epidermidis* (Normal commensal of skin but may cause stitch abscesses or systemic infection if introduced by contaminated sutures or instruments)

Family: NEISSERIACEAE

Gram-negative diplococci; some are parasitic, others saprophytic	—*Neisseria gonorrhoeae* (The agent of gonorrhea: the gonococcus) —*Neisseria meningitidis* (One agent of bacterial meningitis) —*Neisseria catarrhalis* and others (Normal nasopharynx; sometimes associated with chronic upper respiratory infections or with meningitis)

Family: LACTOBACILLACEAE

Gram-positive cocci and bacilli; ferment carbohydrates, forming lactic acid and other end products; normally found on mucosal surfaces, especially mouth, throat, intestinal tract, and vagina; some species have pathogenic properties	—*Diplococcus pneumoniae* (An agent of bacterial pneumonia) —*Streptococcus pyogenes* (Beta-hemolytic strains associated with scarlet fever, sore throat, erysipelas, puerperal fever, wound and burn infections, and other serious diseases) —*Streptococcus viridans* group (Associated with normal respiratory mucosa, chronic mucosal infections, and subacute bacterial endocarditis) —*Streptococcus faecalis* and other species of "enterococci" (Associated with normal intestinal tract, respiratory and urinary tract infections; subacute endocarditis)

Table 12–3. (Cont.)

—*Streptococcus mitis*
(Normal respiratory tract, and occasional cases of bacterial endocarditis)
—*Streptococcus salivarius*
(Normal oral mucosa)
—*Lactobacillus* species
(Normal oral, intestinal, and genitourinary mucosa)

Family: CORYNEBACTERIACEAE

Gram-positive, nonspore-forming rods, aerobic, saprophytic or parasitic	—*Corynebacterium diphtheriae* (The agent of diphtheria) —*Listeria monocytogenes* (A bacterial agent of meningitis, congenital infection of infants, and infectious disease of animals)

Family: BACILLACEAE

Gram-positive endospore-forming bacilli Bacillus species are aerobic Clostridium species are anaerobic Saprophytic, but can induce threatening infections in animals and human beings	—*Bacillus subtilis* (A common environmental contaminant) —*Bacillus anthracis* (The agent of anthrax) —*Clostridium botulinum* (Produces the toxin that causes botulism) —*Clostridium tetani* (The agent of tetanus) —*Clostridium perfringens* —*Clostridium novyi* —*Clostridium septicum* —*Clostridium histolyticum* (The agents of gas gangrene)

Order: ACTINOMYCETALES

Family: MYCOBACTERIACEAE

The "higher" bacteria Filamentous rods Gram-positive; many are acid-fast Some form reproductive spores (not endospores) Some display true branching (like fungi) Many are saprophytic in soil or on human mucosal surfaces; some are parasitic	Acid-fast, Gram-positive bacilli; no true branching; aerobic; saprophytic and parasitic	—*Mycobacterium tuberculosis* (The agent of tuberculosis) —*Mycobacterium leprae* (The agent of leprosy) —Atypical *Mycobacteria* (Associated with human disease similar to tuberculosis) —*Mycobacterium smegmatis* and others (Saprophytic species found on human and animal mucosa, and in environment)

Table 12–3. *(Cont.)*

Family: ACTINOMYCETACEAE	
Slender, filamentous branching rods; some are acid-fast; some produce spores; aerobic and anaerobic Saprophytic and parasitic	—*Actinomyces israeli* (Normal oral mucosa) —*Actinomyces bovis* (Animal strain) (Either may cause actinomycosis) —*Nocardia asteroides* (The agent of nocardiosis, a systemic infection; also associated with mycetoma, a deep tissue infection of foot or other extremity)
Family: STREPTOMYCETACEAE	
	—*Streptomyces* species ← *good* (Many produce antibiotic substances, such as tetracyclines, chloramphenicol, streptomycin)

Order: SPIROCHAETALES — **Family: TREPONEMATACEAE**

Order: SPIROCHAETALES	Family: TREPONEMATACEAE	
Long, slender, flexible spiraled organisms; rotate on long axis with corkscrew motion; also have undulant motility; divide by fission; do not stain readily, and are not easily cultivated on cell-free culture media; saprophytic and parasitic	*Treponema* species have regular, even, short spirals; do not stain well; dark-field illumination for wet mounts	—*Treponema pallidum* (The agent of syphilis) —*Treponema pertenue* (The agent of yaws) —*Treponema* species (Others associated with nonvenereal diseases similar to yaws)
	Leptospira species have fine, tight, regular spirals, hooked at one or both ends; do not stain well; dark-field illumination for wet mounts	—*Leptospira icterohemorrhagiae* (The agent of Weil's disease; other species also associated with similar infection — infectious jaundice, sometimes aseptic meningitis)
	Borrelia species have coarse irregular spirals; take Gram stain (Gram-negative)	—*Borrelia recurrentis* (The agent of relapsing fever) —*Borrelia vincentii* (Normal oral mucosa, and associated with "Vincent's angina" or trench mouth)

Order: MYCOPLASMATALES — **Family: MYCOPLASMATACEAE**

Order: MYCOPLASMATALES	Family: MYCOPLASMATACEAE	
Extremely pleomorphic; some forms filamentous, some minute, filterable; size range between smallest bacteria and rickettsiae; grow on complex but cell-free media, also in tissue culture or	Cause pleuropneumonia in animals Human strains called "pleuropneumonia-like organisms," or PPLO	—*Mycoplasma pneumoniae* (Eaton agent) (An agent of atypical primary pneumonia) —*Mycoplasma hominis* and others (Found on normal human mucosa;

Table 12–3. (Cont.)

embryonated eggs; Gram-negative, but special stains usually required	may cause urethritis, cervicitis, or other infections) └Mycoplasma species (Agents of pleuropneumonia in animals)

The Laboratory Identification of Bacteria. The bacteria are cultivated on a variety of media. Some organisms have simple nutrient requirements; others will grow only on complex, enriched media. Temperature and atmospheric conditions must also be closely adjusted to meet individual species requirements. Most bacteria stain well with aniline dyes. The staining techniques used most frequently are the Gram stain and the Ziehl-Neelson (acid-fast) technique.

When clinical specimens are submitted to the laboratory for bacteriologic studies, many are examined first by stained smear. In some instances a presumptive identification of bacteria can be made on the basis of microscopic morphology, but confirmation is sought by culture techniques, or by other methods in the case of organisms that do not grow well in vitro. Identification of bacteria growing in culture is made on the basis of colonial and microscopic morphology, biochemical characteristics, and antigenic composition (recognized by serologic reactions), or some appropriate combination of these features. Pathogenicity studies in laboratory animals are sometimes necessary as well. Organisms that do not grow on cell-free media may be cultivated in embryonated eggs, in tissue cultures, or in laboratory animals. In many instances, the laboratory diagnosis of infectious disease may be provided or confirmed through identification of the patient's circulating antibodies.

Table 12–4. Division: Protophyta, Class III. Microtatobiotes (Rickettsia and Viruses)*

(The smallest living organisms. Free-living forms are not known; all appear to be obligate intracellular parasites, in hosts from the highest to the lowest members of the plant and animal kingdoms. Some species require two hosts, in sequence, for perpetuation. Most are filterable, the smallest particles having measurements of the same order as molecules. Propagated in tissue cultures, embryonated eggs, or experimental animals. Identified by pathologic effects in the cells parasitized. Rickettsiae are the largest and may be visualized with the light microscope. The morphology of individual viral particles can be observed only by electron microscopy [except that aggregates may be seen within cells as "inclusion bodies" large enough for visualization with the light microscope]. Also identified by serologic reactivity.)

Order I: RICKETTSIALES   **Family: RICKETTSIACEAE**

	Arthropod Vector:	
Arthropod hosts Obligate parasites of animals	Louse	┌Rickettsia prowazekii (The agent of epidemic typhus fever)
Small coccobacilli, pleomorphic, nonfilterable	Flea	├Rickettsia typhi (The agent of endemic, murine typhus)
Parasitize reticuloendothelial and vascular endothelial cells	Tick	├Rickettsia rickettsii (The agent of Rocky Mountain spotted fever)
Cultivated in tissue culture, embryonated eggs, animals	Tick	└Rickettsia conorii (The agent of boutonneuse fever)

* Systematic classification based on *Bergey's Manual of Determinative Bacteriology.*

Table 12–4. (Cont.)

Require special stains Can be visualized with light microscope (0.5 μ × 1.5 μ average)	Mite	—*Rickettsia tsutsugamushi* (The agent of scrub typhus, or tsutsugamushi fever)
	Mite	—*Rickettsia akari* (The agent of rickettsialpox)
	Tick, but this agent is not dependent on arthropod transmission	—*Coxiella burnetii* (The agent of Q fever)

Family: CHLAMYDIACEAE

| (Large viruses) No arthropod hosts; small coccoid microorganisms, form inclusions within a membrane in cytoplasm of parasitized host cells; can be stained with aniline dyes (Gram-negative) | —*Chlamydia trachomatis†* (The agent of trachoma) —*Chlamydia oculogenitalis†* (The agent of inclusion conjunctivitis, or swimming-pool conjunctivitis) —*Miyagawanella lymphogranulomatis†* (The agent of lymphogranuloma venereum, "LGV") —*Miyagawanella psittaci†* (The agent of psittacosis) —*Miyagawanella ornithosis†* (The agent of ornithosis) |

Family: BARTONELLACEAE

| Arthropod host (sandfly) Pleomorphic coccobacilli; parasitize erythrocytes as well as tissue cells | —*Bartonella bacilliformis* (The agent of Oroya fever and verruga peruana) |

Order II: VIRALES

Viruses are small, filterable, transmissible agents of infectious disease. They are obligate intracellular parasites, cultivable only in living cells (tissue culture, embryonated eggs, or animals). Electron microscopy is required for the visualization of individual viral particles. Some viruses form aggregates within parasitized cells, and these inclusion bodies may be seen with the light microscope when they are stained by special techniques. The classification of the viruses into families, genera, and species has not yet been accomplished. They may be placed in a number of groupings, based on their chemical composition; hemagglutinating capacity; size and shape; their host reservoirs or their affinity for certain types of host cells (neurotropic, viscerotropic, dermotropic, or pantropic viruses); or a requirement for arthropod vector hosts. A given virus may fall into several such groups, however. With respect to clinical disease, some viruses may induce a variety of syndromes, and, conversely, a particular type of infection may be caused by more than one virus. For all these reasons, systematic classification remains a problem for future solution.

  For the convenience of the student and graduate nurse, whose primary interest lies in the clinical picture of viral infections, the following grouping relates the viruses of medical importance to either their route of entry or the type of disease produced:

† The genus name *Bedsonia* is also widely used for these organisms. See Chap. 16, p. 389.

Table 12–4. *(Cont.)*

Respiratory Viruses	**Enteroviruses**	**Arboviruses**
Influenza virus	Poliomyelitis virus	(Arthropod-borne)
Parainfluenza viruses	Coxsackie viruses	(Viscerotropic)
Adenoviruses	ECHO viruses	Yellow fever virus
Rhinoviruses	Infectious hepatitis virus	Dengue fever virus
Respiratory syncitial		Colorado tick fever virus
(RS virus)		Sandfly fever virus
Mumps virus		(Neurotropic)

Respiratory Viruses
Influenza virus
Parainfluenza viruses
Adenoviruses
Rhinoviruses
Respiratory syncitial
 (RS virus)
Mumps virus

Poxviruses
(Dermatropic)
Smallpox (variola virus)
Cowpox virus
Vaccinia virus

Herpesviruses
(Dermatropic)
Chickenpox (varicella virus)
Herpes zoster virus
Herpes simplex virus

Exanthem Viruses
(Dermotropic and Viscerotropic)
Measles (rubeola virus)
German measles (rubella virus)

Enteroviruses
Poliomyelitis virus
Coxsackie viruses
ECHO viruses
Infectious hepatitis virus

CNS Virus
(Neurotropic)
 Rabies virus

Arboviruses
(Arthropod-borne)
 (Viscerotropic)
Yellow fever virus
Dengue fever virus
Colorado tick fever virus
Sandfly fever virus
 (Neurotropic)
Eastern equine encephalitis virus
Western equine encephalitis virus
St. Louis encephalitis virus
Japanese B encephalitis virus

Table 12–5. Classification of the Animal Parasites of Man and Important Arthropod Vectors*

Kingdom : ANIMALIA

  Phylum: PROTOZOA
   Unicellular organisms; cell membrane; well-organized nucleus enclosed in a nuclear membrane

   Subphylum: MASTIGOPHORA '
   Class: ZOOMASTIGOPHOREA
    Flagellated organisms; reproduce by longitudinal binary fission; two groups of medical importance:
    Flagellates of the intestinal and genital mucosa
    — *Giardia lamblia* (sometimes causes a mild diarrheal disease)
    — *Trichomonas hominis* (nonpathogenic inhabitant of the intestinal tract)
    — *Trichomonas vaginalis* (an agent of vaginal pruritus)

* Selected from Classification of Animals Which Parasitize Man, Produce Venenation, or Serve as Vectors of Human Pathogens, in *Craig and Faust's Clinical Parasitology*, by Ernest C. Faust and Paul F. Russell, 7th ed., Lea & Febiger, Philadelphia, 1964, pp. 30–39.

Table 12–5. (Cont.)

Flagellates of the blood and tissues (arthropod-borne)
—*Leishmania donovani* (the agent of *kala-azar,* a visceral leishmaniasis)
—*Leishmania tropica* (the agent of *Oriental sore,* a cutaneous infection)
—*Leishmania braziliensis* (the agent of *espundia,* a mucocutaneous disease)
—*Trypanosoma gambiense* (the agent of *"African sleeping sickness,"* an encephalitis)
—*Trypanosoma rhodesiense* (another agent of *African sleeping sickness*)
—*Trypanosoma cruzi* (the agent of *Chagas' disease,* a systemic infection)

Subphylum: SARCODINA
Class: RHIZOPODEA
Move by means of *pseudopodia* (finger-like projections of cytoplasm) ; reproduce asexually, frequently pass into cyst stages
—*Endamoeba histolytica* (the agent of amebic dysentery)
—*Endamoeba coli* (nonpathogenic inhabitant of the intestinal tract)
—*Iodamoeba butschlii* (nonpathogenic inhabitant of the intestinal tract)
—*Dientamoeba fragilis* (nonpathogenic inhabitant of the intestinal tract)

Subphylum: SPOROZOA
Possess no means of locomotion ; reproduce by alternating sexual multiplication (*sporogony*) and asexual multiplication (*schizogony*) ; parasitic forms only
Class: TELOSPOREA, Subclass: *HAEMOSPORINA*
Parasitize erythrocytes and tissue cells of man and animals
—*Plasmodium vivax*
—*Plasmodium malariae*
—*Plasmodium falciparum*   The agents of *malaria*
—*Plasmodium ovale*
—*Plasmodium knowlesi†*
Class: TOXOPLASMEA: Reproduce by binary fission or sporogony
—*Toxoplasma gondii*   Intra- and extracellular parasites
—*Pneumocystis carinii*   that sometimes cause human
—*Sarcocystis lindemanni*   disease

Subphylum: CILIOPHORA
Locomotion is by means of cilia ; possess a macronucleus and a micronucleus ; reproduce by fission or by sexual conjugation ; may be free-living or parasitic
Class: CILIATEA
—*Balantidium coli* (an agent of ulcerative colitis)

Phylum: PLATYHELMINTHS (Flatworms)
Multicellular invertebrate animals ; bilaterally symmetrical but lack a body cavity ; usually flattened dorsoventrally

Class: TREMATODA (Flukes)
Parasitic worms ; body unsegmented ; hermaphroditic reproduction (usually)
Family: SCHISTOSOMATIDAE
The only bisexual trematodes ; life cycle requires vertebrate and aquatic hosts in sequence

† *Review of Medical Microbiology,* by Ernest Jawetz, J. L. Melnick, and E. A. Adelberg, 7th ed., Lange Medical Publications, Los Altos, Calif., 1966, p. 460.

Table 12–5. (Cont.)

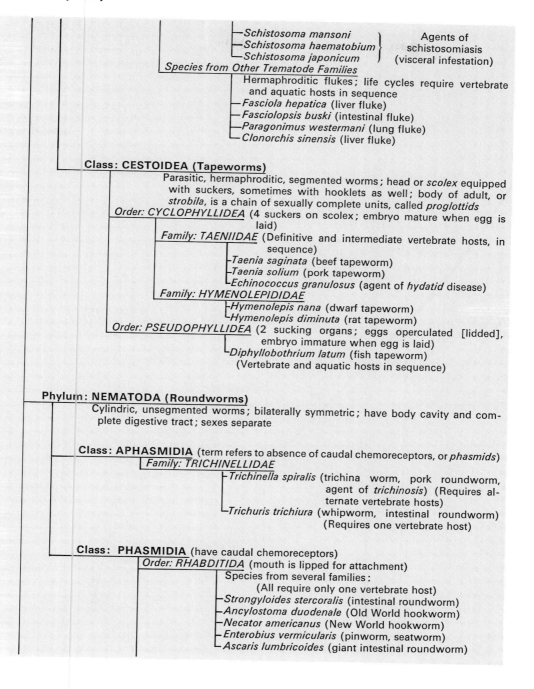

Schistosoma mansoni ⎫ Agents of
Schistosoma haematobium ⎬ schistosomiasis
Schistosoma japonicum ⎭ (visceral infestation)

Species from Other Trematode Families
Hermaphroditic flukes; life cycles require vertebrate and aquatic hosts in sequence
Fasciola hepatica (liver fluke)
Fasciolopsis buski (intestinal fluke)
Paragonimus westermani (lung fluke)
Clonorchis sinensis (liver fluke)

Class: CESTOIDEA (Tapeworms)
Parasitic, hermaphroditic, segmented worms; head or *scolex* equipped with suckers, sometimes with hooklets as well; body of adult, or *strobila*, is a chain of sexually complete units, called *proglottids*
Order: CYCLOPHYLLIDEA (4 suckers on scolex; embryo mature when egg is laid)
Family: TAENIIDAE (Definitive and intermediate vertebrate hosts, in sequence)
Taenia saginata (beef tapeworm)
Taenia solium (pork tapeworm)
Echinococcus granulosus (agent of *hydatid* disease)
Family: HYMENOLEPIDIDAE
Hymenolepis nana (dwarf tapeworm)
Hymenolepis diminuta (rat tapeworm)
Order: PSEUDOPHYLLIDEA (2 sucking organs; eggs operculated [lidded], embryo immature when egg is laid)
Diphyllobothrium latum (fish tapeworm)
(Vertebrate and aquatic hosts in sequence)

Phylum: NEMATODA (Roundworms)
Cylindric, unsegmented worms; bilaterally symmetric; have body cavity and complete digestive tract; sexes separate

Class: APHASMIDIA (term refers to absence of caudal chemoreceptors, or *phasmids*)
Family: TRICHINELLIDAE
Trichinella spiralis (trichina worm, pork roundworm, agent of *trichinosis*) (Requires alternate vertebrate hosts)
Trichuris trichiura (whipworm, intestinal roundworm) (Requires one vertebrate host)

Class: PHASMIDIA (have caudal chemoreceptors)
Order: RHABDITIDA (mouth is lipped for attachment)
Species from several families:
(All require only one vertebrate host)
Strongyloides stercoralis (intestinal roundworm)
Ancylostoma duodenale (Old World hookworm)
Necator americanus (New World hookworm)
Enterobius vermicularis (pinworm, seatworm)
Ascaris lumbricoides (giant intestinal roundworm)

Table 12–5. (*Cont.*)

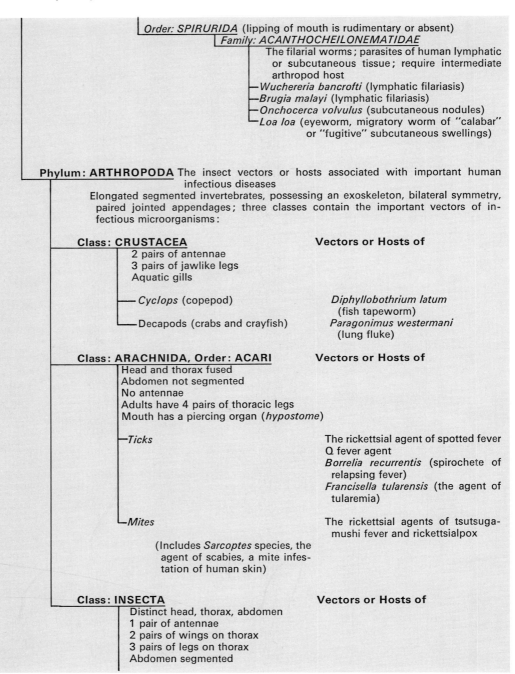

Order: SPIRURIDA (lipping of mouth is rudimentary or absent)
    Family: ACANTHOCHEILONEMATIDAE

The filarial worms; parasites of human lymphatic or subcutaneous tissue; require intermediate arthropod host

— *Wuchereria bancrofti* (lymphatic filariasis)
— *Brugia malayi* (lymphatic filariasis)
— *Onchocerca volvulus* (subcutaneous nodules)
— *Loa loa* (eyeworm, migratory worm of "calabar" or "fugitive" subcutaneous swellings)

Phylum: ARTHROPODA The insect vectors or hosts associated with important human infectious diseases

Elongated segmented invertebrates, possessing an exoskeleton, bilateral symmetry, paired jointed appendages; three classes contain the important vectors of infectious microorganisms:

Class: CRUSTACEA   **Vectors or Hosts of**

2 pairs of antennae
3 pairs of jawlike legs
Aquatic gills

— *Cyclops* (copepod)   *Diphyllobothrium latum* (fish tapeworm)
— Decapods (crabs and crayfish)   *Paragonimus westermani* (lung fluke)

Class: ARACHNIDA, Order: ACARI   **Vectors or Hosts of**

Head and thorax fused
Abdomen not segmented
No antennae
Adults have 4 pairs of thoracic legs
Mouth has a piercing organ (*hypostome*)

— Ticks   The rickettsial agent of spotted fever
                            Q fever agent
                            Borrelia recurrentis (spirochete of relapsing fever)
                            Francisella tularensis (the agent of tularemia)

— Mites   The rickettsial agents of tsutsugamushi fever and rickettsialpox

(Includes *Sarcoptes* species, the agent of scabies, a mite infestation of human skin)

Class: INSECTA   **Vectors or Hosts of**

Distinct head, thorax, abdomen
1 pair of antennae
2 pairs of wings on thorax
3 pairs of legs on thorax
Abdomen segmented

Table 12–5. (*Cont.*)

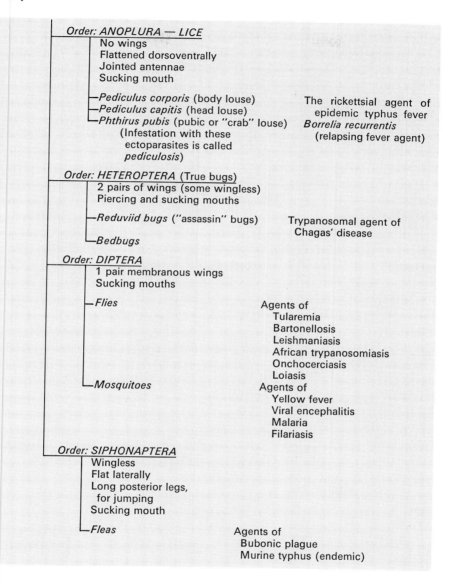

Order: ANOPLURA — LICE
No wings
Flattened dorsoventrally
Jointed antennae
Sucking mouth

—*Pediculus corporis* (body louse)   The rickettsial agent of
—*Pediculus capitis* (head louse)   epidemic typhus fever
—*Phthirus pubis* (pubic or "crab" louse)   *Borrelia recurrentis*
    (Infestation with these   (relapsing fever agent)
    ectoparasites is called
    pediculosis)

Order: HETEROPTERA (True bugs)
    2 pairs of wings (some wingless)
    Piercing and sucking mouths

    —*Reduviid bugs* ("assassin" bugs)   Trypanosomal agent of
                                          Chagas' disease
    —*Bedbugs*

Order: DIPTERA
    1 pair membranous wings
    Sucking mouths

    —*Flies*   Agents of
                                        Tularemia
                                        Bartonellosis
                                        Leishmaniasis
                                        African trypanosomiasis
                                        Onchocerciasis
                                        Loiasis
    —*Mosquitoes*   Agents of
                                        Yellow fever
                                        Viral encephalitis
                                        Malaria
                                        Filariasis

Order: SIPHONAPTERA
    Wingless
    Flat laterally
    Long posterior legs,
      for jumping
    Sucking mouth

    —*Fleas*   Agents of
                                    Bubonic plague
                                    Murine typhus (endemic)

Section IV The Infectious Diseases Acquired Through the Respiratory Tract

13 The Epidemiology of Infections Acquired Through the Respiratory Portal

The human respiratory tract affords a site of entry and initial multiplication, though not necessarily *local* disease, to a large and highly diverse number of microbial agents. The three major groups represented are *bacteria*, *viruses*, and *fungi*. There are also a few microorganisms whose classification is intermediate between bacteria, rickettsiae, and viruses. The diseases associated with these organisms are described in separate chapters of this section, according to the nature of their causative agents.*

Many of the agents classified together on the basis of their morphology and growth characteristics produce diseases of widely divergent types. Thus, among the bacterial diseases, entities such as scarlet fever, whooping cough, and tuberculosis have few, if any, clinical relationships. However, one of the common signs of bacterial infection is the leukocytic response the body makes. This is usually polymorphonuclear in character and can be observed at the site of bacterial localizations or in white blood cell counts made from the circulating blood. In tuberculosis, however, the tissue response is quite different, resembling that induced by fungi, while in diphtheria and scarlet fever the production of bacterial toxins changes the entire clinical picture from one of mere infection to that of systemic toxicity. Some of the viruses display even more

* References for Chaps. 13 to 17 are located at the end of Sec. IV (pp. 411–15).

clinical versatility, a number of them being associated with various syndromes, ranging from the mildest respiratory illness to severe disease in or beyond the pulmonary system. Furthermore, a particular clinical syndrome, such as "bronchitis," "pneumonia," or "aseptic meningitis," may be caused by any one of a number of different, unrelated viruses. The viral diseases are usually acute and self-limited. A characteristic feature of viral and rickettsial infections is the intracellular localizations of the parasites. They do not elicit large cellular responses from the body as a rule, and the leukocytic force that does meet them is of the mononuclear rather than the polymorphonuclear type. On the other hand, the fungi that cause systemic disease are met by a fairly uniform type of local tissue reaction designed to wall them off and contain them through the activity of mononuclear cells of the reticuloendothelial system, locally assigned throughout the body to resist the intrusion of foreign bodies wherever they may enter. The pathogenic fungi are relatively inert in the strange medium of human tissues (they normally live a saprophytic life in the soil), but they are often capable of survival and slow multiplication in the face of the best defenses the human body can offer, as are the "higher bacteria," which include the tubercle bacillus and related species. These organisms produce chronic diseases characterized by the production of slowly progressive lesions. The cellular formations mustered by the body surround and fight them every step of the way, but they are sometimes defeated in this effort by an overreactivity (hypersensitivity) of immunologic defense.

From the nursing point of view, another important feature of infectious disease is its *communicability* and the *route of its transmission.* This is determined both by the portal of entry of the microbial agent and by the portal of its exit. The latter is, in turn, determined by the localization of the organism in different tissues of the human body, their responses to it, the routes of escape left open, and the organism's requirements for survival outside the human host. Although the infectious agents and the diseases described in the ensuing chapters of this section

are quite diverse, it is important from the epidemiologic and nursing viewpoint, to recognize that they have a common entry point in the respiratory tract. From this initial point of localization, even though it be transient, further extensions may occur in the respiratory tract or to other parts of the body. Also, during the time respiratory localizations persist, the infectious agent may be present in mucous secretions or sputum and transmissible to others through nasal and oral discharges.

As a portal of entry, the respiratory tract appears to be very vulnerable to microorganisms disseminated in the air or carried into the mouth on fingers, objects, food, or water. However, many defensive mechanisms operate effectively to prevent exogenous infection. The flushing action of saliva and nasal mucus, the lymphoid tissue of the pharynx and nasopharynx, and the constant action of the "ciliary mucous escalator" of the tract all function to prevent air-borne particles from reaching the lower bronchial tract or the lungs, as discussed fully in Chapter 6.

As a portal of exit, the respiratory tract has no equal in the ease and frequency with which it permits transfer of the microorganisms contained in sputum, saliva, or throat secretions to the outside environment. Even in ordinary speaking, or clearing of the throat, a minor spray may be ejected, but in coughing or sneezing not only is the spray projected farther but the secretions are nebulized, so that many more droplets and smaller ones are disseminated in the air (see Fig. 13–1). The smaller and lighter droplets may hang suspended for a time, settling slowly and drying to droplet nuclei, which can then remain in the air or be swept back into it from dry surfaces, such as clothing, bed linens, dustcloths, or dry mops. When such droplets reach food, milk, or water the organisms they contain may find an even wider dissemination, although not all of them survive or multiply under these conditions, nor do they necessarily survive gastrointestinal entry to the body.

The *successful transfer of infection* to the respiratory tracts of other persons by the oral and nasal discharges of infected individuals often depends also on the closeness of contacts, the

numbers of organisms inhaled, and the site of their localization. Some of the viral diseases, such as influenza and measles, are highly contagious, probably because their infectious agents are capable of quick and easy implantation in the cells of the upper respiratory membranes, and also because they are transferred in fairly large numbers in pharyngeal secretions. Tuberculous infection may result from the inhalation of a single tubercle bacillus (or of a few in one droplet nucleus), but it must be deposited deep in the respiratory tract, beyond the ciliated epithelium. The same thing applies to bacterial spores (anthrax), to psittacosis virus, and to the spores of fungi, which do not implant in the upper respiratory tract and, indeed, may be easily eliminated if they are not deeply inhaled. The ability of microorganisms to survive in the air or on inanimate surfaces and the duration and intimacy of contacts are also factors to be considered in judging the communicability of infection.

Fig. 13–1.   Sneezes. *A*. Droplet spray ejected by the sneeze of a person with a head cold. *B*. A sneeze sprayed through a mask. *C*. A sneeze directed at a culture dish containing nutrient agar. *D*. The culture dish after incubation showing the bacterial colonies that have developed from the droplet spray. (Reproduced from Jennison, Marshall W.: The Dynamics of Sneezing — Studies by High Speed Photography, *Sci. Monthly*, **52**:24–33, 1941.)

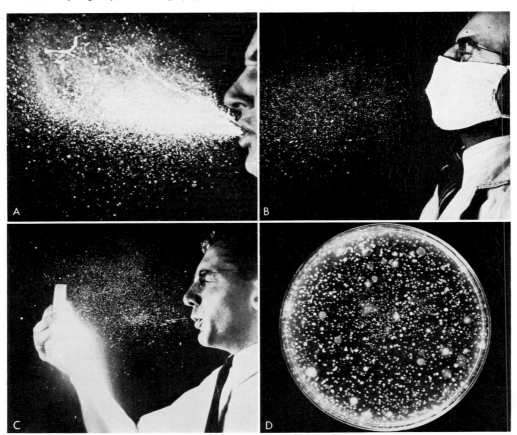

When infection acquired by the respiratory route extends from the initial site to systemic localizations, other portals of exit may become available to the microorganism. Thus, in small-pox the virus is present in the discharges from open vesicular and pustular skin lesions as well as in similar foci on the oral membranes, so that transmission may occur from both avenues. Smallpox infection is acquired, however, only through respiratory entry, not directly through the skin. In poliomyelitis, virus implantation first occurs in the pharyngeal membranes, and the virus can be transmitted from them early in the disease, but later it is excreted primarily by the fecal route from its sites of intestinal localization. Of equal importance is the fact that some of the infectious diseases acquired by man through the respiratory tract (or other route) are not trans-missible by him at all. This is particularly true of the systemic mycoses, and for this reason they are discussed together in one chapter of this section (Chap. 17), although they do not have a common entry point. Some are acquired by in-halation of spores, but a number of fungi of exogenous origin can gain entry to the body by the parenteral route, being introduced to deep tissues through injury to the skin. Others have an endogenous source as members of the com-mensalistic flora of superficial mucous mem-branes, and these may also produce disease if they gain a parenteral entry through traumatized surfaces. Two of the diseases discussed in Chap-ter 16, namely Q fever and psittacosis, also are not usually transmitted directly from person to person, and the same is true for some bacterial diseases (anthrax, brucellosis, tularemia) that can be acquired through the respiratory tract.

The discussion of each disease in the following chapters includes a brief account of the prom-inent epidemiologic features that determine the nature and extent of the nursing precautions that should be followed in each case. The epidemi-ology of the fungous diseases is discussed as for a single entity, however, since these are not com-municable diseases. It should be recognized that measures taken for the control of an active in-fection acquired through or transferred from the respiratory tract must be based on existing knowledge of the infectious agent as to its localizations and activities during different clin-ical stages of disease and its capacity for retaining infectivity in the outside environment.

Respiratory precautions in nursing begin with the effort to control the spread of infectious oral and nasal secretions at their point of origin in the infected patient. One or more of the following general types of procedures may be indicated, depending on the nature of the disease or the immediacy with which the diagnosis can be confirmed (see also Chap. 10, pp. 240 to 246):

1. The patient is isolated from other sick persons, and his contacts with healthy persons are limited. The degree of isolation required varies with the suspected or confirmed nature of his infection.

2. The patient is instructed as to the impor-tance of his own control of respiratory dis-charges. Adequate muffling of coughs and sneezes with paper handkerchiefs and the disposal of secretions in a bag or other container that can be incinerated are often of foremost importance.

3. Masks are occasionally useful for persons in close attendance of patients who cannot, or will not, cooperate effectively. The patient himself may be masked under certain circumstances that require removing him from his room for treat-ment or special examination.

4. Medical and nursing equipment is in-dividualized for the patient insofar as possible or necessary. Concurrent disinfection or sterilization techniques are carried out, with special attention to thermometers, oxygen masks (or tents), aspiration tubing and collectors, airways, laryn-goscopes, emesis basins, and other items directly contaminated with infectious secretions or vomitus.

5. Dishes and eating utensils used by all patients should be washed by sterilizing tech-niques. The chief precaution indicated for patients with respiratory infections is the instruc-tion of dietary personnel in careful hand-washing after handling used trays. In some instances added emphasis can be given by placing the finished tray in a large paper or plastic bag before it is removed from the patient's room.

6. Laundry techniques should routinely assure

the disinfection of all linen and the protection of clean laundry from contamination. Soiled linen should be handled with an economy of motion to prevent shaking infectious organisms into the air with lint. As in the case of soiled dishes, laundry can be placed in marked bags to emphasize the hazard it represents. Blankets, mattresses, and pillows may also require special attention in many instances. Protection of mattresses and pillows with plastic covers or other impervious materials is helpful provided the technique for disinfection of their surfaces is adequate.

7. Clean gowns protect the clothing from contamination. They should be worn by all who come into close contact with the patient.

8. Additional precautions may be indicated in the case of diseases that can be transmitted by feces, or by discharges from skin lesions, as well as by respiratory secretions.

9. Terminal disinfection-cleaning of the room or unit is often indicated, with special attention to the horizontal surfaces of furniture, bed frames, and floors, which hold the settled accumulations of infectious droplets or droplet nuclei.

10. Hand-washing comes first as well as last. The hands are one of the most important agents of infection transfer, and the easiest to control — simply by awareness of their role.

Questions

1. From a nursing viewpoint, what are the important features of infectious diseases?
2. What defense mechanisms operate to prevent exogenous infection?
3. How are microorganisms transmitted from the respiratory tract to the outside environment?
4. What contributes to the successful transfer of infection to the respiratory tract?
5. Where do respiratory precautions in the nursing care of a patient begin?

14 Bacterial Diseases Acquired Through the Respiratory Tract

The bacterial diseases that are acquired by way of the respiratory tract include some of the most important and serious infectious problems man has known. They are important because the respiratory route of access makes their control difficult and assures their widespread distribution in populations everywhere. This means that not only are low-grade but debilitating infections with some of these bacterial agents very common, but also the threat of devastating epidemics of acute infections must be continuously and vigilantly controlled.

The diseases described in this chapter are diverse in their nature and symptomatology, but bacterial infections share a few common features. Some pathogenic bacteria are called *pyogenic* because the body responds to them with the defensive production of pus. Purulent exudates at the site of microbial localizations in the tissues are one of the most frequent signs of bacterial infection, whether it be pharyngitis, pneumonia, meningitis, or a focal abscess. When infection is severe, a general leukocytic response occurs, with elevated white blood cell counts, the height of which is often an indication of severity as well as of the patient's capacity for reaction. Some bacteria produce additional effects through the toxicity for human cells of their components or secretions.

For bacterial diseases easily acquired by the respiratory route control and prevention are

most effective when they can be accomplished by immune mechanisms. Bacterial vaccines or toxoids used on a large or small scale as required by the distribution of particular agents of infection have done much to eliminate the threat of epidemic diseases such as diphtheria and whooping cough. Artificially acquired immunity must be maintained, however, by continuing immunization programs for populations whose natural experience with such infections is dwindling. Naturally acquired active immunity, hypersensitivity, and nonspecific resistance play their own important roles in many of the bacterial diseases described here.

Antibiotic therapy of manifest infection constitutes the next strong control measure against bacterial diseases, but it is not unaccompanied by serious problems, as discussed in Chapter 10. Many of the acute bacterial infections that were once accompanied by crippling or fatal effects (pneumococcal or streptococcal pneumonia, meningococcal meningitis, scarlet fever, and diphtheria) can now be controlled promptly by early, effective use of antibiotics. Chronic infections, in particular those caused by bacterial strains indigenous to the body, are a more difficult problem, and the increasing frequency of infections of this type caused by antibiotic-resistant microorganisms presents a growing challenge.

These factors are considered for each of the diseases described, together with the nursing precautions required for the control of active infection and the public health measures appropriate to the control or prevention of epidemics.

Upper Respiratory Infections (URI)

The Clinical Disease. Many of the common bacterial infections of the upper respiratory tract are nonspecific as to symptoms, pathology, and etiology. They may be acute, chronic, or recurrent. Febrile reactions are mild or do not occur. The basic picture is one of inflammation and hyperemia (congestion). Terms such as "pharyngitis," "laryngitis," "tonsillitis," and "sinusitis" indicate the regional mucous membranes involved. Otitis media, or inflammation of the middle ear,

may result from the extension of pharyngeal infection through the eustachian canal. Mucosal injury following viral infections, inhalation of toxic vapors or smoke, excessive dryness, pollen or dust allergies — all may permit unusual growth and activity of members of the indigenous bacterial flora (see Chap. 30). These secondary, or opportunistic, infections may be further characterized by the formation of purulent or serous exudates, localizing abscesses, and hyperplasia of tissues chronically involved (adenitis, adenoiditis, follicular tonsillitis). Persistent infections are frequently marked by the enhanced tissue reactivity of bacterial allergy, that is, by hypersensitive responses to bacterial cells or their products. More specific symptoms and pathology may be produced by pathogenic invaders (the hemolytic streptococci of scarlet fever and related infections, the diphtheria bacillus, measles and mumps viruses, and others whose characteristic diseases are described elsewhere).

The Organisms. Nonspecific bacterial infections of upper respiratory mucosa may be caused by coagulase-positive strains of staphylococci, pneumococci, various strains of streptococci (alpha-hemolytic strains, often grouped under the term "*Streptococcus viridans*"; nonhemolytic streptococci; and fecal strains, or enterococci), *Hemophilus influenzae* and *parainfluenzae*, and *Klebsiella pneumoniae* (Friedlander's bacillus). Nonpathogenic *Neisseria* (*catarrhalis, sicca*) are sometimes involved, as are Gram-negative enteric bacilli (*E. coli, Proteus* species, *Pseudomonas aeruginosa*). (See Chap. 12 for classifications.)

Laboratory Diagnosis. Smears and cultures may be unrewarding in distinguishing from among the normal microbial flora of upper respiratory mucosa those which are responsible for nonspecific infections. However, *cultures taken with thin swabs or wire loops* aimed with discriminating care at the site of principal lesions may reveal the causative microorganisms with some precision. In the collection of such cultures care must be taken to avoid contaminating the swab or loop with saliva or the mucous secretions of uninvolved tissues. The collected material should be placed

immediately in a supportive broth medium ("transport broth") pending its transport to the laboratory or streaked out on a <u>blood agar plate</u>. Swabs should never be replaced in empty tubes where they may dry out before laboratory culture can be initiated, because fastidious streptococci and *Hemophilus* species may die, and even the hardier organisms (staphylococci or enteric bacilli) may be greatly reduced in numbers, so that their significance in culture is missed. In the laboratory, transport broth media are streaked on appropriate agar plates and incubated under conditions that support fastidious microaerophilic bacteria. Isolated colonies appearing on incubated plates are identified and, if indicated, tested in pure culture for antibiotic susceptibility. In general, pneumococci and streptococci appearing on such plates are not routinely tested with antibiotics: pneumococci, because they are uniformly susceptible to penicillin or its derivatives; streptococci, because their association with clinical disease should first be confirmed. Serologic tests are not appropriate in nonspecific infections of the upper respiratory tract, because antibody levels induced by normal flora are not significantly higher than those seen in persons free of symptoms.

Epidemiology

I. Communicability of Infection

A. RESERVOIR, SOURCES, AND TRANSMISSION ROUTES. The reservoir of these infections is man, and the source is usually endogenous (see Chap. 30). When man-to-man transmission is involved, the route is by air-borne droplets or direct contact with the secretions from the nose and throat of infected persons.

B. INCUBATION PERIOD. Unknown for endogenous infection; probably very short (one to two days) when transmissible.

C. COMMUNICABLE PERIOD. During time of active inflammation, excessive mucous production, or drainage of purulent exudates from nose and throat.

D. IMMUNITY. Specific immune responses to the organisms usually involved either do not occur naturally or are not protective. The nonspecific resistance of normal, healthy tissues appears to constitute the major defense mechanism. Local injury to mucosal surfaces predisposes to

infection of endogenous origin and increases susceptibility to exogenous infections should exposure occur.

II. Control of Active Infection

A. ISOLATION. Not warranted, but patient should avoid directly exposing those who may be unusually susceptible to infection (infants, aged people, surgical or obstetric patients).

B. PRECAUTIONS. Infected persons should practice careful personal hygiene: cover coughs and sneezes, collect nasal discharges in disposable tissues and discard these in closed paper or plastic bags for incineration, wash hands frequently with good technique.

C. TREATMENT. Nonspecific supportive measures designed to remove surface accumulations of exudates, promote blood supply, and reduce allergic reactivity of tissues, if any. Specific antibiotics are sometimes effective, but they should be reserved until adequate clinical observation and laboratory studies have demonstrated their suitability in the individual case.

D. CONTROL OF CONTACTS

Quarantine: Not applicable.

Prophylaxis: No value.

Case finding: Indicated only when the risk of infection to exposed persons is great, as in hospital nurseries, operating rooms, or intensive-care units. Infectious personnel working in these areas should be removed from this duty until their infections are no longer communicable.

E. EPIDEMIC CONTROLS. Not applicable. These bacterial infections do not usually display epidemic patterns of spread.

III. Prevention

A. IMMUNIZATION. Limited value. The use of autogenous bacterial vaccines (killed suspensions of bacteria isolated from the patient's lesions) and toxoids may be effective in reducing the hypersensitive response of tissues to these agents, provided a causal relationship exists between the organisms chosen for the vaccine and the active infection. Desensitization with bacterial antigens requires the repeated injection of increasing quantities of pertinent antigen over long periods of time (usually many months); the intermittent use

SCHEMATIC DIAGRAM OF PNEUMONIC LESION

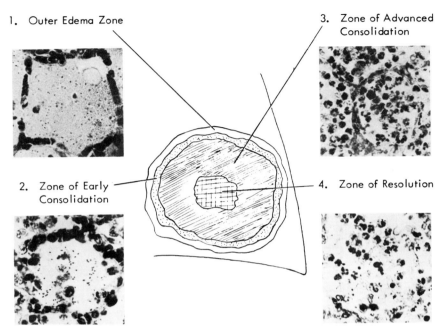

1. Outer Edema Zone

3. Zone of Advanced Consolidation

2. Zone of Early Consolidation

4. Zone of Resolution

Fig. 14–1. A diagram of a pneumonic lesion illustrated with photomicrographs. The center of the pneumonic lesion contains a *zone of resolution* where the earliest damage caused by the infection is being cleared away. This is surrounded by a *zone of advanced consolidation* that is filled with a fibrinous exudate containing red blood cells and polymorphonuclear leukocytes. Infection is no longer active in this area, and many of the invading microorganisms have been phagocytized. Beyond this is a *zone of early consolidation* where the microorganisms are multiplying and the infection is advancing. The whole area is surrounded by an *outer zone of edema* caused by the seepage of plasma from dilated blood vessels as the inflammatory response continues at the expanding margin of the lesion. (Reproduced from Wood, W. Barry: Studies on the Mechanism of Recovery in Pneumococcal Pneumonia, *J. Exp. Med.*, **84**: 355–402, 1946.)

of vaccines has little justification. Protective antibody is not produced in response to these vaccines. Passive immunization is not appropriate for the same reason.

B. CONTROL OF RESERVOIRS, SOURCES, AND TRANSMISSION ROUTES. Remains in the hands of the infected individual, both literally and figuratively. The principles of personal hygiene and the support of healthy resistance are most important.

The Bacterial Pneumonias

Pneumococcal Pneumonia

The Clinical Disease. The bacterial pneumonias, lobar or bronchial, are most frequently of pneumococcal origin (see the description of the organism in the following section). These are acute infectious diseases involving the alveolar or bronchial structures of the lungs, or both. The onset

is sudden and is marked by chills, fever, chest pain, difficult breathing (dyspnea), and cough. The sputum produced is characteristically bright or rusty with blood. In *acute lobar pneumonia*, the alveolar spaces of an involved lobe fill with a fibrinous exudate containing red blood cells and polymorphonuclear leukocytes, and the lung becomes consolidated. (See Fig. 14–1). Pneumococci are present in large numbers in the exudate and within the phagocytic polymorphonuclear cells; they may also be found in the blood stream during the early stages of disease, or persistently if the infection is not arrested. Antibody production reaches a peak between the fifth and tenth days and may bring about dramatically sudden recovery of untreated cases by "crisis." Specific antimicrobial therapy given early may prevent or arrest lobar consolidation and terminate the disease promptly. Pulmonary damage is not permanent because pneumococci produce no injury to lung tissue cells.

Bronchopneumonia is more diffuse and less localized than the lobar variety. Distribution of the infectious process through the bronchial tree is frequent among the very young and the very old, for whom the disease is most severe.

As in the case of many other respiratory infections of bacterial etiology, pneumococcal pneumonia is seldom a primary infection, but occurs as a secondary result of injury induced by other causes, e.g., virus infection, chemical irritation, allergic damage, impaired pulmonary circulation (as in chest surgery or cardiac disease), and other factors that bring about locally or systemically depressed resistance. Pneumococci are members of the upper respiratory flora in 40 to 70 per cent of normal persons. They may extend from this endogenous source to produce active infection in the carriers themselves if their resistance to pneumococci is reduced by a predisposing cause, or they may be transmitted to others by asymptomatic infected persons.

The factors that predispose to pneumococcal pneumonia may similarly lead to the extension of infection along mucosal surfaces of the upper as well as the lower respiratory tract. Pneumococcal sinusitis and otitis media may occur, and

extension to the mastoid surfaces may lead to the further threat of pneumococcal meningitis. Pneumococci circulating in the blood stream may reach the brain by this route as well, to localize on the meninges or even within the brain.

Laboratory Diagnosis

I. Identification of the Organism (*Diplococcus pneumoniae*)

A. MICROSCOPIC CHARACTERISTICS. The pneumococcus is characteristically a Gram-positive diplococcus; it occurs in pairs or in short chains of pairs. The cocci are lancet-shaped, the broad ends of a pair adjacent, the thinner ends pointing away from each other (see Fig. 14–2).

B. CULTURE CHARACTERISTICS. Pneumococci are somewhat fastidious and do not survive well in competition with the hardier organisms of the mixed flora of throat and sputum specimens. For this reason, throat swabs or sputum specimens submitted to the laboratory for the confirmation of pneumococcal infection should be clearly identified as to purpose, so that appropriate culture techniques can be initiated.

Pneumococci are also sensitive to the acid end products of their own utilization of glucose. Therefore, specimens of cerebrospinal fluid (which contain abnormal quantities of glucose when pneumococcal or other bacterial infection of the meninges exists) must be cultured promptly before the organisms are lysed by the acid accumulating from glucose breakdown.

Pneumococci are well supported by enriched culture media containing blood, incubated under microaerophilic conditions. The colonies growing on blood agar plates are often mucoid (see Fig. 14–3, *A*) and surrounded by a zone of incomplete (alpha) hemolysis, usually accompanied by greening. In this respect they resemble alpha-hemolytic streptococci, but can be differentiated from the latter by differences in colony morphology, some biochemical reactions to carbohydrates, and their greater sensitivity to bile salts and other surface-active agents. The latter point has further practical significance: because pneumococci are more readily killed by soaps and detergents than are many other bacteria, specimens for their culture must be collected in sterile vessels free of trace contamination with cleaning agents.

C. SEROLOGIC METHODS OF IDENTIFICATION. Pneumococci capsules are composed of an anti-

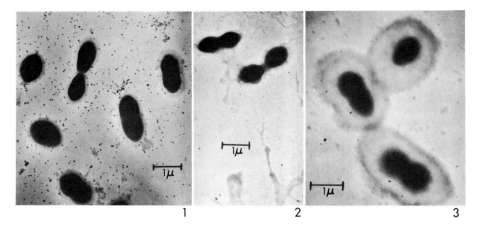

1 – Diplococcus pneumoniae, type 3.
2 – Diplococcus pneumoniae, type 3 in type 1 serum.
3 – Diplococcus pneumoniae, type 1 in type 1 serum.

Fig. 14–2. These photographs of *Diplococcus pneumoniae*, types 1 and 3, were taken with an electron microscope. Note the lancet shape of these diplococci, particularly as seen in the photograph on the left and in the one in the center.

1. These organisms were not exposed to pneumococcus antiserum. Their capsules are visible only as faint aureoles surrounding the bacterial bodies.

2. Type 3 pneumococci were exposed to a heterologous antipneumococcal serum prepared with type 1 organisms. The appearance of the capsules does not differ from those seen in the photograph to the left.

3. Type 1 pneumococci were exposed to a homologous type 1 antipneumococcal serum. A strong "quellung" reaction has occurred. The capsules appear to be swollen, and their margins are well demarcated. This visible change is the result of the specific combination of antibody with the capsular antigen. (Reproduced from Mudd, Stuart; Heinmets, Ferdinand; and Anderson, Thomas F.: The Pneumococcal Capsular Reaction, Studied with the Aid of the Electron Microscope, *J. Exp. Med.,* **78** : 327–32, 1943.)

genic polysaccharide that stimulates antibody production. In active infection, the presence of the capsule prevents effective ingestion of pneumococci by phagocytes. When anticapsular antibody is formed, however, it combines with the polysaccharide and changes the capsular properties so that phagocytosis may proceed normally. When the combination of antibody with capsulated pneumococci is viewed under the microscope, the capsule appears to swell and its outer edge becomes sharply demarcated (see Fig. 14–2). This reaction (often identified by the German word for swelling, *quellung*) is applied in the laboratory identification of pneumococci and in the serologic recognition of their many different antigenic types.

About 75 serologic types of pneumococci (designated by roman numerals) have been distinguished

on the basis of differences in the structure of their antigenic capsular polysaccharides, as detected by specific antiserums (see Chap. 7, pp. 136 and 138). Only a few of these types are associated with pneumococcal disease, however, types I to VIII accounting for most cases of adult pneumococcal pneumonia, while these plus types XIV and XIX are responsible for most cases in children.

The serologic identification of pneumococcal strains was a matter of clinical urgency before penicillin and other antimicrobial drugs were developed for therapeutic use because antiserums of homologous type were used in the treatment of pneumococcal infections. Passive immunization with antibody directed against the specific serologic type of pneumococcus causing infection was of immediate value to the patient who had not yet

developed his own active pneumococcus antibody. Chemotherapeutic methods have obviated the clinical need for pneumococcus typing, but the procedure remains valuable in tracing the epidemiology of pneumococcal disease.

II. Identification of Patient's Serum Antibodies.
Impractical in view of cultural methods of laboratory diagnosis and the usual efficacy of prompt chemotherapy.

III. Specimens for Diagnosis (submitted, whenever possible, *before* antibiotic therapy is started.)
A. Blood samples drawn in the early febrile stage of disease may yield pneumococci promptly upon appropriate culture.

B. Sputum specimens for *smear* and *culture*: Gram-stained smears can be made and examined immediately for the presence of typical Gram-positive diplococci. Culture confirmation is usually possible within 24 to 48 hours.

C. Spinal fluid (only if pneumococcal meningitis or other CNS involvement is suspected) for *smear* and *culture*.

IV. Special Laboratory Tests (for problem cases)

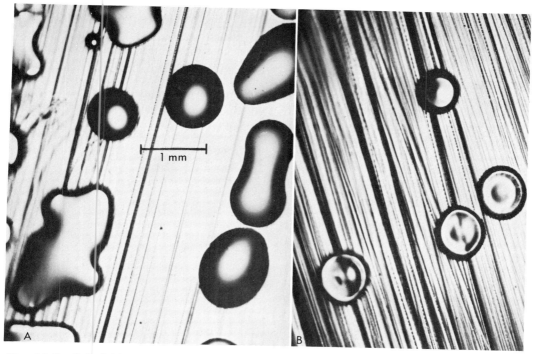

Fig. 14–3. Colonial forms of *Diplococcus pneumoniae. A.* These are colonies of a strain of pneumococcus, type 3, that is producing large amounts of viscous polysaccharide capsular material. Note the mucoid appearance of these colonies and the bulging variation in their shapes. *B.* These are colonies of a strain of pneumococcus, type 2, that is not producing an excessive quantity of capsular substance. The colonies are glistening and mucoid, but their shapes and appearance are uniform. Note the raised rim and umbilicate mound in the center of these colonies. This is the characteristic morphology of most pneumococcal strains. Note also that both types of colonies are surrounded by dark zones of alpha hemolysis. (Reproduced from Austrian, Robert: Morphologic Variation in Pneumococcus. I, An Analysis of the Basis for Morphologic Variation in Pneumococcus and Description of a Hitherto Undefined Morphologic Variant, *J. Exp. Med.,* **98**:21, 1953.)

A. Sputum or spinal fluid specimens that are positive by Gram stain for pneumococci can be tested immediately with antiserum. *The quellung reaction* confirms the diagnosis and identifies the pneumococci by type. This test can also be done later on cultures of the organism isolated from any specimen.

B. Sputum or spinal fluid specimens containing Gram-positive diplococci can be inoculated intraperitoneally into mice. These animals are highly susceptible and may provide a more rapid means of isolating and identifying penumococci than artificial culture media. Heart's blood and peritoneal exudates of animals dying within 12 to 24 hours are examined directly for pneumococci, identified and typed by the capsule swelling reaction, and cultured for final confirmation.

Epidemiology

I. *Communicability of Infection*

A. RESERVOIR, SOURCES, AND TRANSMISSION ROUTES.   Man is the reservoir; the organisms are present in the respiratory secretions of asymptomatic carriers and patients with active infection. Transmission is by direct contact with infected persons, by droplet spread, and by indirect contact with infectious secretions on recently contaminated surfaces.

B. INCUBATION PERIOD.   Unknown for infection of endogenous origin; probably very short (one to two days) for transmitted infection.

C. COMMUNICABLE PERIOD.   Probably during time when pneumococci are present in large numbers in nasal and oral secretions. Prompt chemotherapy reduces these numbers sharply and shortens the communicable period (two to three days).

D. IMMUNITY.   The nonspecific resistance of normal healthy tissues constitutes the major defense mechanism, holding most infections to an inapparent level. The immunity following an attack is type-specific; its duration depends on the level of antibody reached before antibiotic therapy eliminated the antigenic stimulus.

II. *Control of Active Infection*

A. ISOLATION.   For at least one day following the start of antibiotic therapy.

B. PRECAUTIONS.   During the communicable period, concurrent disinfection of respiratory secretions and of items contaminated by them. Terminal cleaning should include disinfection of furniture and floor.

C. TREATMENT.   Penicillin is the usual drug of choice. Pneumococci are also susceptible to a wide range of antimicrobial drugs (e.g., erythromycin, tetracyclines, sulfonamides). The route of administration (oral, intramuscular, or intravenous) depends on the severity of symptoms, localization of the infection, characteristics of the drug, and response of the patient.

D. CONTROL OF CONTACTS
Quarantine: Not indicated.
Prophylaxis: Not indicated.
Case Finding: Not indicated.

E. EPIDEMIC CONTROLS.   Generally not necessary, unless outbreaks are threatened in closed populations with uniformly low resistance (pediatric wards, geriatric institutions, military hospitals, prisons). Vigorous sanitary and hygienic measures may be indicated, together with chemoprophylaxis for the unusually susceptible. Epidemic outbreaks must be reported to the local health department; individual case reports are not required.

III. *Prevention*

A. IMMUNIZATION.   Active immunization with bacterial vaccines or polysaccharide antigens is possible but impractical.

B. CONTROL OF RESERVOIR, SOURCES, AND TRANSMISSION ROUTES.   Public education on the principles of personal hygiene and the support of good health. Institutional practices should include good sanitation and uncrowded living conditions.

Common Bacterial Pneumonias Other Than Pneumococcal

The Clinical Disease.   About 20 per cent of bacterial pneumonias are caused by organisms other than the pneumococcus. They are acute febrile infections that may localize in any segment of the bronchopulmonary system. As in the case of pneumococcal pneumonia, they are not primary infections but are often sequels to virus infections

(influenza, viral pneumonia) or other injury. The degree of permanent damage done to lung tissues varies with the capacities of the causative organisms to induce injury of parenchymal cells. Unlike the pneumococcus, other invasive bacteria may have a necrotic effect on local tissues or blood vessel walls through the action of exo- or endotoxins. The hemolytic toxins of strains of *Staphylococcus aureus* and *Streptococcus pyogenes* may produce a hemorrhagic necrosis of lung parenchyma. This damage is resolved with difficulty and is often replaced by permanent scarring, or fibrosis. *Klebsiella pneumoniae* (Friedlander's bacillus) also produces a hemorrhagic consolidation of the lung, presumably through the action of its endotoxins as well as its capsular substances. The incidence of these pneumonias is not high, but their morbidity and fatality depend on the resistance of the patient (children and aged persons are least resistant) and the speed and adequacy of chemotherapy. Pulmonary abscesses may develop in chronic persistent infections and generally require surgical intervention to effect drainage and elimination of the microbial focus.

Laboratory Diagnosis

I. The Organisms

A. STREPTOCOCCI — hemolytic strains of serologic group A (the human pathogens). Microscopically, these are Gram-positive cocci occurring in chains of medium to great length. In culture they are somewhat fastidious but are supported by blood-enriched media incubated aerobically or under microaerophilic conditions. Colonies on blood agar are surrounded by a zone of complete (beta) hemolysis. Serologic identification is based on differentiation, with antiserum, of their somatic polysaccharide antigens. Numerous groups, designated by letters, are recognized but most of the strains associated with human disease fall into group A. (See the discussion of streptococcal diseases elsewhere in this chapter.)

B. STAPHYLOCOCCI — microscopically, Gram-positive cocci in clustered arrangements, resembling grapes. These organisms grow readily in most simple nutrient media. Strains most frequently associated with human pathogenicity are hemolytic on blood agar, display a golden pigment, and produce a plasma-coagulating enzyme. When these characteristics are seen, strains are reported

as "hemolytic *Staphylococcus aureus*, coagulase positive." (See the discussion of staphylococcal diseases in Chap. 23.)

C. KLEBSIELLA PNEUMONIAE — microscopically, Gram-negative plump, short bacilli with large capsules. They are nonsporing and nonmotile. Klebsiellae grow with ease on most nutrient media, their colonies being quite mucoid because of capsular polysaccharide production. The latter are antigenic and can be identified by serologic methods such as the quellung reaction. Most of the strains that cause human respiratory infection fall into capsular types 1 and 2. (Other serologic types are associated with urinary tract infections.)

D. HEMOPHILUS INFLUENZAE — microscopically, a Gram-negative bacillus, slender but pleomorphic. Most are short and coccoid, but long filamentous rods may also be seen. This organism is nonmotile and nonsporulating. It requires enriched media and microaerophilic incubation for growth. *H. influenzae* produces antigenic capsular polysaccharides identifiable by the quellung technique. This organism is a frequent commensal of the upper respiratory mucosa, but like the streptococci, staphylococci, and pneumococci that also reside there normally, it has a pathogenic potential as a secondary invader of injured tissues. It is frequently involved in upper and lower respiratory tract infections and is an important cause of meningitis in children, especially those under three years of age. (See Bacterial Meningitis, this chapter.)

II. Identification of Patient's Serum Antibodies.
Except in the case of streptococcal infection, serologic diagnosis is generally unrewarding because antibody production does not occur to significant degree. Serologic methods applicable to the diagnosis of streptococcal infection are discussed in the section of this chapter dealing with the primary streptococcal diseases.

III. Specimens for Diagnosis
A. Sputum specimens for smear and culture.

B. Blood specimens for culture.

C. Throat or nasopharyngeal swabs, in transport broth, may be useful for culture, particularly if concurrent URI exists.

D. Specimens should be collected for laboratory diagnosis before antibiotic therapy is started, whenever possible. Prompt transport to the laboratory is essential to the successful isolation of fastidious pathogens, such as *Hemophilus* and streptococci.

IV. Special Laboratory Tests

A. Following isolation of organisms clinically interpreted as significant to the patient's disease, antibiotic susceptibility testing is done when requested. Isolates can be tested while identification methods are in progress.

Epidemiology

I. Communicability of Infection

A. RESERVOIR, SOURCES, AND TRANSMISSION ROUTES. See Pneumococcal Pneumonia.

B. INCUBATION PERIOD. See Pneumococcal Pneumonia.

C. COMMUNICABLE PERIOD. See Pneumococcal Pneumonia.

D. IMMUNITY. Specific immunity plays a minimal role in these bacterial pneumonias, with the exception of group A streptococcal infections (discussed later in this chapter). Most infections with these organisms are inapparent, nonspecific resistance being the most important defense.

II. Control of Active Infection. The discussion of pneumococcal pneumonia under this heading applies here as well. Specific antimicrobial therapy is based on the nature of the infectious agent and its response to in vitro antibiotic susceptibility testing.

III. Prevention. Immunization, active or passive, is not applicable in these pneumonias. Preventive controls center on the support and maintenance of health by good personal hygiene and a clean environment.

Primary Plague Pneumonia

The Clinical Disease. Plague is essentially an endemic infection of rats and other wild rodents, maintained among them by a flea vector. Man is also victimized by this flea and, if infected, develops the bubonic form of plague (see Chap. 27). In late or terminal stages of bubonic plague, the invading organism (*Pasteurella pestis*) may be disseminated to the lung, where it localizes and multiplies to large numbers. The sputum and respiratory secretions of such patients are extremely infectious and can transmit the organism directly to others. The respiratory entry of the infectious agent may result in primary plague pneumonia. This is not a common disease but it may occur in epidemic patterns among persons closely exposed to a plague source and to each other. It is also a highly fatal infection, characterized by rigor, severe headache and generalized pain, difficult breathing, and productive cough, with high fever. Sputum is watery, frothy, and easily projected in a droplet spray for several feet by the coughing patient. Prompt diagnosis and antibiotic therapy may be lifesaving.

Plague in man is rare in the United States today, but it remains endemic among wild rodents in the West Coast and Gulf states where it remains a potential source of epidemics. It is also endemic in India; the countries of Southeast Asia, including Vietnam; China; and parts of Africa where infected rodent populations abound.

The *laboratory diagnosis* and the *epidemiology* of plague are discussed in Chapter 27.

Bacterial Meningitis

General Comments

The term "meningitis" signifies an acute inflammation of the meningeal membranes of the brain and spinal cord. It may be associated with a variety of nonspecific injuries, but it is also commonly caused by the localization of an infectious microorganism on the meninges. The microbial agent may be of bacterial, viral, or fungal nature.

The clinical as well as the epidemiologic pattern of infectious meningitis varies greatly with the type of organism involved. Clinically, *bacterial* meningitis is acute and characterized by an outpouring of purulent exudate over the membrane surfaces. (The spirochetal meningitides are an exception, as discussed below.) The exudate is largely composed of polmorphonuclear leukocytes, which appear in great numbers in the spinal fluid. Epidemiologically, most types of bacterial meningitis are associated with respiratory routes

of entry and transmission. Many of the bacterial agents display an ability for commensalism on the human respiratory mucosa. From this local and relatively harmless situation they may be catapulted into deeper tissues by unusual circumstances that either accentuate their own capacities for virulence or depress the host's resistance to such penetration, or both.

Viral meningitis is clinically a more benign disease, of relatively short duration. The cellular reaction is less marked than in bacterial infections and is characterized by a predominance of lymphocytic cells. (This type of infection is sometimes called *aseptic meningitis* because it is non-bacterial.) The epidemiology of the several viral agents of meningitis is similar to that of the bacterial organisms, with respiratory or oral routes of entry and transfer. Gastrointestinal localizations of some of these viruses also occur, so that fecal transmission is possible as well. Some viruses of meningitis (such as the adenoviruses) also appear to be commensals of the normal upper respiratory mucosa, but these relationships are more difficult to document by laboratory methods.

The meningitis that sometimes complicates systemic *fungal* diseases is very different clinically and epidemiologically from bacterial or viral meningeal disease. These fungi are air-borne, and they usually enter the body by the respiratory route, but they come from *soil* reservoirs. Man is not a reservoir for these organisms, and he does not transmit them directly (see Chap. 9, p. 185). The clinical infections induced by the pathogenic fungi are chronic, persistent, and slowly progressive. From primary localizations in the lungs, or the reticuloendothelial system, they may be disseminated to other organs or to the meninges. When meningitis occurs it is also chronic, progressive, and usually fatal. The cellular reaction is predominantly lymphocytic.

The *spirochetal* meningitides have another epidemiologic pattern. These bacterial agents (*Leptospira* and the *Treponema* of syphilis) enter the body through skin and mucosal barriers, rather than the respiratory route. As in the case of the fungi, they are disseminated from primary localizations to other sites in the body, and the me-

ninges may become a secondary focus of infection. Man is an accidental host for leptospirae and does not transmit them directly (see Chap. 9, p. 184). The transmission of syphilis is almost always venereal, but it may sometimes occur through other direct contacts during the stage of generalized dissemination of spirochetes to the skin and mucous membranes. The meningeal and other secondary lesions of syphilis subside spontaneously. Leptospiral meningitis is clinically benign. In both these infections, the cellular response as seen in the spinal fluid is usually not heavy and is primarily lymphocytic.

Descriptions of specific meningeal infections are arranged in this book according to their epidemiologic significance. The bacterial and viral meningitides that may arise as a fairly direct result of respiratory entry and transmission are discussed as primary or secondary entities in the large section dealing with diseases acquired through the respiratory tract: the bacterial infections in the ensuing subsection of this chapter; the viral meningitis group in Chapter 15. Other routes of entry that are available to these agents are noted in context with their transmission and communicability.

In other instances, where meningitis is the result of an extension of infection from primary active lesions elsewhere, the agent and its epidemiology are discussed under the principal disease heading. Thus, tuberculous meningitis is considered in the subsection of this chapter that deals with tuberculosis; the systemic fungous diseases are described in Chapter 17; syphilis and leptospirosis in sections on diseases acquired through the normal skin and mucosa in Chapters 23 and 25, respectively.

Meningococcal Meningitis

The Clinical Disease. Meningococcal meningitis is an acute bacterial disease characterized by the sudden onset of fever, severe headache, painful rigidity of the neck, nausea, and vomiting. Convulsions are often seen in children. Delirium or coma is also frequent. The meninges are involved in an acute inflammatory reaction characterized

by a purulent exudate. If the disease is not arrested before this exudate becomes abundant, the meninges later become thickened as the inflammation is organized. Hemorrhage and thrombosis of small blood vessels contribute to the damage, which may be residual if treatment is delayed or ineffective.

Meningococci enter the body through the nasopharynx and localize there. They may remain there without any injury to tissues, or they may induce a local inflammation. In a small proportion of cases, meningococci enter the blood stream. They may be filtered out and killed by the body's defensive mechanisms, or meningococcemia may ensue, with a possible distribution of the organisms to many foci of multiplication throughout the body, notably the skin, joints, lungs, adrenal glands, and central nervous system. Destruction of capillary walls by meningococci leads to small petechial hemorrhages in the skin and other affected tissues. Fulminating infections may lead to adrenal hemorrhage, circulatory collapse, and shock (Waterhouse-Friderichsen syndrome). The usual clinical appearance of meningococcemia is marked by fever, chills, acute malaise, petechial rash, and prostration. Meningitis is usually, but not always, quickly apparent.

The most probable route of entry of meningococci to the meninges is from the circulating blood, but it is possible that they may extend or penetrate directly through the thin bony lamina posterior and superior to the nasopharynx.

Laboratory Diagnosis

I. Identification of the Organism (*Neisseria meningitidis;* also called *Neisseria intracellularis*)

A. MICROSCOPIC CHARACTERISTICS. The organism is a Gram-negative diplococcus. Each member of a pair is characteristically flattened on its adjoining side and rounded on its outer edge, so that it resembles a kidney bean. In direct stained smears of purulent spinal fluid the diplococci are often seen in intracellular positions within the polymorphonuclear phagocytes.

B. CULTURE CHARACTERISTICS. Meningococci belong to the genus *Neisseria*, which contains one other important pathogen (*Neisseria gonorrhoeae*) and several species that are members of the normal respiratory flora (*N. catarrhalis, N. sicca*).

These organisms are aerobic, nonsporulating, and nonmotile. The two pathogenic species are much more fastidious in their growth requirements than the commensal species. Meningococci grow best on blood-enriched media incubated microaerophilically, and with added CO_2. Their colonies are transparent, glistening, and nonhemolytic. They are distinguished from gonococci and other *Neisseria* by differences in their ability to ferment carbohydrates.

C. SEROLOGIC METHODS OF IDENTIFICATION. The recognition of meningococcal antigens seldom has practical importance in diagnosis.

II. Identification of Patient's Serum Antibodies. A rising titer of antibodies (agglutinins) produced during the course of illness can be demonstrated by agglutination techniques, but this is seldom necessary or practical.

III. Specimens for Diagnosis

A. Blood samples drawn as soon as possible after onset of symptoms.

B. Spinal fluid samples for *immediate* reading of Gram-stained smears and initiation of culture. Cell counts and chemical analysis for glucose and protein are also essential.

C. Nasopharyngeal swabs, in transport broth, may detect carriers.

D. Petechial lesions on the skin may be scraped or punctured and submitted for smears and culture.

IV. Special Considerations

A. Infectious meningitis is a medical emergency requiring prompt, accurate diagnosis and therapy. Permanent tissue damage or death may result from delay. Pretreatment specimens, aseptically collected in adequate quantity and promptly examined, are essential to the laboratory diagnosis.

B. Spinal fluid must be analyzed by chemical and cytologic methods, as well as by culture techniques. Collection in three separate sterile tubes is recommended for speedy and efficient distribution to appropriate sections of the laboratory. The quantity per tube should be predetermined by consultation with the laboratory so that the requirements of its methods can be met. If only one tube is used for collection, it should be submitted *first* to the microbiology laboratory for aseptic withdrawal of an aliquot for smear and culture.

C. Any material submitted for culture of men-

ingococci should be clearly identified for this purpose so that appropriate examinations may be made promptly by the laboratory.

D. Meningococci lyse rapidly in extravasated body fluids without nutrient. This happens at room temperature and even more rapidly at the higher temperatures of incubators. Meningococci are also sensitive to cold. For all these reasons, specimens for meningococcus culture should be delivered *without delay* to the laboratory and placed in the hands of the bacteriologist, not in incubators, in refrigerators, or on unattended laboratory benches.

Epidemiology

I. Communicability of Infection

A. RESERVOIR, SOURCES, AND TRANSMISSION ROUTES. Man is the only known reservoir. The nasal and oral secretions of infected persons are the principal source. Epidemics are spread primarily by asymptomatic carriers rather than by infectious cases. Transmission is by direct contact or droplet spread. Meningococci do not survive long in exposed situations.

B. INCUBATION PERIOD. The extremes are two and ten days, the average being three to four days.

C. COMMUNICABLE PERIOD. The disease is transmissible while meningococci are present in respiratory discharges. In the individual patient, the spread of petechial lesions or an increasing intensity of symptoms is further evidence that the disease is in a communicable stage. Effective chemotherapy generally clears the nasopharyngeal focus within 24 to 48 hours.

D. IMMUNITY. Asymptomatic carriers greatly outnumber cases of infectious disease, indicating a generally high resistance to the clinical illness. Specific immunity following recovery from the disease is of uncertain importance in providing future protection. Effective agents for artificial active immunization have not been developed.

II. Control of Active Infection

A. ISOLATION. For 24 hours following initiation of specific therapy, or until the nasopharynx is culturally negative.

B. PRECAUTIONS. During the communicable period, concurrent disinfection of respiratory se-

cretions and of items contaminated by them. Terminal cleaning should include disinfection of furniture and floor.

C. TREATMENT. Penicillin and/or the sulfonamides are the most effective of the therapeutic drugs. Meningococci are also susceptible to chloramphenicol and the tetracyclines. Intravenous administration of antimicrobial drugs is usual in the early acute stage of disease. Many supportive methods are often indicated as well.

D. CONTROL OF CONTACTS

1. *Quarantine.* Limited to surveillance (see Chap. 10, p. 207).

2. *Prophylaxis.* Immunization methods are not available. Chemoprophylaxis with sulfonamide drugs given orally is generally recommended. Local health departments can provide advice as to currently accepted dose regimens.

3. *Case Finding.* Unnecessary.

E. EPIDEMIC CONTROLS. Individual cases must be reported to local health departments. Chemoprophylaxis of exposed contacts and surveillance of their health and living conditions may limit the spread of an outbreak by reducing the number of carriers and permitting early segregation of the clinically ill. Outbreaks occur most frequently among closed populations, in military barracks, schools, camps, and institutions. Physical separation, increased ventilation of quarters, and vigorous insistence on good personal hygiene help to limit outbreaks.

III. Prevention

A. IMMUNIZATION. None.

B. CONTROL OF RESERVOIRS, SOURCES, AND TRANSMISSION ROUTES. Public education concerning the source of infection, the necessity for respiratory hygiene, the avoidance of direct contacts, and the hazards of crowding in living, working, or traveling conditions.

Listeriosis

The Clinical Disease. Listeriosis is a disease of animals and man that has attracted new interest in recent years. It is a sporadic disease in man, or so it would seem because of the difficulty of

clinical recognition and bacteriologic confirmation. Increasing awareness of listeriosis, however, has led to more frequent reporting of its incidence. It is described here because clinically apparent infection often begins as an acute meningitis, with a possible respiratory tract entry. The epidemiology of *Listeria* infections has not been clearly defined, but the disease has a widespread distribution among many hosts and may be acquired by man through inhalation, ingestion, venereal contacts, or congenital transfer. The probability is that the organism is readily transmissible, meets with resistance in the normal human adult, but lives commensalistically on his tissues until he becomes more susceptible to infection. Adults with underlying debilitating diseases (such as neoplasms) and particularly those who are maintained on steroid therapy, may develop listeriosis, manifest usually as an acute meningitis. The organisms survive on adult genital mucosa and can be transferred by venereal contacts. The clinical result of venereal transfer among adults is not remarkable and may be undetected, but if conception occurs the fetus may be severely involved. Fetal infection may lead to abortion, stillbirth, or neonatal disease (frequently fatal also).

Acute listerial meningitis may begin with or without signs of blood stream transfer (septicemia). The onset is sudden, signaled by fever, chills, acute headache, stiff neck, and other signs of purulent bacterial meningitis (see pp. 320 and 321). Delirium is common; coma or the collapse of shock may also occur. The clinical signs indicate a bacterial type of infection, which may be confirmed by laboratory examination of spinal fluid.

Pregnant women infected by venereal contact may display mild febrile symptoms related to a light septicemic spread of the organisms. Infants acquire the infection in utero. The fetus may be aborted or stillborn. Those who survive the prenatal period may have a massive septicemia, manifest at birth by multiple infectious abscesses in internal organs and on external surfaces (granulomatosis infantiseptica); others may develop meningitis neonatally.

The disease appears to have a worldwide distribution among animals but is reported only sporadically, though increasingly, in man. Infants manifest the disease within three weeks of birth, adults in middle life or later, possibly because other physiologic stresses are greatest in this period.

Laboratory Diagnosis

I. Identification of the Organism   (*Listeria monocytogenes*)

A. MICROSCOPIC CHARACTERSITICS. The organism is a Gram-positive, nonsporulating aerobic bacillus and is a member of the family of bacteria known as *Corynebacteriaeceae*, which also includes the diphtheria bacillus. Unlike the latter *Listeria* is motile and hemolytic on blood agar.

B. CULTURE CHARACTERISTICS. Listeria is sometimes difficult to grow in primary isolation on artificial culture media from clinical specimens. When it does appear on blood agar plates among the mixed flora of vaginal or other mucosal cultures, its small hemolytic colonies may be mistakenly interpreted as streptococci if they are not smeared. Microscopically, *Listeria* resembles the nonpathogenic members of the *Corynebacterium* genus (diphtheroids), which are common commensals of mucosal and skin flora. Accurate bacteriologic diagnosis depends, therefore, on the recognition of *Listeria* as a Gram-positive rod (not a coccus) displaying hemolytic properties and motility (unlike diphtheroids).

Cultures of spinal fluid and deep tissue abscesses from cases of listeriosis yield the organism in pure culture, but sometimes with difficulty on initial attempts. Storage of such specimens at refrigerator temperatures for days, or weeks, often leads to more successful recovery of *Listeria* upon subculture.

C. SEROLOGIC METHODS FOR IDENTIFICATION. Not useful.

II. Identification of Patient's Serum Antibodies. Not routine.

III. Specimens for Diagnosis

A. Spinal fluid for smear and culture.

B. Blood for culture in the early stages of meningitis.

C. From postpartum mothers with infected infants, cultures of vaginal discharge, placenta, milk.

D. From infected infants, cultures of blood, urine, meconium, lesions.

IV. Special Laboratory Tests

A. Specimens for culture are divided in the laboratory for immediate culture and for repeated subculture after refrigerator storage.

B. Suspicious organisms isolated from cultures may be instilled in a rabbit's eye. *Listeria* produce a characteristic keratoconjunctivitis.

Epidemiology

I. Communicability of Infection. See initial discussion.

II. Control of Active Infection

A. ISOLATION. Since human resistance appears to be normally high, disease is not readily communicable, although the organisms are transmissible. Therefore, isolation of adult meningitis cases is usually not warranted. Infectious infants and mothers should be isolated until lesions are healed or discharges are bacteriologically negative for *Listeria*.

B. PRECAUTIONS. Concurrent disinfection of all items associated with care of infectious infants or the vaginal discharges of mothers. Disinfection of respiratory secretions of meningitis patients during the acute stage. Terminal disinfection of units.

C. TREATMENT. Antibiotics chosen on the basis of laboratory susceptibility testing, when possible. Tetracycline therapy is the usual choice; penicillin and streptomycin in combination are also used.

D. CONTROL OF CONTACTS. Not indicated.

E. EPIDEMIC CONTROLS. None indicated. Cases should be reported to local health departments for the record, but this is not a feature of control.

III. Prevention

A. IMMUNIZATION. Immunizing agents are not available. (Protective immunity is apparently not acquired as a result of disease.)

B. CONTROL OF RESERVOIRS, SOURCES, AND TRANSMISSION ROUTES. Education of persons (especially pregnant women) continuously exposed to domestic animals, with particular regard to precautionary techniques for handling diseased animals.

Secondary Bacterial Meningitis

The Clinical Disease. Acute bacterial meningitis may be secondary to respiratory tract infections caused by organisms of the indigenous flora. Entry of these organisms into the blood stream from the site of active lesions in the upper or lower respiratory tract probably constitutes their chief route of access to localization on the meninges. The latter event does not occur frequently, presumably because the blood's defensive barriers are effective in eliminating most bacteremic infections. Bacteria of enteric origin are also sometimes responsible for acute meningitis if they find a disseminating route from colonizing sites in the bowel or in parenteral tissues. The clinical disease produced in these situations resembles meningococcal meningitis in every way, except that the petechial lesions characteristic of meningococcal injury are not seen in other bacterial infections.

Laboratory Diagnosis

I. Identification of the Organisms. Differentiation of these meningitides requires bacteriologic recognition of their agents. The organisms most frequently involved are among those that are also associated with the bacterial pneumonias, notably *Hemophilus influenzae*, pneumococci, streptococci, and staphylococci. A bacteriologic description of these organisms is given earlier in this chapter. The *Klebsiella* strain described earlier may also induce acute meningitis, as may a number of the commensalistic or pathogenic Gram-negative bacilli of the intestinal tract. These include *Escherichia coli* and species of *Proteus, Pseudomonas*, and *Salmonella*. The bacteriology of the enteric bacilli is described in Chapter 19.

II. Identification of Patient's Serum Antibodies. Serologic diagnosis is seldom helpful in these infections.

III. Specimens for Diagnosis

A. Blood for culture, particularly in the early stage of disease.

B. Spinal fluid for smear and culture.

C. Throat swabs or sputum specimens sometimes help in recognizing the endogenous sources of meningeal infection.

IV. Special Considerations. Acute infectious meningitis is a medical emergency. See "Special Considerations" in the laboratory diagnosis of meningococcal meningitis, items A, B, and C.

Epidemiology

I. Communicability of Infection

A. RESERVOIR, SOURCES, AND TRANSMISSION ROUTES. Man is the reservoir for these infections. Endogenous infectious lesions in the respiratory tract or other organs are often an immediate source of meningeal infection. The nasal, oral, and intestinal discharges of infected persons may be a source for susceptible individuals, however. Transmission is by direct contact, by droplet spread, or, in limited instances, by the fecal-oral route.

B. INCUBATION PERIOD. Not measurable in secondary meningitis.

C. COMMUNICABLE PERIOD. The organisms are readily transmissible as noted, but the communicability of disease depends on the susceptibility of contacts.

D. IMMUNITY. General resistance to the pathogenic potential of these organisms is high, but children are often more susceptible than adults, particularly in the case of *H. influenzae*. This organism is one of the most common causes of meningitis in infants and children. Antibody response may lower susceptibility to severe *H. influenzae* infection, but in general the role of specific immunity to other organisms of this group is not significant in the development or prevention of meningitis.

II. Control of Active Infection

A. ISOLATION. Not generally necessary, provided the possibility of epidemic spread of meningococcal meningitis has been ruled out by prompt bacteriologic diagnosis.

B. PRECAUTIONS. Concurrent disinfection of respiratory secretions or other discharges as indicated by the possible systemic foci of infection. Special care in the disposal of urine and feces may be indicated, for example, if *Salmonella* or other pathogenic enteric bacillary agents of meningitis

are localized primarily in the kidney or gallbladder.

C. TREATMENT. Antibiotic drugs are effective, particularly when given promptly on onset of symptoms. Speed is essential in identifying the causative organism and determining its susceptibility to antibiotics. Pending preliminary and confirmed information from the laboratory, antibiotics are given empirically to control the disease.

D. CONTROL OF CONTACTS. Generally not indicated except in the case of *Salmonella* infections, whose epidemiology is discussed in Chapter 19.

E. EPIDEMIC CONTROLS. Generally not applicable. Case reports should be sent to local health departments.

III. Prevention

A. IMMUNIZATION. None.

B. Avoidance of infectious contacts by susceptible persons, particularly children. Support and maintenance of healthy resistance.

Streptococcal Diseases

Acute Streptococcal Infections: General Comments

Hemolytic streptococci of group A are capable of producing injury to almost any human tissue in which they are localized. Also, some of the toxic products they secrete may be disseminated through the body and exert damaging effects on cells and tissues very distant from the focus of multiplication. Streptococci may find several routes of entry into the body, such as the respiratory tract, the normal skin and mucosa, or traumatized tissues. Four of the important streptococcal diseases are associated with these entry portals: *streptococcal sore throat*, *scarlet fever*, *erysipelas*, and *puerperal fever*. The first two of these are associated with the upper respiratory mucosa and are discussed here. Erysipelas is a systemic infection characterized by spreading localizations of the organism in deep tissues of the skin. It may be acquired through minor breaks

in the skin exposed to infectious sources and is described in Chapter 23. Puerperal fever is an acute sepsis of the genital tract of the postpartum patient. Hemolytic streptococci and a number of other bacterial species may produce this disease if they are introduced to genital mucosa traumatized by delivery or abortion. A discussion of puerperal fever is given in Chapter 29.

In addition to these rather specific disease entities, the hemolytic streptococci may cause severe infections in a variety of systemic localizations. Diseases such as osteomyelitis, mastoiditis, lymphadenitis, and peritonitis may be of streptococcal origin. In skin diseases, such as impetigo, or in infected wounds, hemolytic streptococci are often found together with other bacterial strains, notably staphylococci, in mixed infections.

Streptococcal Virulence. The pathogenicity and virulence of the hemolytic streptococci are related to their production of extracellular substances that have a toxic effect on human cells. Bacterial products of this type were discussed in Chapter 6 (pp. 114 to 115).

The *hemolytic toxins*, or *streptolysins*, of these strains distinguish them from other streptococci found more usually among the commensal flora of the upper respiratory tract. The streptolysins of virulent strains completely destroy red blood cells in laboratory media. This property is referred to as *beta* hemolysis. Strains of the *Streptococcus viridans* group (which occur most frequently in the throat) grown on blood agar plates effect an incomplete hemolysis of blood cells termed *alpha* hemolysis. It is often accompanied by a green discoloration of the zone of incomplete lysis surrounding the *viridans* colonies. Nonhemolytic streptococci are referred to as *indifferent*, or *gamma*, strains. The streptolysins of beta streptococci are antigenic. The specific antibodies produced in response to their presence in the body during active streptococcal infection are called *antistreptolysins*. The laboratory detection of antistreptolysins in a patient's serum indicates present or past infection with beta-hemolytic streptococci.

In addition to hemolytic toxins, the virulent streptococci often produce the enzymes *hyaluroni-* *dase* and *streptokinase*, as well as a *leukocidin*. Hyaluronidase production probably accounts for some of the invasive properties of these organisms, assisting in their spread through local tissues by breaking down connective-tissue matrix. It is called a "spreading factor" on these grounds. Streptokinase activity may also assist in invasive spread because of its defibrinating effect on blood plasma, while leukocidin is destructive to phagocytes. These substances do not stimulate antibody formation to a significant degree.

An *erythrogenic toxin* produced by some strains of beta streptococci is responsible for the skin rash of scarlet fever. The soluble toxin is distributed through the body via the blood stream from a site of streptococcal infection in the throat. Its toxicity for cells in the skin results in the characteristic diffuse reddening of the scarlatinal rash. This substance is antigenic and stimulates the formation of an antibody capable of neutralizing its effects on the dermal tissues.

The capacity of beta-hemolytic streptococci to produce some or all of these substances contributes to their virulence and is manifest in their clinical infections as invasiveness, or toxigenicity, or both.

The Somatic Antigens of Hemolytic Streptococci. The somatic substances of these organisms (as opposed to the extracellular products described above) also have antigenicity, and their serologic classification has some epidemiologic importance. The method recognizes differences in the somatic antigens of different hemolytic strains and separates them into groups (lettered) and distinct types (numbered) within the groups. Most of the strains of pathogenic importance to man fall into group A (hence the frequent use of this term), while many of the animal pathogens occur in groups B and C. Group D contains the fecal streptococci, or enterococci, which are commensalistic in the human intestinal tract but potentially pathogenic for systemic tissues (they are often involved in urinary tract and wound infections and are important agents of subacute bacterial endocarditis). A number of other serologic groups exist (E through O) but these strains are rarely associated with human disease.

Within group A, many type-specific strains can also be recognized serologically.

The grouping and typing of beta streptococci are not essential to routine bacteriologic diagnosis, but they can be very useful in the epidemiologic identification of the sources of sporadic or epidemic streptococcal disease. Also, some of the important noninfectious sequelae of streptococcal infection, such as rheumatic fever and acute glomerulonephritis, are associated with certain types of group A strains.

Antibacterial immunity is acquired during the course of natural, active infection with the hemolytic streptococci. Antibodies directed against the type-specific somatic antigens of the group A strain that induced the disease may persist in the body for several years. They are not protective, however, against the other types within the group.

The alpha and gamma strains of streptococci are not easily classified by serologic methods, and immune reactions with these strains have no apparent significance.

The Clinical Streptococcal Diseases of Respiratory Entry

1. Streptococcal Sore Throat. Streptococcal infection of the pharyngeal tissues is characterized by edema and reddening of the posterior and anterior surfaces of the throat and soft palate. (They have a swollen, "beefy" look.) Petechial lesions are sometimes seen. When the tonsils and other lymphoid tissue are involved, an acute exudative response occurs. The draining cervical lymph nodes may become tender and enlarged; fever and malaise are frequent.

2. Scarlet Fever. This disease results when (1) the causative strain involved in streptococcal sore throat produces *erythrogenic toxin*, or (2) the person in whom this occurs is *not* immune to the toxin. In addition to the lesions visible in the throat, symptoms of generalized toxemia appear together with the characteristic skin rash. The febrile reaction intensifies, nausea and vomiting may occur, and the white blood cell count rises. The rash is distributed to the neck and chest, the

axillary and inguinal folds, and the soft skin of the inner sides of the arms and thighs. (Desquamation of these skin areas, and also of the hands and feet, occurs during convalescence from the disease.) The tongue is also involved in the mucosal reactions. It becomes swollen and reddened, and the papillae protrude, giving an effect described as "strawberry tongue."

The erythrogenic toxin is antigenic, stimulating the production of specific antitoxin. As antitoxin levels rise in the circulating blood, the skin reaction begins to subside. The neutralization of toxin by antibody at the sites of the rash forms the basis for an immunologically diagnostic skin test: the *Schultz-Charlton reaction*. Scarlatinal antitoxin injected intradermally into the center of a reddened area of skin produces visible blanching at the site of injection, within a few hours. Antitoxin levels produced during the course of the disease are durable and protect the individual from the erythrogenic effects of future streptococcal throat infections. This probably accounts for the fact that many cases of streptococcal sore throat occur without the development of scarlet fever. The incidence and severity of scarlet fever have been declining in this country for a number of years, but this fact is probably related not only to antitoxin immunity, but also to the frequent therapeutic use of penicillin and other antibiotics to which beta streptococci are highly susceptible. Prompt therapy of the initial throat infection effectively prevents the development of scarlet fever by also aborting the production of erythrogenic toxin by the infecting strain.

The Dick test is an immunologic method of demonstrating scarlatinal antitoxin immunity in healthy individuals. This test is similar to the Schick test used to determine diphtheria antitoxin immunity. In both instances, a small amount of the pertinent bacterial toxin is injected into the skin (intradermally). If little or no antitoxin is available in the circulating blood to neutralize the effects of the toxin, local damage to the skin at the injection site will occur in a few hours. If the individual possesses a protective level of antitoxin, however, the toxin introduced will be neutralized, and the injection site will remain essentially normal in appearance.

Laboratory Diagnosis

I. Identification of the Organism (*Streptococcus pyogenes*)

The microscopic, cultural, and serologic characteristics of the virulent streptococci may be summarized as follows:

A. They are Gram-positive cocci that grow in chains (see Fig. 14–4).

B. They are aerobic organisms that grow best on blood-enriched media. Microaerophilic incubation (decreased atmospheric O_2 and increased CO_2 provided in a "candle jar") enhances the speed and extent of their growth. Isolated colonies on blood agar media are characteristically surrounded by zones of *beta hemolysis*.

C. They may be serologically identified by grouping and typing methods when epidemiologic considerations warrant. Most of the pathogenic strains that cause human disease fall into serologic group A.

D. See also Chapter 12 and pages 319 and 327 to 328 of this chapter.

II. Identification of Patient's Serum Antibodies

A. Antibacterial (somatic) antibodies are type-specific. They have no practical value in the diagnosis of current infection because they arise late in disease. Type-specific antibodies present in the early stages of an infection probably reflect previous encounters with strains other than that causing the current disease.

B. Antistreptolysin titers are indicative of current or past infection with beta-hemolytic strains of streptococci. The titer (level of antibody) is a clue to the recency of infection.

C. The Schultz-Charlton skin test with scarlatinal *antitoxin* may have diagnostic value in the recognition of the scarlet fever rash.

D. The skin test with Dick *toxin* may be useful for determining antitoxic immunity for scarlatinal disease in healthy individuals who may have previously encountered erythrogenic strains of beta streptococci. This test does not diagnose scarlet fever. It is applied when epidemiologic information is desired as to the history of previous infection with erythrogenic strains. Dick-negative persons are immune to the toxic effects of scarlet fever, but not to the bacterial infection of streptococcal sore throat.

III. Specimens for Diagnosis

A. Throat or nasopharyngeal swabs, in transport broth, for smear and culture. (Smears may be inconclusive since several varieties of streptococci are normally present in the throat.)

B. Whole blood (or serum) for antistreptolysin titer. At least two samples should be submitted: one collected during the acute stage of illness (when the titer may be low), and another taken in the late or convalescent stage to determine whether the antibody level has increased.

IV. Special Laboratory Tests

A. The fluorescent antibody technique may be applied, if locally available, to the recognition of group A streptococci in respiratory secretions.

Epidemiology

I. Communicability of Infection

A. RESERVOIR, SOURCES, AND TRANSMISSION ROUTES. Man is the reservoir for group A strep-

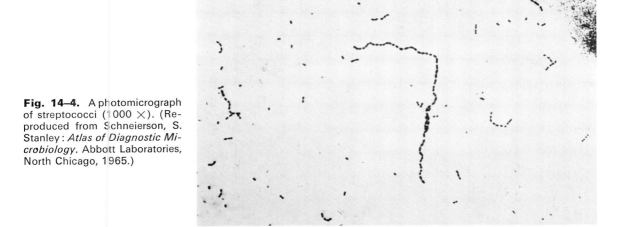

Fig. 14–4. A photomicrograph of streptococci (1000 ✕). (Reproduced from Schneierson, S. Stanley: *Atlas of Diagnostic Microbiology.* Abbott Laboratories, North Chicago, 1965.)

tococci. Asymptomatic carriers as well as patients in the acute and convalescent stages of disease shed these organisms in their respiratory secretions. Transmission is by droplet spread, direct contact, and indirect contact with many temporarily contaminated environmental sources, including milk or food. Contaminated hands may carry these organisms everywhere: from handkerchiefs to clothing, skin, and food, as well as objects handled. Droplet spray contaminates many nearby surfaces also, including the faces of close contacts.

B. INCUBATION PERIOD. Rarely more than three days.

C. COMMUNICABLE PERIOD. Persists during the incubation period and throughout clinical illness or longer, unless adequately treated with specific antimicrobial drugs. The carrier state may last for many months, and untreated persons with exudative lesions are a constant source of virulent organisms. Adequate antibiotic therapy can eliminate the communicability of disease, if not all streptococci, within 24 to 48 hours. Repeated cultures may be useful in marking the end of the communicable period.

D. IMMUNITY. Susceptibility to streptococcal sore throat and scarlet fever is general, although certain immunities develop as noted: antitoxin immunity to erythrogenic toxin prevents scarlet fever but not sore throat; antibacterial immunity is specific for the infecting type but does not prevent repeated infection with other types. Artificial immunization, active or passive, is not practical with toxins or antitoxins and not effective with vaccines or antibacterial sera.

II. Control of Active Infection

A. ISOLATION. For 24 to 48 hours from the start of antibiotic therapy, provided the latter is continued until infection is eliminated. This varies with the severity of the individual case, but the average course of therapy is one week to ten days. Infection control may be verified by repeated throat cultures.

B. PRECAUTIONS. Concurrent disinfection of respiratory discharges and all items contaminated thereby. Terminal disinfectant-cleaning.

C. TREATMENT. Penicillin is the usual drug of choice. Streptococci are also susceptible to erythromycin and the tetracyclines. Dose and route of administration are chosen to achieve a maximum effect as promptly as possible.

D. CONTROL OF CONTACTS

1. *Quarantine.* Not indicated.

2. *Prophylaxis.* Immunization not available. Chemoprophylaxis is sometimes indicated for unusually susceptible contacts for whom the hazards of infectious disease are great (the very young, the very old or debilitated.)

3. *Case Finding.* Not indicated except in outbreaks.

E. EPIDEMIC CONTROLS. Local health departments require individual case reports of scarlet fever. For other streptococcal diseases, reports of epidemics are required. In the latter situation, control methods begin with efforts to find the source and mode of transmission. Serologic identification of the group and type of streptococcal strain involved in active infections is of importance in the detection of sources. Suspected persons, milk, or food can then be checked by bacteriologic and serologic techniques. People involved in epidemic outbreaks are isolated and treated with antibiotics. Contaminated commercial supplies of food or milk are removed from the market. The latter sources may be pinpointed by examining the distribution of cases and their possible exposure to common transmission routes.

III. Prevention

A. Public education on the ease and the hazards of the transmission of streptococcal diseases; the need for personal hygienic controls and for prompt medical control of developing illness.

B. Control of food- and milk-handlers.
   Inspection of dairy cows for mastitis or other infection.
   Sanitation of dairy establishments.
   Pasteurization of milk (boil or discard if evidence of streptococcal contamination exists).

C. Penicillin prophylaxis for children and others for whom the risk of repeated infection is great. The group includes those who have had rheumatic fever or other diseases as an aftermath to streptococcal infection (see below).

Sequelae of Group A Streptococcal Infections

Late manifestations or consequences of streptococcal throat infections are recognized in the development of *rheumatic fever, acute hemorrhagic glomerulonephritis,* or *erythema nodosum* in a small proportion of patients. These diseases are neither infectious nor communicable. They are believed to develop as a consequence of delayed hypersensitive responses to streptococcal antigens.

1. Rheumatic Fever.   This is the most important and frequent of the poststreptococcal diseases. Following upper respiratory tract infection with group A beta streptococci, about 1 to 3 per cent of patients (the incidence is highest in childhood) develop rheumatic fever after an average interval of three weeks. The major clinical symptoms include fever, carditis, and polyarthritis (inflammatory involvement of joints, usually migratory in pattern). The severity of symptoms varies from the mild and scarcely noticeable to acute illness with irreversible cardiac damage. The lesions of the disease may include skin involvement (subcutaneous nodules), and central nervous system injury (chorea). Rheumatic fever may persist as a chronic disease for years, or it may be a recurrent acute or subacute problem following repeated streptococcal infections. Most of the serologic types of the group A strains have been demonstrated in the predisposing throat infections. When numerous cases of rheumatic fever are grouped as an aftermath of a streptococcal epidemic, epidemiologic studies usually relate them to the specific infecting strain.

2. Acute Hemorrhagic Glomerulonephritis.   Hemorrhagic lesions in the glomeruli may develop following streptococcal infection. The clinical accompaniment of this injury includes hematuria, albuminuria, generalized edema, and hypertension. The average interval between infection and this type of sequel is shorter than for rheumatic fever. Glomerulonephritis is usually an acute disease from which most patients recover without residual damage, and recurrent episodes of this type are rare. Occasionally, however, symptoms of rheumatic fever may occur together with those of glomerulonephritis, in a more serious and generalized hypersensitive response to streptococcal proteins or toxins.

3. Erythema Nodosum.   This disease is not always specifically related to preceding streptococcal infection, but it can appear as a recurring sequel to repeated bouts with hemolytic streptococci. It is characterized by the cropping of tender, red, subcutaneous nodules, distributed chiefly over the arms and legs, accompanied by fever and general malaise. This type of lesion is sometimes seen in rheumatic fever, but it occurs more usually as a distinct entity from which recovery is complete.

> *The laboratory diagnosis* of these diseases is retrospective with regard to previous bacteriologic evidence of streptococcal infection. Current demonstration of significant titers of antistreptolysins in the patient's serum gives support to the clinical diagnosis.

The epidemiology of the streptococcal sequelae does not include considerations of their *control,* since they are not communicable. The primary concern is *prevention,* particularly of rheumatic fever with its potential for permanent cardiac damage. The prompt therapy of active streptococcal disease, with a course of antibiotic at levels geared to eliminate the organism quickly and completely, may prevent or limit the distribution of sensitizing streptococcal proteins through the body and reduce the incidence of rheumatic fever. Penicillin prophylaxis for children or others who have had rheumatic fever can successfully prevent its recurrence.

Subacute Bacterial Endocarditis

Subacute bacterial endocarditis (often abbreviated to SBE) is included in this section dealing with the streptococcal diseases because it is so often associated with *Streptococcus viridans* or other streptococci indigenous to the respiratory

and oral flora. Other commensalistic organisms of the normal mucosal surfaces may be involved in SBE, however, including various species of the Gram-negative enteric bacilli.

This disease is not communicable. Its epidemiology reveals no relationship to the entry of infectious pathogenic microorganisms by respiratory or other routes. SBE is an infection of *endogenous* origin (see Chap. 30), involving the localization of organisms from indigenous sources at some site of previous injury on the endocardium, usually a valve surface. At least two factors appear to be essential to the development of subacute bacterial endocarditis: (1) a pre-existing defect of valvular endocardium (though this may not be clinically detectable before the onset of SBE), and (2) bacteremic distribution of microorganisms from a resident focus on a skin or mucosal surface disrupted by trauma, surgery, or some manipulation.

The great majority of patients with SBE (better than 75 per cent) have a history of rheumatic fever as the most probable cause of the preexisting cardiac damage. Congenital cardiac defects and the valvular injuries induced by arteriosclerosis or syphilis may also set the scene for SBE.

Minor dental or throat surgery (tonsillectomy, adenoidectomy) is often considered to be the initiating cause of transient bacteremias that may lead to SBE. Many other possibilities exist as well, however: nonsurgical manipulation of genitourinary tissues (catheterization, cystoscopy, prostatic massage), ulcerative erosions or perforating lesions of the bowel, or the surgical transection of surfaces with a normal flora — all represent possible mechanisms by which commensalistic microorganisms may be introduced into the blood stream. Ordinarily these bacteremias are terminated rapidly, the organisms being incapable of localization in normal systemic human tissues. SBE may develop, however, if the microorganisms localize on damaged valvular surfaces and multiply there. The site may characteristically be involved in a fibrinous response to injury, and small aggregates of platelets in fibrin may be formed. Microorganisms can grow in this milieu protected from the action of phago-

cytes or other bactericidal components of blood. Their presence accelerates fibrinous tissue reaction, however, and "vegetations" are built up around their proliferating growth. From time to time bacteria are spilled into the blood stream from these aggregates. The bacteremia of SBE is usually intermittent and is heralded by spikes of fever as bacterial cells and their proteins are circulated. Increasing valvular dysfunction leads to symptoms of cardiac distress. If the situation is not arrested by antimicrobial treatment, the valve may be occluded by the vegetative growth or fail to function because of loss of elasticity, with fatal results in either case. These vegetations are friable; that is, small pieces may break off in the surging flow of blood propelled through the valve by ventricular contraction. These infectious emboli then travel down the arterial vessels, finally lodging in and occluding vessels that are too small to pass them further. The seriousness of this situation depends on the nature of the tissue thus deprived of its blood supply and also on the capacity of the organisms to continue multiplying at the new site.

The laboratory diagnosis of SBE depends on the successful isolation of the causative organism from blood cultures taken at the time of bacteremic episodes. There is sometimes a fairly continuous release of small numbers of organisms from the valvular lesions, but more often the bacteremia is intermittent. When very few organisms are present in samples of blood drawn for culture, several days may be required for their growth and identification. The collection of blood for culture should be timed to coincide with febrile episodes reflecting a "shower" of organisms into the circulation. Several samples should be drawn during the course of spiking fever to improve the odds for securing a diagnostic culture.

Strains of *Streptococcus viridans* (alpha-hemolytic) are most frequently isolated from blood cultures in SBE. The fecal streptococci (enterococci) are less common, and coliform bacilli and anaerobic organisms are still less frequent.

It should be noted that modern methods of heart surgery, including the use of arterial catheters, open easy avenues for infection of damaged

or prosthetic valves. The most rigorous aseptic precautions are required to protect patients undergoing cardiac surgery or catheterization from directly implanted infection. The most successful results of these surgical techniques may be compromised or negated by microbial contamination that develops into infection, whether it be low-grade but persistent, or acute to fulminating. The organisms most frequently involved in this situation are staphylococci of the skin and mucosa. Some are the benign coagulase-negative strains of the resident skin flora (*Staphylococcus epidermidis*), which generally induce subacute but troublesome problems; others are the virulent coagulase-positive pigmented variety (*Staphylococcus aureus*) capable of causing acute or overwhelming infection, particularly of traumatized or malfunctioning tissues. (See Chap. 29.)

The treatment of subacute bacterial endocarditis of streptococcal origin generally employs penicillin and streptomycin in combination. When the agent is obtained in laboratory culture, antibiotic susceptibility testing is useful in indicating the choice of drugs. The physician may find it of even greater value, however, to know what quantities of the drug of his choice are required to kill, rather than merely suppress, the organism. Quantitative tube dilution assays of the antibiotic are performed with the organism isolated from the patient, so that the size, frequency, and route of administration of the drug may be adjusted to maintain a bactericidal level of antibiotic in the blood stream and tissues. The patient's blood serum can also be assayed for its bactericidal activity against the causative agent as a further measure of the adequacy of therapy and of response to it. (See Chap. 6.)

The epidemiology of SBE points to the need for preventive measures (not for communicable infection controls): prevention of the causes of endocardial injury (rheumatic fever is the primary target), and control of the transmission of the infecting organisms from their sources. Chemoprophylaxis has helped to reduce the incidence of rheumatic fever, and it is also useful in decreasing the occurrence of bacteremia after surgery or other provocative procedures. In the latter application, antibiotics are given before, during, and after surgery, but this practice should take into consideration the susceptibility of the cardiac patient to the risk of infection as opposed to others for whom a transient bacteremia is not a major challenge. Antibiotic-induced changes in the normal flora and the emergence of resistant bacterial strains counterbalance the prophylactic use of antibiotics in nonselective situations.

Whooping Cough (Pertussis)

The Clinical Disease

Whooping cough is a highly communicable, acute respiratory disease, particularly prevalent in children. It begins with a catarrhal stage that resembles a cold, except that it persists for 10 to 12 days, the initial mild cough becoming more progressively irritating, and finally paroxysmal. At this time, the organism is extending on a path of descent from its first upper respiratory localizations downward along the mucosal surfaces of the larynx, trachea, and the bronchial tree. The epithelial tissue along the way is injured and a leukocytic exudate is formed. Pneumonia may develop if the deep structures of the lung are reached and the organisms multiply there in the interstitial tissues. Secondary opportunists may proliferate in alveolar exudates, but the pneumonia of pertussis is interstitial. Excessive mucous production in the bronchial tract may plug the lower airways. This is the cause of the paroxysm, which is characterized by a series of struggling coughs on a single inhalation ending with an involuntary "whoop" of inspiration through narrowed, mucus-filled passages. The mucus is clear but very tenacious and difficult to expel. Its obstruction of airways, together with the thickening of interstitial tissue in the lung itself, reduces the amount of oxygen available for the blood. Convulsions may ensue if the hypoxia continues. Antimicrobial drugs and immunotherapy may reduce the severity of the disease, but they do not change its course to any marked degree. The paroxysmal stage may remain acute for two to three weeks and persist for one or two months.

The mortality rate is low (about 0.2 per cent in the United States) for the general population but

high for infants: about 80 per cent of the deaths occur in children under one year of age. Active immunization programs have greatly reduced the incidence of this disease in the past 20 years, but epidemic cycles continue every two to four years. Pertussis may occur in all seasons, but the epidemic incidence is highest in the winter and early spring.

Laboratory Diagnosis

I. Identification of the Organism (*Bordetella pertussis*; formerly called *Hemophilus pertussis*)

A. Microscopic Characteristics. The organism is a small Gram-negative bacillus closely resembling the *Hemophilus* species with which it was once classified. (See Chap. 12, p. 293.)

B. Culture Characteristics. The pertussis bacillus requires complex media for its isolation and growth. An agar medium devised in 1906 is still among the most satisfactory in use. Called Bordet-Gengou medium (for the Belgian workers who formulated it), this is a mixture of potato infusion, glycerol, blood, and agar. It may be used in a Petri dish as a "cough plate," held a few inches in front of the patient's mouth during his coughing, or it may be inoculated with a nasopharyngeal swab. Penicillin is usually added to the medium to inhibit the growth of the other respiratory flora. The pertussis bacillus, which is resistant to penicillin, may then grow well as small transparent colonies surrounded by a zone of dark discoloration of the medium.

C. Serologic Methods of Identification. This organism possesses several components that are antigenic. Suspensions of the bacterial growth are agglutinated by specific antibodies in antiserum. The agglutination technique can be used, if necessary, to confirm the identity of isolated organisms.

II. Identification of Patient's Serum Antibodies. Agglutinins for *B. pertussis* appear in the patient's serum during an attack of whooping cough. They do not rise to significant levels until the third or fourth week, however, and are of little diagnostic value for this reason.

III. Specimens for Diagnosis

A. Nasopharyngeal swabs, in transport broth, for culture.

B. Cough plates are a useful alternative to swabs.

C. Blood for white cell counts. (Leukocytosis is striking [15,000 to 30,000], with a predominance of lymphocytes unusual in bacterial infections of the respiratory tract.)

IV. Special Laboratory Tests. The fluorescent antibody technique may be applied, if locally available, to the recognition of pertussis bacilli in respiratory secretions.

Epidemiology

I. Communicability of Infection

A. Reservoir, Sources, and Transmission Routes. Man is the only reservoir. Infectious respiratory secretions transmit the infection directly by droplet spread or indirectly by contamination of objects in the environment (including hands and handkerchiefs).

B. Incubation Period. Not more than 21 days, usually within seven to ten days.

C. Communicable Period. Communicability is highest in the late days of the incubation period and during the catarrhal stage. Familial contacts continue to run a high risk of infection until the paroxysmal stage begins to subside. In the schoolroom or out of doors, communicability is reduced by distance and by the susceptibility of the organism to the effects of drying. For general control, the disease should be considered communicable for a period extending from the seventh day following exposure to the end of the third week of the paroxysmal stage.

D. Immunity. Resistance to pertussis depends on specific immunity. The incidence of the clinical disease and of inapparent or atypical infections is highest in childhood, and especially in the preschool years. Active immunity acquired during an attack of the disease in childhood is durable, but occasional second attacks occur in exposed adults. Artificial active immunization is effective and should be started in infancy.

II. Control of Active Infection

A. Isolation. Children and other patients hospitalized with severe pertussis pneumonia must be isolated. Precautions are of most urgent

importance in hospital nurseries and pediatric wards. At home, the sick child should be separated from susceptible children (particularly young infants) insofar as practical. Outdoor play for the afebrile patient is better than confinement in close quarters. The school-age patient must be kept at home for the duration of the recognized communicable period (usually about four weeks).

B. PRECAUTIONS. Concurrent disinfection of nasal and oral secretions, vomitus, and all articles contaminated with these discharges. Hospital units are cleaned and disinfected terminally. At home, frequent cleaning and disinfection of the sickroom should be practiced. The protection of susceptible children includes separating and boiling dishes used by the infectious patient.

C. TREATMENT. Antibiotic therapy is not markedly effective but may help to modify the most severe symptoms, prevent secondary pulmonary infection, and shorten the communicable period. Chloramphenicol and the tetracyclines are the drugs of choice. In severe cases, human gamma globulin may be given to provide the support of passive antibody.

D. CONTROL OF CONTACTS

1. *Quarantine.* Nonimmune children *exposed* to whooping cough must be excluded from school or other public contacts with susceptible children for a two-week period. This time corresponds with the incubation and communicability of the disease. Exceptions may be granted for public schools that have adequate surveillance programs for the detection of early illness in children. Younger children and infants must be guarded from infection with particular care.

2. *Prophylaxis.* Susceptible children and adults exposed to whooping cough are candidates for an injection of gamma globulin. *Passive* immunization following exposure may ameliorate the disease or prevent it. *Active* immunization with vaccine is not usually prophylactic for exposed individuals because antibody response is too slow to be protective during the time when the causative organism implants and multiplies on susceptible respiratory membranes.

3. *Case Finding.* The obvious case may be found and isolated easily. Atypical cases, or those

that have been misdiagnosed, must also be found if adequate control is to be exercised.

E. EPIDEMIC CONTROLS. Individual cases must be reported to local health departments. Beyond this, alert and accurate case finding of unrecognized (and therefore unreported) active infections is the key to controlling further spread of the disease.

III. Prevention

A. IMMUNIZATION. Artificial active immunization during infancy now affords the best protection against whooping cough. Killed bacterial vaccines are available that effectively stimulate the production of protective antibody. Pertussis vaccine (usually combined with diphtheria and tetanus toxoids (DTP) may be given to infants two or three months of age. Timing should be geared to the seasonal and familial risk of infection. Effective artificial active immunization with currently available vaccine requires three injections at monthly intervals during the first year of life. A booster dose of the triple vaccine is advisable during the second year and another when school age is reached. Once the active immune process is underway, subsequent exposures to infection are minimized as to risk and result.

B. CONTROL OF RESERVOIR, SOURCES, AND TRANSMISSION ROUTES. The most effective control of the reservoir and sources of infection is accomplished by specific immunity actively acquired through the natural route of infection or, more safely, by artificial immunization programs. The availability of such programs, coupled with the education of the public as to their value, has undoubtedly contributed to the declining incidence and fatality rates of pertussis in the United States and other countries.

Diphtheria

The Clinical Disease. Diphtheria is not seen today on the frightening epidemic scale of former years. It remains a potential threat, however, as evidenced by sporadic cases and small outbreaks that occur among persons who lack naturally or

artificially acquired active immunity against the toxic components of infection. While the incidence of clinical diphtheria has sharply declined since the introduction of nearly universal artificial immunization, the case fatality rate of 5 to 10 per cent has not changed significantly.

Diphtheria begins as an acute infection of the mucous membranes of the upper respiratory tract. As the diphtheria bacilli grow, they produce a toxin that destroys the local epithelial cells and induces an inflammatory response at the site. The necrotic surface epithelium becomes enmeshed in a fibrinous and cellular exudate that lies like a membrane over the involved area. This *pseudomembrane* formation advances as the organisms continue to grow. It may cover the tonsils and pharynx or extend downward to the larynx and trachea. Laryngeal diphtheria may cause death by suffocation, particularly when it occurs in infants or young children. The pseudomembrane is tough and cannot be lifted without tearing the structures beneath, leaving an exposed, bleeding undersurface.

Patients often appear extremely toxic, even though fever is moderate (100° to 102° F). The cervical lymph nodes become enlarged and tender, and there may be extensive edema of the neck. The organisms continue to proliferate in the pseudomembrane and to produce toxin, which is absorbed and distributed through the body. The toxin may cause severe injury to the parenchymal cells of the liver, adrenals, kidneys, and (a more immediate threat) the myocardium. Cardiac deaths are frequent among patients succumbing in the stage of systemic toxic involvement. Cranial and peripheral nerves, both motor and sensory, may also be damaged, with resulting paralysis of ocular muscles, the soft palate, or the extremities, depending on the nerve affected by toxin localization.

Aside from this picture of classical diphtheria as an acute infectious disease of the upper respiratory tract, accompanied by systemic toxicity, the diphtheria bacillus is sometimes associated with wound or skin infections. These superficial infections may also be marked by local membrane formation, but absorption of toxin with resulting systemic toxicity either does not occur or is very

minor in effect. Diphtheritic skin or wound infections are not common in areas of temperate climate but may be frequent in tropical countries. The lesions may persist without healing for weeks or months.

The severity of diphtheria infections is a reflection of the capacity of the organism to establish itself, multiply, and produce its exotoxin. The speed of multiplication and the amount of toxin produced (and absorbed) are a measure of virulence. The most severe disease is produced by strains that elaborate large quantities of toxin in a short time.

Prompt *clinical* diagnosis of diphtheria is the most important factor in the prevention of crippling or fatal toxicity. Immediate passive immunization with antitoxin provides circulating antibody to neutralize toxin *before* it can attach to cells in the myocardium or elsewhere and cause irreparable damage. Simultaneous therapy with an appropriate antibiotic then eliminates the infectious agent, and the source of toxin, from localization in the throat. The diagnosis is confirmed in the laboratory by demonstration of the organism in smears and cultures of the throat exudate.

Laboratory Diagnosis

I. Identification of the Organism (*Corynebacterium diphtheriae*) (*Klebs-Loeffler bacillus*). The diphtheria bacillus is one of several species belonging to the genus *Corynebacterium*, but it is the only one of pathogenic importance. The others are common commensals of the skin and mucous membranes, however, and the bacteriologist must distinguish these "diphtheroid" species from *C. diphtheriae* in cultures of material from the nose and throat.

A. MICROSCOPIC CHARACTERISTICS. The corynebacteria are Gram-positive bacilli, nonspore-forming, and nonmotile. *C. diphtheriae* is a slender, rather attenuated bacillus, with granular contents that stain irregularly and give it a beaded or barred appearance. Individual rods are often club-shaped, being more swollen at one end than the other. They lie in characteristic "V" and "Y" formations, or in palisaded groups (see Fig. 14–5). The diphtheroids appear in this arrangement also, but they are usually shorter, thicker rods than diphtheria bacilli and have a coarser appearance.

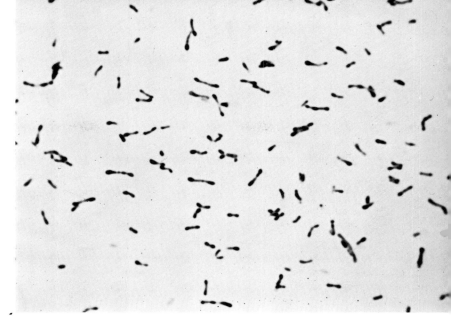

Fig. 14–5. *Corynebacterium diphtheriae,* the organism that causes diphtheria. Note the club shapes, beading, and V and Y figures. (Reprinted with permission of U.S. Public Health Service Audiovisual Facility, Atlanta, Ga.)

The distinction may be very difficult to make in direct smears of throat exudate, but the smear report is evaluated by the physician in the light of clinical findings. If these suggest diphtheria, the decision to give antitoxin is made at once, with or without bacteriologic confirmation.

B. CULTURE CHARACTERISTICS. All the coryne-bacteria grow aerobically on blood agar, but certain special media are useful in the selection and differentiation of the diphtheria bacillus from other organisms present in throat cultures. Loefflers' medium is often used because it does not support the growth of streptococci and pneumococci, but offers enough nutrient for the growth of *C. diphtheriae.* The addition of potassium tellurite to blood agar inhibits the development of many throat organisms and also distinguishes colonies of *C. diphtheriae* from other bacteria that are capable of growing in the presence of this chemical. The former take up the tellurite and react with it, the result being a gray to black coloration of the *C. diphtheriae* colonies, which makes them stand out from others.

The colonial growth of *C. diphtheriae* is confirmed by Gram-stained smears, and the virulence of the isolate is then tested in laboratory animals. Since the virulence of this organism depends on its toxigenicity, animal tests are designed to show whether or not the isolated organism, or its products, can produce a toxic effect and, if so, whether this effect can be forestalled by diphtheria antitoxin. There are a number of ways of performing a virulence test, but the following description

of one convenient method should suffice to illustrate the principle:

The pure culture growth of the organism on a solid medium is emulsified in broth. The shaved side of a guinea pig or a rabbit is injected intracutaneously with 0.1 to 0.2 ml of this suspension. The suspension is then set aside in the refrigerator. After four hours, the animal is given 500 units of antitoxin by intraperitoneal inoculation. Within 30 minutes, the suspension of organisms is injected intracutaneously into a second shaved site. Both sites may show some inflammation within the next day or so, but if injury was due to specific diphtheria toxin, only the site injected *before* antitoxin was given will continue to develop a necrotizing lesion during the second and third days. If the organism is not virulent, the original injection will not produce a significant reaction.

The genetic mechanism of toxin production by virulent strains of *C. diphtheriae* was explained some years ago (1951) when it was discovered that a bacterial virus (bacteriophage) infecting the toxin-producers was responsible for directing the cellular manufacture of the toxic substance. The virus acts as a gene within the bacterial cell it infects. When it is present, the cells are toxigenic. In the absence of the bacteriophage gene, the diphtheria bacillus is incapable of toxin production, though it retains its ability to invade and multiply in human epithelial tissue.

II. Identification of Patient's Serum Antibodies. The demonstration of circulating antitoxin is not appropriate in the diagnosis of diphtheria, because

active production of antibody in the sick individual occurs much too late to have diagnostic value. Healthy individuals may be tested for antitoxin immunity, however, by a skin test with diphtheria toxin. This is the *Schick test* described previously (Chap. 7). Intracutaneous injection of the toxin induces no local reaction in persons with protective levels of circulating antitoxin, but a Schick-positive reaction indicates an inadequate immunity and the need for artificial active immunization with diphtheria toxoid.

III. Specimens for Diagnosis. Material from the suspected lesion in the throat is submitted for smear and culture. This is the only type of specimen of diagnostic value, since diphtheria bacilli do not invade the body widely, nor do they enter the blood stream. Material is best collected by running a thin swab or wire loop under the lifted edge of the pseudomembrane, for the organisms may be present in nearly pure culture in the active area beneath, but many saprophytic organisms may be living on the dead tissue at the surface of this membrane.

Epidemiology

I. Communicability of Infection

A. Reservoir, Sources, and Transmission Routes. The reservoir is man, clinically or inapparently infected. Discharges from the normal respiratory membranes of carriers are a source of infection as well as those from active throat or skin lesions. The organism is transmitted in direct contacts, by droplet spread, and through indirect contacts with objects contaminated by respiratory secretions. Milk contaminated after pasteurization or raw milk may transmit the infection.

B. Incubation Period. Usually only a few days (two to five).

C. Communicable Period. This varies with the persistence of the diphtheria bacilli in the lesions or on the recovering mucous membranes. The carrier state may persist for many weeks following convalescence. Some health department regulations require continued quarantine of the convalescent until two or three negative nose-and-throat cultures have been obtained on consecutive days. Antibiotic therapy, or the surgical removal of tonsils and other harboring tissues when indicated, reduces the number of carriers in a shorter time, but these measures have not eliminated the problem completely.

D. Immunity. Resistance to the clinical disease is chiefly dependent on antitoxin immunity, passively or actively acquired, by natural or artificial means. An attack of the disease usually confers a durable active immunity (the passive antibody acquired through antitoxin administration in the acute stage of infection does not persist for more than two to three weeks). Infants born of immune mothers acquire passive immunity congenitally, but this does not last more than five or six months. Artificial active immunization with diphtheria toxoid affords the most effective control.

II. Control of Active Infection

A. Isolation. Patients ill with diphtheria should be isolated until bacteriologically negative throat-and-nose cultures can be demonstrated after antibiotic therapy has ceased. Two cultures from the nose and two from the throat, taken on consecutive days, are required as a basic rule. When cultures continue to be positive after clinical recovery is complete, a negative virulence test on the latest organism recovered can release the patient from isolation. If the culture is of demonstrated virulence, however, a course of antibiotic therapy is repeated. In situations or areas where laboratory evidence is difficult to obtain, isolation may be terminated 14 days after onset with fair assurance of safety.

B. Precautions. Concurrent disinfection of all articles involved in the respiratory transfer of infection. Terminal cleaning-disinfection of the room should be thorough.

C. Treatment. Antitoxin is given in a single dose of 20,000 to 80,000 units as indicated by the duration and severity of symptoms, after careful predetermination of hypersensitivity to horse serum proteins. Penicillin and erythromycin are the antibiotics of choice for antibacterial therapy,

but they have no effect on diphtheria toxin or the toxic symptoms of the disease.

D. CONTROL OF CONTACTS

1. *Quarantine.* Intimate susceptible contacts of an active case should be held in *modified* quarantine (see Chap. 10, p. 207) until nose and throat cultures are reported to be negative. Adult contacts who care for children or handle food should be removed from these occupations until bacteriologic evidence shows them not to be carriers. Contacts who are found to have inapparent infections should be placed on a course of antibiotic therapy.

2. *Prophylaxis.* The prophylactic use of antitoxin is indicated for nonimmune children under ten years of age who have been intimately exposed to the disease. These children should also be started on a course of active immunization with toxoid. The physician may determine the need for active or passive immunization of older children and adults exposed to the disease if he can obtain an accurate history of previous immunization. If not, the Schick test may be applied. Whether or not they require *passive* immunization, Schick-positive persons exposed to diphtheria should receive toxoid immunization, as a primary course or in a booster dose, depending on the history. Immunization may be particularly important for older people whose immunity has waned.

3. *Case Finding.* In communities where the population has been universally immunized, carriers and atypical cases are rare. When an unusual incidence of clinical diphtheria begins to appear in any community, however, a careful search for possible sources should be made.

E. EPIDEMIC CONTROLS. Immediate surveys are made to determine the general level of immunity in the population involved. Active immunization is conducted on the scale indicated, concentrating on the youngest children but extending to all age groups. The search for contacts and sources is intensified. Individual case reporting is required as a rule in this country and others. The international control of diphtheria requires the recent immunization of persons traveling in or through endemic areas.

III. Prevention

A. IMMUNIZATION. Artificial active immunization with diphtheria toxoid on a mass scale has provided effective control of the human reservoir of this disease. It should be provided early in life, preferably at three to four months of age, and reinforced at intervals, at least through adolescence. In infancy, purified alum-precipitated toxoid (see Chap. 7, p. 145) is given together with tetanus toxoid and pertussis vaccine, in a combined preparation known as *DTP*. The initial series requires several injections at four-to-six-week intervals.

This preparation combining three immunizing agents may be used in an initial program for children up to the age of four years. Nonimmune children between the ages of 4 and 12 are given diphtheria and tetanus toxoid only, and this is feasible for nonimmune adults also. Booster toxoids for adults are adjusted in their preparation to avoid the complication of hypersensitive reactions to bacterial proteins encountered naturally or through previous immunizations.

It has become clear in recent years that artificial immunization begun in infancy must be reinforced at primary school age and again during adolescence. During the past two decades an increased age incidence of clinical diphtheria has been observed in all countries where mass immunization of children has been practiced. This is because the organism tends to die away in immunized populations, so that there is no repeated, natural stimulus to immunity through inapparent infection. As artificially acquired immunity wanes, therefore, it is not reinforced by natural infection, and the adult population slowly becomes more susceptible. The introduction of carriers into such a population may lead to an outbreak involving the nonimmune of all ages, as reported from Holland during World War II and more recently from Denmark and Great Britain. (Mass immunization to diphtheria began in this country in 1922 when William H. Park, of the New York City Department of Health, first applied the principle to the large-scale protection of children.)

Adults who are unusually subject to the risk of

exposure to diphtheria-carriers or infectious patients should have a booster dose of the type of toxoid prepared for their age group. Diphtheria exposure is particularly likely for hospital personnel who work closely with patients, for military personnel traveling to or stationed in endemic areas, and for professional travelers (such as airline hostesses), teachers, and others in contact with many people from different parts of the world.

The future control of diphtheria depends on the continuing education of people everywhere as to the necessity of adequate artificial active immunization.

Tuberculosis

The Clinical Disease. Tuberculosis is a chronic bacterial disease, characterized in its course by a continuing interplay between the durable invading organism and the host's mechanisms for resistance, the latter being greatly affected by the development of hypersensitive host responses as well. Specific immunity is primarily of the hypersensitive type, but nonspecific resistance is also extremely important.

Pathogenesis. The virulence of tubercle bacilli is associated with their capacity for establishment and multiplication in the human host and with the degree of their resistance to his defenses. After first entry of the bacilli into a susceptible host, production, progression, or healing of tuberculous lesions depends on the numbers of invading organisms and their success in multiplying locally despite nonspecific host resistance.

When lesions are produced, they appear as one of two types, depending on the local host reaction. *Exudative lesions* are formed by an acute inflammatory reaction, with engulfment of tubercle bacilli in a fluid exudate containing polymorphonuclear and monocytic cells. This type of lesion may subside and heal; it may progress and lead to necrosis of local tissue; or it may develop into a *tubercle*. This second type of lesion is called *productive* (i.e., producing new tissue) because it consists of cells (without exudate) organized in a

fairly definite way around the offending organisms. It is also called a *granuloma* because it resembles a tumor and is composed of granulation tissue. In the central part of the tubercle there is a compact mass of large multinucleated cells (giant cells), formed by the coalescence of mononuclear cells. Surrounding this is a zone of "epithelioid" cells, and the outer zone is composed of lymphocytes, monocytes, and fibroblasts. The tubercle bacilli reside in the center of the tubercle, principally intracellularly, within the giant cells or mononuclear cells (see Fig. 14–6). Eventually the tubercle may become fibrous at its periphery and calcified within. The organisms may remain viable for years even under these conditions, or they may slowly dwindle and die. Often, however, the central area of the tubercle becomes soft and cheesy, in a process called *caseation* or *caseation necrosis*. Caseous tubercles sometimes break open, spilling their contents into surrounding tissue and forming a cavity that then may heal by fibrosis and calcification.

Spread of the organisms through the body may occur in a number of ways. From exudative lesions or cavitating tubercles they may extend directly into adjacent tissue, enter the blood stream or the lymphatic flow, or find their way along mucosal surfaces. The cavitation of a caseous tubercle in the lung, for example, may spill organisms into a bronchus. From here they may pass downward into the lung or be coughed up into the throat, swallowed, and passed into the gastrointestinal tract. When tubercle bacilli *initially* enter the body through the respiratory or alimentary routes, they are spread from their original site through the lymphatic ducts into the regional lymph nodes.

Patterns of Disease. Two types of tuberculosis are recognized: the *primary*, or first-infection type, and *reinfection* tuberculosis.

In primary tuberculosis, the initial lesion is of the acute exudative type from which a rapid spread occurs via the lymphatics to the regional nodes. The exudative lesion may quickly resorb and heal, usually with some residual fibrosis and scarring, but the involved lymph nodes become caseous. With time, the lymph nodes generally

are calcified to some degree. Primary tuberculosis occurs most frequently in childhood, but it may also be seen in adults who have not acquired infection previously. In first infections the primary lesion may occur in any part of the lung.

Reinfection tuberculosis is a more chronic disease, characterized by lesions of the productive type. Reinfection may be acquired from new exogenous sources, or it may be caused by organisms that survive in and extend from the primary lesions (endogenous reinfection). The regional lymph nodes are seldom involved in reinfection. The prominent lesions of this type of disease almost always begin in the apex of a lung and progress downward. Tubercles form, become caseous, and cavitate; the organisms pass down the bronchial tree to new sites where tubercle formation again resists their spread.

Endogenous reinfection may occur many months or years after first infections appear to be healed. Fibrosis and calcification are not always sufficient to suppress and finally destroy the organism. Lowered resistance of the host, possibly accompanied by increased hypersensitivity, may permit a breakthrough of organisms from a primary focus or a regional lymph node, with a resulting distribution and spread as described previously. Occasionally, organisms from a cavitating focus enter the blood or lymph stream in sufficient numbers to assure widespread distribution throughout the body. General infection then ensues, with tubercle formation in many organs. This distribution is called *miliary* tuberculosis because the tubercles are small and hard and resemble millet seed.

Resistance, Hypersensitivity, and Immunity. The speed and extent with which reinfection tuberculosis progresses are partly determined by the numbers of organisms released from productive foci and the route of spread available to them. Progress of the disease is also determined by the increasing capacity of the host to resist: that is, to localize the bacilli and retard their growth or destroy them and thus limit their dissemination. The nonspecific resistance of the inflammatory process and of the reticuloendothelial cells plays a primary role in first infection. The reactivity of the mononuclear cells increases, however, as a result of the first experience. They become more adept at phagocytosis of tubercle bacilli, and tubercle formation is often more rapid. This altered tissue reactivity is called *allergy*, or *hypersensitivity* (see Chap. 7). It confers a significant degree of increased (though still inadequate) resistance on the reinfected host, but at the same time it can lead to more extensive damage in tuberculous disease. The amount of caseation within tubercles, for example, is related to the hypersensitive response of mononuclear cells. Extensive caseation can lead to sloughing, cavitation, and further spread of organisms.

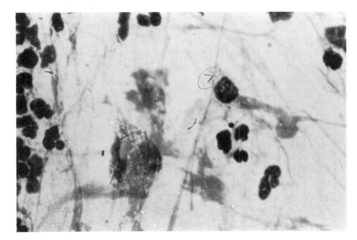

Fig. 14–6. A photomicrograph of a portion of a tubercle. Note the rod-shaped, granular tubercle bacilli. Some are lying within the mononuclear cell (upper right center); others are within the large multinuclear cell at lower left center (1000 ✕). (Courtesy of Dr. Kendall K. Kane, St. Luke's Hospital Center, New York, N.Y.)

The tuberculin skin test for hypersensitivity to the proteins of tubercle bacilli becomes positive during the course of first infection and remains so. Circulating antibodies specific for the cellular substances of tubercle bacilli also appear in tuberculosis but appear to play no part in the acquired resistance of reinfection. The role of the specific hypersensitive response in acquired resistance as compared with that of nonspecific factors still awaits more complete explanation.

Clinical Symptoms. The wide variety of symptoms in tuberculosis reflects the fact that the organism may involve any organ to which circumstances permit its spread. The intensity of symptoms depends on the numbers and location of foci and the host response to them. There may be no symptoms at all in a first infection, or the primary course may be rapidly progressive and sometimes fatal. The signs of reinfection tuberculosis may also be minimal or prominent. Common symptoms include fever and malaise, easy fatigue, and loss of weight. In pulmonary disease there may be a productive cough yielding blood as well as sputum. Tuberculosis of kidney, liver, bone, genital organs, or other tissues may occur simultaneously by hematogenous spread, usually from a pulmonary focus, or one or another of these sites may be involved separately, with symptoms characteristic of the localization.

Tuberculous meningitis may occur as a result of bacteremia. It is more commonly seen in children following first infection than in adults. The symptoms are more chronic and slowly progressive than those of the acute bacterial meningitides (see Bacterial Meningitis, this chapter), with lower cell counts that are predominantly lymphocytic. The clinical form of tuberculous meningitis is similar in some basic respects to that seen in extensions of fungous disease.

Laboratory Diagnosis

I. Identification of the Organism (*Mycobacterium tuberculosis*). The tubercle bacillus belongs to the genus Mycobacterium, which contains another well-known pathogen, *M. leprae*, the causative agent of leprosy (see Chap. 23). There are many saprophytic forms in the genus, a number that are associated with diseases of animals, and,

of increasing importance, an "atypical" group that resembles the human pathogen in some respects, including the production of human disease closely similar to tuberculosis.

A. MICROSCOPIC CHARACTERISTICS. The mycobacteria are bacilli that stain with difficulty. Once they take an appropriate stain, however, they resist decolorization, even by acids, and are referred to as "acid-fast" bacilli because of this property. The Ziehl-Neelsen stain (see Chap. 4) is most commonly used to identify them, the organisms appearing red against a blue background.

Tubercle bacilli are slender straight rods, often granular or beaded in appearance. Like the corynebacteria (see Diphtheria, this chapter), they are often seen in palisade formations, or in "V" and "L" positions that suggest a snapped stick. (The colloquial phrase "red snapper" is often quite appropriate.) (See Fig. 14–7.)

B. CULTURE CHARACTERISTICS. The growth rate of tubercle bacilli and most mycobacteria is much slower than that of other bacteria. Several days or weeks are required for their primary isolation, with an average incubation time of three to six weeks on laboratory media of most practical value. They are aerobic organisms, but their growth may be enhanced with increased atmospheric CO_2. Incubation is at 37° C.

A number of media are available for the culture of tubercle bacilli. Some of these contain complex nutrients, such as egg, potato, and serum. Others are simpler media formulated to provide the factors best known to promote growth. Many laboratories use two or more different media to ensure successful cultures.

Since tubercle bacilli may produce lesions in many parts of the body, many types of specimens can be appropriate for culture. Some of these, however, contain a number of commensalistic organisms indigenous to the region (sputum, uncatheterized urine, etc.). Many of these bacterial species will also grow on the media used for isolation of tubercle bacilli, and they grow very much faster. Their multiplication on the media depletes it rapidly of nutrient, and also makes the search for tubercle bacilli virtually impossible in the mixed culture. For these reasons it is necessary, prior to culture, to treat such specimens with chemicals that destroy bacteria other than *M. tuberculosis*. This takes advantage of the latter's greater resistance to alkalies, acids, quaternary ammonium compounds, and other chemical agents. The chemical treatment is carefully con-

trolled to avoid undue suppression of the tubercle bacilli themselves. Fluid specimens are then concentrated by centrifugation and the sediment is inoculated on appropriate culture media. Cultures are routinely examined every week for developing growth of *M. tuberculosis*, or every day in cases of clinical urgency. Negative cultures are not discarded until they have been incubated for at least eight weeks.

The lipoid, hydrophobic nature of the surface of tubercle bacilli accounts for their heaped, clumped colonial growth on the surface of solid media. Certain compounds with a detergent or wetting action (for example, Tween 80) are used in liquid media to permit more dispersed, and often more rapid, growth. It should also be noted that the waxy character of the surface of this organism contributes to its resistance to chemical and physical agents. Tubercle bacilli are not as readily killed by antiseptics or disinfectants as are other vegetative microorganisms. They are also more resistant to drying and are capable of surviving for long periods in dried sputum or other infectious discharges. For this reason, special care must be taken in the selection of chemical disinfectants, in the adjustment of their concentrations, and in timing of the disinfection period when tubercle bacilli are to be killed by chemical methods. Specific recommendations for the chemical disinfection of medical and surgical materials are to be found in Appendix VII.

C. Serologic Methods of Identification. None.

II. Identification of Patient's Antibodies

A. Circulating Antibodies. These occur in the serum of tuberculous patients. Circulating antibodies are measurable by complement fixation and other tests, but they have *no* diagnostic value.

B. Skin Tests. The *sensitizing* antibody of tuberculin allergy (see Chap. 7, p. 147) is associated with mononuclear cells wherever they occur in the body, including epidermal tissue. Skin tests using extracted protein antigens of tubercle bacilli can detect this antibody of hypersensitivity. When antigen is injected into the skin it reacts with cell-attached antibody, and this interreaction induces injury to the hypersensitive cells at the local site of injection. Since the hypersensitivity of tuberculosis is long-lasting, a positive skin reaction indicates past infection that may or may not be currently active. (The possibility of current infec-

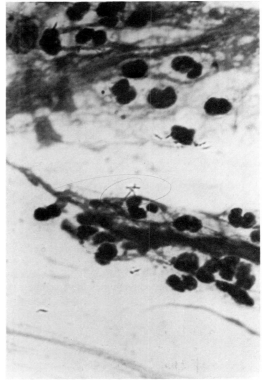

Fig. 14–7. A photomicrograph of a smear of concentrated sputum stained by the Ziehl-Neelsen method. Tubercle bacilli (*Mycobacterium tuberculosis*) can be seen as small, dark, rod-shaped organisms. The large dark objects are stained white blood cells. (Courtesy of Dr. Kendall K. Kane, St. Luke's Hospital Center, New York, N.Y.)

tion must then be determined by clinical findings, x-ray, and bacteriologic methods.) A negative tuberculin reaction is displayed by individuals who have never been infected and by those who are in the preallergic early stage of first infection.

1. *Skin-Testing Antigens.* Old tuberculin (OT) is a concentrated filtrate of a broth culture of tubercle bacilli. It contains, in addition to the tuberculoproteins derived from the organism, a number of irrelevant constituents of the bacilli and of the medium that may induce nonspecific reactions in the skin. A purified protein derivative (PPD) is obtained by chemical fractionation and purification of OT. This purified antigen is preferred for skin testing.

2. *Skin Test Doses.* Hypersensitive persons may have severe local reactions to tuberculin. Introduction of the antigen into the skin may also induce renewed or increased reactivity at *focal* sites of infection elsewhere in the body. For this reason, caution must be exercised in skin testing. A series of skin test doses may be given, beginning with very dilute material. If no reaction occurs, repeated doses may be given, each in an increased concentration, until some hypersensitivity is displayed. If even a fully concentrated dose fails to elicit a skin response, the individual is considered tuberculin-negative.

3. *Skin-Testing Methods.* A number of techniques have been devised for introducing tuberculins to the cells of the skin. The goal of each is to detect hypersensitivity with accuracy, without inducing untoward reactions. *Accuracy* can be increased by using purified antigens, as described. *Safety* is promoted by using minimal doses, or by applying them at superficial levels of skin, where reactivity is less intense and absorption of antigen to systemic foci less likely. Some of the techniques currently available are described below, together with their advantages and disadvantages:

The Vollmer patch test utilizes OT in a gauze strip (with lanolin) applied to the *surface* of the skin. This is the least accurate but the safest way to test for tuberculin hypersensitivity. The antigen is not pure, but the skin is not very absorptive, and reactions, when they occur, are seldom intense. It is a reasonable screening method for groups of children or adults who may be expected to display a high rate of infection.

The Heaf test utilizes OT for the *intracutaneous* introduction of antigen. A "gun" device is used to inject antigen from six spring-released needle points, which enter only the epidermal layer. The method is convenient and safe for mass surveys, but its accuracy is not quantitative.

The tine test employs dried OT on multiple metal tines held in a round plastic head. The tines are pressed against the skin for intracutaneous insertion of antigen. Each unit is used once and discarded. This method is similar to the Heaf test in advantages and limitations (see Fig. 14–8).

The Mantoux test requires the *intradermal* injection of antigen, which may be either OT or PPD. This is the most accurate method of tuberculin skin testing. An aliquot of 0.1 ml of quantitatively diluted antigen is introduced from a needle and syringe into a site just within the epidermal layer. Specificity is gained by using purified antigen; safety is controlled by adjusting the dose dilution and by making successive tests, if necessary, with increasing concentrations. The necessity for individual syringes and needles is of some disadvantage in mass surveys. The choice of method depends largely on considerations of the epidemiologic background of the group or individual to be tested and of the risk of excessive reactivity.

4. *Reading and Interpreting Tuberculin Skin Tests.* The application, reading, and interpretation of skin tests are the physician's prerogative and responsibility, because these tests involve clinical reactivity of diagnostic import. Nursing and laboratory personnel should be well informed, however, as to the nature of the materials used, the

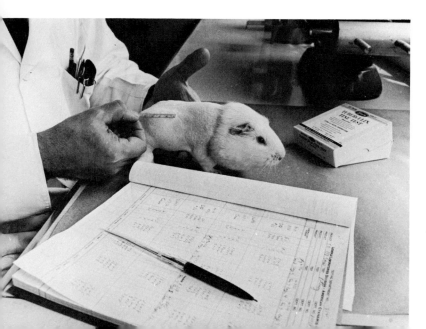

Fig. 14–8. The potency of the diagnostic tine test material is measured in the skin of guinea pigs that are hypersensitive to tuberculin. During the several months required for the production of each batch of tine tests, as many as six such tests may be performed. (Courtesy of Lederle Laboratories Division of American Cyanamid Company, Pearl River, N.Y.)

method of application, and the significance of results.

Tuberculin reactivity is of the delayed type, and of relatively long duration. Positive reactions require several hours to begin; they reach a maximum in one to three days. Skin tests should be read in 48 hours, or no later than 72 hours. They are interpreted as positive if the injection site shows an area of induration of at least 10 mm diameter. Edema and erythema may also be seen, and intense reactions proceed to central necrosis. Strongly positive reactions may persist for several days, but weak ones disappear quickly after 72 hours. Nonspecific reactions may appear during the first 24 hours but do not persist to the second day.

Tuberculin reactivity begins within four to six weeks after infection and persists for long periods. It may be lost in the presence of overwhelming tuberculous infection, or during the course of such diseases as measles, sarcoid, and Hodgkin's. As pointed out previously, a positive test does not necessarily denote present infection, nor does it imply immunity. In the absence of *current* infection it may signify an increased resistance to superinfection. This expectation must be guarded, however, in view of the increased *reactivity* of hypersensitive persons, which may contribute to extension of focal infection.

III. Specimens for Bacteriologic Diagnosis

A. In *pulmonary* tuberculosis, sputum collections and gastric washings are the most appropriate and useful specimens for smear and culture. In *disseminated*, or *miliary*, forms of the disease, any specimen that can represent a suspected focus of infection may be relevant: pleural fluid, synovial fluid, peritoneal fluid, or spinal fluid; urine, aspirated bone marrow, or exudate from lesions in bone, biopsied tissue, and other suspected material. Blood cultures are sometimes rewarding if blood is drawn during a period of active bacteremia, but they are less satisfactory than material obtained from a focal lesion. Stool specimens have the least value and offer the greatest technical difficulties. They may be warranted only in rare instances of suspected involvement of intestinal lymphatic tissue, when this cannot be confirmed by other means.

B. *Sputum* collected over a 24-hour period may contain more tubercle bacilli than a single ex-

pectoration and is therefore more valuable for culture than a casual specimen, unless the latter appears to contain caseous particles. Twenty-four-hour collections are made in sterile glass jars or plastic cups *without* added preservative. A tightly fitted cap must be kept in place at all times. The patient should be instructed to avoid the collection of saliva and to handle the container hygienically. Containers must not be overfilled lest their contents leak through the cap. When the containers are ready for transport to the laboratory, the outer surfaces should be wiped clean with disinfectant, the cap again tested for fit, and the transporter instructed to carry the container in an upright position, within a paper or plastic bag.

C. *Urine* may also be collected over a 24-hour period into a pooling container. A single collection of the first morning specimen is often considered equally satisfactory, however, and presents fewer technical problems to the nurse and the laboratory alike.

D. The *precautions* described in B above for the collection of sputum should be intelligently applied to the collection and transport of *any specimen, fluid or solid.*

E. *Smears* can be made directly from clinical specimens, or from their concentrates. A smear report indicating the presence of acid-fast bacilli must be considered presumptive evidence of tuberculosis, but it is important to remember that acid-fast saprophytic organisms may be found in sputum, urine, gastric washings, and similar specimens. The growth characteristics of the organisms must be identified in culture, or in inoculated animals, to confirm the laboratory diagnosis.

F. *Cultures* are made directly or on centrifuged concentrates of fluid or other specimens that do not have a mixed, commensalistic flora. Sputum and other contaminated materials are first treated with a bactericidal agent that does not destroy the tubercle bacillus as well. Inoculated media are incubated until mycobacterial growth is observed, or for a minimum of eight weeks. Identification of growth is made on the basis of microscopic and colonial appearance, pigmentation, and a few important biochemical properties.

IV. Special Laboratory Tests

A. ANIMAL INOCULATIONS. Guinea pigs are highly susceptible to tuberculous infection. They may be inoculated subcutaneously with a portion

of the clinical specimen that has been prepared for simultaneous culture. Animals are observed for signs of developing infection, tuberculin-tested in three to four weeks. and autopsied after six weeks. Gross evidence of infection is confirmed by smears and cultures of involved tissues. This method of laboratory diagnosis is expensive and hazardous. Culture methods are generally of equal reliability when competently performed and are preferred for their ease, economy, and safety. The use of guinea pigs should be reserved for those cases in which clinical and cultural diagnosis is difficult or inconclusive.

Guinea pigs, rabbits, and other animals may sometimes be used to establish the virulence of a strain of *Mycobacterium* isolated in culture. Animals vary in their susceptibility to strains of *M. tuberculosis* from human, bovine, or other sources, a fact that may be of value in determining both the origin and virulent properties of a pure culture. For example, rabbits and guinea pigs used together can distinguish virulent human and bovine strains. Both animal species develop severe infection with tubercle bacilli of bovine origin, but guinea pigs are also susceptible to human strains, while rabbits are relatively resistant to the latter.

B. *Antibiotic susceptibility testing* is of particular value in determining the emergence of resistance in strains from treated cases of tuberculosis. (See the later discussion of treatment.)

Epidemiology

I. Communicability of Infection

A. Reservoir, Sources, and Transmission Routes.   Man is the most common reservoir of human tuberculosis, the source of infection being the respiratory secretions of persons with active pulmonary lesions. Transmission may occur by direct or indirect contact with patients with open lesions, but the most probable and usual route is by the inhalation of air-borne droplet nuclei. The closed conditions of familial, military, or institutional living may permit prolonged exposure to an active case if the latter is unrecognized. This type of situation most frequently contributes to the spread of infection and the incidence of active cases. A dramatic illustration of this point was provided in the report (in 1961) of a naval medical officer who discovered 62 cases of tu-

berculosis aboard a navy vessel at sea. All these cases were traceable to one infectious sailor who had been previously exposed to a civilian case. Within 18 months of their close associations on board ship, 62 men out of 236, or 26 per cent, acquired active tuberculosis.*

Diseased cattle are a reservoir for the bovine variety of *M. tuberculosis*, which also causes human disease. The usual source of infection for man is raw milk (or other dairy products) from tuberculous cattle. The lesions acquired through gastrointestinal entry are usually extrapulmonary, and this type of infection is not directly transmitted by man. Bovine tuberculosis may also be acquired through the inhalation of air-borne infection in and around barns housing diseased animals or by handling infectious animal products. Human pulmonary infection with bovine strains is communicable. The cattle reservoir of tuberculosis in this country has been largely controlled or eliminated through continuous programs for the tuberculin testing of herds and pasteurization of milk.

B. Incubation Period. The period from known effective exposure to the appearance of a primary lesion of first infection is usually about four to six weeks. The time required for the development of new lesions following reinfection varies with host resistance and with the source and numbers of organisms. The interval between first infection and reinfection tuberculosis may be of many years' duration.

C. Communicability.   The communicable *period* persists for a given patient for as long as he discharges tubercle bacilli. The *degree* of communicability depends on the intensity of contamination of the air with infectious droplets. This is influenced by the coughing habits of the patient, as well as by the dynamics of air circulation and fallout. Actual transmission to another person during the communicable period depends on inhalation of at least one infectious droplet nucleus. Inhaled tubercle bacilli must be carried far down the airways to a point in the lung where fixed mononuclear phagocytes can pick them up and their intracellular multiplication can begin.

* Ochs, Lt. Charles W.: The Epidemiology of Tuberculosis, *J.A.M.A.*, **129**:247, Jan., 1962.

The sputum of an infected patient must carry fair numbers of bacilli to assure this process. It becomes a most dangerous source of communicable infection when it is sprayed into the air by forceful coughing or sneezing. In a closed environment, shared by a number of people, the communicability of infection from an active case may be high.

D. IMMUNITY. The basis for resistance to tuberculosis was described in the discussion of the clinical disease. Susceptibility to infection is general but is influenced by factors of age, sex, race, nutrition, and general health. Children under three years of age are most susceptible, but the incidence of tuberculosis in older children has declined sharply with improved controls on bovine tuberculosis. In 1964, the U.S. Department of Health, Education, and Welfare reported the incidence of new active cases to be lowest in children between the ages of 5 and 14, and rising rapidly in the age group beyond 65. The largest total number of active cases occurred, however, in groups under the age of 45 (see Fig. 14–9).

The white races appear to be generally less susceptible than are Negroes and American Indians. It is not certain whether the higher resistance of Caucasians is related to a longer history of endemic infection, with selection of resistant survivors, or to what extent differences in living conditions and nutrition are important.

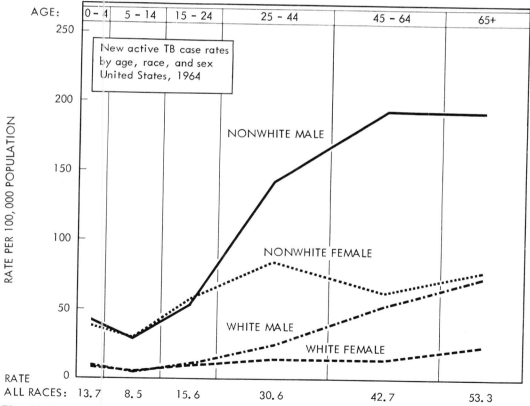

Fig. 14–9. New active tuberculosis case rates by age, race, and sex—United States, 1964. (Reproduced from *Reported Tuberculosis Data—1964*. Communicable Disease Center, U.S. Public Health Service, Atlanta, Ga.)

The death rate from tuberculosis is highest among nonwhites of both sexes (see Table 14–1). In terms of incidence, however, more than 50 per cent of all cases occur among white males, although the number of new cases in this country is highest among nonwhite males (see Table 14–2). The differences observed in the incidence of tuberculosis in men and women may be a reflection of physiologic influences or of different degrees of exposure under varying living conditions.

A bacterial vaccine is available that confers a definite degree of increased resistance to tu-

berculosis. This vaccine is known as BCG, in recognition of the French workers who first suggested its possible value ("bacille de Calmette et Guérin"). The immunizing material is a living, attenuated strain of tubercle bacilli of bovine origin. The evidence has been considered convincing that BCG provides some protection against naturally acquired human tuberculosis. Accordingly, its use is recommended for tuberculin-negative individuals who run a high risk of continuing exposure to infection, a group that includes medical students, physicians, nurses, and

Table 14–1. Tuberculosis Death Rates* by Age, Race, and Sex: United States, 1964

Age Groups	Total	White			Nonwhite		
		Total	Male	Female	Total	Male	Female
All Ages	4.3	3.6	5.5	1.8	9.8	13.9	5.9
0– 4	0.4	0.3	0.3	0.2	1.1	1.0	1.1
5–14	0.1	0.1	0.1	(**)	0.3	0.3	0.5
15–24	0.4	0.2	0.2	0.2	1.8	1.4	2.1
25–44	2.4	1.4	1.7	1.1	10.4	12.7	8.4
45–64	8.3	6.6	10.9	2.7	24.2	38.5	10.9
65+	21.0	18.8	31.8	8.7	48.0	77.4	22.9

* Rate per 100,000 population.
** Less than 0.05.
Reproduced from *Reported Tuberculosis Data — 1964*, U.S. Dept. of Health, Education, and Welfare, Public Health Service.

Table 14–2. Tuberculosis Deaths by Age, Race, and Sex: United States, 1964

Age Groups	Total	White			Nonwhite		
		Total	Male	Female	Total	Male	Female
All Ages	8,303	6,092	4,528	1,564	2,211	1,527	684
0– 4	79	45	26	19	34	17	17
5–14	36	18	11	7	18	5	13
15–24	109	46	24	22	63	24	39
25–44	1,119	567	338	229	552	314	238
45–64	3,197	2,313	1,833	480	884	677	207
65+	3,759	3,102	2,295	807	657	487	170

NOTE: Totals include 1 death in a white male and 3 deaths in nonwhite males with age not stated.
Reproduced from *Reported Tuberculosis Data — 1964*, U.S. Dept. of Health, Education, and Welfare, Public Health Service.

laboratory personnel. Vaccinated persons become tuberculin-positive and display an increased resistance to new natural infection with virulent organisms. Under the auspices of the World Health Organization, tuberculin testing has been completed for more than 200 million people, and 75 million have been vaccinated with BCG. An 80 per cent protection rate has been shown in some controlled epidemiologic studies of the vaccine's effect. There have been no authenticated cases of progressive tuberculosis related to a virulent mutation of the attenuated vaccine. Extremely rare cases of tuberculosis have followed its use in individuals lacking normal resistant responses.

II. Control of Active Infection

A. ISOLATION. The communicability of tuberculosis can be brought under control by specific antimicrobial therapy coupled with effective hygienic practices. Patients with active infection should be hospitalized for treatment, at least until sputum (or other discharge) is bacteriologically negative. During their stay in a general hospital, patients should be assigned to private rooms while their disease is communicable. In the tuberculosis hospital, or the general hospital with a tuberculosis service, patients are usually grouped in separated wards, with assignments on the basis of positive or negative sputum. If the patient must be treated at home, the principles of isolation should be observed while he remains in a communicable stage of disease. This is particularly important if there are young children, or other highly susceptible individuals, in the family. Public health nursing supervision should be provided, with instruction for all members of the family, as well as the patient, in the hygiene of tuberculosis prevention.

B. PRECAUTIONS. During the communicable period, the care of hospitalized patients should be individualized, with concurrent disinfection of sputum and for articles exposed to it. Since tuberculosis is chiefly an air-borne infection, the most effective precautions are those that prevent tubercle bacilli from reaching the air in significant numbers.

The patient is taught to muffle coughing or sneezing with paper handkerchiefs, which are then carefully disposed of in paper bags for incineration. Effective masks are appropriate for the patient, nursing personnel, visitors, and others, under special circumstances in which coughing is uncontrolled or that contribute to dissemination of the organism into the air from environmental sources. Uninformed or uncooperative patients are sometimes a problem, but failure to cooperate may also be involuntary (as in throat or laryngeal examination). Bed-making, the handling of sputum-contaminated clothing, and dry-dusting may stir drying droplet nuclei into the air, together with lint and dust. Gowns are of considerable value, for the clothing of persons who come into close contact with the infectious patient or his immediate surroundings can be grossly contaminated with respiratory discharges. When such material dries, it is easily shaken into the air, together with viable tubercle bacilli. A clean gown worn for occasions of close patient contact, and discarded thereafter, protects clothing and prevents subsequent shedding of organisms in other areas.

The selection of good tuberculocidal disinfectant agents (see Appendix VII), and their proper use in the routine disinfection of thermometers and other equipment, or for daily cleaning of floors and furniture, are essential precautions in the care of the hospitalized patient.

When the tuberculous patient has become sputum-negative on antimicrobial therapy, the precautions of ordinary hygienic practices are sufficient for the continuing control of infection.

C. TREATMENT. Most first infections heal without recognition or treatment. Recognized, active cases of tuberculosis should be hospitalized, to prevent a chain of contact infections and to give the patient the immediate support of specific and other therapy.

Currently, the most useful antituberculous drugs are streptomycin, isoniazid (INH), and para-aminosalicylic acid (PAS). They are generally used in one or another combination, because drug resistance to any one of them may develop quickly in infecting strains of tubercle bacilli. Laboratory testing of drug susceptibility

should be done on initial cultures of tubercle bacilli and repeated if the patient's sputum remains bacteriologically positive after six months or reverts after being negative. Changes in the therapeutic regimen may be necessary if laboratory studies demonstrate drug resistance.

Surgical techniques are also used in the treatment of tuberculosis. When anatomically and medically feasible, the removal of diseased tissue, under cover of antimicrobial therapy, can prevent further systemic extension of the infection. In pulmonary tuberculosis, the collapse of a lung by the artificial introduction of air (pneumothorax) is sometimes useful in restricting the spread of organisms from cavitating lesions. This technique also permits the affected lung to rest temporarily. In other instances, lobectomy may be the most satisfactory solution. When systemic infection is extensive, as in miliary tuberculosis, or localized in vital organs, as in tuberculous meningitis, intensive antimicrobial therapy is used, but the fatality rates in these situations remain high.

D. CONTROL OF CONTACTS

1. *Quarantine* of contacts is not indicated.

2. *Prophylaxis.* The immunoprophylactic use of BCG vaccine may be warranted for the close contacts of active cases who are *tuberculin-negative*. Household and medical contacts might be included in this group.

The chemoprophylactic use of isoniazid may be indicated for those contacts of active cases for whom the risk of infection is particularly grave. This group includes *tuberculin-positive* individuals who can be expected to display unusual susceptibility to reinfection; for example, children under three years of age, diabetics, and patients on steroid therapy for other conditions (steroids reduce the inflammatory response that is so important in resistance to infection).

3. *Case Finding.* Chest x-ray and tuberculin test surveys of contacts are of particular value. In view of the recognized hazards of repeated x-irradiation, tuberculin skin testing is preferred for the *continuing* surveillance of exposed negative reactors. This should be done on a semiannual basis for children, and at least on an annual basis for adults (particularly nursing, medical, and laboratory personnel). If negative skin reactors

convert to a positive tuberculin response, chest x-ray and other intensive studies are useful in detecting early infection. Prompt chemotherapy may then abort the development of serious disease.

E. EPIDEMIC CONTROLS. Case reports to local health departments are obligatory in most communities of this and other countries. This procedure permits epidemiologic analysis of the distribution of cases, so that unusual grouping and incidence of cases may be promptly recognized and an immediate search made for the origins of infection. International control calls for the x-ray screening of immigrants.

III. Prevention

A. IMMUNIZATION. BCG vaccination is at present the only method available for providing some protection of specific value. When properly performed, BCG vaccination converts at least 90 per cent of tuberculin-negative persons to a state of skin sensitivity. The protection afforded is only partial, and its duration remains undetermined. Mass vaccination with BCG is applicable only in situations where the risk of infection and the number of tuberculin-negative contacts of active disease are both high.

B. CONTROL OF RESERVOIRS, SOURCES, AND TRANSMISSION ROUTES. These factors have each been discussed previously. Methods for their control that are important to the prevention of further infection may be summarized here as follows:

1. Find and treat active tuberculosis as rapidly as possible.

2. Find the source (or sources) of each active case, isolate the individual, and apply chemotherapeutic methods as indicated.

3. Continue and widen the search for bovine tuberculosis. Eliminate tuberculin-reactive cattle. Pasteurize milk.

4. Provide BCG vaccination for tuberculin-negative persons who are closely or continuously exposed to risk of infection.

5. Provide chemotherapy for tuberculin-positive *exposed* individuals for whom the risk of infection is great.

6. Conduct frequent community surveys by

skin testing or roentgenographic methods (see 1 and 2 above).

7. Provide public health nursing supervision of active cases under treatment at home.

8. Provide continuing public education concerning the importance, origin, and control of tuberculosis.

Atypical Mycobacteria.   In recent years there has been an increasing awareness of the pathologic significance of a group of acid-fast mycobacteria that resemble the tubercle bacillus in some respects but are atypical in others. The "atypical" characteristics are largely cultural and microscopic: they possess pigments, enzymes, or biochemical properties not seen in *M. tuberculosis;* they grow more rapidly, sometimes at lower temperatures; and they lack some of the surface characters of tubercle bacilli. They have been isolated from human sputum, urine, and other specimens, but, more importantly, they have been associated with progressive pulmonary diseases very similar clinically, and pathologically, to tuberculosis.

The medical significance and the frequency of infection produced by these organisms have yet to be determined, but it is of practical concern that they are relatively resistant to the antituberculous drugs in common use. Furthermore, their distribution in the general population appears to be common, as evident from the fact that their protein extracts (equivalent to PPD) produce skin reactions in many persons tested. Since even tuberculin-negative persons may react to these "atypical" protein extracts, it would appear that the skin reactivity is not necessarily related to hypersensitivity to the tubercle bacillus.

Air-Borne Bacterial Diseases (Zoonoses) Not Communicable by Man

A few of the bacterial infections of animals can be transmitted to man by air-borne or direct routes that permit respiratory entry of the organism. The most notable of these are anthrax, brucellosis, and tularemia, each a serious disease when it occurs in man. The respiratory tract is not the only site of entry for the infectious agents of these diseases, nor is it the usual one, but its role as a portal of infection constitutes an important epidemiologic consideration in the control of these diseases.

Man is not a reservoir for these diseases and does not communicate them to others. In the case of anthrax and brucellosis, respiratory entry does not lead to pulmonary involvement; the infecting bacteria extend to systemic localizations, probably by way of the lymphatics to the regional lymph nodes and then elsewhere. On the other hand, pneumonia is common in tularemia, whether the organism enters by the respiratory tract or some other route. Although the causative agents may be found in the discharges and secretions of human patients, they are rarely if ever transmissible to other human beings from these sources.

The principal discussion of these diseases, including their epidemiology, is given in chapters relating them to their most frequent routes of entry (anthrax and tularemia, Chap. 24; brucellosis, Chap. 19). In this section, a brief description is given of the establishment of these infections through the inhalation route.

Inhalation Anthrax

This is an acute bacterial disease most commonly seen as a skin infection (malignant pustule) complicated by septicemia with resultant systemic involvement. The mortality rate in anthrax septicemia is high, as it may also be when infection results from respiratory entry. Inhalation anthrax is not commonly seen today in this country because better protections exist for people exposed to the source of this infection: the contaminated hides and hair of animals. The organism (*B. anthracis*) is an aerobic sporeforming bacillus with a natural reservoir in domestic animals, such as cattle, sheep, and horses (see Chap. 11, p. 277, and Chap. 9, p. 184). Anthrax spores (derived from the vegative bacilli that proliferate in the tissues of fatally infected animals) can survive for long periods in the wool, hair, or hides of such animals. When these spores are inhaled by human

Table 14–3. Summary: Bacterial Diseases Acquired Through the Respiratory Tract

Clinical Disease	Causative Organism	Other Possible Entry Routes	Incubation Period	Communic Period
I. Upper Respiratory Infections				
Pharyngitis	*Streptococcus* species		1–2 days	During time active infla mation
Laryngitis	*Staphylococcus aureus*			
Tonsillitis	*Pneumococcus*			
Sinusitis	*Hemophilus influenzae*			
Otitis media	Gram-negative enteric bacilli			
II. Bacterial Pneumonias				
A. Pneumococcal pneumonia	*Diplococcus pneumoniae*		1–2 days	Probably du time spu is bacteriol cally positi
B. Other bacterial pneumonias	*Streptococcus pyogenes* *Staphylococcus aureus* *Klebsiella pneumoniae* *Hemophilus influenzae*		1–2 days	As above
C. Primary plague pneumonia	*Pasteurella pestis*	Bubonic plague is arthropod-borne (see Chap. 27)	3–4 days	As above
III. Bacterial Meningitis				
A. Meningococcal meningitis	*Neisseria meningitidis*		3–4 days	While naso-pharynx is bacteriolog cally positi
B. Listeriosis	*Listeria monocytogenes*	Venereal contact Congenital transfer Ingestion (animal sources)	Unknown	Man-to-man transfer un usual excep for congen infection
C. Secondary bacterial meningitis	*Hemophilus influenzae* *Diplococcus pneumoniae* *Streptococcus pyogenes* *Staphylococcus aureus* Gram-negative enteric bacilli	Enteric bacteria possibly enter by fecal-oral route	Unknown	Respiratory transmissio does not necessarily lead to mer geal infecti
IV. Streptococcal Diseases				
A. Strep sore throat	*Streptococcus pyogenes*		1–3 days	While throat secretions a bacteriolog cally positi

pecimens Required	Laboratory Diagnosis	Immunization	Treatment	Nursing Care
at swab	Smear and culture	Limited value	Antibiotic choice depends on testing of isolated organisms	Principles of personal hygiene, support of healthy resistance
um d	Smear and culture Culture	None	Penicillin	Isolation for 1st day of therapy; concurrent disinfection of respiratory secretions
at and opharyngeal bs um d	Smear and culture Smear and culture Culture	None	Antibiotic choice depends on testing of isolated organisms	As above
um d n	Smear and culture Smear and culture Serology	Killed vaccine	Sulfonamides Tetracyclines Streptomycin	*Stringent* respiratory precautions
al fluid d	Smear and culture Culture	None	Penicillin Sulfonamides	Isolation and respiratory precautions for the first day after therapy initiated
al fluid d rnal vaginal harge, enta ted infant's d, lesions	Smear and culture Culture Smear and culture Smear and culture	None	Tetracyclines Penicillin Streptomycin	Isolation of infants Concurrent disinfection in care of infants and infected mothers
al fluid d t swabs um	Smear and culture Culture Smear and culture Smear and culture	None	Antibiotic choice depends on testing of isolated organism	Concurrent disinfection of respiratory secretions; special care in case of enteric bacterial agents focused in kidney or gallbladder
at or opharyngeal bs	Smear and culture	None	Penicillin	Isolation for 1 or 2 days following initiation of antibiotic therapy

353

Table 14–3. (Cont.)

Clinical Disease	Causative Organism	Other Possible Entry Routes	Incubation Period	Communic Period
B. Scarlet fever	*Streptococcus pyogenes*		1–3 days	As above
C. *Sequelae of group A strep infections:* Rheumatic fever			3 weeks post-infection	Not communic
Acute hemorrhagic glomerulo-nephritis			1–3 weeks post-infection	Not communic
Erythema nodosum			Post-strep infection	Not communic
D. Subacute bacterial endocarditis	*Streptococcus viridans* *Streptococcus faecalis* Gram-negative enteric bacilli and others		Unknown	Not communic
V. Whooping Cough	*Bordetella pertussis*		7–10 days, not more than 21	Highest dur late incuba and catarr stages
VI. Diphtheria	*Corynebacterium diphtheriae*		2–5 days	Carrier state may be persistent
VII. Tuberculosis	*Mycobacterium tuberculosis*	Gastrointestinal (bovine strains)	4–6 weeks for primary infection	While sputu is bacterio-logically positive

(handwritten annotations near Streptococcus pyogenes: "Beta", "gram +")

ecimens equired	Laboratory Diagnosis	Immunization	Treatment	Nursing Care
ove	As above (Schultz-Charlton skin test with scarlatinal antitoxin)	None	Penicillin	As above
n	Antistreptolysin titer	None	Penicillin	No special precautions
n	Antistreptolysin titer Microscopic analysis (no culture)	None	Penicillin	No special precautions
n	Antistreptolysin titer	None	Penicillin	No special precautions
d (during r spike)	Culture	None	Penicillin Streptomycin	No special precautions
pharyngeal bs h plates d	Smear and culture Culture White blood cell count	Killed vaccine	Chloramphenicol Tetracycline	Hospital isolation (especially on pediatric service) Concurrent disinfection of nasal and oral secretions, vomitus, and contaminated articles
of susted lesion roat	Smear and culture Animal inoculation	Toxoid	Diphtheria antitoxin Penicillin Erythromycin	Isolation until bacteriologically negative; concurrent disinfection of nasal and oral secretions and contaminated articles
um ic washings fluids ates from lized ons d (rarely) s (rarely)	Smear and culture Smear and culture Smear and culture Smear and culture Culture Culture	BCG vaccine for persons at risk	Streptomycin Isoniazid (INH) Para-amino salicylic acid (PAS) Pneumothorax? Surgery?	Isolation while sputum or other discharges are bacteriologically positive Concurrent disinfection of respiratory secretions and contaminated articles (see Appendix VII)

beings who prepare animal skins or wool for commercial uses, serious infection (once known as "woolsorter's disease") can result. The initial respiratory symptoms are mild and nonspecific, resembling those of many common upper respiratory infections or irritations. Ensuing symptoms are quite severe however, and are related to the dissemination of vegetating bacilli from the lung into the mediastinal lymph nodes and thence to the blood stream. Fever and shock follow rapidly upon septicemia, and death commonly occurs within five to six days.

The etiology, diagnosis, and epidemiology of anthrax are described in Chapter 24, together with other diseases associated with direct contacts with animals.

Brucellosis

Clinical infection with organisms of the *Brucella* group is a systemic disease, with localizations in the lymphatic system, spleen, and numerous other tissues, including the reproductive organs in females. The reservoir of brucellosis is in infected domestic animals, notably swine, cattle, sheep, and goats. The human disease is usually acquired through the ingestion of contaminated milk or dairy products (Chap. 19), or by direct contacts with infected animal tissues (Chap. 24). Airborne infection occurs in situations permitting an unusually dense contamination of the air. Barns and stables housing infectious animals and abattoirs where extensive contamination of

the environment can occur are examples of areas in which inhalation infection may occur. Respiratory entry of the organisms may be marked by the development of bronchitis, but the serious aspects of the disease are caused by the organism's entry into systemic tissues by way of the lymphatic system and the blood stream. Brucellosis is a chronic disease that may last for many months, and occasionally for several years. The principal discussion of its causative agent, diagnosis, and epidemiology can be found in Chapter 19.

Tularemia   *Rabbit*

The reservoir for tularemia infection is in a number of wild animal species, some of which are popular targets for game-hunters. Man acquires it through his direct contacts with wild game, but he may be infected in a number of other ways also. The ingestion of infected, partially cooked meat or of contaminated water, the bites of insect vectors, and the inhalation of air containing numerous organisms constitute other common routes. The latter situation may arise for laboratory workers when they handle cultures or infected experimental animals. Pulmonary involvement is common in tularemia, occurring as a result of respiratory tract entry or as an extension of disease acquired through other routes. The organisms may localize in many tissues, reached from the point of entry by dissemination through lymphatic channels and the blood. The disease is described more fully in Chapter 24.

Questions

1. Name several microorganisms that cause bacterial pneumonias.
2. What specimens are used for diagnosis of pneumonia?
3. Can immunization be used to control these diseases? Why?
4. What organism causes meningococcal meningitis?
5. What nursing precautions are exercised while caring for a patient with meningococcal meningitis?
6. What extracellular substances contribute to streptococcal virulence?
7. Name the clinical streptococcal diseases of respiratory entry.
8. What is the Schultz-Charlton reaction?
9. What is the Dick test?
10. Describe the morphology of streptococci.

11. Name the reservoir of group A streptococci and the transmission routes.
12. Name several sequelae of group A streptococcal infections.
13. What is the causative agent of pertussis?
14. What specimens are used for diagnosis of pertussis?
15. What methods are used to control the active infection?
16. How can pertussis be prevented?
17. What factors contribute to the severity of diphtheria infections?
18. Why is it necessary to administer antitoxin immediately to a patient with diphtheria?
19. Describe the genetic mechanism of toxin production by virulent strains of *C. diphtheriae*.
20. On what factors does the future control of diphtheria depend?
21. What organism causes tuberculosis?
22. What is a tubercle?
23. How is the tuberculosis organism spread through the body?
24. Describe primary tuberculosis; reinfection tuberculosis.
25. Describe the hypersensitive response to tuberculosis.
26. Why is the tuberculosis organism often referred to as the "acid-fast" bacillus?
27. What does a positive tuberculin skin test signify?
28. How long does the communicable period persist for a patient with tuberculosis?
29. What nursing measures are necessary in the care of a patient with active tuberculosis?
30. Name the antituberculosis drugs.
31. When is BCG vaccination used?
32. Give the cultural characteristics of *B. anthracis* and its natural reservoir.
33. To what occupation is anthrax a hazard? Why?

15 Viral Diseases Acquired Through the Respiratory Route

The viral diseases that are acquired by respiratory transmission and entry include some of the most contagious infections known to human populations. Influenza, for example, is one of the most rapidly spreading infections when it assumes epidemic form, and the common viral diseases of childhood, such as mumps, chickenpox, and especially measles, are similarly so highly communicable that they are not often escaped.

The diseases of this chapter are presented in three major sections: (1) those whose agents infect the upper or lower respiratory tract following respiratory entry; (2) those that are systemic infections induced by agents entering by the respiratory route (these include mumps, measles, and the pox diseases); and (3) the systemic viral diseases, which may have either a respiratory or an alimentary tract entry. The principal discussion of the latter, which include poliomyelitis and infectious hepatitis, is given in Chapter 20, with emphasis on the gastrointestinal route of spread and entry, but the possible importance of the respiratory route is pointed out here to underline the need for suitable nursing precautions in the care of patients.

Unlike many of the bacterial infections considered in Chapter 14, and particularly those of the upper respiratory tract where chronic bacterial entrenchments can occur so frequently, the viral diseases described in this chapter are always

acute and self-limited, although they may leave residual damage behind. They do not respond to antibiotic therapy, but are resolved by the body's defensive mechanisms. Specific immunity, artificial or natural, plays a large role in this in some instances, notably smallpox, chickenpox, measles, mumps, and poliomyelitis. The viral diseases of the respiratory tract itself, however, such as influenza or the common cold induce only transient immunity. Artificial immunization is of limited value in controlling the latter infections, but it has been of major importance in controlling the serious systemic viral diseases, namely smallpox and poliomyelitis.

The easy and frequent communicability of these infections by the respiratory route accounts for their epidemic character and presents a difficult challenge in their nursing care, especially when this must be provided in hospitals. In some instances (e.g., smallpox or measles) even the most rigid techniques may not accomplish their purpose fully, but they must be maintained with careful attention to principle and detail for the greatest possible safety of all concerned.

Viral Diseases of the Respiratory Tract

Influenza

not pyogenic
not intestinal

The Clinical Disease. Influenza is an acute respiratory infection accompanied by fever, chills, and general malaise. Headache, muscular aches and pains, and a feeling of exhaustion that borders on prostration are common. The tissues of the upper respiratory tract are inflamed and have a bright red, mucoid appearance. Lymphoid tissue is often enlarged, but there is no purulent exudate. There is some coryza but it is not so prominent in influenza as it is in "head colds" or in bacterial infections of the upper respiratory tract. A dry, hacking cough is usual, and there may be laryngitis with hoarseness. The disease is usually self-limited, with fever for about three days and recovery in a week or so.

The chief complication of influenza is pneumonia, resulting from initial *viral* injury extending to the epithelium of the bronchial tract and the alveoli, and frequently followed secondarily by *bacterial* invasion of these tissues. The most common secondary invaders are *Hemophilus influenzae*, staphylococci, streptococci, and pneumococci (see Chap. 14, pp. 315 and 319).

When influenza occurs in epidemic form, it spreads very rapidly through large segments of the communities involved. Under these circumstances many people with chronic debilitating diseases or other reason for lowered resistance are among those infected, and it is for this group that the risk of complication and death is greatest. The death rate is highest among elderly people with underlying cardiac, pulmonary, or renal diseases and pregnant women, secondary bacterial pneumonia being the most notable of the serious complications. During epidemic years, the general mortality may greatly exceed the normal expectancy. The 1963 epidemic of influenza in the United States resulted in approximately 57,000 deaths in excess of the nonepidemic rate.

During epidemic periods influenza is usually diagnosed on a clinical basis, but sporadic cases can be identified only by laboratory findings. Mild or asymptomatic infections probably go unrecognized for the most part.

Laboratory Diagnosis
I. Identification of the Organism

A. Influenza virus can be recovered from throat secretions by inoculating these into embryonated chicken eggs. The virus multiplies in the amniotic and allantoic fluids, which can be harvested from the eggs in three to four days and tested for virus activity. One of the properties of this virus that is most easily recognized is its ability to agglutinate the red blood cells of several animal species. Some other viruses* also have hemagglutinating properties, however, so that it is necessary to test the harvested fluid in the presence of specific influenza

---

* Influenza, mumps, and measles viruses belong to a group known as the "myxoviruses." The prefix *myxo* means slime and refers to an affinity for mucin. Red blood cells contain a mucoprotein to which virus attaches, the result being agglutination of the cells.

antiserums. When antibody combines with the virus the hemagglutinating property of the latter is specifically inhibited.

B. The serologic identification of influenza virus includes the recognition of antigenically distinct strains. There are three immunologic types of influenza virus, known as A, B, and C. The A and B strains have been of major importance in epidemics. The antigenic composition of these organisms is subject to frequent change, however, as a result of mutations while passing through populations, so that new variant types appear from time to time, such as the Asian, or A_2, strain that swept around the world in 1957 (see Fig. 15-1). The recognition of type-specific variants is important not only to the identification of virus in epidemic or sporadic cases, but to the preparation of immunologically effective vaccines.

When virus is isolated from throats by passage of throat washings through embryonated eggs, it is first tested for hemagglutinins. If results are positive, type-specific influenza antiserums (prepared by immunizing animals) are mixed with virus suspensions. The serum, which causes hemagglutination inhibition, identifies the virus type.

II. Identification of Patient's Serum Antibodies. Antibody production occurs during a clinical attack of influenza. Antibodies appear in the circulating blood in increasing concentration following onset and the acute stage, reaching a peak level in about two weeks and persisting for about four weeks. Thereafter the level gradually falls until a new infection is acquired.

The patient's antibodies can be identified by the complement-fixation technique, or by the hemagglutination-inhibition method described above, using laboratory-propagated virus. For diagnostic purposes, it is important that two specimens of serum be tested: one obtained during the *acute* stage of illness and one taken about two weeks later in the *convalescent* stage. The serologic diagnosis is made on the basis of a *rising titer* of antibody during the course of the disease, the changing level indicating an active immune process. This pairing of serums is necessary, because low levels of influenza antibody persist in normal persons, between infections, and do not signify current disease.

III. Specimens for Diagnosis

A. *Throat washings*, or garglings, for virus isolation. The patient's mouth should first be rinsed with a mild antiseptic, followed by water, to clear out saliva and many commensalistic mouth bacteria. A gargling solution should be obtained from the virus laboratory. The solution is a transport medium (buffered saline or broth) to be used as a throat rinse and returned to its container. Washings should be sent immediately to the virus laboratory, or frozen until their transport can be arranged.

B. An "acute" serum taken within a day or two of the onset of illness.

C. A "convalescent" serum taken two weeks after *onset.*

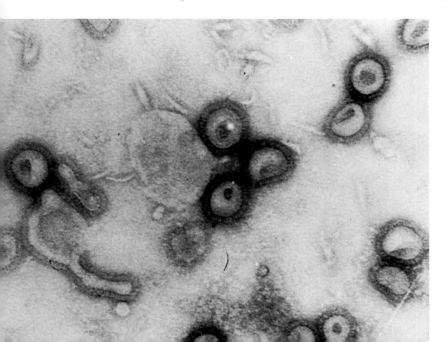

Fig. 15–1. Electron micrograph of Asian influenza virus, magnified 160,000 ×, shows fine structure of the virus particles. (Courtesy of Lederle Laboratories Division of American Cyanamid Company, Pearl River, N.Y.)

Note: The first serum specimen can be retained in the refrigerator until the second blood is drawn and the two sent to the virus laboratory as a pair. To prevent hemolysis in storage or transit, serum should be separated from whole blood and stored in a sterile tube using aseptic technique to prevent bacterial contamination and deterioration of the serum.

D. A brief clinical history and tentative diagnosis, specifying the dates of onset and of specimen collection, should accompany every patient's specimens.

Epidemiology

I. Communicability of Infection

A. RESERVOIR, SOURCES, AND TRANSMISSION ROUTES. The reservoir for influenza is man, his respiratory secretions being the source of infection. Transmission is by droplet spread on airborne routes, by direct contact, and by indirect contamination of fomites. The virus probably does not survive for long periods outside of the body, under natural conditions, so that droplet and other contacts must be reasonably close and indirect contacts fresh.

B. INCUBATION PERIOD. Very short, usually only one or two days.

C. COMMUNICABLE PERIOD. Probably does not extend past the acute febrile stage (three to four days).

D. IMMUNITY. Specific active immunity confers resistance, but antibodies must be present at the site of virus entry to be protective. An effective concentration of antibody in respiratory secretions is not possible unless high levels exist in the circulating blood. The immunity following disease is transient, probably because the virus is limited to the superficial respiratory membranes and does not provide an effective systemic stimulus to antibody production. Repeated infections with different types of influenza broaden the immunity. Protective immunity can also be obtained with influenza vaccines, the scope of the preventive effect depending on the antigenic types incorporated in the immunizing material.

In the absence of type-specific immunity, human beings are universally susceptible. The incidence of infections with respect to age groups reflects the opportunity for previous exposure, and this in turn is influenced by social and environmental factors. In general the incidence is highest in schoolchildren, lower in children under six, and decreases progressively among adults of advancing age. When populations encounter new strains, or when old ones recur after some time, age incidence becomes more uniform. The duration of immunity to a single type, or to closely related strains, has always been difficult to evaluate.

II. Control of Active Infection

A. ISOLATION. Patients may be isolated during the acute stage if their close contacts include those for whom the risk of infection might be serious.

B. PRECAUTIONS. For hospitalized patients, nursing precautions should include concurrent disinfection of respiratory discharges and of items or equipment contaminated by these secretions during the acute stage. The patient should be taught handkerchief control of coughing and sneezing, whether he is at home or in the hospital.

C. TREATMENT. There is no specific therapy for influenza. Antimicrobial drugs are ineffective for the virus and should be used only when secondary bacterial complications are threatened.

D. EPIDEMIC CONTROLS. Individual contact controls are not feasible in influenza, and sporadic cases are not reported unless specific information is available as to the laboratory diagnosis of type specificity. Health departments maintain surveillance programs to determine the prevailing types and the patterns of epidemics. This information is exchanged at state, national, and international levels so that vaccine manufacture may keep pace with epidemic expectancy. Appropriate vaccines must be available and administered as indicated, *before* epidemics get underway, because the disease develops and spreads rapidly, outstripping the immune response to active immunization.

During epidemics unnecessary public gatherings should be avoided, but the disruption of office, school, or other institutional functions is not warranted. Hospital admission of influenza

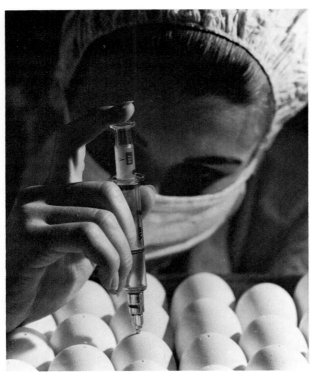

Fig. 15–2. Inoculating fertile eggs. One of the first steps in the production of many virus vaccines is the inoculation of fertile eggs with the seed virus dilution. After injection, the egg is sealed with collodion and incubated to permit maximum virus growth. During all these operations complete sterility is maintained— the eggs are frequently brushed with an antiseptic, and the syringe needle is frequently passed through the flame of a bunsen burner. (Courtesy of Lederle Laboratories Division of American Cyanamid Company, Pearl River, N.Y.)

cases should be avoided except for patients of high risk or those with complications. Hospital rules should include control of personnel with active infection.

III. Prevention

A. IMMUNIZATION. Mass immunization of whole populations has not been practiced, because uniform vaccine production has been limited. Vaccines in routine use contain a pool of antigens (see Fig. 15–2). They are effective when they immunize against current strains, in advance of expected epidemics. They may also establish a base of resistance to related strains for which a given population has little or no current immunity. The U.S. Public Health Service recommends annual vaccination of persons of all ages who may risk serious illness as a result of influenza infection. These include people with cardiac, pulmonary, renal, or metabolic disease; pregnant women; and people over 65 years of age. Vaccination is also advisable for all hospital personnel and for others in public services.

The Common Cold and Other Acute Viral Respiratory Diseases

Clinical Diseases. The common cold and a number of other acute infections of the upper, and sometimes the lower, respiratory tract are caused by viruses. These infections are seldom marked by clinical features of individually diagnostic value, and their viral agents fall into diverse classifications. *Clinically*, two types of problem are recognized: nonfebrile illnesses with symptoms localized in the upper respiratory tract, and more severe involvements of the lower respiratory structures, with constitutional symptoms, including fever, general malaise, and, sometimes, gastrointestinal disturbances. (See also Primary Atypical Pneumonia, Chap. 16, p. 385.) *Virologically*, differences are noted in the localization and type of cellular injury produced by different viruses, as well as their antigenic and biologic properties. *Epidemiologically*, these diseases are characterized by an easy distribution from the human reservoir by respiratory transmission routes, general susceptibility, and high incidence rates with varying degrees of immune response.

1. *The common cold* is recognized by everyone as a catarrhal infection of the nose and throat, characterized by the local discomfort of congestion and excessive mucous secretion, as well as general malaise and fatigue. Fever is rare and the duration is generally limited to a few days or a week. Secondary bacterial infections of involved mucous membranes are rather frequent, inducing sinusitis, laryngitis, tracheitis, bronchitis, otitis media, or, upon occasion, combinations of these syndromes.

2. *Febrile* viral diseases of the respiratory tract generally involve either the underlying lymphoid tissue and the superficial membranes of the upper respiratory tract or the vulnerable tissues extending downward from the larynx and trachea into the bronchial tree and the lungs. Localizing signs are related to the nature and site of viral injury: e.g., lymphoid swelling; hoarseness and croup; the dry, irritated cough of laryngeal or tracheal involvement; the productive cough of bronchitis or pneumonia; or deep pulmonary infection, which may lead to interstitial reactions or the production of consolidating alveolar exudates.

> **Virologic Diagnosis.** The recognition and identification of the individual viral agents of these diseases are difficult and time-consuming at the practical level. Continuing study, however, has led to the association of numerous viruses with upper and lower respiratory diseases. Some of them belong to virus groups capable of diverse localizations in human tissues other than those of the respiratory tract. Designations and classifications of viruses are difficult when clinical entities are not distinctive, and the diversity of names given to these organisms reflects the variety of situations in which they have been identified, as well as their biologic relationships. Table 15–1 lists some of the viruses associated with colds or more serious respiratory diseases and indicates their relationship to other epidemiologically or clinically distinct infections.

Epidemiology

Communicability of Infection. Man is the only reservoir for these viruses, so far as is known. They are transmitted in respiratory discharges by droplets spread on air-borne routes, by direct contacts, or by indirect contamination of the immediate environment. Some may also be spread by the fecal-oral route.

The incubation period for the common cold is generally quite short, usually a matter of one to two days. The infectious agent is probably communicable for a day or so before symptoms begin, and throughout the course of active infection. In the more acute diseases, involving less accessible

tissues, the incubation period is somewhat longer: from a few days to a week or more. The infections are communicable while active symptoms persist.

Susceptibility to these infections is quite general, although young children and infants are more frequently and seriously involved than adults. Specific immunity is induced by these diseases, but it is often short-lived. Reinfections are common but they may be milder than preceding attacks because of lingering immunity.

The control and prevention of the common viral respiratory infections remain a difficult problem, whose importance can be judged by the frequency of attack and the extent to which disability interferes with school or work. These viral infections often predispose to secondary bacterial complications that may become entrenched, chronic, and marked by continuing hypersensitive responses. Personal and public attention to the hygienic and sanitary measures that limit the respiratory and oral spread of infection constitutes the chief control within families and groups. Antibiotics have no effect on viral infections and should be used only when bacterial complications arise. In those situations, antibiotics should be selected on the basis of laboratory recognition of significant bacterial strains, individually tested for susceptibility.

Killed vaccines have been prepared with adenoviruses and some others, but their use has thus far been limited to special or experimental situations, and their efficacy remains to be evaluated.

Systemic Viral Disease Entities Acquired by the Respiratory Route

Mumps

The Clinical Disease. Mumps is a familiar disease easily recognized by its characteristic involvement of the parotid glands, on one or both sides. The infection is usually generalized, however, because viremia frequently occurs after the virus has multiplied in the parotid gland, or in the superficial epithelium of the upper respiratory tract. The virus may localize subsequently in other salivary glands; the testes or ovaries, espe-

Table 15–1. Viruses Associated with Respiratory Diseases

Virus	Isolation from:	Associated Disease
Rhinoviruses (at least 60 are recognized)	Nasopharyngeal washings	Common colds (adults and children)
Adenoviruses (at least 30 types)	Normal and infected adenoids and tonsils Phayngeal washings Infected conjunctiva Stools and rectal swabs in infected cases	Undifferentiated acute respiratory disease (ARD) Acute pharyngitis Acute conjunctivitis Pharyngoconjunctival fever Epidemic keratoconjunctivitis Bronchitis and bronchial pneumonia⎫ Gastroenteritis ⎬(children)
Para-influenza viruses (4 antigenic groups, each with several virus types)	Nasal and pharyngeal washings Lung tissue	Mild or acute upper respiratory infection Laryngotracheobronchitis (croup) Bronchitis Pneumonia
Respiratory syncytial (RS virus)	Pharyngeal washings	Infant bronchiolitis and pneumonia Acute upper respiratory illness in childhood
Coxsackie viruses (enterovirus family) (2 antigenic groups, at least 29 types) (named for a town in New York State where first isolated)	Stool specimens Throat washings Spinal fluid	Common colds Herpangina (vesicular pharyngitis) Pleurodynia (epidemic, febrile myalgia, usually thoracic) Aseptic meningitis, sometimes with paresis resembling poliomyelitis Neonatal myocarditis
ECHO viruses (enterovirus family) (at least 31 antigenic types) (Enterocytopathogenic Human Orphan Virus = ECHO)	Stool specimens Throat washings Spinal fluid	Common colds Undifferentiated respiratory or enteric illness Aseptic meningitis, often with rash

cially in adolescents or adults; the thyroid gland; and occasionally the central nervous system.

Mumps begins typically as a parotitis, with sudden onset of fever and swelling and tenderness of one or both parotids, followed sometimes by enlargement of the sublingual or submaxillary glands. The tissue damage is not great, but the swelling causes pain, particularly with the pressure of mouth and throat movements. The swelling reaches a peak in about two days and persists for a week to ten days, outlasting the fever. When other localizations occur, they generally follow

the salivary gland inflammation in about a week, but they can occur simultaneously or even in the absence of parotitis. Tissue injury is not severe or permanent, except in the testis, which may be compressed by the swelling within its limiting membrane and later atrophied. If bilateral orchitis occurs (which is not usual), the damage may lead to sterility. Ovarian infection does not result in sterility, because the ovaries can swell without compression by a limiting anatomic sheath. Meningoencephalitis occurs in fewer than 10 per cent of cases; fatality is rare.

Laboratory Diagnosis. Mumps parotitis is diagnosed clinically, without need for laboratory studies, but when other involvements occur without the characteristic initial syndrome, the virus laboratory may be needed to establish the diagnosis.

I. Identification of the Organism. Mumps virus can be propagated in chick embryos or in monkey kidney tissue culture. It can be identified as a *myxo*virus (see footnote, p. 359) by its hemagglutinating property. It is also characterized by its ability to lyse red blood cells, as well as agglutinate them. Serologic identification of the virus is made by demonstrating the specific neutralization of these properties by mumps antiserum.

II. Identification of Patient's Serum Antibodies. A serologic diagnosis of mumps can be made by demonstrating a rising titer of specific antibody following an attack of mumps. A sample of serum taken soon after the onset of symptoms is compared with another one drawn about two or three weeks later. The titer of the "convalescent" serum must be at least four times higher than that of the "acute" serum, to confirm a mumps diagnosis.

Hemagglutination-inhibition (see the diagnosis of influenza virus, pp. 359 to 360), complement-fixation, and neutralization techniques are employed. The latter method involves neutralization by antibody of mumps virus infectivity for eggs or for tissue cultures.

III. Specimens for Diagnosis
A. Saliva, spinal fluid, or urine may be collected for virus isolation, as indicated by the localization of symptoms, a few days after onset.
B. An "acute" serum taken within a day or two of onset.
C. A "convalescent" serum collected two to three weeks after onset.
D. A brief clinical history and tentative diagnosis with recorded dates of onset and specimen collection must accompany the specimens.

Epidemiology

I. Communicability of Infection
A. Reservoir, Sources, and Transmission Routes. Mumps is a human disease, the virus source being the saliva of infected persons. It is transmitted by air-borne droplets, by direct contacts, and by articles freshly contaminated by infectious saliva. The transfer must be rapid to be effective, apparently through close contacts.

B. Incubation Period. May be as short as 12 days or as long as a month, but the average time is 18 days to three weeks.

C. Communicable Period. Mumps is most communicable at the time symptoms begin, but virus may be present in saliva from about four days prior to onset until nine days after the first swelling.

D. Immunity. Mumps is generally a mild disease of childhood and confers a lasting immunity. Inapparent infections are frequent and also lead to antibody production as well as skin hypersensitivity. Mumps does not occur with as much regularity as other childhood virus infections, and consequently many adults may be susceptible. When the risk of infection among adults is high (young adults in schools or military camps, hospital personnel, parents exposed to infected children), a skin test for hypersensitivity can be used to detect those who have had previous infection, even though inapparent, and who are therefore probably immune. Susceptible individuals are skin-negative and may be candidates for mumps vaccine.

II. Control of Active Infection
A. Isolation. The patient should be isolated from *new* contacts for as many days as indicated by the persistence of active symptoms of parotitis, usually seven to nine days. His contacts of the previous week presumably were exposed and should be watched for signs of developing infection.

B. Precautions. Respiratory and oral secretions are infectious. Concurrent disinfection of dishes and other contaminated articles should be carried out. The hospitalized patient should have individualized care in isolation.

C. Treatment. There is no specific treatment for mumps, but gamma globulin prepared from mumps convalescent serum (not from normal human serum, which may be deficient in protective antibody) may lower the risk of orchitis if given immediately upon the onset of parotitis.

D. CONTROL OF CONTACTS. The routine investigation or quarantine of contacts is not warranted, especially if they are children. On the other hand, surveillance of exposed, susceptible (skin-negative) adults may help to prevent serious effects if passive immunoprophylaxis is given at the first sign of developing symptoms.

E. EPIDEMIC CONTROLS. When epidemics are underway, there are no recognized measures of practical value in control.

III. Prevention

A. ACTIVE IMMUNIZATION. Mumps vaccines, of live or inactivated types, are available, but artificially induced immunity is not durable. Their use is not indicated for children, because the mild, natural disease of childhood confers a better protection against the possible consequences of later infection. Vaccines have a greater value for non-immune adults whose circumstances include the risk of exposure (see Immunity, p. 365, this chapter), but active immunization must be provided before exposure occurs.

Measles (Rubeola)

The Clinical Disease. Measles is a common, but sometimes severe, infectious disease of childhood. It begins with fever and the sneezing, coughing, and conjunctival irritation so usual in colds or other upper respiratory infections, but the patient often appears sicker than a mere cold would warrant. In three or four days, the characteristic blotchy, dark-red rash appears on the face to confirm the impression that something more serious than a cold is developing. The skin rash, or exanthem, progresses quite dramatically within the next 24 or 48 hours, extending to the neck, the chest, and finally the entire trunk. In the meantime, systemic features of the disease have intensified, the fever reaching 104° to 105° F, the cough deepening to an obvious symptom of bronchitis, the patient becoming progressively irritable and dyspneic. Physical examination of the mouth and throat reveals rashy lesions (enanthem) on the buccal mucosa and the palate. These mucosal lesions, or Koplik's spots as they are called, often

appear before the skin rash is visible and may provide the first grounds for clinical diagnosis.

In about a week or ten days the rash begins to lose its angry red look and slowly becomes brownish. Fever and respiratory symptoms subside rapidly at the same time, barring complications, and an uneventful recovery ensues. The symptoms of measles are referable to the activities of rubeola virus, which enters the body by the respiratory route, localizes, and multiplies, probably in the lymphoid tissue of the pharynx. After about ten days of incubation, as the catarrhal period begins, viremia occurs, and the virus can be found not only in the respiratory discharges, but also in conjunctival secretions and in the blood for at least two days after the rash appears. The superficial capillaries in the skin are injured either by virus or by virus-antibody interactions, and it is this pathology that leads to the rash. Koplik's spots on the oral mucous membranes also reflect little focal areas of capillary damage and consequent formation of cellular exudate at the site. A generalized lymphoid tissue reaction also occurs in response to virus activity.

Both the upper and lower respiratory tracts become more susceptible to secondary bacterial infection, and this is the most frequent complication of measles. Hemolytic streptococci, in particular, may superimpose new injury, causing a more severe bronchitis or bronchopneumonia, but this can usually be well controlled with antibiotic therapy. A rare, but more serious, complication arises if the virus enters the central nervous system (1 in 1000 cases). The encephalomyelitis that results is fatal in up to 30 per cent of cases displaying this syndrome, and about 40 per cent of the survivors are left with residual damage expressed as mental or physical disorders.

Laboratory Diagnosis. Measles is usually diagnosed on the basis of its characteristic clinical appearance. When the rash is atypical, or Koplik's spots fail to appear, differentiation from other virus exanthems may be difficult, however, and in such cases laboratory confirmation of the diagnosis may be valuable.

I. Identification of the Organism. Measles virus can be propagated in tissue cultures of human cells, such as kidney and amnion cell cultures. It produces characteristic changes in these prepara-

tions, and its typical inclusion bodies can be seen in the nuclei of invaded cells. When harvested from tissue cultures, rubeola, which is a myxovirus, can be demonstrated to have hemagglutinating properties (see Influenza, pp. 359 to 360, this chapter). Serologic identification of the virus is obtained with measles antiserum, which specifically inhibits the hemagglutinating activity of rubeola or neutralizes its infectivity for human cell cultures.

II. Identification of Patient's Serum Antibodies. Specific measles antibody appears in the patient's serum during the course of the disease, rising in titer from the acute to the convalescent period. These antibodies may persist for many years following an attack of measles and are sufficiently protective to make second attacks infrequent. However, in suspected cases of adult measles, the serologic diagnosis depends particularly on the comparison of antibody titer during the convalescent stage of disease with that of the acute period, which may reflect a titer lingering from previous encounters with the virus. At least a fourfold rise above this level must be demonstrated in the second sample to provide serologic evidence of current infection.

The patient's serum is tested for its ability to react with known strains of measles virus, by complement fixation, neutralization of infectivity, or inhibition of red cell agglutination.

III. Specimens for Diagnosis.

A. Nasopharyngeal washings and blood samples can be submitted for *virus isolation* in the early acute phase, within 24 hours of the first appearance of rash. Blood should be defibrinated or anticoagulated; throat secretions should be placed in holding medium provided by the laboratory. These materials should be sent immediately for culture or frozen pending their transport.

B. An "acute" serum sample taken at the time the rash appears.

C. A "convalescent" serum collected two to three weeks after onset.

D. A brief history and tentative clinical diagnosis with recorded dates of onset and specimen collection must accompany the specimens.

Epidemiology

I. Communicability of Infection

A. RESERVOIR, SOURCES, AND TRANSMISSION ROUTES. Measles is one of the most readily transmissible of infectious diseases, with a human reservoir. It is spread by air-borne droplets derived from the respiratory discharges of infected persons, who may remain infectious from the time of onset of symptoms, throughout the catarrhal period, and for four or five days of the eruptive stage. Infectious droplets can be transferred directly or indirectly by contamination of clothing or other articles with secretions from the nose and throat. Subsequent drying releases into the air droplet nuclei containing viable rubeola virus.

B. INCUBATION PERIOD. From exposure to the time of first symptoms of fever and "cold," usually about ten days. Development of the rash requires another three to four days.

C. COMMUNICABLE PERIOD. See I, A above.

D. IMMUNITY. Generally, a single attack of measles confers a lifelong protective immunity. Following a mild, or aborted, case, immunity may be less durable, however, and in these instances second attacks of unmodified measles may occur. Maternal antibody is transferred in utero, but congenitally acquired immunity does not persist in the newborn for more than a few months. Artificial passive immunization is sometimes of value in aborting the disease, as discussed below with regard to the control of contacts.

Measles is endemic in all habitable parts of the world and is most prevalent in winter and spring. The immune state of the population in any given area is the principal determining factor in the frequency of epidemics. Susceptibility is universal, but the disease is most common and widespread among children, so that about 90 per cent of people reaching age 20 have acquired immunity through infection. In large urban communities the disease is endemic, but it appears in epidemic patterns of mild disease among the susceptible young or the newcomers about every second year. In rural or isolated areas, the intervals between outbreaks are longer, but the epidemic distribution includes people of all ages who have not been previously exposed, and the disease is often more severe.

II. Control of Active Infection

A. ISOLATION. The patient should be isolated for a period of seven days from the time the

rash appears to minimize the risk of further exposure of susceptible contacts, particularly if these include infants or small children for whom the disease may be serious. The patient should be protected against the possibility of secondary bacterial complications, particularly if he is hospitalized.

B. PRECAUTIONS. Nursing techniques are directed at the control of the respiratory route of spread. Concurrent disinfection of all articles contaminated by nose-and-throat secretions is indicated, and terminal disinfection is wise in view of the possible survival, for a short time, of the virus within the protective protein coats of settled droplet nuclei.

When measles is prevalent or epidemic in the surrounding community, hospitals should be particularly careful to protect their very young or very sick patients from infection acquired through visitors or through new, unscreened admissions.

C. TREATMENT. There is no specific treatment for measles. The use of antimicrobial drugs is aimed at the prevention of secondary bacterial infections (especially in patients with underlying debilities), or at the treatment of complications as they arise.

D. CONTROL OF CONTACTS. The isolation of cases and the quarantine of susceptible contacts have very little effect on the epidemic spread of measles, but they are of value in protecting those for whom the risk of severe disease is high, notably children under three or four years of age and people sick with other conditions. During epidemics, pre-school-age children should be kept at home. When outbreaks occur in institutions housing little children, strict isolation of the sick is warranted, as well as a quarantine of infants. In isolated rural communities measles can be a severe disease, with mortality rates as high as 25 per cent, a situation that justifies every effective protective effort.

Passive immunoprophylaxis is of value for exposed susceptible persons who risk serious consequences of measles infection. Human gamma globulin given in a single dose can avert or modify the disease if it is given within three days of known first exposure. Antiserum given later than the

sixth day of the incubation period has very little modifying effect on the course of the disease. Its use is not recommended for healthy children of school age who have been exposed, partly because prevention or modification of the disease also prevents or modifies the immune response to active measles and because the long-lasting immunity conferred by a disease that is usually mild in the schoolchild is preferable. Measles vaccines that are effective in the active immunization of children have become available in recent years. Their value in the prevention of the disease is discussed in the final section.

E. EPIDEMIC CONTROLS. Case reporting is required by most health departments, because it provides the best opportunity for prompt protection of the most vulnerable contacts. Where these are concentrated in institutions or isolated villages, public health measures include, as indicated by the local situation, isolation of the sick, quarantine of contacts, and passive immunoprophylaxis, as discussed above. When sufficient time is permitted by the slow progression of an epidemic, active immunization of the susceptibles in the involved community may help to retard or restrict further spread.

III. Prevention

IMMUNIZATION. Inactivated, and live attenuated, measles virus vaccines have been given to several million children in different parts of the world during the past few years. Current evaluations are quite optimistic regarding the success of these vaccines in inducing effective active immunity.

Live attenuated vaccine given in a single injection has provided 95 per cent of the immunized children with antibody levels similar to those that occur after the natural disease, and this immunity has held during a five-and-one-half-year period of study. The majority of children develop fever and rash following vaccination, but these symptoms are minimal and subside quickly. They can be reduced or avoided for children who can be expected to react adversely by the simultaneous injection of immune globulin at a different site.

Inactivated vaccine produces reactions only

rarely, but it must be given in at least three doses at monthly intervals, and the immunity provided does not persist for more than a year or so.

Combined immunization with an initial injection of inactivated vaccine followed in a few months by attenuated virus reduces the reactions to the latter and confers a lasting immunity.

When measles vaccines are employed, they should be given in the first year of life (inactivated vaccine at three to six months, live attenuated virus at 9 to 12 months). Their use for older children is limited to those who have no history of measles, particularly if they are institutionalized or if they have underlying pulmonary or cardiac disease. Measles vaccine should not be given to persons who are receiving steroid or other therapy that depresses the normal mechanisms of resistance.

Vaccination may prove to be a valuable public health measure in many of the isolated or underdeveloped areas of the world where measles is a severe disease of great frequency and high mortality. As in the case of other infectious diseases controlled by immunization, however, the price of artificially induced immunity includes continuing evaluation of its durability, with repeated booster doses of antigen as indicated. This is necessary to avoid a widening accumulation of susceptibles among older populations who have never experienced infection and whose artificial immunity has waned. This in turn must be weighed against the severity of the disease or its consequences in people of all ages.

German Measles (Rubella)

The Clinical Disease. German measles is one of the frequent but mild viral exanthems of childhood. Its chief importance lies in the effect it may have on infants born of mothers who contract the infection during the early months of pregnancy.

Rubella virus probably enters the body through the respiratory tract, but is disseminated by the blood stream. Symptoms begin with a mild upper respiratory disturbance, followed by the enlarge-

ment of cervical lymph nodes, characteristically those of the back of the neck, and finally include the eruption of a generalized macular rash. The rash is distributed first on the face and head, spreads rapidly to the neck and trunk, but subsides in two or three days. Rapid recovery without complication is the rule, but in adults occasional complications result from virus localization in joints or the central nervous system.

When rubella occurs in pregnant women, transfer of the virus across the placenta to the fetus may cause serious and permanent damage to the developing embryonic tissues, particularly if they are infected during the stage of their earliest, most rapid formation. The danger of such effects diminishes after the fourth or fifth month of pregnancy. Stillbirths and spontaneous abortions may occur, and babies brought to term may display one or more serious anomalies, such as heart defects, liver and spleen enlargements with dysfunction, deafness, cataracts, mental retardation, or other brain damage.

Laboratory Diagnosis. Clinically, rubella must be distinguished from measles, scarlet fever, and a number of rash-producing virus infections. The laboratory diagnosis has been difficult, but the recent development of techniques for the isolation of rubella virus from throat washings, blood, and urine or stool specimens and for assay of serum antibodies may lead to the general availability of reliable methods.

Epidemiology

I. *Communicability of Infection*

A. RESERVOIR, SOURCES, AND TRANSMISSION ROUTES. So far as is known, man is the only reservoir for the virus of German measles. The nasopharyngeal secretions of infected persons contain the virus and transmit it when they are sprayed into the air. Air-borne droplet nuclei and direct or indirect contacts are the usual transferral routes.

B. INCUBATION PERIOD. Virus multiplication in the body requires about 14 to 21 days before symptoms become apparent. The average period is 18 days.

C. COMMUNICABLE PERIOD. This disease is very communicable during the week before *and* the week after the appearance of the rash.

D. IMMUNITY. A single attack of German measles appears to provide a permanent immunity. The disease often appears in epidemic form among children, particularly in the winter and spring, but it is not so frequent as measles, and consequently many young adults remain susceptible. Epidemics are also frequent in the latter group, especially during their school or military associations.

II. Control of Contacts. German measles is such a mild disease that controls are neither necessary nor desirable under ordinary circumstances. The situation is different, however, in the case of rubella contracted by pregnant women.

The epidemiology of congenital rubella is related to the fact that outbreaks of German measles can and do occur after childhood. In the spring of 1964 this country experienced a large epidemic, which resulted in congenital disaster for thousands of babies. Improved laboratory techniques made it possible to study many of those infants extensively. It was discovered that they remain infectious for many months after birth, the virus being recoverable from throat secretions or spinal fluid up to 18 months postnatally. It is thought that this continuing infection with rubella virus may account for the progression of symptoms observed in the affected babies, especially those with central nervous system defects.

It is also important to recognize that congenitally infected infants are capable of transmitting the virus to susceptible adults who care for them. The hazard is great only for young women in the first trimester of pregnancy. If these contract the disease, a 30 per cent incidence of congenital infection can be expected in the first three months, weighted by an 80 per cent record of infection in the initial four weeks of pregnancy. Furthermore, it is now known that apparently normal babies, born of mothers who were infected, may shed the virus, and that inapparent infections of mothers may affect the fetus to the same degree as those characterized by rash. For all these reasons, it is considered

advisable for susceptible pregnant women to avoid unnecessary contacts with newborn babies, especially during the first trimester, until the situation has been further clarified.

The prophylactic use of human gamma globulin has been tried without proven success in preventing rubella infection in either the pregnant patient or the developing fetus.

Vaccines designed to prevent the disease by artificially induced active immunity are in the formative stage now that the virus can be successfully cultivated in the laboratory.

Chickenpox and Herpes Zoster

The Clinical Disease. Chickenpox (varicella) and herpes zoster (shingles) have been a part of the human scene for many centuries, but it is only in recent years that the relationship of their viral agents has become apparent. *Chickenpox* is a mild but highly communicable disease of childhood, characterized by fever, malaise, and an itching vesicular skin eruption. Epidemiologically and clinically, its chief importance lies in its resemblance to mild or modified smallpox, from which it must be carefully differentiated. *Zoster*, or shingles, bears little clinical resemblance to chickenpox but is apparently a recurrent manifestation of persistent infection with the same virus. It occurs sporadically in adults, who develop an incapacitating, painful inflammation of posterior nerve roots and ganglia, the path of the affected sensory nerves being marked by crops of vesicular eruptions of the skin of the area. These vesicles are morphologically identical with those of chickenpox, but the clinical appearance of zoster is quite distinct from the childhood disease.

Varicella virus is believed to enter the body through the respiratory mucosa and, after a period of viremia, to localize in the cells of the skin. The first symptoms of fever and malaise appear about 12 to 14 days after exposure. As skin localization occurs, the rash appears first on the trunk, then progresses to the face, limbs, and sometimes the mucosa of the mouth and throat. The lesions are often more abundant on covered than on exposed areas of the body, and they appear in successive crops for three to four days,

so that different stages of pock development may be seen at the same time. The pocks begins as papules, then develop into weepy vesicles, which become crusted as they begin to heal. The lesions resolve without scarring as a rule, and recovery is usually rapid and uneventful. The disease has an extremely low mortality rate and only occasionally may lead to dangerous complications, such as viral pneumonia in adults or encephalitis in children.

Zoster also begins with fever and malaise as virus multiplication proceeds, and extreme tenderness develops along the dorsal nerve roots where virus localization has occurred. In a few days crops of vesicles appear on the skin area supplied by the sensory nerves of the affected root. The eruption is generally unilateral, appearing most commonly on the trunk along the lower rib line. Other frequent areas are the shoulders, neck, or head. Zoster is a sporadic infection chiefly seen in older adults.

Laboratory Diagnosis. Clinically, the appearance and sequence of distribution of skin lesions usually distinguish chickenpox from other "pox" diseases. When epidemiologic considerations raise doubts concerning the possibility of smallpox, however, laboratory identification of these viruses or of the patient's specific immune response becomes imperative.

Morphologically, varicella and smallpox viruses have much in common, but distinctions can be made in the location of inclusion bodies within infected host cells or in the cells of tissue cultures. Positive identification of virus can be made by cultivating vesicle fluid in tissue culture or chick embryos and by confirming morphologic features of inclusion bodies or the damage they induce with serologic tests using specific antibody. Similarly, patient's serum antibodies can be identified in tests with known strains of viruses.

Epidemiology

I. *Communicability of Infection*

A. Reservoir, Sources, and Transmission Routes.   Man appears to be the only susceptible host for chickenpox and zoster virus, the infected portion of the human population being the reservoir. Chickenpox is one of the most highly communicable and common epidemic diseases of childhood. It spreads rapidly from person to person, the chief source of infection being respiratory secretions or discharges from early vesicular lesions of the mucous membranes or the skin. Air-borne droplets as well as direct and indirect contacts with infectious secretions carry infection into the respiratory tract of exposed contacts. Infection does not occur directly through the skin.

B. Incubation Period.   Two to three weeks are commonly required for virus multiplication following exposure. The average case becomes symptomatic in about 14 to 16 days.

C. Communicable Period.   Infectivity is greatest from a day or so before the rash appears to the fifth or sixth day of the eruption. Scabs are not infective, but the disease remains communicable while fresh crops of vesicles are appearing. Zoster is not readily communicable because the virus is not present in the respiratory tract, but this infection can be the source of varicella in children and has been known to initiate epidemics.

D. Immunity.   Infection with either varicella or zoster confers a long-lasting immunity to the respective diseases. Children who have recovered from experimentally induced zoster or varicella show a cross-immunity to both, but zoster may occur in adults who have had a natural varicella infection at an early age.

Susceptibility is universal among those who have not had the disease, but chickenpox in adults is often more severe than it is in children, and this sometimes contributes to the difficulty of distinguishing it from smallpox. In temperate zones, chickenpox is most prevalent in the winter and spring, but zoster occurs sporadically, without seasonal incidence.

The viruses isolated from chickenpox and from zoster are either identical or share closely related antigens. The most workable theory concerning the relationship of their diseases is that chickenpox virus may sometimes infect nerve cells and remain latent and inactive within them for long periods. A stress or physiologic insult of unknown influence may later provide an opportunity for the activation of the latent virus, with the characteristic result known as zoster.

II. *Control of Active Infection*

A. Isolation.   Children are rarely hospital-

ized with chickenpox, and should not be, unless complications or other problems require it. By the time complications appear, chickenpox is usually no longer communicable. Cases sometimes develop in patients already in the hospital, however, and in this situation every precaution must be taken to prevent the spread of chickenpox to other susceptible children, infants, or adults. The patient should be strictly isolated, and susceptible contacts quarantined. It is particularly important to protect other patients who may be on steroid or other therapy that suppresses the immune mechanism. Children with leukemia, for example, are subject to severe or possibly fatal consequences if they contract chickenpox.

In the community, the isolation of sick children is not effective in stopping the spread of epidemics, but they should be kept out of school for the week of the eruptive stage, and away from very young susceptible contacts.

B. Precautions. In the hospital, the nursing care of chickenpox requires the concurrent disinfection of objects contaminated by respiratory secretions or the discharges of fresh skin lesions. The patient's care should be individualized; gowns should be worn; and particular attention should be given to proper techniques for handling soiled bedclothing and linens. Terminal disinfection of the isolation room is recommended also.

C. Treatment. There is no specific treatment for chickenpox or varicella. Scratching of the very itchy eruption may lead to secondary bacterial infection of open vesicles, however. This can usually be controlled locally by the use of ointments that reduce itching. In this connection, it is important for the nurse to assist the patient in maintaining strict cleanliness of the skin, with careful attention to hands and fingernails. Hand and nail scrubbing is essential also for the nurse and physician who have been in close contact with the patient.

D. Control of Contact. The quarantine of contacts is ordinarily not effective, and prophylactic measures are not indicated, except possibly for exposed susceptibles for whom chickenpox might be a serious disease (children or adults on antibody-suppressive drugs). Gamma globulin

has been recommended in these occasional situations, in the hope of achieving modification of the infection.

Chickenpox is not a reportable disease except for adult cases occurring in areas where smallpox is not endemic.

III. Prevention. There are no specific means of preventing chickenpox. Vaccines are not available and the therapeutic use of gamma globulin ordinarily is not justified. Of chief concern is the early distinction of chickenpox from smallpox in adolescents or adults.

Smallpox

The Clinical Disease. Smallpox, also referred to as *variola major*, is a severe, acute infectious disease that has been recognized and feared for many centuries in all parts of the world. The recorded descriptions of its epidemic effects extend from the writings of Galen in the second century to the reports of observers of our own day. Wherever it has been carried by the infected and introduced into noninfected, susceptible populations, it has left a trail of suffering, disfigurement, and death. It has been brought under partial control by the success of artificial immunization, but it remains worldwide in distribution as a sporadic, endemic, or epidemic disease, depending on the immune status of populations as well as their socioeconomic condition. Its continued control, or eventual elimination, requires a constant, vigorous effort to achieve and maintain universal immunization. In an age of ever-increasing physical contacts among the people of the world, the threat of smallpox demands continuing vigilance.

Variola virus enters the susceptible host through the upper respiratory mucosa. During the incubation period (6 to 21 days), virus multiplication proceeds in lymphoid tissue, and blood stream distribution occurs, with localization of virus in reticuloendothelial cells in many parts of the body. More virus is released from these cells to the circulating blood and localization then begins

in the cells of the skin. Symptoms begin when the second stage of viremia becomes intense. The onset of fever and chills with intensifying malaise is usually sudden but may occur gradually. The skin rash begins to appear after one or several days of fever, erupting first on the face and then symmetrically on the arms, trunk, and legs (see Fig. 15–3). The exanthem progresses through macular, papular, and vesicular stages to the formation of pustules about the eighth or ninth day. Crusts harden on the pustules and fall off after another ten days or two weeks.

The nature and full development of the rash are an index of the severity of the disease and of the extent of the patient's immunity. A partially immune person, such as a vaccinated contact who has not yet developed full immunity or an individual whose immunity is waning between vaccinations, may develop fever and all the symptoms of the pre-eruptive stage, but experience little or no further progression of disease. In severe cases, however, the rash may become confluent, and even hemorrhagic. There is a direct correlation between the death rates and the extent and character of the rash.

Recovery is signaled by the drying of the pustular lesions. Successive crops of eruptions do not occur in smallpox, so that individual pocks all begin to heal at about the same time. As the scabs fall away, healing is usually accompanied by scarring, the pitted scars fading gradually from pink to white.

The complications that may occur during smallpox infection include secondary bacterial invasion of the skin lesions, sometimes with resultant septicemia. Patients who die in the first week of illness often show evidence of heart failure and pneumonia, as a result either of overwhelming virus infection or of secondary bacterial invasion. The majority of deaths occur in the second or third week, however, at the height of the pustular phase. There may be hemorrhages in the skin, conjunctiva, the oral mucosa, bowel, uterus, or vagina. Pregnant women with smallpox frequently abort, but if the infection occurs near the end of pregnancy the child may be brought to term. Infants may acquire the disease in utero,

or at the time of birth if the mother's infection is still active at that time.

A mild form of smallpox called *alastrim* is caused by a variant of the smallpox virus known as *variola minor*. The eruption is less profuse and malignant, symptoms are less profound, and the disease is seldom fatal. When this form of smallpox is transmitted to susceptible contacts, they, too, develop a light disease. On the other hand, when mild smallpox is the result of modification of *variola major* in a partially immune individual, transmission to a susceptible person can give rise to typically severe smallpox if that contact possesses no immunity.

Laboratory Diagnosis.   Most cases of smallpox can be diagnosed clinically on the basis of the

Fig. 15–3.   A young girl in Southeast Asia with smallpox. Her parents have dressed her in her finest clothes as if to protect her from evil. (WHO photo by WHO sanitarian, W. Wilkie.)

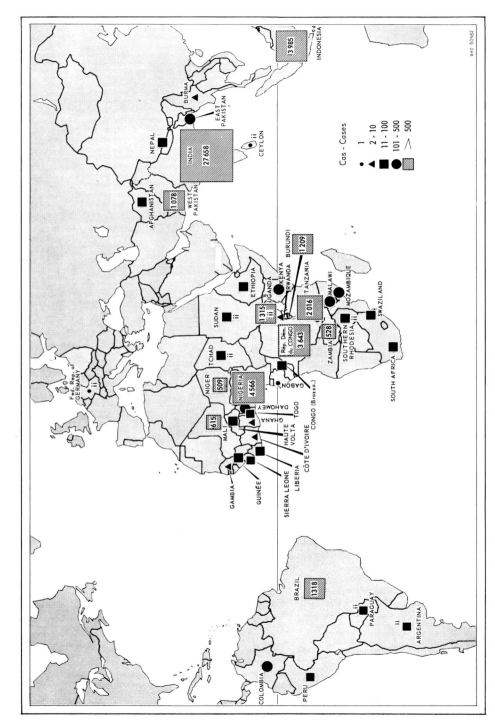

Fig. 15-4. The distribution of smallpox throughout the world in 1965. Vaccination programs could eliminate this disease. (Courtesy of World Health Organization, Geneva, Switzerland.)

appearance, development, and distribution of the skin eruptions, together with a history of sudden febrile illness preceding the exanthem. A history of possible contact must be sought, including the question of travel in parts of the world where smallpox is endemic or of recent contact with persons who reside in those areas. The clinical suspicion of smallpox calls for immediate preventive measures to be instituted for all the patient's contacts, even before laboratory confirmation can be obtained. Clinical diagnosis is most difficult in cases of modified variola major, or of alastrim, when the pocks may appear atypical. Smallpox must also be distinguished, however, from chickenpox, drug eruptions, meningococcemia, and other viral diseases accompanied by skin eruption.

The diagnostic virus laboratory can provide confirmation of clinical smallpox, or be of assistance in doubtful cases, by the following means:

I. Identification of the Organism

A. By examination of stained smears of material from skin lesions. The report is presumptive but it can be obtained quickly; i.e., within an hour of the laboratory's receipt of suitable material. The smallpox viruses are rather large, being about one third the size of the smallest bacteria. They can be seen as aggregates, or inclusions called Guarnieri bodies, within the cytoplasm of infected cells. These bodies can be stained and visualized with the ordinary light microscope.

B. By culture of appropriate material in chick embryos. This method may provide confirmation of the diagnosis within three to five days. The material to be cultured includes blood, if it can be obtained during the febrile pre-eruptive stage, scrapings from the early papular lesions, fluid from vesicles or pustules, and crusts. Virus can usually be seen in material from the skin lesions and propagated in eggs. Smears of blood are not rewarding, but cultures may be successful.

C. Serologic confirmation of the nature of the virus harvested from chick embryo cultures is obtained by complement-fixation tests, or by demonstrating neutralization of virus infectivity for eggs by specific smallpox antiserum.

II. Identification of Patient's Serum Antibodies.
Circulating antibody can be detected in the patient's serum only after several days or a week of illness. Complement-fixation and hemagglutination-inhibition tests (see Influenza Diagnosis pp. 359–60, this chapter) are generally employed with well known strains of smallpox virus. The serologic diagnosis of smallpox requires the demonstration of a rising titer of antibody during the course of the disease, with a "convalescent" serum titer at least four times higher than the "acute" serum titer. The first specimen of blood for serologic testing should be drawn immediately upon appearance of the rash, the second one in two or three weeks.

Epidemiology

I. Communicability of Infection

A. Reservoir, Sources, and Transmission Routes. Smallpox is a human disease, the reservoir and source of virus being the infected person. From the early stages of the eruption, virus is present in the oral and respiratory secretions, as a result of erosion of focal lesions in the mucous membranes. When the vesicular skin lesions rupture, their discharges are also a source of infection. Transmission of smallpox does not occur through skin-to-skin contacts and entry, but through introduction of the virus into the respiratory tract of a susceptible contact. Direct contacts may easily convey the virus, but indirect contacts and air-borne droplet nuclei or dust may transmit infection. Smallpox virus can survive drying for long periods, and scabs that have fallen off may remain infectious for years. This means that contacts need not be close, and that contamination of the air may result not only from the patient's respiratory secretions but also from the dissemination of skin discharges, drying particles, and dust stirred into the air. The hands and clothing of nurses and other attendants, bedclothes and linens, bedside equipment, furniture, floor, walls, and curtains all may be contaminated by virus in a drying but viable state, scattered on air currents or deposited directly. The virus may also be transported for long distances to induce new outbreaks, as reported for cases occurring in England that were traced to cotton imported from an endemic area. (See Fig. 15–4.)

B. Incubation Period. The virus requires from 7 to 16 days for multiplication before the first symptoms appear. The average time is 9 to 12 days from exposure to onset, and another three or four days to skin eruption.

C. Communicable Period. The patient must be considered infectious from the time of onset

of fever and other initial symptoms until all scabs have dropped away. Communicability is greatest during the early stages of the rash.

D. IMMUNITY. Resistance to smallpox depends on specific immunity, conferred either by an attack of the disease, by vaccination, or by congenital transfer of maternal antibody. The latter does not persist long after birth, and children should be vaccinated within the first year of life for this reason. Following vaccination, antibodies can be demonstrated within 9 to 14 days, reach a maximum titer within two or three weeks, and remain demonstrable for a few years. Revaccination every three to five years maintains immunity at a protective level and is considered adequate in nonendemic areas. In countries where smallpox persists (Asia, Africa, South America), revaccination at more frequent intervals may be necessary. It is particularly important that persons whose exposure risk is continuously high maintain an effective vaccination schedule. Such persons include customs and quarantine officers, international travelers, military personnel, and all hospital employees. In this connection, it should be remembered that a partially immune individual in contact with an active case of smallpox may develop a modified, sometimes unrecognized form of the disease but he can transmit it, in fully virulent form, to a nonimmune person and thus be responsible for continuation of an outbreak, or initiation of a new one (see p. 373). Smallpox vaccine and vaccination schedules are discussed below under Prevention.

II. Control of Active Infection

A. ISOLATION. Smallpox requires immediate consultation between the physician and appropriate public health authorities. The strictest isolation and precautions are required for the protection of nonimmune contacts, either at home or in the hospital. Only persons whose vaccination is current can safely care for the patient, and even these persons should be promptly revaccinated at this time. In the hospital, the patient should be assigned to an individual room, particularly if he represents a sporadic case appearing in a nonendemic area. When several cases are being cared for simultaneously, screened areas or cubicles are generally considered acceptable.

B. PRECAUTIONS. Careful techniques must be employed for the concurrent disinfection of all articles associated with the patient, particularly if they must be taken from the area. Individualized equipment should be used whenever possible. Oral and nasal discharges are deposited in containers suitable for burning, and other disposable items also are incinerated. Steam pressure sterilization or boiling is used for nondisposable items when possible; otherwise thorough disinfection and cleaning procedures must be used. Clean gowns should be worn by all who enter the patient's room and carefully discarded so that clothing is not contaminated in the process. Nonimmune personnel or visitors may not be admitted to the patient's room, and even immune visitors should be discouraged during the communicable period because they may carry the infection out of the hospital to others.

Particular attention must be given to the handling and disposal of soiled bedclothes and bedding, because virus can be disseminated easily from such items in lint. Susceptible laundry workers may acquire smallpox through the handling of contaminated linen, also. Soiled linens, blankets, and gowns should be carefully folded with their contaminated sides turned inward (without shaking), and placed in marked, sealed bags impermeable to moisture for transport to the laundry. If available laundry techniques cannot be relied upon to disinfect soiled linen, it should be placed loosely in a permeable bag and sterilized in the autoclave before washing.

Isolation and precautions are maintained until the patient displays no residual scabs. Terminal disinfection-cleaning should be thorough and includes the sterilization of pillows, mattresses, and other bedding.

C. TREATMENT. There is no specific therapy for smallpox. Antibiotics are of value in preventing or controlling secondary bacterial infections during the pustular stage. The use of gamma globulin after smallpox has become clinically apparent is not valuable because by that time the patient's own antibody level is as high as that

attainable by passive immunization. Gamma globulin has prophylactic value during the incubation period, however, as discussed below.

D. CONTROL OF CONTACTS. All of the patient's contacts are promptly vaccinated, or re-vaccinated, or quarantined for a period of 16 days timed from the last exposure. These precautions apply to all persons who have lived or worked on the same premises as the patient or have had other close contacts. Nonimmune newly vaccinated persons are kept under surveillance for a 16-day period, while persons with evidence of previously acquired immunity are carefully watched until the height of reaction to the current vaccination has passed. Any contact who develops a febrile illness during the period of quarantine or surveillance is promptly isolated until smallpox can be ruled out.

Passive as well as active immunization may be of value for nonimmune contacts. Gamma globulin is obtained from servicemen who have been recently vaccinated. It should be given together with vaccine as soon as possible after exposure.

Case finding is of ultimate importance in smallpox. The source of each patient's infection is of primary concern to all health authorities, who make a careful review of all associated cases with exanthematous or other suggestive symptoms.

E. EPIDEMIC CONTROLS. Case reporting of smallpox is required everywhere, under international law. If an epidemic threat occurs, local health authorities institute rigorous enforcement of quarantine on all contacts until evidence of successful vaccination is obtained. Surveillance is maintained after vaccination for a 16-day period. The public is informed of the necessity and nature of controls, and of the availability of vaccine. Physicians and hospitals are supplied with fresh, potent vaccine, and public vaccination stations may be established as well. If the disease appears to be spreading to a material extent, mass immunization of partial or whole populations within the affected area may be attempted. In 1947 this procedure was credited with the prevention of what might have been a major outbreak in New York City following the entry of a primary case and the development of several secondary cases.

The vaccination of several million people successfully aborted the epidemic. In 1962 another imported case appeared in New York City, but no transmissions occurred.

International requirements for the control of smallpox include government notification of the World Health Organization as well as adjacent countries of new cases appearing in a nonendemic area. The International Sanitary Regulations of WHO provide special measures for vehicles arriving by any route from countries where smallpox persists. Strict regulations prevent the travel of infected persons, and many countries, including the United States, require all entering travelers to provide evidence of successful vaccination or of previous infection. Vaccination certificates are valid for a period of three years.

III. Prevention

A. IMMUNIZATION. Active immunization by vaccination affords the only effective or reliable means of controlling smallpox. The more universally it is practiced, beginning in infancy, the less prevalent smallpox becomes. In the early part of the twentieth century, the annual case rate in the United States was over 40,000. By 1942 the number of annual cases had been reduced to less than 1000, and in the current decade only an occasional imported case has been reported, with few, if any, secondary transmissions.

The idea of protecting human beings from the effects of smallpox by injecting them with a small dose of material obtained from a mild case was first introduced about two thousand years ago by the Chinese. In our own time, the first safe application of this technique dates from 1798 with Jenner's use of cowpox virus to accomplish the same purpose (see Chap. 11, p. 270). Cowpox is a mild exanthematous disease of cattle caused by a virus immunologically related to variola. Jenner observed that it caused a similarly mild disease in milkmaids and other dairy workers who were then impervious to the effects of epidemic smallpox, which at the time was taking an enormous toll of other members of the English population. He called his technique "vaccination" to relate it to the Latin word for cow, which is

vacca. Jenner's success with cowpox virus led to its continuing use for many years and the gradual decline of smallpox as an epidemic disease in the populations of Western Europe and America. In the course of time another virus, called "vaccinia," emerged during the laboratory propagation of cowpox and variola viruses. Its origin is not known, but it is also antigenically very similar to variola and even more attenuated for man, so that vaccinia virus has become the variant of choice for the preparation of the immunizing vaccine for smallpox.

Vaccinia virus is propagated in calves and harvested from their skin lesions for vaccine manufacture. Calf lymph vaccine thus contains live attenuated virus. When introduced into human skin it produces a localized infection at the site of inoculation and stimulates the production of antibodies that are effectively capable of preventing the development of smallpox infection. To accomplish this purpose the vaccine must be fresh and potent at the time of inoculation. Under rare and unusual circumstances it is capable of causing generalized skin or systemic infections. It must be correctly applied and its effect properly interpreted if it is to achieve the desired result. The following factors are of greatest importance:

1. *Time and Frequency of Vaccination.* Vaccination must be successfully completed *before* exposure to smallpox if it is to afford a guarantee of protection.

Primary vaccination should be carried out in children between 6 and 18 months of age and repeated at school age. This general rule applies in countries where smallpox is not endemic. In areas where the disease is seen with frequency, children should be vaccinated first at three to six months, and revaccinated about one year later.

Revaccination every three to five years is indicated for people who live in nonendemic countries; more frequently if the exposure risk is high and sustained.

Hospital personnel and all others under special risk should maintain immunity through vaccination programs instituted upon employment and continued at regular intervals as indicated.

Contraindications to vaccination include skin diseases (such as eczema), agammaglobulinemia,

and leukemia, particularly when these occur in young children. Because the vaccine is live, the risk of generalized vaccinia infection is higher in patients with pre-existing skin lesions or suppressed mechanisms for immunity. For the same reason, eczematous patients should not be permitted to come in contact with recently vaccinated persons, and the eyes of young children should be protected against secondary inoculation of virus from their own or others' fresh vaccinations. Also, primary vaccination should not be given to pregnant women. If the danger of active smallpox is real, vaccination may be considered the lesser risk in these situations, and it is performed simultaneously with the administration of vaccinia gamma globulin.

2. *Technique of Vaccination.* Vaccine is pressed into the most superficial layer of epidermis by a multiple pressure method. The site is first prepared by wiping away excess skin oil with acetone or ether. When the skin is dry (this is quite important because these solvents may affect the virus), a drop of vaccine is placed on it and pressed in lightly by stroking through it several times with the side of a sterile needle. The needle should not draw blood or involve an area more than 3 mm wide in any direction. Excess vaccine is removed with a sterile swab or gauze pad (carefully discarded into a container for incineration), and the site is left to dry *without* a protective covering. The preferred site of vaccination is the deltoid surface of the arm. Leg vaccination is not recommended because the irritation of clothing can enlarge the lesion or encourage secondary bacterial infection.

3. *Interpretation of Reactions to Vaccine.* Vaccination sites should be observed, and reactions recorded, at least twice (preferably the third and the ninth days), because the time of development of the maximum reaction has a bearing on the immunologic interpretation of the reaction, as follows:

A *primary* reaction, or "take" (also called *vaccinia reaction*), occurs in a *nonimmune*, fully susceptible person. A local lesion is formed, but does not reach its maximum development before the seventh to ninth day. During the first three or four days there may be no visible reaction. Then

a papule appears, surrounded by a small area of erythema. The papule progresses toward the vesicular stage on the fifth or sixth day, the vesicle reaching full development on or about the ninth day. It becomes pustular thereafter, and a crust forms, dries, and drops away usually by the end of the second week. The small scar that is left is usually permanent. It will be noted that this sequence of events for the single lesion of vaccination in a nonimmune person is entirely similar to that which occurs as the multiple eruptions of smallpox develop in a susceptible individual.

An *accelerated* reaction (also called *vaccinoid*) occurs in an individual with *partial immunity*. The sequence of development is the same as that described above, but it occurs more rapidly, and the lesion is usually less conspicuous. A small vesicle is formed by the third to the seventh day, and the *total* sequence is completed by the tenth day. This muted reaction reflects the presence of residual antibody in the vaccinated individual, the antibody neutralizing some of the vaccinia virus activity.

An *immediate* reaction (also called an *immune* or *early reaction*) should occur if the vaccinated individual is *fully immune* to smallpox. A small papule develops within the first three days and promptly disappears.

Errors in interpretation most often surround the immediate reaction. Unfortunately, this type of response may also occur if the vaccine is not potent, and even if the virus is dead. It may also occur if the individual is allergic to vaccine components other than virus, or if the skin is injured unduly by the vaccinating technique. Proof that the vaccine batch used was potent can only be obtained by observing its capacity to induce accelerated reactions in revaccinated persons or primary results in nonimmune, previously unvaccinated persons. If this proof cannot be obtained, or if there is any other reason for doubt, individuals displaying immediate reactions should be revaccinated. In any case, an immediate reaction cannot be accepted as valid for a person without a history of an attack of smallpox or of previous vaccination.

Proper technique and potent vaccine applied together cannot fail to produce one of the three types of reactions. Most or all first vaccinations should result in the primary, vaccinia reaction. About 50 per cent of persons revaccinated after more than ten years should develop accelerated reactions, the remainder show the primary response. Persons who maintain a vaccination schedule at regular intervals display immune or accelerated reactions.

A completely negative response to vaccine has no immunologic significance. The failure, or "no take," usually means inactive vaccine, or inadequate technique, or both. The vaccination should always be repeated in such case.

Systemic Viral Disease Entities Acquired by the Respiratory and Alimentary Routes

A few of the pathogenic viruses that are associated with the fecal-oral route of transfer and that localize in the intestinal tract may also find a respiratory route of entry and site of primary multiplication. The most notable of the disease entities to be recognized in this connection are *poliomyelitis* and *infectious hepatitis*. The important features of these diseases, and their epidemiology, are discussed in Chapter 20 of Section V where other diseases of intestinal tract entry are grouped. At this point, emphasis is placed on the possible role of the respiratory tract in their transmission.

Poliomyelitis

The virus of poliomyelitis is the best-known and most outstanding member of a family group called the *enteroviruses*. Two other types of viruses belonging to this family were mentioned earlier in this chapter for their association with respiratory infections. These are the Coxsackie and ECHO viruses (see page 364), which may produce injury in a variety of tissue sites. All of these organisms, including poliovirus, are known for their ability to implant, multiply, and persist in the intestinal tract where they produce little if any injury, their effects being exerted in other

Table 15–2. Summary : Viral Diseases Acquired by the Respiratory Tract

Clinical Disease	Causative Organism	Other Possible Entry Routes	Incubation Period	Communicable Period	Specimens Required
Influenza	Influenza virus		1–2 days	Acute febrile stage (3–4 days)	Throat washi or garglings "Acute" and convalescer serums
Common cold	Rhinoviruses Adeno-viruses Coxsackie viruses ECHO viruses	By fecal-oral route	1–2 days	During time of active symptoms	
Mumps	Mumps virus		18 days to 3 weeks	4 days prior to onset of symptoms until 9 days after first swelling	"Acute" and convalescer serums
Measles (rubeola)	Measles virus		About 10 days	From onset of symptoms through catar-rhal period and for 4–5 days of eruptive stage	Blood serum Nasopharyng washings
German measles (rubella)	Rubella virus	Transfer of virus across placenta	14–21 days	Week prior and subsequent to appearance of rash	Throat washi blood, urine specimens
Chickenpox and herpes zoster	Varicella virus		2–3 weeks	Greatest from a day before rash appears to 5th or 6th day of eruption	Throat washi Blood serum
Smallpox	Variola virus	Transfer of virus across placenta	7–16 days	Onset of fever until all scabs have dropped away ; greatest during early stages of rash	Exudate from skin lesions Blood serum

3day

Laboratory Diagnosis	Immunization	Treatment	Nursing Management
us isolation tibody titer	Killed vaccine	None specific	Isolation during the acute stage if close contacts are high risks
ologic diagnosis fficult and time-onsuming at actical level	Killed vaccine for adenoviruses, use limited	None specific	Principles of personal hygiene, support of healthy resistance
tibody titer	Live and inactivated vaccines	None specific: gamma globulin if orchitis risk is great	Isolation from new contacts; concurrent disinfection of dishes and other contaminated articles; hospitalized patient should be isolated
ibody titer us isolation	Inactivated and live vaccines Gamma globulin for high-risk individuals	None specific	Isolation; concurrent disinfection of articles contaminated by nose-and-throat secretions; terminal disinfection
's isolation not ne routinely	None	None specific	Isolation not necessary or desirable except to protect pregnant women
s isolation to stinguish from allpox virus body titer	None	None specific	Isolation in hospital to protect susceptible children, infants and adults
ar; to seek arnieri bodies s isolation in ck embryo body titer	Live vaccinia virus	None specific	Strictest isolation; only personnel with current vaccination should care for patient; concurrent and terminal disinfection until patient no longer displays residual scabs

tissues when they reach the blood stream and are disseminated. Their transfer to other hosts by way of fecal contamination is common, but transmission from respiratory sites of implantation and multiplication is also possible.

The exact mechanism of poliovirus transmission is not known, but it is obvious that close personal contacts are required. The infection rates among susceptible members of a household are quite high, especially among very young children whose unsanitary habits need no description. Polioviruses can usually be found in the throat during the early stages of infection, and this fact correlates with epidemiologic evidence that the disease is most communicable during the early days. On the other hand, the infectious period also parallels the time of maximum fecal excretion of the virus, and the communicability of polio is influenced by environmental sanitation in a way that is not usually seen in infections transmitted by respiratory routes.

Current evidence points to the probability that both the respiratory and alimentary tracts are involved in the spread of poliovirus. The role that either one plays depends on community and personal standards of sanitation and hygiene. When these conditions are optimal, the opportunity for virus transfer by the fecal-oral route is minimal (except in the case of children under two years of age who may disseminate virus to others of all ages), and respiratory transmission, always difficult to control, becomes more important. On the other hand, crowded, unsanitary, poor living conditions greatly enhance the opportunities for fecal contamination and spread of the disease through the oral route of entry.

From the nursing point of view, it is important to recognize both possibilities when poliomyelitis cases are to be cared for, at home or in the hos-

pital. Polio patients should be isolated during the first days following the onset of symptoms, particularly if they are admitted to the hospital during this period. If they are cared for at home, there is little value in isolation, because other household members have presumably already been well exposed during the patient's prodromal period. Nursing precautions for the hospitalized patient should include the concurrent disinfection of respiratory secretions and of fomites contaminated by them, as well as the proper disposal of feces and of bed linens or other items exposed to fecal contamination.

Infectious Hepatitis

The transmission mechanisms for this disease are not known precisely, but here the evidence seems better that intestinal transfer and oral entry occur most frequently, and that respiratory transmission is less likely, though possible. As is the case in poliomyelitis, infectious hepatitis is communicable during subclinical as well as clinically apparent periods of infection. Close personal contacts during prodromal or carrier stages of infection probably account for most orally acquired cases of infectious hepatitis, while water-, food-, and milk-borne transmission accounts for others, sometimes in epidemic patterns.

Enteric precautions are of particular importance in the care of infectious patients. Thermometers and other items that come in contact with oral secretions should be individualized, and later either discarded or sterilized (not merely disinfected). The question of accidental transfer of hepatitis virus by contaminated needles and syringes first used for infected cases is also of vital importance, as discussed in Chapters 20 and 29.

Questions

1. What is the chief complication of influenza? Name the most common secondary invaders.
2. What is the reservoir of influenza?
3. What nursing precautions are exercised for hospitalized patients with influenza?
4. What glands are affected in mumps?
5. Why can mumps cause sterility in the adult male patient?

6. What are the communicable and incubation periods for mumps?
7. When is active immunization for mumps indicated?
8. What is a serious complication of measles?
9. How is measles transmitted?
10. Why is antiserum not given later than the sixth day of exposure to measles? For whom is passive immunity recommended?
11. What vaccines are used to establish active immunity for measles?
12. Why is German measles of clinical importance?
13. Why is it considered advisable for susceptible pregnant women to avoid unnecessary contacts with newborn babies?
14. What are the incubation and communicable periods for chickenpox?
15. What nursing precautions are required in the care of a hospitalized patient with chicken-pox? Of a patient in the community?
16. Describe the transmission routes of smallpox. What is the portal of entry?
17. What people are considered high exposure risks to smallpox?
18. How long is a patient with smallpox isolated?
19. How are contacts with smallpox controlled?
20. What is the only effective and reliable means of controlling smallpox?
21. When should primary vaccination be given?
22. When is vaccination contraindicated?

16 Primary Atypical Pneumonia, Q Fever, and Psittacosis

The diseases discussed in this chapter are associated with agents whose classification presents some problem. They are a heterogeneous group, completely unrelated to each other biologically and epidemiologically, except for their common capacity to induce disease in man following an effective respiratory tract entry. By morphologic and physiologic criteria each falls into a different intermediate position, somewhere between the classical definitions of bacteria, rickettsiae, and viruses.

Pneumonia is the single outstanding feature induced by the first of the agents described here, *Mycoplasma pneumoniae*. Q fever and psittacosis, on the other hand, are systemic infections. Pulmonary disease is a constant feature of psittacosis, but does not invariably occur in Q fever. The clinical picture of pneumonia as it occurs in these diseases is quite different from that seen in bacterial infections of the lungs, and for this reason it is often spoken of as being "atypical" (see p. 385).

There are marked epidemiologic differences in these diseases, particularly with regard to reservoirs, sources of infection, and transmission routes. *Mycoplasma* belongs to a group known as pleuropneumonia-like organisms (PPLO). The pneumonia-associated strain has a natural reservoir in man and is directly transmissible from person to person, although its communicability

is apparently not great. Q fever is transmitted to man from its animal reservoirs; its direct transmission from man to man is rare. The reservoir for psittacosis is in birds. Transfer of infection to man is primarily from avian sources but occasionally occurs by person-to-person contacts.

Primary Atypical Pneumonia

The Clinical Disease. The term "primary atypical pneumonia" refers to a clinical syndrome rather than to any one of the several infectious agents that may induce it. Clinically, the phrase implies an acute lower respiratory infection of primary origin, that is, unrelated to any other disorder, whether or not it is coexistent. The disease is characterized by fever and other constitutional symptoms, and some degree of pulmonary infiltration, this being patchy, irregular, or diffuse, but seldom if ever consolidated. There is usually not a marked leukocytic response, the white blood cell count remaining within normal limits. This picture is "atypical" with respect to most bacterial infections, which characteristically induce exudative reactions in the lungs or bronchi. In bacterial pneumonia, bronchial exudates are often purulent; alveolar exudates may be abundant, collect rapidly, and consolidate; and general leukocytosis is the rule.

The nonbacterial infectious pneumonias of the infiltrative type are caused by a number of different microbial agents. A large and heterogeneous group of *viruses* has been associated with a variety of respiratory infections, including primary pneumonitis. These are listed in Table 15–1 (p. 364) and include both respiratory and enteroviruses. In addition to these, the pleuropneumonia-like organism now designated as *Mycoplasma pneumoniae* is known to be responsible for some cases of primary atypical pneumonia.

Laboratory Diagnosis
I. Identification of the Organism. The PPLO group, or pleuropneumonia-like organisms, are so designated because of their resemblance to the infectious agent of pleuropneumonia in cattle.

They have properties intermediate to the bacteria and rickettsiae on the one hand and the viruses on the other, but in their general properties they are unique and distinct from all three. They are characterized by a lack of a rigid cell wall, such as bacteria possess, and by a very pleomorphic morphology. They display many different forms: long filaments, bacillary and coccal shapes, disks, and granular bodies (see Fig. 16–1, *B*, *C*). Because of their plasticity and extremely small breadth, even the longest forms are filterable. Like the rickettsiae and viruses, they are intracellular parasites in vivo, but the PPLO differ from these organisms in their ability to grow on cell-free media in vitro. Like bacteria, they appear to reproduce by binary fission. They are the smallest microorganisms known to be capable of a saprophytic nutrition. On agar media, however, their colonies are difficult to see without a microscope lens because the delicate, protoplastic cells extend through and within the medium rather than over its surface (see Fig. 16–1, *A*).

The PPLO are now recognized as very prevalent in man, in both health and disease, as well as in many species of animals with which he has contact. One group of these strains has been placed together in the *Mycoplasma* genus. They are found among the normal flora of the mucosa of the respiratory and genital tract as well as in association with inflammatory conditions of these tissues (cervicitis, urethritis, prostatitis) or, more rarely, in synovial or pleural effusions and deep tissue abscesses.

Mycoplasma pneumoniae was identified in the early 1960's as the cause of those cases of atypical pneumonia that are associated with the development of "cold agglutinins" in the serum. The latter term refers to the fact that the patient's serum agglutinates human erythrocytes in the cold, at 4° C, but not at 37° C (group O cells must be used). This activity is not displayed by normal serum, but increases markedly in cases of mycoplasmal pneumonia. For a number of years the agent of these penumonias associated with cold agglutinins was thought to be a virus, and it was referred to only as the *Eaton agent* prior to its recognition as a PPLO.

II. Identification of Patient's Serum Antibodies. In addition to a rising titer of cold agglutinins, patients with mycoplasmal pneumonia develop specific antibodies, which are demonstrable by the immunofluorescent staining technique and by complement fixation.

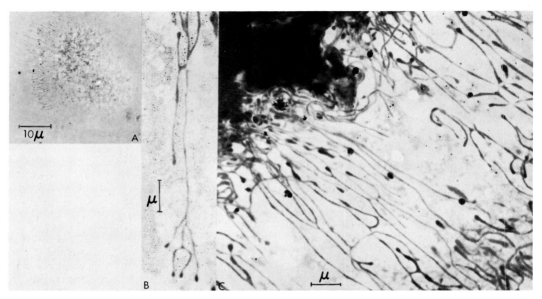

Fig. 16–1. *Mycoplasma pneumoniae.* Photomicrographs of (*A*) a colony growing in agar; (*B*) long, branching filamentous forms of the organism; and (*C*) the filamentous edge of a colony. (Reproduced from Freundt, E. A.: Morphological Studies of Pleuropneumonia Organism, *Acta Path. Microbiol. Scand.,* **31**:508–29, 1952.)

III. Specimens for Diagnosis

A. Pharyngeal swabs and sputum for isolation of *M. pneumoniae.*

B. An "acute" serum taken soon after the onset of symptoms.

C. A "convalescent" serum taken about two weeks after the date of onset.

Epidemiology

I. Communicability of Infection

A. Reservoir, Source, and Transmission. The reservoir of mycoplasmal infection is man, its source being the nasal and oral secretions of infected persons. Infection is transferred by droplet inhalation, or by direct and indirect contacts.

B. Incubation Period. Usually about two weeks, but may be from 7 to 21 days.

C. Communicability is probably highest during the first week of illness.

D. Immunity. Immunologic evidence, as well as the incidence of *M. pneumoniae* in normal persons and in patients with primary atypical pneumonia or febrile upper respiratory illness, indicates that this organism is widely disseminated. The incidence of disease in the general population is low, but the attack rate is higher among children and young adults. Epidemics occur most frequently among military and institutional populations.

II. Control of Active Infection. The control of mycoplasmal pneumonia does not appear to hinge on specific preventive measures. The hospitalized patient does not require isolation, although suitable precautions should be taken with respiratory secretions. When an outbreak appears to be spreading, isolation of the sick may be useful in control.

The tetracycline antibiotics are useful in severe cases of mycoplasma infection, but in the absence of specific laboratory diagnosis the use of antibiotics is generally avoided since the same symptoms may also be of viral etiology.

III. Prevention. No immunizing or other specific preventive measures are available.

Q Fever

The Clinical Disease. Q fever was first recognized as a clinical entity in the mid-1930's in Australia. It was named by the letter Q to indicate "query," pending the demonstration of its agent, soon identified as a rickettsia. Q fever is an acute systemic disease with a sudden onset of fever and chills, myalgia, and severe headache. The upper respiratory tract is not commonly involved, but an interstitial pneumonia is frequent, with chest pain and cough. Nausea and vomiting often occur, and in some cases symptoms may be referable to hepatic or meningeal involvement or endocarditis. Chronic infection persisting for a few months has been noted, but usually recovery is complete in about three weeks.

Laboratory Diagnosis. Clinical and x-ray diagnosis reveals signs of viral (atypical) pneumonia, but these are not specific for Q fever. Laboratory studies such as blood counts and tests for cold agglutinins (negative in Q fever but positive in mycoplasmal pneumonia) are also nonspecific. Laboratory diagnosis is best provided by identification of the organism or the demonstration of specific antibodies in the patient's serum, or both.

I. Identification of the Organism. The causative agent, *Coxiella burnetii*, is an obligate, intracellular parasite, like other rickettsiae. Important differences are noted for this organism as compared with other organisms of its type. Its morphology is irregular, with forms large enough to be mistaken for bacteria, or so minute as to be barely visible in stained preparations examined by the light microscope (see Fig. 16–2). It is filterable and resistant to physical and chemical agents. It is the only one of the rickettsiae that does not produce a cutaneous rash and does not require an arthropod vector to maintain itself in nature. The organism infects ticks, lice, mites, and other arthropods, and these probably have a role in its transmission among animals, but human infection with *Coxiella* can be acquired by inhalation, by ingestion in unpasteurized milk, through the conjunctiva, or through minor lesions in the skin. This distinction from other rickettsiae, all of which are transmitted to man by insect vectors (see Chap. 27), together with the other differences noted, is the basis for the genus name *Coxiella* rather than *Rickettsia*, although the organism remains classified with the family Rickettsiaceae.

II. Identification of Patient's Serum Antibodies. Tests for specific antibody in the patient's serum, early and late in the disease, are performed by complement-fixation and agglutination methods. Agglutinin titers are significantly high by the end of the second week; complement-fixing antibody titers, by the end of the fourth week.

III. Specimens for Diagnosis
A. Specimens of blood taken during the febrile period, as well as sputum, urine, or spinal fluid (as indicated by symptomatology), are injected into small laboratory animals or chick embryos for isolation of the organism. Laboratory facilities for

Fig. 16–2. An electron micrograph of *Coxiella burnetii*, the rickettsial agent of Q fever (40,000 ×). (Courtesy of Dr. R. L. Anacker. Electron micrograph by Mr. W. R. Brown, Rocky Mountain Laboratory, U.S. Public Health Service, Hamilton, Mont.)

this work should include special safeguards against the high risk of infection of laboratory personnel and others who work in the same building.

B. Serologic diagnosis is simpler, safer, and preferred by the diagnostic laboratory. "Acute" and "convalescent" samples of serum, timed as indicated in II above, are submitted for testing. A brief clinical history should accompany these specimens, indicating the tentative diagnosis and the dates of onset and serum collection.

Epidemiology

I. Communicability of Infection

A. RESERVOIR, SOURCES, AND TRANSMISSION ROUTES. Domestic animals and ticks (possibly other arthropods as well) are the natural reservoirs of this infection, man being an incidental victim and unimportant to its natural maintenance. As a zoonosis, Q fever is typically an inapparent infection with a worldwide distribution in domestic livestock. Animals with inapparent infections may shed large numbers of the organisms in milk, urine, and feces, and in placental tissues and blood. Raw milk from infected animals is probably a source of infection for man, but the richest common source of the organisms is the dust of pasture soil and of barns housing infected animals. The inhalation of airborne rickettsiae is thought to be the most important route of transmission. Q fever may be an occupational hazard for workers in abattoirs, in plants where wool or hides are processed, and also in laboratories where the organism is handled. Direct person-to-person transmission does not ordinarily occur, but Q fever has been reported as a hospital cross-infection and as a contact infection for nurses and physicians, particularly at postmortem examination.

B. INCUBATION PERIOD. The range is from two to four weeks, with an average time of 18 to 21 days.

C. COMMUNICABLE PERIOD. Not ordinarily transmissible from man to man (see I, A above).

D. IMMUNITY. Susceptibility to Q fever appears to be general in areas where the organism is endemic in animals. In the United States, Q fever is endemic in California and some other states where it occurs among farmers, dairy workers, veterinarians, and others who work with domestic animals.

II. Control of Active Infection

A. ISOLATION. Person-to-person transmission is unusual and does not warrant isolation.

B. PRECAUTIONS. Blood, sputum, feces, and urine should be disposed of by sterilizing methods. The organism can survive for months on clothing, on farm implements, in dust and dirt, and presumably on hospital equipment. Concurrent disinfection techniques should be practiced in the hospital unit where the Q fever patient is cared for, and terminal disinfection-cleaning is advisable as well.

C. TREATMENT. Tetracyclines are effective in the therapy of Q fever and are the drugs of choice. Chloramphenicol is also useful.

D. CONTROL OF CONTACTS. Human contacts are usually not infected, but a search should be made for the source of infection in contacts with animals, unpasteurized milk, or laboratory work.

E. EPIDEMIC CONTROLS. Case reports are indicated in areas where Q fever is endemic. Persons exposed in an outbreak are kept under observation for development of symptoms of Q fever and are promptly treated with antibiotics should such symptoms occur.

III. Prevention

A. *Immunization* can be afforded with an inactivated vaccine. This procedure is recommended for laboratory workers and others whose risk of infection is high.

B. The pasteurization of milk prevents dissemination of this infection and is particularly important in areas where the zoonosis is endemic.

C. Control of the disease in man depends on limiting the spread of infection from animals, by hygienic practices in the handling of milk or other animal products, by regulations on the importation and shipment of livestock, and possibly by the vaccination of animals, although the latter measure is not always economically feasible.

Psittacosis

The Clinical Disease. Psittacosis (alternately known as parrot fever, or ornithosis) is a respiratory and systemic viral disease of man transmitted to him by birds, such as parrots, parakeets, and lovebirds (known as psittacine birds), pigeons, and farmyard fowl, particularly ducks and turkeys. When the clinical disease of man was first recognized and associated with psittacine birds, it was called psittacosis to emphasize this relationship. Later it became obvious that a large variety of birds and domestic poultry may transmit the disease, and the more general term "ornithosis" was introduced to describe these infections when they occur in, or are acquired from, birds other than the psittacine variety.

Human infection may occur without clinical symptoms, or as a mild disease, but it may also be seen as a severe pneumonia. The infectious agent gains entry to the body through the respiratory tract. Localization occurs primarily in cells of the reticuloendothelial system. After a period of multiplication, the organism is distributed through the body in the blood stream, signaled by a sudden onset of fever, chills, headache, and malaise. The respiratory tract involvement may resemble influenza or primary atypical pneumonia. In mild cases, this may be the extent of symptoms, with recovery in about a week. Pulmonary infection may be severe, however, with a cough productive of mucopurulent sputum. Fatalities seldom occur with treatment, but when they do they are attributable to vascular damage. Rose spots are seen in the skin as a result of capillary flushing, nosebleeds are common, and thrombophlebitis may occur, with threat of embolism. Early and adequate antibiotic therapy of recognized psittacosis usually assures recovery without circulatory or other complications.

Because of its localization in reticuloendothelial cells, the psittacosis agent may be widely disseminated through the body, so that a variety of complications, involving the function of many organs, may be seen. At autopsy, a patchy inflammation of the lungs is usually found, sometimes with areas of consolidation resembling bacterial infection. Lesions may also be observed in the liver, spleen, heart, and kidney, as well as the brain or spinal cord. Intracytoplasmic localizations of the agent can be observed in stained tissue sections.

Laboratory Diagnosis. The clinical diagnosis of psittacosis can be confirmed in the laboratory by isolation and identification of the agent from human cases, or suspected bird sources, and by serologic methods.

I. Identification of the Organism. The agents of psittacosis and ornithosis are intracellular parasites that form a distinct biologic group. They have several properties in common with the microbial agents of two other very different kinds of human disease: lymphogranuloma venereum, a venereal disease, and trachoma, a serious eye infection (see Chap. 23, Sec. VI). In the past, this group of microorganisms has been classified with the viruses, because of small size, filterability, and obligate intracellular parasitism. These organisms are large for viruses, however, and the observation of other properties, such as susceptibility to antibiotics and the type of response they induce in human infections, has led to the current belief that they are either rickettsiae or small bacteria. The genus name *Bedsonia* (derived from the name of an investigator) has been assigned to them because it is noncommittal as to their nature, properties, or origin, pending further study.

In the laboratory, the psittacosis agent can be readily cultivated in chick embryos, mice, and other small laboratory animals, and in tissue culture. Unlike bacteria, it does not grow on cell-free media, but its multiplication in living cells is inhibited by drugs effective against bacteria, such as the tetracyclines, chloramphenicol, and penicillin. The agent is identified by its morphology in infected cells of living animals or tissue culture, and also by its reactivity with specific antiserums.

II. Identification of Patient's Serum Antibodies. Serologic diagnosis is made by testing two samples of the patient's serum, one taken during the early, acute phase of disease and another after at least two weeks. Antibodies can be demonstrated by complement-fixation and agglutination techniques, or by neutralization of infectivity of the agent for animal cells. However, antibody production may be delayed in the antibiotic-treated patient,

Table 16–1. Summary : Primary Atypical Pneumonia, Q Fever, and Psittacosis

Clinical Disease	Causative Organisms	Other Possible Entry Routes	Incubation Period	Communicable Period	Specimen Required
Primary atypical pneumonia (Eaton agent)	*Mycoplasma pneumoniae*		7–21 days	During first week of illness	Pharyngeal sw and sputum "Acute" and "convalescen blood serum
Q fever	*Coxiella burnetii*	Ingestion (milk), through conjunctiva and minor skin lesions	2–4 weeks	Ordinarily not communicable from man to man	Blood, spinal fluid, sputur urine "Acute" and "convalescen serums
Psittacosis	*Bedsonia* psittacosis agent	Sputum of infected person	4–15 days	Acute stage of illness, especially when coughing	Blood, throat washings, sputum, vom "Acute" and "convalescen blood serums

and a two-week serum sample may not show a significant rise in titer over the "acute" serum in such cases. Repeated serologic testing done at three and four weeks after onset may confirm the diagnosis in treated cases.

III. *Specimens for Diagnosis*

A. Specimens of blood, throat washings, sputum, or vomitus are submitted for isolation of psittacosis agent. Suspected bird tissues also yield psittacosis agent.

B. "Acute" and "convalescent" serum samples are drawn at appropriate intervals, as described in II above, and submitted to the laboratory for serologic diagnosis.

C. A brief clinical history should accompany specimens for laboratory study. The tentative clinical diagnosis should be stated, together with a notation of the date of onset of symptoms and the dates on which specimens were collected.

Epidemiology

I. *Communicability of Infection*

A. Reservoir, Sources, and Transmission Routes. The psittacosis agent is transmitted to man primarily from a reservoir in infected birds, but person-to-person transmission also occurs occasionally. Birds bred for sale as pets, such as parrots, parakeets, lovebirds, canaries, and thrushes, are frequently involved. Other important reservoirs for ornithosis are found among domestic fowl, particularly turkeys, ducks, and geese, and also pigeons and some water birds. Infection rates are high among workers in pet shops and aviaries, poultry farmers, pluckers, and processors. Infected birds may show symptoms such as diarrhea, droopiness, ruffled feathers; but often they do not appear to be ill. The infectious agent is present in the respiratory secretions of infected birds and also in the droppings. It spreads readily among birds by contact

ratory gnosis	Immunization	Treatment	Nursing Management
re g titer of lutinins	None	None specific	Concurrent disinfection of respiratory secretions
tion of anism in nal or k ryo g titer	Inactivated vaccine	Tetracyclines, chloramphenicol	Isolation not warranted (see text for exceptions)
ion of anism g titer	None	Tetracyclines	Isolation during acute febrile stage, respiratory precautions, masks for personnel if patient cannot control coughing; concurrent disinfection of all discharges; terminal disinfection

and on air routes. The dust from dried, infected droppings is widely disseminated on air currents created by the motion of wings and feathers. Young birds may receive the infection from their parents while still in the nest, and although the infection is often inapparent, they continue to excrete the agent for long periods.

Human infection is principally contracted through the inhalation of infected droplets or dust particles. When direct man-to-man transmission occurs, the source of infection is the sputum of infected persons, the agent being spread in air-borne droplets or possibly through indirect contacts with sputum-contaminated articles. Nurses and others who care for psittacosis patients are sometimes involved in outbreaks of the disease.

B. INCUBATION PERIOD.   About ten days are required for symptoms to appear following exposure, the range being 4 to 15 days.

C. COMMUNICABLE PERIOD.   Human patients are infectious during the acute stage of illness, particularly when coughing. Birds may be infectious for long periods, whether or not they show symptoms.

D. IMMUNITY.   An attack of the disease confers some protective immunity, but second attacks do occur, because of either inadequate resistance or a very heavy exposure. Psittacosis has a worldwide, nonseasonal distribution. The number of cases reported annually is directly related to the volume of traffic in birds. In the general population it is a sporadic disease, with occasional family outbreaks stemming from an infected pet bird.

II. Control of Active Infection. Isolation of the patient is important during the acute febrile stage of illness. Respiratory precautions should be carefully and fully observed, with concurrent disinfection of all discharges. Masks should be worn by nurses or others in close, continuous

contact with patients whose coughing cannot be properly shielded (very young, very ill, or uncooperative persons). Terminal disinfection-cleaning of the unit should be thorough in view of this organism's capacity for survival in dust.

Treatment with the tetracycline antibiotics is often effective, particularly when it is begun early in the disease with large doses and continued for several days after fever and other symptoms have subsided. Relapses occur when specific therapy is inadequate. The tetracyclines are also used in the treatment of sick birds. These drugs are helpful, though not always fully effective, in preventing or eliminating flock infection.

Contacts should be investigated, but neither quarantine nor immunization is recommended. Identification of the source of infection in diseased birds is essential to control, not only to prevent further spread of human cases from a current source, but to prevent a widening flock epidemic. Infected pet birds are traced to their pet shop or aviary origin; domestic flocks are examined closely if they are involved. Microbiologic diagnosis is made at autopsy of infected

birds, and appropriate flock controls are instituted. These may include mass dosing with tetracycline, elimination of sick birds and incineration of their bodies, and thorough cleaning and disinfection of premises, nests, and roosts.

To ensure effective application of control measures at the source of infection, it is important that every human case be reported to the local health authority.

III. Prevention. Effective immunizing vaccines are not available for the prevention of psittacosis. Prevention is best achieved by national regulations on the import of and traffic in psittacine birds, with quarantine of imports as indicated or of pet shops associated with cases. Improved methods for raising birds for pet sales and the prophylactic feeding of tetracyclines have helped to prevent the spread of infection in aviaries. The public has become better educated concerning the nature of this disease and its association with pet birds, but continuing emphasis is important.

Questions

1. What is the reservoir of psittacosis?
2. What are the morphologic and cultural characteristics of PPLO?
3. What is the reservoir of mycoplasmal infection?
4. What is the causative agent of Q fever infection?
5. What are the natural reservoirs for Q fever infections?
6. What methods are used to confirm the clinical diagnosis of psittacosis?
7. What nursing measures are necessary in the control of active psittacosis infection?
8. How is the spread of psittacosis prevented?

17 The Systemic Mycoses: Fungous Diseases Acquired Through Respiratory, Parenteral, and Endogenous Routes

Mycotic Infections: Clinical and Epidemiologic Distinctions

Clinically, the mycotic diseases of man fall into two distinct patterns: the *superficial infections* that involve only the outermost epithelial structures of the body (skin, hair, and nails) and the *systemic mycoses* that arise from fungal infection of deep tissues. The former are usually chronic and difficult to treat, but they are not a threat to general health because their fungal agents do not invade or survive in deeper tissues and are not disseminated. The fungi responsible for systemic infections, on the other hand, can survive in the body for long periods. They may remain inactive, or be held in a quiescent condition by the body's defensive reactions, producing few if any symptoms of importance; or they may cause progressively advancing disease.

Important *epidemiologic* distinctions can also be made for these two types of mycosis. The fungi of superficial infections have found a natural reservoir in man and some animals, and they are directly transmissible, by close or indirect contacts between infected individuals. Most of the agents of the deep mycoses, however, appear to have a reservoir only in the soil, where they live as saprophytes. When they find themselves

in human tissues, they are capable of parasitism, but in this condition they are not directly transmissible from one person to another.

In view of these considerations, the superficial fungus infections are described in Section VI, together with other diseases acquired and transmitted through skin contacts (Chap. 23). The systemic mycoses are grouped together here because, irrespective of their routes of entry, the basic patterns of their pathogenesis and epidemiology are closely similar.

Systemic Mycoses: Sources, Entry Routes, Pathogenesis, Epidemiology

Sources. There are several species of fungi associated with systemic disease in man. Most of these are derived from an exogenous soil reservoir, but there are two varieties that live as saprophytic commensals on human mucosal surfaces. From this endogenous source they can induce serious infection if trauma or other circumstance permits their introduction into deep tissues. The important diseases, and their agents, are listed in Table 17–1. They fall into three groups with respect to source, possible routes of entry, and resultant type of primary disease.

The free-living fungi from exogenous sources are not ubiquitously distributed in nature; often they are concentrated in particular areas where soil conditions permit their growth. Some fungous diseases occur in widely scattered parts of the world, others in limited geographic regions. Little is known about the natural life of these fungi or about the factors that determine their geographic distribution. At least two of the pathogenic species, *Cryptococcus* and *Histoplasma*, are often harbored by birds, such as pigeons, chickens, starlings, and others. They may be spread in

Table 17–1. Systemic Mycoses: Source, Entry Routes, Primary Disease

Disease	Causative Organism
Exogenous Sources	
Group 1: Respiratory or Parenteral Entry Routes (Traumatized Skin or Mucosa)	
Primary Diseases Pulmonary or Extrapulmonary	
Histoplasmosis	*Histoplasma capsulatum*
Coccidioidomycosis	*Coccidioides immitis*
Blastomycosis (North American)	*Blastomyces dermatitidis*
Cryptococcosis	*Cryptococcus neoformans*
Nocardiosis	*Nocardia asteroides**
Exogenous Sources	
Group 2: Parenteral Entry Route (Traumatized Skin or Mucosa)	
Primary Disease Extrapulmonary	
Blastomycosis (South American)	*Blastomyces brasiliensis*
Sporotrichosis	*Sporotrichum schenckii*
Chromoblastomycosis	Dark-pigmented fungi (*Hormodendrum* and *Phialophora* species)
Mycetoma (Madura foot)	*Madurella, Nocardia* species, and others
Endogenous Origin	
Group 3: Entry Through Traumatized Skin or Mucosa	
Primary Disease Pulmonary or Extrapulmonary	
Actinomycosis	*Actinomyces bovis**
Candidiasis (moniliasis)	*Candida albicans*

* Note: *Nocardia* and *Actinomyces* species are not true fungi. They are members of the Actinomycetales family of "higher" bacteria, which includes the mycobacteria. They produce disease with many features of mycosis, including nontransmissibility.

bird droppings or be carried on their contaminated feathers and distributed widely on air currents.

Entry Routes. In the soil, these primitive plants produce many spores, which are capable of long survival with or without moisture, in drying earth, or superficial dusty layers, on wood or plant surfaces. When spore-laden dust is stirred up by feet, by shovels or bulldozers, or by wind currents, the air-borne spores may be inhaled in sufficient numbers to reach the lungs and induce tissue reaction. Subcutaneous introduction of spores may also occur, through minor skin injuries incurred by people working with contaminated soil, plants, or wood. Splinters and thorns are common agents of such injuries.

The endogenous species of *Actinomyces* and *Candida* that normally live on mucous membranes may be introduced into deep tissues in several ways. *Actinomyces* may be found around carious teeth and in tonsillar crypts. Tooth extraction or other trauma to local tissues may permit entry to the tissues of the face and neck, with a resultant infection known as "lumpy jaw." Pulmonary actinomycosis may result from aspiration of the organisms, and abdominal infection sometimes occurs if they are swallowed. *Candida* strains can be isolated from the normal skin and from the normal oral, vaginal, or intestinal mucosa. They may induce local tissue damage to these surfaces if circumstances permit their unchecked overgrowth or their establishment in traumatized areas of skin or membrane. Superficial candidiasis is much more frequent than systemic *Candida* infection, but the latter may involve the lungs, meninges, endocardium, or other tissues.

Pathogenesis. The typical tissue reaction to fungi reaching systemic positions is a chronic granuloma with necrosis or abscess formation. This is the same general type of lesion that develops in tuberculosis (see Chap. 14, p. 340), with certain differences characteristic of the proliferating organism or of its site of localization. Mononuclear, epithelioid, and giant cells surround and attempt to contain the organism, and this group is surrounded peripherally by dense accumulations of lymphocytes and fibroblasts. The different fungal agents germinate and reproduce in different ways. Under the pressure of human tissue opposition, proliferation may be halted or held to a minimum for long periods of time, or it may advance progressively as conditions permit. A necrotizing or suppurating granuloma may release fungi into adjacent tissues where new reaction to them occurs, or into lymphatic channels or blood vessels that distribute them widely in the body to other foci of localization.

Primary pulmonary mycosis may result from the inhalation of fungous spores (Group 1, Table 17–1, p. 394). Granulomatous lesions may be distributed through the lungs, and progressively to other tissues (liver, spleen, kidneys, brain and meninges, bone, and skin may be variously involved, sometimes in patterns characteristic of a particular disease). Skin and subcutaneous lesions sometimes develop by extension from systemic foci, or they may represent the primary form of disease at the site of entry of the agent. Cutaneous granulomas may be nodular or ulcerative. Nodular lesions developing subcutaneously tend to soften, break down, and discharge through the surface.

The primary route of entry of the fungi involved in the diseases of Group 2 (Table 17–1) is extrapulmonary. For South American blastomycosis, the entry is through the oral mucous membranes, the mucocutaneous borders of the mouth and nose, or the gastrointestinal tract, with subsequent lymphatic distribution. The other diseases of this group (sporotrichosis, chromoblastomycosis, and mycetoma) begin with the local introduction of a fungal agent into the skin or subcutaneous tissues of some part of the body exposed to a contaminated source of infection. Minor injuries to the skin of the hands or arms, feet or legs may admit the fungal spores from thorns, splintered wood, or soil. In sporotrichosis, the organism advances from the site of entry with subcutaneous nodule formation along the course of the regional draining lymphatics. Disseminated forms of this disease occur but are not common. The lesions of chromoblastomycosis and mycetoma are characteristically limited to the tissues of the extremity originally exposed to the infection.

Immunity of protective value does not develop in the mycotic diseases. Circulating antibodies measurable by complement-fixation or precipitation methods appear in certain mycoses. Their appearance sometimes has diagnostic value but does not contribute to resistance. The characteristic immunologic response to mycosis is a developing *hypersensitivity* to the chemical constituents of the invading fungus. This specifically altered reactivity of the tissues probably contributes, in many instances, to the necrosis of granulomatous lesions and the progressive advance of infection, as it may do in tuberculosis of the reinfection type (see Chap. 14, p. 341). In some of the mycoses, hypersensitivity develops to a degree that is measurable by *skin tests* of the tuberculin type, using specific fungal antigens extracted from the organism. Positive reactions are of the delayed type and indicate either currently active or past (possibly healed) infection. Skin tests coupled with serologic tests may be of diagnostic value particularly in histoplasmosis, coccidioidomycosis, and blastomycosis.

The clinical symptoms vary among these diseases, or for a particular mycosis, with the localization of the organism and the degree of nonspecific as well as hypersensitive reactivity evoked. Pulmonary mycosis often begins as a subacute respiratory infection, with low-grade fever, dyspnea, and unproductive cough. As the disease progresses, these symptoms intensify, but the cough becomes productive of purulent sputum. Pain in the chest, loss of weight, fatigue, and night sweats may ensue. Disseminated disease produces symptoms referable to the involvement of other organs.

The diagnosis is sometimes difficult because the characteristics of systemic mycotic lesions are very similar to those of tuberculosis and other granulomatous diseases with protean symptomatology. The laboratory identification of the causative fungus in smears and cultures of sputum, body fluids, or pus from localized lesions usually affords a secure diagnosis. Skin tests and serologic methods can be applied in some cases, as previously indicated.

It should also be noted here that the microscopic characteristics of many of the pathogenic fungi as they are seen in the tissues, or in direct smears and wet mounts made from clinical specimens, are different from those that appear when the organisms grow saprophytically in culture. This difference in the structure of parasitic and saprophytic phases of the same fungus is of some epidemiologic interest, because infected human beings do not transmit the parasitic fungi directly to others. It is only when the parasitic forms have converted to a saprophytic type of growth outside of the body that spores or other structures with an infectious potential are produced.

Epidemiology. The systemic mycoses are frequently limited to particular geographic areas of the world. Within these areas a majority of people may acquire the fungous infection, but a very small minority of these develop serious progressive disease. Some of the mycoses, such as histoplasmosis and coccidioidomycosis, appear to be increasing in importance, but this may be a reflection of improved diagnosis, an increased rate of exposure among the ever-larger traveling public, or a greater number of people with heightened susceptibility. Some of the factors that lower resistance to mycotic infection are: (1) other persistent, debilitating disease (cancer, diabetes, tuberculosis, malnutrition); (2) the widespread use of chemotherapeutic drugs and hormones that alter human metabolism and disturb the balances among commensalistic flora of the body; and (3) local traumatization that permits fungi to enter deep tissues (accidental or surgical trauma; ulcerative lesions of skin or oral or intestinal membranes; or the lesions of avitaminosis, x-irradiation).

The incubation period of systemic mycosis varies somewhat with the numbers of organisms introduced and the ease of their access to sites where they can proliferate. The fungi do not multiply rapidly, and as a general rule it requires at least ten days to two weeks for the first symptoms of infection to appear. In many instances, the incubation period may extend from three to five weeks, or it may be impossible to define.

The control of active mycotic infection does *not* require isolation of the patient or any special measures to protect his contacts. The nursing care of these diseases does include, however, the application of concurrent disinfection techniques to sputum or other discharges (as may be clinically appropriate), as well as to contaminated articles. Terminal disinfection-cleaning should be provided for the patient's room or unit. These precautions are necessary to prevent possible conversion of the fungus from the parasitic to saprophytic forms, with resultant unusual concentrations of the latter. When epidemics of airborne mycoses occur (coccidioidomycosis, histoplasmosis), recognition of their sources may make it possible to apply dust control measures or to eliminate heavy concentrations of fungus in limited areas (chicken houses, barns, starling roosts may be the sources of *Histoplasma* infection). These and similar procedures may be of preventive value when applied on a routine basis in endemic areas.

The treatment of the deep fungous infections varies with the disease. In recent years an antibiotic substance called *amphotericin B* has been used in the treatment of some of the disseminated mycoses. It appears to be the most effective drug available for these diseases, but its success is limited. Its use is further complicated by toxic effects, which include fever, nausea and vomiting, anemia, and renal failure. Other drugs, such as stilbamidine, are also used with varying effects on prognosis. The antibiotics useful in bacterial infections have no value in the mycoses. (In the case of nocardiosis and actinomycosis, whose agents are "higher" bacteria rather than true fungi [see Chap. 12], the sulfonamide drugs are useful. Actinomycosis also responds to penicillin and some other antibiotics.)

Systemic Mycotic Diseases

Individual mycotic diseases are briefly described in outline form on the following pages. The preceding section should be consulted for general information when a particular disease is being studied. Specific details are inserted only when they represent an exception to the general features of mycosis.

Histoplasmosis

Causative Organism.   *Histoplasma capsulatum.*

The Clinical Disease.   Primary pulmonary infection is frequent in endemic areas, but usually asymptomatic. Small granulomas in the lung heal with calcification, as evidenced by chest x-ray and histoplasmin-positive and tuberculin-negative skin tests. (The calcified lung lesions cannot be distinguished from healed tuberculosis, or coccidioidomycosis, by x-ray alone.) With heavy exposure to air-borne infection, clinical pneumonia develops. The illness may be prolonged. It can subside with spontaneous healing or continue to disseminated disease in a small minority of cases. When dissemination occurs, the reticuloendothelial system is particularly involved, with localizations in lymph nodes, spleen, and liver. Granulomatous lesions may be found in many organs. Progressive histoplasmosis is usually fatal, its course being more rapid in children than in adults.

Source and Occurrence.   The organism is found in the soil and bird-contaminated dust of chicken coops, pigeon roosts, caves, and barns. Endemic areas in this country occur in many central and eastern states, including Tennessee, Maryland, Ohio, Indiana, Missouri, and Arkansas. Infection is usually air-borne.

Incubation Period.   When infection can be traced, about 5 to 18 days.

Diagnosis
I. Skin Tests.   Positive for histoplasmin extract; *negative* for coccidioidin, blastomycin, and tuberculin, unless past or present infection with these organisms is also involved.

II. Laboratory. Specimens of sputum; pus aspirated from lesions; biopsies from bone marrow, lymph nodes, skin.

Microscopic examination reveals small, oval, yeastlike budding cells occurring intracellularly in reticuloendothelial cells.

In culture the organism is *dimorphic:* at 37° C on enriched media simulating in vivo conditions the organism is yeastlike, as it is in tissues. At atmospheric temperature on ordinary media a saprophytic mold appears, with mycelium, micro-conidia, and characteristic spiny ("tuberculate") chlamydospores (see Figs. 17–1 and 17–2).

Epidemiology. See pages 396 and 397 of this chapter for the control and treatment of active mycotic infections.

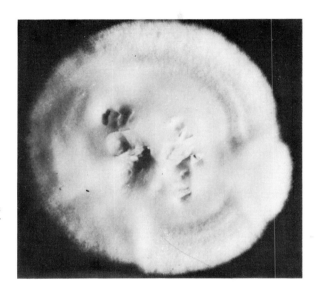

Fig. 17–1. *Histoplasma capsulatum* grows as a white, cottony mold on Sabouraud's agar at room temperature.

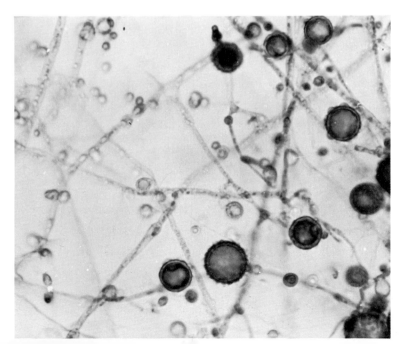

Fig. 17–2. A photomicrograph of the mycelial phase of *Histoplasma capsulatum* grown on Sabouraud's agar at room temperature. Note the large, spiny (tuberculate) chlamydospores and many small conidia (2250 ×). (Courtesy of Mr. Coy D. Smith, University of Kentucky College of Medicine, Lexington, Ky.)

Coccidioidomycosis

Causative Organism.   *Coccidioides immitis.*

The Clinical Disease.   This mycosis always begins as a respiratory infection. The primary infection may be asymptomatic or it may resemble acute influenzal illness, with fever, chills, cough, and chest pain. These symptoms may subside without residual traces, or healing may be accompanied by fibrosis and calcification of granulomatous lesions in the chest. Rarely, the disease progresses to a disseminated form resembling tuberculosis, with lesions in the lungs, bones, joints, subcutaneous tissues, skin, internal organs, brain, and meninges. With widespread dissemination, symptoms are acute; prostration and death may occur within a few weeks.

Source and Occurrence.   Soil and spore-laden dust are the sources of infection for man and a number of domestic animals. In this country the disease is endemic in the southwest, particularly the San Joaquin Valley of southern California. Other endemic areas are found in Argentina, Mexico, Central America, and parts of southeastern Europe.

Incubation Period.   For primary infection, between ten days and three weeks.

Diagnosis

I. Skin Tests.   *Positive* for coccidioidin extract, *negative* for histoplasmin, blastomycin, and tuberculin (in the absence of multiple infection).

II. Laboratory.   *Specimens* of sputum; pus from aspirated lesions; biopsies; gastric washings; spinal fluid if indicated by symptoms.

Microscopic examination reveals thick-walled spheric structures (spherules) containing many endospores. In tissue sections or biopsies of granulomas, the spherules may be seen within giant cells, or in the acellular areas of central necrosis (see Fig. 17–3). They may also be found empty, having erupted their contents.

In culture it is difficult to reproduce the in vivo conditions that encourage spherule production (the endospores are yeastlike but do not reproduce by budding). At atmospheric temperature on ordinary media the saprophytic growth consists of an abundant aerial mycelium. The branching hyphae develop into chains of fragmenting arthrospores, which are easily disseminated and highly infectious.

Epidemiology.   See pages 396 and 397 of this chapter for the control and treatment of active mycotic infections. In endemic areas, infection rates for this air-borne disease are highest in the dry months of summer and fall. Dust control measures are of value in suppressing the spread of coccidioidomycosis.

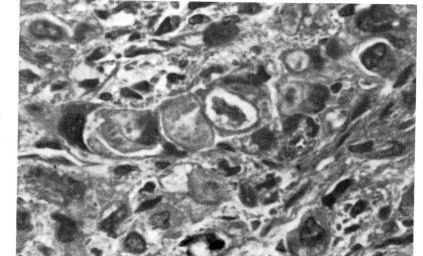

Fig. 17–3.   Photomicrograph of a histologic section of a granuloma containing *Coccidioides immitis* spherules. Each spherule is a thick-walled sporangium containing many small endospores.

North American Blastomycosis

Causative Organism.   *Blastomyces dermatitidis.*

The Clinical Disease. Systemic blastomycosis usually begins as a primary pulmonary infection acquired through the inhalation of spores. Initial symptoms are those of an upper respiratory viral infection, but progressive infection leads to severe pulmonary involvement and dissemination to subcutaneous tissues, bones, genital and visceral organs, and the central nervous system. Cutaneous blastomycosis may be an extension of systemic disease (highly fatal) or a primary infection resulting from local entry of the organisms into the skin.

Source and Occurrence. The exogenous source of this infection is probably soil. The infection appears to be confined to the United States and Canada. It is an uncommon disease, reported occasionally also in dogs and horses.

Incubation Period. Difficult to define; probably a few weeks.

Diagnosis
I. Skin Tests.   *Positive* for blastomycin extract; *negative* for histoplasmin, coccidioidin, and tuberculin except in multiple infections.

II. Laboratory.   *Specimens* of sputum; pus and exudates from lesions; biopsy of skin granulomas.
Microscopic examination reveals the tissue form to be a large, thick-walled budding yeastlike organism.
In culture the organism grows in the in vivo yeastlike form on blood agar incubated at 37° C. At room temperature on ordinary media the saprophytic form is an undistinguished mycelial mold (see Fig. 17-4).

Epidemiology. See pages 396 and 397 of this chapter for the control and treatment of active mycotic infections.

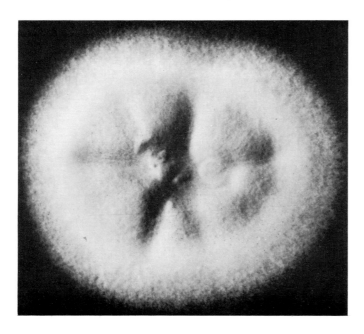

Fig. 17–4. *Blastomyces dermatitidis* grows as a white, cottony mold on Sabouraud's agar at room temperature.

Cryptococcosis

Causative Organism.   *Cryptococcus neoformans.*

The Clinical Disease.   Infection in man probably occurs through the respiratory tract as a rule, with resulting mild pulmonary infection frequently undiagnosed. The most common clinical extension of cryptococcosis in man is the slow development of a chronic meningitis. The course of cryptococcal meningitis may extend over several years, resembling degenerative central nervous system disease, syphilitic or tuberculous meningitis, or brain tumor. The organism may also gain entry to the body through the skin, or the mucosa of the upper respiratory or intestinal tracts, with isolated lesions in the subcutaneous tissues, lymph nodes, tongue, muscles of the back, and other areas. Lesions of this type may remain localized or extend to the brain and meninges.

Source and Occurrence.   The organism is found in saprophytic growth in the external environment, particularly in accumulations of pigeon droppings. Infection is thought to occur through the inhalation of contaminated dust, but the development of disease depends on the intensity of exposure and the containment of organisms in the respiratory tract. Sporadic cases occur in many parts of the world, in domestic animals as well as man.

Incubation Period.   Not defined; meningitis follows usually upon inapparent pulmonary infection.

Laboratory Diagnosis.   *Specimens* for smear and culture include spinal fluid, sputum, and exudates from cutaneous lesions if they occur. *Microscopic* examination of wet mounts of centrifuged spinal fluid or other specimens reveals a budding yeast surrounded by a large capsule (see Fig. 17–5). The latter can also be seen against a dark background, obtained by suspending the material to be examined in India ink.

In culture the organism grows as a yeast on all media at temperatures ranging from 20° to 37° C. Capsule production can be demonstrated on special media or by mouse inoculation.

Epidemiology.   See pages 396 and 397 for the control and treatment of active mycotic infections. When outbreaks of acute pneumonitis occur, the source of common exposure may be eliminated if it is reasonably limited, geographically.

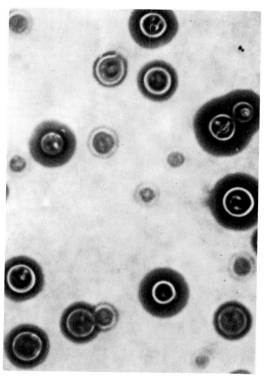

Fig. 17–5.   Photomicrograph of a preparation of spinal fluid containing *Cryptococcus neoformans.* One can readily see the large clear capsule surrounding each cell. (Courtesy of Mr. Coy D. Smith, University of Kentucky College of Medicine, Lexington Ky.)

Nocardiosis

Causative Organism. *Nocardia asteroides.*

The Clinical Disease. Systemic nocardiosis is a chronic pulmonary disease simulating tuberculosis clinically and bacteriologically. The organisms are acid-fast filamentous bacilli resembling *M. tuberculosis* in microscopic appearance, but their culture characteristics are distinctive (see below). Dissemination of the organism from the pulmonary lesions results in scattered abscesses in subcutaneous tissues, the peritoneum, and the brain. The disease has a high mortality rate unless diagnosed before widespread metastases have occurred. The sulfonamides are the drugs of choice.

Nocardia species are also among the organisms associated with mycetoma (see Mycetoma, p. 404), a subcutaneous infection limited to an extremity.

Source and Occurrence. Contaminated soil or dust is the source of infection. Air-borne organisms are presumably the source of pulmonary disease; local tissue entry through minor wounds of skin is the origin of mycetoma. This disease is sporadic in all parts of the world.

Incubation Period. Not known.

Laboratory Diagnosis. *Specimens* for smear and culture include sputum, spinal fluid, exudates, biopsies. Examination of clinical specimens may reveal pigmented flecks or *granules.*

Microscopically, granules appear as tangled masses of filamentous, branching bacillary forms. The organisms are Gram-positive and acid-fast.

In culture the organism grows slowly on ordinary media at room temperature or 37° C. It is *aerobic.* The colony is often waxy and folded. Orange, yellow, and red pigments are produced by different strains. (See also the laboratory diagnosis of actinomycosis, p. 405 and Fig. 17–9.)

Epidemiology. See page 397 of this chapter for comments on the control of active infection.

South American Blastomycosis

Causative Organism. *Blastomyces brasiliensis.*

The Clinical Disease. This disease is endemic in South America, particularly Brazil. It is often called *paracoccidioidal granuloma* because it was once thought that the tissue form of the organism resembled *Coccidioides.* The organism is of the *Blastomyces* type, however. It produces a chronic granulomatous disease of the skin, the mucocutaneous membranes of the face (see Fig. 17–6), oral membranes, lymph nodes, and visceral organs. Cervical lymphadenopathy may resemble that of Hodgkin's disease. Disseminated infection is highly fatal; localized disease may persist for years if untreated. The sulfonamide drugs can provide rapid clinical cure.

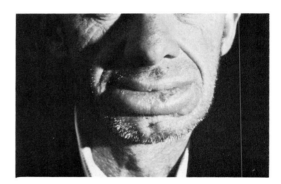

Fig. 17–6. The mucocutaneous form of South American blastomycosis. (Courtesy of Dr. E. S. Beneke, Michigan State University, East Lansing, Mich.)

Source and Occurrence. The organism is thought to originate in soil or wood. The infection is usually introduced parenterally through the skin or the oral membranes, presumably by contact with contaminated vegetative material. Pulmonary disease is not primary but may occur as a secondary extension from visceral sites. The highest incidence is in young male adults whose manual labor brings them in contact with the

fungus, but the disease is sporadic rather than epidemic.

Incubation Period.   A few weeks.

Diagnosis

Skin Tests.   Positive for "paracoccidioidin," an extract from the organism; *negative* for other fungi and tuberculin except in multiple infections.

Laboratory. Specimens of pus from lesions, biopsies. Sputum if pulmonary disease occurs.

Microscopically, the tissue form of the organism is a large, thick-walled budding yeast resembling *Blastomyces dermatitidis*, except that each cell shows *multiple budding*.

In culture, the tissue form grows at 37° C on blood agar (see Fig. 17-7). At room temperature on ordinary media the organism is a saprophytic mold.

Epidemiology.   See page 397 for control of active infection. Epidemic measures are not applicable to this disease.

Sporotrichosis

Causative Organism.   *Sprotrichum schenckii.*

The Clinical Disease.   This is a chronic infection usually initiated by entry of the organism through the skin of an extremity (frequently a hand or arm) and characterized by the development of nodular lesions in the subcutaneous tissues along the path of the regional lymphatic drainage. The nodules frequently soften, ulcerate at the surface, and discharge this pus. The clinical picture is highly characteristic. Dissemination of the organism to other parts of the body occurs rarely. The disease responds well to treatment with potassium iodide.

Source and Occurrence.   The organism grows in soil, on wood, and on vegetation. Infection is a sporadic occupational hazard of gardeners and farmers. An epidemic was reported from South Africa, involving about 3000 gold-mine workers commonly infected by contaminated mine timbers. The disease has been reported from all parts

Fig. 17-7. *Blastomyces brasiliensis.* The photomicrograph shows the multiple budding of yeast cells that grew on blood agar at 37° C (2500 ×).

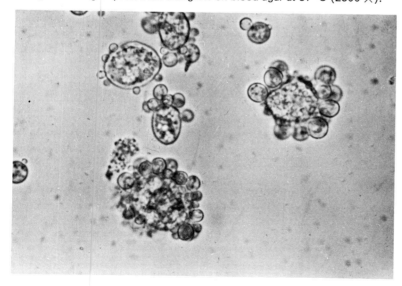

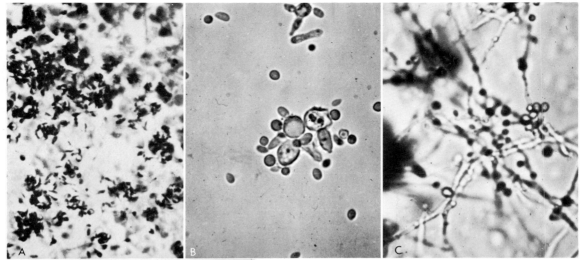

Fig. 17–8. *Sporotrichum schenkii. A.* Cigar-shaped budding (yeast) cells in a histologic section of a nodular lesion. *B.* Yeastlike cells taken from a culture grown on blood agar at 37° C. *C.* A microscopic view of the mycelial growth obtained at room temperature (note the delicate spores). *D.* Colonial appearance at room temperature.

of the world and has been seen in animals as well as man.

Incubation Period. The initial lesion may be seen within three weeks, or it may require up to three months to appear.

Laboratory Diagnosis

Specimens. Pus or biopsy from subcutaneous lesions for smear and culture.

Microscopic examination of pus does not always reveal the tissue phase (Fig. 17–8, *A*) of the orga-

nism, which is a small, Gram-positive, cigar-shaped, budding cell.

In culture the yeastlike tissue form grows on enriched media at 37° C. (Fig. 17–8, *B*). At room temperature on simple media the organism is a mold, often darkly pigmented (Fig. 17–8, *D*). Delicate hyphae on the aerial mycelium carry small ovoid spores in petal-like clusters (Fig. 17–8, *C*).

Epidemiology. See page 397 for control of active infection. Contaminated dressings may be infectious for persons with open skin lesions.

Chromoblastomycosis (Verrucous Dermatitis)

Causative Organism.   Several species of darkly pigmented fungi, notably of the *Hormodendrum* and *Phialophora* genera.

The Clinical Disease.   This is a chronic, slowly progressive, granulomatous infection of the skin and lymphatics. Warty cutaneous nodules develop very slowly. They become prominent vegetations that do not always ulcerate. The lesions are located as a rule on an exposed extremity and are almost always unilateral. The feet and legs are generally involved, possibly because they are frequently exposed to the soil source of the organism. Surgical excision of early lesions and treatment with iodides help to limit the slow progression of the disease. The infection does not become generalized.

Source and Occurrence.   The organisms probably exist in wood, soil, or vegetation and are introduced through traumatized tissue. Sporadic cases occur in many parts of the world, but this is primarily a disease of rural tropical regions (the West Indies, Central and South America, the Orient). It is seen most frequently in adult male laborers.

Incubation Period.   Unknown, but probably requires weeks or months.

Laboratory Diagnosis
Specimens.   The crusts of lesions or biopsy material.
Microscopic examination of the tissue reveals dark-brown, thick-walled septate bodies about the size of a leukocyte. These structures reproduce by splitting rather than budding. The several fungi that cause this disease produce the same form in tissues.
In culture these fungous species produce dark-brown or black mold colonies at room temperature on simple media. They do not grow at 37° C.

Epidemiology.   See page 397 for control of active infection.

Mycetoma (Madura Foot, Maduromycosis)

Causative Organism.   Numerous soil fungi, including *Madurella*, *Actinomyces*, and *Nocardia* species.

The Clinical Disease.   This is a chronic infection of subcutaneous tissues, characterized by swelling and nodule and abscess formation, with suppurative extension through sinus tracts or fistulae. The foot is commonly involved, especially in tropical areas where people go without shoes. Deep extension of the infection involves muscles and bones. The affected area swells to a globular shape, losing its structural form. Sulfonamide or antibiotic therapy is of value if the infecting organism is one of the "higher" bacteria of the *Actinomyces-Nocardia* group. The true fungi that cause this disease do not yield to these drugs, but may respond to amphotericin therapy. Intractable disease may require amputation to save the patient from death by secondary bacterial infection.

Source and Occurrence.   Mycetomas are seen most frequently in tropical and semitropical areas where people acquire the infection through the injured skin of bare feet. The disease is seen occasionally in scattered areas of the United States, and in Mexico, South America, Africa, and Asia.

Incubation Period.   The first lesions may require months to develop; progression takes place over a period of years.

Laboratory Diagnosis
Specimens.   Draining pus from sinus tracts or biopsy material.
Microscopic examination and *culture* may reveal bacillary forms or fungi. Culture techniques should include methods appropriate for the growth of either.

Epidemiology.   See page 397 for the control of active infection. The simplest and most practical means of preventing this disease is to protect the feet with shoes.

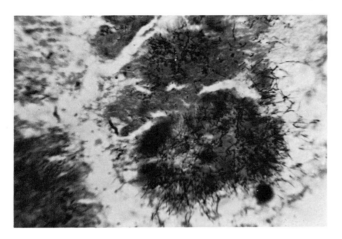

Fig. 17–9. Actinomycotic sulfur granule. Note the tangled, filamentous, beaded, branching organisms.

Actinomycosis

Causative Organism. *Actinomyces israeli* (human oral mucosa). *Actinomyces bovis* (sometimes transmitted from cattle).

The Clinical Disease. Actinomycosis is a chronic granulomatous and suppurative disease of endogenous origin. The localization of primary infection depends on access of the organisms to deep tissues from their original sites on normal upper respiratory membranes. Tooth extraction or other injury to the mouth or jaw may lead to cervicofacial infections. Aspiration of the organism into the lungs may result in primary pulmonary disease, while gastrointestinal entry may permit primary infection of the abdominal wall. Abdominal actinomycosis can also extend to secondary pulmonary involvement. The lesions are granulomas that frequently break down to suppurative abscesses. Multiple sinus tracts are formed, which drain off pus to adjacent tissues or to the surface. The drainage contains so-called "sulfur granules," which are actually tangled masses of the infectious organism. The disease is treated with penicillin and other antibiotics, or the sulfonamides.

Source and Occurrence. These organisms have a natural reservoir in man and also in cattle. The organisms are presumably transmissible, but *disease* is not communicable. This type of disease is not frequent in man, but occurs sporadically in all parts of the world, the frequency being highest in adult males.

Incubation Period. Not easily defined; may require days or months after trauma permits tissue penetration.

Laboratory Diagnosis
Specimens. Sputum, pus from draining sinus tracts, or biopsy as indicated by clinical symptoms.

Microscopic examination of pus should reveal tiny hard "sulfur granules," about the size of a pinhead. Their presence may give the drainage a gritty quality. On *microscopic* examination the granules are seen to be composed of matted, tangled bacillary filaments (see Fig. 17–9). These organisms are Gram-positive and *some* are acid-fast. They cannot be distinguished from *Nocardia* by microscopic means alone.

In culture, *Actinomyces* species are anaerobic. Culture techniques must include aerobic incubation of suitable media to rule out *Nocardia.* Actinomyces species require enriched media incubated at 37° C. The filamentous bacilli display true branching.

Epidemiology. See page 397 for control of active infection. Epidemic measures are not applicable to this sporadic, endogenous disease.

Candidiasis

Causative Organism.   *Candida albicans.*

The Clinical Disease.   Candidiasis is usually a superficial mycosis of the skin or mucous membranes, where the organism is ordinarily a member of the normal flora. A number of factors involving injury to or unusual susceptibility of tissues may permit local entry of the organism or the development of systemic progressive disease. These factors are stated below in the section on susceptibility.

Several types of clinical candidiasis may be described briefly, as follows:

Oral candidiasis (thrush) is particularly frequent in infants. Loosely adherent, white, pseudomembranous patches of the fungous growth occur on the tongue and the buccal mucosa.

Vaginal infection is common in pregnancy and in diabetic women. It involves the vulvar surfaces as well as the vagina, producing irritation, intense pruritus, and discharge.

Cutaneous candidiasis often involves the smooth skin of the intertriginous folds, particularly in the axillary, inguinal, and inframammary regions. The interdigital folds of the feet and hands may also be involved. The cutaneous form may also be quite generalized (see Fig. 17–10). These areas become reddened and weepy with exudate from small vesicles or pustules.

Nail infections, onychia and paronychia, are common. Swellings develop around or in the nailbed, and the nails become thick, hard, and deeply grooved.

Systemic candidiasis may begin as bronchial, pulmonary, or renal infection, usually in persons debilitated by coexisting disease. Dissemination of the organisms through the blood stream may lead to grave extensions of infection to the meninges or the brain, and sometimes the endocardium.

Superficial infections may respond to the antibiotic nystatin or to the local application of iodides, permanganate, or gentian violet. Therapy with amphotericin B is required for generalized disease.

Source and Occurrence.   *Candida* infections of the skin and mucous membranes arise from endogenous sources. Strains of *Candida*, including the pathogenic species *C. albicans*, may be found on normal skin, on the oral and genital mucosa, and in the stools of healthy persons. From these sources, mycotic *Candida* lesions may be induced in superficial or deep tissues predisposed to infection by a number of factors.

Susceptibility.   The factors that commonly predispose to *Candida* infection include the following:

1. Antibiotic therapy, which disturbs the normal bacterial flora that holds *Candida* in check under ordinary circumstances.

2. Debilitating organic disease, particularly diabetes.

3. Chronic infectious disease, such as tuberculosis.

4. Malignant tumors and leukemia.

5. Nutritional deficiencies.

Fig. 17–10.   Generalized cutaneous moniliasis. (Courtesy of Dr. Margarita Silva-Hutner, College of Physicians and Surgeons of Columbia University, New York, N.Y.)

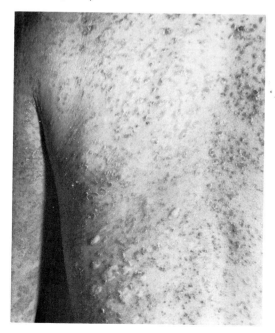

6. Continuing maceration of tissues caused by, for example, frequent or prolonged immersion of the hands in water; or excessive perspiration in the frictional, intertriginous folds (axillary, inguinal, inframammary, interdigital).

Increased susceptibility to oral and dermal *Candida* infections is also seen in newborn infants, particularly premature babies and others with underlying organic problems. *Thrush*, as these superficial infections are often called, is frequently communicable in the nursery situation. It may be transmitted to babies by nursing mothers with breast infection, and it may also appear as a nursery outbreak arising from a common environmental source, such as inadequately sterilized rubber nipples.

Incubation Period. Infant thrush develops within two to five days of exposure.

> **Laboratory Diagnosis**
> *Specimens.* Scrapings or pus from surface lesions, sputum, stools, spinal fluid, as indicated by clinical symptoms.
> *Microscopic* examination of clinical specimens

in wet mounts or stained smears reveals an oval, budding yeast. Very often the pseudomycelium produced by these organisms in culture is also seen in the tissues.

In culture, the organism grows well on simple media both at room temperature and at 37° C. Under both conditions it is a yeastlike fungus, with a pseudomycelium produced by the elongation and pinching-off of germinating cells. When grown on media deficient in nutrient, *Candida albicans* produces clusters of thick-walled chlamydospores (resting spores). This feature is often used to distinguish this species from other members of the *Candida* genus that are not frequently associated with mycosis (see Fig. 17–11).

Epidemiology. In the control of active infection, isolation is necessary only in the case of infected newborn babies in nurseries. When nursery epidemics occur, every effort must be made to find the source of infection. (Rubber nipples should be considered as the first possibility.) Concurrent disinfection and terminal cleaning techniques must be carefully maintained. In these situations, swabs can be used to collect material from the mouths of all new babies entering the nursery.

Table 17–2. Summary: Mycotic Infections

Clinical Disease	Causative Organisms	Other Possible Entry Routes	Incubation Period	Communic Period
Histoplasmosis	*Histoplasma capsulatum*	Respiratory Parenteral	5–18 days	Not usually communical from man to
Coccidioidomycosis	*Coccidioides immitis*	Respiratory Parenteral	10 days to 3 weeks	Same as abo

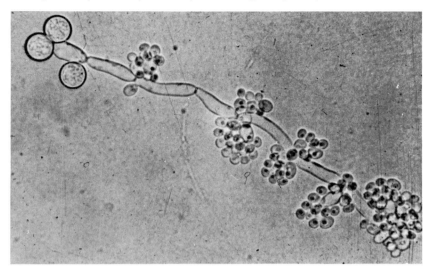

Fig. 17–11.   Slide culture of *Candida albicans* (1290 ×). Note the pseudomycelium, clusters of small blastospores, and three large terminal chlamydospores. (Courtesy of Mr. Coy D. Smith, University of Kentucky College of Medicine, Lexington, Ky.)

Swabs can be sent to the laboratory, in sterile saline or in transport broth, for microscopic examination, and for culture. If *Candida albicans* is demonstrated, these babies should be segregated also whether or not they display active thrush. The laboratory can provide smear reports on the day the specimen is received, with culture results following on the second or third day.

Specimens Required	Laboratory Diagnosis	Immunization	Treatment	Nursing Management
um, pus from ons	Smear and culture	None	Amphotericin B	Isolation not necessary; concurrent disinfection of discharges and contaminated articles prevents possible conversion of fungus from parasitic to saprophytic form
sies of bone row, lymph nodes,	Smear and culture			
test	Positive for histoplasmin extract			
um, pus from ons, gastric hings, spinal fluid	Smear and culture	None	Same as above	Same as above
test	Positive for coccidioidin extract			

Table 17–2. *(Cont.)*

Clinical Disease	Causative Organisms	Other Possible Entry Routes	Incubation Period	Communic Period
Blastomycosis (North American)	*Blastomyces dermatitidis*	Respiratory Parenteral	Probably a few weeks	Same as abov
Cryptococcosis	*Cryptococcus neoformans*	Respiratory Parenteral	Not defined	Same as abov
Nocardiosis	*Nocardia asteroides*	Respiratory Parenteral	Unknown	Same as abov
Blastomycosis (South American)	*Blastomyces brasiliensis*	Parenteral	A few weeks	Same as abov
Sporotrichosis	*Sporotrichum schenckii*	Parenteral	3 weeks to 3 months	Same as abov
Chromoblastomycosis	Dark-pigmented fungi (*Hormodendrum* and *Phialo-phora*) species	Parenteral	Unknown	Same as abov
Mycetoma	*Madurella, Nocardia* species	Parenteral	First lesions may take months to develop	Same as abov
Actinomycosis	*Actinomyces bovis Actinomyces israelii*	Through traumatized skin or mucosa	May require days or months	Not usually communica from man t man
Candidiasis	*Candida albicans*	Same as above	Infants (thrush), 3–5 days	During time of lesions

Specimens Required	Laboratory Diagnosis	Immunization	Treatment	Nursing Management
ːum, pus and ▯dates ▯sies of skin, ▯nulomas ▯ test	Smear and culture Smear and culture Positive for blastomycin extract	None	Same as above	Same as above
ːum, spinal fluid, ▯dates from ▯ons	Smear and culture	None	Same as above	Same as above
ːum, spinal fluid, ▯dates, biopsies	Smear and culture	None	Sulfonamides	Same as above
▯from lesions, ▯psies, sputum ▯ test	Smear and culture Positive for "para-coccidioidin"	None	Amphotericin B	Same as above
▯or biopsy of ▯cutaneous lesions	Smear and culture	None	Same as above	Same as above
▯ts of lesions ▯sy material	Smear and culture Smear and culture	None	Same as above	Same as above
▯ning pus or biopsy ▯terial	Smear and culture	None	Same as above	Same as above
ːum, pus from ▯ining sinus tracts, ▯psies as indicated ▯symptoms	Smear and culture	None	Sulfonamides	Not usually communicable from man to man
▯pings or pus ▯n surface lesions, ▯tum stools, spinal ▯d, as indicated by ▯ical symptoms	Smear and culture	None	Amphotericin B Mycostatin	Isolation of infants with thrush; con-current disinfection and terminal cleaning techniques must be carefully maintained; every effort must be made to find the source of infection in the nursery

Questions

1. What is the typical tissue reaction to fungi reaching systemic positions?
2. Why is the diagnosis of systemic mycoses sometimes difficult?
3. What factors lower resistance to mycotic infections?
4. Briefly describe the nursing care in active mycotic infections.
5. What is the causative agent of histoplasmosis? Coccidioidomycosis? Cryptococcosis? Blastomycosis?
6. Briefly describe oral and vaginal candidiasis.
7. What factors commonly predispose to *Candida* infection?
8. When is isolation necessary in *Candida* infections?

Question for Discussion — Section IV

Mrs. Martinez is admitted with a lobar pneumonia. She has a frequent productive cough and difficulty breathing. Her temperature is 103° F. The physician orders immediate blood culture and a sputum smear and culture with antibiotic sensitivities. When questioned, Mrs. Martinez states she "broke out in a rash" the last time she had penicillin. The doctor orders a tetracycline instead.

1. What special measures to prevent dissemination of her infection to others should be explained to Mrs. Martinez and instituted?
2. Explain the doctor's decision about drug therapy.
3. Why should the blood and sputum specimens be collected before giving the first tetracycline dose?
4. Since drug therapy is already started, why is the doctor interested in culture and antibiotic sensitivities?
5. Why does Mrs. Martinez have breathing difficulty?
6. Of what value is a high fluid intake for this patient?

References — Section IV

Textbooks

Conant, Norman, Smith, D. T., Baker, R. D., Callaway, T. L., and Martin, D. S.: *Manual of Clinical Mycology*. W. B. Saunders, Philadelphia and London, 1954.

Dubos, René J., and Hirsch, James G. (eds.): *Bacterial and Mycotic Infections of Man*, 4th ed. J. B. Lippincott, Philadelphia, 1965.

Horsfall, Frank L., Jr., and Tamm, Igor (eds.): *Viral and Rickettsial Infections of Man*, 4th ed. J. B. Lippincott, Philadelphia, 1965.

Jawetz, Ernest, Melnick, J. L., and Adelberg, E. A.: *Review of Medical Microbiology*, 8th ed. Lange Medical Publications, Los Altos, Calif., 1968.

Riley, Richard, and O'Grady, Francis: *Airborne Infections: Transmission and Control*. The Macmillan Co., New York, 1961.

Pertinent References

GENERAL

Riley, Richard L.: Airborne Infections, *Amer. J. Nurs.*, **60**:1246, Sept., 1960.

Safer Ways in Nursing — To Protect Against Airborne Infections. Nursing Advisory Service of the National T.B. Association and the National League for Nursing, National Tuberculosis Association, 1962.

STREPTOCOCCAL INFECTIONS
Calafiore, Dorothy C.: Streptococcal Infections, *Nurs. Outlook*, **7**:12, Dec., 1959.

STAPHYLOCOCCAL INFECTIONS
Brown, Regina, and Myra S. Wagner,: A Family's Battle with Staphylococcus, *Amer. J. Nurs.*, **64**:136, Sept., 1964.
Cohen, Lawrence S., Fekety, R. F., and Cluff, Leighton E.: Studies of the Epidemiology of Staphylococcal Infection, *J.A.M.A.*, **180**:805, June 9, 1962.
Colbeck, John C.: Environmental Aspects of Staphylococcal Infections Acquired, *J. Public Health*, **50**:468, April, 1960.
Hamil, Evelyn R.: The Role of the Nurse in the Control of Staphylococcal Infections in Hospitals, *Calif. Health*, **17**:July 15, 1959.
Kline, Patricia A.: Isolating Patients with Staphylococcal Infections, *Amer. J. Nurs.*, **65**:102, Jan., 1965.
Lester, Mary: An Annotated Bibliography on Staphylococcal Infections, *Amer. J. Nurs.*, **59**:1801, Dec., 1959.
Miller, Adah, and McDonald, Ellen: Staphylococcal Infections — A Community Problem, *Nurs. Outlook*, **7**:584, Oct., 1959.
Mortimer, Edward, Fischer, P., Jenkins, N., and McGirr, D.: Staphylococcus in the Nursery, *Amer. J. Nurs.*, **61**:56, Oct., 1961.
Mudd, Stuart: The Staphylococcus Problem, *Sci. Amer.*, **200**:1, Jan., 1959.
Murray, E. G. D.: About the Staphylococcus, *Canad. Nurse*, **55**:787, Sept., 1959.
Nichols, Leola F.: When Staph Comes Home to Roost, *Amer. J. Nurs.*, **63**:75, April, 1963.
Pratt, Mary, Walsh, Helen, and Hazelhurst, Robert C.: A VNA Combats Staph Infection, *Nurs. Outlook*, **8**:310, June, 1960.
Rakich, Jennie H., Thomas, Margaret W., and Lester, Mary R.: Nurses Are Asking About Staphylococcal Infections, *Amer. J. Nurs.*, **60**:1766, Dec., 1960.
———, ———, and ———: Nurses Are Asking About Staphylococcal Infections in the Obstetric Department, *Amer. J. Nurs.*, **60**:1632, Nov., 1960.
Ravenholt, Reimert, and Nixon, Mary: The Telephone in the Epidemiology of Staphylococcal Disease, *Amer. J. Nurs.*, **61**:61, Aug., 1961.
Rogers, David E.: Staphylococcal Diseases on General Medical Service, *Amer. J. Nurs.*, **59**:842, June, 1959.
Selected Materials on Staphylococcal Disease. CDC Training Program, U.S. Dept. HEW, Public Health Service, Washington, D.C., Oct., 1958.
Smith, Ian Maclean: Death from Staphylococci, *Sci. Amer.*, **218**:84, Feb., 1968.
Staphylococcal Disease. Selected Materials on Nursing Aspects, CDC U.S. Dept. HEW, Public Health Service, Washington, D.C., 1960.
Thompson, LaVerne R.: Staphylococcus Aureus, *Amer. J. Nurs.*, **58**:1098, Aug., 1958.

DIPHTHERIA
Doege, Theodore, Heath, Clark W., Jr., and Sherman, Ida L.: Diphtheria in the United States, 1959–1960, *Pediatrics*, **30**:194, Aug., 1962.
Edsall, Geoffrey: Diphtheria, Tetanus, Pertussis Vaccine, *J.A.M.A.*, **178**:97, Oct. 7, 1961.
Page, Malcolm I.: The Present Problem of Diphtheria Control in the United States, *Amer. J. Public Health*, **52**:68, Jan., 1962.
Styler, Herman: Napoleon's Prize Contest, in *Plague Fighters*. Chilton Co., Philadelphia, 1960.
Wood, Barry W.: *From Miasmas to Molecules.* Columbia University Press, New York and London, 1961.

TUBERCULOSIS
Andelman, Samuel L.: Tuberculosis in Large Urban Centers, *Amer. J. Public Health*, **56**:1546, Sept., 1966.

Bettag, O. L., and Hall, C.: Mantoux Tuberculin Testing: Standard Method vs. Jet Injection, *Dis. Chest*, **51**:530, May, 1967.

Bullough, Bonnie: Where Should Isolation Stop?, *Amer. J. Nurs.*, **62**:86, Oct., 1962.

Creighton, Helen, and Tayrien, Dorothy P.: The Enigma That Was Annabelle, *Amer. J. Nurs.*, **60**:987, July, 1960.

Diagnostic Standards and Classification of Tuberculosis. National Tuberculosis Association, New York, 1961.

Dubos, René, and Dubos, Jean: *The White Plague.* Little, Brown and Co., Boston, 1952.

────── and ──────: Consumption and the Romantic Age, in Rouché, Berton (ed.): *Curiosities of Medicine.* Berkeley Medallion, New York, 1964.

Frenay, Sister Mary Agnes Clare: Drugs in T.B. Control, *Amer. J. Nurs.*, **61**:82, April, 1961.

Long, Esmond R.: The Germ of Tuberculosis, *Sci. Amer.*, **192**:102, June, 1955.

Mushlin, Irving, and Amberson, J. Burns: Tracking down Tuberculosis, *Amer. J. Nurs.*, **64**:91, Dec., 1965.

New Antituberculous Agents: Laboratory and Clinical Studies. *Ann. N.Y. Acad. Sci.*, **135**:681, 1966.

Ochs, Charles W.: The Epidemiology of Tuberculosis, *J.A.M.A.*, **179**:247, Jan. 27, 1962.

Rosenthal, Sol Ray, Afremow, M. L., Nikurs, L., Loewinsohn, E., Leppman, M., Katele, E., Liveright, D., Thorne, M.: BCG Vaccination and Tuberculosis in Students of Nursing, *Amer. J. Nurs.*, **63**:88, June, 1963.

Schaefer, George, Taggart, Eleanor, and Ivey, Elizabeth: The Pregnant Woman with Tuberculosis, *Amer. J. Nurs.*, **63**:68, Aug., 1963.

South, Jean: Nursing Implications (TB), *Nurs. Outlook*, **9**:33, Jan., 1961.

──────: *Tuberculosis Handbook for Public Health Nurses*, 4th ed. National Tuberculosis Association, New York, 1965.

────── Public Health Nursing Services in Tuberculosis Control Programs, *Nurs. Outlook*, **15**:46, Jan., 1967.

Spahn, Caroline H.: Tuberculosis or Coccidioidomycosis, *Nurs. Outlook*, **8**:25, Jan., 1960.

Tuberculosis in 1963: An Overview. U.S. Dept. HEW, Public Health Service, Washington, D.C., 1963.

Wilson, Alberta B.: The Big Push to Eliminate Tuberculosis, *Amer. J. Nurs.*, **61**:110, Oct., 1961.

ATYPICAL MYCOBACTERIA

Chapman, John S.: The Atypical Mycobacteria, Their Significance in Human Disease, *Amer. J. Nurs.*, **67**:1031, May, 1967.

Hohle, Beth: The Atypical Mycobacteria, Patient Care at Home, *Amer. J. Nurs.*, **67**:1033, May, 1967.

BRUCELLOSIS

Brucellosis. U.S. Dept. HEW, #42, Health Information Series, Washington, D.C., revised 1965.

INFLUENZA

Blankenship, Marilyn: Influenza Immunization and Industrial Absenteeism, *Amer. J. Assoc. Industr. Nurses J.*, **12**:16, June, 1964.

Geister, Janet: The Flu Epidemic of 1918, *Nurs. Outlook*, **5**:583, Oct., 1957.

Stewart, Alleen Cole: Ready to Serve, *Amer. J. Nurs.*, **63**:85, Sept., 1964.

COLDS AND RESPIRATORY DISEASE VIRUSES

Andrewes, Christopher H.: The Viruses of the Common Cold, *Sci. Amer.*, **203**:88, Dec., 1960.

Conference on Newer Respiratory Disease Viruses, *Amer. Rev. Resp. Dis.*, **88**:1–419, Sept., 1963.

Johnson, Karl M.: Some Newly Discovered Respiratory Disease Viruses, *Amer. J. Nurs.*, **63**:67, Nov., 1963.

Lefkowitz, Lewis B., Jr.: The Common Cold Syndrome, *Amer. J. Nurs.*, **63**:70, Dec., 1963.

GERMAN MEASLES AND MEASLES

Brody, Jacob A.: The Infectiousness of Rubella and the Possibility of Reinfection, *Amer. J. Public Health*, **56**:1082, July, 1966.

Calafiore, Dorothy: Eradication of Measles in the United States, *Amer. J. Nurs.*, **67**:1871, Sept., 1967.

Cooper, Louis: German Measles, *Sci. Amer.*, **215**:30, July, 1966.

Douglas, Gordan W.: Rubella in Pregnancy, *Amer. J. Nurs.*, **66**:2664, Dec., 1966.

Enemies of the Unborn, *Time*, p. 100, Sept. 20, 1963.

James, Patrick J.: Measles Meets Its Match, *Health News*, **44**:8, Oct., 1967.

Krugman, Saul: Rubella — New Light on an Old Disease, *Amer. J. Nurs.*, **65**:126, Oct., 1965.

Lennon, Richard G., Turnbull, C. D., Elsea, W. R., Karzon, D. T., and Winkelstein, W.: Measles Immunization in a Northeastern Metropolitan County, *J.A.M.A.*, **200**:815, June 5, 1967.

Nader, Philip R., Sills, J. R., Calafiore, D., and Warren, R. J.: Measles Epidemic Control in Mason County, Kentucky, 1965–1966, *J.A.M.A.*, **200**:811, June 5, 1967.

Panum, Peter Ludwig: Observations Made During the Epidemic of Measles on the Faroe Islands in the Year 1846, in Roueché, Berton (ed.): *Curiosities of Medicine*. Berkley Medallion, New York, 1964.

The Status of Measles Vaccines, *Amer. J. Nurs.*, **63**:72, May, 1963.

Warren, Joel, and Cutchins, Ernest: Immunization of Man Against Measles: Potential Vaccines and Problems, *Amer. J. Public Health*, **52**:80, Jan., 1962.

SMALLPOX

Benenson, Abram S.: Why Does Smallpox Exist? *Amer. J. Nurs.*, **62**:77, Sept., 1962.

Bowles, Cynthia: Taking Part in Smallpox Research in India, *Amer. J. Nurs.*, **61**:92, Dec., 1962.

Cockburn, W. Charles: Progress in International Smallpox Eradication, *Amer. J. Public Health*, **56**:1628, Oct., 1966.

Dolan, Edward, Jr.: *Jenner and The Miracle of Vaccine*. Dodd, Mead and Co., New York, 1960.

Roueché, Berton: A Man from Mexico, in *Eleven Blue Men*. Berkley Medallion, New York, 1965.

Smith, J. W., Seidl, L. G., and Johnson, J. E.: Smallpox Vaccination in Hospital Personnel, *J.A.M.A.*, **197**:309, Aug. 1, 1966.

Soper, Fred L.: Smallpox — World Changes and Implications for Eradication, *Amer. J. Public Health*, **56**:1652, Oct., 1966.

Trevor, Elleston: *Pillars of Midnight*. William Morrow Co., New York, 1958.

Q FEVER

Council Report: Q Fever, *J. Amer. Vet. Med. Ass.*, **138**:64, Jan. 15, 1961.

GENERAL MYCOSIS

Mold and Fungus Diseases: A Growing Public Health Problem, *Consumer Rep.*, Jan., 1955.

Second Conference on Medical Mycology, *Ann. N.Y. Acad., Sci.*, **89**:1–282, 1960.

Utz, John T., and Benson, Margaret E.: The Systemic Mycoses, *Amer. J. Nurs.*, **65**:103, Sept., 1965.

HISTOPLASMOSIS

Bird Borne Diseases in Man, *What's New*, **228**:27, Summer, 1962.

Furcolow, Michael L.: Histoplasmosis, *Amer. J. Nurs.*, **59**:79, Jan., 1959.

Menges, Robert W.: *Histoplasmosis.* U.S. Dept. HEW, Public Health Service, Kansas City
  Field Station, Kansas City, Kan.
Rakich, Jennie H.: Nursing Aspects of Histoplasmosis, *Amer. J. Nurs.*, **59**:81, Jan., 1959.
Roueché, Berton: Liberace Room, *The New Yorker*, Sept. 17, 1960.
———: The Liberace Room, in *A Man Named Hoffman.* Little, Brown and Co., Boston, 1965.

Cryptococcus Infection
Devlin, John C.: Pigeons Blamed in Two Deaths Here, *New York Times*, Oct. 1, 1963.

Candidiasis
Burchall, Dorothy Peterson: Caring for the Infant with Thrush, *Amer. J. Nurs.*, **61**:55,
  Jan., 1961.
Kazinn, Phillip, and Taschidjian, Claire L.: Candidiasis, *Amer. J. Nurs.*, **61**:52, Jan., 1961.

Section V The Infectious Diseases Acquired Through the Gastrointestinal Route

18 The Epidemiology of Infections Acquired Through the Alimentary Portal

The gastrointestinal tract is the site of entry of many varieties of microorganisms, carried in with food and water and also by hands or by objects placed in the mouth. Many of these organisms do not survive their trip through the alimentary canal, being killed by the stomach's acidity or crowded out by the microbial competitions of the commensalistic intestinal flora. Many that do survive are unable to implant, and these are simply eliminated. The mechanisms associated with the alimentary portal of entry are discussed in some detail in Chapter 6 (pp. 104 to 107), together with a review of the major groups of microorganisms that are capable of causing disease by this route.

The three types of organisms primarily responsible for the orally acquired diseases described in this section are *bacteria*, *viruses*, and *animal parasites*. Most of the *bacterial* diseases involved are caused by members of the group known as "enteric bacteria." They are Gram-negative, aerobic, motile bacilli similar in morphology and in some biochemical respects to the large group of coliform bacilli that normally inhabit the human or animal intestinal tract. These diseases are described in Chapter 19, together with a few others that are caused by bacteria of other families. The *viral* diseases of enteric origin are induced by agents classified as "enteroviruses," the most important being poliomyelitis

virus. The agent of infectious hepatitis appears to have many of the epidemiologic features of an enterovirus, but until it is isolated and identified by laboratory methods it must remain unclassified. These diseases are described in Chapter 20. The *animal parasites* that gain oral entry to the body represent every major class of the pathogenic species: *Protozoa, Nematoda* (roundworms of both the intestinal and tissue-invading types), *Cestoda* (tapeworms capable of intestinal infestation and some that invade parenteral tissues), and *Trematoda* (the liver, intestinal, and lung flukes). The diseases associated with ingestion of infective parasitic forms are reviewed in Chapter 21.*

Important aspects of the epidemiology of these diseases relate to the gastrointestinal tract as a *portal of exit*, as well as an entry site, and to infective human feces as a transmitting agent for pathogenic microorganisms. Adequate nursing management of active infections must be based on both considerations, as are preventive measures applied on either a personal or a public scale. The majority of diseases acquired by the alimentary route are transmitted from that source as well. The exceptions to this rule are found mainly among the parasitic diseases induced by parasites lodged in parenteral tissues from which they cannot escape (trichinosis, echinococcosis, cysticercosis), and a few systemic bacterial infections in which ingested organisms invade the tissues from the bowel but do not remain implanted in the latter site (brucellosis, bovine tuberculosis, tularemia).

The *transmission* of infection from the intestinal tract may be accomplished in several ways: (1) by direct simple fecal-oral transfer from one person to another, soiled hands being the agent; (2) by indirect contacts with fecally contaminated objects placed in the mouth; (3) indirectly through the contamination of food or water; (4) indirectly from fecally polluted soil; and (5) by a circuitous route through animal or plant hosts that not only infect man but may be infected by human fecal sources of pathogenic organisms. The communicable bacterial diseases, as well as the viral and protozoan infections with which we

are concerned here, are transmissible from person to person by one of the first three methods. This is true also of one of the roundworms (pinworm), but the other animal parasites are not directly communicable. The eggs of two of the nematode species (*Trichuris* and *Ascaris*) require a period of maturation in the soil before they become infective, but this indirect route of transfer is much less involved than that required by other helminths that undergo cyclic development in different host species.

Direct fecal-oral transmission is always a matter of poor or inadequate personal hygiene. Improper toilet habits and failures in hand-washing after defecation or before eating are chiefly at fault. Diseases spread in this way are often seen in outbreaks among familial or close institutional contacts. In families, young children are the most frequent disseminators of microorganisms, and this is difficult, if not impossible, to control even in the best regulated households with high sanitary and hygienic standards. The situation is difficult in certain kinds of institutions, also, particularly those that care for children or for persons who are mentally incompetent. Overcrowding contributes to disease transmission by contact, as does negligent staff control of sanitary facilities. The threat of epidemics through contact transmissions is limited to the number of susceptible persons who can be exposed, but it is also influenced by the numbers of persons whose infection is unrecognized and the extent to which they can spread disease before they are detected. A number of enteric diseases are transmissible during the prodromal stage of infection, before symptoms become apparent, a notable example being poliomyelitis. When this situation is coupled with generally unsanitary standards of living within a community, poor socioeconomic conditions, the malnutrition of poverty, and a climate that encourages spread, infection fans out rapidly through the susceptibles, and those who develop disease provide the visible framework of the epidemic. The persistence of inapparent, asymptomatic carriers within a group constitutes another silent source of infection for

* References for Chapters 18 to 21 are located at the end of Section V (pp. 488 to 490).

susceptible contacts. The infant members of any population are always the most vulnerable, even to organisms that live as harmless commensals in adults. The early days of life are always the most critical in this respect, and, for infants, the closed situation of the modern hospital nursery may sometimes provide a serious threat of epidemic infection, spread rapidly by contacts that for adults would be casual or insignificant. The best control of infections derived from the intestinal tract, and easily spread by direct transmission, begins with sanitary toilet practices scrupulously followed by adults and taught to children from the earliest possible time. Thorough hand-washing is an essential feature of the control of all directly transmissible diseases, but particularly those of enteric origin.

Indirect contact with fecally contaminated objects usually transfers infection to the hands, and from there to new objects, to food, or directly to the mouth. Here again, personal hygiene is important in preventing such transfers, which may begin with soiled hands and end by soiling the hands of others. Mechanical vectors, especially flies, may play a role in this, bringing infection from their breeding places in fecal deposits, when these are available to them. Both public and personal measures are required to control the potential spread of disease by flies and other insects. Adequate screening and the use of insecticides keep flies out of houses, but their breeding can be controlled only by community-wide vigilance, usually maintained by health departments. Procedures include the sanitary disposal of raw sewage, as well as the judicious application of insecticides on a large scale.

The indirect transmission of disease through contaminated food or water may provide a serious public health hazard when large and often mixed groups of people are exposed to the same source of infection. Food is usually contaminated by persons with inapparent infections, or by those who have recognizable but ignored infectious conditions (mild diarrhea, colds, sore throats, pimples or boils, skin "rashes" that are really sources of multiplying microorganisms). Food contamination may involve small family groups,

larger numbers of people fed from institutional kitchens, or the general public that frequents a restaurant. Its control is difficult at best and can be achieved only when general education and community understanding of the problem support the efforts of public health authorities to find and remove the sources of infection shared through common food supplies (Chap. 11, pp. 274–75). Every food handler should develop an awareness of his possible role in transmitting disease and a corresponding sense of responsibility. Educational campaigns and good supervision assist in this, but it is also important to find effective relief from the economic pressures that create fear of occupational losses and prevent personnel from reporting minor disabilities that may affect the health of others as well as themselves. The latter problem has another facet in the irresponsibility of paid "sick leaves" without basic justification. These social and economic problems not infrequently contribute to the total problem of protecting the public health.

The protection of water supplies is also difficult and is achieved only by continuous supervision and guidance of public habits with the support of an educated community. Much is taken for granted, today, in countries that have achieved a good measure of public sanitary controls. One has only to look at areas of the world where such measures have not been well established (or glance back a few decades at the history of infectious diseases in this country and others that learned their epidemiology slowly) to realize that continuing safety is a matter of continual effective control of sewage wastes and the protection of water from human or other sources of contamination (see Chap. 11, pp. 262–67). Water is a ubiquitous medium, necessary and utilized by all forms of life. The control of its pollution, however, is now primarily dependent upon applied human knowledge and intelligence. In terms of human communicable diseases of microbial origin, contaminated water is one of the most frequent sources of explosive epidemics when these are related to microorganisms capable of survival and dissemination in this milieu. Food-borne epidemics are often more limited in distri-

bution, as are those induced by direct human contacts, because the ultimate sources of infection are seldom so widely disseminated as they may be by water.

Indirect disease transmission from contaminated soil is often quite effective, but it is limited to those pathogenic microorganisms that can establish a reservoir in this medium. These include the fungi that induce systemic mycoses (Chap. 17), the larval forms of animal parasites that mature in the soil and enter the human body through the skin (see hookworm disease, Chap. 25), and those intestinal roundworms of man whose ova require development under conditions offered in soil. The latter (*Trichuris* and *Ascaris*) are appropriate for discussion in this section (Chap. 21) because their epidemiology involves their transmission to soil through infective feces and back to human beings through the oral route of entry.

The tapeworm and trematode diseases of man are for the most part not directly transmissible to other persons, but man transmits many of them indirectly, through environmental reservoirs, to animal hosts that continue the parasite's cycle. Human excreta containing parasite ova, when permitted to contaminate soil or water, are a source of infection for animals or aquatic species. Man acquires these parasites by ingesting them in an infective stage developed in the animal host. The only exception to the alimentary route of entry for the trematode diseases is schistosomiasis, which is acquired when free-swimming larvae in infested water penetrate the skin (Chap. 25). The human transmission of schistosomal ova back to the aquatic host (snails) occurs by the same excretory route, however, and the pollution of water with infective fecal or urinary discharges.

The control of diseases perpetuated by human contamination of soil or water begins with the sanitary disposal of feces, either through sewerage systems, well-constructed septic tanks, or chemically disinfected privies. In areas of the world where sanitary standards are not well controlled, it is useful to apply additional measures designed to interrupt the chain of transfer when this involves animal hosts. Domestic animals that serve as intermediate or alternate hosts can be protected

from infection from human sources. When animals such as rats or snails are involved in the chain they can be eliminated, or at least held in control. Continuing educational campaigns are required, however, to inform the public of the nature and sources of these diseases, and of the necessity for good sanitation, care in choosing meats and other foods, and adequate cooking methods.

The nursing precautions required in the management of patients with infections acquired through and transmitted by the gastrointestinal route are centered in the control of spread through infectious feces. Hospitalized patients should not be permitted, during the communicable stage of their infections, to share bathroom facilities with uninfected patients. Bedpan collections may be emptied directly into toilets or hoppers if the local sewerage system is adequate and properly maintained. If not, the bedpan contents must first be chemically disinfected for a time (see Appendix V). Bedpans, enema equipment, rectal tubes, and similar items should be individualized for infectious patients, if possible. In any case, bedpans, rectal thermometers, and enema nozzles should be safe for every patient's use. The continuing problem of inapparent carriers also provides strong reasons for sterilizing bedpans between each use, either by steam or by boiling water. Autoclave sterilization is appropriate for most other equipment involved, but thermometers must either be discarded or disinfected by methods relevant to the nature of the infectious organism concerned (see Appendix VII).

Patients with gastrointestinal infections do not, in general, require isolation in a private room but may be segregated in cubicle units. Exceptions to this rule include patients with infectious hepatitis or poliomyelitis (during the first week of illness) and nursery babies with diarrhea. Gowns should be worn by those in contact with infectious patients, and particular attention should be given to hand-washing techniques (the patient also should be instructed in this, if possible). Laundry techniques should include the disinfection of bedclothing and linen, the latter to be transported, when soiled, in closed

bags marked to indicate the need for caution. Soiled dishes must be handled with care, but they can be put through the routine cleaning process if this provides safe disinfection. If not, contaminated dishes and eating utensils should be handled separately and disinfected in very hot soapy water followed by boiling rinse water.

Everyone who handles dishes from an infectious case should be alert to the necessity for careful hand-washing.

In the following chapters, precautions pertinent to the nursing care of these infections are indicated in the discussion of each disease.

Questions

1. On what considerations must adequate nursing management of active intestinal infections be based?
2. In what ways can the transmission of infection from the intestinal tract be accomplished?
3. What nursing precautions are required in the management of patients with infections acquired through and transmitted by the gastrointestinal tract?

19 Bacterial Diseases Acquired Through the Alimentary Route

Many of the bacterial infections of the gastrointestinal tract are highly communicable, by direct contact transmission or through contaminated food or water. Their public control depends on the protection of general food supplies, the purification of drinking or swimming water, and the safe disposal of sewage. These same principles apply in hospitals that care for patients who are ill with these diseases, and of course the provision of safe food, milk, and water supplies is essential for all hospital patients. Food must be protected from environmental contamination and from handlers who may be carriers of infection. Hospital health service programs include screening employees for active or asymptomatic infections, and employees themselves must have responsible attitudes with regard to reporting their infections, so that suitable safeguards may be set up to prevent their spread to patients.

Enteric precautions, as described in the preceding chapter, must be followed carefully in the management of most of these diseases, with exceptions as noted in individual cases (intoxications resulting from bacterial food poisoning, brucellosis, and the diseases grouped in the last section of this chapter. In enteric diseases, the patient's feces, urine, and vomitus should be considered infectious, or potentially so. The organisms involved may contaminate bedding, clothing, dishes, bedpans, hands, and everything

423

they touch. The hands and clothing of those who attend the patient may be similarly contaminated and can carry the infection to others unless hand-washing and gown techniques are used effectively. Concurrent disinfection of equipment in the patient's unit, and of objects handled by him, is necessary, as well as good terminal disinfection-cleaning.

Salmonellosis

The *Salmonella* genus is a remarkable one because of its size, its wide distribution in nature, and the nearly uniform pathogenicity of its many species for man, animals, and birds. Some species are more frequently associated with one type of host than with another, but all of them have pathogenicity for man. *Salmonella typhosa*, the agent of typhoid fever, is the only one of these species that appears to be restricted to a human reservoir.

The salmonellae are usually associated with an intestinal route of entry and transmission. Morphologically, they are indistinguishable from those members of the normal intestinal flora that are grouped together as "Gram-negative enteric bacteria." The latter include the coliform bacilli (*Escherichia coli*, *Klebsiella* and *Aerobacter* species), the related paracolon (*Citrobacter*) strains, *Proteus*, and *Pseudomonas* species. (These indigenous organisms are described as a group in Chap. 12. Their recognition has importance when they cause infection in parenteral tissues, such as the urinary or respiratory tracts, or in surgical wounds, as a result of conditions that permit their extension from their endogenous intestinal site.) Like many of these organisms, the salmonellae are Gram-negative, aerobic, nonsporeforming, usually motile bacilli. In the laboratory, they are distinguished from the others by differences in their biochemical properties (chiefly those involved in the fermentation of carbohydrates, such as lactose, dextrose, sucrose, and a number of others), and by recognition of their specific antigenic components. The biochemical characteristics of the *Salmonella* group are fairly uniform, but their antigenic classification recognizes a large number of species.

Salmonella infections are most often acquired through the oral route, usually by the ingestion of food or water contaminated with these bacilli derived from a fecal source. Soiled hands frequently play a role in implanting these organisms in food, or directly into the mouth. Meat and other products of infected animals, eggs from infected birds, and shellfish are also often involved in the far-flung distribution of salmonellosis. As in the case of many other pathogenic microorganisms, inapparent human infection is a common source of sporadic or epidemic disease because it is unrecognized.

Clinical disease produced by *Salmonella* infection may be one of three major types, and, sometimes, a combination of these: *enteric fever*, *septicemia*, or *gastroenteritis*. The first two of these are systemic infections resulting from distribution of the organisms through the blood stream following their intestinal tract entry, while the third (and most common) is intestinally localized infection. All species of *Salmonella* have the potential to produce any of these clinical situations, but certain strains are characteristically associated with either systemic or intestinal infection. Typhoid fever is the prototype of severe enteric fever and is classically associated with *Salmonella typhosa*. Paratyphoid fever is a milder form of enteric fever, most frequently caused by *Salmonella paratyphi* or by some others such as *S. schottmulleri* or *S. hirschfeldii* (these organisms have been named most often for the scientists who discovered them, or for the places where they have been discovered, e.g., *S. miami* or *S. cubana*). Septicemia is a more fulminant systemic invasion, with a wide dissemination of focal abscesses. *S. choleraesuis* is characteristically associated with this type of problem. By far the largest number of salmonellae are found in cases of gastroenteritis. They are an enormously diverse group antigenically, but from the clinical and epidemiologic points of view their potential is very similar. Some of the strains frequently involved in gastroenteritis are *S. typhimurium*, *S. enteritidis*,

S. *derby*, S. *heidelberg*, S. *oranienburg*, and S. *newport*, to name just a few. Occasionally more than one strain of *Salmonella* may be found in a patient's stool, and sometimes, also, a case that begins as a gastroenteritis may develop into enteric fever. The latter commonly begins, however, with little or no evidence of intestinal localization or irritation.

The Enteric Fevers (Typhoid and Paratyphoid Fever)

Typhoid Fever. Following its ingestion in contaminated food or water, S. *typhosa* first localizes in the deep lymphoid tissue of the intestinal wall (Peyer's patches). The lymph flow carries the organisms into the thoracic duct, and from there they reach the blood stream. They may be widely disseminated, but they localize most usually in the liver and gallbladder. The kidneys may also be infected, as well as the spleen, bone marrow, or lungs. In organs such as liver and kidneys there is focal necrosis of the parenchymal cells at the site of colonization; lymphoid tissue becomes enlarged and more cellular (hyperplastic). The gallbladder is always infected and is a major source of the organisms that appear in the stool during the course of the disease and often continuing into convalescence. Localization in the lungs produces a bronchitis or pneumonitis. The cellular response is mononuclear rather than polymorphonuclear, and the total number of white blood cells in the circulating blood is often depressed.

Clinically, the symptoms of typhoid fever include a gradual, insidious onset, with fever rising in steps to an average height of 104° F, with a relatively slow pulse. There is often abdominal tenderness, but constipation is more frequent than diarrhea. Rose spots on the trunk are a frequent sign during the first or second week, together with symptoms of pulmonary involvement. In severe cases, the patient may become delirious or stuporous (the Greek word for stupor is *typhos*).

The organisms may be recovered from cultures of the blood during the first week to ten days when bacteremia and dissemination occur. Stool cultures are usually positive from the onset and may remain so, even long after convalescence. Urine cultures may yield the organisms in the second and third weeks, and also may continue to do so for long periods thereafter. The organisms may be found in bone marrow, bile drainage, or sputum if localization in bone, the gallbladder, or the lungs has occurred.

The patient's immune response to typhoid fever begins in the early days of infection, and recovery is associated with a rising titer of antibodies during the second and third weeks. Then organisms can no longer be found in the blood stream, the temperature gradually returns to normal levels, and the convalescent stage ensues. Foci of typhoid bacilli may nonetheless persist in the tissues, particularly in the gallbladder, spleen, or kidney. They are found within mononuclear cells, out of reach of circulating antibody, where they may continue to multiply. From such sites they may continue to be shed into the intestinal tract (by way of the common bile duct when the gallbladder is involved) or excreted in urine. The patient remains asymptomatic, but he may become a persistent carrier.

Paratyphoid Fever. This is a milder type of disease than typhoid fever. It usually has a more rapid onset, with fever, involvement of lymphoid tissue in the intestine, and spleen enlargement. In more severe cases there may be rose spots and many other resemblances to typhoid, but the causative organism is a strain of *Salmonella* other than S. *typhosa*. S *paratyphi* and others closely related to it may produce disease similar to typhoid but not fully typical in all respects. The duration of symptoms of active infection may be from one to three weeks.

Salmonella Septicemia

Blood stream invasion may result in some instances (particularly in S. *cholerasuis* infection)

in even wider dissemination and localization of organisms, in any tissue, with the production of local abscesses. There may be perineal and pelvic abscesses, meningitis, endocarditis, pyelonephritis, arthritis, osteomyelitis, or pneumonia.

Gastroenteritis (Salmonella Food Poisoning)

The clinical symptoms of this infection are familiar to many people. They begin from 8 to 48 hours following the ingestion of the organisms, with the sudden onset of abdominal pain, nausea, vomiting, and diarrhea, often accompanied by fever and chills. In severe cases, the patient may be prostrate. The signs are those of severe irritation of the intestinal mucous membranes, probably from the release of endotoxic components of the cells when large numbers are ingested, multiply rapidly, and begin to die. The organisms do not enter the blood stream ordinarily (although occasionally they do so, some time later after the enteritis has subsided), but they can be recovered from stools and vomitus.

Laboratory Diagnosis

I. Identification of the Organism. The microscopic characteristics of the salmonellae were described on the first page of this section. These organisms grow with relative ease in laboratory culture, but their isolation from the mixture of bacteria present in stools (and sometimes in urine also) presents some difficulty. This problem is overcome by the use of selective agar media that suppress the growth of coliform and other enteric organisms but permit *Salmonella* species to grow. The incorporation of lactose in these media, together with an indicator that responds with a color change when acid is produced, serves to differentiate the colonies that grow. *Salmonella* species are always indifferent to lactose and do not break it down into acid end products. Their colonies are therefore colorless in appearance on differential media. Coliform bacilli, on the other hand, characteristically fermet lactose. Their colonies take on the indicator color as the pH changes with breakdown of the sugar to acid products. This color differentiation makes it possible to select the suspicious, colorless colonies from the plates and

to inoculate them as pure cultures into other media necessary for their identification. Certain other organisms normally found in stool specimens, such as *Proteus* and *Pseudomonas* species, are also lactose-negative and must be differentiated from *Salmonella*, by recognition of a combination of biochemical characteristics, such as the fermentation of other carbohydrates (dextrose, sucrose, salicin, etc.), the production of certain enzymes or pigments, and so on.

Serologic identification of isolated organisms biochemically typical of the *Salmonella* genus is accomplished with specific antiserums, by simple slide agglutination techniques. The somatic antigens of *Salmonella* fall into several groups. Antisera containing group-specific antibodies identify the isolated strain, as a member of a *Salmonella* group. Species identification of the strain then depends on recognition of individual flagellar antigens, using antisera that contain specific flagellar antibodies. (See Chap. 7, p. 135.)

II. Identification of Patient's Serum Antibodies. The *Widal test* is a method for identifying the agglutinating antibodies that arise in the patient's serum during *systemic Salmonella* infection. It is particularly useful in typhoid and paratyphoid fevers, and in *Salmonella* septicemias, when the presence of the organisms in parenteral tissues stimulates antibody formation. In gastroenteritis without blood stream invasion, however, there is usually no antibody response, and the Widal test is not helpful in those instances.

Known *Salmonella* O (somatic) and H (flagellar) antigens are mixed separately with the patient's serum, the latter being diluted serially to find its maximum capacity (titer) for agglutinating the antigen. A *rising* titer of agglutinins occurring from the onset through the course of the disease signifies active infection. A single finding of typhoid or paratyphoid agglutinins, in only one serum sample, may not distinguish antibody persisting from a previous infection, from vaccination, or during the carrier state.

III. Specimens for Diagnosis. In enteric fevers and septicemia:

A. Blood cultures should be taken frequently, especially during the first week of disease. Bone marrow cultures may also be useful in demonstrating bacteremic or septicemic spread.

B. Stool specimens should be submitted for

culture at frequent intervals, particularly after the first week of disease.

C. Urine specimens may be positive for *Salmonella* culture, usually in the second and third weeks of infection.

D. Bile drainage may be collected for culture, particularly during convalescence, or later, to check for the persistence of the carrier state, and to demonstrate biliary tract localization of the organisms.

E. Sputum, pus from abscesses, synovial fluid, spinal fluid, and similar collections as indicated by the clinical signs of infection may yield the organisms in culture.

F. An "acute" serum taken during the first week of disease, as close to onset as possible, should be submitted for the Widal test. (The term "febrile agglutinins" is sometimes used to identify this test.)

G. A "convalescent" serum should be collected after ten days to two weeks for a second Widal titer to demonstrate a rising antibody response to active infection.

In gastroenteritis, repeated stool specimens should be submitted for culture during the acute stage. The culture of vomitus is sometimes useful, if stool results are negative. When positive stool results are obtained, cultures should be repeated a week or so after the patient has returned to normal, to check on the possibility of lingering infection and the establishment of the intestinal carrier state. Other cultures and serologic testing are not indicated unless signs of enteric fever or septicemia develop.

Epidemiology

I. Communicability of Infection

A. RESERVOIR, SOURCES, AND TRANSMISSION ROUTES. Man is the only reservoir for *Salmonella typhosa*, and the *primary* reservoir for *S. paratyphi* and its close relatives. Other strains have a worldwide distribution in domestic and wild animals, some amphibians such as turtles, and poultry. The source of infection is the feces of infected animals or persons, and the environmental reservoir is usually either (1) food derived from an infected animal (meats, eggs, milk and other dairy products), (2) food contaminated during storage by the feces of infected animals,

especially rodents, (3) food contaminated by an infected person during its processing or preparation (meats, eggs, milk), (4) water contaminated by infectious sewage, (5) food obtained from contaminated water (shellfish), or (6) direct or indirect contact with persons having clinical or inapparent infection. When infection is derived from any of the first five of these sources, the result is likely to be an outbreak among persons sharing the contaminated food or water supply. The numbers of cases resulting from contact with an infected individual depend on the nature and closeness of the contacts and on the activities of the infected person, with particular respect to food-handling for family or public consumption. One of the most famous typhoid carriers (Mary Mallon, or "Typhoid Mary") is known to have been responsible for 10 outbreaks of typhoid fever, involving 51 cases and 3 deaths. Flies have frequently been incriminated as mechanical vectors of *Salmonella* infection, particularly in areas where sanitation and living conditions are poor. They may carry the organisms from infected fecal deposits (where flies usually feed) and deposit them on food or on kitchen surfaces. If the food thus contaminated is eaten without subsequent cooking, the organisms may multiply in the small intestine and induce gastroenteritis or other *Salmonella* infection.

B. INCUBATION PERIOD. For typhoid fever, usually one to two weeks, sometimes three weeks; for paratyphoid fever, about one to ten days; for gastroenteritis, from about eight to ten hours, up to 48 hours.

C. COMMUNICABLE PERIOD. Communicability continues throughout active infection, and for as long as salmonellae are shed in excreta. Following typhoid fever, about 10 per cent of convalescents shed the bacilli for varying periods up to three months, and about 2 to 5 per cent become permanent carriers. The carrier rate is variable in paratyphoid fever and in gastroenteritis, permanent carriers being unusual, but the carrier state may persist for a few days or a few weeks following recovery. Babies and very young children sometimes shed the organisms for months.

D. IMMUNITY. Human populations show a general susceptibility to *Salmonella* infections,

with more severe reactions among the very young and the very old. Exposure to systemic infection generally results in immunity, but the degree and duration are variable. Second attacks occur but are not usual after age 30 or 40. Gastrointestinal infection produces little or no immunity, however, and attacks of this type of disease may be experienced at any time exposure occurs. Artificial active immunization is available, and useful, for those who are in situations where risk of exposure to systemic infection is high (hospital personnel, travelers to, or residents in, areas of high endemic incidence), as discussed under Prevention.

II. Control of Active Infection

A. ISOLATION. Patients with typhoid or other enteric fever of *Salmonella* origin should at least be segregated from others when they are treated in hospitals. They should not be cared for at home unless adequate sanitary and living conditions permit, and good nursing care is available. Their rooms should be screened from flies and kept scrupulously clean. In hospitals, such patients should be assigned to cubicle space in wards or semiprivate areas, or to private rooms. They must not share bathroom facilities with other patients. They may not be released to resume general activities, especially if these include food-handling, until stool and urine cultures appear to be safely free of salmonellae. This assurance is usually based on three negative cultures of stool (and urine, if indicated) obtained on successive days during the convalescent stage. If any one of these cultures is positive, supervision is continued for one month's time. If three negative cultures can then be obtained, the patient may be released from supervision; if not, this requirement may be continued by health authorities for as along as the individual situation appears to demand. Patients with gastrointestinal salmonella infections also are followed with stool cultures and excluded from food-handling while they remain culture-positive.

B. PRECAUTIONS. These include the concurrent disinfection of all infectious excreta, and of objects contaminated by them (bedpans, bedlinens, rectal thermometers, enema equipment, clothing). When community sewage disposal systems are adequate, toilet facilities may be used directly, or for bedpan contents. Disinfection techniques should be used frequently for toilet seats and other bathroom facilities, especially when these are shared. In hospitals, individual bedpans or toilets should be provided for patients with enteric infections, or arrangements should be made for the sterilization of all bedpans. The latter may be accomplished with specialized steam sterilizing equipment, or by boiling. When good sewage disposal is not available, preliminary treatment of bedpan contents with chemical disinfectants is necessary. Gowns should be worn, and hand-washing should be practiced with scrupulous care, by the patient as well as by personnel in attendance.

C. TREATMENT. Chloramphenicol or the tetracyclines are effective in the therapy of *Salmonella* infections, but with limitations. They are of less value in gastrointestinal than in systemic disease. In the latter they help to suppress active, continuing infection, but they do not necessarily eliminate the organisms, particularly when the latter have become entrenched in intracellular locations.

When the carrier state persists and can be related to continuing localization of the organisms in the gallbladder, surgical removal of this organ may solve the problem. When the organisms persist in the kidney and are excreted in the urine, however, the surgical approach is of graver concern, and not undertaken lightly.

D. CONTROL OF CONTACTS. Food-handlers are the particular targets of efforts to prevent the spread of *Salmonella* infection. The close contacts of actual cases of *Salmonella* diseases are excluded from food-processing until cultures prove them to be free from inapparent infection. When cases of enteric fever occur, household and medical personnel may be actively immunized with vaccine to prevent their own infection, but this has no value in protecting against gastroenteritic infections.

The source of every case of typhoid or other enteric fever is investigated. Sporadic cases of gastroenteritis are difficult to trace, but every effort is made to find the common source of outbreaks. The possibilities of unreported cases

or inapparent carriers are explored, together with the question of contaminated food or water supplies offering a common exposure.

E. EPIDEMIC CONTROLS. When typhoid or paratyphoid fever occurs, individual case reports are required by local health authorities, but this is not necessary for *Salmonella* gastroenteritis, unless it occurs in epidemic form. Such reports guide the efforts of epidemiologists to find the active case, carrier, or food or water source. One outbreak of *Salmonella* infections led to the recognition of a strain, later known as *Salmonella miami*, that had originally contaminated a certain batch of watermelons sold to a particular market. When customers wanted only part of a melon, a single knife was used to cut the portions. That knife, once it had been inoculated with *S. miami* from the contaminated melons, contributed to the spread of *Salmonella* gastroenteritis to many of the market's customers, until the outbreak led to a successful search for its source. Similar situations may arise in hospitals, as in the case of a *Salmonella*-contaminated dye administered by gastric intubation to patients undergoing studies of abdominal tumors. Another type of outbreak was seen in 1964 in northeastern sectors of the United States, but localized particularly in the greater New York area, with the highest incidence among hospitalized patients. This was an outbreak of *Salmonella derby*, which was not pinpointed definitively but was traced with fairly reliable evidence to eggs marketed by local poultry farmers. The hospital incidence of this infection was associated with the practice of serving raw eggs in milk shakes, or other form, to nutritionally debilitated patients. The susceptibility of this group to any type of infection provides reason for stricter controls on poultry farms and careful judgment on the part of hospital purchasers, physicians, and dietitians in selecting, prescribing, and serving eggs, particularly if they are not to be cooked. Other recent *Salmonella* infections that have threatened or reached limited epidemic proportions have been associated, on different occasions, with a fish-processing plant where infected handlers were involved, contaminated powdered milk, and a popular brand of candy prepared from contaminated ingredients.

These incidents point up the necessity for continuing awareness of the many living and environmental reservoirs of *Salmonella* infection, and for controls on the obvious sources. When outbreaks occur, these controls are tightened, with the exclusion of suspected foods from the market; recommendations for the pasteurization, boiling, or exclusion of milk; thorough cooking of eggs, poultry, and meats; and chlorination or boiling of water, depending on the epidemiologic evidence pertinent to the situation.

III. Prevention

A. IMMUNIZATION. Bacterial vaccines do not confer protection against *Salmonella* gastroenteritis, but they are of value in preventing typhoid and paratyphoid fevers. A triple vaccine is available, containing typhoid and two species of paratyphoid bacilli in heat-killed suspension. It is not recommended for use on a mass scale because it provides only partial resistance, which must be renewed at intervals of three years. Used on a selective basis, however, for persons subject to a frequent or high risk of exposure, typhoid-paratyphoid vaccine has a distinct value. Candidates for current vaccination include laboratory and other hospital personnel, travelers, military personnel, and persons visiting or living in areas where sanitation is poor and *Salmonella* infection is endemic.

The vaccine is initially given in two subcutaneous doses, separated by an interval of two or three weeks. A single booster dose given once in three years reinforces the immunity. Vaccine elicits the production of agglutinating antibodies, which appear in the circulating blood and persist for some time. When serum from patients with febrile disease of suspected *Salmonella* origin is tested for typhoid or paratyphoid agglutinins, a positive titer must be interpreted in the light of a history of vaccination, or of repeated natural exposure to, or active infection with, these organisms.

B. CONTROL OF RESERVOIRS, SOURCES, AND TRANSMISSION ROUTES. Many of the factors involved in the prevention of salmonellosis have been described in the preceding discussion. They may be summarized here as follows:

1. Public water supplies must be protected, purified, and chlorinated (see Chap. 11). Private water supplies must also be protected. When doubt exists concerning the safety of water for drinking or washing, it should be either boiled or disinfected with chlorine or iodine preparations. Disinfectants are available for individual use for this purpose.

2. The adequate disposal of sewage is essential.

3. Meats, eggs, and milk must be protected by sanitary processing. Infection should be eliminated at the animal source, insofar as possible. Stored foods should be safeguarded from possible contamination by rodent feces.

4. Shellfish should be protected by the control of sewage disposal in waters from which they are harvested.

5. Milk should be pasteurized; eggs, meats, and shellfish should be cooked when questions concerning their purity arise.

6. Food-handlers and the methods for preparing foods in public places should be under continuing supervision by local health departments.

7. Flies should be controlled by adequate screening and the judicious use of insecticides at their breeding places or entry routes. Fly-breeding can be reduced by adequate methods for the collection and disposal of garbage, and of human feces.

8. Carriers of *Salmonella typhosa* must be supervised and restricted from occupations that offer a public health hazard, notably food-handling. When the carrier state threatens to be permanent, gallbladder removal may be effective in ending it. Antibiotic therapy prolonged over a long period is sometimes helpful, also. Release from supervision requires six consecutive negative cultures of feces and urine, taken one month apart, when the carrier state has persisted for more than a year. Carriers sometimes become impatient and uncooperative under surveillance, and this may necessitate authentication of specimens yielding negative cultures.

9. Patients convalescing from enteric fevers must be warned of the significance of the carrier state, if they remain culture-positive. They should be given special instruction in personal hygiene, in hand-washing after use of the toilet and before meals, and in the sanitation of excreta when adequate public sewers are not available. They must be excluded from food-handling until satisfactorily demonstrated to be free of continuing infection.

10. Food-handlers and the public at large must be continuously educated as to the sources and transmission of typhoid fever and other *Salmonella* infections.

Shigellosis (Bacillary Dysentery)

The Clinical Disease. The bacterial genus *Shigella* contains a group of pathogenic species of major importance because of its wide distribution and its potential for producing severe human disease.

Shigellosis, or bacillary dysentery as it is often called, is an acute intestinal disease characterized by diarrhea with abdominal cramps, vomiting, and fever. The liquid stools often contain blood and mucus, and they are passed with difficulty because of rectal spasm (tenesmus). The large bowel is inflamed. Damage to the mucous membrane leads to ulceration and bleeding and the formation of a "pseudomembranous" exudate on the ulcerated areas. The infection is usually self-limited, but when it subsides the intestinal ulcers heal by granulation and are filled in with scar tissue. Uncomplicated recovery is the usual rule, although the clinical severity varies with the causative strain, the age of the patient, and his general condition. Young children and older persons are most seriously affected, particularly if they are malnourished or otherwise debilitated. Ordinarily the case fatality rate is less than 1 per cent, but in epidemics in tropical countries where living conditions and sanitation are poor, the disease may be rapidly fatal to as many as 20 per cent of the cases.

The intestinal injury that results from *Shigella* infection is thought to be caused by the toxicity of the somatic antigens (endotoxins), released from the organisms as they die and lyse. One of the strains, *Shigella dysenteriae*, also secretes an exotoxin that adds to the damage. Infection with this particular species usually leads to more seri-

ous disease, marked by a general intoxication. Unlike the salmonellae, which invade the blood stream and cause enteric fever, the shigellae do not enter the parenteral tissues but remain in the bowel. The fever that often accompanies shigellosis is probably due to some absorption of toxic products and to the dehydrating effects of the diarrhea.

Laboratory Diagnosis
I. Identification of the Organism

A. Microscopic Characteristics. The shigellae closely resemble the other enteric bacteria in appearance, except that they are nonmotile. They are Gram-negative, nonsporulating bacilli that grow aerobically.

B. Cultural Characteristics. Methods for the isolation of *Shigella* species from stool specimens are very similar to those described for salmonellae. The chief problem is to distinguish them from the nonpathogenic enteric bacteria that are usually abundant in feces. This can be done by using selective and differential agar media that contain inhibitors for the coliform group, and lactose, with an indicator. *Shigella* species are indifferent to lactose (one ferments it very slowly), and therefore, their colonies are colorless on these plates, in contrast to lactose-fermenting coliform bacilli, which take on the indicator color. Colorless colonies are fished from the plates for further identification. They are distinguished from *Salmonella* and other species by their lack of motility and by the fact that those carbohydrates that they do utilize are fermented without gas production.

C. Serologic Identification. The final identification of isolated *Shigella* species is accomplished by slide agglutination tests of the growth mixed with specific *Shigella* antisera. The genus contains four major antigenic groups: group A (*Sh. dysenteriae*), group B (*Sh. flexneri*), group C (*Sh. boydii*), and group D (*Sh. sonnei*). Some of these groups contain more than one strain, but those named are the prototype species.

II. Identification of Patient's Serum Antibodies.
Circulating antibodies (agglutinins) appear in the blood during shigellosis but they do not appear to be correlated with recovery from infection nor with protective resistance to second attacks. It is seldom practical to test for these antibodies as a diagnostic procedure because they are frequently found in normal persons who have had previous infection, and because bacteriologic and clinical diagnosis is generally more reliable.

III. Specimens for Diagnosis. Bowel contents only are suitable for the culture of *Shigella* species. Specimens should be received by the laboratory in the freshest possible condition, because these organisms are undergoing autolysis in the bowel during the symptomatic stage of disease, and the survivors may be neither numerous nor metabolically active. Also, they are in competition for nutrient with other bacteria present, and for this reason, also, fresh material should be cultured promptly.

The organisms are often concentrated in the flecks of mucus and blood present in diarrheic stools, and these may profitably be selected for culture.

Rectal swabs have a clinical and nursing advantage and yield good bacteriologic results. If the patient is examined by sigmoidoscopy, cultures may be taken from the ulcerative lesions visualized through the instrument.

If serologic diagnosis is attempted, serum samples should be taken during the acute and convalescent stages, separated by at least ten days, so that a rising titer of antibody may be recognized if it occurs.

Epidemiology

I. Communicability of Infection

A. Reservoir, Sources, and Transmission Routes. The reservoir for the shigellae is the human intestinal tract, and infected feces are always the source. Transmission may occur by the direct fecal-oral route, or indirectly through contaminated objects and hands (sometimes with the help of mechanical vectors such as flies), but the contamination of water or food enables the widest distribution.

B. Incubation Period. Usually short, within one to four days, but not more than seven days.

C. Communicable Period. For as long as the organisms are present in feces. The carrier state does not develop so frequently in shigellosis as it does in salmonellosis. Most convalescents do not shed the bacilli for more than two or three

weeks, but occasional persons remain chronically infected and may suffer relapses.

D. IMMUNITY. As mentioned in the discussion of laboratory diagnosis, specific antibodies develop during the course of disease but they are not protective against new infections. People of all ages are susceptible to this disease, but it is often more serious in children and in debilitated adults. It has a worldwide distribution, but epidemics are more frequent and severe in tropical and other areas where nutrition is poor, living conditions are marked by poverty, and sanitation is inadequate. Outbreaks are often associated also with institutional living, particularly in orphanages, convalescent homes for children, mental hospitals, and jails.

II. Control of Active Infection

A. ISOLATION. Patients must be isolated during the acute stage of illness. A private hospital room is not necessary, however, provided the patient's unit can be segregated from others, and precaution techniques are carefully carried out. The patient should not be permitted to share bathroom facilities with noninfected patients.

B. PRECAUTIONS. These include the concurrent disinfection of feces and of contaminated objects (bedpans, toilet seats, bed linens, rectal thermometers, sigmoidoscopes, enema equipment, clothing). Feces may be disposed of directly into the sewage system if this is adequate; if not, fecal matter should first be disinfected chemically. Gowns should be worn by all who come in contact with the patient, and scrupulous attention should be given to hand-washing, both by the patient and by personnel attending him.

C. TREATMENT. Antibiotics such as chloramphenicol, the tetracyclines, and streptomycin (also the sulfonamides) are effective in relieving the acute stage of illness, but they do not always eliminate the organism from the bowel or prevent the carrier state from developing. Polymyxin therapy is sometimes effective in terminating the chronic carrier state. The most important supportive therapy is the control of dehydration.

D. CONTROL OF CONTACTS. As in the case of salmonellosis, the control of food-handlers is important in epidemiology of this disease. When the contacts of active cases include food-handlers, the latter are excluded from this occupation until they are proved to be bacteriologically negative by fecal culture. A search is made among contacts for other cases of active shigellosis, atypical cases, and carriers.

E. EPIDEMIC CONTROLS. Individual as well as group cases of this disease must be reported so that the source of infection may be found in the population or in the environment. With regard to the latter, investigations are centered on common water, food, and milk supplies.

III. Prevention

A. IMMUNIZATION. Effective vaccines are not available.

B. The prevention of shigellosis is based on control of its human reservoir, as outlined in the previous section, and sanitary control of its environmental sources, through the purification and chlorination of water, adequate sewage disposal, fly control, and the protection of food, water, and milk from human or mechanical vectors.

Bacterial Food Poisoning

The term "bacterial food poisoning" traditionally refers to diseases of bacterial origin that develop abruptly after the ingestion of food. They often involve many, if not all, of the persons who shared the food, their respective symptoms developing simultaneously or within close time periods. The illnesses are enteric in nature, with the notable exception of botulism. (See also Chap. 6, pp. 106 to 107.) Numerous infectious diseases are, or may be, transmitted through food, but they are not "poisonings" in the sense defined here.

The three major types of food poisoning referable to bacteria are *Salmonella gastroenteritis*, *staphylococcal intoxication*, and *botulism*. The first of these is an acute enteric *infection*, characterized by symptoms of intestinal irritation caused by endotoxins released from the infecting organisms when they begin to lyse and die following active multiplication in the intestinal tract. *Sal-*

monella gastroenteritis, and its epidemiology, are described earlier in this chapter, together with other clinical syndromes caused by salmonellae. It is reviewed briefly here for purposes of comparison with the other two types of food poisoning, both of which result from the ingestion of *preformed* bacterial toxins rather than from infection. (See Table 19–1.)

Salmonellosis   6 hrs.

Salmonella gastroenteritis has an acute onset that begins after an incubation period of *at least six to eight hours*, during which time the organism multiplies actively in the small intestine. Symptoms begin when some of these organisms begin to die and endotoxic components are released that have an irritating effect on the bowel mucosa. Symptoms persist while the organisms continue to multiply and die within the intestinal tract, usually for several days. Vomiting, diarrhea, abdominal pain, and fever are the most usual and constant signs of infection. The infection is generally self-limited, although antibiotic therapy may help to shorten the illness. It does not necessarily eliminate the organisms from the bowel, however. They may persist after symptoms have subsided, and the infection may sometimes develop into an enteric fever.

The foods most commonly involved are meats and poultry, eggs, and dairy products obtained from infected animal sources and eaten raw or with insufficient cooking to kill the salmonellae. The human food-handler infected with salmonellae may, however, contaminate any food. If it is eaten without cooking, or contaminated subsequent to cooking, cases of salmonellosis may result from consumption of the food. Time is not required for the organism to multiply in food. Once it finds its way there it need only survive (as it will do in the refrigerator) until it is ingested. Multiplication then proceeds in the human intestinal tract, whether or not it has done so previously in the food. Measures for the control of this problem are discussed fully on pages 428 to 430.

Staphylococcal Enterotoxin Poisoning   2 hr.

Acute food poisoning due to staphylococcal *enterotoxin* is one of the principal forms of bacterial enteric poisoning in the United States. This illness is not an infection, but an intoxication induced by *preformed toxin* produced by staphylococci multiplying actively in food *before* it is consumed. Symptoms begin within *one to six hours*, usually about two to four hours after the contaminated food is eaten. The onset is abrupt, and often violent, with nausea and vomiting, cramps, and diarrhea. The patient may be prostrate, with a depressed temperature and blood pressure. Severe as these symptoms are, they pass rather quickly, usually within a day or so, as the toxin is eliminated and the insulted intestinal mucosa recovers.

> The *diagnosis* of staphylococcal intoxication can be made tentatively from clinical symptoms, supported by the isolation of staphylococci in significantly large numbers from the suspected food if it is still available for testing. The presence of many staphylococci in vomitus is also significant, but their isolation from fecal specimens has little meaning, because these organisms may be found among the normal intestinal flora. When staphylococci are isolated from food or stomach contents, they may be tested for enterotoxin production or typed by their reactions with bacteriophages (see Chap. 3, p. 45, and Chap. 23, p. 514), because only a relatively few strains are capable of secreting this toxin.

The *source* of staphylococcal contamination of food is usually a person with an infected lesion on hands, arms, or face, although these organisms may also reside on healthy skin and respiratory mucosa. A great variety of foods may support the growth of staphylococci, but those most often involved are custards and pastries made with cream, salads and salad dressings, and meats that have been sliced or ground. When staphylococci are implanted into foods they require a few hours to grow and elaborate the toxin. Growth and multiplication occur most rapidly in warm

rooms. Cooking kills the organisms, but if the toxin has already been formed it may survive, for it is stable to heat. Refrigeration does not kill the organisms, or the toxin, but it inhibits microbial growth and thus prevents enterotoxin formation. For this reason, meats and foods prepared in advance of meals must be kept under refrigeration until they are eaten or cooked.

The *control* of staphylococcal food poisoning depends on the recognition of cases (outbreaks must be reported to health departments), of the food source, and of the infected human reservoir. Bacteriologic cultures are made of suspected food and of handlers (from lesions, or from the nose), and also from patients' vomitus, when possible. Strains of staphylococci isolated from these sources are then compared as to phage type, enterotoxin production, and other properties to relate them to the case and its source. The control of food-handlers includes their education in personal hygiene and their supervision in maintaining sanitary techniques for handling, preparing, and refrigerating foods. Persons with obvious skin infections should not be permitted to handle foods until the condition has been treated and cured. In many areas the public health laws require the refrigeration of foods prepared for public consumption, particularly those that are most dangerous as possible sources of *Staphylococcus* poisoning, such as custards, salads, and meats.

Botulism

This acute and often fatal disease results from the ingestion of a *toxin preformed* in foods by the anaerobic bacterial species *Clostridium botulinum*. Unlike other forms of bacterial food poisoning, botulism is a systemic intoxication. The powerful toxin is absorbed from the intestinal tract and exerts effects on motor nerves of the central nervous system that are sometimes irreversible and fatal. Symptoms sometimes, but not always, begin with gastrointestinal irritation, vomiting, and diarrhea. Often, however, the first signs are related to neurotoxin activity: headache

and dizziness, ocular disturbances (double vision), with paralysis of oculomotor nerves. Neuromuscular involvement of the intestinal wall may lead to severe constipation; death is usually the result of respiratory paralysis or cardiac failure. An incubation period of *12 to 36 hours*, rarely longer, reflects the time required for the toxin to be absorbed from the intestinal tract, disseminated through the body, and attached to the peripheral nerves. The amount of toxin ingested may also affect the length of the incubation period, although this is a very powerful substance, capable of exerting effects in very small doses. Patients who recover do so slowly, as toxin is inactivated and eliminated, and the lesions at the myoneural junctions slowly regress. They may require artificial respiration for some time. Immunotherapy with *botulinum* antitoxin is sometimes lifesaving.

The *diagnosis* of botulism can often be made on clinical grounds but requires bacteriologic confirmation and identification of its source. The organism may be isolated from the suspected food, if it is available for testing, but the best proof lies in demonstrating (1) that the food is toxic for mice, and (2) that this toxicity can be specifically neutralized by botulinum antitoxin. When canned foods are involved, related lots or batches are tested. *Cl. botulinum* is an anaerobic, sporeforming, motile, Gram-positive bacillus, normally found in the soil and in the intestinal tract of animals and fish (see Fig. 19–1, A–C). Its spores may contaminate vegetables and other foods. When these are preserved by canning techniques, the spores may survive inadequate processing and germinate later under the anaerobic conditions provided in the can or jar. The vegetative bacilli then proliferate and elaborate toxin. Canned foods are frequently eaten with little or no subsequent cooking, and under these circumstances active toxin is ingested. Boiling of foods for at least ten minutes will inactivate the toxin, but the chief danger lies in the fact that these foods may display little or no change in appearance or odor or at least none related to the presence of toxin, so that the urgent necessity for boiling them may not be apparent. The foods most commonly involved are home-canned vegetables, olives, mushrooms, corn, spinach, and string beans. Commercial can-

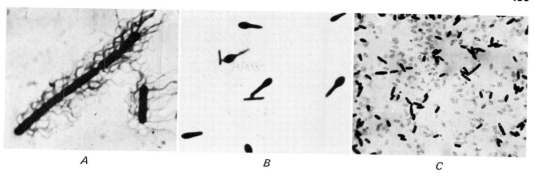

Fig. 19–1. *Clostridium botulinum. A.* A chain of vegetative bacilli stained to demonstrate their flagella. *B.* The vegetative bacilli are sporulating. Note their swollen tips. *C.* Vegetative bacilli and many free spores. Note that the latter are resistant to staining. (Reproduced, with permission, from Dolman, C. E.: Botulism, *Amer. J. Nurs.,* **64**:119, Sept., 1964.)

ning processes have largely overcome the problem, but recently cases have been related to commercially packed tuna fish, smoked fish, and fresh fish sealed in vacuum-packed plastic bags.

The *control* of botulism hinges on the use of safe measures for processing foods (especially those likely to harbor *Cl. botulinum*), the prompt recognition of the disease and its source, and recall from the market of suspected foods. Cases must be reported so that a search for the source can be made without delay. Other persons known to have eaten the incriminated food may be treated prophylactically with botulinum antitoxin. This procedure is most effective if antitoxin reaches the blood stream before the toxin does so. There are two types of *Cl. botulinum* and several antigenic types of toxins (A through E). It is essential, therefore, that prophylactic antiserum contain antibodies specific to the type involved in the disease, if this can be determined, or that polyvalent antiserum, containing several type-specific antibodies, be used.

Government controls now provide for the regulation and inspection of commercially canned foods, although occasionally new problems arise. It is vitally important, however, that housewives educate themselves, or receive instruction, in safe methods for preparing home-canned foods. The spores of *Cl. botulinum* may survive long periods of boiling, especially in neutral or alkaline foods, so that unless the food has an acid reaction it cannot be safely processed except in a pressure cooker. If there is the slightest reason for doubt, home-canned nonacid foods should be boiled for at least ten minutes before they are served or even tasted by the cook.

Epidemic Diarrhea in Nurseries

The Clinical Disease. Epidemic diarrhea is a clinical syndrome sometimes seen in hospital nurseries for the newborn and for older infants on pediatric services. The epidemic pattern can be alarming, with swift spread from one baby to another. Clinically, there is severe diarrhea with dehydration; stools are watery and yellow but they are seldom mucoid, and they do not contain pus cells or blood. This prostrating syndrome is not seen in the general community, but in hospital nurseries it may have a high case fatality rate. It is not related to the sporadic cases or community epidemics that sometimes result from the spread of infectious agents by poor sanitation and are made more serious by the malnutrition of poverty, but instead occurs among

Table 19–1. Summary of Bacterial Food Poisoning

Disease	Agent	Incubation Period	Communicable Person to Person	Symptoms	Control
Salmonella gastroenteritis	*Salmonella* species infecting gastrointestinal tract	8–48 hr	Yes	Fever, N, V, D,* for several days	Prevent contamination of food, water; control carriers, especially food-handlers
Staphylococcal intoxication	Preformed enterotoxin of staphylococci	1–6 hr	No	Acute abdominal cramps, N, V, D* 1 or 2 days; subnormal temperature	Prevent contamination and multiplication of staph in food; control food-handlers
Botulism	Preformed toxins of *Cl. botulinum*	12–36 hr	No	Central nervous system intoxication; double vision; flaccid paralysis	Prevent spore contamination of canned foods; prevent germination of spores in canned foods; reheat canned foods before serving (boil 10 min); antitoxin for all who have eaten suspected food

*N,V,D = nausea, vomiting, diarrhea.

babies, healthy or sick, who are under hospital supervision.

Laboratory Diagnosis

I. Identification of Organisms. Very often the causative agent cannot be identified. In some cases ECHO, Coxsackie, or other enteroviruses (see Chap. 15, p. 364, and Chap. 20, p. 451) can be isolated. Numerous bacterial strains common to the normal flora of the adult intestinal tract have been incriminated. These include *Proteus* and *Pseudomonas* species, fecal streptococci (entero-

cocci), staphylococci, *Clostridium* strains, and coliform bacilli (see Chap. 5, pp. 94 to 95, and Chap. 30, p. 633). It is thought that these bacterial species that are well adapted to a commensalistic life on the adult intestinal mucosa or other surfaces (and vice versa) may be separately, or sometimes collectively, quite pathogenic for babies who have not yet adjusted to life in the microbial world. When babies are exposed to such organisms, in excessive numbers derived from environmental or human reservoirs, they may be overwhelmed by infection. Infected babies then become new, rich sources of multiplying microorganisms, and the

infection spreads rapidly from one bassinet or crib to another.

One group of organisms that has received particular interest in recent years should be emphasized. This is a group biochemically identified with *Escherichia coli*, a normal resident of the adult intestinal tract. A number of species of *E. coli* have been associated with epidemic diarrhea in babies, and these have been found to possess distinctive antigenic components, recognizable by serologic techniques. There are about a dozen such serotypes of *E. coli* that have been identified as one cause of infant diarrhea and also of infections in adults in parenteral tissues beyond the intestinal tract (particularly the urinary tract, as discussed in Chap. 29). The pathogenic serotypes of *E. coli* are identified with specific antiserums and reported by numbers assigned to their different somatic (or 0) antigens: e.g., 0111, 055, 0119.

II. Identification of Patient's Serum Antibodies. It is not always possible to make a serologic diagnosis of these infections, for several reasons: the antibody-forming mechanism is not well developed in babies; these diarrheal infections may be too fulminating, or too short-lived, to permit antibody response; serologic testing depends on the use of specific antigens, whose identity may not be suggested by clinical or bacteriologic evaluations. However, many of the agents mentioned above, particularly the viruses and the pathogenic serotypes of *E. coli*, have been confirmed as causative agents in individual outbreaks by the recognition of rising titers of specific antibodies in infants' serums.

III. Specimens for Diagnosis. Stool specimens may be submitted for bacteriologic or virologic examination, but results must be interpreted with caution. The diagnostic bacteriologic laboratory is particularly alert to the necessity for the serologic identification, if possible, of strains of *E. coli* isolated from the feces of infants less than one year of age. Other organisms may be described in terms of their relative numbers or predominance in culture, a finding that may be of some clinical value in the choice of antibiotic therapy or of epidemiologic significance in controlling the infection.

Serum samples are not often of value in routine diagnostic testing, for reasons described in II above. They may sometimes be submitted for special testing, however, or for referral to large diagnostic centers. Serum collections should always be paired, when possible, an "acute" and a "convalescent" specimen being drawn, respectively, at onset of symptoms and ten days to two weeks later.

Epidemiology

I. Communicability of Infection

A. RESERVOIR, SOURCES, AND TRANSMISSION ROUTES. The adults who surround babies in hospitals are the probable reservoir of these infections: mothers, physicians, nurses, and other attendants. Since the organisms involved are often members of the adult intestinal flora, the source of infection is probably fecal. The transfer may be direct from the contaminated hands of adults, or indirect through the contamination of environmental surfaces or objects to which hospitalized babies are commonly exposed, e.g., shared bath tables, weighing scales, and the contaminated dust of ill-kept nurseries. Formulae may also be an indirect source of infection if they are contaminated by personnel during their preparation, improperly sterilized or pasteurized, stored in inadequate refrigerators, or saved for another feeding after a first try. Pathogenic serotypes of *E. coli*, for example, have been found on the bassinet linen and clothing of babies, in nursery dust and dirt, in solutions and formulae, on instruments and weighing scales, and in cultures taken from attendant personnel — their feces, hands, and clothing. These organisms, and others of similar origin, may also be present in large numbers on the mother's perineum or as contaminants of her birth canal at time of delivery, if she is not properly prepared. Breast-fed babies may acquire their infections, also, at feeding times, from the mother's soiled hands, breasts, or sheets. In premature nurseries, the humidity chambers of incubators are often a colonizing site for *Pseudomonas* strains.

B. INCUBATION PERIOD. This is often difficult to determine, but incubation of organisms infectious for babies probably does not require

more than two to four days, with a maximum estimate of three weeks.

C. COMMUNICABLE PERIOD. Epidemics of diarrheal disease are communicable among nursery infants for as long as symptomatic babies remain in the area, the environmental source persists, or the adult carrier of infection remains undetected.

D. IMMUNITY. Babies are not immune to this type of infection. They are most susceptible during the first year of life, but epidemics are most common in nurseries for the newborn or for older babies sick with other diseases. Premature babies are even more susceptible to this, or any, type of infection. Congenital immunity does not exist, and the mother's milk does not contain protective antibodies against the etiologic agents. Disease occurs as readily among breast-fed babies as it does among those on formula. The source of infection, the numbers of infecting organisms, and the baby's age and nonspecific resistance are the principal factors in determining the severity of resulting diseases.

II. Control of Active Infection. Symptomatic babies should be immediately isolated, and "infection security" must be tightened in the nursery. Cleaning procedures may have to be revised, disinfectant practices reviewed, and personnel instructed authoritatively in the principles of hygiene as they relate to their own persons or to their techniques in attending to babies. It is imperative that hands be carefully washed, not only after the personal toilet, but after each infant's diaper change.

Case reports should be made when no more than two cases have appeared concurrently within a nursery, for this may be the start of an epidemic whose source should be found without delay. The isolation of babies under these circumstances requires the establishment of two completely separated units: a "contaminated" and a "clean" nursery, with different facilities and personnel for each. There should be no interconnecting links between them. When the safety of the clean nursery for new babies remains in doubt, it may be necessary to close the maternity service until the source of the infection is found or the prob-

lem is solved by vigorous, thorough disinfection-cleaning. Newborn infants may not be admitted to the contaminated nursery. This should remain closed until the sick babies have recovered and been discharged. Contact infants in the closed area should remain under close observation for at least two weeks from the time of their last exposure to an infected baby, although they are not necessarily kept in the hospital throughout this period if they appear to be well and progressing normally. While in the hospital these babies should have individualized care. When the last contact or infected baby has left the contaminated nursery, it may be reopened after thorough, detailed disinfection-cleaning.

Other steps indicated by epidemic emergencies include the following:

A. Call consultative meetings of the hospital's infection control committee to evaluate the problem and the efficacy of measures taken to combat it. Local health departments may also be of epidemiologic assistance.

B. Survey mothers and obstetric and nursery personnel for symptoms of illness or for bacteriologic evidence relating them to infant cases.

C. Survey babies discharged from the hospital within the preceding weeks for evidence of a missed case, or a late-developing infection.

D. Review methods for formula preparation.

E. Review methods for nursery or general hospital sanitation.

F. Review nursing techniques in the delivery room and on the obstetric service, as well as in the nursery.

G. Take stool cultures from sick or exposed babies, mothers, and personnel to determine the predominating flora, and the infectious agent of the epidemic, if possible.

H. Establish firmer standards for asepsis wherever weaknesses are noted.

Antimicrobial therapy is based on clinical and microbiologic evidence of its efficacy and relevance. Antibiotics may have prophylactic as well as therapeutic value in epidemics of bacterial origin, or in reducing secondary bacterial problems in viral epidemics. The antibiotic resistance of bacterial strains derived from the adult population is a serious problem, however, and may

hamper efforts to achieve specific therapeutic control of the situation.

III. Prevention. The general principles followed in the prevention of serious cross-infections in nurseries fall under two major headings:

A. ASEPSIS. The control of the general environment of the nursery should be rigid and detailed. The safety of formula preparations is particularly vital. Laundry techniques must assure the return of nursery laundry that is disinfected as well as clean. Cleaning techniques should include the routine use of effective disinfectants, properly chosen for their purpose. The humidity chambers and the inner walls of incubators should receive particular attention: interior surfaces should be disinfected daily; chambers, as indicated by periodic bacteriologic testing. (Consult the manufacturer's instructions for methods of disinfecting humidity chambers or plastic walls.) Sinks and basins, examining tables, weighing scales, and other equipment shared by infants must be disinfected between uses. Individual sterile pads should be used for babies placed on surfaces in common use.

B. PERSONAL CONTACTS. Good floor-planning and traffic control are essential to protect babies from cross-infection. Separate, disconnected facilities should be provided for newborns, premature infants, and older babies. Newborn and premature units should offer individualized equipment for each infant. Isolation facilities must be available for the segregation of sick or quarantined babies. Infants born of mothers with any recognized infection should be quarantined for at least one week, or until clinical and microbiologic evidence warrant release. Babies admitted from other hospitals or from the community also should be quarantined pending evaluation.

Nursery and formula room personnel should not do double-duty in other areas of the hospital, and the formula staff should not have direct contact with babies. Access to the nursery area is not permitted for unauthorized visitors. All others are required to put on a clean gown and, if they are to handle babies, to scrub their hands.

On the obstetric service, mothers who breast-feed their babies are carefully instructed in hygienic technique. Babies should not be breast-fed or visit with mothers who have infections of their own.

The diagnostic microbiology laboratory can play an essential and informative role in the control and prevention of nursery infections. Nursing supervisors on maternity services and responsible laboratory personnel should establish and maintain close liaison, develop effective techniques for periodic bacteriologic checking, and be prepared to prevent trouble by recognizing and reporting the earliest signs.

Cholera

The Clinical Disease. Cholera is an acute bacterial disease caused by infection of the large intestine with an organism known as *Vibrio comma,* or *Vibrio cholerae.* Following their ingestion in fecally contaminated water, or by other oral access, the organisms localize in the intestinal tract, multiply, lyse, and release endotoxic substances that damage the mucosal epithelium of the large bowel. Failure in function of the intestinal membrane results in an outpouring of fluid and salts. There is a profuse diarrhea, with "rice water" stools containing mucus and mucosal epithelial cells. The onset is sudden, and accompanied by nausea, vomiting, abdominal pain, and severe dehydration. Collapse and shock may ensue, and death follows if the patient is not promptly and continuously rehydrated until infection subsides. This disease may occur in explosive epidemic patterns in susceptible populations, with death rates as high as 75 per cent under these circumstances. In endemic areas the fatality rate varies from 5 to 15 per cent.

Cholera is strictly an intestinal infection. The organisms do not reach the blood stream or establish systemic foci. Consequently, the disease is ordinarily self-limited. Recovery, when it occurs, is usually quite rapid, with no signs of residual damage. Convalescents may shed vibrios in feces for two or three weeks, but the carrier state does not appear to be permanent.

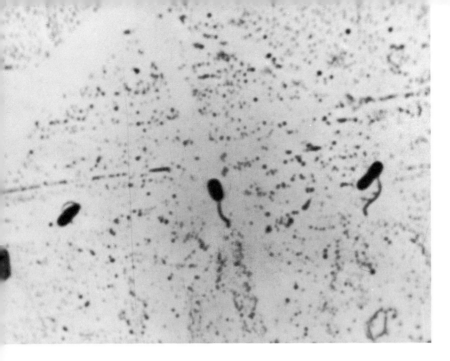

Fig. 19–2. Electron micrograph of *Vibrio comma* (*V. cholerae*). (Reprinted with permission of the U.S. Public Health Service Audiovisual Facility, Atlanta, Ga.)

Laboratory Diagnosis

I. Identification of the Organism. Microscopically, the vibrios are small Gram-negative bacilli, curved in the shape of a comma. They have a single polar flagellum, which gives them very rapid motility (see Fig. 19–2). They are not sporeforming.

Culturally, the vibrios are aerobic and grow readily on ordinary laboratory media. Two of the individual metabolic features by which they are recognized are their ability to grow in media with a strongly alkaline pH (8.5 to 9.5) and their capacity to produce indole and reduce nitrate in peptone media. The indicator system used to detect these reactions produces a red color when they occur, and the method is therefore called the "cholera red test."

Serologically, vibrios can be identified by slide agglutination tests, using specific antiserum.

II. Identification of Patient's Serum Antibodies. Specific agglutinating antibodies appear in the patient's serum during cholera infection (the reasons for this are not clear, since cholera is apparently not a systemic infection). They do not provide long-term protection against reinfection, but their presence provides a basis for serologic diagnosis of current disease. A significant increase in antibody titer must be demonstrated in the convalescent stage as compared with the acute stage of disease.

III. Specimens for Diagnosis. Stool specimens or vomitus should be sent for bacteriologic culture.

An "acute" and a "convalescent" pair of serum samples may be submitted for serologic diagnosis. The time interval between collection of these samples should be at least seven, preferably ten, days.

Epidemiology

I. Communicability of Infection

A. RESERVOIR, SOURCES, AND TRANSMISSION ROUTES. Cholera is a human disease, transmitted by infected persons in their feces or vomitus. Contaminated water supplies are the usual vehicle for epidemic spread. Food is not ordinarily involved in epidemics, but may be the source of sporadic cases in endemic areas where mild cases of cholera continue. In the latter situation, water is less important as a transmitting agent than direct contacts of the household variety. Hands, utensils, clothing, and flies may contaminate food or carry the infection directly to the mouth.

B. INCUBATION PERIOD. Usually a matter of two to three days, but in rapidly spreading cholera, many cases begin within a few hours of exposure.

C. Communicable Period.   Cholera is transmissible so long as vibrios are present in vomitus or feces. They usually persist in the intestinal tract for several weeks after recovery.

D. Immunity.   Active immunity results from an attack of the disease or from artificial immunization with bacterial vaccine, but it is not durable for more than about six months. Human susceptibility to this disease is not consistent. Cholera is currently endemic among people of the eastern hemisphere, particularly those of the poorest socioeconomic circumstances. From endemic areas in India, Indonesia, Vietnam, Thailand, Hong Kong, the Philippines, and others, it spreads from time to time in epidemic patterns to adjacent susceptible populations, or to incoming armies. Susceptible travelers may acquire and spread the disease also. Repeated vaccination is required, therefore, for military personnel and others under continuing risk of exposure.

II. Control of Active Infection

A. Isolation.   Cholera patients should be cared for under conditions of hospital isolation. The sporadic case in a nonendemic area should be assigned to a private room. In epidemics, or in endemic regions, patients may be grouped in areas where screens or cubicles can provide reasonable barriers to cross-infection.

B. Precautions.   These include the concurrent disinfection of feces, vomitus, contaminated equipment and bedding, or other objects. Chemical disinfection of feces must be carried out when adequate sewerage systems are not available. Nurses and others in contact with the patient must wear clean gowns and give particular attention to careful hand-washing.

C. Treatment.   Adequate rehydration of the patient with restoration of electrolyte balance is the most important feature of therapy. Tetracycline antibiotics may be of value in eliminating infection.

D. Control of Contacts.   Exposed contacts are kept under surveillance for several days. If fecal cultures are positive for vibrios, longer periods of observation may be required. Vaccination at time of exposure may not prevent current infection, and passive immunization is not applicable. A search is made for other cases of cholera, and for possible sources in common water supplies, or household contacts.

E. Epidemic Controls.   Case reporting is required by the International Sanitary Regulations of WHO. Measures described above are expanded to the entire community when epidemics threaten. When the general water supply cannot be immediately purified, water used for drinking or any household purpose must be boiled. Cases are isolated, and the exposed community is vaccinated. Supervisory controls are tightened on members of households where cholera has occurred, and on public eating places, and renewed battles are waged against flies, particularly at their breeding places. Ships, airplanes, and other carriers are not permitted to discharge susceptible persons (any who have not been vaccinated within six months) in epidemic areas, and, conversely, cholera patients and exposed contacts are not permitted to travel to other countries. Vaccination within six months is required of travelers who have lived or visited in endemic areas.

III. Prevention.   Cholera prevention depends on continuing application of the principles of control outlined in the preceding sections. Immunization has a short-term value only, and in endemic areas cholera vaccine must be given repeatedly to persons who run the risk of frequent exposure. Personal and public sanitary measures remain the best protection.

Brucellosis

The Clinical Disease.   Brucellosis is a systemic infection, characterized by *variability* — of entry route, of tissue localizations, of onset and symptoms. It is really a disease of domestic animals. Called Bang's disease when it affects cattle, it also occurs in hogs, sheep, goats, and horses. It is sometimes transmitted to man through infectious tissues or milk. The ingestion of contaminated milk, cream, cheese, or other dairy products af-

fords one of the major entry routes of this infection, but the organisms also frequently enter the body through skin contacts (see Chap. 24, p. 537) or on inhalation (see Chap. 14, p. 356).

Whatever their portal of entry, the organisms usually find their way through lymphatic channels to regional lymph nodes, the thoracic duct, and the blood stream, with eventual dissemination to many organs. They are localized most frequently in tissues of the reticuloendothelial system, because they are taken up by the mononuclear phagocytes of tissues such as the spleen, liver, bone marrow, and lymph nodes. The *cellular* reaction around them is granulomatous, as noted so often in chronic infectious diseases (compare tuberculosis and the systemic mycoses). The nodules frequently undergo central necrosis, and if they break down, extension of the infection results. Extension from the liver may lead to cholecystitis; bone marrow invasion may result in chronic osteomyelitis; and meningitis sometimes occurs, presumably from blood stream dissemination. The *immune* reaction to *Brucella* organisms is one of hypersensitivity, as evidenced by febrile responses and skin sensitivity to endotoxins extracted from the bacterial cells.

The symptoms of brucellosis reflect this dissemination and localization of the organisms and the hypersensitive tissue responses evoked. The onset is usually insidious, with malaise and weakness, assorted muscle aches and pains, and an intermittent fever that arises late in the day but falls during the night, the patient being drenched with sweat at that time. With abrupt, acute onset, fever and chills are more pronounced, though characteristically intermittent, and there may be severe headache, backache and exhaustion. There may be gastrointestinal symptoms, enlarged lymph nodes and spleen, hepatitis with jaundice, and mental depression. These generalized symptoms may subside after several weeks, but the disease often becomes chronic, with persisting or extending lesions. Endocarditis or pyelonephritis may develop, endometritis may occur in women, and various forms of nervous system disease may be seen, such as meningoencephalitis, neuritis, and psychiatric changes sometimes interpreted as neuroses.

Gradual recovery may occur, often with residual allergy or damage to bones and other tissues; or the infection may become latent and asymptomatic, with recurrent chills and fever occurring at times over the years as old lesions are reactivated and produce symptoms.

Laboratory Diagnosis

I. Identification of the Organisms. There are three major species of the *Brucella* genus: *Brucella abortus* (the primary reservoir is in cattle), *Brucella melitensis* (goats are the chief reservoir), and *Brucella suis* (swine are the principal hosts). Any of these strains may infect man or animals other than the principal host.

Microscopically, the brucellae are very small Gram-negative coccobacilli, nonmotile and nonsporeforming. They are much smaller and more delicate in appearance than the enteric bacilli of the human intestinal tract.

Culturally, these organisms are quite fastidious. They require enriched culture media, and some of them will not grow unless additional atmospheric CO_2 is provided during 37° C incubation. They are differentiated from other Gram-negative bacilli and from each other by a few biochemical reactions and by serologic agglutination with strain-specific *Brucella* antisera.

II. Identification of Patient's Serum Antibodies. *Agglutinating* antibodies appear in the circulating blood during the early stages of infection and persist for some time, but are not always in high titer during the later, chronic stages of disease. *Opsonins* also develop, as recognized by tests that demonstrate enhanced phagocytosis of brucellae in the presence of the patient's serum (opsonocytophagic test) (see Chap. 7, p. 137). *Precipitating* antibodies can be recognized during the acute stage of active infection and may be diagnostic at that time, but they disappear when infection subsides and disappears or becomes latent. The evanescent nature of the immune response with respect to humoral antibodies makes serologic diagnosis difficult, particularly during the chronic and persistent stages of brucellosis. The results of these tests must be interpreted in the light of the patient's history with regard to time of possible exposure, onset, and the current stage of symptoms.

Hypersensitive antibodies can be demonstrated by skin tests, using an extract of *Brucella* endotoxins. This product is called "brucellergen" and elicits skin reactions of the delayed type in indi-

viduals who have experienced *Brucella* infection. Limitations on interpretation exist in this case also, because a positive test does not necessarily indicate current *active* infection, and a negative result may be obtained during acute infection, before the hypersensitive response has begun.

III. Specimens for Diagnosis

A. Repeated blood cultures are useful during the early stages of acute infection, or during febrile periods of the chronic disease. Cultures of bone marrow may yield the organism also.

B. Biopsies of lymph nodes, spleen, liver, or other tissues apparently involved in infection; body fluids, such as spinal fluid; or sections of nodules in tissues removed by surgery may be bacteriologically diagnostic.

C. Serum samples for agglutination, precipitation, or opsonocytophagic tests may be submitted. Only the first of these is performed on a routine basis, however, and the results of each of these tests must be interpreted in the light of the difficulties in serologic diagnosis discussed in II above.

Epidemiology

I. Communicability of Infection

A. RESERVOIRS, SOURCES, AND TRANSMISSION ROUTES. From domestic animal reservoirs, brucellosis is transmitted to man through direct contacts with animal tissues (placentas, aborted fetuses, slaughterhouse blood and meat), the inhalation of contaminated dust of barns or abattoirs, or the ingestion of unpasteurized milk or other dairy products from infected animals. It is rarely transmitted from person to person, even when the organisms are present in urine, respiratory secretions, or other discharges from the infected human case.

B. INCUBATION PERIOD. When the onset is slow and insidious, the incubation period is difficult to determine, but it may be estimated, variably, at two or three weeks or several months. In cases with an acute onset, the incubation period has been observed to require from one to three weeks.

C. COMMUNICABLE PERIOD. Brucellosis is not ordinarily communicable among human beings.

D. IMMUNITY. The duration and effectiveness of active immunity resulting from disease are uncertain. Reinfections may occur if exposure is massive or strains possess particular virulence. Judging by the numbers of people who can be infected through ingestion of contaminated milk, it would appear that a majority of human beings are susceptible to *Brucella* infection. However, the widespread, controlled practice of pasteurizing milk prevents this form of exposure on any large scale, and brucellosis remains primarily an occupational hazard for farmers, veterinarians, and slaughterhouse workers exposed to infected animals. Artificial active immunization is not available for persons exposed to risk of infection, but a bacterial vaccine is used for calves in areas where the disease is endemic in cattle.

II. Control of Active Infection

A. *Isolation* of the patient with brucellosis is not necessary, and infection precautions are followed only as normally indicated for the safe disposal of excreta and secretions.

B. *Treatment* of diagnosed *Brucella* infection with antimicrobial drugs generally must be prolonged to eradicate the organisms from their protected intracellular sites in granulomatous nodules, and relapses may be frequent. The drugs of choice are the tetracyclines and streptomycin, usually administered in combination

C. *Contact controls* are applicable only to infected animal reservoirs, or to the detection of sources of infection in unpasteurized milk and other dairy products from infected herds. Suspected animals are tested for skin hypersensitivity and for agglutinating serum antibodies. If these tests provide evidence of infection, reactive animals are slaughtered.

D. *Epidemic controls* depend on good case reporting of human infections. These may often be mild or unrecognized because of the variety of clinical symptoms presented and the difficulties inherent in bacteriologic or serologic diagnosis. When brucellosis is suspected or confirmed, however, local health agencies can provide effective investigation of sources and set up appropriate controls on infected animals or their products, as described above.

Table 19–2. Summary: Bacterial Disease Acquired Through the Alimentary Route

Clinical Disease	Causative Organism	Other Possible Entry Routes	Incubation Period	Communicable Period
Typhoid fever	*Salmonella typhosa*		1–2 weeks, sometimes 3 weeks	Through active infe tion, and as long a salmonellae are sh in excreta; 10% of convalescents she bacilli up to 3 mo 2–5% become per manent carriers
Paratyphoid fever	*Salmonella paratyphi* (A) *Salmonella schottmulleri* (B) *Salmonella hirschfeldii* (C)		1–10 days	Through active infe and for as long as salmonellae are sh in excreta; carrier rate is variable
Gastroenteritis (*Salmonella* food poisoning)	*Salmonella typhimurium* *Salmonella enteritidis* *Salmonella derby* *Salmonella heidelberg* *Salmonella oranienburg* *Salmonella newport* and others		8–10 hours, up to 48 hours	Same as above
Shigellosis (bacillary dysentery)	*Shigella dysenteriae* *Shigella flexneri* *Shigella boydii* *Shigella sonnei*		1–4 days, not more than 7 days	As long as organism in feces

ecimens equired	Laboratory Diagnosis	Immunization	Treatment	Nursing Management
d cultures e marrow ures l specimens e specimens drainage um from cesses vial fluid al fluid appropriate ically) te" and valescent od serums	Culture Smear and culture Widal titer	Heat-killed vaccine	Choramphenicol Tetracyclines	Isolation from others while in hospital by cubicles in semiprivate areas or private rooms; must not share bathroom facilities with other patients; concurrent disinfection of all infectious excreta and contaminated objects; individual toilets or bedpans for patients with enteric infections; chemical disinfection of excreta if sewage disposal is inadequate; gowns for personnel and *hand-washing* by patient and personnel.
e as above	Same as above	Same as above	Same as above	Same as above
l specimens tus	Culture Culture	None	None (unless enteric fever develops)	Same as above
el contents al swabs ires taken n ulcerative ons during moidoscopy	Culture Culture Culture	None	Chloramphenicol Tetracyclines Streptomycin Sulfonamides	Isolation during acute stage; concurrent disinfection of feces (if sewage system is not adequate); of contaminated objects such as bedpans, toilet seats, bed linens, rectal thermometers, enema equipment, clothing, sigmoidoscopes; gowns should be worn, scrupulous attention to *hand-washing;* patient must not share bathroom facilities with other noninfected patients

Table 19–2. *(Cont.)*

Clinical Disease	Causative Organisms	Other Possible Entry Routes	Incubation Period	Communicable Period
Bacterial food poisoning Gastroenteritis	*Salmonella* strains, see Gastroenteritis above			
Staphylococcal intoxication	Staphylococcal *enterotoxin*		1–6 hours	Not communicable from person to person
Botulism	*Clostridium botulinum* toxin		12–36 hours	Not communicable from person to person
Epidemic diarrhea in nurseries	Pathogenic *Escherichia coli* (other bacterial strains common to the normal flora of the adult intestinal tract have been incriminated)		2–4 days; maximum of 3 weeks	As long as babies remain symptomatic and the adult carrier environmental source remains undetected
Cholera	*Vibrio comma* (*V. cholerae*)		2–3 days; few hours during outbreak of cholera	While organisms are present in vomitus and feces; may persist in intestinal tract for several weeks after recovery

cimens quired	Laboratory Diagnosis	Immunization	Treatment	Nursing Management
us cted food ailable)	Smear and culture Isolation of staphylococci Bacteriophage typing Enterotoxin production	None	None specific	No specific nursing precautions
cted food	Smear and culture Toxicity for mice	None	Antitoxin	No specific nursing precautions
from and sed babies from ers and nnel	Culture Virus isolation Culture for predominating flora	None	Antibiotic choice depends on testing of isolated organism	Isolation of symptomatic babies; review of disinfection practices; personnel instructed authoritatively in principles of hygiene; careful *hand-washing* after each infant's diaper change and personal toilet; set up clean and contaminated nurseries; meeting with infection control committee; review methods of formula preparation, nursery and general hospital sanitation, nursing techniques in the delivery room, obstetric service, and nursery; surveys of mothers and obstetric personnel for symptoms of illness; survey of recently discharged babies for evidence of possible missed case; establish firmer standards for asepsis wherever weaknesses are noted
us e" and alescent ns	Smear and culture	Killed vaccine	Tetracyclines	Isolation, gowns and careful *hand-washing;* concurrent disinfection of feces, vomitus, equipment, and bedding

447

Table 19–2. (*Cont.*)

Clinical Disease	Causative Organism	Other Possible Entry Routes	Incubation Period	Communicable Period
Brucellosis	*Brucella abortus* *Brucella melitensis* *Brucella suis*	Inhalation Skin contacts	1–3 weeks	Not ordinarily communicable fro[m] person to person

III. Prevention. The prevention of brucellosis depends on recognition of its sources in animals; limitation of its spread among them; and control of occupational hazards, infected meats, milk, and other animal foods.

Other Bacterial Diseases Sometimes Acquired Through Contaminated Food, Milk, or Water

A number of other serious bacterial infections of man can be acquired through the gastrointestinal route. Most of these diseases are systemic in nature, and all of them have another portal of entry, usually more important than this one, if not to the infected individual, at least to the epidemiologist and others who think in terms of public health hazards. The principal discussion of these diseases is given in other chapters of this text, to emphasize the epidemiology of the most frequent entry. They are mentioned here to assist the practicing nurse who must understand the individual case in terms of its own epidemiology.

All these diseases have a reservoir in animals, and some of them may also have a human reservoir. When they are acquired by man through the gastrointestinal route, it is because infected animal foods provide the source, or because infected human beings have contaminated food during its processing.

Gastrointestinal Anthrax

Man is an accidental victim, not a reservoir for anthrax. The disease is not communicable among human beings and is usually acquired by them from their contacts with infected animals. This infection is troublesome for two reasons: the bacterial agent is an aerobic sporeformer whose spores can remain viable and infectious for years, and systemic infections caused by this organism are highly fatal, although not common. When acquired by the respiratory or gastrointestinal routes, systemic localizations are reached rapidly. The more usual entry through the skin meets with greater local tissue resistance, and therefore often (but not always) the disease remains more localized, and less threatening.

Gastrointestinal anthrax results from the ingestion of infected, poorly cooked meat. In the United States and many other countries, this form of anthrax is rare, because people do not eat the meat of animals that have died of disease. In those areas of the world where primitive conditions still exist, however, and where animal foods are at a premium, such practices are not uncommon. Ingestion of the spores of the anthrax bacillus leads to the germination of vegetative bacilli, which enter the regional lymphoid tissue of the intestinal tract and are disseminated from there to the thoracic duct and the blood stream. Multiplication of the organisms in the blood and tissues leads to fulminating febrile illness, with shock and early death. (See Inhalation Anthrax, Chap. 14; Cutaneous Anthrax, Chap. 24.)

Leptospirosis

This is a spirochetal disease with a reservoir in domestic animals (including dogs) and also in rodents and wild animals (deer, foxes, skunks,

ecimens equired	Laboratory Diagnosis	Immunization	Treatment	Nursing Management
ated blood ures marrow sies of ph nodes, en, liver; al fluid n samples	Smear and culture	None available for humans *Aves*	Tetracyclines Streptomycin	Isolation is not necessary, safe disposal of excreta and secretions
	Agglutinin titers			

and reptiles). The organism usually finds a portal of exit in the urine of infected animals, and from this source it may infect the water of small brooks and ponds, irrigation canals, and rice and sugar cane fields. People who work or swim in such waters, or drink from them, are most liable to infection. Entry of the organism probably occurs most commonly through minor lesions in the skin or in the mucous membranes of the respiratory tract or the conjunctiva. It may also occur through the gastrointestinal route, following the ingestion of contaminated water or of the infected meat of domestic animals, such as cattle. Any of these entry portals may afford the organism access to the blood stream, and from there to visceral organs. Liver and kidneys are most often involved, but there may be lesions in the central nervous system, skin, muscles, and other tissues. Leptospirosis is not directly communicable from person to person. (See Chap. 25.)

Listeriosis

This infection is described in Chapter 14, page 323. It is a disease of animals and man that has not been well defined in terms of source and transmission routes. It is apparently widely distributed among many animal hosts, however, and may infect man in a variety of ways. The gastrointestinal route has been associated with milk from infected cows. Organisms derived from this or other exogenous sources are apparently not very pathogenic for human adults, but if they infect pregnant women they may be transferred to fetal tissues, for which they are highly pathogenic. Active listerial infection in adults is sporadic, and rarely communicable except by the congenital route.

Streptococcal Sore Throat

Beta-hemolytic streptococci of human or bovine origin may readily find their way into milk, either from cows with streptococcal mastitis or from dairy workers. Explosive outbreaks of streptococcal sore throat (with the potential threat of scarlet fever) have resulted from such distribution of these organisms. The pasteurization of milk provides an effective control of this type of infection, but its prevention also depends on the use of carefully aseptic techniques in the subsequent bottling, refrigeration, and distribution of milk supplies. (See Chap. 11, p. 268.)

Bovine Tuberculosis

Milk from tuberculous cattle has been a prominent cause of human tuberculosis in the past. The disease acquired by the gastrointestinal route is usually extrapulmonary, involving first the regional lymph nodes of the alimentary tract (cervical nodes are involved in the disease known as "scrofula," once commonly seen among children; mesenteric nodes and the lymphatic tissues of the intestinal wall may be localizing sites as well). Extension of tuberculous lesions from these foci usually occurs, but the disease is not ordinarily communicable to others from extrapulmonary lesions. The bovine reservoir of tuberculosis has been well controlled in this and many other countries by the tuberculin testing of dairy herds,

elimination of infected cows, and pasteurization of public milk supplies. (See Chap. 14, pp. 340 to 351.)

Tularemia

This infection has a reservoir in many wild animal species, from which it may be transmitted to man. The most common route of entry is through minor lesions of the skin or mucosa as a result of direct contact with the infected tissues of small game animals (notably rabbits), but infection may also be acquired through the ingestion of inadequately cooked meat from these animals. Other entry routes are also possible, but all lead to systemic infection, with localization of the organisms in a variety of tissues following lymphatic or blood stream dissemination. Like many other infections accidentally acquired by man from animal reservoirs, this disease is not directly communicable from person to person. See Chapter 14, page 356, for a note on transmission by inhalation, and Chapter 24 for the principal discussion of tularemia.

Questions

1. How are *Salmonella* infections most often acquired? food-mouth
2. Describe the dissemination of *Salmonella typhosa* in the body.
3. Where do the typhoid bacilli usually localize? What implications does this have for public health?
4. What is the Widal test?
5. What specimens are used in the diagnosis of enteric fevers?
6. What is the communicable period for *Salmonella* infections?
7. What nursing precautions are required in the care of patients with *Salmonella* infections?
8. What is the causative organism of bacillary dysentery? Shigellosis
9. Why is it necessary to send a stool culture to the laboratory immediately? autolysis pg 43)
10. Name the three major types of food poisoning referable to bacteria.
11. How does botulism differ from other bacterial food poisoning? toxin
12. What conditions are necessary for *Cl. botulinum* to produce toxin? anaerobic
13. How can the disease botulism be controlled? Cook 10 min
14. What is epidemic diarrhea?
15. What is believed to be the causative agent? E coli
16. What is the probable reservoir of infection for epidemic diarrhea? nurseries personal.
17. Describe the effects of the *Vibrio comma* on the human intestines. How do these lead to the typical symptoms of cholera?
18. How is brucellosis transmitted to man?
19. What control measures are necessary for an active brucellosis infection?

20 Viral Diseases Acquired Through the Alimentary Route

Enterovirus Diseases

The term "enterovirus" groups together three families of viruses associated with an ability to localize in the human intestinal tract. Many of them have been identified as causative agents of a variety of human diseases, but some are known only as transient members of the intestinal flora and have not yet been correlated with clinically obvious infections. The enterovirus family includes (1) the viruses of *poliomyelitis*, (2) the *Coxsackie* viruses, and (3) a group known as ECHO viruses (these initials are derived from the phrase "*entero*cytopathogenic *h*uman *o*rphan" viruses, originally meant to describe the fact that these organisms were isolated from enteric human sources, produced injury to the cells of human tissue cultures, but were considered to be "orphans" in the sense that they were not immediately recognizable as the agents of clinical diseases). All these viruses are widely distributed in the human population, and all of them, including the polioviruses, are far more commonly associated with asymptomatic infection of the intestinal tract than they are with clinically apparent disease. When they do induce injury to human tissues, the clinical and epidemiologic patterns of enterovirus infections are varied. Primary entry, localization, and subsequent transmission may relate the enteroviruses to the tissues of the upper respiratory tract, but they usually

implant more permanently in the bowel. From the latter site they may be disseminated to parenteral tissues of the infected host, causing cell damage and host reaction, and they may also be transmitted, by the fecal-oral route, to the oropharynx of neighboring human hosts.

The clinical patterns of diseases produced by enterovirus infection differ in the nature and the tissue focus of lesions produced, and in the severity of damage induced. They range from simple upper respiratory syndromes, such as the common cold, to serious illnesses, including paralytic poliomyelitis, myocarditis, or meningitis. Some of the Coxsackie and ECHO virus types have been associated only with diseases of the respiratory tract, but others are known to produce several kinds of systemic infections. Conversely, a particular clinical entity (meningitis, bronchitis, pneumonitis) may be caused by any one of several different enteroviruses. The clinical classification of these viruses is, therefore, not very satisfactory, except for their common relationship to the alimentary route of entry, implantation, and

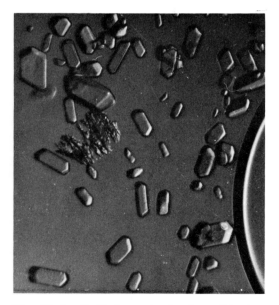

Fig. 20–1. Purified crystals of poliomyelitis virus. (Courtesy of Dr. F. L. Schaffer, Naval Biological Laboratory, Virology Division, University of California, Berkeley, Calif.)

transmission. Virologically, they have some physical and chemical properties in common. They are small viruses, their particles being in the range of 17 to 28 mμ in size; their architecture is similar, as revealed by electron micrography; and their nucleic acid structures are closely related. Antigenically, the three families of poliomyelitis, Coxsackie, and ECHO viruses represent distinct groups. The poliovirus group contains three major types, while the other two contain a much larger number each.

Poliomyelitis

The Clinical Disease.   Poliovirus infection is usually inapparent. The virus (see Fig. 20–1) has a worldwide distribution in the human population, but only about 1 per cent of infected persons develop a clinically recognizable disease. This may take one of three forms, or a combination of these merging together. (1) Most commonly, poliomyelitis begins and ends as a mild, *nonparalytic* illness characterized as a gastrointestinal disturbance, with fever, nausea and vomiting, headache, sore throat, and drowsiness. The course is short, with recovery in a few days. This syndrome can be diagnosed as an abortive poliomyelitis only by laboratory identification of the virus or of specific antibody response. (2) Patients with nonparalytic poliomyelitis may develop symptoms of meningitis, with stiffness and pain in the neck and back. This is an *aseptic meningitis*, typical of the kind produced by many viruses (see Chap. 14, p. 321). These symptoms may continue up to about ten days and be followed by rapid, complete recovery. Again, the diagnosis can be confirmed only by laboratory findings, although the clinical diagnosis is often based on the prevalence of typical poliomyelitis among the patient's contacts. (3) Paralytic poliomyelitis may develop without preliminary warning, but more usually follows the initial, mild form of febrile illness. Viral damage to lower motor neurons results in a flaccid paralysis, usually asymmetric and commonly involving the lower extremities, although this varies with the site of virus localization. In bulbar polio, there may be brainstem invasion

with paralysis of the respiratory muscles or spasm and incoordination of nonparalyzed muscles.

Poliovirus enters the body through the mouth, transmitted by fecally contaminated objects or hands or by infectious pharyngeal secretions (see Chap. 15, p. 382). It implants in the lymphoid tissue of the pharynx (tonsils) and the intestinal wall (Peyer's patches) and multiplies in these sites. Virus can be isolated both from the throat and from feces during the incubation period and in the early days of illness, but after a week it is difficult to recover from the throat. It is excreted in feces, however, for a number of weeks and is often identified in the stools of persons with inapparent infection, also. Studies in chimpanzees have shown that continuing viral multiplication in lymphoid tissue may extend from the tonsils to the draining cervical lymph nodes, and from Peyer's patches to the lymph nodes of the mes-

entery. From these tissues, the virus may invade the blood stream and be disseminated to other lymphoid structures and, more importantly, to susceptible cells of the central nervous system (see Fig. 20–2). Virus can be isolated from the blood of patients with nonparalytic polio, and from others in the preparalytic stage of central nervous system disease.

The virus spreads along the peripheral nerves to the nerve fiber paths in the CNS. The cells of the CNS most susceptible to its intracellular localization and multiplication are the anterior horn cells of the spinal cord. Sometimes in its spread within the CNS, the posterior horn cells and sensory ganglia are also involved, as well as the intermediate gray matter. The damage to these cells may be severe and it may proceed rapidly to complete distruction. Cells that are not destroyed, however, may later recover their

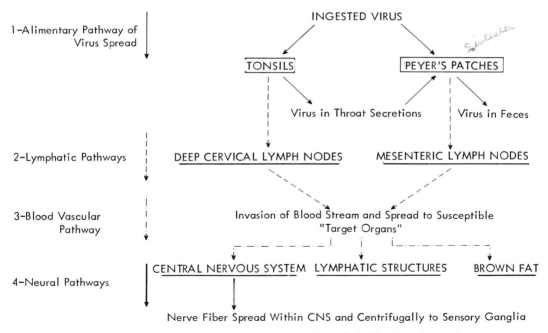

Fig. 20–2. This schematic diagram illustrates the primary sites of viral implantation and multiplication after the ingestion of poliomyelitis virus (by chimpanzees) and the pathways of subsequent viral spread in the body. This concept of the pathogenesis of poliomyelitis is based on studies of poliomyelitis in man as well as in chimpanzees. (Reproduced from Bodian, David: Emerging Concepts of Poliomyelitis Infection, *Science,* **122**:105–108, 1955.)

function. Inflammation appears at the site where the neurons are attacked, with focal collections of mononuclear cells and some polymorphonuclears. The virus does not affect the peripheral nerves and muscles directly, but these undergo changes reflecting the motor neuron damage. Muscle involvement usually reaches its peak quickly, within a few days.

Although poliovirus infection may be persistent, it is usually asymptomatic. When disease results, it is of the acute rather than the chronically progressive type. Recovery from paralytic polio is slower than in most acute infections, however, requiring several months, and the residual damage sometimes remains crippling for a lifetime.

Laboratory Diagnosis

I. Identification of the Organism. Polio virus can be propagated in the cells of human or monkey tissue cultures. It can be identified by complement-fixation tests with specific antisera or, more usually, by antibody neutralization of its infectivity for tissue cultures. There are three antigenic types of poliovirus, numbered 1, 2, and 3.

II. Identification of Patient's Serum Antibodies. Antibodies to poliovirus appear early in the disease, whether it is abortive or paralytic. They may also be detected in the blood of persons with inapparent infection, however, and for this reason the serologic diagnosis of illness requires a pair of serum samples, one collected as soon after onset as possible and one taken three or four weeks after the start of symptoms. Serums are tested with the three antigenic types of polio virus by neutralization or complement-fixation techniques. The titer of the second sample must be at least four times greater than that of the first to be considered diagnostically significant of active disease.

III. Specimens for Diagnosis

A. Throat swabs collected within a few days of onset of symptoms may be submitted for virus isolation. These are placed in a transport broth supplied by the laboratory and kept frozen until they can be transported to the diagnostic virus lab.

B. Rectal swabs (also in transport broth) or fecal specimens may be collected at any time during the course of the illness, and for some time during or after convalescence, but the optimum time for virus recovery is during the first two weeks. These materials also should be frozen at once, pending their culture for virus.

C. Acute and convalescent serums. See II above.

Epidemiology

I. Communicability of Infection

A. RESERVOIR, SOURCES, AND TRANSMISSION ROUTES. Man is the only known reservoir of poliovirus infection. The probability is that both respiratory secretions and fecal contamination are sources of infection during the incubation period and for a short time after onset. That contacts must be fairly close and direct is evident from the fact that infection rates are highest in familial households, with rapid virus dissemination among family members. When good standards of sanitation and hygiene prevail, direct and indirect oral contacts probably account for the transmission of virus, but in areas where living conditions are poor, spread of the disease from fecal sources is undoubtedly of great importance. The latter type of spread is enhanced by a warm climate and is greatest during the summer season of temperate climate zones. (See also Chap. 15, pp. 379–82.) During epidemic periods, poliovirus has been recovered from flies, roaches, and sewage. The role played by contaminated vectors, food, or water does not appear to be prominent, however, direct human contacts being the most usual factor in transmission.

B. INCUBATION PERIOD. Usually between one and two weeks, but may range from three days to four or five weeks.

C. COMMUNICABLE PERIOD. Virus is present in throat secretions and in feces before the onset of illness. It usually persists in the throat for about a week, and in the feces for varying periods, up to about six weeks.

D. IMMUNITY. Type-specific antibodies induced both by clinically inapparent and by recognizable infection confer a durable resistance to reinfection. When second attacks do occur, rarely, they are related to infection with a different type of poliovirus. Congenital passive immunity is acquired by infants in utero, but does not persist

for more than about six months, neonatally. Artificial active immunization with poliovirus vaccines provides a good level of immunity to all three types of virus. This immunity is durable, provided vaccine is given in adequate initial and booster doses.

Human populations all over the world are susceptible at all ages to poliomyelitis. Many adults have acquired immunity, but those who have not been exposed or vaccinated remain susceptible, as do most children. In areas where the majority of children become immune early in life because of repeated exposures under poor and unsanitary living conditions, poliovirus is maintained in only a small portion of the population. In temperate zones, and among people who maintain good hygienic standards, there may be a high percentage of susceptibles of all ages, subject to an epidemic pattern of spread if poliovirus is introduced. Following such epidemics, the virus is spread in a slow fashion, restricted by sanitary controls, until a new generation grows to the age when it participates most actively in transmission (the preschool years). When strains of high virulence are spread under conditions that promote rapid dissemination (as in the warm weather influence on human contacts, and possibly on environmental reservoirs and vectors), and the proportion of susceptibles is high, a new epidemic breaks out. The majority of infections in epidemics are inapparent, with about 1 per cent of those infected actually displaying clinical disease, as previously pointed out.

II. *Control of Infection*

A. ISOLATION.   When patients suspected of poliomyelitis are hospitalized, they should be isolated for a period of one week after the onset of symptoms. Isolation at home has little value for the previously exposed contacts, but new exposures should be avoided.

B. PRECAUTIONS.   During the first week of illness, respiratory precautions should be followed as well as concurrent disinfection techniques for fecal excreta and of articles exposed to fecal contamination. When adequate sewage disposal systems are not available, bedpan collections must be chemically disinfected before discard.

The hospitalized poliomyelitis patient should not share bathroom facilities with uninfected patients. Terminal disinfection-cleaning is necessary for the patient's bathroom and unit.

C. TREATMENT.   There is no specific antimicrobial therapy for poliomyelitis. Passive immunotherapy appears to have no value by the time symptoms have begun.

D. CONTROL OF CONTACTS.   *Quarantine* of contacts does not appear to be justified in view of the usual wide spread of virus before the active cases appear. In individual situations, however, it may sometimes be effective to limit the activities of family members to prevent their contacts with persons they have not previously exposed.

Prophylaxis with gamma globulin is of value in preventing paralytic disease, but not infection. It must be given well ahead of the viremic stage, however, for once virus has reached the peripheral nerves or the CNS, it is out of reach of antibody. Gamma globulin should be given within a day or two of known exposure if it is to be effective. Active immunization after exposure has no protective value for the immediate situation, but vaccination for the children of the neighborhood or school related to a case may be useful if their exposure is not certain.

Case finding among the contacts of the sick individual is important from the point of view of assuring their treatment and preventing further spread, insofar as possible.

E. EPIDEMIC CONTROLS.   Case reporting is required almost universally so that community protection from epidemic polio can be provided without delay. Since the development of effective vaccines, mass immunization has produced a striking reduction in the incidence of paralytic poliomyelitis. Paralytic cases now occur chiefly in pre-school-age children who have not been vaccinated or have not received adequate doses of vaccine. These are usually children whose families live under the poorest socioeconomic conditions.

When the incidence of reported cases indicates the possibility of an outbreak, mass immunization for the involved community is practiced as rapidly as possible. Oral vaccines are chosen particularly for this purpose because of the ease

with which they can be administered to large numbers of people in a very short time, from vaccine centers set up throughout the town or city.

III. Prevention

A. IMMUNIZATION. Two types of poliovaccine are available and effective in providing durable active immunity:

The Salk vaccine contains formalin-inactivated viruses of the three types of polioviruses. It is given in a series of four injections, the first three doses at six-week intervals, and the last one after about six months. This series may be given at any age, from early infancy on. The killed virus is disseminated through the body and stimulates the production of circulating antibody, which can then neutralize the activity of infective viruses if they reach the blood stream from intestinal sites. It does not prevent intestinal infection, or the excretion of virus in the feces of infected persons, but it prevents the development of paralytic disease if live virus reaches the blood stream.

Oral poliovirus vaccines contain live attenuated strains. They are used in the United States as single-strain (monovalent) vaccines, each type of virus being given in one separate dose, the series requiring six-to-eight-week intervals between doses. The types are given in order of their prevalence in the country, beginning with type 2 and continuing with type 1, then type 3. After six months, a booster dose of triple (trivalent) oral vaccine is given. The trivalent vaccine may also be used for the basic regimen, being given initially in two doses six weeks apart, followed by a third dose in six months. The live viruses present in these vaccines multiply in intestinal sites and induce resistance of the alimentary tract to later infection. They also stimulate the production of circulating antibodies that prevent CNS localization of infective virus.

Solid immunity is best obtained by several annual boosters with trivalent vaccines of either type. Preimmunized children should be given a booster dose at the time they enter school. Under epidemic conditions, reinforcement immunization should be given to persons of all ages who run special risks of infection, such as young children, hospital personnel, travelers, and others directly exposed to active cases, and nonimmune persons should receive oral vaccine immediately.

B. OTHER PREVENTIVE MEASURES. If and when epidemics of poliomyelitis appear again in the community, children and others who may be susceptible, and exposed to risk, should be protected. Booster immunization or gamma globulin may be indicated for prophylaxis. Febrile conditions should be treated with particular care, because undue exertion may promote viremia and CNS involvement in polio infections. Tonsillectomies or other nose, throat, and oral surgery should be avoided for nonimmunized children during seasons in which poliovirus infections are frequent because if the children are harboring the virus in the lymphoid tissue of the oropharynx, such operations may release the organism to the blood stream or directly to adjacent peripheral nerves, and thence to the central nervous system.

The advent of effective vaccines has brought poliomyelitis under control for the first time. The price of artificial control is clear, however, in this as in many other infectious diseases. Mass immunization procedures are followed by a dwindling but persistent appearance of the infectious microbe in the general population. At the same time, the immunity that results from natural encounters with the organism also declines, so that larger and larger numbers of susceptible persons accumulate, *unless* artificial exposures to the causative agent are voluntarily maintained on a large scale. Epidemics are generated by the coexistence of susceptible hosts and virulent organisms. A solution to the problem of the persisting microorganism is offered through a rational approach to its immunologic defeat. The continuing efficacy of this solution depends on the increasing education and comprehension of the general public as to the difference between natural and artificial immunity and their respective, accompanying risks.

Coxsackie Virus Diseases

Clinical Syndromes. The Coxsackie viruses were first recognized in a study of an outbreak of a disease that simulated paralytic poliomyelitis but

was milder and did not leave residual paralysis. Clinically, this syndrome was one of aseptic meningitis with some muscle weakness, or paresis. In the laboratory, the virus isolated from these cases was shown to be distinct from poliovirus in its antigenic and infective properties, and so it was named for the town (Coxsackie, New York) in which it had caused an epidemic. Since that time (1948), Coxsackie viruses have been found to have a worldwide distribution and to be associated with a number of acute illnesses, most of which are of short duration and without serious consequence.

In addition to *aseptic meningitis*, which must be distinguished from mild poliomyelitis, Coxsackie viruses have been recognized as causative agents of the following clinical syndromes:

Common Colds. Coxsackie and other enteroviruses are among the many viral agents associated with colds. (See Chap. 15, p. 364.)

Herpangina. This is an acute but brief illness characterized by fever, a sore throat, difficulty in swallowing, vomiting, and abdominal pain. The pharynx typically shows many vesicular lesions. Recovery occurs within two to four days. "Summer grippe" of Coxsackie origin resembles herpangina, but it is not known whether the throat lesions are always present or not.

Pleurodynia. Fever and acute muscle pain, usually in the chest wall, characterize this disease. The pain is sometimes abdominal, rather than thoracic, and there are usually malaise, headache, and other ill-defined symptoms of illness. Symptoms may disappear quickly or persist for a week or two, but recovery is complete.

Neonatal Myocarditis. Neonatal myocarditis or encephalomyocarditis is associated with Coxsackie viruses, but it is not known how babies acquire this infection. During the first week of life, signs of lethargy, diarrhea, vomiting, and feeding problems, sometimes with fever, may occur. These symptoms may disappear without further difficulty, or there may be rapid development of cardiac and respiratory distress, the baby being cyanotic and dyspneic, with a rapid pulse

and other evidence of myocarditis. The disease may be fatal but infants who recover do not display residual damage.

Laboratory Diagnosis

I. Identification of the Organism. These viruses can be propagated in tissue cultures or in neonatal (suckling) mice and recognized by distinctive pathogenic effects. A large number of antigenic types have been identified by the use of specific antisera that neutralize the infectivity of the viruses or induce complement fixation when combined with viral antigen.

II. Identification of Patient's Serum Antibodies. Rising titers of neutralizing antibodies appear in patients' serums during the course of these viral infections. Their identification with known strains of viruses provides serologic confirmation of Coxsackie disease.

III. Specimens for Diagnosis. Throat or nasopharyngeal washings and stool specimens are submitted for viral isolation in most of these infections. Spinal fluid may yield the virus in aseptic meningitis, and fecal specimens are positive in this instance also.

"Acute" and "convalescent" serum samples are useful for serologic diagnosis. The first serum collection is made as soon as possible after onset; the second, in about two weeks.

Epidemiology

I. Communicability of Infection. Coxsackie viruses appear to have a human reservoir only. Their frequent presence in throat washings or feces and the easy spread of infections such as herpangina among familial contacts suggest transmission by fecal-oral or oral-oral direct or indirect contacts. The incubation period is usually short, a matter of a few days, and the communicable period is probably associated with the acute, febrile stages of illness. Encounters with these viruses appear to be very frequent, resulting in the formation of antibodies that persist for years. Many more adults possess antibodies to a wider variety of antigenic types than do children.

II. Control of Active Infection. The question of the isolation and precautionary care of these

infections is often entirely academic, because virologic diagnosis is seldom complete until long after the patient's recovery, and clinical diagnosis is difficult or, of necessity, inconclusive. It has been recommended that cases of aseptic meningitis, particularly if they resemble poliomyelitis, be isolated during the febrile stage. The basic precautions that apply to any infectious disease should be followed, with hygienic control of respiratory secretions and sanitary disposal of excreta.

Attempts to control contacts are not practical, and there are no feasible measures for restricting epidemics.

ECHO Virus Diseases

Clinical Syndromes.   The ECHO viruses are isolated from the human intestinal tract far more frequently than they can be documented as the causative agents of recognizable diseases. When they do induce clinical disease, the diagnosis is entirely dependent on laboratory tests in which the virus is isolated and identified, or serum antibodies are detected in significant titer, or both.

The diseases that ECHO viruses can produce range from common colds to febrile respiratory illnesses, sometimes accompanied by a rash; epidemic diarrhea in infants (see Chap. 19, p. 435); and aseptic meningitis. The latter syndrome may include some degree of muscle weakness and spasm and must be differentiated from poliomyelitis. This type of disease in young children is also often accompanied by a rash.

> **Laboratory Diagnosis.**   The ECHO viruses are cultivated in monkey kidney tissues. Their isolation from clinical material, such as throat washings or feces, and spinal fluid, in aseptic meningitis, affords the best means of making a laboratory diagnosis. More than 30 antigenic types of ECHO viruses have been recognized, and it is not uncommon to find more than one type in a given specimen. The size of this group makes serologic diagnosis difficult under ordinary circumstances, for the patient's serum must be tested against the entire battery, often by more than one serologic method.

Epidemiology.   As in the case of other enteroviruses, the ECHO group appears to have a worldwide distribution in the human population. Infections occur more frequently during infancy and childhood than in later years, and the viruses have a rapid spread among intimate contacts. Acute febrile illness with rash, aseptic meningitis, and epidemic diarrhea in newborn nurseries constitute the more serious problems. In the latter situation, effective controls can and must be instituted, as described in Chapter 19. ECHO infections probably occur far more widely in the community than is recognized on the basis of the incidence seen in hospitalized patients, but there are no effective means of controlling community spread. The protection of young infants from older children or adults with acute febrile illnesses is always advisable, however.

Infectious Hepatitis

The Clinical Disease.   There are two forms of hepatitis thought to be caused by viruses. One of these is called *infectious hepatitis*, sometimes known also as *epidemic jaundice*, or *viral hepatitis A*. This is an "enteric" disease that involves the liver. It is acquired through alimentary tract entry of the agent (respiratory entry may also be possible). Infected human beings are the reservoir, and their feces, urine, or blood is the source of infection. This disease is transmitted by natural contacts between people, and it may also be transferred by the transfusion of blood, serum, or plasma containing the virus, or by contaminated syringes or needles. In addition, infectious hepatitis can be transmitted from environmental sources, such as water and food, contaminated by infective feces or urine. The spread of disease from water or food is very likely to take an epidemic pattern. This disease is discussed in some detail in this chapter.

The other form of infectious liver disease is called *serum hepatitis*, or *viral hepatitis B.* It is clinically similar to infectious hepatitis, but its agent, development, and epidemiology are different. Man is the only reservoir, but the blood of infected persons is the sole source of infection

and is transferred only by inoculation. This disease is discussed in more detail in Chapter 29, with other infections acquired through parenteral routes.

Clinically, infectious hepatitis begins as many other infections do, with fever, malaise, vomiting, anorexia, and discomfort. These symptoms subside after a few days and are succeeded by jaundice. The liver may be enlarged and tender, and bile may appear in the urine. The injury induced by the causative agent appears to be restricted to the liver, the degree of destruction to parenchymal cells determining the severity and the mortality of the disease. In the most fulminating cases, which are unusual, death may occur within about ten days; in more slowly advancing cases death occurs in one or two months. The fatality rate is low, however, and the majority of cases recover, though residual liver damage may take some time to repair. The disease in children is mild and probably occurs more frequently than is recognized. In adults, the infection is more severe, particularly in those with underlying liver disorders and in pregnant women.

Laboratory Diagnosis
I. Identification of the Organism. The agent of infectious hepatitis has not yet been successfully cultivated in tissue culture or in laboratory animals. The little that is known of its properties and infectious nature has been gained from studies made in human volunteers. It is known to resist heating at 56° C for 30 minutes and a concentration of 1 ppm of chlorine for the same time period (the usual concentration of chlorine in drinking water and swimming pools is 2 ppm). When frozen it remains viable for long periods.

The virus can be recovered from the feces of infected persons during the incubation period, that is, about two to three weeks before the onset of icteric symptoms. It appears to localize first in the intestinal tract, as do the enteroviruses. It can be recovered from blood after the prodromal period of fever and malaise, before jaundice is noted.

II. Identification of Patient's Serum Antibodies. Information is not available about the nature of antibodies that arise during attacks of infectious hepatitis, since the virus has not been isolated.

It is apparent, however, that circulating antibodies do appear and that they contribute to resistance. They can be transferred passively in gamma globulin, which has a protective effect if given during the incubation period, after known exposure to infection.

III. Specimens for Diagnosis. Laboratory tests for virus isolation or antibody identification are not yet available. The diagnosis is made on clinical grounds, supported by tests for abnormal liver function.

Epidemiology

I. Communicability of Infection
A. RESERVOIR, SOURCES, AND TRANSMISSION ROUTES. See the first paragraph of discussion of infectious hepatitis, page 458. Some additional sources of infection should be emphasized here. Explosive epidemics have been known to originate from drinking water, particularly during the summer months under conditions of camp life. Sewage contamination of water may also infect oysters and clams, a subsequent source of infection when they are eaten raw. Transmission among members of a family or within institutional populations may also lead to epidemics. When transferred parenterally through the use of contaminated syringes or needles, or in transfused infectious blood or serum, the new infection has all the characteristics of infectious hepatitis. (See Table 29–2, p. 626, comparing this disease with serum hepatitis.)

B. INCUBATION PERIOD. Varies from 15 to 40 days, with an average of three weeks.

C. COMMUNICABLE PERIOD. Appears to be communicable during the incubation period and at least through the first week of symptoms.

D. IMMUNITY. Immunity appears to be widespread in the adult population as a result of childhood infection. Second attacks of clinically apparent infectious jaundice are rare. Early infections are probably largely inapparent, or so mild as to escape recognition. The persistence of antibodies in adult serum and their concentration in preparations of gamma globulin make it

Table 20–1. Summary: Viral Diseases Acquired Through the Alimentary Route

Clinical Disease	Causative Organism	Other Possible Entry Routes	Incubation Period	Communicable Period
Poliomyelitis	Poliomyelitis virus	Respiratory tract	Usually 1–2 weeks, may range from 3 days to 4–5 weeks	Prior to onset of symptom and during infection
Coxsackie virus diseases	Coxsackie viruses	Respiratory tract	3–5 days	During acute, febrile stag of illness
ECHO virus diseases	ECHO viruses	Respiratory tract	Unknown	During acute, febrile stag of illness
Infectious hepatitis	Hepatitis virus A	Respiratory tract Parenteral route	15–40 days	During incubation period at least through first wee of symptoms

possible to provide passive immunoprophylaxis for contacts.

II. Control of Active Infection

A. ISOLATION. Patients should be isolated, at home or in the hospital, for at least the first week of illness.

B. PRECAUTIONS. Enteric precautions are emphasized in the care of infectious hepatitis patients. The stools should be considered potentially infectious for at least four weeks from the onset of symptoms. Thermometers should be individualized and later discarded. The possible transfer of this organism in respiratory secretions should

be considered during the early days of illness, although this is probably accomplished, if at all, only by very close contacts. Concurrent disinfection is required for nose and throat discharges and for feces or fecally contaminated articles. Individual toilet facilities are indicated for the hospitalized patient. Terminal cleaning should be thorough. (See Chap. 15, p. 382.)

If they are not disposable, needles, syringes, and other instruments soiled with the blood of infectious hepatitis patients must be carefully sterilized before reuse, as, indeed, they must be in any case. Suitable sterilization techniques are (1) autoclaving for 30 minutes at 121° C; (2) dry

cimens equired	Laboratory Diagnosis	Immunization	Treatment	Nursing Management
t swab in port broth swab in port broth and alescent m	Virus isolation Rising antibody titer	Salk vaccine _shot_ (killed) Sabin vaccine (live) _oral_	None specific	Isolation for one week from onset of symptoms; respiratory precautions; concurrent disinfection of articles contaminated with feces; terminal disinfection
t and pharyngeal ings specimens and alescent m	Virus isolation Rising titer	None	None specific	Isolation during febrile stages: hygienic control of respiratory secretions and sanitary disposal of excreta
t washings, , spinal	Virus isolation	None	None specific	See above: If organism is incriminated in epidemic diarrhea in infants, see summary under Epidemic Diarrhea, Chapter 19
crobiologic available	None	None	None specific	Isolation, for at least the first week of illness; enteric precautions; stools potentially infectious for four weeks; individual thermometers, discard later; concurrent disinfection of respiratory secretions and fecally contaminated articles; individual toilet facilities for the hospitalized patient; disposable needles and syringes

heat for one hour at 180° C or for two hours at 170° C; or (3) boiling in water for 30 minutes.* The use of sterile disposable needles and syringes provides a convenient solution to this problem.

C. TREATMENT. There is no specific antimicrobial therapy for infectious hepatitis.

D. CONTROL OF CONTACTS. Quarantine of contacts is not indicated, but case finding is important so that close contacts may receive the protection of gamma globulin. Passive antibodies provide protection for about two months if given within the first week after exposure. Later im-

munization may also be effective, however, and if the exposure is prolonged, a second dose may be indicated.

E. EPIDEMIC CONTROLS. Case reports are advisable in order to protect contacts and to prevent possible epidemic outbreaks. A search is made for the source of infection when the incidence of cases is unusually great. Mass immunization with gamma globulin is sometimes indicated when institutional outbreaks occur. Sanitary and hygienic standards are reviewed and strengthened as indicated, with particular regard to sewage dis-

* See *Guide to Control of Infections in Hospital*, New York State Department of Health, p. 36.

posal and the protection of food and water supplies. When outbreaks are associated with hospitals or physicians' offices, a careful review of sterilizing practices is indicated, giving special attention to syringes, needles, and small instruments. The source of blood or blood products given by injection is also investigated. Records are made available to commercial and hospital blood banks regarding the incidence of hepatitis occurring in patients who were recipients of blood from known donors and such donors are not used thereafter.

III. Prevention.   Passive immunization may be useful for travelers or others who can anticipate a certain risk of exposure.

Controls applicable to blood bank practices are described in the discussion of serum hepatitis, Chapter 29 (pp. 627 to 628).

Questions

1. What viruses are found in the enterovirus family?
2. What cells of the CNS are most susceptible to the poliovirus's intracellular multiplication and localization?
3. What is the reservoir of poliovirus infection?
4. How long is the isolation period for a patient with poliomyelitis?
5. When should gamma globulin be given prophylactically to be effective?
6. What two types of polio vaccine are available?
7. What preventive measures can be taken during a polio epidemic?
8. Name the clinical syndromes for which Coxsackie viruses are recognized as causative agents.
9. What diseases can the ECHO viruses produce?
10. How is infectious hepatitis transmitted?
11. What methods are used to diagnose infectious hepatitis?
12. How long should patients with infectious hepatitis be isolated?
13. What epidemic controls are necessary if an outbreak of infectious hepatitis is associated with hospitals or physicians' offices?

21 Parasitic Diseases Acquired Through the Alimentary Route

The General Nature of Parasitic Diseases

The animal parasites capable of living in or on human tissues usually induce some degree of noticeable injury at the sites of their localizations in the body. There are some exceptions to this general rule. There are a few protozoans that are commensal inhabitants of the human bowel, and some of the helminths (both roundworms and tapeworms) that infest the intestinal tract live there as saprophytes. For the most part, however, these organisms are truly parasitic. They are dependent on one or more hosts to maintain them in nature, and they produce damage to the host as an incidental result of parasitic activities. Some of the injury is simply due to their size. Even the small protozoans, and the immature forms of the helminths, although they are microscopic in size, can induce structural damage within tissues. Coupled with this feature is the fact that they are living, metabolizing organisms, competing for nutrient with the body's own cells. Many utilize the body's materials for their own sustenance and add injury to insult by excreting metabolic end products that are toxic to the cells around them, or to distant tissues if they are disseminated.

Parenteral Infestations

When animal parasites gain entrance to parenteral tissues, either from intestinal sites or directly through the skin (by way of insect vectors or their own penetrative capacity), the body attempts to deal with them as it does with any foreign object, marshaling phagocytic cells and fibrinous exudates to contain them. If this succeeds, scar tissue formation and continuing deposit of calcium complete the job. The resulting degree of impairment of local tissue function depends on the extent of the infestation; it may be minor and unnoticeable, or permanently handicapping. The total effect on health depends also, of course, on the nature of the tissue involved and the extent to which it contributes to the body's vital functions.

The immune response to the antigenic components of animal parasites or their products is usually one of hypersensitivity. This response may occur when antigenic products of intestinal parasites are absorbed from the bowel, but the allergic reaction is often a particularly prominent feature of parasitic diseases characterized by parenteral localizations of the parasite, in either adult or immature stages. The eosinophilic polymorphonuclear cells, which frequently play a role in allergic responses, are characteristically seen in markedly increased numbers in the circulating blood in several of the parasitic diseases. Hypersensitivity can be demonstrated, in many cases, by the use of skin-testing antigens extracted from the parasites. These antigens evoke skin reactions of the delayed type of hypersensitivity.

Intestinal Infestations

Those protozoans and helminths that parasitize the bowel produce varying degrees of surface injury to the intestinal lining. The most invasive of the protozoans, *Endamoeba histolytica*, actually erodes the surface, penetrating into the submucosa and producing undermined, ulcerative lesions. One of the ciliated protozoans, *Balantidium coli*, may also induce ulcerative lesions, but these are usually not deeply erosive. Some species of amoebae and flagellates live as saprophytes in the bowel, inducing no injury unless their numbers become excessive, and in this case their motility, activity, or accumulating metabolites may be irritating to the lining cells.

Helminth infestation of the bowel is usually not serious per se, unless the worm actually parasitizes the tissues from that site, or its larval forms migrate through the body beyond the bowel. The *hookworm* is a notable example of a

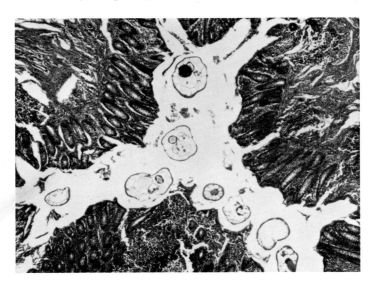

Fig. 21–1. *Enterobius vermicularis* in the appendix (400 ×). Several adult worms are seen in cross section within the lumen of the appendix.

helminth adult that parasitizes the body from an intestinal site, attaching itself to the mucosa with a cutting mouth through which it ingests the host's blood. This situation is debilitating and can lead eventually to a severe anemia if many worms are involved, or if it continues unchecked. In trichinosis and ascariasis, larval migrations into parenteral tissues occur, and these, rather than intestinal infestation, constitute the serious aspects of these diseases. In the former case, intestinal infestation by the adult worm is brief and of little consequence. *Ascaris* adults persist in the bowel, but their presence there creates little disturbance unless by virtue of their size (they are the largest of the parasitic roundworms, measuring 7 to 9 in.) and numbers they obstruct the flow of intestinal contents.

Like *Ascaris*, many of the intestinal roundworms and tapeworms live saprophytically in the bowel. Some of them hold on with hooklets and suckers and irritate the mucosa in this way, but they derive their nutrient from bowel contents, not from living tissue. Some have no means of attachment, but their activities or products may be locally injurious. If they are numerous enough and large enough (some species of tapeworm may reach up to 20 ft in length), they can sometimes create an intestinal obstruction. The small intestinal roundworms that are not equipped for holding on, for example the pinworm (*Enterobius*) or the whipworm (*Trichuris*), often find their way, or are pushed, into the cul-de-sac of the appendix. This seldom causes any difficulty, however, and is usually just an incidental finding in appendices that have been surgically removed for some other reason (see Fig. 21–1).

Laboratory Diagnosis of Parasitic Diseases

Parasitic infestations are sometimes recognizable on clinical grounds but usually require laboratory confirmation, most readily supplied by microscopic examination of appropriate specimens for ova, larvae, or adult forms of the suspected parasite. Stool specimens are relevant when intestinal infestations by protozoa or helminths are suspected. Small, selected portions of feces may be suspended in saline or water for direct examination as wet-mount cover slip preparations. The numbers of ova or other developmental stages of the parasite may be few, however, in proportion to the quantity of feces passed at any one time, and it is often necessary to eliminate the bulk of the fecal material and thereby increase the density of parasitic forms present in the remainder. When parenteral infestations are suspected, specimens of urine, sputum, or blood may be relevant, depending on the nature of the parasite in question and clinical indication of its tissue localization. In some instances, parenteral lodgments of parasitic forms do not permit their migration into excreta, secretions from superficial tissues, or the blood stream, and in such cases biopsies of involved tissue may reveal the organisms.

The various forms of animal parasites that may be present in such clinical specimens are usually easily identified by microscopic examination. The ova, larvae, and adult forms of helminthic parasites are large, readily visualized (even without staining, as a rule), and identified by characteristic morphologic features (see Chap. 2, pp. 17 to 24). Protozoan parasites are also recognizable by microscopic techniques, but they are smaller and sometimes difficult to find in clinical specimens. A few of the protozoans can be cultivated on artificial laboratory media (e.g., *Endamoeba histolytica*, *Trichomonas*, *Leishmania*, or *Trypanosoma*) or propagated in laboratory animals (*Toxoplasma*), but some of these techniques require expert knowledge, and they are not always available on a routine basis.

When laboratory techniques for the direct microscopic identification of parasites are unrewarding, efforts are sometimes made to identify an immunologic response in the patient. Unfortunately, the immune response does not ordinarily involve the production of circulating (humoral) antibodies to a significant degree, and tests for agglutinins, precipitins, and complement-fixing or other antibodies are often unreliable, although a few exceptions may be noted in certain individual diseases (trichinosis, echinococcosis, or toxoplasmosis). Skin tests for the cell-fixed antibodies of

hypersensitivity are sometimes diagnostically useful, particularly in parenteral infestations that are difficult to diagnose by other clinical or laboratory methods.

Epidemiology of Parasitic Diseases Acquired by the Alimentary Route

The animal parasites gain entry to the human body through one of three major routes: the *alimentary tract*, the *intact skin or mucosa*, or the direct *parenteral route*. The majority are taken in through the mouth, being derived from the feces of other infected persons or eaten in infected animal or aquatic plant foods. These are the diseases described in the remainder of this chapter. The larval forms of the hookworm and *Schistosoma* families of parasites are noted for their ability to penetrate the skin and establish themselves in sites distant from this portal. The diseases they induce are discussed in Chapter 25. Several important protozoan parasites (the malaria parasites, *Trypanosoma*, and *Leishmania*) and one family of roundworms (the filarial parasites) parasitize the blood and parenteral tissues. These organisms are maintained, in sequence, first by human or animal hosts, then by insect hosts that support a part of their developmental life cycle and reintroduce them directly into human or animal tissues. The important human diseases acquired in this manner are described in Chapter 27.

The control and prevention of parasitic diseases are based, as in other infections, on a knowledge of their communicability, but this knowledge depends on an understanding of the developmental requirements of the parasites and their sometimes prolonged life cycles. The life cycles of the animal parasites, and their communicability, are described in Chapter 9 (pp. 190 to 198).

The parasitic organisms that establish disease following oral entry represent all the major taxonomic groups (protozoans, nematodes, cestodes, and trematodes) and three of the four types of life cycle development displayed by animal parasites:

Type 1, in which the cycle is maintained in one definitive host, and infection transfer occurs either directly from fecal sources or indirectly from fecally contaminated soil where parasite maturation occurs. This group includes the *intestinal* protozoans and nematodes, such as *Endamoeba*, *Enterobius*, *Trichuris*, and *Ascaris*, acquired orally.

Type 2, with a cycle maintained by alternate hosts. *Trichinella spiralis* is the only parasite of importance to man that displays this type of cycle. Its development in each host follows the same pattern, from adult maturation in the intestinal tract following the ingestion of larvae encysted in the flesh of an infected animal to the production and dissemination of larvae through the tissues of the new host. Pork is the infected animal source for man.

Type 4, in which the cycle is maintained by a definitive host, together with one or more intermediate hosts. This group includes the *intestinal* cestodes, acquired by ingestion of the larvae-infected flesh of animals (beef, pork, or fish); the *tissue* cestode, *Echinococcus*, acquired by ingestion of the ovum derived from the intestinal tract of a definitive host (usually the dog); and some of the trematodes whose larval forms are encysted in marine animals or plants that are eaten (the liver and lung flukes).

It will be noted that most of the parasites that enter by the alimentary route localize in the intestinal tract, but a few of them produce parenteral disease by penetrating into adjacent tissues, or by disseminating larvae to systemic localizations.

The control of patients with active parasitic infestations never requires their isolation, but suitable precautions must be taken with feces or other excretions in which infective forms may leave the body. When infection can be acquired by direct transfer, as in amebiasis, or in pinworm infestation, measures appropriate to the individual situation are taken. For example, people with active amebiasis should not be involved in food-handling until the disease has been treated, because amoebae may be transmitted by this route, but controlling the spread of pinworm requires more stringent precautions, because the ova are

present on perianal skin, not merely in feces, and are easily transferred by contaminated hands to many surfaces from which they can find their way into the mouth.

The source of any parasitic infestation should be sought, whether it is an infected human contact or an animal food, so that further spread of disease can be prevented. Preventive measures are based on interrupting the chain of transfer of parasites to other hosts in which they can develop. Sanitary disposal of feces and urine, sewage control, and the protection of drinking-water supplies are important in any event (the latter can spread amebiasis); animal farming should include measures that prevent the infection of animals raised for meat, and meat inspection provides further preventive control. Education of the public in the nature of these diseases, the necessity for careful selection of government-inspected meats and for their adequate cooking, or both, is the final link in the chain of prevention in some cases, while in others it rests on public understanding of the role played by certain fish and aquatic plants that are eaten without thorough cooking.

In the following sections of this chapter, individual parasitic diseases acquired by the oral route are described in semioutline form, highlighting the cyclic development of each parasite in the human host, other hosts, or the environment; the general characteristics of the human infestation; and the most useful methods of diagnosis in each case. Special features of control are indicated in a few instances, but reference should be made in most cases to the general discussion of epidemiology above, or to the bibliography if further detail is desired. These diseases are arranged in groups according to the nature of the parasite and its intestinal or tissue localization.

Intestinal Protozoan Diseases

Amebiasis (Amebic Dysentery)

Organism. *Endamoeba histolytica.*
An amoebic protozoan (subphylum Sarcodina)

with two developmental stages: the *trophozoite* or vegetative form, and a *cyst* stage.

The trophozoite (18 to 20μ in diameter) is two and one-half to three times the size of a red blood cell, has one nucleus, multiplies by fission, has an active amoeboid motion, and is capable of ingesting red blood cells when it is parasitizing the human body. It can be cultivated through several generations on artificial laboratory media if these are properly enriched.

The cyst is somewhat smaller than the trophozoite, is rounded and nonmotile, and is more resistant than the trophozoite to environmental pressures. When mature it contains four nuclei, each capable of meiotic division, so that one cyst can give rise to eight trophozoites.

Details of nuclear structure, cytoplasmic inclusions, and motility (in the case of trophozoites) distinguish this organism from other intestinal amoebae when they are examined microscopically.

Life Cycle (Type 1)

I. Definitive Host. Man (the only reservoir).

II. Intermediate Host. None.

III. Human Infestation

A. SOURCE OF INFECTION. Infected human feces. Can be spread by direct fecal-oral contact, or through contaminated food or water. Water may be a source of epidemics.

B. INFECTIVE FORM. Usually cysts, which can survive in environmental sources; trophozoites are infective if transferred directly.

C. LOCALIZATION AND DEVELOPMENT. Trophozoites parasitize the large bowel. They enter the cystic stage when body defenses create adverse circumstances. Cystic forms may persist and be responsible for chronic lesions or an asymptomatic carrier state. Erosion of capillaries in intestinal lesions may lead to dissemination of the organisms to the liver, lung, brain, or other organs.

D. EXIT ROUTE. Feces. Trophozoites are found in active intestinal infections; cysts in chronic intestinal disease or carrier state. When

other localizations occur, either form may be found in pus from the localized lesion; sometimes in sputum if pulmonary abscess location permits bronchial discharge of pus.

IV. Cyclic Development Outside of the Human Body

A. IN ENVIRONMENT. Trophozoites may pass into cyst stage, but are easily destroyed by chemical or physical pressures before this occurs. Cysts may survive for some time but do not evolve into trophozoites until ingested by human host.

B. IN HOSTS OTHER THAN MAN. Does not establish disease in other hosts.

Characteristics of Human Disease. Amebiasis may be acute, chronic, or asymptomatic. Amoebic trophozoites invade the wall of the large bowel, feeding on red blood cells. They may erode the local area, creating ulcerative lesions that can extend deeply through the submucosa under the entry point, with undermining of the mucosal surface (see Fig. 21–2). In acute dysentery, there may be profuse bloody diarrhea, with mucus in the stool but few pus cells. Chronic amebic dysentery is characterized by intermittent mucoid diarrhea, sometimes with blood and some pus cells, or there may be only occasional discomfort with mild diarrhea or constipation. When extension to parenteral sites occur, the tissue response is one of abscess formation at the focus of infection in the liver, lung, brain or elsewhere. The organism may extend to new sites if these abscesses rupture.

Diagnostic Methods. Microscopic examination of feces is indicated when intestinal infection is suspected. Trophozoites remain active for a very short time only, and for this reason stool specimens should be kept warm during their transport to the laboratory. Cold, casual specimens of stool are ordinarily not satisfactory for the diagnosis of amebiasis. When chronic or asymptomatic amebiasis is suspected, mild purgatives are sometimes useful in increasing the concentration of cysts in stool specimens and facilitating laboratory diagnosis.

Aspirated pus from parenteral lesions, or sputum, may reveal the organisms when systemic localizations are suspected.

Culture techniques are sometimes useful when microscopic examination fails to reveal the amoebae or cysts.

Immunologic techniques are not dependable.

Special Features of Control

I. Treatment. The tetracycline antibiotics are useful in therapy of intestinal amebiasis when

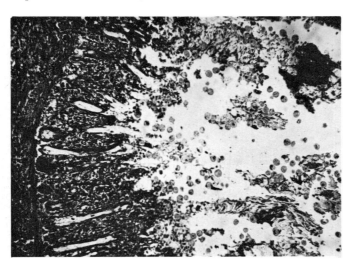

Fig. 21–2. Typical "flask"-shaped ulcer of the colon containing *Endamoeba histolytica* (100 ×). (Courtesy of Dr. Kenneth Phifer, Rockville, Md.)

they are combined with emetine. Arsenical drugs such as diodaquin or carbasone are also used following the preliminary treatment to eradicate the infection.

Parenteral abscesses may require surgical drainage. They are treated with quinine derivatives such as chloroquine, coupled with antibiotics to control secondary bacterial infection.

II. Other. Patients with amoebic infections should be removed from food-handling occupations until freed of the organism. Sources of infection among the patient's contacts or in his environment should be found if possible, using laboratory techniques for examination.

Preventive measures on a public scale involve sanitary controls on feces and sewage disposal, the protection of water supplies, and health agency supervision of public restaurants.

Balantidiasis

Organism. *Balantidium coli.*

A ciliated protozoan (subphylum Ciliophora) with two developmental stages, a *trophozoite* and a *cyst.* The trophozoite has a rapid motility imparted by the beating of cilia that cover its outer surface. Both forms possess two nuclei, one quite large (macronucleus) and the other small (micronucleus). This organism is the largest of the parasitic protozoa, measuring 50 to 200μ in length and 40 to 70μ in breadth.

Life Cycle (Type 1)

I. Definitive Host. Swine and rats; man an occasional victim.

II. Intermediate Host. None.

III. Human Infestation
A. SOURCE OF INFECTION.   Infected human or swine feces (the latter exposure occurs on farms or in abattoirs).
B. INFECTIVE FORM.   Cysts from indirect, environmental sources; trophozoites by direct human contacts.

C. LOCALIZATION AND DEVELOPMENT.   Motile trophozoites pass into the large bowel and burrow into the mucosal surface, producing ulcers similar to those of *E. histolytica*, except that they are more shallow and less undermined or eroded. Penetration into parenteral tissues is rare but may occur.

D. EXIT ROUTE.   Feces. Trophozoites are found in active diarrheal infections; cysts are the usual finding in chronic infections.

IV. Cyclic Development Outside of the Human Host
A. IN ENVIRONMENT.   Trophozoites pass into more resistant cyst stage.
B. IN HOSTS OTHER THAN MAN.   The two forms are the same as those seen in man.

Characteristics of Human Disease.   Balantidia produce ulcers or subsurface abscesses in the mucosa and submucosa of the large intestine (see Fig. 21–3). Infection may be acute, chronic, or asymptomatic. In acute cases, severe dysentery with bloody, mucoid stools may develop. Chronic cases may display diarrhea alternating with constipation. Extraintestinal extensions have been reported producing cases of balantidial peritonitis, pyelonephritis, and vaginitis.

Fig. 21–3.   An ulcerative lesion in the human bowel wall caused by *Balantidium coli.* This large protozoan organism can be seen among the inflammatory cells. Arrows *A* and *B* point, respectively, to a micronucleus and a macronucleus in one of the parasites (100 ×). (Courtesy of Dr. Kenneth Phifer, Rockville, Md.)

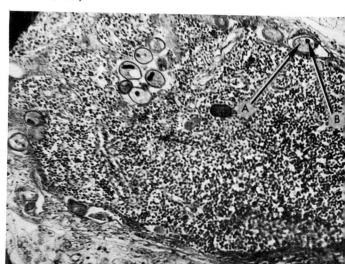

Diagnostic Methods. Microscopic examination of feces may demonstrate trophozoites or cysts. Cultural methods may also be employed, as in the diagnosis of *Endamoeba histolytica* infections.

Special Features of Control

I. Treatment. Antibiotic (tetracycline) and quinine (diodaquine) drugs are effective in eliminating this parasite.

II. Other. Balantidium-infected swine are the chief source of infection, but when human infections become established, prevention of spread depends on improved sanitation and hygiene.

Giardiasis

Organism. *Giardia lamblia.*

A flagellated protozoan (subphylum Mastigophora) with two developmental stages: a *trophozoite*, which has a tumbling, vibrant motility imparted by several pairs of flagellae located on one side of the pear-shaped body, and a pair of symmetrically located nuclei, which look like spectacles. It is about twice the size of a red blood cell in length, and half this in diameter. The *cyst* is nonmotile, is oval in shape, and has four nuclei when mature. Flagellar protoplasts can be seen within the cytoplasm.

Life Cycle (Type 1)

I. Definitive Host. Man is the reservoir.

II. Intermediate Host. None.

III. Human Infestation
A. SOURCE OF INFECTION. Infected human feces.
B. INFECTIVE FORM. Cysts from direct contacts.
C. LOCALIZATION AND DEVELOPMENT. These organisms reproduce in the upper small intestine.

They do not invade intestinal tissue, but feed on mucous secretions.
D. EXIT ROUTE. Feces. Trophozoites and cysts may both be found.

IV. Cyclic Development Outside of the Human Host. Probably none.

Characteristics of Disease. This organism ordinarily lives saprophytically in the duodenum and jejunum, producing no symptoms. It may cause symptoms in children or adults when it reaches sufficient numbers to involve large surface areas of the upper intestine. There is chronic diarrhea, dehydration, excessive mucous secretion, and flatulence, and the stools are pale in color, possibly because of interference with fat absorption.

Diagnostic Methods. Recognition of both forms of the organism in large numbers in feces.

Special Features of Control. The training of children and their parents in effective habits of personal hygiene.

Treatment. Atabrine and other derivatives of quinine.

Intestinal Nematode (Roundworm) Diseases

Enterobiasis

Organism. *Enterobius vermicularis* (pinworm).

The smallest of the parasitic intestinal roundworms, females measuring about 13 mm in length ($\frac{1}{2}$ to $\frac{3}{4}$ in.), the male about 5 mm (see Fig. 21–4). The gravid female produces eggs containing well-developed larvae, many of them motile within their shells. The ova are broadly oval, are flattened on one side, and measure about $60 \times 30\mu$ (compare this with the red blood cell's $7\text{-}\mu$ diameter).

Life Cycle (Type 1)

I. Definitive Host. Man.

II. Intermediate Host. None.

III. Human Infestation

A. SOURCE OF INFECTION. Feces or the perianal skin of infected persons. Direct or indirect transfer, via clothing, bedding, toys, or other objects, and sometimes food.

B. INFECTIVE FORM. Ingested ovum.

C. LOCALIZATION AND DEVELOPMENT. Following ingestion of ova, the larvae hatch and develop into adults in the intestinal tract. After copulation, the female usually migrates to the anus where she produces thousands of eggs. The adults die, but reinfection from the ova is common, as well as transfer of infection.

D. EXIT ROUTE. Anus and perianal region.

IV. Cyclic Development Outside of the Human Body

A. *Environmental* development of the embryonated ova occurs within a few hours, usually while eggs are still clinging to the skin. These ova are resistant to drying and to disinfectants and may remain infective in dust, or on surfaces, for many days.

B. *Hosts other than man* are not involved in the cycle.

Characteristics of Human Disease. Intestinal infestation with adult worms produces few, if any, symptoms. Perianal migrations of the female and oviposition in that region cause an intense local pruritus. This is often particularly irritating at night, inducing restlessness, insomnia, and incessant scratching. Children are frequently infected by other youngsters, but they can transfer the infestation to an entire family household. (See also Fig. 9–10.)

Diagnostic Methods. Pinworm ova may be seen by microscopic examination of Scotch tape or other sticky materials applied to the

Fig. 21–4. A male pinworm (*Enterobius vermicularis*). Note that the posterior end is sharply twisted, as it is in most male roundworms. The pinworm is a common parasite of children (20 ×).

perianal skin. The eggs may also be present in feces, or in material scraped from beneath the fingernails. Adult worms, females and sometimes males, can also be found on the skin of the perianal region.

Special Features of Control

I. Treatment. Piperazine salts are effective. When several members of a household are infected, they should be treated simultaneously so that reinfections will not permit new adult worms to generate.

II. Other. Chemotherapy should be combined with vigorous methods of household disin-

fection, involving bathrooms, bed linens, bedroom dust. Careful personal hygiene is also important, particularly with regard to the cleanliness of hands and fingernails.

Trichuriasis

Organism. *Trichuris trichiura* (whipworm).

A slender little roundworm shaped like a whip, the posterior end being thickened, the anterior slim and drawn out. It is about twice the size of the pinworm, measuring up to 2 in., the male a little shorter.

The characteristic ovum is barrel-shaped, thick-shelled, with a bulging protuberance at each pole.

Life Cycle (Type 1)

I. Definitive Host. Man.

II. Intermediate Host. None.

III. Human Infestation
A. SOURCE OF INFECTION. Soil in which eggs from human feces have matured.
B. INFECTIVE FORM. Embryonated egg.
C. LOCALIZATION AND DEVELOPMENT. After ingestion, the shell of the ovum is digested away; the larva emerges and develops into an adult in the small intestine. Adults attach to the wall of the cecum. Each female can produce five or six thousand eggs per day.
D. EXIT FROM BODY. Eggs discharged in feces.

IV. Cyclic Development Outside of Human Body
IN ENVIRONMENT. Ova require 10 to 14 days in soil for further development of embryo before they are infective. Other living hosts not involved.

Characteristics of Disease. Light infestations produce few, if any, symptoms. Massive infestations may occur in children, with worm attachments extending far down the colon. Inflammation of the mucosa, mucous diarrhea, systemic toxicity, and anemia may result in severe un-

treated cases. These symptoms may resemble those of hookworm disease. Adult infestations are usually asymptomatic.

Diagnostic Methods. Demonstration of the *Trichuris* ova in feces, by microscopic examination.

Special Features of Control

I. Treatment. Dithiazanine, a cyanine dye, is given in small oral doses daily for a week, followed by a high retention enema to remove worms from the colon.

II. Other. Control depends on preventing contamination of soil with infective feces. This is a disease of rural areas where facilities for sewage disposal are poor, social conditions are uncontrolled, and small children pollute the ground frequently, then infect themselves with soiled hands or playthings. (See Fig. 9–11.)

Ascariasis

Organism. *Ascaris lumbricoides.*

The largest of the roundworms, cylindric, tapered, measuring 8 to 12 in. in length.

The ovum is large ($50 \times 75\mu$), spheric to ovoid, with a very thick, rough outer shell. Some infertile eggs, lacking the shell, are often produced also.

Life Cycle (Type 1)

I. Definitive Host. Man.

II. Intermediate Host. None.

III. Human Infestation
A. SOURCE OF INFECTION. Soil in which eggs from human feces have matured.
B. INFECTIVE FORM. Embryonated egg.
C. LOCALIZATION AND DEVELOPMENT. After ingestion, larvae hatch from the ova in the duodenum. They penetrate the wall of the small in-

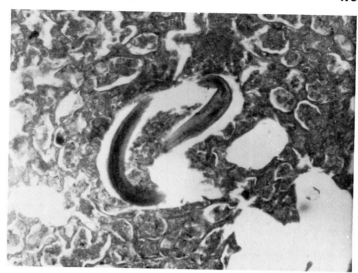

Fig. 21–5. *Ascaris lumbricoides* larvae in lung tissue (800 ×).

testine, reach the portal circulation, and are carried through the right side of the heart into the lungs. They may remain in the lungs for several days (see Fig. 21–5), then penetrate the pulmonary capillaries, reach the alveoli, and work their way up the bronchial tree. They are coughed up through the epiglottis, swallowed, and on rearrival in the small intestine, develop into adult males and females.

D. EXIT FROM BODY. Ova are discharged in feces. (Each female can produce approximately 200,000 eggs per day.)

IV. Cyclic Development Outside of the Human Body

IN ENVIRONMENT. Ova require two to three weeks of incubation in the soil for maturation of the embryo before they are infective. Other living hosts not involved. (See Fig. 9–11.)

Characteristics of Disease

Intestinal infestation may be mild and asymptomatic, or produce abdominal pain, vomiting, diarrhea, indigestion. Masses of worms can cause intestinal obstruction, and systemic toxicities may occur.

Pulmonary infestation with migrating larvae may induce a severe pneumonitis, sometimes with secondary bacterial complications. Fever, spasms of coughing, and asthmatic breathing are characteristic, and allergic reactions indicate hypersensitivity to the ascarids. These may include urticarial rashes and eosinophilia.

Larvae sometimes reach the general circulation and are lodged in other tissues, producing severe symptoms if they reach such organs as the kidney or brain.

Diagnostic Methods. *Ascaris* pneumonitis is diagnosed clinically and by radiologic techniques. Occasionally, larvae may be seen in sputum. Later, the recognition of ova in feces during intestinal infestation confirms the diagnosis (see Fig. 21–6).

Special Features of Control

I. Treatment. Piperazine salts are used to treat intestinal ascariasis. There is no specific therapy for migrating larvae.

II. Other. As in trichuriasis, control depends on preventing contamination of soil with infective feces, education of children and adults in techniques of sanitation and hygiene.

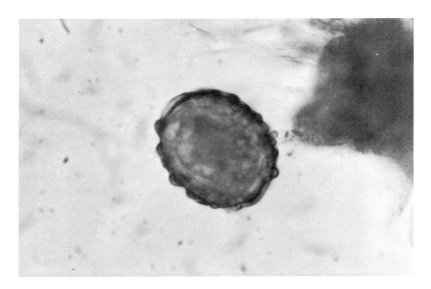

Fig. 21–6. The ovum of *Ascaris lumbricoides* (1000 ×).

Tissue Nematode (Roundworm) Disease

Trichinosis

Organism. *Trichinella spiralis.*

A minute worm, smaller than the pinworm, just visible to the unaided eye. The female is *viviparous*; that is, she deposits viable larvae rather than eggs.

Life Cycle (Type 2)

I. Definitive Hosts. Swine, rats, and wild animals are alternate hosts. Man becomes an alternate host by eating infected meat, but does not maintain the parasite in nature.

II. Intermediate Host. None.

III. Human Infestation

A. SOURCE OF INFECTION. Meat of infected animal (pork, bear meat).

B. INFECTIVE FORM. Viable larvae encysted in muscle tissue of animal.

C. LOCALIZATION AND DEVELOPMENT. After being swallowed, the larvae are set free from their encystment during gastric digestion of the meat. They pass into the duodenum and develop into male and female adults within four or five days. The females burrow into the mucosa of the villi, or even into submucosal layers or mesenteric

lymph nodes, and begin to deposit larvae, which reach the lymphatic and blood circulation and are distributed through the body. Larvae may lodge temporarily in a variety of tissues from which they re-enter the circulation. When they reach striated muscle tissue, they become encysted. Muscles most frequently involved are the diaphragm, those of the thoracic and abdominal walls, the tongue, biceps, and deltoid. Larvae cannot develop into adults unless they subsequently are ingested by an alternate host.

D. EXIT FROM HUMAN BODY. None, not communicable by man.

IV. Cyclic Development Outside of the Human Body

A. IN ENVIRONMENT. None.

B. IN HOSTS OTHER THAN MAN. Carnivorous animals maintain this parasite. Swine are infected from garbage scraps containing infected meat. Adult and larval trichinae both develop in one host, but each worm requires two hosts to complete its development. (See Fig. 9–12.)

Characteristics of Human Disease. Trichinosis often appears as a small, sporadic outbreak among family or other groups who have gathered around the same infected, undercooked roast pig or bear roast. (Sausages and other products may also contain infective larvae.) The severity of the resulting disease depends on the number of viable larvae eaten. Trichinosis may be a mild

infestation, or a serious and threatening disease. Initially there may be some gastrointestinal discomfort as the larvae invade the intestinal mucosa and develop into adults. During larval migration there is fever, often a characteristic periorbital edema, and then in a few days muscle pain, chills, weakness, and sometimes prostration. Eosinophilia is usually marked. There may be widespread injury due to localization of larvae. Respiratory distress and myocardial involvement constitute the most threatening events and may cause death. Recovery begins when larval migration ceases, the time varying between three and eight weeks. Residual handicap to muscle function depends on the numbers and location of encysted larvae. These are slowly calcified, but may remain viable for many months.

Diagnostic Methods. Visualization of the parasite in the laboratory requires examination of muscle tissue taken by biopsy (see Fig. 21–7). Bits of muscle may be sectioned and stained by histologic techniques, or they can be digested by proteolytic enzymes and examined microscopically for freed, motile larvae.

A skin-testing antigen is available that induces a delayed type of hypersensitive skin reaction. Hypersensitivity to trichina antigen persists for many years following an attack of trichinosis, however, so that a positive skin reaction is not of itself indicative of current disease.

Precipitating antibodies appear in the patient's serum after two or three weeks and provide a useful basis for serologic confirmation of a positive skin reaction.

Special Features of Control

I. Treatment. There are no specific drugs for the treatment of trichinosis.

II. Other. The control and prevention of trichinosis depend on eliminating the sources of infection for hogs (feeding cooked garbage, eliminating infested animals detected by skin testing, destroying rats), processing meat by adequate cold storage or freezing, and final thorough cooking.

Intestinal Cestode (Tapeworm) Diseases

Taeniasis

Organisms. *Taenia saginata* (beef tapeworm), *Taenia solium* (pork tapeworm).

The adult parasites are closely similar morphologically, differing in details of structure of the

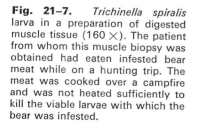

Fig. 21–7. *Trichinella spiralis* larva in a preparation of digested muscle tissue (160 ×). The patient from whom this muscle biopsy was obtained had eaten infested bear meat while on a hunting trip. The meat was cooked over a campfire and was not heated sufficiently to kill the viable larvae with which the bear was infested.

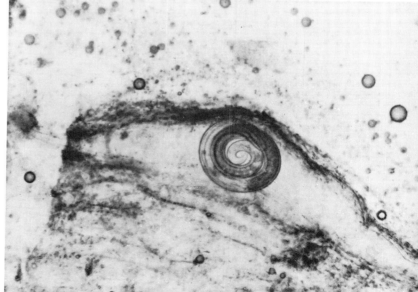

scolex (*T. solium* possesses a crown of hooklets, *T. saginata* is unarmed) and internal features of the proglottids (see Figs. 21–8 and 21–9). Adults are seldom less than 6 ft in length and may reach 20 ft (see Fig. 2–6, p. 221). The ova of the two species are morphologically identical. They are spheric (35 to 40μ in diameter), have a striated outer shell, and the embryo within possesses hooklets (see Fig. 21–10).

Life Cycle (Type 4)

I. Definitive Host.   Man.

II. Intermediate Host.   Cattle (*T. saginata*) and swine (*T. solium*).   Man can also serve as an intermediate host for *T. solium*.

III. Human Infestation

A. SOURCE OF INFECTION. Infected, inadequately cooked flesh of beef or pork.

B. INFECTIVE FORM. Viable larvae encysted in muscle tissue of animals. (See Fig. 9–14.)

C. LOCALIZATION AND DEVELOPMENT. Following ingestion, larvae are excysted in the stomach and pass into the small intestine where the scolex attaches to the intestinal wall, developing into a mature worm within 5 to 12 weeks. The hermaphroditic proglottids produce many eggs.

D. EXIT FROM HUMAN BODY. Eggs are discharged in the feces. Gravid proglottids break off easily and may also be passed in the stool.

IV. Cyclic Development Outside of the Human Body

Animal hosts ingest the eggs derived from infective human feces if this is deposited on soil where animals graze. When the eggs reach the animal's intestinal tract, the larvae are hatched, penetrate the intestinal wall, and are distributed through the body by the blood stream. They localize and encyst in skeletal muscle, in forms referred to as *bladder worms*, or *cysticerci*.

Human cysticercosis may result from the ingestion of the eggs of *Taenia solium* derived from the feces of a person with an intestinal infestation with this worm. The eggs hatch in the intestine, the larvae penetrate through the intestinal wall and are carried by the blood stream into striated muscle tissue, subcutaneous loci, and sometimes to vital organs, where the development of a cysticercus may have severe consequences. When human infection of this type develops, no further development of the parasite is possible, for it finds no exit route by which it can reach another host. (*T. saginata* eggs are not infective for human beings.)

Characteristics of Human Disease.   Intestinal infestation with either of these species is relatively mild. There may be diarrhea, epigastric distress and vomiting, and weight loss in persistent infections. Symptoms of cysticercosis are referrable to the localization of the bladder worms. They have been reported most frequently in subcutaneous

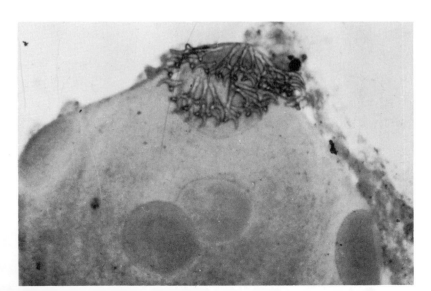

Fig. 21–8. The scolex of *Taenia solium* (40 ✕). Note the crown of hooklets and the four muscular suckers. Compare with the scolex of *Taenia saginata* (the beef tapeworm), which also possesses suckers but no hooklets. (See Fig. 1–2, p. 8.)

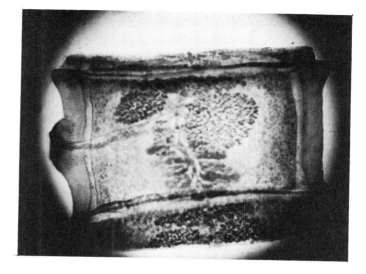

Fig. 21–9. A proglottid of *Taenia solium*. Note the central uterine canal and its few bilateral branches. Mature ova pass from the uterus along the genital canal (seen extending to the left in the photograph) and escape through the prominent lateral genital pore (10 ×).

tissue, but also in the eye, brain, muscles, and visceral organs.

Diagnostic Methods. Laboratory diagnosis of intestinal taeniasis is provided by gross recognition of proglottids passed in feces, or microscopic identification of *Taenia* ova.

The diagnosis of cysticerosis requires the excision of the encysted larvae and their microscopic examination. When biopsy is not feasible, skin tests and serologic recognition of precipitating antibodies may be helpful.

Special Features of Control

I. Treatment. Quinacrine or oleoresin of aspidium is used in the treatment of intestinal infestations of these worms, but there is no specific therapy for the tissue stage of *T. solium* infection. Treatment must successfully eliminate the scolex, for, if not, a new adult worm will be generated.

II. Other. The control and prevention of *Taenia* infestations depend on the sanitary disposal of human feces and the protection of

Fig. 21–10. An ovum of a *Taenia* species in a direct wet-mount of feces (1000 ×).

animal feeding grounds. Government meat inspectors find and reject grossly infected meats in abattoirs (bladder worms can be seen and felt in the tissues), but thorough cooking provides the final safeguard.

Diphyllobothriasis

Organism. *Diphyllobothrium latum* (fish tapeworm).

This tapeworm, like the *Taenia* species, can reach great lengths. The structure of the scolex differs from that of the taeniae (see Fig. 21–11), the proglottids are very much broader than long, and the ovum is larger (about $50 \times 75\mu$). The ovum is broadly oval and has a rather thin shell with a lidded opening (operculum) at one end. As in the *Taenia* eggs, however, the embryo within has hooklets.

Life Cycle (Type 4)

I. Definitive Host. Man and many animals (cats, dogs, bears, foxes, walruses, etc.).

II. Intermediate Hosts. Copepods (aquatic arthropods) and fish.

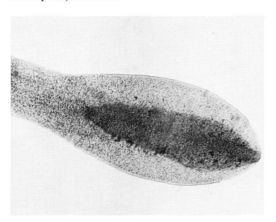

Fig. 21–11. Scolex of *Diphyllobothrium latum* (25 ×). Note the long, deep muscular cleft by which this tapeworm attaches to the intestinal wall. Compare with the scolex of *Taenia solium* (Fig. 21–8) and *Taenia saginata* (Fig. 1–2). (Courtesy of Dr. Kenneth Phifer, Rockville, Md.)

III. Human Infestation

A. SOURCE OF INFECTION. The flesh of infected fresh-water fish.

B. INFECTIVE FORM. Viable larvae encysted in fish tissues.

C. LOCALIZATION AND DEVELOPMENT. After they are swallowed, larvae excyst in the stomach, and pass into the small intestine. The scolex attaches to the wall and develops into a mature, egg-producing worm.

D. EXIT FROM HUMAN BODY. Eggs are discharged in feces. These are not infective for humans.

IV. Cyclic Development Outside of the Human Body. *Aquatic hosts* ingest the embryos derived from eggs passed in human feces which is deposited in water or contaminates water from draining sewage. When the ova reach fresh water, their ciliated embryos are released and swim about until ingested by the copepod, the first intermediate host. The parasite undergoes some development within the arthropod for two or three weeks. If the latter is then eaten by a fish, the larval form develops further and migrates into the fish's muscles. Fish-eating marine or land animals, including man, then acquire the intestinal infestation by eating the fish raw. Man can avoid the problem by cooking fish thoroughly, or by freezing it for 24 hours at −10° C. (See Fig. 9–14.)

Characteristics of Human Disease. The fish tapeworm does not ordinarily produce serious intestinal symptoms unless it becomes obstructive. Systemic intoxication sometimes results from absorbed metabolic wastes; and in some instances there is a severe primary anemia, produced because the worm in the intestine deprives the host of the vitamin B_{12} contained in his food and thus interferes with red blood cell formation.

Diagnostic Methods. The characteristic eggs are identified by microscopic examination of feces. Proglottids and segments of worms are sometimes passed as well.

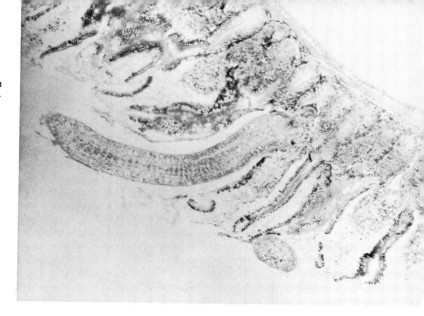

Fig. 21–12. *Hymenolepis nana.* An adult tapeworm in the human intestinal tract (10 ✕).

Special Features of Control

I. Treatment. As in taeniasis, quinacrine or oleoresin of aspidium is used. If treatment does not release the scolex from its point of attachment, a new worm will be generated.

II. Other. Diphyllobothriasis is endemic in northern and central Europe, parts of the Near and Far East, and on this continent, in Canada and the Great Lakes region, Alaska, and Florida. These are all areas where fresh-water fish are an important food, and where rural systems for sewage disposal may fail to protect fresh water from contamination. Infected human beings are the primary source of the fish infestation in endemic areas. Control and prevention require the protection of fresh water from human fecal pollution, as well as the education of housewives in the preparation of fish and the dangers of sampling partially cooked fish foods.

Hymenolepiasis

Organisms. *Hymenolepis nana* (dwarf tapeworm), *Hymenolepis diminuta* (rat tapeworm).

These are the smallest of the intestinal tapeworms, measuring only about 1 to 2 in. in length.

Hymenolepis nana infections are common, particularly in the southern United States. Its life cycle (type 1) is unusual, for it is the only tapeworm that does not require an intermediate host. The adult worm lives in the human intestinal tract, producing ova that are discharged in the feces and are directly infective for others if swallowed. Ova remaining in the bowel, however, may also hatch into larval forms within the intestinal villi and continue their development into adult forms within the bowel lumen (see Fig. 21–12). This means that a single host may harbor the parasite indefinitely, as well as pass it along to others. Dwarf tapeworm infestation is generally mild until large numbers of adult worms are formed, causing intestinal irritation and systemic intoxication from the absorption of worm products. Hexylresorcinol or quinacrine is used in treatment of this disease. Its control depends on breaking the chain of transfer among human contacts by improved sanitation and hygiene.

Hymenolepis diminuta infests man infrequently. It is primarily an intestinal infestation of rats, kept going by fleas that ingest the ova passed in rat feces. (The fleas are scavengers as well as blood-sucking insects). The larval stage of development occurs in the arthropod host, which is then ingested by the rat host it parasitizes, and the intestinal cycle begins again (type 4). Human intestinal infection results from accidental swallowing of an infected flea or other arthropod. This situation can arise under squalid, rat-

infested living conditions. Rat extermination, relief of poverty, and improvement of living conditions reduce the possibility of human exposure to this parasite.

Tissue Cestode (Tapeworm) Diseases

Echinococcosis (Hydatid Cyst)

Organism. *Echinococcus granulosus.*

This is a small tapeworm having only four segments: a scolex, an immature proglottid, one maturing and one gravid proglottid (see Fig. 21–13, *A*). The ovum is indistinguishable from that of the *Taenia* species.

Life Cycle (Type 4)

I. Definitive Host. Domestic dogs and wild canines.

II. Intermediate Hosts. Sheep, cattle, swine, and sometimes man.

III. Human Infestation
   A. SOURCE OF INFECTION. Feces from infected animals, usually domestic dogs.
   B. INFECTIVE FORM. Egg derived from adult worm living in canine intestine.
   C. LOCALIZATION AND DEVELOPMENT. After being swallowed, the eggs hatch in the duodenum, the embryos migrate through the intestinal wall, enter the portal blood stream, and eventually lodge in capillary filter beds, in the liver and various other tissues. A fluid-filled sac, or *hydatid cyst*, forms at sites of tissue localization. Within the cysts many immature scolices develop but cannot mature. The cysts enlarge, creating pressure, and architectural damage to tissues (see Fig. 21–13, *B–D*). They may rupture and extend their contents to adjacent areas, where new cysts are formed.
   D. EXIT ROUTE FROM THE HUMAN BODY. None, not communicable by man.

IV. Cyclic Development in Nature. Dogs and sheep (or other domestic animals raised for meat)

ordinarily maintain this parasite. Sheep ingest the ova when they graze in pastures contaminated by infective dog feces, and they develop the larval form of tissue infestation described above for man. In rural areas, dogs usually have access to the discarded portions of slaughtered animals. They ingest the larvae in these tissues and develop an intestinal infestation, which completes the cycle. (See Fig. 9–15.)

Characteristics of Human Disease. Echinococcosis is usually quite serious, although symptoms depend on the size and location of the cysts. They sometimes cause death, but they may also persist throughout life, producing little difficulty.

Diagnostic Methods. Diagnosis is usually made on the basis of clinical and radiologic findings. Skin tests for hypersensitivity and serologic methods are sometimes useful. Direct laboratory recognition of the cysts and the embryos within them is not possible until they have been surgically removed. (In some locations, however, the cysts may rupture and discharge their contents to an orifice, such as the bowel, the urinary tract, or the bronchial tree. In such case, examination of feces, urine, or sputum may reveal immature scolices.)

Special Features of Control

I. Treatment. There is no specific chemotherapy of this disease. Surgical techniques are useful if the cysts lie in operable sites, and if they have not extended too widely. Cautious surgical dissection is important, because the cysts are easily nicked or broken and may spill their infectious contents into the tissues of the surgical field.

II. Other. This disease is most common on other continents (South America, the Mediterranean area of Europe and Africa, and Australia), although it occurs in Canada and Alaska as well. Its control and prevention depend on breaking the chain of transfer, particularly from sheep, cattle, or other animals to dogs. The disease

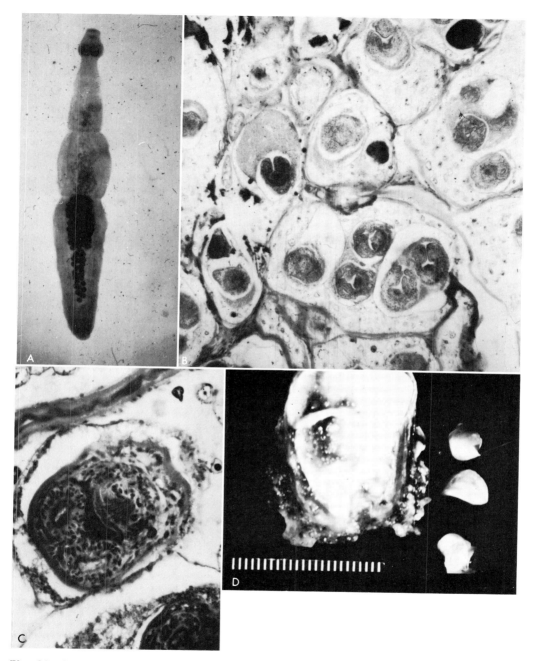

Fig. 21–13. *Echinococcus granulosus. A.* The adult tapeworm (10 ✕). *B.* Histologic section of cysts in the liver showing many immature scolices (400 ✕). *C.* Photomicrograph of an immature scolex found in hydatid cyst fluid (1000 ✕). *D.* Cysts removed from the liver of a human case.

declines when strict controls keep dogs away from slaughtered animal tissues. The human disease can be prevented by good household and personal hygiene, particularly when dogs are free-roaming members of the household in an endemic area.

Cysticercosis

This parenteral tapeworm larval infestation is discussed on page 476. The causative organism, *Taenia solium* (pork tapeworm), ordinarily is seen as an intestinal parasite in man, who ingests the larval forms in infected animal meats. However, ingestion of the eggs, derived from the feces of intestinally infected persons, may result in migration of larvae into the tissues.

Tissue Trematode Diseases (Liver, Intestinal, and Lung Flukes)

The trematode diseases, which are described here briefly, are caused by a small group of animal parasites with many biologic features in common. They share the same group of definitive hosts (man, and some domesticated animals, such as dogs, cats, sheep, and swine) that acquire them by the common route of ingestion; and their cyclic development in intermediate hosts is similar, although this may differ in some details. They differ from the blood flukes (*Schistosoma* species) in that their adult forms are hermaphroditic, while the related schistosomal flukes are bisexual. The latter live in such close association, however, that the distinction is not extremely important. The more useful epidemiologic distinction lies in the fact that the larval forms of the *Schistosoma* find their way into the body by penetrating the exposed skin or mucosa from their environmental sources (see Chap. 25), while the flukes discussed here have an alimentary route of entry. (See list below.)

Life Cycle (Type 4)

I. Definitive Hosts. Man, dogs, cats, sheep, and swine.

II. Intermediate Hosts. Two are usual: Snails are the first intermediate host. Marine animals (crayfish, crabs, or fish) or aquatic plants (water chestnuts and others) act as second intermediate hosts. These are ingested by man and other land animals.

III. Human Infestation
A. SOURCE OF INFECTION. Infective marine life eaten raw or partially cooked.
B. INFECTIVE FORM. Larvae (metacercariae) encysted in marine animals or plants.
C. LOCALIZATION AND DEVELOPMENT. After they are eaten, the encysted larvae are freed, by digestion, of surrounding plant or animal tissue. *Fasciolopsis buski*, the intestinal fluke, fastens to the intestinal wall and develops into an adult at that site (see Fig. 21–14). Larvae of the other species of this group penetrate the intestinal wall and travel through body cavities or ducts to reach their respective sites of choice. The liver flukes (*Clonorchis* and *Fasciola*) usually settle down in the bile ducts within the liver, while the lung fluke (*Paragonimus*) finds its way from the abdominal cavity through the diaphragm into the pleural cavity, the lungs, or, finally, the bronchioles. The development of larvae into adult flukes is completed in these locations, usually after several weeks, and the hermaphroditic adult worms begin to produce eggs. Depending on the location of

Trematode Diseases and Organisms with an Alimentary Entry Route

Clonorchiasis	Clonorchis sinensis (liver fluke)
Fascioliasis	Fasciola hepatica (liver fluke)
Fasciolopsiasis	Fasciolopsis buski (intestinal fluke)
Paragonimiasis	Paragonimus westermani (lung fluke)

the adult worm, ova may find their way directly into feces (*Fasciolopsis*), down the bile ducts into the bowel and the feces (*Clonorchis* and *Fasciola*), or up the bronchial tree with sputum (*Paragonimus*). Some eggs may be deflected from these paths, and be caught in surrounding parenchymal tissues, where defensive host reactions embroil them in cellular exudates that hold the ova but also disrupt local tissue functions (as the adult worm may do as well).

D. Exit Routes from Human Body. Ova of liver and intestinal flukes exit through fecal discharges. Lung fluke ova exit in sputum. Other sites are possible if adults locate in aberrant positions. These ova are not infective for human beings.

IV. Cyclic Development Outside the Human Body

A. In Environment. The ova of these parasites must reach water to continue their developmental cycles. Ciliated embryos (miracidia) escape from their shells and swim about until they are taken up by snails.

B. In Hosts Other than Man. Snails are the *first* intermediate host for each of these species (and also for the schistosomal flukes). The parasites go through maturation stages in snails and emerge again as free-swimming forms called cercariae. These larval forms then encyst again in a second aquatic host — fish, crustaceans, or water plants — until they are ingested by a mammalian host that offers suitable conditions for their maturation as adults. The second intermediate host differs for each of these species. (The schistosomal cercariae do not require a second aquatic host at all, but are directly infective for their final human hosts because they are capable of penetrating his skin. See Fig. 9–16.)

Clonorchiasis

The *Clonorchis* adult lodges in the bile ducts. Symptoms may result from obstruction of the ducts, with jaundice or liver disease due to short migrations of the ova into hepatic tissue, with accompanying cellular reactions. The liver may

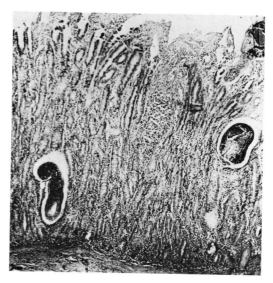

Fig. 21–14. *Fasciolopsis buski* in the small intestines (2 ✕). (Courtesy of Dr. Kenneth Phifer, Rockville, Md.)

become enlarged, tender, and cirrhotic. Symptoms may persist for many years. Satisfactorily curative drugs have not been developed for this infestation. The disease is acquired through ingestion of larvae encysted in fish. Its control requires the sanitary disposal of human feces so that the ova of human infections do not reach water where snail and fish hosts may perpetuate the cycle. Thorough cooking of fish is another measure necessary in endemic areas (the Far East and Southeast Asia, including Hawaii, Korea, and Vietnam).

Fascioliasis

This disease occurs in sheep-raising countries around the world, including the United States. The adult worm, *Fasciola hepatica*, develops from larvae ingested with infected water plants (such as water cress). It inhabits the bile ducts and produces symptoms referable to obstructive jaundice. Emetine treatment or surgical removal of the adult worm may be effective. Sheep are the principal animal reservoir. The control of this disease

Table 21–1. Summary: Parasitic Diseases Acquired by the Alimentary Route

Clinical Disease	Causative Organisms	Other Possible Entry Routes	Incubation Period	Communicable Period
Amebiasis	*Endamoeba histolytica*		Usually 3–4 weeks	During the time parasite persists in intestines
Balantidiasis	*Balantidium coli*		Unknown	Same as above
Giardiasis	*Giardia lamblia*		Unknown	Same as above
Enterobiasis	*Enterobius vermicularis*		3–6-week life cycle	Same as above
Trichiuriasis	*Trichuris trichiura*		Long, variable	Not communicable from man to man, ova require period maturation in soil
Ascariasis	*Ascaris lumbricoides*		Several months	Same as above
Trichinosis	*Trichinella spiralis*		2–28 days	Not communicable from man to man
Taeniasis	*Taenia saginata Taenia solium* (see Cysticercosis below)		8–10 weeks	Same as above
Diphyllobothriasis	*Diphyllobothrium latum*		3–6 weeks	Same as above
Hymenolepiasis	*Hymenolepis nana Hymenolepis diminuta*		Unknown	*H. nana* communic while parasite per in intestines *H. diminuta* not communicable fro man to man

pecimens Required	Laboratory Diagnosis	Immunization	Treatment	Nursing Management
stools	Trophozoites or cysts by microscopic examination Culture	None	Tetracyclines Diodaquin Carbasone	Isolation not necessary, concurrent disinfection of fecally contaminated objects; sanitary disposal of feces
s	Same as above	None	Tetracyclines Quinine	Same as above
s	Same as above	None	Atabrine Quinine	Same as above
h tape of nal area	Ova or adults	None	Piperazine salts	In home: vigorous disinfection involving bathroom, bed linens, bedroom dust, hands, fingernails; in hospital: concurrent disinfection of fecally contaminated objects, careful handwashing
s	Ova	None	Dithiazanine	Sanitary disposal of feces
m s	Larvae Ova or adults	None	Piperazine salts	Same as above
le biopsy	Larvae	None	None specific	No special precautions necessary
s	Ova or proglottids	None	Oleoresin of aspidium Quinacrine	Sanitary disposal of feces (see Cysticercosis below)
s	Ova or proglottids	None	Same as above	Sanitary disposal of feces
s	Ova	None	Same as above	*H. nana:* Sanitary disposal of feces, careful handwashing before eating and after defecation; *H. diminuta:* no special precautions necessary

Table 21–1. *(Cont.)*

Clinical Disease	Causative Organisms	Other Possible Entry Routes	Incubation Period	Communicable Period
Echinococcosis	*Echinococcus granulosus*		Long, months to years	Not communicable from man to man
Cysticercosis	*Taenia solium*	Migration of larvae into the tissues		As long as *T. solium* persists in intestine
Clonorchiasis	*Clonorchis sinensis*		Unknown	Not communicable from man to man
Fascioliasis	*Fasciola hepatica*			Same as above
Fasciolopsiasis	*Fasciolopsis buski*		About 3 months	Same as above
Paragonimiasis	*Paragonimus westermani*		Unknown	Same as above

depends on the elimination of infected animals, snail eradication, and the sanitary protection of water greens cultivated for animal or human consumption.

Fasciolopsiasis

The adult trematode, *Fasciolopis buski*, infests the intestinal tract, producing local irritation with resultant diarrhea, vomiting, anorexia, and other gastrointestinal discomfort. Absorption of toxic products produced by the worm induces systemic reactions and allergy. The face becomes edematous; the abdomen may be distended and painful with ascites, as well as with allergic edema of the wall. Treatment with hexylresorcinol is effective in clearing the worms from their intestinal attachments, and recovery is good if the accompanying intoxication has not been too damaging. This is primarily a disease of the Orient. Human beings and some of their domestic animals maintain the parasite. Fecal contamination of water leads to the parasite's further development in snails and eventual encystment on water plants, particularly the popular water chestnut, which is often eaten raw. Control can be achieved by the sanitary disposal of feces, or its disinfection before use as a fertilizer; the destruction of snail hosts in areas where water plants are harvested; or the preliminary treatment of such vegetables by a few seconds' dip in boiling water.

Paragonimiasis

The adult lung fluke, *Paragonimus westermani*, infests pulmonary tissues. The ova may be coughed out in sputum, or swallowed and discharged in feces. When they reach water and a snail host, larval development proceeds. Cercariae emerging from snails find their way into crayfish or crabs, and encyst in these second intermediate hosts. Man and other animals (dogs,

pecimens equired	Laboratory Diagnosis	Immunization	Treatment	Nursing Management
serum	Rising titer of antibodies	None	None specific	No special precautions necessary
cal specimens	Recognition of cysts and contents			
biopsy	Ova Larvae	None	Oleoresin of aspidium Quinacrine	Careful hand-washing before eating and after defecation; sanitary disposal of feces
	Ova	None	None specific	Sanitary disposal of feces
	Ova	None	Emetine	Same as above
	Ova	None	Hexyresorcinol	Same as above
m	Ova	None	Emetine	Same as above

cats, wild carnivores) that eat these infected crustaceans perpetuate the parasite. The human infestation can be treated with emetine and related drugs. It can be prevented by adequate cooking of crustacean foods. In areas of the world where this disease is endemic and the parasite is maintained by numerous animal species (the Far East, and parts of India, Africa, and South America) control of the snail host is important.

Questions

1. Through what major routes do animal parasites gain entry to the human body?
2. What are the two stages in the development of *Endamoeba histolytica*? Which is the most resistant?
3. How is *E. histolytica* transmitted?
4. How is the disease enterobiasis transmitted?
5. Describe the development of *Ascaris lumbricoides* after ingestion of the egg.
6. What are the definitive hosts of *Trichinella spiralis*?
7. Why is man an alternate host for *Trichinella spiralis*?
8. How can trichinosis be controlled?
9. What is the source of infection for taeniasis?
10. What are the intermediate hosts for *Taenia saginata* and *Taenia solium*?
11. Why must treatment of the tapeworms successfully eliminate the scolex?
12. How can diphyllobothriasis be prevented and controlled?
13. What is the portal of entry for the liver, intestinal, and lung flukes?

Questions for Discussion — Section V

Four young adults hurriedly terminate a picnic at the beach and appear in a local hospital's emergency room. All are complaining of a sudden severe onset of abdominal cramps, nausea, vomiting, and diarrhea. They give a history of having lunched on hot dogs and potato salad brought from home.
1. What is the most probable cause of illness?
2. How can this illness be avoided?
3. Why are stool specimens of no value as a diagnostic tool in this situation?
4. What reassurance could you offer these people as to the length of illness?

References — Section V

Textbooks

Conant, Norman F., Smith, D. T., Baker, R. D., Callaway, J. L., and Martin, D. S.: *Manual of Clinical Mycology*. W. B. Saunders, Philadelphia and London, 1954.

Dubos, René J., and Hirsch, James G. (eds.): *Bacterial and Mycotic Infections of Man*, 4th ed. J. B. Lippincott, Philadelphia, 1965.

Faust, Ernest, and Russell, Paul Farr: *Craig and Faust's Clinical Parasitology*, 7th ed. Lea & Febiger, Philadelphia, 1965.

Horsfall, Frank L., Jr., and Tamm, Igor (eds.): *Viral and Rickettsial Infections of Man*, 4th ed. J. B. Lippincott, Philadelphia, 1965.

Hunter, George W., Frye, William W., and Swartzwelder, J. Clyde: *A Manual of Tropical Medicine*, 4th ed. W. B. Saunders, Philadelphia and London, 1966.

Jawetz, Ernest, Melnick, J. L., and Adelberg, E. A.: *Review of Medical Microbiology*, 7th ed. Lange Medical Publications, Los Altos, Calif., 1966.

Pertinent References

GENERAL

Coerver, R. M.: One Man's Meat, *Amer. J. Nurs.*, **58**:690, May, 1958.

Dauer, Carl C.: 1960 Summary of Disease Outbreaks and a 10 Year Resume, *Public Health Rep.* **76**:915, Oct., 1961.

Fason, M. Fitzpatrick: Controlling Bacterial Growth in Tube Feedings, *Amer. J. Nurs.*, **67**:1246, June, 1967.

Food Service Sanitation Manual. U.S. Dept. HEW, Public Health Service, #934, Washington, D.C., 1962.

Melnick, Joseph L.: Enteroviruses, *Sci. Amer.*, **200**:89, Feb., 1959.

TYPHOID FEVER

Budd, William: Two Outbreaks of Typhoid Fever, in Roueché, Berton (ed.): *Curiosities of Medicine*. Berkley Medallion, New York, 1963.

Collins, R. N., Marine, W. H., and Nahmias, A. J.: The 1964 Epidemic of Typhoid Fever in Atlanta, *J.A.M.A.*, **197**:179, July 18, 1966.

Edsall, Geoffrey: Typhoid Fever, *Amer. J. Nurs.*, **59**:989, July, 1959.

Hailey, Arthur: *The Final Diagnosis*. Doubleday & Co., Inc., Garden City, N.Y., 1959.

PasYotis, Frances: Typhoid Fever, Circa 1958, *Nurs. Outlook*, **7**:85, Feb., 1959.

Roueché, Berton: A Game of Wild Indians, in *Eleven Blue Men*. Berkley Medallion, New York, 1965.

Salmonella

Newell, Kenneth W.: Possibilities for Investigation and Control of Salmonellosis for This Decade, *Amer. J. Public Health*, **57**:472, March, 1967.
Roueché, Berton: *S. miami, The New Yorker*, Dec. 2, 1961.
———— *Salmonella miami*, in *A Man Named Hoffman*. Little, Brown & Co., Boston, 1965.
Werrin, Milton, and Kronick, David: Salmonella Control in Hospitals, *Amer. J. Nurs.*, **66**:528, March, 1966.

Shigellosis

Levin, Beatrice: For More Effective Shigellosis Control, *Amer. J. Nurs.*, **61**:104, Nov., 1961.

Staphylococcal Food Poisoning

Hodge, Benjamin E.: Control of Staphylococcus Food Poisoning, *Public Health Rep.*, **75**:355, April, 1960.

Botulism

Berland, Theodore: Botulism: The Killer Who Came to Dinner, *The Saturday Evening Post*, March 7, 1964.
Dolman, C. E.: Botulism, *Amer. J. Nursing*, **64**:119, Sept., 1964.
Roueché, Berton: Family Reunion, in *Eleven Blue Men*. Berkley Medallion, New York, 1965.

Epidemic Infantile Diarrhea

Shaker, Yehia, Aziz, Rauouf, and Abu El Naga, Amal: A Preliminary Study of Infantile Diarrhea in Kuwait, *Amer. J. Public Health*, **56**:1580, Sept. 1966.

Cholera

Cahill, Kevin M.: Cholera, *New York J. Med.*, **63**:2672, Sept. 15, 1963.
McGrew, Roderick E.: *Russia and the Cholera*, 1823–1832. University of Wisconsin Press, Madison, 1965.
Woodham-Smith, Cecil: *The Great Hunger*, chap. 12. Harper & Row, New York, 1962.

Leptospiroses

Ager, Ernest: The Leptospiroses, *Nurs. Outlook*, **10**:260, April, 1962.
Alston, J. M., and Broom, J. C.: *Leptospirosis in Man and Animals*. E. & S. Livingstone Ltd., Edinburgh and London, 1958.
Council Report: Leptospirosis, *J. Amer. Vet. Med. Ass.*, **138**:2, Jan. 15, 1961.
Galton, Mildred, Menges, Robert W., Shotts, Emmett B., Nahmias, Andre J., and Heath, Clara W.: *Leptospirosis — Epidemiology; Clinical Manifestations in Man and Animals and Methods in Laboratory Diagnosis*. U. S. Dept. HEW, CDC, Atlanta, Ga.
Leptospirosis: U.S. Dept. HEW, Health Information Series, Washington, D.C., 93, 1963.
Menges, Robert W.: Control of Leptospirosis in Man and Animals, *Public Health Rep.*, **74**:149, Feb., 1959.

Hepatitis

Barton, Jane: What Hospitals Should Know About Hepatitis, *Mod. Hosp.*, **96**:69, May, 1961.
Dull, J. C.: Syringe Transmitted Hepatitis, *J.A.M.A.*, **176**:413, May 6, 1961.
Eichenwald, Heinz F., and Mosley, James W.: *Viral Hepatitis — Clinical and Public Health Aspects*. U.S. Dept. HEW, #435, Washington, D.C., 1959.
———— and ————: Viral Hepatitis — Clinical and Public Health Aspects, *Nurs. Outlook*, **8**:295, June, 1960.
Eisenmenger, William J.: Viral Hepatitis, from a Medical Viewpoint, *Amer. J. Nurs.*, **61**:56, Nov., 1961.
Finlayson, Eleanor: Operation Big Switch, *Nurs. Outlook*, **9**:680, Nov., 1961.
Sullivan, Walter: Hepatitis Traced to an Oysterman, *New York Times*, Nov. 19, 1961.
Uhl, Marilyn, and Lydon, Joan: Viral Hepatitis, from a Nursing Viewpoint, *Amer. J. Nurs.*, **61**:58, Nov., 1961.

POLIOMYELITIS

Engel, Leonard: Why We Don't Wipe Out Polio, *Harper's*, Sept., 1961.

Rooney, Alyce: A Polio Epidemic Is Averted, *Amer. J. Nurs.*, **62**:71, May, 1962.

PARASITIC DISEASES

Krehl, Willard A.: Intestinal Flora and Parasites — Their Effect on Nutrition, *Borden Rev. Nutr. Res.*, **20**:1 Jan., Feb., 1959.

Litter, Leo: Pinworms, a Ten Year Study, *Arch. Pediat.*, Nov., 1961.

Melvin, Dorothy M., Brooke, M. M., and Sadun, E. H.: *Common Intestinal Helminths of Man (Life Cycle Charts)*. U.S. Dept. HEW, CDC, 1235, Atlanta, Ga., April, 1965.

Mizer, Helen E.: The Tapeworm and the Noodle, *Amer. J. Nurs.*, **63**:102, July, 1963.

Roueché, Berton: A Pig from New Jersey, in *Eleven Blue Men*. Berkley Medallion, New York, 1965.

Section VI The Infectious Diseases Acquired Through the Intact Skin and Mucosa

22 The Epidemiology of Infections Acquired Through Intact Skin and Mucosa

The unbroken skin and mucous membranes offer a very effective barrier to most microorganisms, for anatomic and physiologic reasons previously described (Chap. 7, pp. 122 to 123). Under normal circumstances, however, there is a good deal of wear and tear on these surfaces, and although they may appear to be intact, minor breaks may frequently occur. Such openings can afford a route of entry to the body for a number of microorganisms whose pathogenic properties permit them to establish themselves, multiply, and induce tissue reaction and injury. In some instances organisms introduced through the skin or mucosa remain localized there, the disease process affecting only the superficial tissues, but in many cases wide dissemination of the pathogen may occur, and infection becomes systemic. The microorganisms capable of establishing human disease through entry portals in the superficial tissues represent all the major groups of pathogens, but epidemiologically it is important to distinguish between those that can be transmitted through minor breaks in "intact" skin and those that usually must be introduced through penetrative or deep injury. The latter group includes the arthropod-borne infectious diseases as well as those associated with accidental or surgical injury, and they are discussed in the chapters of Section VII.*

* References for Chaps. 22 to 25 are at the end of Sec. VI (pp. 551 to 553).

The pathogenic organisms that can enter through "intact" skin are usually transmitted to man through simple, direct contacts with a source of infection. The most important and largest group of the contact diseases of man have a human reservoir, their sources are infected persons, and they are transmitted directly through human contacts. They include the venereal diseases, a number of staphylococcal and streptococcal infections of the skin, leprosy, a few spirochetal diseases, the superficial fungous infections, and the bacterial and viral diseases of the conjunctiva and other ocular structures. These diseases associated with *human contacts* are discussed in Chapter 23.

Infectious diseases acquired through *animal contacts* include anthrax and tularemia. These diseases can be transmitted to man through other routes as well, as has been noted in previous sections (Chap. 14 and Chap. 19) but cutaneous entry is frequent and important, so that these diseases should be recognized as contact zoonoses, as described in Chapter 24. Some other infectious diseases such as brucellosis, leptospirosis, and ringworm infections may also be contracted through direct contacts with animals, but in these instances we have emphasized an epidemiologic route of spread and entry that is either more frequent or involves larger numbers of people. Brucellosis, for example, can be transmitted in unpasteurized milk from infected cows, involving many more people than those in direct contact with the infectious source. For this reason, the principal discussion of this disease is placed in Chapter 19, together with other bacterial infections acquired through the alimentary route. The fungi associated with ringworm diseases often infect dogs, cats, and domestic farm animals and can be transmitted by them to man, but they are frequently and easily spread through human contacts and are discussed in this context in Chapter 23.

Leptospirosis is an enzootic spirochetal infection of wild animals, dogs, and rodents. Man seldom acquires the disease directly from these animals, but he is infected through contacts with *intermediate environmental sources* contaminated by organisms shed through the urinary tract of infected animals. Soil and water may also be the source of certain parasitic diseases, notably hookworm and schistosomiasis. The hookworm larvae require a period of maturation in the soil, after being passed in human feces, and they are then capable of penetrating the intact human skin to begin their cycle of development in a new host. *Schistosoma* larvae (or cercariae, as they are called) also enter the body by wriggling through the skin from their source in infested water. This parasite is maintained in its life cycle by man and by intermediate snail hosts. Man contaminates water with ova shed in feces or urine, and the snail liberates cercariae that have undergone development in its body. The skin itself is merely the entry point for these infectious organisms and is not importantly involved in disease, although sometimes parasitic larvae find themselves unable to progress beyond the skin by way of lymphatic or blood routes. Local tissue reactions may block them, or they may be physiologically incapable of further penetration. Their presence in the skin is irritating, however, and induces a dermatitis called "ground itch" in the case of hookworm species, or "swimmer's itch" when *Schistosoma* are involved. These diseases that man acquires through skin contacts with environmental sources of the organism are described in Chapter 25.

Infectious lesions of the skin and mucosal surfaces represent the portal of exit and transmission of the human contact diseases, but man does not transmit the diseases he acquires from animal contacts. He is an accidental victim of these, and also of leptospirosis, and does not contribute to their maintenance in nature. In the case of the parasitic diseases, the organisms are perpetuated by human infections, but they are transmitted through and acquired from indirect environmental sources only.

The nursing management of the contact diseases is based on a knowledge of their transmissibility from skin lesions and the route of entry their infectious agents may follow on transfer to another individual. Communicability varies greatly in this group, and the necessity for precautionary techniques is correspondingly diverse. Leprosy, for example, is a disease of very low communicability requiring only those precautions that are directed

at the disposal of nasal and skin discharges. Staphylococcal and streptococcal infections, on the other hand, are highly communicable, requiring isolation of the patient as well as strict precautions in the control of infectious material. The venereal diseases are transmitted principally through sexual contacts, but when they are treated in the hospital during acute stages, medical personnel must take particular care that they themselves do not become infected while treating the patient or handling infectious material. Syphilis and gonorrhea yield rapidly to antibiotic therapy, under most circumstances, so that precautions are seldom indicated after 24 hours of therapy. In the case of animal contact diseases, such as anthrax or tularemia, direct transmission does not normally occur, but here again some caution is indicated in the handling of infectious blood or skin discharges, because infections may be accidentally acquired through injured skin, penetrative wounds inflicted by a contaminated needle (and syringe), or other exposure routes. (Laboratory workers are subject to risk when handling some of these infectious agents in culture or studying their effects in experimental animals.)

The epidemiology of these diseases is described in the following chapters of this section, and established requirements for isolation and nursing precautions are stated for each. General recommendations for the nursing management of diseases transmissible through skin or mucosal contacts may be summarized as follows:

1. The patient may be placed in partial or complete isolation, depending on the nature of his infection and its communicability. *Complete* isolation is indicated for staphylococcal and streptococcal infections (especially impetigo and erysipelas). *Partial* isolation should be provided for secondary-stage syphilis, acute gonorrhea, acute infectious conjunctivitis of the newborn, leprosy, anthrax, and the superficial mycoses (especially those of the body or scalp). Isolation is generally *not indicated* for cases of tularemia, brucellosis, or leptospirosis and is not necessary for hookworm disease or schistosomiasis.

2. Precautions include the use of gowns by those who attend the patient directly and scrupulous attention to hand-washing immediately following such care.

3. Concurrent disinfection varies in detail but should always include the incineration of contaminated dressings or mucosal discharges (in paper bags).

4. Soiled bedclothing and linens should be packaged for the laundry in individual marked bags, to ensure extra care in transport and handling prior to actual washing. The routine laundry technique should assure adequate disinfection of all laundry, with the exception of that contaminated by pathogenic sporeformers (such as the anthrax bacillus or clostridial species).

5. Linens, instruments, and equipment contaminated with sporebearing organisms should be sterilized *prior* to their inclusion with materials to be handled by routine procedures. Depending on the nature of the material, sterilization may be accomplished by autoclaving, gas sterilization, or incineration.

6. Concurrent techniques for the cleaning and/or disinfection of units in which patients with infectious diseases are treated should always be performed with particular care and attention to detail.

7. The use of special precautionary techniques (other than those listed above) must be based on the individual case, the stage of infection, the site of the infectious agent, and the epidemiology of the disease in question.

Questions

1. List the general recommendations for the nursing management of diseases transmissible through skin or mucosal contacts.
2. For what diseases in this group is isolation generally not indicated?
3. For what diseases in this group is complete isolation indicated?

Note: Diseases acquired through the upper respiratory and oral mucosa are discussed in Sections IV and V, respectively.

Diseases acquired through penetrative or other injury to the skin or mucosa are discussed in the chapters of Section VII.

23 Infectious Diseases Acquired Through Intact Skin and Mucosa, Transmitted by Human Contacts

The Venereal Diseases

This group of diseases is referred to as "venereal" because their causative infectious agents are most commonly spread by sexual contacts with infected persons. It is not usual for these infections to spread by other means, for two reasons: (1) the microorganisms involved are obligate parasites of human hosts and do not survive for any significant time in the environment outside of the body; and (2) these organisms do not penetrate normal skin, but must come into close, intimate contact with mucosal surfaces if they are to gain entry. For most of them the genital tract constitutes the usual route of entry, but other mucosal surfaces may also be traversed. Ordinarily, these are diseases of adults or adolescents, but children can acquire infections through close contacts with adults, and infants may be infected at birth, or in utero. Infection from environmental rather than personal sources is rare in either children or adults, but accidental transfer from freshly contaminated objects, infectious discharges, or transfused blood is occasionally reported, particularly in medical or laboratory personnel, or young infants. The susceptibility of the latter to infections of all kinds always increases the hazards of their exposures to communicable diseases.

A variety of organisms of potential or established pathogenicity can be transferred by vene-

real contacts. Among these, there are five that are consistently associated with resultant disease in adults; the spirochete of syphilis; the bacterial agents of gonorrhea, chancroid, and granuloma inguinale; and the filterable agent of lymphogranuloma venereum. In most of these infections, the disease process is one of acute or chronic reactions in tissues adjacent to the site of entry. Syphilis, however, develops as a slowly progressive, chronic systemic infection. In some instances, microorganisms transmitted through the genital route produce infections of little or no consequence in adults, but intrauterine infection of infants born of infected mothers may be severe or fatal. This may be the case with the *Listeria* bacillus, for example (see Chap. 14), or the herpes simplex virus (see p. 520).

The prevention of venereal diseases remains an unsolved problem. Their control depends on the promptness of diagnosis and the adequacy of treatment, and this in turn demands a vigorous communitywide effort. Educational campaigns are conducted constantly to inform the public of the nature and dangers of untreated venereal diseases; physicians and laboratories make prompt reports of diagnosed cases; and local health agencies deploy trained workers to interview patients, find the sources of their infections, and locate their contacts so that treatment may be administered if indicated. Such treatment is usually offered without charge, at government expense, in hospital or health department clinics. Where syphilis is concerned, efforts to detect and control it include compulsory serologic tests for applicants for marriage licenses, pregnant women, military personnel, and others. Personnel health services in hospitals and most business corporations also require that new employees have a serologic test for syphilis (STS). Active cases of these infections seldom require isolation, particularly if treatment is under way; but personal hygiene must be reinforced, sexual contacts must be avoided until cure is effected, and careful disinfection of infectious discharges and of freshly contaminated objects is indicated to prevent further spread.

In the following discussions of individual venereal diseases, special features of their epidemiology are mentioned when significant.

Syphilis

The Clinical Disease. In adults, untreated syphilis progresses through three stages extending over many years, with long intervening periods of latency. The spirochetes usually enter the body through intact mucous membranes but sometimes penetrate through breaks in skin at the site of their deposit. During the *primary* stage of disease, they multiply locally, producing a superficial lesion called a *chancre*. Some also reach the draining lymph nodes of the area and spread to the blood stream. The chancre usually requires about three to six weeks to develop. It is a painless ulcer with a hard, firm base, located usually on the penis in the male, and on the labia, vaginal wall, or cervix of the female. Depending on the mode of infection, the chancre may appear at other sites, including the rectum, the lip, or the palm of the hand, but only one lesion is formed. The adjacent lymph node often becomes hard and firm, but it is also painless. The chancre heals spontaneously, with or without treatment, but systemic infection continues.

The *secondary* stage begins in the next month or two (two to ten weeks). A rash of red papular lesions appears on the skin, and often in the pharynx as well. The rash may be generalized, or localized, often appearing on the palms of the hands and on the feet. These lesions represent foci of disseminated spirochetes, and they may occur at countless sites, in the bones and joints, the eyes, or the central nervous system, as well as in the skin and mucosa. Like the primary chancre, the superficial lesions of the secondary stage are teeming with spirochetes, and they are infectious. The secondary stage also subsides spontaneously, the disease entering a latent period of variable length.

The *tertiary* stage does not always develop. When it does, it is characterized by the formation of soft granulomatous lesions, called *gummas*, which may be located in a variety of tissues: skin, bones, blood vessels, liver, or central nervous system. The spirochetes are not numerous in these lesions, and it is thought that gummas represent a hypersensitive host response to the organism or its products. The location, number, and effects of these lesions are extremely varied,

producing symptoms that may imitate many other chronic diseases. (Syphilis has often been called "The Great Imitator" for this reason.) There may be cardiovascular disease (syphilitic aortic aneurysm is not uncommon); malfunctions of involved organs; and with CNS involvement, general *paresis*, *tabes dorsalis* (sensory tract degenerations in the cord result in a particular kind of difficulty in walking, called *locomotor ataxia*), deafness, blindness, or insanity.

Congenital Syphilis. Untreated syphilis in pregnant women may produce congenital disease of the fetus. The spirochete crosses the placental barrier and actively infects the fetal tissues. Miscarriages and stillbirths occur, but the greatest tragedy may involve live infants brought to term with generalized lesions, including CNS disorders. Sometimes there are no obvious signs of syphilis at birth, but months or years later the congenital case develops blindness, deafness, or insanity. The superficial lesions of congenital syphilis are as infectious as those of the disease acquired in any other way. Syphilitic babies may transfer the disease to adults who fondle and kiss them, and conversely, normal babies may be infected in this way by persons in primary or secondary stages of infection.

Laboratory Diagnosis. Syphilis is often readily diagnosed clinically from the appearance of characteristic lesions and a history of sexual contact with an infected case, but this disease is so protean in its symptomatology that laboratory confirmation is always sought.

I. Identification of the Organism (*Treponema pallidum*)

A. MICROSCOPIC CHARACTERISTICS. The treponemal spirochetes are slender spirals with about 8 to 15 coils evenly spaced at $1-\mu$ distances, so that the entire length is from 8 to 15μ. They are very thin (about 0.2μ in width), and their cell walls are rather membranous and flexible. They are actively motile, with a rapid corkscrew rotation on their long axis. Their bodies also may curve in graceful, slowly undulating motions, or even bend into a circle for a few moments (see Fig. 23–1).

Treponemes do not take ordinary stains, but they can be visualized in tissue sections treated with silver nitrate. Metallic silver precipitates on the surface of the spirochetes, making them appear black against a light background of tissue.

They can be visualized in wet preparations of material taken from chancres if the microscope is adjusted for *dark-field* illumination. The condenser used for dark-field lighting blocks out the light from underneath the stage that would pass directly upward through the specimen from an ordinary condenser. (Remember that the spirochetes are slender, transparent, and difficult to stain except with metallic precipitates. They would not be seen in ordinary preparations by the usual *transmitted* light.) Instead, light is directed at the specimen from an angle almost parallel to the stage, and the eye sees light that is reflected from the object. Particles in suspension are brightly illuminated (and may appear larger because the reflected light

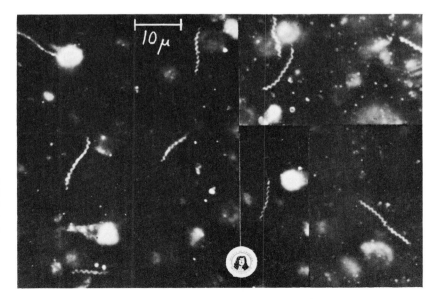

Fig. 23–1. Dark-field photomicrograph of *Treponema pallidum* (1500 ×). (Courtesy of Dr. Theodore Rosebury, Washington University, St. Louis, Mo.)

spreads outward in a cone); the background is almost black because light that is not reflected from a particle does not enter the lens. When spirochetes are viewed in this way, they can be seen distinctly, gleaming with light in the dark field. Other particles in the preparation also shine, of course, but the treponemes can be readily distinguished from other bacteria that may be present in the chancre exudate, by their characteristic motility and morphology.

Treponema pallidum has not been successfully cultivated on artificial laboratory media, nor does it grow in embryonated chick eggs or in tissue cultures. It must be diagnosed on the basis of microscopic characteristics, in material obtained from active lesions or, in the absence of the latter, by serologic testing of the patient's serum.

II. Identification of Patient's Serum Antibodies.

Two types of antibodies develop during the course of syphilitic infection, and both can be detected in the circulating blood. One is called *reagin*. In the test tube, reagins react with lipid antigens extracted from beef heart (cardiolipin) and other mammalian tissue, combining with them to fix complement or producing flocculation. Although the antigen is not derived from the spirochete, it is thought to be closely similar to lipid material formed in the body as a result of tissue destruction during active infection or to resemble some antigenic component of the organism. In any case, the antibody formed in response to a lipid that appears during the disease process gives positive reactions in the Wassermann or Kolmer complement-fixation tests and in several flocculation tests. The one used most frequently today is the VDRL slide flocculation test (developed by the Venereal Disease Research Laboratory of the U.S. Public Health Service, hence its name). These are the common and routine serologic tests for syphilis (STS). They all detect reagin, but they may also detect it in nonsyphilitic infections in which immune reactivity to lipid apparently also occurs. False-positive tests for syphilis may be obtained with cardiolipin antigens in diseases such as malaria, tuberculosis and leprosy, infectious mononucleosis, and infectious hepatitis, as well as other spirochetal infections. Reagins also appear in the spinal fluid during syphilitic infections of the central nervous system and can be detected by complement fixation with lipid antigens. There is very little likelihood of obtaining a false-positive test with spinal fluid; a negative result, however, merely excludes

CNS disease but does not rule out systemic syphilitic infection elsewhere in the body.

Specific treponemal antibodies also arise during the course of disease. A number of serologic tests for these have been developed during the last two decades, using as antigens either live treponemes or antigenic fractions extracted from the spirochetes. In the former case, the spirochete must be cultivated in living animals. Methods have been found to propagate them in rabbit testes, and to extract them from the chancre that develops, without affecting their active motility. When they are mixed with serum from a syphilitic patient, they are immobilized by the antibody that coats their surfaces. In the presence of normal serum they remain typically active. This test is referred to as "treponema immobilization," or the *TPI test*.

The organisms harvested from rabbit testes are also used in fluorescent antibody techniques (*FTA test*). They need not be fresh and alive in this case, but can also be frozen or dried. They are first mixed with the patient's serum, so that antibody, if it is present, will coat their surfaces. Then a fluorescent-labeled antibody against human globulin is added, and this combines with the human serum coat on the treponemes. When examined microscopically by ultraviolet light the spirochetes that have combined with antibody appear to fluoresce. If the patient's serum contained no antibody there will be no combination with the fluorescent antiglobulin, and the spirochetes will not be visible (see Chap. 7, p. 138 and Fig. 7–5).

A strain of spirochete other than *T. pallidum* that has been cultivated in rabbits is known as "Reiter's spirochete." Antigenic extracts from this organism will fix complement when mixed with human syphilitic antiserum (see Chap. 7, p. 137). This method of testing for treponemal antibody is referred to as the *Reiter complement-fixation test* and is to be distinguished from the Kolmer or Wassermann complement-fixation methods, which utilize lipid antigens in testing for reagin.

The serologic tests for specific treponemal antibodies in patients' serums present numerous technical difficulties. Their use is generally reserved, therefore, for those patients whose reagin tests are inconclusive or are suspected of being falsely positive.

III. Specimens for Diagnosis

A. Tissue fluid aspirated or expressed from primary or secondary superficial lesions is sub-

mitted for dark-field examination. Arrangements must be made with the laboratory for immediate examination of this material, because the spirochetes die rapidly when they leave the body and cannot be identified with certainty when they are dead. Patients presenting with primary chancres should be questioned as to any self-treatment they may have attempted. Ointments, salves, and other home remedies do not influence the lesion, but they may inactivate spirochetes at the surface, so that the dark-field examination is unsuccessful. In such instances, the lesion should be carefully cleansed with a bland soap or detergent and water, and the patient instructed to return in a few hours, or the following day, having used nothing but water to clean the area. Repeated dark-field examination may then be successful. If this approach creates a risk of losing control of the patient or his contacts, prior to treatment, the physician must weigh the value of a confirmed laboratory diagnosis against this risk in deciding whether or not to initiate treatment on clinical evidence alone, without a positive dark-field result. The spirochetes disappear from the superficial lesions within a very few hours of antibiotic therapy, and there is usually no later opportunity to demonstrate them in the treated case. Presumptive serologic evidence can be obtained rapidly with the VDRL or other screening slide test, and if this is positive the diagnostic problem is solved. However, the primary lesion not infrequently appears a week or more in advance of detectable levels of reagin, so that a negative STS is not conclusive at this stage.

B. Late syphilis can be diagnosed in the laboratory by the histologic examination of gummatous lesions removed by surgery or biopsied. Silver impregnation techniques are used to demonstrate the organisms in tissues.

C. Serologic tests for reagin (VDRL, Kolmer) become positive between the third and sixth weeks of infection, in the case of serum antibody, and between the fourth and eighth weeks, when spinal fluid is tested from cases with CNS involvement. These antibodies may persist for months or years, even in treated cases, but in latent syphilis a small percentage of patients become reagin-negative.

D. Serologic tests for treponemal antibodies (TPI, FTA, and Reiter's complement-fixation) in the serum become positive after the second week of infection and remain so for many years, even in treated cases.

Three particular problems should be noted in the serologic diagnosis of syphilis:

1. The patient with a history of treated syphilis who displays both reagin and treponemal antibody some years later has not necessarily been reinfected. A drop in titer over the years, followed by a new rise, is suggestive, however, either of reinfection or of reactivation of an inadequately treated earlier infection.

2. The patient with clinical evidence suggestive of latent syphilis may be reagin-negative. In such cases, the TPI test or other method of detecting treponemal antibody is valuable, for these specific tests are usually positive.

3. The patient whose reagin tests are positive but unsupported by clinical or historical evidence of syphilis may be a "biologic false-positive." Tests of his serum for specific treponemal antibodies will be negative if this is, indeed, the case.

Epidemiology

I. Communicability of Infection

A. RESERVOIR, SOURCES, AND TRANSMISSION ROUTES.   See pages 495 to 497.

B. INCUBATION PERIOD.   Average time from exposure to development of primary lesion is about three weeks, but this period may be as short as ten days.

C. COMMUNICABLE PERIOD.   Untreated syphilis may be communicable, on the basis of intermittently active infection, throughout the two to four years of the primary and secondary stages, and during the first years of latency. With adequate treatment, infectivity ceases after about one day.

D. IMMUNITY.   There is no natural resistance to syphilis among human beings of any age, sex, or race, but infection slowly leads to some immunity against reinfection, probably because of the development of specific treponemal antibodies. (Reagins do not play a protective role.) When syphilis is treated adequately during its early stages, however, eradication of infection returns the individual to a state of full susceptibility.

II. Control of Active Infection

A. ISOLATION.   Antibiotic therapy of active syphilis eliminates the threat of communicability within 24 hours. Patients in the primary stage of

disease do not require hospitalization in any case. Those who are hospitalized with severe secondary lesions should be placed in partial isolation (cubicle space) for the first day following institution of specific therapy. Patients treated in the clinic should be warned against sexual contacts, particularly with those who may be infected but not under treatment.

B. PRECAUTIONS. The nursing care of patients with active superficial lesions includes the concurrent disinfection of discharges from open lesions and of objects freshly contaminated through direct contacts. Nurses and others in close attendance during the communicable period should wear gowns, be alert to the necessity of keeping the hands clean and well scrubbed, and guard against careless handling of hypodermic needles or other sharp instruments that may be contaminated after use for the patient. Terminal cleaning of the unit does not require special techniques.

C. TREATMENT. *Treponema pallidum* is highly sensitive to penicillin, and long-acting formulations of this drug, such as benzathine penicillin G, are customarily used to treat early or latent syphilis. The drug is given in two intramuscular doses of 2.4 million units each, separated by an interval of two weeks. Patients with hypersensitivity to penicillin may be treated with other antibiotics, such as the tetracyclines, or erythromycin, but these drugs are not so effectively treponemicidal as penicillin, and a watch must be kept for remittent symptoms of active infection. Mercuric and arsenical drugs used prior to the discovery of penicillin and other antibiotics have now been abandoned. They are toxic for the patient and not very actively spirocheticidal, but between the time of Paul Ehrlich's formulation of salvarsan, the "magic bullet" (an arsenical compound), at the turn of the twentieth century and the first practical applications of the newly discovered penicillin during World War II, compounds of mercury, arsenic, or bismuth were the drugs of choice for syphilis.

If syphilitic pregnant women are treated during the first weeks of pregnancy, congenital disease can be avoided for the fetus. After the eighteenth week, however, in utero treatment of the baby is indicated, as well as specific therapy for the mother.

The Herxheimer reaction is a febrile response to specific therapy that may occur in patients in the secondary or later stages of syphilis who are being treated for the first time. During the preceding weeks or months of spirochetal multiplication and dissemination throughout the body, hypersensitivity develops to the antigenic components of these organisms, and many tissues may contain cell-fixed antibodies to these antigens (see Chap. 7, pp. 146 to 153). The sudden killing effect of penicillin or other treponemicidal drugs on numerous spirochetes localized throughout the body releases their components and elicits a generalized allergic tissue response characterized by fever and chills. The reaction usually occurs within 12 hours following the first dose of penicillin and subsides within the next 24 hours. It is not likely to occur when syphilis is treated in its primary stage, before hypersensitivity is well developed.

C. CONTROL OF CONTACTS. Prophylactic methods appear to be quite unreliable for the control of syphilis. The use of condoms and diaphragms, soaps and antiseptics is limited by practical considerations of ignorance or carelessness. Prostitution and other forms of sexual promiscuity also appear to assure the continuation of this disease, which has been steadily on the rise during the last few years, after an initial decline following the institution of antibiotic therapy. Case finding through the investigation of contacts of known syphilitic infections remains the most effective form of control, through its offer of treatment for otherwise undetected cases. Tracing the contacts of a known case is a job for public health nurses or epidemiologists trained in interview techniques and in the clinical implications of syphilis in its various stages. When a primary case is involved, the contacts of the previous three months should be investigated. A case of secondary or early latent syphilis may have spread the disease for six months to a year, while the discovery of a case of tertiary syphilis, or one of long latency, raises the possibility that marital contacts and children may have become infected. However, when syphilis is not diagnosed

until it has reached the tertiary stage, it may be unrewarding, at that point, to search for contacts beyond the household. With the diagnosis of a case of congenital syphilis, all family members and household or other significant contacts must be investigated. Sources of infection should be sought in advanced, as well as currently communicable, stages of disease.

E. EPIDEMIC CONTROLS. All state health departments require individual case reports so that efforts can be made to find and treat contacts who represent sources of the infection. Yet in spite of countrywide and international measures to control it, the disease appears to be expanding in new epidemic patterns, particularly among adolescents. Syphilis can be widely disseminated from a single active case, and each new transfer has the same potential for fanning out widely, particularly among the sexually promiscuous (see Fig. 23–2). The comfortable thought that it can now be cured promptly, and with relative ease, by penicillin has perhaps been misleading. The early cure of infection is essential in controlling its spread, but it leaves little or no residual resistance to reinfection. Furthermore, primary infection may go unnoticed (particularly in women) and therefore untreated, being spread from such silent sources to large numbers of contacts, including the children congenitally infected. Renewed and intensified efforts are being made by health agencies to maintain control through case finding and treatment (see the methods outlined on page 496).

III. Prevention. The prevention of this and other veneral diseases depends on the efforts of an informed public, armed with a basic knowledge of sex and health, to promote the social and physical welfare of its young people, in particular. Working together, the general public, its public health services, and the medical community could resolve the problem.

Gonorrhea

The Clinical Disease. Gonorrhea is a venereal disease of worldwide distribution, maintained as a genitourinary tract infection of adults, but sometimes also affecting young female children as a vulvovaginitis or newborn infants as a severe ophthalmic infection. The incidence of the adult disease has been steadily increasing from year to year for the past decade, the actual incidence probably being several times greater than the number of reported cases. Gonorrhea, like syphilis, is a disease that is widely disseminated by sexual promiscuity.

Gonorrhea in the adult male begins as an acute urethritis, manifest by a thick, purulent discharge. If untreated, it may extend to an epididymitis or prostatitis. Not uncommonly, systemic involvements also occur, notably arthritis and sometimes endocarditis. *In the adult female,* the initial localization of infection may be in the urethra, the vagina, or the cervix, but it is often mild at this stage, and the discharge may not be noticed. If it is not treated, the infection may extend upward into the fallopian tubes and on into the pelvic peritoneum. The resultant salpingitis and pelvic inflammation may be healed by scarring when the suppurative process subsides, and this may lead to obstruction of the tubes and sterility. Urethral scarring in the male may produce strictures requiring surgical relief. Chronic, residual infection in untreated cases, particularly in women, is often responsible for the continuing spread of the disease to new contacts.

Gonorrhea in female children who have not reached puberty is a more superficial infection of the genital labia and the vagina. In severe cases, extension occurs into the urethra and bladder. The mucous membranes are inflamed, and there may be a profuse leukorrheal discharge. Sexual or other intimate contacts with infected adults appear to be responsible for most of these cases. There is little or no bacteriologic evidence that gonococcal infections can be transmitted through indirect environmental contacts with such items as toilet seats or towels used in common. The bacterial agent of gonorrhea is fragile and fastidious. It does not survive outside of the body unless provided with special conditions for growth on enriched media, as may be done in the laboratory. However, if objects contaminated with fresh infectious discharges come into direct con-

1960

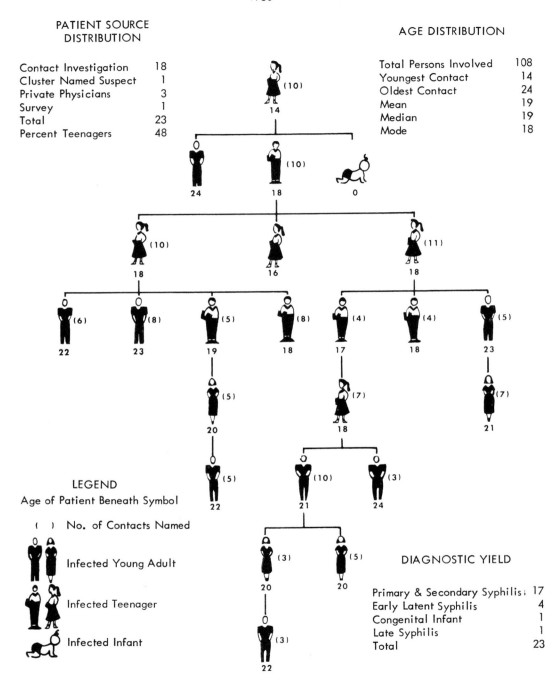

PATIENT SOURCE
DISTRIBUTION

Contact Investigation	18
Cluster Named Suspect	1
Private Physicians	3
Survey	1
Total	23
Percent Teenagers	48

AGE DISTRIBUTION

Total Persons Involved	108
Youngest Contact	14
Oldest Contact	24
Mean	19
Median	19
Mode	18

LEGEND
Age of Patient Beneath Symbol

( ) No. of Contacts Named

Infected Young Adult

Infected Teenager

Infected Infant

DIAGNOSTIC YIELD

Primary & Secondary Syphilis	17
Early Latent Syphilis	4
Congenital Infant	1
Late Syphilis	1
Total	23

Fig. 23–2. A syphilis outbreak in a southern town in 1960. Note how the chain of infection spread from one infected individual. (Reproduced from *Today's VD Control Program*, March, 1961. Courtesy of American Social Health Association, New York, N.Y.)

tact with the genital mucosa (or the conjunctival membrane) they may transfer infection.

Gonococcal ophthalmia of the newborn (*ophthalmia neonatorum*) may be a serious consequence of maternal disease that is untreated and undetected. The eyes of a newborn baby become infected at the time of delivery, during passage through the vaginal canal, if the mother has active gonorrhea. If not promptly treated, infection begins as an acute conjunctivitis, which rapidly involves the cornea and other structures and commonly ends in blindness. This problem can be readily avoided by prophylactically treating the eyes of all newborn babies with silver nitrate solution or penicillin, a procedure required by the law of most states.

Gonococcal conjunctivitis may be acquired by people of all ages, usually through the transfer of genital infection by contaminated hands. Patients may infect themselves in this way, and medical personnel may do so as well if they are careless about hand-washing after contact with infectious discharges.

Laboratory Diagnosis. The genital and conjunctival infections described above are often very difficult to distinguish clinically from other acute bacterial infections. For this reason, and because the control of gonorrhea depends on its recognition not only in the individual case but in the contacts of that case, it is essential that laboratory confirmation be obtained whenever possible.

I. Identification of the Organism (*Neisseria gonorrhoeae*)

A. MICROSCOPIC CHARACTERISTICS. The gonococcus is a Gram-negative, bean-shaped diplococcus, morphologically indistinguishable from the meningococcus (see Chap. 14, p. 322). When seen in stained smears of purulent exudates, gonococci are characteristically found in intracellular positions within the polymorphonuclear leukocytes (see Fig. 23–3). They cannot be identified on the basis of morphology alone, however. Other Gram-negative organisms that normally inhabit the mucosal surfaces, or that may be associated with infections, may look very much like gonococci. Confusion has frequently arisen with members of the *Mima-Herellea* group of Gram-negative coccobacilli, which have been recognized in recent years as the agents of a variety of infections, including a urethritis resembling gonorrhea. (See Chap. 30.)

With these considerations in mind, the laboratory sends a guarded report of the findings in a smear of exudate. The language is descriptive, but avoids a commitment as to identification. When suspicious organisms are found, the report may read, "Gram-negative intracellular diplococci resembling gonococci were seen." If other organisms are present, they are also described, together with the numbers and types of leukocytes seen.

B. CULTURE CHARACTERISTICS. The presumptive diagnosis of gonorrhea is confirmed by culture techniques. *N. gonorrhoeae* is a fastidious organism, requiring enriched media containing heated, defibrinated blood (chocolate blood agar). It grows best under microaerophilic conditions at 37° C. It is distinguished from the meningococcus and other *Neisseria* by its behavior in carbohydrate media.

C. SEROLOGIC METHODS FOR IDENTIFICATION. The usual serologic techniques are of little or no

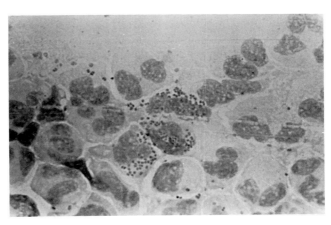

Fig. 23–3. *Neisseria gonorrhoeae* in a urethral smear. Note the intracellular position of the bean-shaped diplococci (1000 ×). (Courtesy of Dr. Kendall K. Kane, St. Luke's Hospital Center, New York, N.Y.)

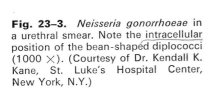

value in the identification of gonococci, but the fluorescent antibody (FA) technique is sometimes of value in identifying an isolated strain, or in locating organisms in smears of pus examined during late chronic stages when the diplococci are most difficult to find or to culture. When smears are coated with fluorescein-tagged antibody, the latter combines with the gonococci specifically. Examined microscopically with ultraviolet light, the organisms are visible as the only fluorescent objects in an otherwise dark field. The indirect FA technique is also used. (See Chap. 7, p. 138.)

II. Identification of Patient's Serum Antibodies. Serologic methods for diagnosis of gonorrhea are not reliable. Complement-fixation tests have been largely abandoned because they lack specificity, and antibody response during the course of disease is often irregular, even in chronic infections.

III. Specimens for Diagnosis. Exudates from genitourinary mucosal membranes for smear and culture.

In the female, cervical discharges are most likely to yield the organisms.

In the male, exudates from the urethra or prostate are submitted.

In gonococcal ophthalmia, pus from the conunctiva is collected.

It is of critical importance that specimens be transported to the laboratory with all possible speed, because gonococci are extremely susceptible to the effects of drying and to the competition for nutrient offered by commensal flora of the genitourinary tract. A transport medium should be used whenever possible for swabs containing suspected material.

Epidemiology

I. Communicability of Infection

A. RESERVOIR, SOURCES, AND TRANSMISSION ROUTES. Gonorrhea is a human disease. Exudates from the involved mucous membranes of infected persons are the source of infection, transmitted by direct contact, usually sexual.

B. INCUBATION PERIOD. Usually three to nine days, except in the case of ophthalmia neonatorum, which develops within 36 to 48 hours.

C. COMMUNICABLE PERIOD. If specific antibiotic therapy is given, symptoms and communicability subside within a day or so. Without therapy, adult gonorrhea may remain communicable for months or years. The disease in children generally does not persist for more than about six months. Conjunctival membranes should be considered infectious until all discharge has ceased.

D. IMMUNITY. Effective natural immunity to gonorrhea does not develop as the result of an attack, and artificial immunization is not available. Susceptibility to this disease is universal without respect to age, sex, or race, and reinfection may readily occur.

II. Control of Active Infection

A. ISOLATION. Hospitalized patients (especially children and infants) should be kept in partial isolation for 24 hours following the institution of antibiotic therapy. Private isolation is not necessary, but cubicle barriers may be used to prevent children from intermingling. Infected babies in newborn nurseries should be kept in isolation until all signs of infection have ceased.

B. PRECAUTIONS. The nursing care of gonococcal infections includes the use of gowns for those who come in contact with the patient, his bedclothing, or items contaminated with infectious discharges. Soiled laundry should be bagged and marked for careful handling on its way to the laundry. Concurrent disinfection of exudates from lesions or articles soiled by them should be carried out, and particular care should be taken with hand-washing. Nurses and physicians should be aware of the susceptibility of the conjunctival membranes to this organism. Routine terminal cleaning of the unit is satisfactory. Special precautions are not indicated when symptoms have subsided following antibiotic therapy.

C. TREATMENT. Penicillin is the drug of choice. In uncomplicated cases, it is given in one intramuscular dose of a long-lasting form (benzathine penicillin G or procaine penicillin). Patients with hypersensitivity to penicillin can be treated with other antibiotics. It is not uncommon for syphilis and gonorrhea to be contracted simultaneously, and since the primary lesion of syphilis may not appear for a week or more after symptoms of gonorrhea begin, the antibiotic dose level is often adjusted to cure one and abort the other.

The question of syphilis infection should then be followed with serologic testing at monthly intervals for at least four months.

D. CONTROL OF CONTACTS. Rapid case finding to locate and treat the source of infection is essential to the control of this disease. Treatment is also given to the female contacts of male cases on empiric grounds, because the mildness of gonorrhea in women, as well as its tendency toward chronicity, often makes diagnosis difficult. The problem is compounded by the fact that effective immunity does not develop for this disease, with or without treatment, and, indeed, early therapy often increases the opportunity for reinfection, this situation being very similar to that which now applies in the case of syphilis. The lack of a serologic tool for large-scale detection of gonorrhea is another feature that makes control difficult to establish.

See the initial discussion of venereal diseases (pp. 495 to 496) and comments on the control of syphilis (pp. 499 to 501) for similarities in the problems of control and prevention.

Chancroid

The Clinical Disease. This venereal disease is relatively widespread, but is particularly well known to military personnel in tropical areas. It is also a disease of seaports and overcrowded cities. The chancroid is the initial lesion that occurs on the genitalia: a *soft* chancre with ragged edges. Unlike the hard chancre of syphilis, the ulcer is swollen and painful, as are the regional lymph nodes. The chancroid and the nodes become suppurative and necrotic. The pus-filled inguinal nodes may break down and suppurate to the surface. These "buboes" exude the causative bacteria, which may then be inoculated into new sites. Extragenital lesions may be seen on other mucosal and skin surfaces (tongue, lip, breast, umbilicus).

Laboratory Diagnosis. *Hemophilus ducreyi* is the responsible agent. This is a small, Gram-negative bacillus, nonmotile and nonsporeforming. It is classified in the same genus as *Hemophilus in-*

fluenzae (see Chap. 14, p. 319), but it is culturally more fastidious, requiring heavy blood enrichment as well as microaerophilic incubation. It can be visualized in Gram-stained smears of exudates from the chancroid or from the buboes as chaining rows of bacilli.

A skin-testing antigen containing heat-killed bacilli is available. Infected individuals display the delayed type of hypersensitive skin reaction to this material.

The differential diagnosis of chancroid includes dark-field examinations of exudate and serologic testing to rule out syphilis.

Special Features of Control

Treatment. Sulfonamides are the drugs of choice. Tetracylines and other antibiotics are also effective, but they can mask concurrent syphilis; therefore, careful diagnostic techniques for the latter disease must be used.

Chancroid has a relatively short incubation period of three to five days and is communicable through the infectious discharges of the genital lesions and buboes.

Measures for the control and prevention of this disease are similar to those described for syphilis and gonorrhea.

Granuloma Inguinale

The Clinical Disease. Granuloma inguinale is a chronic venereal disease chiefly seen in tropical areas but also found in temperate zones. A small nodule appears initially at the site of entry of the organism on the genital mucosa. When the nodule ulcerates, it may be mistaken for the hard chancre of syphilis, or the soft one of chancroid. As disease progresses, however, the ulcer spreads peripherally and may superficially involve a large area of the mucous membrane.

Laboratory Diagnosis. The causative organism has recently been classified with the generic name *Calymmatobacterium granulomatis.* Formerly known as *Donovania granulomatis* or, simply as "Donovan bodies," these organisms appear in biopsies of the lesions as short, Gram-negative bacilli crowded into mononuclear cells (see

Fig. 23–4). They have been cultivated in embryonated eggs, and also on complex artificial media, and found to resemble the Friedlander's bacillus (*Klebsiella*; see Chap. 14, p. 319).

Special Features of Control

Treatment. These organisms respond to antibiotic therapy. Streptomycin, the tetracyclines, and chloramphenical have been used with good effect.

This disease is not necessarily transmitted by sexual contact only. It appears to be an infection of the poverty-stricken who do not, or cannot, maintain standards of cleanliness. It can be controlled by the usual case finding among marital or other contacts, but the framework for improved standards of living must also be provided (see pp. 495 to 496, and 500 to 501).

Lymphogranuloma Venereum

The Clinical Disease. This disease has a world-wide distribution, but it is most common in tropical or semitropical areas. In the United States it is endemic in southern regions bordering the Gulf of Mexico. It is a venereal infection to which all ages and races are susceptible, but it is most common in sexually active young adults. Lymphogranuloma venereum (LGV) begins, as a rule, with a small, painless primary lesion on the genital mucosa marking the site of entry. This may be a papule or an ulcerated lesion. Clinical

evidence of systemic infection begins within about two weeks, with enlargement of the regional lymph nodes, which may proceed to suppurate and drain, and with fever, general malaise, and sometimes the involvement of membranous surfaces of the joints, the eye, or the brain. Chronic infection within the pelvic lymphatics may be of long standing, eventually inducing blockade, with resultant elephantiasis of genital tissues, and strictures.

Laboratory Diagnosis. The agent of this disease was formerly classified as a "large virus." Its morphologic and biologic properties relate it to the agents of psittacosis (see Chap. 16, p. 389) and trachoma (p. 509). The genus name *Bedsonia* has recently been suggested for this group of organisms pending further study of their characteristics, which resemble in many respects those of rickettsiae or of very small bacteria rather than viruses.

With special staining techniques this organism can be visualized within the mononuclear cells of exudates obtained from draining lymph nodes, or in tissue biopsies. It can also be cultivated in the yolk sacs of embryonated eggs, or in mice. In preparations harvested from these sources it is identified by microscopic morphology together with serologic identification of its antigenic properties.

Antibodies produced during the course of LGV infection can be identified by complement-fixation tests, in a serologic confirmation of the clinical diagnosis. The specific hypersensitivity that develops in this disease can also be recognized by the use of a skin-testing antigen, prepared from the organism cultivated in a chick embryo. This

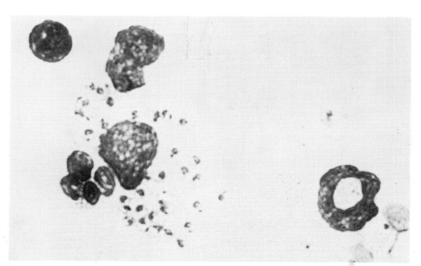

Fig. 23–4. Photomicrograph of cells from a lesion produced by *Calymmatobacterium granulomatis*. The large monocytic cell to the left contains many Donovan bodies. These short, plump bacilli are Gram-negative. When stained with Wright's or Giemsa's stain, the bacterial bodies are dark blue, and the surrounding capsular material takes on a pink or light purple color (1250 ×). (Courtesy of Dr. S. Stanley Schneierson, The Mount Sinai Hospital, New York, N.Y.)

is known as the "Frei antigen," or the "Frei test," which elicits a reaction of the delayed hypersensitive type in infected persons. The antigen that induces this reaction is shared by other microorganisms of the psittacosis-lymphogranuloma-trachoma group, which means that the Frei test is not specific for LGV alone but may also be positive in persons infected with related organisms.

Special Features of Control

Treatment. Antimicrobial drugs are effective in treating this disease. The sulfonamides are useful in the early stages, but the broad-spectrum antibiotics are more effective in curing the systemic phases of disease.

The incubation period may require from one to three or four weeks. The primary lesion usually appears within 7 to 12 days, but, if it fails to develop, the first sign of infection may be an inguinal bubo appearing about a month after exposure. Untreated LGV may be communicable for months or years. With treatment the lesions are slowly healed.

Resistance to reinfection develops during the course of this disease, but the infecting organism may remain latent and viable within tissues, unaffected by antibody production.

LGV is primarily a venereal infection, but it is also sometimes transmitted to children through contacts with freshly contaminated environmental sources. The control and prevention of the disease depend on the detection and treatment of sexual contacts, as outlined for syphilis and gonorrhea (pp. 495 to 496, 500 to 501, and 504 to 505).

almost never produces any symptoms. When transferred to women, however, it may induce a chronic vaginitis characterized by a profuse, malodorous discharge. Other bacteria (lactobacilli) that normally live in the vagina, maintaining the acidity of the membrane, are displaced by the trichomonads. The latter feed on bacteria and also on the leukocytes that are marshaled in response to their invasion. The membranes become superficially inflamed, and there is usually an intense pruritus of the vagina and vulva. *Trichomoniasis* is easily diagnosed by microscopic examination of vaginal secretions, or of seminal discharge from the male. The organisms are often present in urine as well. The actively motile parasite can be seen in unstained wet mounts (see Fig. 23–5). It can be cultured, also, on a medium similar to that used for amebic protozoans (see Chap. 21, p. 465). Trichomoniasis can be treated effectively with quinoline drugs or tetracyclines, which kill the protozoans. These drugs may be given orally or applied locally in suppositories. Restoration of the normally acid pH of the vagina is also important and is accomplished with mild douches that have a cleansing action as well. The control of this infection in women depends on simultaneous treatment of their male partners.

As pointed out in the general discussion of the venereal diseases (pp. 495 to 496 of this chapter), some microorganisms that are transferred among adults during sexual intercourse may have consequence only for the fetus or the infant born of an infected mother. Two examples can be cited

Other Microbial Diseases Transmissible by Venereal Contacts

The genital transfer of infection may involve quite a number of organisms that ordinarily do not result in serious, or even noticeable, disease of adults. One of those that sometimes causes women a great deal of annoyance is the flagellated protozoan *Trichomonas vaginalis*. This organism often lives commensalistically on the genital mucosa. In men it lives on the urethral ·surfaces or in the prostate and seminal vesicles, where it

Fig. 23–5. The flagellated protozoan, *Trichomonas vaginalis* (1000 ×). (Courtesy of Dr. Thomas W. M. Cameron, McGill University, Montreal, Canada.)

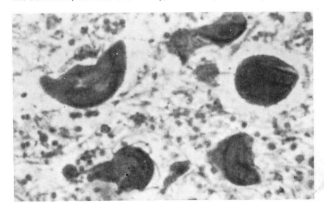

in which disastrous intrauterine or neonatal disease may occur as a result of venereal infection. One is the fetal disease *granulomatosis infantiseptica*, caused by the *Listeria* bacillus. This organism is sometimes associated with serious or mild nonvenereal disease in adults also, as discussed in Chapter 14 (pp. 323 to 325). Respiratory, alimentary, or cutaneous portals of entry appear to have importance in the acquisition of adult listerial disease. The wide distribution of the organism among animal hosts and increasing awareness of its incidence in man suggest that it may persist unrecognized on human tissues, be transmitted in personal contacts, but cause disease only when adult resistance is lowered by other factors, or when it finds its way into the highly susceptible tissues of a developing human embryo.

Another example of this type is *herpes simplex* virus infection, which may occur in babies born of mothers who were newly infected. As in the case of gonococcal ophthalmia, the infant is probably infected during passage through the birth canal by exposure to primary herpetic lesions on the mother's vulval mucosa. Herpes simplex (see the discussion later in this chapter) is a virus that is rather constantly associated with man, causing recurrent infections and persisting in long periods of latency. Antibodies are produced in the course of active infection, and during pregnancy they are transferred to the fetus, so that ordinarily the newborn child is protected from critical infections during the first months of life. If the mother acquires her first infection during pregnancy, however, and the child is born before sufficient protective maternal antibody can be transferred placentally, severe neonatal infection may ensue, usually with fatal consequences. The virus is widely disseminated in infant tissues, producing necrotizing lesions in the skin and mucosa, the liver and brain. Herpes simplex virus usually enters the body through the skin and mucous membranes, causing local but sometimes generalized infections. It is transmitted by direct personal contacts and is not infrequently seen as a mild venereal infection.

Other organisms acquired through sexual contacts may have similar effects on fetal or infant tissues, but the evidence is often not clear, particularly in the absence of maternal signs of infection. It should be noted that intrauterine infections are acquired in two epidemiologically distinct ways: by extension of the mother's venereally acquired infection, or by extension of maternal infection acquired through another portal of entry, as in the case of the rubella syndrome (see Chap. 15, pp. 369 to 370). Infectious diseases of the newborn, on the other hand, have several epidemiologic origins. At the time of delivery the baby may acquire infection of venereal origin, or one that is simply related to the mother's indigenous mucosal flora. The latter situation may be due to faulty preparation of the mother for delivery or breaks in aseptic technique. Postnatally, the infectious diseases of infants are acquired through the usual routes of transfer from infected or asymptomatic adult carriers, or from environmental sources (see Chap. 19, pp. 435 to 439).

Infectious Diseases of the Eye

The infectious eye diseases that can be acquired through direct or indirect contacts with infected persons fall into two groups, those of *bacterial* etiology, and those caused by *viral* agents, including members of the "large virus," or *Bedsonia*, group. Numerous strains of pathogenic bacteria are associated with eye infections, but the clinical result is similar in each case: there is an acute conjunctivitis, with production of a purulent exudate. Bacteria generally do not invade the epithelial cells of the conjunctiva or surrounding tissues, but multiply in extracellular positions where they may be taken up by the phagocytes marshaled in the exudate. The clinical and pathologic features of viral infection, on the other hand, are related to the invasion of the conjunctival epithelium, or the cells of other ocular tissues, and to the intracellular activities of the infectious agent. In most viral infections, the initial acute conjunctivitis may be succeeded by a chronic stage of slow destruction with scarring which can lead to blindness.

Acute Bacterial Conjunctivitis

The Clinical Picture.   Bacterial infections of the eye begin with symptoms of local irritation, tearing, and congestion of the small blood vessels of the conjunctiva over the cornea and under the eyelids. As infection proceeds, the eyelids may become swollen and reddened, and a reactive, cellular exudate is formed. The affected eye (both or only one may be involved) becomes sensitive to light and feels hot and painful to the patient. These symptoms vary in degree, being mild and scarcely noticeable in some cases. They are more severe in patients who have been heavily infected, or in those who have little resistance, and neglect may lead to chronicity with more serious involvement of deep tissues. As a rule, however, these infections respond well to treatment and heal without scarring or other residual damage. Because vascular injection is often a marked feature of bacterial conjunctivitis, the popular word for this type of infection is "pinkeye."

Laboratory Diagnosis.   Microscopic examination of the exudate from eye infections caused by bacteria usually reveals the organism, and culture techniques provide final identification. The agents identified most commonly are strains of pneumococci or species of *Hemophilus* and *Moraxella*. Other organisms associated with the respiratory membranes, such as streptococci or staphylococci, may also be responsible for conjunctivitis. These bacterial strains are described in Chapter 14 as agents of pneumonia (p. 319), except for *Moraxella*, which is described in Chapter 12 (p. 293). It should be remembered, also, that gonococci from infected genital membranes can establish themselves on the conjunctival mucosa and produce severe infection in adults as well as in babies born of mothers with gonorrhea (see p. 503 of this chapter).

Epidemiology.   These infections are most common among young children, or others with lowered resistance. They are spread from infectious throat or conjunctival discharges and may pass rapidly from one small child to another (in kindergartens, nursery schools, playgrounds). They often yield to local antibiotic therapy, but systemic dosage is sometimes also required. Healing is usually rapid, without residual damage if treated early. The best control lies in prompt therapy and careful attention to the hygienic care of normal eyes. Children should be taught as early as possible to respect their eyes, and to avoid rubbing them, especially with dirty hands. Parents and nurses both should be alert to the child who rubs his eyes to an unusual extent, for this may be the first symptom of a developing infection.

Viral Diseases of the Eye

Trachoma.   This is a serious communicable disease of the eye prevalent in the hot, dry areas of the world, particularly among people who live under the overcrowded and unsanitary conditions of poverty. It is widespread in the Mediterranean countries, parts of Africa, the Middle East, Asia, and South America. In the United States it is a public health problem on the Indian reservations of the Southwest.

Trachoma is caused by one of the "large viruses" of the *Bedsonia* group, now thought to be small bacteria or rickettsiae rather than true viruses. Two other diseases associated with agents of this group were discussed previously: psittacosis (Chap. 16) and lymphogranuloma venereum (p. 506). Trachoma and inclusion conjunctivitis are caused by closely related agents, but they differ in clinical and epidemiologic features. Like the others of this type, these microorganisms are obligate intracellular parasites that can be seen in clumped masses (inclusion bodies) within the cytoplasm of invaded cells. In these eye diseases the inclusions are seen within the epithelial cells of the conjunctiva.

Trachoma begins as an acute inflammatory conjunctivitis, but it is later characterized by excessive accumulations of tissue cells in tumor-like formations. Lymphocytes accumulating in and beneath the conjunctiva form lymphoid "follicles." This hyperplasia usually involves the conjunctiva of the upper lid and may extend under the mucosa covering the upper half of the cornea. The cornea becomes vascularized, and

as affected cells die they are filled in by fibro-blastic scar tissue. The corneal epithelium is not infected, but it becomes keratinized as a result of the tissue reaction, and this, together with scarring, not only deforms the eye but threatens blindness because of corneal opacity. Secondary bacterial infection is common and inflicts further damage on the cornea, usually with total loss of vision.

Epidemiology. Trachoma is spread by direct or indirect contacts with the conjunctival discharges from infected persons. It can be treated successfully if discovered early, so that the detection and prompt diagnosis of the disease constitute the chief means of control of its spread. The tetracycline antibiotics are applied locally, and oral doses of sulfonamides are usually given at the same time. Children are more frequently affected than adults, and they must be diagnosed and treated before the disease has advanced to the point of scar formation if their recovery is to be complete. In areas where the disease is prevalent, treatment programs coupled with efforts to improve sanitary standards and general living conditions have been effective in control.

Inclusion Conjunctivitis. This is an acute conjunctivitis of newborn babies and is another example of maternal venereal infection transfer. The causative agent appears to reside in the genital tract of adults and can be transferred among them without producing injury or disease. Infants are infected during birth, as they pass through the vaginal canal. The organism appears to have a worldwide distribution, but conjunctivitis occurs only sporadically. It is rarely acquired by adults from infected babies' eyes, but is sometimes seen in children and adults as a "swimming-pool" conjunctivitis acquired from nonchlorinated swimming water contaminated from genital sources.

The disease is less severe than trachoma, but if untreated it may persist in a chronic stage for several months. The incubation period is from 5 to 14 days (in the newborn this distinguishes it from gonococcal ophthalmia, which usually begins within 36 hours of birth). Infant conjunc-

tivitis is characterized by an acute inflammation, particularly of the lower lids. A purulent exudate is produced, but there is no lymphoid follicle formation or scarring. In older children and adults, there is lymphoid hyperplasia, as in trachoma, but it is most marked on the lower lids, and it resolves without scarring. Unlike trachoma, there is no involvement of the cornea in inclusion conjunctivitis.

Confirmation of the diagnosis can be obtained by laboratory demonstration of inclusion bodies within epithelial cells scraped gently from the conjunctival surface of the lower lid. The infection responds rapidly to tetracycline and sulfonamide therapy. The newborn disease is difficult to prevent, since the mother's infection is usually inapparent, and neither penicillin nor silver nitrate instillation in babies' eyes affects the microorganism. Outbreaks associated with swimming pools are very simply prevented by adequate chlorination of the water.

Keratoconjunctivitis. Acute conjunctivitis is also associated with at least two of the true viruses. One of the *adenoviruses* (see Chap. 15, p. 364) is known to be responsible for an acute conjunctivitis that is usually accompanied by symptoms of general infection as well, with low-grade fever, headache, and edema of the tissues around the eyes. The conjunctivae are inflamed, and the cornea may become keratinized and opaque, although this is seldom permanent. Most patients recover completely within a few weeks. This disease is sometimes seen in small outbreaks occurring in shipyards and industrial plants where eyes may be traumatized by foreign objects and then infected from common sources in dispensaries and clinics where they are treated without due attention to strict asepsis. The conjunctival discharges are directly infectious and may remain so on objects contaminated by them. The virus may also be spread through infectious nasal secretions. There is no specific therapy for adenovirus conjunctivitis, and its control depends primarily on industrial safety measures that protect the eyes, as well as careful technique in dispensaries. Sterilized instruments, general cleanliness, and well-scrubbed hands are essential in

clinics where industrial injuries are frequently treated.

Herpes simplex virus may also infect the conjunctival membrane or the cornea. Infections of the eye may accompany herpetic lesions in the mouth and throat, or they may be confined to the ocular tissues. They are sometimes superficial and quickly resolved, but more usually they offer a serious threat of blindness. The cornea may be ulcerated and scarred, or keratinized. Antiviral drugs are now available for the treatment of herpetic eye infections but these are chiefly of value in suppressing the organism when it is located in superficial cells. Deep infections often require treatment by techniques of ophthalmic surgery. There are no specific control measures applicable to herpes simplex virus, for this is an organism that is constantly associated with man, and the vast majority of infections are latent, or of minor importance (see p. 520 of this chapter).

Infectious Diseases Involving, or Entering Through, the "Intact" Skin

Staphylococcal Infections

Staphylococci are among the most constant members of the resident flora of man's superficial tissues. Biologically speaking, there are two types of these organisms, both of which ordinarily live commensalistically on the skin and mucous membranes: one type has very few of the properties required for pathogenicity (i.e., it is *relatively* avirulent) and produces disease only if it is given unusual opportunities for entry into the tissues of persons whose defensive mechanisms are not in good working order; the other type has several virulent properties and probably always has a potential for pathogenicity, but it is normally held in check by the many physiologic conditions that make for good general health and for the integrity of the superficial barrier tissues. The current classification of the staphylococci assigns the species name *Staphylococcus epidermidis* to those strains that fail to display the properties

associated with virulence *when tested in the laboratory*. Those strains that do possess properties that contribute to virulence are given the species name *Staphylococcus aureus*. It must be emphasized that these distinctions are made in the laboratory when strains are isolated from clinical specimens and tested for certain characteristics in vitro. This testing must, of course, be accurately performed with controlled techniques (see Laboratory Diagnosis). The laboratory's report, however, should never be construed as an assignment of the pathogenic role played by a particular strain in an individual situation. This must be done on the basis of the clinical evidence, supported by laboratory studies and sometimes by epidemiologic data as well. Nevertheless, the greater potential for pathogenicity possessed by strains of *S. aureus* should always be recognized.

The diseases produced by staphylococci cover a very wide spectrum, from the simplest localized infection of the skin, or focal infections of deep tissues, to septicemia, disseminating disease, and death. The source of invading organisms is sometimes endogenous, the resident staphylococci entering deep tissues through broken skin or mucosal barriers or multiplying vigorously at some local site because the physiologic barriers have broken down. Probably more often the source of infection is the purulent discharge from the active lesion of another person or the asymptomatic nasal carrier of a virulent strain. Any portal of entry may be involved, but the gastrointestinal tract is ordinarily not susceptible to staphylococcal infection from exogenous sources. The bowel mucosa may be seriously injured by overgrowth of endogenous staphylococci when antibiotic therapy or some other factor has reduced the numbers of Gram-negative enteric bacteria and upset the normal balance of microbial competitions in the bowel; and it may be acutely irritated by ingested staphylococcal *enterotoxin*, as described in the discussion of bacterial food poisoning in Chapter 19 (p. 433). With this exception, staphylococci may enter through any route if the local circumstances permit. However, the skin is not only a very frequent route, but also the most common site of localized staphylococcal infection. For this reason, as well as

for convenience, the staphylococcal diseases are grouped together here as *superficial* or *deep-tissue* infections.

1. Superficial Staphylococcal Infections. The typical lesion produced in response to staphylococcal infection is an abscess (see Chap. 6, p. 108, and Chap. 7, p. 129). Skin abscesses may range in size and severity from the small but annoying *pimple*, to the larger and more painful furuncles (boils) and carbuncles. *Furuncles* arise from abscesses localized in hair follicles. They are uncommon on the scalp, but they may occur on many other hairy surfaces of the body, frequent sites being the axillae, the back of the neck, and the buttocks. (Abscesses arising in the follicles of the eyelashes are called *sties*.) *Carbuncles* are deep-seated abscesses of subcutaneous tissues. They are large, lumpy, and painful because there may be several closely associated, or intercommunicating, pockets of pus. These infections and others, such as staphylococcal *paronychia* (inflammation of the soft tissues around the nails) and *decubitus ulcers* (bedsores), usually arise at sites of minor but continuously irritating injuries to the skin. Such injuries may be caused by the constant pressure of clothing, the macerating effect of heat and moisture, or both of these physical effects coupled with lowered physiologic resistance. Bedridden patients who do not receive proper nursing care probably suffer most from these infections, which add their toll to the underlying debility that confines them to bed and subjects them to another physical problem.

Acne is another type of skin infection commonly associated with staphylococci, but also with other bacterial species that live commensalistically on the skin. This is a problem of adolescence that appears to be primarily associated with physiologic changes related to hormone output. Dietary factors may also play a role, as well as hypersensitivity to components of the persistently infecting organisms. Acne is characterized by the recurrent appearance of crops of pimples on the face, often developing in such density that the epithelium cannot recover and is replaced by scar tissue. It can be controlled by the use of skin soaps that reduce the normal bacterial flora, judicious hormone therapy, some

dietary restrictions, and desensitization with bacterial antigens, these procedures being programmed collectively.

Staphylococcal skin infections can be particularly serious in young children and infants who have fewer defenses against virulent strains than do adults. *Impetigo* (from the Latin word *impetare* meaning to attack) is the clinical term given to the contagious form of skin disease sometimes displayed by children. It is characterized by the formation of vesicles that form on the exposed parts of the body. These are rather large "blisters" with an underlying base of inflammatory tissue. The serous fluid that fills them contains staphylococci, often in association with streptococci. The vesicles rupture and then crust over, healing later with some scarring. Fluid from ruptured vesicles is infectious for susceptible young contacts, and the infection may spread in an epidemic fashion among nursery school or backyard playmates. It may spread in even more rapid patterns through a newborn nursery where susceptibility is greatest. (Impetigo of the newborn is sometimes called *pemphigus neonatorum*, but should not be confused with the noninfectious pemphigus of adults.)

2. Deep-Tissue Infections Caused by Staphylococci. Within the tissues staphylococci may localize anywhere, depending on the route of entry and their accessibility to the blood stream. From the upper respiratory tract they may extend to the sinuses or to the middle ear and mastoid, or downward to the bronchial tract and the pulmonary beds. Staphylococcal pneumonia is one of the most serious of the bacterial pneumonias, because the organism and its toxins produce hemorrhagic, necrotizing lesions in the lung parenchyma (see Chap. 14, p. 319). Within the upper respiratory tract itself, entrenched staphylococcal infection of the tonsils and other lymphoid tissues can be a stubborn and difficult problem, particularly when the causative strain is resistant to antibiotics.

Staphylococci are sometimes the cause of puerperal fever, gaining access to the pelvic tract from the superficial genital mucosa when these are injured and exposed to infection during childbirth. Streptococci are also associated with this type of

disease, perhaps more frequently (see Sec. VII, Chap. 29, p. 619).

From systemic locations, introduced across membranous surfaces, through skin wounds, or from skin abscesses, staphylococci may gain access to the blood stream and be distributed to various sites. They are capable of growing in any tissue, and if the local defenses are not adequate, abscess formation may occur in the bone marrow (*osteomyelitis*), in the covering tissue that sheathes bone (*periostitis*), in the liver or spleen, in the kidney pelvis (*pyelitis*), in the urinary bladder (*cystitis*), or in the brain (*meningitis* or *encephalitis*). Usually focal lesions in one or more of these sites are involved, reflecting the site of entry, but if a fulminating septicemia occurs there may be miliary abscess formation and death. Generalized infections are more frequent and more dangerous in those of highest susceptibility: the very young, the very old, and those with problems that open the door to superimposed infection. The latter include surgical and obstetric patients, people with respiratory diseases, patients with renal or bladder dysfunctions (especially those that require the introduction of catheters through the urethra or ureter, or blood vessel catheterization as in the use of the artificial kidney apparatus), diabetic patients and others with endocrine disorders that affect resistance, and those with cardiac problems requiring arterial catheterization or open-heart surgery. Staphylococci (or other organisms) introduced to the endocardium directly by the latter techniques may result in a rapidly fatal *endocarditis*, or septicemia with generalized infection. Even a minor abscess in the skin may be the source of infection disseminated to systemic tissues if the fibrous capsule encasing it is broken by the pressure of squeezing, so that microorganisms within the lesion are released to surrounding tissues and to adjacent capillaries. It is particularly dangerous to squeeze pimples and boils that appear on the face, because the draining lymphatics and blood capillaries may carry released staphylococci directly into areas contiguous with the brain.

Laboratory Diagnosis

I. Identification of the Organism (*Staphylococcus aureus*) (*Staphylococcus epidermidis*)

A. MICROSCOPIC CHARACTERISTICS. Strains of *Staphylococcus* are indistinguishable by microscopic examination. They are Gram-positive cocci, typically arranged in grapelike clusters, nonmotile, and nonsporeforming.

B. CULTURE CHARACTERISTICS. Strains of *S. aureus* grow well under aerobic or anaerobic conditions on ordinary laboratory media. On blood agar they characteristically possess the *golden-yellow pigment* from which their name was derived. They are often *hemolytic*, and virulent strains associated with lesions usually produce a substance called *coagulase* that causes clotting of plasma (see Chap. 6, p. 114).

Strains of *S. epidermidis* grow under the same conditions, but they usually possess a *white pigment* (they are often called *S. albus* because of this). They are generally *nonhemolytic* and *coagulase-negative*.

These findings represent the general rule but variations may occur. Occasional strains of *S. albus* may be either hemolytic or coagulase-positive, or both, and strains of *S. aureus* may be nonhemolytic or coagulase-negative. Variants of either type may be associated with human lesions, sometimes with minor superficial infections of surgical wounds (e.g., stitch abscesses), or with chronic, low-grade, but threatening systemic infections occurring most frequently as an aftermath of cardiac surgery or catheterization.

C. SEROLOGIC METHODS OF IDENTIFICATION. Serologic methods are generally not applicable because the staphylococci are a large and heterogeneous group antigenically. The tools most useful in recognizing strains of common epidemiologic importance in hospital or community cross-infections are phage typing, and antibiotic susceptibility testing (see Special Laboratory Tests below).

II. Identification of Patient's Serum Antibodies. The serum of most normal adults contains antibodies against numerous staphylococcal products and components: hemolysins, coagulase, leukocidin, hyaluronidase, and others. However, there seems to be no correlation between the titer of these antibodies and resistance to reinfection, and analysis of these titers has no practical diagnostic value.

III. Specimens for Diagnosis. Pus or fluid from any lesion in any part of the body may be submitted for smear and culture. Blood cultures, spinal fluid culture, or pleural, abdominal, or synovial

fluid each may be appropriate depending on clinical circumstances.

Stained smears of the exudate are reported for the presence of clumped organisms resembling staphylococci. Culture reports indicate pigment, hemolysis, and coagulase activity, or they may read simply "*Staph. aureus*" or "*Staph. epidermidis*," implying the combination of properties described above.

IV. Special Laboratory Tests. When it is suspected that cross-infections have been incurred from a single source of infection, two types of laboratory information may support or confirm this:

Fig. 23–6. Phage typing of staphylococci. The photograph above shows an agar plate that was first seeded with staphylococci, then inoculated with a series of 24 numbered bacteriophages, each placed in a separate small area on the surface of the plate. The test strain of *Staphylococcus* was resistant to most of the phages but was lysed by five of them, as evidenced by clear zones at the sites where these viruses were placed and have killed the bacteria. The phage type of this strain of *Staphylococcus* is 6, 47, 53, 81, 83. Bacteriophages are used as an epidemiologic tool to identify individual strains of staphylococci, and to study and control the source of staphylococcal infections. (Reprinted with permission of the U.S. Department of Health, Education, and Welfare, Public Health Service, Communicable Disease Center, Atlanta, Ga.)

A. The "*antibiograms*" of staphylococci isolated from a series of infected patients may be compared. An antibiogram is the pattern of susceptibility and resistance shown by a given strain to a battery of antibiotics. When all the isolated strains show similar or identical patterns, this constitutes presumptive evidence of their epidemiologic relationship.

B. The *phage types* of strains isolated from a series of infections may be compared. The coagulase-positive strains of *Staphylococcus* are generally sensitive to the action of bacteriophages, each being lysed by a particular phage or group of phages. Staphylococcal bacteriophages are given numbers instead of names, and the type of a strain of *Staphylococcus* is indicated by the phages to which it is sensitive (see Fig. 23–6). Thus, *Staph. aureus* of phage type 80/81 is a strain that is lysed by each of the two phages indicated by number. This has little significance of itself, but if many strains isolated from numbers of patients involved in an outbreak of staphylococcal infection all are reported from the laboratory as being of phage type 80/81 (or some other type), this means that the epidemic probably arose from a strain of this type disseminated from a common source that should be identified and eliminated if possible. The strain may be spread by the respiratory secretions, hands, or clothing of an asymptomatic nasal carrier, or from active lesions on the skin or membranes of an infected person. Strains of phage type 80/81 appear to have added virulence in that systemic or localized lesions seen in individuals involved in outbreaks of this type are sometimes more severe than those caused by other types. However, other phage types are also virulent and quite capable of spreading in epidemic patterns when circumstances permit. Some appear to spread more rapidly than others, and to acquire drug resistance with greater speed than others.

Epidemiology

I. Communicability of Infection

A. Reservoir, Sources, and Transmission Routes. Staphylococcal infections have their primary reservoir in man. They are spread from colonizing sources on normal human membranes (usually in the anterior part of the nose) or in open furuncles, draining sinuses, tonsillar abscesses, and similar lesions. They may be trans-

mitted in direct personal contacts or indirectly through contaminated hands and objects. Airborne transfers may be important for viable organisms in dust, or in droplet nuclei from respiratory sources. In hospitals, dirty dry mops and dustcloths may contribute to their spread, as well as soiled bed linens, dressings, and the unwashed hands of personnel that make contact with one patient after another.

B. INCUBATION PERIOD. This varies a great deal and depends largely on the route of entry and resistance of the infected individual, as well as the numbers of virulent organisms introduced. In surgical wounds, infection may appear within a day or two. When organisms are introduced directly into the blood stream, symptoms may ensue within hours. Infections of normal "intact" skin, such as impetigo, boils, or other abscesses, usually require from four to ten days to appear following exposure.

C. COMMUNICABLE PERIOD. Staphylococcal infection is presumably transmissible throughout the time purulent discharges drain from open lesions or the nasal carrier state persists.

D. IMMUNITY. Resistance to staphylococcal infections is based primarily on nonspecific mechanisms. Antibody titers are not consistent and seem to have little relationship to immunity against reinfection. Susceptibility is fairly general, but those at greatest risk are the newborn, those who are debilitated by chronic diseases (e.g., diabetes) or by age, surgical patients, and those who must undergo protracted medical or surgical therapy for underlying organic diseases (see p. 513).

II. Control of Active Infection

A. ISOLATION. It is seldom necessary or feasible to isolate the patient being treated *at home*, but he should be kept away from infants or family members who are ill and debilitated. In the *hospital*, the prompt isolation of all patients with staphylococcal infections is indicated, but the degree of isolation warranted may vary. In the newborn nursery, isolation should be complete and rigidly maintained (this and all other precautions described in Chap. 19, pp. 435 to 439, for the control of epidemic diarrhea in the nursery

apply here as well). On the medical wards, all cases of staphylococcal pneumonia should be isolated in private rooms, but the isolation of other types of infection depends on the degree of risk offered by the draining lesion and the capability of available techniques and staff to contain the infection. In general, private-room isolation of all patients with staphylococcal infections provides the best guarantee of safety to the hospital at large, but if it is to be effective it must be faithfully carried out with attention to every detail of aseptic technique, including the use of gowns and scrupulous hand-washing. Reliance on occlusive dressing for the patient with an infected surgical wound or skin lesion is dangerous under most hospital circumstances.

B. PRECAUTIONS. Dressings from discharging lesions should be placed in a paper or plastic bag, sealed, and burned. Bed linens and clothing should be carefully placed in bags that can be tightly closed, and these are marked for care in transport and handling prior to laundering. If the laundering routine cannot assure disinfection, sheets and bedclothes should be autoclaved or washed in boiling water with detergent. Concurrent disinfection must be carried out for all items and equipment in the patient's room that might be contaminated by infectious discharges or by drying droplet nuclei disseminated from the patient's secretions or exudates. A clean gown should be worn by each person who enters the room, including visitors. Upon leaving, each person discards the gown in a hamper provided near the hand-washing facility and carefully washes his hands with a disinfectant liquid soap, drying them with paper towels. Terminal cleaning-disinfection must be thorough.

C. TREATMENT. Superficial skin lesions are treated by medical or surgical methods designed to promote drainage. Antibiotics are sometimes applied locally but are not given systemically unless parenteral extension of infection is threatened. Antibiotics must be chosen on the basis of laboratory determination of individual strain sensitivity, since many differences in drug resistance exist among staphylococci, especially those encountered in hospitals where antibiotic drugs are in constant use.

D. CONTROL OF STAPHYLOCOCCAL INFECTIONS IN HOSPITALS. The control of hospital infections with these organisms is threefold and is based on an understanding of the three major reasons that hospitals represent the most dangerous focus for staphylococci:

1. Staphylococci rapidly become drug-resistant. When constantly exposed to antibiotics, resistant mutants emerge, and sensitive strains are destroyed. In hospitals, the constant use of antimicrobial drugs encourages the replacement of sensitive strains with resistant ones, in patients, personnel, and the environment. The prevention and control of this situation depend on the prompt and vigorous therapy of known staphylococcal infections with adequate doses of the most effective antibiotics continued for a period of time sufficient to eliminate the causative strain of the individual infection. An important corollary to this approach is to restrict antistaphylococcal drugs to use for staphylococcal infections only and to employ other antibiotics for specific therapy of serious infection as indicated. The indiscriminate use of antibiotics for minor infections or for general prophylaxis has done much to create a resistant bacterial population, particularly in hospitals. Sound laboratory studies should be used as a guide in instituting and maintaining antibiotic therapy in individual cases.

2. Persons who run the greatest risk of serious staphylococcal infections are concentrated in hospitals (see pp. 513 and 515 above), and they should have the greatest protection. The prompt identification and isolation of cases should be accompanied by efforts to find and eliminate the sources so that others will not also be involved. Patients at particular risk (the newborn, those who have undergone prolonged surgery, or those under continuing vascular or urinary catheterization) should be protected from infection by rigid aseptic techniques, using "reverse precautions."

3. Patients and hospital personnel alike become carriers of drug-resistant strains after very short periods of exposure to hospital life. Both may be a source of the organisms for exposed susceptible patients, but personnel constitute the most frequent, permanent, and mobile sources

(see Fig. 29–1, p. 611). When demonstrated to be active shedders of virulent strains that are antibiotic-resistant and belong to phage types frequently associated with the hospital's most common sporadic or epidemic infections, such personnel should be removed from work involving patient contacts, particularly with patients in the high-risk group.

When epidemic outbreaks occur in nurseries, surgical wards, or elsewhere in the hospital, cultures are taken from infected patients, from the noses and lesions of contact personnel, and from environmental sources that might constitute a reservoir for persistent organisms. Antibiograms and phage types are obtained for all isolates of *S. aureus*, and the data are analyzed for a common source. Infected patients are isolated from others, aseptic techniques are reviewed and tightened, and personnel harboring the epidemic strain are removed from the area. Usually they are placed on antibiotic therapy, but this is not always an effective procedure in eliminating a carrier strain, or in ensuring its permanent displacement.

Strict principles of personal hygiene should be applied to patients, and practiced by personnel in all hospital situations, but particularly when the threat of staphylococcal outbreaks occurs. Recurring infections often can be controlled by the judicious use of disinfectant skin soaps as a continuous routine, brief daily ultraviolet exposures for carriers, laundry disinfection of clothing, and careful disinfectant-cleaning of the immediate environment (including bathroom facilities and towels, bedside furniture, and personal toilet items).

III. Prevention

A. IMMUNIZATION. Vaccines prepared from killed cultures of staphylococci and toxoids containing several of the antigenic but inactivated toxic products of staphylococci are often used in the treatment of recurrent furunculosis. Their success as immunizing agents has been difficult to establish, for they fail as often as they seem to improve the patient's resistance. They may be effective, however, in conjunction with vigorous methods of skin and environmental asepsis as outlined above.

B. The prevention of staphylococcal infections in hospitals requires the coordination of methods and the cooperation of all responsible for the safety of the hospital patient (see Chap. 10, pp. 233 to 246).

Erysipelas

The Clinical Disease. Erysipelas is an infection of the skin caused by strains of beta-hemolytic streptococci of group A (see Chap. 14, p. 326). Systemic infection also occurs, with bacteremia, fever, malaise, and marked leukocytosis. The skin lesions occur most frequently on the face and legs, beginning at an inconspicuous portal of entry of the organism in the skin (perhaps rubbed into an abrasion or a hair follicle). The lesion is tender and red and spreads rapidly, having a raised advancing margin. On the face, erysipelas spreads often from the nose, bilaterally across the cheeks in a "butterfly" pattern. The infection is more severe in patients with debilitating conditions, and it is also highly contagious.

Laboratory Diagnosis. See Chapter 14, page 329. Specimens for smear and culture should be taken from the raised peripheral border of the lesions. Blood cultures may yield the organisms also, if taken during the febrile periods.

Epidemiology. Erysipelas occurs most frequently in the older age groups and in infants and is characterized by recurrences in the same individual, possibly because of developing hypersensitivity and reinfection from endogenous sources. Its epidemiology is very similar to that of the other streptococcal diseases described in Chapter 14. Hospitalized patients should be isolated, and strictest precautions should be followed, particularly if the newborn nursery is involved.

Leprosy (Hansen's Disease)

The Clinical Disease. Leprosy is a chronic, very slowly progressive disease. It requires many years to develop but is perhaps the least communicable of infectious diseases. When untreated, however, its progressive development leads to disfigurements that have been greeted for centuries with horror and fear. No social ostracism could be more complete, perhaps, and no physical exclusion more dreadful than that to which lepers have been subjected throughout human history. In recent years, medical knowledge has shed some light and a good deal of objectivity on the problem, so that some of the pressure on the leprous patient has been relieved.

Two forms of leprosy are recognized. Both require many years to develop, and both may be present in the same patient. One is a form characterized by the development of granulomatous nodules, called *lepromas*, in the skin, the mucous membranes (especially those of the upper respiratory tract), and some of the visceral organs. This nodular form is often spoken of as *lepromatous, or cutaneous*, leprosy (see Fig. 23-7, *A*). The other form involves the development of lesions around peripheral nerves, which leads to sensory damage, anesthesia, and atrophy of muscle, skin, and bone, particularly in the extremities. This *tuberculoid, or neural*, form of leprosy may lead to injuries of the hands or feet that are mutilating and leave the patient open to secondary infections that result in the loss of fingers and toes, nasal cartilage, and other affected tissues.

Laboratory Diagnosis

I. Identification of the Organism (*Mycobacterium leprae*). The organism of this disease has never been satisfactorily cultivated or demonstrated to have pathogenicity for animal hosts fully comparable to that seen in human beings. It is visualized in smears and scrapings from the skin or mucous membranes of patients with lepromatous nodules as an acid-fast bacillus. Aggregates of *M. leprae* (Hansen's bacillus) look like tubercle bacilli, lying in parallel bundles within the cells of granulomatous tissue, particularly the epithelioid cells or other monocytes. When they are injected into the footpads of mice they produce granulomatous lesions locally but not progressive infection. The nature of this organism and its role in the pathogenesis of human leprosy remain a problem for continuing study.

II. Identification of Patient's Serum Antibodies. Serologic tests for leprosy are not reliable, but it

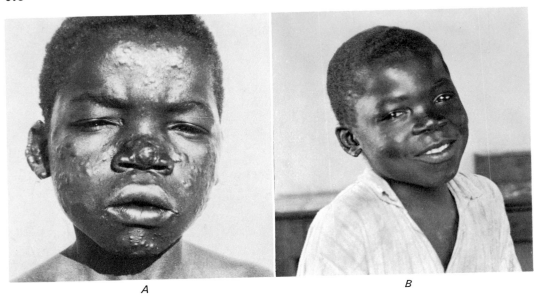

A   *B*

Fig. 23–7. *A.* An early case of cutaneous (lepromatous) leprosy. *B.* The same child following treatment with antileprosy drugs. (Courtesy of American Leprosy Missions, Inc., New York, N.Y.)

should be remembered that sera from leprous patients give false-positive results in tests for syphilis.

Lepromin is an extract of leprous tissue used as a skin antigen. It produces a skin reaction of the hypersensitive type in patients with the neural type of leprosy but is negative in lepromatous cases. As a diagnostic agent, therefore, lepromin has limited value.

III. Specimens for Diagnosis. Scrapings or biopsies of skin lesions are submitted for acid-fast stains by the Ziehl-Neelsen technique and microscopic examination for intracellular acid-fast bacilli. The nasal mucosa is a preferred area for sampling, or the active periphery of a nodule cut through its epidermal layer and scraped along the inner edge of the cut for cells representing the central portion of the granuloma. Acid-fast bacilli are seen within the mononuclear cells.

Cultures and animal inoculations are attempted with this material to establish the fact that the organism cannot be propagated and that it is not *M. tuberculosis.*

Epidemiology

I. Communicability of Infection

A. RESERVOIR, SOURCES, AND TRANSMISSION ROUTES. This disease has a human reservoir only. The organisms present in the discharges of infectious lesions are thought to be transmitted through the skin or mucous membranes of susceptible contacts. Infants and young children are the most susceptible, but their contacts with infectious parents or other adults must be long and intimate if they are to contract leprosy.

B. INCUBATION PERIOD. Very long periods of exposure are required, the average time for appearance of symptoms being three to five years. Infants who were heavily exposed from birth have been known to develop the disease in as short a time as seven months or, more usually, one to two years.

C. COMMUNICABLE PERIOD. Leprosy is considered infectious if bacilli can be demonstrated in skin or mucosal lesions. Usually many more

organisms are demonstrable in lepromatous nodules than in the tuberculoid, neural lesions.

D. IMMUNITY. Human susceptibility to leprosy is universal but greatest during childhood. Immunity is of the hypersensitive type, as indicated by reactivity to lepromin. Patients with the more progressive lepromatous type of infection have no resistance and are lepromin-negative, whereas tuberculoid patients as well as infected but asymptomatic persons are lepromin-positive. The long incubation period and the closeness of contact required for transmission of the disease indicate a low communicability; increasing resistance with age is reflected in the diminished communicability of leprosy in older children and adults.

Leprosy is distributed primarily in the tropical and semitropical areas of the world. There are an estimated ten million total cases, half of which are found in China and India. The African continent has the next highest incidence, and there is a spotty distribution of foci in Mediterranean Europe, Hawaii, the Caribbean, and the southern Gulf States in the United States.

II. Control of Active Infection

A. ISOLATION. It is no longer believed that lepers should be rigidly isolated. During active stages of the disease they are best treated in leprosaria, such as the National Leprosy Hospital in Carville, Louisiana, where experienced methods of medical treatment and control offer hope for suppression of clinical symptoms and a return to community living. Many patients with inactive lesions are treated at home.

B. PRECAUTIONS. Nursing care is very similar to that of the tuberculous patient. Respiratory and skin discharges should be disposed of by incineration. Bed linens and clothing should be carefully handled and bagged for transport to the laundry. If the patient is in an active lepromatous stage, a gown is advisable to protect the clothing of the nurse or others who are in close contact, and hand-washing is as vital as in the care of any other infectious disease. Terminal disinfection-cleaning should be thorough.

C. TREATMENT. The sulfone drugs (diaminodiphenyl-sulfone, promin, and diasone) have proved effective in arresting the active disease and in preventing reactivation of old lesions. Antituberculous drugs, such as streptomycin, also have value, and other antibiotics are also used to control secondary bacterial infection. The sulfones are given in gradually increased doses until a maintenance plateau is reached and continued for three or more years (see Fig. 23-7, B).

D. CONTROL OF CONTACTS. The chief method of control involves case finding, especially among the family contacts of the newly diagnosed individual case. Newborn infants are separated from leprous parents, but older children who have already been exposed are not segregated from their families. All active cases are reported and registered so that they can be periodically examined and referred to treatment clinics or hospitals when necessary.

III. Prevention.

The appearance of new cases can be markedly reduced by protecting or segregating the children born into families where leprosy exists. In endemic areas, survey and treatment clinics and health education of the public have helped to control the disease and to alleviate both suffering and fear.

Yaws

The Clinical Disease. Yaws is one of several nonvenereal diseases caused by spirochetes of the treponemal group. (*Bejel* and *pinta* are related syndromes.) It is an acute infection that becomes chronic and relapsing if not treated. The primary lesion, or "mother yaw," appears in three to six weeks at the site of skin exposure and inoculation. This lesion is a papule that enlarges into a papilloma, or tumor-like growth of epithelial cells. Mild symptoms of systemic involvement occur and after some weeks successive crops of papules appear on the skin, persisting for months. There may also be destructive lesions in bone. The disease is marked by periods of latency and reactivation of progressive lesions that can be

quite disfiguring. The superficial lesions are distributed on the arms and legs, palms and soles, but may also occur on the trunk and on the oral and nasal mucosa.

> **Laboratory Diagnosis.** Clinical diagnosis is based on the appearance and distribution of the lesions and is supported by the laboratory demonstration of spirochetes in the eroding and ulcerating papillomas. Dark-field examination or special staining of the exudates is necessary. The causative organism is *Treponema pertenue.*
>
> The sera of patients with yaws or other treponematoses give positive results in the serologic tests for syphilis.

Epidemiology. The reservoir for this disease is man. The exudates of eroding skin lesions contain the organisms, which are transmitted by direct contact, or indirectly by contaminated objects. It is thought that flies may play a role in transmission, but this is probably less frequent than personal contact.

Yaws is a disease of tropical and semitropical countries around the world. It occurs most frequently in children, and in areas where living conditions are poorest. The disease responds to a single intramuscular injection of penicillin in a long-lasting form, so that early diagnosis and prompt treatment constitute the best hope for control. Concerted efforts are being made through the World Health Organization to eliminate yaws in its endemic foci in many countries, through case finding and mass treatment programs, as well as through efforts to improve standards of living.

Herpes Simplex Virus

Herpesvirus Infections. Herpes simplex belongs to the group of viruses that includes the varicella (chickenpox) and herpes zoster agents. It produces vesicular eruptions of the skin or mucous membranes that are similar to those of zoster (see Chap. 15, pp. 370 to 371), but it differs antigenically, and in its epidemiologic patterns of spread. Herpes simplex virus often establishes a lifelong association with infected human beings. It may involve various mucous membranes (oral, pharyngeal, conjunctival, genital) or mucocutaneous areas in recurrent infections interspersed with long periods of asymptomatic latency. Most active herpetic infections are mild, but they may take severe forms, as in neonatal disease derived from maternal lesions of the genital mucosa (see pp. 507 to 508) or keratoconjunctivitis (pp. 510 to 511).

Other severe forms of herpes simplex virus infection include meningoencephalitis and herpetic eczema. These diseases are considerably more rare than the primary acute *stomatitis* (inflammation of the oral membranes) that is seen in infants and small children or the recurrent *herpes labialis* of adults. The latter is familiar to everyone as the "cold sore" or "fever blister" that crops up again and again in some individuals at a mucocutaneous margin of the lip.

> **Laboratory Diagnosis.** Severe infections of herpesvirus origin require laboratory confirmation of the diagnosis. The virus can be isolated from specimens of saliva, throat washings, or stools. These are inoculated into chick embryos, tissue cultures, or the cornea of a rabbit. Harvested virus is identified by the typical cellular pathology it produces in these cultures, and by specific antisera that neutralize its infectivity. The patient's serum also contain antibodies that rise in titer during the course of infection and can be serologically demonstrated with known herpesvirus.

Epidemiology. Man is the reservoir for herpesviruses. Herpes simplex may be present in the saliva or respiratory secretions of infected persons, in stools, in discharges from the conjunctiva of herpes-infected eyes, and on the genital mucosa. It is transmitted by direct personal contacts of all kinds and, by the same token, is seen most frequently among people who live together under crowded conditions, with poor hygienic standards.

There are no specific treatment for herpetic infections and no special measures for control other than those of careful personal hygiene and the avoidance of contact with obviously infected persons.

The Superficial Mycoses

Ringworm Infections. The superficial mycotic diseases of hair, skin, or nails are generally referred to collectively as ringworm infections. The clinical term for ringworm is *tinea* (derived from the Latin word for "worm"). In medical usage, this term is modified by another Latin word indicating the part of the body affected, e.g., *tinea capitis* (ringworm of the scalp), *tinea corporis* (ringworm of the body), *tinea pedis* (ringworm of the feet), and *tinea unguium* (ringworm of the nails). Many other more specific anatomic terms may be used for fungous infections of particular areas of the body, such as *tinea barbae* (the bearded area of the face and neck are involved) or *tinea cruris* (the inguinal folds are infected), but the four major terms above are used with greatest frequency.

These "dermatomycoses" are caused by members of a group of fungi called *dermatophytes*, because they are capable of invading skin or its keratinized appendages, but they do not infect systemic tissues. There are three important genera of dermatophytes (*Epidermophyton*, *Microsporum*, and *Trichophyton*), which are described briefly below, under Laboratory Diagnosis. A particular species of dermatophyte may cause a variety of clinical lesions in different areas of the body, and, conversely, different fungi may cause similar clinical manifestations. For this reason the superficial mycoses are generally classified according to the part of the body infected.

Epidemiologically these infections have much in common. Some of the causative fungi have a reservoir in both man and animals, some in man only, but all of them are directly transmissible from person to person, unlike the systemic mycoses (see Chap. 17). The route of transmission may be through direct contact with infected persons (or animals) or from indirect sources of environmental contamination derived from active cases. Methods for the control and treatment of these infections are very similar and are described in outline form at the end of this section (see Table 23–1), following a brief description of the four major clinical forms of dermatomycosis and the causative fungi.

1. *Tinea capitis* (Ringworm of the Scalp). This infection usually begins with the appearance of a small scaling papule which is red and itchy. Numerous papules may appear and spread peripherally. The hair of the affected area becomes brittle and is easily broken off, leaving patches of baldness (alopecia). Sometimes the underlying tissue becomes inflamed and ulcerated, this type of lesion being called a *kerion*. The hair shafts themselves are infected with the fungus (see Fig. 23–8). Some of the fungi (*Microsporum* species) are fluorescent in ultraviolet light. This can be an aid to diagnosis: that is, the suspected area of the scalp can be examined under an ultraviolet ("Wood's") lamp, and fluorescing hairs can be removed with forceps for laboratory examination (see Fig. 23–9).

Some *Trichophyton* species create a lesion known as "black dot" ringworm, the effect being created by the dark broken stumps of hair shafts sticking up in an area of alopecia and scaling. These fungi do not fluoresce under the Wood's lamp.

Tinea favosa is a clinical lesion of the scalp caused by a particular species of *Trichophyton*

Fig. 23–8. *Microsporum* species on a hair shaft (100 ×). Note the clusters of spores clinging to and growing on the surface of the hair. Fine branching mycelial threads can also be seen extending from the spore masses.

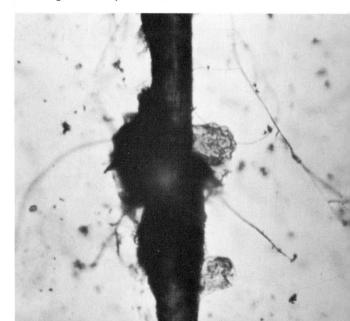

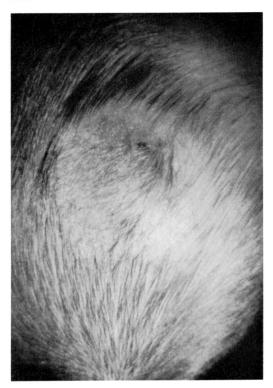

Fig. 23–9. Tinea capitis, or ringworm of the scalp, often occurs in childhood. Under the Wood's light the infected hairs fluoresce. (Courtesy of Dr. Lamar S. Osment, Medical College of Alabama, Birmingham, Ala.)

(*T. schoenleinii*). Cup-shaped yellowish crusts, called *scutula*, are formed. The lesion is deep and may heal by scarring, with permanent destruction of the hair follicles.

2. Tinea corporis (Ringworm of the Body). This term refers to fungous infections of the glabrous (smooth, nonhairy) skin anywhere on the body. The lesions are characteristically flat, spreading, and ring-shaped. The periphery of the lesion is always the most active, being raised, erythematous, sometimes vesicular and weeping, sometimes dry and scaling. Moist lesions may form crusts as they heal. The infection advances peripherally, leaving a central area of healing, normal skin in many instances.

3. Tinea pedis (Ringworm of the Feet). "Athlete's foot" is one of the most common and widespread of the superficial fungous infections. It may often appear as nothing more than a scaling or cracking of the skin, particularly between the toes; but it may become chronic and severe, with vesicle formation and maceration of tissues. Scaling may extend over the heels and soles of the feet, sometimes with vesicular eruptions or acute excematoid reactions. The tissues of the sole may be undermined by ulcerations, with resulting cellulitis, lymphangitis, and systemic reaction. This form of *tinea pedis* can be chronically disabling. The hands may also become infected, and allergic skin reactions to fungal products may appear on many parts of the body, but particularly the arms and legs.

4. Tinea unguium (Ringworm of the Nails). The nails of the hands or feet may become involved in chronic infections caused by the dermatophytic fungi. (Infections with *Candida albicans* are also common, but they have a somewhat different epidemiology, being of endogenous origin [see Chap. 30].) The affected nails become discolored, thickened, brittle, and often deeply grooved or pitted. Caseous epidermal debris accumulates under the nail, and the top may separate. Eventually the entire nail may be destroyed if the fungus invades the entire plate. Unlike *Candida* or staphylococcal infections, there is usually no paronychial involvement.

Laboratory Diagnosis. The characteristic features of the three genera of dermatophytes may be summarized as follows:

Epidermophyton. The colony is velvety and greenish-yellow, with radiating furrows. Microscopically, the macroconidia identify the fungus. These are large, club-shaped, septate, smooth bodies usually born in clusters on the hyphae. The only important species is *E. floccosum.*

Microsporum. Colonies are velvety, woolly, or powdery, depending on the species. They also vary in color, one species being light gray to brown; the other two, bright orange or yellow. The macroconidia are spindle-shaped, septate, thick-walled, and rough-surfaced (see Fig. 23–10). The three important species are *M. audouini*, *M. canis*, and *M. gypseum.*

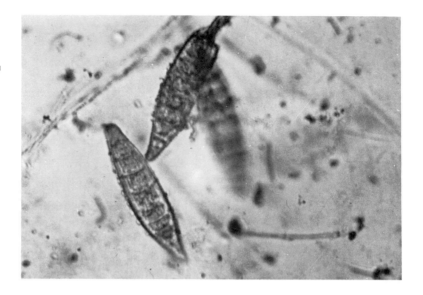

Fig. 23–10. Macroconidia of a *Microsporum* species (1000 ×).

Trichophyton. There are many species, displaying a variety of colony forms and pigments. On microscopic examination, these fungi are seen to produce many microconidia and few macroconidia. The latter are thin, pencil-shaped bodies, multiseptate, thin-walled, and smooth (see Fig. 23–11). Some of the important species are *T. mentagrophytes*, *T. rubrum*, *T. tonsurans*, *T. violaceum*, and *T. schoenleinii*.

Most of these fungi grow slowly in the laboratory, requiring two to four weeks for maturation and identification of characteristic reproductive structures. They are strict aerobes that grow best at room temperature (22° to 28° C) rather than at body temperature.

Specimens for Diagnosis. Scrapings of involved areas of skin, vesicular fluid, exudates, or hairs may be submitted for microscopic examination and culture. In general, it is best to take material from the active margins of advancing lesions, scraping deeply under the lip of crateriform lesions or into the inflamed base of vesicles or papules. Hairs and skin scrapings may be examined under the microscope directly, using a 10 per cent hydroxide solution to clear cellular debris. When infected hair is examined, fungous spores may be seen invading the shaft itself (*endothrix*) or clinging to its external surfaces (*ectothrix*). Skin scrapings usually reveal branching hyphal fragments without spores.

These materials may be satisfactorily cultured on a variety of simple media, the most common of which is Sabouraud's glucose agar, usually containing antibiotics to inhibit the growth of contaminating bacteria.

Fig. 23–11. The pencil-shaped object is a macroconidium of a *Trichophyton* species (1000 ×). Compare with the shape and appearance of the *Microsporum* macroconidia shown in Figure 23–10.

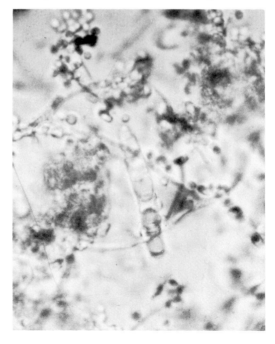

Table 23–1. The Epidemiology of the Superficial Mycoses

Disease	Causative Fungus	Reservoir	Sources	Transmission	Incubation Period
Tinea capitis	*Microsporum* sp. *Trichophyton* sp.	Man Dogs Cats Cattle	Lesions Combs Toilet articles Barber's tools Head rests of upholstered seats in theatres, trains, etc.	Direct or indirect contacts	10 to 14
Tinea favosa	*T. schoenleinii*	Man	Crusts from scutula	Direct or indirect (favored by crowding and filth)	10 to 14
Tinea corporis	*Epidermophyton Microsporum* sp. *Trichophyton* sp.	Man and animals	Lesions Clothing Floors Shower stalls	Direct or indirect contacts	10 to 14
Tinea pedis	*Epidermophyton Trichophyton* sp.	Man	Lesions Shoes and socks Floors Shower stalls	Direct or indirect contacts	10 to 14
Tinea unguium	*Epidermophyton Trichophyton* sp.	Man	Lesions	Person-to-person transmission unusual, but may extend to other nails of infected individual	Source and time of exposure usually unknown

municable eriod	Special* Treatment	Precautions	Other Controls
lesions in active	Daily shampoo Fungicidal ointment Protect with skullcap At night, pull out infected hairs and reapply ointment Griseofulvin by mouth, especially for *M. audouini* infections X-ray epilation if indicated	Keep head covered with cotton cap that can be sterilized frequently by boiling or autoclaving	Investigate household for other infected cases Look for infection among pet animals or farm animal contacts
lesions in active	Epilation usually essential Other therapy as above	As above	This infection more common in central and southeast Europe than in U.S.A.; seen in Russian and Polish immigrants from refugee camps; these are usually detained and treated before entry
lesions in active	Keep skin very clean by soap-and-water bathing Clean away crusts and scabs, if any, and apply fungicidal ointments Griseofulvin by mouth	Infected persons should not frequent public pools and gymnasiums Clothing, especially underclothes, should be disinfected if in contact with lesions	Look for source of infection among human or animal contacts
lesions in active	As above Keep feet clean and dry; expose to air as much as possible	Cotton socks or stockings should be worn and disinfected between uses, preferably by boiling; shoes can be fumigated with formaldehyde	Infected persons should not frequent public pools and gymnasiums; the care of such places includes daily disinfectant cleaning
lesions n active, ttle nuni- ty for s	Nail is kept closely pared and filed Fungicidal soaks and ointments topically Griseofulvin by mouth X-radiation sometimes necessary but recurrences are frequent	As above if toenails are involved When fingernails are infected, gloves should be worn only to maintain contact with fungicides; otherwise nails should be kept clean and dry	As above if toenails are involved

text discussion also.

Table 23–2. Summary: Infectious Diseases Acquired Through Intact Skin and Mucosa, Transmitted by Human Contacts

Clinical Disease	Causative Organism	Other Possible Entry Routes	Incubation Period	Communicabl Period
I. Venereal Diseases				
Syphilis	*Treponema pallidum*	Parenteral, or transfer across placenta	10 to 21 days	Probably commur cable during 2–4 years of primary secondary stages and during first y of latency
Gonorrhea	*Neisseria gonorrhoeae*	Ophthalmic route for newborns	3–9 days; in ophthalmia neonatorum 36–48 hours	In adults, com- municable for ye if not treated; conjunctival mer branes are infect until discharges
Chancroid	*Hemophilus ducreyi*		3–5 days	Communicable th infectious discha of genital lesions and buboes
Granuloma inguinale	*Calymmatobacterium granulomatis*		Unknown	While infective ag is found in lesior
Lymphogranuloma venereum	Filterable "large virus" of *Bedsonia* species		1–4 weeks	Untreated LGV m communicable fe months or years

ecimens equired	Laboratory Diagnosis	Immunization	Treatment	Nursing Management
e fluid rations natous lesion sy serum	Dark-field examination for spirochete Silver impregnation demonstrates spirochete Positive for reagin (VDRL, Kolmer) Positive for treponemal antibodies (TPI, FTA, Reiter's test)	None	Penicillin Tetracyclines Erythromycin	Isolation (antibiotic therapy eliminates threat of communicability in 24 hrs); concurrent disinfection of discharges from open lesions and of objects freshly contaminated by direct contacts; gown during communicable period; careful *handwashing;* guard against careless handling of hypodermic needles and other sharp instruments after use
te from ns	Smear and culture	None	Penicillin	Hospitalized patients are isolated or partially isolated in cubicles until 24 hours after antibiotic therapy has been instituted (isolate infected babies in nurseries); concurrent disinfection of articles; *handwashing*
te from ns	Smear and culture	None	Sulfonamides	Similar to above
y of lesions	Isolation of organism in chick embryos	None	Streptomycin Tetracyclines Chloramphenicol	Concurrent disinfection of exudates from lesions and contaminated articles
te from ns biopsy serum	Smear and isolation in embryonated eggs Rising titer of antibodies	None	Sulfonamides Tetracycline	Same as above

Table 23–2. (Cont.)

Clinical Disease	Causative Organism	Other Possible Entry Routes	Incubation Period	Communicable Period
II. Eye Diseases				
Acute bacterial conjunctivitis	Streptococci Staphylococci Pneumococci *Hemophilus* species Gonococci	Respiratory Skin	Short, 24–72 hours	During active infection
Trachoma	Filterable agent of *Bedsonia* group		About 5–12 days	During active infection
Inclusion conjunctivitis (newborn)	Filterable agent of *Bedsonia* group	Contaminated swimming-pool water	Unknown	During active infection
Keratoconjunctivitis	Adenovirus Herpes simplex virus	Respiratory	Unknown	During active inf
III. Skin Contact Diseases				
Staphylococcal infections	*Staphylococcus aureus*	Respiratory Gastrointestinal Parenteral	Variable, in surgical wounds 1–2 days Impetigo, boils, 4–10 days	During time of purulent dischar of open lesion; as long as nasal carrier state persists
Erysipelas	Beta-hemolytic streptococci of group A	Respiratory	Unknown, probably about 2 days	During active inf no longer comm cable 24 hours a institution of ant biotic therapy

pecimens Required	Laboratory Diagnosis	Immunization	Treatment	Nursing Management
ate or dis-ge from eye	Smear and culture	None	Tetracycline Ophthalmic ointment Sulfonamide ophthalmic ointment	Concurrent disinfection of exudate and articles contaminated by exudate
ate from eye	Smear for cyto-plasmic inclusion bodies	None	Tetracycline ophthalmic ointment; sulfonamides	Same as above
elial cells ped gently eyelids	Same as above	None	Tetracycline Sulfonamides	Same as above and isolate infected babies in nurseries
as above	Virus isolation	None	Nonspecific	Careful aseptic techniques in dispensaries and industrial clinics
te from ns fluid l fluid ninal fluid ial fluid	Smear and culture Antibiograms Phage typing	Killed vaccines and toxoids	Antibiotics chosen on basis of sensitivity	Hospital isolation; very stringent aseptic techniques including burning of dressings, autoclaving of linen if laundry cannot assure disinfection; concurrent disinfection of all articles possibly contaminated by infectious discharges; gown and *hand-washing* with dis-infectant soap; terminal disinfection must be thorough
ngs from d peripheral er of lesions	Smear and culture Smear and culture	None	Penicillin Sulfonamides	Hospital isolation: concurrent disinfection of discharges and dressings from lesions; terminal disinfection should be thorough

Table 23–2. (*Cont.*)

Clinical Disease	Causative Organism	Other Possible Entry Routes	Incubation Period	Communicable Period
Leprosy	*Mycobacterium leprae*		3–5 years	During time bacilli be demonstrated skin or mucosal le
Yaws	*Treponema pertenue*		3–6 weeks	During time of ac infection and wh skin lesions are present
Herpes simplex infection	Herpes simplex virus	Respiratory	Unknown	During active inf

Treatment. The superficial mycotic infections are treated locally with a variety of fungistatic or fungicidal solutions, ointments, lotions, or dusting powders. Potassium permanganate and iodide solutions, dyes such as gentian violet, and salicylic acid have been used for many years. More recently, copper and zinc compounds of undecylenic acid have been found effective, and these are formulated in many dusting powders and ointments. Griseofulvin is an antibiotic synthesized by some species of *Penicillium*. It is not effective in the treatment of the systemic mycoses but is very helpful in suppressing the dermatophytes, particularly some species of *Microsporum* and *Trichophyton*.

Questions

1. Why is it not usual for venereal diseases to be spread by means other than sexual contact?
2. On what factors does the control of venereal disease depend?
3. What is congenital syphilis?
4. Briefly describe the organism *Treponema pallidum*.
5. What is the TPI test?
6. What is the communicable period for syphilis?
7. How can late syphilis be diagnosed in the laboratory?
8. Briefly describe the precautions in the nursing care of a patient with active superficial lesions.
9. When is treatment for the syphilitic pregnant woman effective?
10. What is the Herxheimer reaction?
11. How can venereal disease be prevented?

ecimens equired	Laboratory Diagnosis	Immunization	Treatment	Nursing Management
ngs or sies of skin ns	Smear and culture	None	Sulfones Antituberculous drugs	Rigid isolation not necessary; respiratory and skin discharges are incinerated; bed linens and clothing bagged for transport to laundry; gown and *hand-washing;* terminal disinfection-cleaning should be thorough
tes and ings from Iomas	Dark-field examination Special staining	None	Penicillin	Concurrent disinfection of discharges and contaminated articles
washings	Virus isolation	None	None specific	Careful personal hygiene; avoidance of contact with obviously infected persons

12. Briefly describe four types of the clinical disease gonorrhea.
13. What nursing precautions are necessary in the care of patients with a gonococcal infection?
14. Name three other venereal diseases and their causative organisms.
15. What is trachoma?
16. Briefly describe the superficial skin infections acne and impetigo.
17. What is an antibiogram?
18. What are phage types of staphylococci?
19. What is the communicable period for staphylococcal infections?
20. What three major reasons are responsible for hospitals representing the most dangerous focus for staphylococci?
21. What are the two forms of leprosy?
22. What organism is believed responsible for leprosy?
23. What specimens are used for the diagnosis of leprosy?
24. What is the incubation period for leprosy?
25. What nursing precautions are used in the care of a patient with leprosy?
26. What is yaws?
27. What are the clinical terms for the ringworm infections?
28. What specimens are used for the diagnosis of ringworm infections?

24 Infectious Diseases Acquired Through Intact Skin and Mucosa, Transmitted by Animal Contacts

This chapter highlights two zoonoses that are transmissible from animals to human beings through direct contacts. The first of these is *anthrax*, caused by a bacillus that forms spores that are highly resistant and may persist for years in dried animal products (hides, wool, hair) or in soil. The human disease may be acquired directly from sick or dying animals, from soil, or, more frequently, from animal products being processed in textile and leather manufacture. (See also Chaps. 14 and 19.)

Tularemia is another disease of animals that can be transmitted to man in numerous ways, including transfer through respiratory, alimentary, and arthropod-borne routes (Chaps. 14, 19, and 27), but is frequently acquired during direct contacts with infected small wild game (especially rabbits). Cutaneous or conjunctival infections may be incurred when these animals are skinned and dressed, in the field or in butcher shops.

Other diseases associated with direct animal contacts include brucellosis, leptospirosis, and the superficial fungous infections (ringworm). These are discussed briefly here, with reference to chapters in which other routes of transfer and entry are emphasized.

Anthrax

The Clinical Disease. The bacillary agent of anthrax is an aerobic sporeformer that is primarily associated with severe disease of domestic animals, notably sheep, cattle, and horses. The resistant spore of this organism is capable of surviving for months and years in a dried condition, in soil, and in the hides, hair, and wool of infected animals. Human anthrax has been an occupational disease among people who handle animal products for industrial processing, and it also represents a hazard for farmers and veterinarians who work directly with infected animals. In recent years, however, this disease has become an infrequent problem in this country for several reasons: domestic animal herds have been largely freed of the infection, imported animal products are sterilized either before processing or before final distribution for sale, some effective controls have been instituted for the handling of raw products that would be damaged by sterilization, and immunizing agents are now available for the further protection of exposed workers.

Human anthrax usually begins as an infection of the skin, with the formation of a lesion known as "malignant pustule." The bacilli, or more usually the spores, enter the skin, probably through minor abrasions at the point of pressure contacts with the hide or other product being handled. Within a day or so a papule appears at the site of entry, rapidly develops into a vesicle, becomes pustular, and progresses to necrosis. This necrotic ulcer, or "eschar," is sometimes underlaid by hard, swollen tissues. As the spores germinate, capsulated vegetative bacilli multiply in the wound, and a gelatinous edema affects the surrounding area. The bacilli spread through adjacent lymph channels into the blood stream, multiplying freely. The overwhelming septicemia that results, if untreated, leads to shock and death within a few days. Similar disaster may follow the inhalation of spores (see Chap. 14, pp. 351 to 356) or their ingestion (Chap. 19, p. 448) if this occurs.

Laboratory Diagnosis

I. Identification of the Organism (*Bacillus anthracis*)

A. MICROSCOPIC CHARACTERISTICS. The genus *Bacillus* includes large Gram-positive, sporeforming, aerobic rods. Many of the species of this genus are saprophytes, such as *B. subtilis* or *B. megatherium*, which live in soil, dust, vegetation, or water and are seldom capable of surviving in human tissues or injuring them. *B. anthracis* is the only member of the group that possesses properties that are always pathogenic for man and animals. They can often be distinguished from other species of the genus by the fact that they are *encapsulated* and are *nonmotile*. They line up in chains, with individual ends squared off at regular intervals as though they had been chopped with a knife from a continuing strand of protoplasm (see Fig. 24–1, *D, E*).

B. CULTURE CHARACTERISTICS. *B. anthracis* grows readily on blood agar incubated at 30° C under aerobic conditions. The colonies are nonhemolytic and dull gray. They sometimes have irregular margins but some variants are smooth and discrete (see Fig. 24–1, *A, B, C*). The isolated organism is identified by its typical microscopic appearance, lack of motility, and its virulence for mice or other laboratory animals.

II. Identification of Patient's Serum Antibodies. Serologic identification of the patient's antibodies or of the organism itself is not practical.

III. Specimens for Diagnosis

A. Exudate from the cutaneous lesion is submitted for smear and culture.

B. Sputum specimens may reveal the organisms by smear or culture when inhalation anthrax is suspected.

C. Blood cultures should be collected as soon as the nature of the cutaneous lesion is suspected.

IV. Special Laboratory Tests. Infected tissue taken at autopsy contains an anthrax antigen that gives a precipitin reaction with antianthrax immune serum. This is known as the *Ascoli test*.

Epidemiology

I. Communicability of Infection

A. RESERVOIR, SOURCES, AND TRANSMISSION ROUTES. The reservoir of anthrax infection is

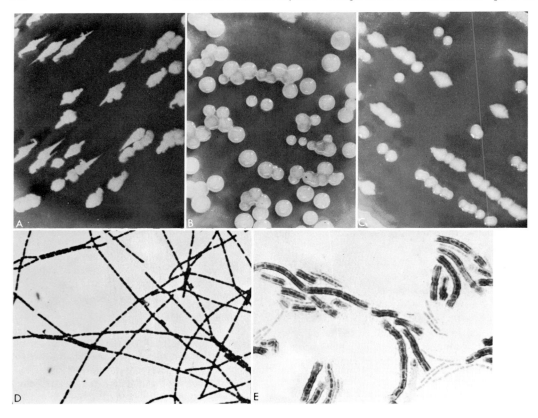

Fig. 24–1. *Bacillus anthracis. A, B,* and *C* are photographs of colonies growing on agar plates. *A.* Rough-surfaced, nonencapsulated colonies. *B.* Smooth mucoid colonies of a strain that is producing capsular substance. *C.* A mixture of smooth and rough colonies growing side by side.

D and *E* are photomicrographs of anthrax bacilli. *D.* Nonencapsulated bacilli from a rough colony. *E.* Encapsulated bacilli from a smooth colony. (Reproduced from Housewright, Riley D., in *The Bacteria — A Treatise on Structure and Function*, Volume III : *Biosynthesis*, edited by I. C. Gunsalus and Roger Y. Stanier. Academic Press, Inc., New York, 1962.)

in a number of domestic animals, mostly herbivorous ruminants, such as cattle, sheep, horses, pigs, or goats. Infected animals die of anthrax, but their tissues may harbor the spores for very long periods. Pasture soil also becomes contaminated and may remain so for years, with infection being spread among animals, from carcasses or from soil, by biting flies or other insects and by vultures. There is no effective method known for disinfecting the soil of these areas where animal anthrax has been prevalent, and this environmental contamination remains a possible source of infection for both animals and man. Anthrax may be transmitted to man from a great variety of animal products, including bone meal, shaving brush bristles, hair or wool used in textile industries, hides processed for leather goods production, and so on. The spores

may be inhaled or ingested (in contaminated meat) or enter through the skin as described above.

B. INCUBATION PERIOD. Usually less than a week.

C. COMMUNICABLE PERIOD. Anthrax is not transmitted from person to person except under rare circumstances. The infectivity of animal or soil sources may persist for years.

D. IMMUNITY. Animals and human beings that survive an attack of the disease are apparently resistant to reinfection. Natural resistance to anthrax varies among animal species and has not been determined with certainty for man. The infection is endemic in agricultural regions, but may fluctuate in its locations with changing soil and climatic conditions, or through the introduction of the organism by vectors or in animal feeds. The incidence of human anthrax similarly varies in different parts of the world. The annual world total is between 20,000 and 100,000 cases, but in this country the figure is now usually less than one hundred in a decade, sporadic cases being associated with occupational hazards, as previously pointed out.

II. Control of Active Infection

A. ISOLATION. Hospitalized patients should be isolated until they have been treated and their lesions are bacteriologically negative. This is advisable from the point of view of preventing contamination of the environment with resistant spores. Cubicle rather than private-room isolation is satisfactory, provided other barrier techniques are observed.

B. PRECAUTIONS. The organisms multiplying in human tissues are in the vegetative state. When they are discharged to the environment in exudates from cutaneous lesions, or in sputum, they convert rapidly to spores, and these can be destroyed only by incineration or steam sterilization. Contaminated dressings should be placed in paper bags and burned. Bedclothing and linens should be autoclaved before laundering. Nursing and medical equipment should be individualized for the patient insofar as possible. Disposable items are placed in bags for incineration; heat-

stable items can be steam-sterilized; heat-sensitive equipment can be sterilized with gas (ETO). Gown technique is essential to prevent contamination of the clothing of those who come in close contact with the patient or his bed, and handwashing facilities must be provided in the unit. Terminal disinfection-cleaning of the patient area is also important.

C. TREATMENT. Because anthrax can develop quickly into a fulminating septicemia, early diagnosis and treatment are essential. The drug of choice is penicillin, but the anthrax bacillus is also quite susceptible to most of the other clinically useful antibiotics. The mortality rate in treated anthrax is essentially zero, as compared with a 5 to 50 per cent fatality among untreated cases, or those diagnosed too late.

D. CONTROL OF CONTACTS. A case report of anthrax leads to an immediate search for the source of infection and the prompt diagnosis and treatment of any other human cases exposed to and infected by the same source. Outbreaks are associated either with industrial workers or with the people of farming areas directly involved in the raising, handling, or slaughter of animals. Control depends on eliminating the animal or environmental sources of infection.

III. Prevention

A. IMMUNIZATION. A vaccine is available for the artificial active immunization of animals and of persons exposed to high occupational risks. The material is a cell-free antigen obtained from anthrax exudate.

B. Control of the natural reservoirs of anthrax requires that special precautions be taken with animals dying of anthrax to prevent contamination of others or of the environment. Carcasses must be either cremated or buried in deep lime pits. In areas where anthrax is prevalent, healthy animals and their human handlers should be vaccinated, at least annually.

Animal products for commercial processing are sterilized as indicated and insofar as is practical. Bone meal is autoclaved before incorporation into animal feeds; fibers used in brushes are sterilized. Hair and wool can be washed with

soap and exposed to formaldehyde. Safety measures for industrial workers include the provision of protective clothing and gloves, as well as immunization programs.

Tularemia

The Clinical Disease. Tularemia is an infectious disease of wild animals, hares and rabbits being among the chief sources of the human disease. The organism may find any one of several portals of entry: the skin or mucous membranes, including the conjunctivae; the respiratory route (see Chap. 14, p. 356); the gastrointestinal tract (Chap. 19, p. 450); or the parenteral route if it is injected by the bite of infective insect vectors (Chap. 27, p. 565).

In some instances infection is limited to the tissues at the portal of entry, with formation of a local ulcer and involvement of the regional lymph glands. Thus, ocular infection may be primary, with a papule on the eyelid, conjunctivitis, and swelling of adjacent lymphoid tissue ("oculoglandular" disease). Primary tularemic pneumonia may follow inhalation of the bacilli. When they are ingested, necrotizing lesions may be formed in the mouth, the pharynx, or the gastrointestinal mucosa. Submaxillary, cervical, or mesenteric lymph nodes are involved, depending on the site of localization. Cutaneous infection is frequent among those who handle or skin infected animals. This takes an "ulceroglandular" form, with an ulcer at the site of entry, usually on the hands, arms, or face, and regional lymphadenopathy. Occasionally tularemia may begin without localizing signs, developing as a febrile systemic infection.

Whatever the site of initial localization, enlargement of the regional lymph nodes may lead to their suppuration, dissemination of the organisms to various tissues of the body, and the formation of granulomatous nodules in systemic foci. These nodules may also break down, and the organisms may be distributed still further in a progressive disease pattern. Fatal septicemia and death may ensue in untreated cases, but early diagnosis and treatment remove this threat.

Laboratory Diagnosis

I. Identification of the Organism (Francisella tularensis; formerly Pasteurella tularensis)

A. MICROSCOPIC CHARACTERISTICS. The organism is a short Gram-negative bacillus, nonmotile, nonsporeforming, aerobic or microaerophilic. Morphologically it is very similar to members of the genus *Pasteurella* with which it was formerly classified. (See the agent of bubonic plague, Chap. 27, p. 562.)

B. CULTURE CHARACTERISTICS. *F. tularensis* grows with some difficulty on laboratory media, requiring blood or tissue enrichments and added concentrations of cystine. Incubation at 37° C for two to three days yields minute colonies, appearing as transparent drops on the surface of blood agar plates.

The organism is identified and distinguished from the *Pasteurella* species by biochemical methods, animal inoculations (this is hazardous, and should be done only with strict precautions for animals and their handlers), and serologic reactions of the isolate with specific antiserum (agglutination or precipitation techniques are used).

II. Identification of Patient's Serum Antibodies. A rising titer of agglutinating and precipitating antibodies occurs during the course of active infection. These may be identified with strains of *F. tularensis* or their extracted antigens. Demonstration of an increasing level of antibody is essential to the serologic diagnosis of this disease, especially in persons who have been previously exposed and have a persisting titer of residual antibody.

III. Specimens for Diagnosis. Exudates from cutaneous or mucosal ulcers, material aspirated from suppurating lymph nodes, blood, or sputum may be appropriate for culture, as indicated by clinical symptoms of localizing infection. These materials should be collected, transported, and handled in the laboratory with strict aseptic technique, and full awareness of the infectivity of these organisms. Laboratory infections have been frequent, particularly when experimental animals are used in virulence studies.

Preliminary reports on stained smears made from these specimens (except blood samples) may sometimes tentatively confirm the clinical diagnosis, but in subacute or chronic infections the organisms may be extremely difficult to see in smears

or to propagate in culture. Serologic diagnosis may be most useful in such cases.

At least two samples of the patient's serum are required for serologic diagnosis: one taken as soon as possible after the onset of symptoms, and one taken about two weeks later, so that a rise in titer can be recognized if it occurs.

Epidemiology

I. Communicability of Infection. The reservoir, sources, and transmission routes of tularemia have been previously discussed. The *incubation period* following exposure to or ingestion of infected animal meat (or contaminated drinking water) is usually about three days, with a possible range of from one to ten days. This disease is *not transmissible* from person to person. Animal meats may remain infective, even though frozen, for periods up to three years.

Immunity follows recovery from active infection and is usually durable and solidly protective. Without acquired immunity, there is no natural resistance to tularemia.

II. Control and Prevention. There is no necessity for isolation of patients with active infection, since this is not a communicable disease. However, mucosal or cutaneous discharges should be disinfected, to avoid accidental transfer of infection from these materials, which can sometimes be teeming with the infecting organism. Dressings should be burned; syringes and needles used to collect blood samples should be handled with particular care and promptly sterilized or incinerated.

Tularemia can be effectively treated with a number of antibiotics, particularly streptomycin, chloramphenicol, or the tetracyclines. Cure is more rapid with early treatment, but in any case specific therapy is continued for several days after fever and other symptoms have subsided to avoid the establishment of chronic, low-grade, persistent infection.

The source of infection is sought in each case, with a view to preventing further incidence from a lingering reservoir, such as remaining portions of game meat stored in the refrigerator. The sale or shipment of infected animals or meats is a matter of concern to public health authorities, who enforce controls on this possible mode of spread. Campaigns are conducted to educate the public, especially hunters, concerning the sources of infection and the techniques of prevention: clothing protective against insect vectors, wearing rubber gloves for protection when dressing wild game, thorough cooking of such meat, and boiling of water obtained in the field in areas where infected animals may have contaminated it.

Immunizing vaccines are available but their use in the United States is restricted to those who must run a high risk of infection, notably laboratory workers.

Other Diseases That May Be Acquired Through Animal Contacts

Three other important types of infection may be acquired through direct contacts with animals, but for each of them other routes of transmission usually constitute a more important public health problem. For this reason, the principal discussion of these diseases and their epidemiology is placed in another chapter emphasizing their most frequent routes of entry and transmission. In individual cases, however, the possibility should be considered that direct animal contacts may be responsible for subsequent transfer of infection through the skin or mucosa.

Brucellosis

This disease is a zoonosis of many domestic animals, transmissible among animals, or from animals to man, but not from man to man. In animals, infection produces systemic disease, which frequently results in abortion. The causative organism is transferred to animals or man through contact with infectious urine, feces, or animal tissues, particularly placentas and aborted fetuses. The accidental human victims of infec-

Table 24–1. Summary: Infectious Diseases Acquired Through "Intact" Skin and Mucosa, Transmitted by Animal Contacts

Clinical Disease	Causative Organism	Other Possible Entry Routes	Incubation Period	Communicable Period
Anthrax	*Bacillus anthracis*	Respiratory Gastrointestinal	Less than 1 week	Not communicable from man to ▮ except under rare circumstances
Tularemia	*Francisella tularensis*	Respiratory Gastrointestinal Parenteral	1–10 days	Not transmissible from man to ma▮

tion acquired from such sources are farmers, veterinarians, slaughterhouse workers, butchers, meat packers, and others who handle animals or their products. For such persons the route of entry of the organisms is often through minor lesions or abrasions of skin, or the respiratory membranes in areas where the dust is heavily laden with organisms (see Chap. 14, p. 356). The widest dissemination of this organism to the general public, however, may occur through the distribution of raw milk obtained from infected animals (cows and goats), or sometimes of pasteurized milk contaminated *after* processing, when it is being bottled. This situation may occur in rural areas where people do not understand the nature of the disease, and where totally inadequate conditions exist for the preparation and local distribution of milk.

Brucellosis and its epidemiology are discussed in Chapter 19 (pp. 441 to 448). The human disease is not greatly influenced by the portal of entry, for the organism finds its way into the lymphatic system and the blood stream and becomes localized in many tissues of the reticuloendothelial system. Prevention and control depend on recognition of the animal sources of infection, elimination of the disease from livestock, and the adequate pasteurization and distribution of milk.

cimens quired	Laboratory Diagnosis	Immunization	Treatment	Nursing Management
te from ns ·m ·	Smear and culture Smear and culture Culture	Cell-free antigen	Penicillin	Hospital isolation until lesions are bacterio-logically negative (*prevents contamination of environment with spores*) ; contaminated dressings and disposable items are bagged and burned; bed linens and blankets are autoclaved before laundering; steam sterilization of heat-stable items; gas sterilization for heat-sensitive items; gown technique and *hand-washing* essential; terminal disinfection-cleaning important
tes from ·rs, ·ated ·rial from ·urating ·h nodes · ·m · and ·valescent	Smear and culture Rising titer of antibodies	Killed vaccines	Streptomycin Tetracyclines Chloramphenicol	Isolation not required; concurrent disinfection of discharges, dressings should be burned, syringes and needles should be handled with care and sterilized or burned immediately after use, *hand-washing* important

Leptospirosis

This is a spirochetal disease with a reservoir in some domestic animals (dogs, cattle, swine), a number of wild animal species (deer, foxes, racoons), rats, and other rodents. Like some of the other animal diseases, it can be transferred to man, but is seldom if ever transmitted from man to man. It may be acquired as a result of direct contacts with infected animals, which shed the organisms in their urine, but a wider distribution of human infection may occur through contacts with water or soil contaminated by the urine of infected animals. People who work or

swim in such water, or drink it, are subject to infection, the organism entering through abraded skin, the conjunctival membrane, or the gastro-intestinal mucosa. The disease, its victims, and its epidemiology are discussed in Chapter 25 (p. 542) together with other infections acquired primarily from an intermediate environmental reservoir.

Ringworm Infections (The Superficial Mycoses)

Some of the fungi responsible for infections of skin and hair have a reservoir in domestic ani-

mals (dogs, cats, cattle) as well as in man. These mycoses are directly transmissible from person to person, or through indirect contacts with human or animal sources. For this reason their epidemiology is discussed in Chapter 23 (pp. 521 to 530).

Questions

1. Why has anthrax become an infrequent problem in the United States?
2. What is the reservoir for anthrax infection?
3. What type of organism is found in the genus *Bacillus*?
4. Why is it necessary to incinerate or steam-sterilize when disposing of articles contaminated with *Bacillus anthracis*?
5. What organism causes tularemia?
6. Why is isolation not indicated for a patient with tularemia?
7. Who are the accidental victims of brucellosis infection? How do they become infected?

25 Infectious Diseases Acquired Through Intact Skin and Mucosa, Transmitted from Intermediate Environmental Sources

The infective agents of the four diseases described in this chapter have little or nothing in common except the epidemiologic importance of their intermediate sources in water or soil and their common route of entry through the "intact" human skin or mucosal surfaces. The spirochetal agent of leptospirosis has a primary reservoir in infected animals; the other three organisms are animal parasites. The hookworm and *Strongyloides* species are intestinal roundworms maintained in man, with intermediate periods of maturation in soil (life cycle type I), and the schistosomes are trematodes (the blood flukes) that display a rotational cycle of development in man or animals, the definitive hosts, and in aquatic intermediate hosts. The infective form of each of these organisms is found in water or soil to which man may be exposed with some frequency, under defined circumstances, and each of them is capable of penetrating the skin and establishing human disease by this route.

The control and prevention of these diseases depend in part on protecting man from contaminated water and soil, but perhaps more importantly on protecting the environment from sources of infection in the primary human or

541

animal reservoirs. It is also important to note the epidemiologic implications of the development or routing of these organisms in nature. They are not directly transmissible from man to man, but in the case of the animal parasites man contributes to their perpetuation. It should be noted, further, that these are really parenteral, or systemic, infections, which exert major effects through deep-tissue passage or localizations. The skin itself is seldom involved in any but minor skirmishes with the penetrating organism. The epidemiologic point to be remembered is that these diseases can be acquired through simple environmental contacts, without noticeable injury to the skin.

Leptospirosis (Weil's Disease)

The Clinical Disease. Leptospirosis is an acute infection characterized by fever, chills, headache,

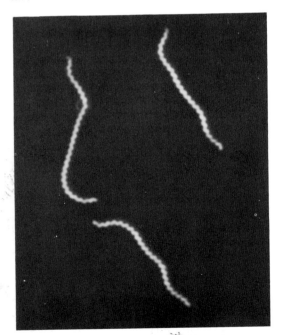

Fig. 25–1. *Leptospira icterohaemorrhagiae* (2500 ×). (Courtesy of Drs. J. D. Fulton and D. F. Spooner, London School of Hygiene and Tropical Medicine, London, England.)

malaise and often by jaundice. Localization of the organisms occurs chiefly in the liver and kidneys, producing necrosis of tissue and dysfunction of the affected organ. In addition to jaundice, there may be hemorrhage, hemolytic anemia, and nitrogen retention. The organism may be disseminated to other areas also, such as skin and muscle, or to the central nervous system. Leptospiral meningitis is clinically of the benign aseptic type (see Chap. 14, p. 321). The duration of this acute illness is from one to three weeks, with possible recurrences. The mortality is low, the outcome usually reflecting the severity of damage to hepatic or renal tissues.

Laboratory Diagnosis

I. Identification of the Organism (*Leptospira icterohaemorrhagiae*). *Leptospira* pathogenic for man include at least eight species, distributed among animal hosts in different parts of the world. They are morphologically indistinguishable but display antigenic differences as well as some variety in the degree and severity of clinical disease. *L. icterohaemorrhagiae* is presented here as the prototype agent of the disease described above.

Leptospira species are very tightly coiled spirochetes. They are about the same length as the treponemal agent of syphilis (Chap. 23, p. 497), but their spirals are much finer, being only about 0.1 to $0.2\,\mu$ wide (see Fig. 25–1). One or both ends of the organism are often bent into a hook. These spirochetes have a very active corkscrew rotation and are so delicate that in dark-field preparations this combination of factors sometimes creates the illusion that they are chains of tiny cocci in rapid undulant motion. Like the treponemes, these spirochetes do not stain well but can be impregnated with silver.

Leptospira can be propagated in chick embryos, and also in a liquid or semisolid medium containing rather concentrated serum, enriched with peptones, incubated at 30° C.

II. Identification of Patient's Serum Antibodies. Agglutinating antibodies develop during leptospiral infection but do not reach a peak level until five to eight weeks after the onset of infection. Antibodies can also be demonstrated by complement-fixation techniques. The antigens used in these tests are derived from leptospirae grown in broth media or chick eggs.

III. Specimens for Diagnosis. Blood, urine, or spinal fluid may be submitted for dark-field examination or for culture, the choice of specimen depending on the clinical symptoms. These specimens may be inoculated into culture media, chick embryos, or guinea pigs or hamsters. The latter animals are very susceptible to *Leptospira* infection and die in a few days with jaundice and extensive hemorrhagic disease. The spirochetes can be demonstrated in large numbers in their tissues, blood, or urine.

Urine submitted for laboratory studies should be of a neutral or slightly alkaline pH, because leptospirae are extremely sensitive to acid and may be inactivated before the specimen reaches the laboratory. Preliminary alkalinization of the patient affords the best method for assuring survival of the organisms pending their examination and culture from urine.

Epidemiology

I. Communicability of Infection

A. RESERVOIR, SOURCES, AND TRANSMISSION ROUTES. The reservoir of leptospirosis is in domestic and wild animals, including rats and other rodents. Infected animals excrete large numbers of the spirochetes in their urine and may contaminate water used for drinking, swimming, or cultivating crops. People whose occupations may take them into contaminated water include workers in sugar cane and rice fields, sewer men and miners, processors in fish plants, and soldiers dug into trenches or foxholes. The disease may also be acquired by people in direct contact with infected animals, such as farmers, veterinarians, and abattoir workers. The route of entry is probably through the skin, or the conjunctival, oral, or alimentary tract mucosa.

B. INCUBATION PERIOD. The average time required for development of symptoms following exposure is ten days, with a range of from 4 to 19 days.

C. COMMUNICABLE PERIOD. Leptospirosis is not transmitted directly from person to person. Man is an accidental host for this organism.

D. IMMUNITY. Infection confers a long-lasting protective immunity, but otherwise human susceptibility appears to be universal.

II. Control and Prevention. It is not necessary to isolate the infected case or to institute special precautionary measures in the medical or nursing care of such patients. The treatment of this disease is largely supportive, although penicillin and other antibiotics may have some therapeutic effect in the early stages of infection. Antimicrobial drugs do not succeed in eliminating the organisms, however.

Control measures consist of a search for the source of infected water, programs for the extermination of rats and other rodents, and the use of protective clothing by workers who are exposed to this type of infection. Contaminated waters should be closed to swimmers, and domestic animals should not be permitted access to such watering places. Vaccines are available for dogs and other animals, and also for man. They contain leptospiral strains prevalent in the local area and are administered when the risk of infection appears to be high.

Diseases Caused by Animal Parasites

The nature and epidemiology of the parasitic diseases are discussed at some length in Chapter 21 (pp. 463 to 467), together with a review of the major types of life cycles displayed by the animal parasites (see also Chap. 9, pp. 190 to 198). The diseases considered here are presented in the same outline form previously used, describing the cyclic development of each parasite in the human or other living host and its environmental requirements; the characteristics of the human infestation; diagnostic methods; and special features of control. Reference should be made in each case to the general discussions elsewhere in the text, as indicated above.

Hookworm Disease

Organisms. *Necator americanus* (the "American hookworm"), *Ancylostoma duodenale* (the "Old World" hookworm), *Ancylostoma braziliense* (an agent of "creeping eruption"). The small adult roundworms have mouths equipped with chiti-

nous plates, or "teeth," by which they attach themselves to the intestinal mucosa (see Figs. 25–2 and 25–3).

Hookworm ova measure about 40 by 60μ. They are oval in shape with rounded ends and have a thin outer shell. Normally, when they are passed promptly in the feces, the developing embryo has not yet reached a differentiated stage but appears cellular (see Fig. 25–4).

Life Cycle (Type 1)

I. Definitive Host. Man.

II. Intermediate Host. None.

III. Human Infestation

A. SOURCE OF INFECTION. Soil in which larvae have matured after hatching from eggs derived from human feces.

B. INFECTIVE FORM. Larvae that penetrate exposed skin.

C. LOCALIZATION AND DEVELOPMENT. Larvae enter through the skin, reach the lymphatics and the blood stream, and are carried to the lungs. They migrate into the alveoli, up the bronchial

tree to the trachea, epiglottis, and pharynx, are swallowed, and reach the small intestine. They attach to the intestinal mucosa, develop into male and female adults, copulate, and produce eggs.

D. EXIT FROM BODY. Hookworm eggs are discharged in feces.

IV. Cyclic Development Outside of Human Body

IN ENVIRONMENT. In moist, shaded, warm soil eggs hatch in one or two days, and the emerging larvae feed on soil bacteria and organic matter. Larvae go through developmental changes, and in about a week reach a stage that is infective for man. This stage may remain viable in the soil for several weeks. (See Fig. 9–11.)

Characteristics of Human Disease. Hookworm infestation produces a chronic disease with symptoms related to the blood-sucking activities of the intestinal worms. It is estimated that a single hookworm may remove nearly 1 ml of blood per day. When this loss is multiplied by thousands of worms and by all the days of a long infestation, the debilitating effects of this disease may be well understood. Severe anemia of the microcytic,

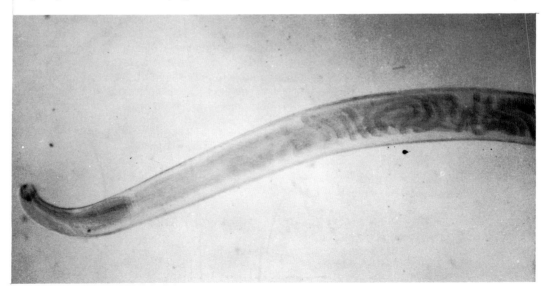

Fig. 25–2. Photomicrograph of *Necator americanus* (hookworm) adult, anterior end (40 ✕).

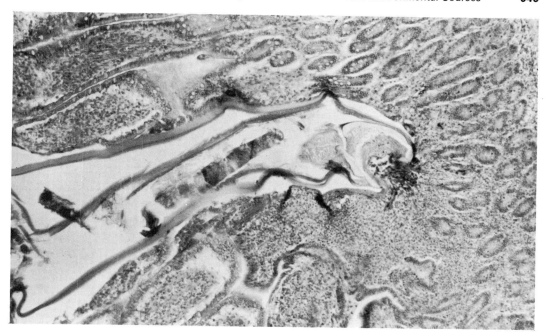

Fig. 25–3. A photomicrograph of a hookworm attached to the intestinal wall (100 ×).

hypochromic type is a characteristic result. Children afflicted with this disease are often malnourished to begin with, and their infestation constitutes an added physical burden, leading to symptoms of weakness, fatigue, pulmonary disability on exertion, physical and even mental retardation.

Light infestations may produce few, if any, symptoms, but the infested individual may nonetheless perpetuate the disease if eggs discharged in feces have an opportunity to mature in soil. Treatment may be indicated for this reason alone.

In the United States, hookworm disease is caused by species of the genus *Necator*, while *Ancylostoma* infestations are common in Europe, Southeast Asia, and the Far East.

Dogs and cats are infested with a species of hookworm, *Ancylostoma braziliense*, that has a similar cycle in the animals' intestine, with larval maturation in the soil. These larvae may also penetrate human skin but are incapable of further migration or development in the human body.

They may remain alive in the epidermal tissues for some time, however, creating serpentine tunnels and producing intense local tissue reactions of erythema, cellular infiltration, induration, and sometimes vesicular eruptions. This form of epidermal hookworm infestation is known as "creeping eruption," or "ground itch."

Fig. 25–4. Photomicrograph of a hookworm ovum (1000 ×).

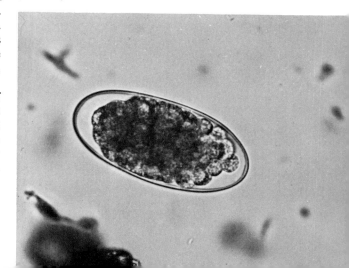

Diagnostic Methods. Diagnosis of intestinal hookworm disease is established by the microscopic identification of hookworm ova in feces (see Fig. 25–4). Quantitative estimation of the daily numbers of eggs being produced is sometimes useful to the physician who might decide not to treat a lightly infected patient if he is unlikely, by virtue of his living conditions and sanitary habits, to perpetuate the organism's life cycle.

Creeping eruption of hookworm origin is diagnosed on the basis of its clinical appearance and a history of exposure to domestic animals who may harbor the intestinal worm.

Special Features of Control

I. Treatment. Hookworm disease is treated with tetrachlorethylene or naphthoate salts (bephenium). A balanced diet and supportive treatment of the accompanying anemia are also essential.

Creeping eruption is treated locally with ethyl chloride spray or carbon dioxide snow to arrest the progress of larvae in the skin, while antihelminthic drugs are given by mouth.

II. Other. The prevention of hookworm disease is primarily a matter of establishing and maintaining sanitary systems for the disposal of feces so that the parasite cannot continue its cycle in soil. Campaigns to promote the wearing of shoes in rural areas where the organism is entrenched in the human population constitute a stopgap measure only. The disease can be eliminated by the installation and maintenance of adequate methods for feces disposal, in privies or latrines that can be chemically disinfected, or in sewerage systems.

Strongyloidiasis

Organism. *Strongyloides stercoralis.* The adult worms are smaller than hookworms and do not possess cutting teeth or plates for attachment.

Life Cycle (Type 1)

I. Definitive Host. Man.

II. Intermediate Host. None.

III. Human Infestation
A. SOURCE OF INFECTION. Soil in which larvae have matured after their discharge in human feces.
B. INFECTIVE FORM. Larvae that penetrate exposed skin.
C. LOCALIZATION AND DEVELOPMENT. Identical with those of hookworm, except that the ova usually hatch in the bowel, before they are discharged in the feces.
D. EXIT FROM BODY. Larval forms are passed in the stool.

IV. Cyclic Development Outside of the Human Body
IN ENVIRONMENT. The larvae mature in the soil and may live freely for several generations. The infective form is closely similar to that of the hookworm, can penetrate human skin, migrate through the body, reach the lungs and then the intestinal tract. (See Fig. 9–11.)

V. Autoinfection. An unusual feature of this parasite is that larval maturation may occur within the infected bowel. Infective larvae may then penetrate the wall of the colon or rectum, enter the tissues, and migrate to the lungs, bronchial tree, and intestinal tract, establishing a new generation of adults. Infestation may be continued in this way for many years, with frequent recurrences of symptoms.

Characteristics of Human Disease. The symptoms of strongyloidiasis vary according to the density of infestation. Migration of larvae through the skin may induce local pruritus; their pulmonary passage sometimes induces pneumonitis or bronchial irritation; but the chief symptoms are related to the burrowing of developing larvae and adults in the villi of the duodenum and small intestine (see Fig. 25–5). Epigastric pain, nausea, vomiting, weight loss, weakness, and disturbances

in bowel function are frequent symptoms, sometimes suggesting peptic ulcer. Allergic skin reactions and eosinophilia also occur with frequency. Light infestations may produce mild variations of these symptoms, or none at all.

Diagnostic Methods. Microscopic examination of the stool usually reveals viable, active *Strongyloides* larvae. These must be distinguished morphologically from hookworm larvae, which occasionally hatch in the bowel before they are discharged in the feces. When strongyloidiasis is suspected but cannot be confirmed by stool examination, aspirated duodenal drainage may reveal the larvae.

Special Features of Control

I. Treatment. Cyanine dyes and dithiazanine iodide are effective agents in the therapy of strongyloidiasis. These drugs are toxic, and patients must be followed closely while under treatment.

II. Other. Measures for the control and prevention of *Strongyloides* infestations are the same as those required for hookworm disease. The most effective and permanent control is provided by the installation of sanitary measures for the disposal of human feces. Shoes are essential in endemic areas where the primary source of infection has not been controlled.

Schistosomiasis

Organisms. *Schistosoma mansoni* (occurs in the Caribbean, South America, Africa), *Schistosoma haematobium* (occurs in Africa, the Middle East, India), *Schistosoma japonicum* (occurs in the Far East and the Philippines). The small adult worms are bisexual, but live in close association (see Fig. 25–6, *A*). The ova are quite large, measuring about 50 μ in diameter and from 100 to 175 μ in length, depending upon the species. They have a transparent shell which in two species is equipped

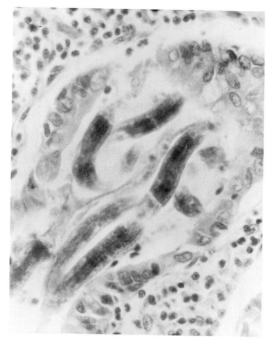

Fig. 25–5. A photomicrograph of *Strongyloides stercoralis*. Adults in the intestinal villi (600 ×).

with a prominent spine (laterally placed on the *S. mansoni* egg [see Fig. 25–7], terminal on the ovum of *S. haematobium*). The ovum of the third species (*S. japonicum*) has a very small, short curved hook on one side. When the embryo within the shell is fully developed, it is ciliated and, upon being hatched, can swim about freely. The hatched embryo is called a *miracidium* (Fig. 25–6 *C*).

Life Cycle (Type 4)

I. Definitive Host. Man and domestic or wild animals.

II. Intermediate Host. Snails.

III. Human Infestation
A. SOURCE OF INFECTION. Water infested with larval forms (cercariae) liberated from the intermediate snail host.

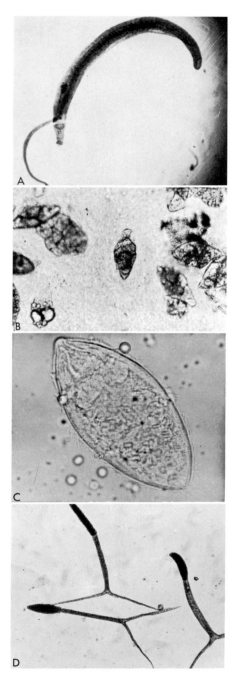

B. Infective Form. Free-swimming larvae ("fork-tailed cercariae," see Fig. 25–6 *D*).

C. Localization and Development. Larvae penetrate the skin of persons swimming, wading, or working in infested water. They enter the blood stream, are carried to the liver, mature to adult forms, and migrate through hepatic vessels or the veins of the abdominal cavity. *S. mansoni* and *S. japonicum* remain in hepatic or mesenteric vessels, but *S. haematobium* usually finds its ways into the venous complex of the pelvis. Deposited eggs find their way out of the venules into the lumen of hepatic ducts, or pass more directly into the bowel, or the urinary bladder (see Fig. 25–6 *B*), depending on the localization of the adult worm. Many ova may be lodged in tissues adjacent to the site of their deposition and be immobilized there by local cellular reactions.

D. Exit from the Body. The ova of *S. mansoni* (see Fig. 25–7) and *S. japonicum* may be discharged with feces; those of *S. haematobium* usually emerge into the bladder and are excreted with urine, but they may also find their way into the colon and be passed in the stool.

IV. Cyclic Development Outside of the Human Body

A. In Environment. *Schistosoma* ova must reach water to begin their maturation. The ciliated embryos (miracidia) (see Fig. 25–6 *C*) break out of their enclosing shells and swim about in water until they are ingested by snails, which serve as intermediate hosts for further development.

B. In Snail Hosts. The parasites undergo several morphologic changes in snail tissues,

Fig. 25–6. Four stages in the life cycle of *Schistosoma haematobium. A. Schistosoma* adults. The small slender female is interlocked with the larger male (10 ×). *B. Schistosoma haematobium* eggs in the urinary bladder of a human case of schistosomiasis (biopsy, 100 ×). *C.* A miracidium hatched from an egg (400 ×). Note the fine rim of cilia on the outer side of the cell membrane. *D.* Fork-tailed cercariae (250 ×). This is the free-swimming form that is infective for man, being capable of penetrating his skin.

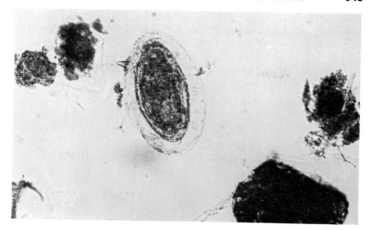

Fig. 25–7. Photomicrograph of an ovum of *Schistosoma mansoni* in a wet-mount of feces. Note that the unhatched embryo (miracidium) is surrounded by a shell equipped with a lateral spine (200 ×).

emerging finally as microscopic larval forms that also can swim freely. The larvae are called *cercariae* and are characterized by having forked tails, their anterior ends being thickened and elongated (Fig. 25–6 *D*). Glands in the anterior section of the larva produce enzymes that assist in the penetration of human skin, once the parasite has become attached. (See Fig. 9–16.)

Characteristics of Human Disease. The symptoms of schistosomiasis are related to the localization of the adult worm and the local damage inflicted on adjacent tissues by the migration of ova. Migration of the bisexual adults, which cling together in their passage through venules, may cause the rupture of small vessels, but chronic injury is induced by the ova wandering in parenchymal tissues. Polymorphonuclear exudates collect around the eggs, and abscess formation results. When the ova lodge in the lumen of hepatic ducts or in the bowel, small ulcers may form around them. The eggs are sometimes dislodged and carried by the blood stream into the lungs, where they may obstruct capillaries and give rise to abscesses in the pulmonary bed. In the liver they may obstruct the portal circulation, and this may lead to enlargement of the spleen. From the venous complex in the pelvis, eggs may reach the bladder, the genital organs, or the colon. Further migration of the adult worms through connecting venules may lead to the de-

position of eggs in other parts of the body, such as the skin, the conjunctiva, or the spinal cord and brain.

During the course of active infestation and egg deposition, allergic reactions characterize the disease. Fever, urticaria, and eosinophilia may be intense. When the eggs trapped in parenchymal tissues eventually die, the surrounding reaction becomes granulomatous in character; pseudotubercles are formed, with foreign-body giant cells surrounding and engulfing the material of the dead ova. The eggs may be removed entirely, or they may become calcified and surrounded by scar tissue. Extensive scarring may disrupt normal tissue architecture and interfere with its function. Obstructions of blood vessels and bile ducts are frequent results of the body's efforts to heal the lesions induced by *Schistosoma* ova.

Diagnostic Methods. The diagnosis of schistosomiasis is confirmed by demonstration of the characteristic eggs in feces, urine, or biopsied tissue. Since dead eggs may be excreted as well as live ones, the viability of the contained embryo should be confirmed by observation of movement, or by encouraging the hatching of the miracidium in a water-diluted specimen incubated at 35° to 37° C. The demonstration of viable eggs indicates

Table 25–1. Summary: Infectious Diseases Acquired Through "Intact" Skin and Mucosa, Transmitted from Intermediate Environmental Sources

Clinical Disease	Causative Organism	Other Possible Entry Routes	Incubation Period	Communicable Period
Leptospirosis	*Leptospira icterohaemorrhagiae* and other species		4–19 days	Not communicable from man to m
Hookworm disease	*Necator americanus Ancylostoma duodenale Ancylostoma braziliense*		Variable; ova are seen in stools 6 weeks after initial infection	Not communicable from man to m
Strongyloidiasis	*Strongyloides stercoralis*		About 17 days	Not communicable from man to m
Schistosomiasis	*Schistosoma mansoni Schistosoma haematobium Schistosoma japonicum*		4–6 weeks	Not communicable from man to m

the presence of active adults, and the necessity for treatment.

Special Features of Control

I. Treatment. Schistosomiasis is usually treated with antimony compounds, such as Fuadin, Stibophen, or Neoantimosan. These are toxic compounds and must be given with caution, especially in the presence of severe liver damage or renal and cardiac insufficiency.

Surgical shunts of the portal or renal circulation are sometimes performed when severe vascular obstruction threatens adequate hepatic function. Recently a new surgical technique has been developed for shunting the patient's blood through a filtration system and back into the body. Adult worms are trapped in the filter and removed, the infestation being greatly reduced or ended.

II. Other. Major control of this disease is achieved by the sanitary disposal of human excreta, which prevents infection of the snail host and perpetuation of the parasite's life cycle. Snail eradication and land reclamation programs afford some relief but cannot eliminate the disease while human infection and unsanitary practices persist.

Questions

1. What kind of organisms are the leptospirae?
2. What is the reservoir of leptospirosis?
3. What people are most likely to become infected with leptospirosis?
4. What measures are taken to control this disease?

imens uired	Laboratory Diagnosis	Immunization	Treatment	Nursing Management
fluid	Culture Animal inoculation	Killed vaccines	Penicillin and other antibiotics suppress but do not eliminate the organism	No special pre-cautionary measures indicated
	Identification of ova		Tetrachlorethylene Naphthoate salts	Sanitary disposal of feces
	Identification of viable, active strongyloid larvae		Cyanine dyes Dithiazanine iodide	Sanitary disposal of feces
	Identification of ova		Antimony compounds, Fuadin, Stibophen Neoantimosan Vascular shunts	Sanitary disposal of feces

5. What is the source of infection for hookworm disease?
6. How is the diagnosis of hookworm disease made?
7. What is the source of infection for schistosomiasis?
8. What drugs are used in the treatment of schistosomiasis?

Question for Discussion — Section VI

Mrs. Mills brings her two youngest children to the Pediatric Clinic where they are being followed for undernutrition and anemia. The nurse notices the mother constantly rubbing her eye. The right eye is tearing and the conjunctiva is red and swollen. Mrs. Mills is persuaded to stop at the eye clinic where simple conjunctivitis is diagnosed. Eye unguentine and warm wet soaks are ordered for home use.

1. What is the probable causative organism of this disease?
2. What instructions for personal hygiene would you give Mrs. Mills and why?

References — Section VI

Textbooks
Conant, Norman F., Smith, D. T., Baker, R. D., Callaway, J. L., and Martin, D. S.: *Manual of Clinical Mycology*. W. B. Saunders, Philadelphia and London, 1954.
Dubos, René J., and Hirsch, James G. (eds.): *Bacterial and Mycotic Infections of Man*, 4th ed. J. B. Lippincott, Philadelphia, 1965.

Faust, Ernest, and Russell, Paul Farr: *Craig and Faust's Clinical Parasitology*, 7th ed. Lea & Febiger, Philadelphia, 1965.

Horsfall, Frank L., Jr., and Tamm, Igor (eds.): *Viral and Rickettsial Infections of Man*, 4th ed. J. B. Lippincott, Philadelphia, 1965.

Hunter, George W., Frye, William W., and Swartzwelder, J. Clyde: *A Manual of Tropical Medicine*, 4th ed. W. B. Saunders, Philadelphia and London, 1966.

Jawetz, E., Melnick, J. L., and Adelberg, E. A.: *Review of Medical Microbiology*, 7th ed. Lange Medical Publications, Los Altos, Calif., 1966.

Pertinent References

GENERAL: VENEREAL DISEASE

Brown, William J.: Venereal Disease Control, *Amer. J. Nurs.*, **61**:94, April, 1961.

Cromwell, G. E.: The Teenager and V.D., *Amer. J. Nurs.*, **59**:1738, Dec., 1959.

Deschin, Cecilia S.: Teen-Agers and Venereal Disease, A Sociological Study of 600 Teen-Agers in New York City's Social Hygiene Clinics, *Public Health News*, **43**:9, Sept., 1962.

————: V.D. and the Adolescent Personality, *Amer. J. Nurs.*, **63**:58, Nov., 1963.

Galton, Lawrence: Why VD Is on the Increase, *Cosmopolitan*, Jan., 1963.

Lefson, Eleanor, Lentz, Josephine, and Gilbertson, Evelyn: Contact Interviews and the Nurse Interviewer, *Nurs. Outlook*, **10**:728, Nov., 1962.

Lentz, John William, and Hall, Madelyn N.: Venereal Disease Control in the Twentieth Century, *Nurs. Outlook*, **10**:722, Nov., 1962.

Maxwell, Margaret: A Careful Look at Venereal Disease Nursing, *Amer. J. Nurs.*, **61**:12, Dec., 1961.

Morton, R. S.: *Venereal Diseases*. Penguin Books, Baltimore, 1966.

Nicol, C. S.: Present Day Incidence and Treatment of V.D., *Nurs. Mirror & Midwives J.*, Feb. 23, 1962.

Notes on Modern Management of VD. U.S. Dept. HEW, #859, Washington, D.C., 1962.

Richman, T. Lefoy: *Venereal Disease, Old Plague, New Challenge.* U.S. Dept. HEW, Public Affairs Pamphlet #292, Washington, D.C., 1960.

Rogers, Garet: *Lancet*, Chap. 26. G. P. Putnam's Sons, New York, 1956.

Syphilis — Modern Diagnosis and Management. U.S. Dept. HEW, #743, Washington, D.C., July, 1961.

Taylor, Susan Daggett: Clinic for Adolescents with Venereal Disease, *Amer. J. Nurs.*, **63**:63, Nov., 1963.

Thomas, Evan W.: *Management of Syphilis.* New York State Dept. of Health, Bureau of Epidemiology and VD Control, Albany, N.Y., 1958.

Today's VD Control Problem. A Joint Statement by The Association of State and Territorial Health Offices, The American Venereal Disease Association, The American Social Health Association, New York, March, 1961.

SYPHILIS

Cleugh, James: *The Secret Enemy, the Story of a Disease.* Thomas Yoseloff, Inc., New York, 1958.

Hunter, John: A Treatise on VD, in Clendening, Logan: *Source Book of Medical History.* Dover Publications, Inc., New York, 1960.

Resurgent Syphilis: It Can Be Eradicated, *Time*, Sept. 21, 1962.

Rusk, Howard A.: Syphilis Cases Rise, *The New York Times*, May 6, 1962.

GONORRHEA

Crede, C. S. F.: The Prophylactic Treatment of Ophthalmia Neonatorum, in Clendening, Logan: *Source Book of Medical History.* Dover Publications, Inc., New York, 1960.

Ormsby, Hugh L.: Prophylaxis of Ophthalmia Neonatorum, *Amer. J. Nurs.*, **57**:1174, Sept., 1957.

LEPROSY

Burgess, Perry: *Who Walk Alone*. Henry Holt and Co., New York, 1940.

Kluth, Frederick C.: The Epidemiology of Hansen's Disease, *Nurs. Outlook*, **4**:77, Feb., 1954.

Martin, Betty (ed. by Evelyn Wells): *Miracle at Carville*. Doubleday & Co., Garden City, N.Y., 1950.

————: *No One Must Ever Know*. Doubleday & Co., Garden City, N.Y., 1950.

Roueché, Berton: A Lonely Road, in *Eleven Blue Men*. Berkley Medallion, New York, 1965.

Shepard, Charles C.: Leprosy: A World Health Problem, *Amer. J. Nurs.*, **63**:112, March, 1963.

SUPERFICIAL MYCOSES

Foley, Anna J.: More Than Skin Deep, *Amer. J. Nurs.*, **60**:1266, Sept., 1960.

Osment, Lamar: Tinea Capitis, *Amer. J. Nurs.*, **60**:1264, Sept., 1960.

Samitz, M. H.: The Industrial Dermatoses, *Amer. J. Nurs.*, **65**:79, Jan., 1965.

ANTHRAX

Roueché, Berton: A Man Named Hoffman, in *A Man Named Hoffman*. Little, Brown & Co., Boston, 1965.

Samitz, M. H.: The Industrial Dermatoses, *Amer. J. Nurs.*, **65**:79, Jan., 1965.

LEPTOSPIROSES

See References, Section V.

SCHISTOSOMIASIS

Ayer, Wardner D.: Napoleon Bonaparte and Schistosomiasis or Bilharziasis, *New York J. Med.*, **66**: 2295, Sept. 1, 1966.

Febles, Francisco, Jr.: Schistosomiasis, a World Health Problem, *Amer. J. Nurs.*, **641**:18, Feb., 1964.

Filtering the Flukes, *The Sciences*, N.Y. Acad. Sci., **7**:32, Sept., 1967.

Roueché, Berton: A Swim in the Nile, in *A Man Named Hoffman*. Little, Brown & Co., Boston, 1965.

Section VII   The Infectious Diseases Acquired Parenterally

26 The Epidemiology of Parenterally Acquired Infections

The diseases discussed in this section have been arranged in four chapters according to the means by which infection is parenterally introduced. All the major infectious diseases that are acquired through the bites of arthropods are described in Chapter 27, where they are divided into four major groups on the basis of the nature of their causative agents (bacterial, rickettsial, viral, and parasitic organisms). Chapter 28 includes the systemic or local infections of soft tissues that can be acquired through accidental injury to the skin or mucosal membranes. They are arranged in three sections according to the nature of the injury — that is, injuries inflicted by the bites of animals, "street wounds," and burns.*

Infections that may arise as a result of medical or surgical techniques are placed in Chapter 29. These include the diseases that can be transmitted through blood transfusions or by contaminated needles and syringes or catheterization procedures, and surgical wound infections. The final chapter (30) recapitulates and summarizes the problem of endogenous infections that may arise as a result of minor injuries to the surface barriers of the body or as a consequence of disability and inadequate mechanisms of resistance. Chapter 30 also includes a summary of the infectious diseases acquired by infants during intrauterine life, at

* References for Chaps. 26 to 30 are located at the end of Sec. VII (pp. 639 to 642).

the time of birth, or during the first few critical postnatal days. Infants represent the most highly susceptible population group because they are born without fully functioning mechanisms of specific immune resistance, and their delicate surface tissues are only a weakly defensive barrier against the parenteral extension of infection from the skin or from the respiratory or alimentary membranes. During fetal development, infections transferred across the placenta or from the maternal blood stream may seriously compromise embryonic tissues, destroying them in active infectious processes or interfering with normal growth and maturation.

Two important epidemiologic points may be made about the diseases presented in this section: (1) the infectious microorganisms are introduced directly into the tissues as a result of injury to (or the inefficacy of) the normal skin or mucosal barriers, and (2) in general these infections are not directly transmitted from person to person. In some cases direct transmission is not possible (for example, the arthropod-borne diseases), and in others it is not usual or probable. The major exceptions to this generality are the infant diseases, which are, in essence, acquired through contacts with human or environmental sources of infections, the route to parenteral tissues often being very direct.

In further consideration of the first point made above, it should be noted that the injuring agent may be both the *reservoir* and the *source* of infection, as in the case of infected arthropods, biting animals, or the wounding environmental object that implants infecting microorganisms into soft tissues. The *source* of injury and infection may also be a surgical instrument, a hypodermic needle, or a catheter, a matter of particularly grave concern in medical and nursing practice. It must also be remembered that exposed, traumatized tissues are vulnerable to infection through contact with a variety of environmental sources. In the case of accidental injuries, contamination with soil or the dirt and dust of the street may lead to the development of serious diseases such as tetanus or gas gangrene, and systemic fungous infections can also be acquired in this way. These sources and possibilities of specific infec-

tions must be anticipated in the treatment and management of "street wounds." Surgical wounds may also be exposed to a number of environmental or human sources of infection, both at the time of surgery and during the early postoperative days. In this case it is of vital importance that potential sources be recognized and controlled to the fullest possible extent, through the use of effective techniques to achieve an aseptic environment (see also Chap. 10, pp. 233 to 246).

With regard to the transmission of these diseases, direct person-to-person transfer does not occur in most instances, since these are parenteral infections requiring deep entry routes. It must be emphasized, however, that under the special circumstances of the surgical ward where patients with postoperative wounds may be in contact with each other, direct transfer of bacterial infections can be a dangerous possibility. The greater and more frequent risk, however, is cross-infection from environmental sources and by way of personnel who may carry infectious microorganisms from one patient to another. Still another important source of infections in hospitals is the staff member who remains on duty, in contact with patients, although he or she has an active, transmissible infection (a sore throat, a febrile "cold," diarrhea, an infectious skin lesion). Any patient may be susceptible (and all the more so because of his underlying illness) and may acquire these infections from personnel through a variety of contacts, but the surgical patient is particularly vulnerable to direct parenteral transfer of pathogenic microorganisms into his wound. Such transfer is accomplished with greatest ease in the operating room while the wound is open, but it may also occur on the surgical ward before the tissues have healed. As a general rule, infections acquired during surgery involve the deep layers of muscle and fascia, while more superficial infections are seen if they are incurred after the wound has been closed and is healing.

The nursing management of parenterally transmissible diseases is varied with respect to the precautions required to control active infection and requires a knowledge of the routes and agents of transfer of each disease. In the case of the

arthropod-borne diseases, the nature and habits of the vector determine the necessity for the isolation or careful screening of the patient in an insect-transmissible stage of infection. Patients with *tick-borne* diseases (for example, Rocky Mountain spotted fever) need not be isolated because ticks are not ubiquitous. They are encountered only in thickly vegetated areas, among thick weeds or bushy undergrowth; therefore, the infected human being who is sick and confined to bed is not a source of infection for this insect. Similarly, cases of diseases that are transmitted by *rat fleas* (bubonic plague or rickettsialpox) do not require isolation provided there is no problem regarding rat control in the immediate area. On the other hand, it is extremely important to isolate cases of yellow fever or malaria when patients remain in an area where the *mosquito vectors* of these diseases are abundant. The isolation need not involve their segregation from other people, but patients should be housed in well-screened rooms and, in endemic areas, be protected at night by bed netting. Without such precautions, mosquitoes that feed on infected persons may spread the disease through a widening area, sometimes in epidemic patterns. *Louse-borne diseases* such as epidemic typhus fever and relapsing fever present a different kind of problem. Here again isolation is not necessary provided the patient has been completely deloused. Lice are ectoparasites that breed and live on the human body, and in clothing and bedding. Under conditions of crowding and filth they pass back and forth readily from one person to another and can spread the diseases they transmit in very rapid fashion. In areas where typhus fever exists, the louse-infested contacts of patients should also be quarantined until they have been deloused.

The isolation of other types of parenterally acquired infections depends on the nature of the organism and its accessibility to patients with open or unhealed wounds, or to infants and others who are highly susceptible. Reference should be made in each case to the requirements for isolation and nursing precautions stated for each disease. General recommendations for the nursing management of diseases acquired through parenteral routes include the following:

1. *Complete* isolation is indicated for patients with wound infections caused by staphylococci, streptococci, or clostridia of the gas gangrene group. This is particularly important for patients on surgical, maternity, or pediatric services. On the maternity service patients with puerperal sepsis or mastitis must be isolated. Newborn babies must not have contacts with mothers who have active infections of any kind. Nursery isolation is indicated for babies whose mothers have infections at the time of delivery and also for infants who develop signs of infectious illness postnatally.

2. *Partial* isolation may be necessary for patients (especially children) with acute conjunctivitis, wound infections other than those mentioned above, or mycotic lesions in an active stage of purulent discharge (see Chap. 17).

3. *No isolation* is necessary for patients with arthropod-borne diseases, but care must be taken to screen patients from mosquito and biting fly vectors in some instances. Adequate delousing is essential to the control of typhus fever and relapsing fever, as discussed above.

4. Special nursing precautions are not indicated in the management of the insect-borne rickettsial, viral, and parasitic diseases. In the case of bubonic plague, however, nurses and all other attendants must take stringent care to protect other patients and themselves if the pneumonic phase of the disease develops.

5. Precautions in the management of wound infections include the use of gowns for those who attend the patient directly, particularly at the time dressings are being changed. Thorough hand-washing is essential before and after wounds are examined or treated. Gloves provide an added safety feature and may be necessary on occasion, but clean hands are one of the most important factors in preventing the spread of infection to environmental reservoirs or directly to other individuals (including oneself).

6. Concurrent disinfection varies in detail but includes the incineration of contaminated dressings, mucosal discharges, or any material obtained from an infectious lesion. Objects contaminated by infectious discharges must be sterilized or carefully disinfected. Terminal

disinfection-cleaning of the patient's unit should be thorough.

7. Soiled clothing and bed linen should be sent to the laundry in marked bags to be handled with care prior to washing.

8. Linens, instruments, and equipment contaminated with sporebearing clostridia from cases of gas gangrene should be sterilized before they are cleaned by routine procedures. Disposable items may be incinerated, others autoclaved or placed in an ethylene oxide sterilizer.

9. Routine sterilization procedures for the preparation of surgical or other supplies should be reviewed at frequent intervals and checked by reliable methods (see Appendixes VI and VII).

10. Hospital areas involved in the care and treatment of patients under special risk of infection must be kept in scrupulously clean condition and protected from avenues of cross-contamination. These critical areas include the operating rooms, recovery rooms, delivery rooms, nurseries, maternity, pediatric, and surgical services, and intensive-care units. Patients for whom the risk of superimposed infection is greatest include newborn infants; burn cases; all surgical patients, but especially those undergoing prolonged surgery, such as open-heart procedures, extensive bowel resection or pelvic evisceration, renal surgery or dialysis, vascular shunts, organ transplants, or the placement of orthopedic prostheses; medical patients with endocrine disorders, notably diabetes; and patients whose resistant mechanisms are suppressed, because of metabolic defects resulting in agammaglobulinemia (reduced production of gamma globulins including those associated with antibody activity) or as a consequence of prolonged steroid therapy (see Chap. 7, pp. 130 and 136). Strict asepsis should always be maintained for these patients throughout the critical periods of their illness, concurrent disinfection techniques should be practiced with attention to every detail so that environmental reservoirs of infection cannot be established, and the sterilization of supplies for these areas should be subjected to critical review at frequent intervals. Such reviews should be conducted by hospital infection control committees, supported by data supplied by the microbiology laboratory.

11. The use of special precautionary techniques, other than those discussed above, must be decided on an individual basis in consideration of the nature of the infection and its probable routes of communicability.

Questions

1. When is complete isolation indicated for parenterally acquired infections?
2. When is isolation not indicated?
3. What precautions are taken in the management of wound infections?
4. For what patients is the risk of superimposed infection the greatest?

27 Infectious Diseases Acquired from Arthropod Vectors

A rather large group of human or animal diseases is perpetuated in nature by arthropod vectors that not only transmit infectious agents to mammalian hosts but also may play a vital role in the developmental cycle of the microorganisms. The microbial agents of this group represent each of the major classes of pathogenic microorganisms except the fungi. The human diseases they induce are presented in this chapter in groups according to the nature of the agent, that is, bacterial, rickettsial, viral, and parasitic infections.

The epidemiology of these infections varies and holds different implications for man. In some instances he is merely an accidental host and victim of parasites maintained primarily by animals and arthropods, but in other cases man is the primary or only mammalian reservoir, sustaining the parasite sequentially with an insect host. (See Chap. 6, pp. 109 to 110.) In general, these diseases are acquired by man only from arthropod vectors and are not directly transmissible from one person to another. Two exceptions to this rule may be noted in the case of tularemia and bubonic plague. The former may be transmitted directly from infected animals to man (see Chap. 24, p. 536) as well as by insects, and the latter may develop, in human cases, into a terminal pneumonia that is directly transmissible to other persons (see Chap. 14, p. 320).

The role of arthropod hosts in the transmission of infectious diseases is discussed more fully in Chapter 9 (pp. 170 to 173) and methods for the control of these vectors are described in Chapter 11 (pp. 280 to 282).

Bacterial Diseases Transmitted by Arthropods

Plague

The Clinical Disease. Plague is a highly fatal infection for man and has threatened him for centuries. The earliest known record of plague in its epidemic form is contained in the Old Testament (the first Book of Samuel, Chaps. 5 and 6). During the course of human history, the Black Death, as this disease has been called, has swept in devastating epidemic waves through populations in various parts of the world. During the Middle Ages, in the crowded cities of Europe, India, and Asia, ravaging epidemics of plague created scenes of horror on numerous occasions, sometimes killing as many as two thirds of a given population. Between the year 1338, when the port city of Genoa in Italy took the brunt of an epidemic that spread into Europe, and 1894, when the last pandemic occurred, beginning in Hong Kong and spreading through most of the world, it is estimated that at least 43 million people died of plague. It was during the last outbreak that the causative organism was discovered, and the epidemiology of the human disease began to be understood. Since that time the disease has come under control in most parts of the world and is rarely seen in epidemic form today. Some of the port cities in the United States, notably San Francisco, Los Angeles, and New Orleans, experienced outbreaks during the early years of this century, but they were well contained. The disease remains a threat in some of our western states and in other areas of the world where the wild rodent population continues to harbor the organism (see Fig. 27–1), but human infection has been limited to sporadic instances of unusual exposure to rodents or their fleas. The vigorous application of public health controls has prevented the spread of infection from such cases.

The plague bacillus can produce two forms of illness in human beings. The *bubonic* form results from the bite of a flea that is carrying the organisms it acquired by previously biting an infected rodent. The injected bacilli are carried along the lymphatic channels into regional lymph nodes the thoracic duct, and the blood stream, which disseminates them throughout the body. The most usual sites of localization are in the spleen, the liver, and the lungs. Symptoms begin suddenly, with fever, chills, severe headache, and exhaustion. There may be vomiting and diarrhea, and the patient often becomes delirious. Damage to the lymph nodes creates hemorrhagic inflammation, swelling, and pain. These swellings are called "buboes" and occur most frequently in the axilla or groin. They may become necrotic and suppurate to the surface. Hemorrhagic lesions in other parts of the body may also become necrotic. In the skin these necrosing areas of hemorrhage look dark and black, giving rise to the term "Black Death." If septicemia ensues there may be destructive lesions in every part of the body, with pleural or peritoneal effusions, pericarditis, or even meningitis. This form of plague is not directly transmissible to other persons, but it may be carried to others by fleas.

The *pneumonic* form of plague results when the organisms become localized in the lungs of the victim of bubonic plague. This form is highly contagious and is spread by the coughing of the infected patient. Cases of *primary* plague pneumonia (see Chap. 14, p. 320) may then occur among people in contact with the patient. The pneumonic illness can spread rapidly and is generally responsible for the epidemic pattern of human plague.

Laboratory Diagnosis. The clinical diagnosis of plague is sometimes difficult until the characteristic buboes appear. In the early stages the symptoms may resemble those of many other diseases, so that laboratory diagnosis may be of critical importance.

I. Identification of the Organism (*Pasteurella pestis*)

Fig. 27–1.   The wild landscape of Kurdistan is today one of the remaining natural hide-outs of bubonic plague. To investigate the upsurges of infection the rodents are trapped and their parasites examined for plague bacilli. In the scene above a rodent has escaped from a cage and is being caught again by hand. (WHO photo by Paul Almasy.)

A. MICROSCOPIC CHARACTERISTICS. The plague bacillus is a short Gram-negative rod, nonmotile and nonsporeforming. The organisms character-istically show a bipolar staining, which gives them the appearance of safety pins, with solid ends and an unstained space between.

B. CULTURE CHARACTERISTICS. *P. pestis* is an aerobic organism that grows best at 30° C, on media enriched with blood or tissue fluids. The colonies are gray and viscous, but they must be distinguished from other species of *Pasteurella* by their biochemical behavior and virulence for animals.

II. Identification of Patient's Serum Antibodies. Agglutination, precipitation, and complement-fixing antibodies arise during the course of infec-tion. Their demonstration in increasing titers pro-vides serologic confirmation of active disease.

III. Specimens for Diagnosis. Blood samples should be collected repeatedly for culture.

Pus aspirated from buboes, paracentesis fluids, spinal fluid, or sputum each may be appropriate for smear and culture if localizing symptoms suggest their value.

Blood should be collected for serologic testing as soon as possible after the onset of symptoms, and again after two or three weeks.

Epidemiology

I. Communicability of Infection. Man is an accidental host for the plague bacillus, which has a primary reservoir in rats and wild rodents (squirrels, field mice, and others). Rodent fleas transmit the infection between animals. When the flea ingests the organisms in a blood meal taken from an infected rodent, the organisms multiply and obstruct its feeding passage. The next time the flea bites, the new meal cannot be swallowed, so that the blood eddies over the obstructing mass of bacilli and is regurgitated back into the bite wound of the current victim, infecting him with its burden of organisms. Fleas are most likely to bite human beings who happen to be around when the rodent host dies, leaving the insect parasite in search of a new source of food.

The *incubation period* for bubonic plague ranges from two to six days. The average time for development of pneumonic plague is three to four days.

The *communicability* of this disease has been described above, and on page 561.

Recovery from plague infection is usually accompanied by a solid, durable immunity. This acquired immunity offers the only natural resistance to the human disease.

II. Control of Active Infection
A. ISOLATION. The patient with bubonic plague should be isolated and treated until all danger of extension of the disease to the pneumonic form has passed. Patients with plague pneumonia are placed in the strictest isolation. In any case of plague, isolation must ensure that neither rats nor their fleas have access to the sickroom.

B. PRECAUTIONS. Nurses and physicians attending pneumonic plague patients must observe stringent precautions, to protect themselves from

infection and to avoid spreading it to others. Hoods, face masks with goggles, gloves, and overall protective clothing are necessary. Further protection can be afforded to personnel by the administration of prophylactic antibiotics or sulfonamides. The patient's excretions, purulent discharges, and sputum must be disinfected, as well as contaminated equipment, bed linens, and other items. Terminal disinfection-cleaning must be performed with care.

C. TREATMENT. Antibiotic or sulfonamide therapy is rapidly effective if it is instituted early. In pneumonic plague the prognosis is best when treatment is begun within 24 hours of the onset of symptoms. Streptomycin and the tetracyclines are the drugs of choice and are often given in combination.

D. CONTROL OF CONTACTS. The immediate concern when cases of plague are reported is the protection of contacts and the prevention of spread by rodent fleas, or by air-borne routes if pneumonic plague develops. Contacts of active cases are quarantined, dusted with insecticide powders, and observed during a six-day period for signs of infection. Antibiotic therapy is instituted with the first evidence of development of a febrile illness. In situations where these procedures are not feasible, chemoprophylactic drugs are administered to contacts on a daily basis throughout the six-day incubation period.

III. Prevention
A. IMMUNIZATION. Killed vaccines are available that provide protective immunity for at least a one-year period. Artificial immunization is recommended for persons who run a high risk of infection. Laboratory workers, medical personnel in areas where the infection is endemic in the rodent population, travelers, and others whose occupation may expose them to the animal source of the infection constitute the group that should be vaccinated.

B. CONTROL OF RESERVOIRS. The most effective methods for preventing plague are centered on the destruction of rats and their fleas. Antirat campaigns begin with measures that eliminate the unsanitary conditions that encourage rat

breeding. When rodent controls are applied on a mass scale, effective measures must be taken simultaneously to eliminate rat fleas, so that hungry infected insects will not spread plague to the adjacent human population.

Public health measures also include the rat-proofing of buildings in sea- and airports, the quarantine of ships or other vessels from areas where plague has been reported, the fumigation of such vessels as indicated, and frequent surveys of the native rodent population for evidence of plague infection. When such evidence is found, efforts are intensified to eradicate the animal reservoir and the arthropod vector.

Relapsing Fever

The Clinical Disease. Relapsing fever is a spirochetal infection characterized by repeated episodes of fever that last two or three days and alternate with afebrile intervals of similar duration. This syndrome of relapse and remission may continue for two or three weeks. The symptoms of the febrile period are related to the presence of spirochetes in the blood stream. Fever, chills, headache, and malaise mark the release of organisms from localizing sites in the spleen, liver, kidneys, and other visceral tissues. There may be three to ten such relapses, of decreasing severity, before symptoms of active infection subside. In epidemic situations the mortality rate may be high (50 per cent) among debilitated victims of this disease, but ordinarily it is in the range of 2 to 10 per cent.

Laboratory Diagnosis
I. Identification of the Organism (*Borrelia recurrentis*). The spirochete of relapsing fever is a long, irregularly coiled, spiraled organism, measuring up to 30μ in length (twice the dimension of species of *Treponema* or *Leptospira*). The coils are haphazardly spaced at distances of 2 to 4μ, and the body is relatively thick (0.3 to 0.4μ). The organism rotates in the characteristic corkscrew fashion of spirochetes, but it is more flexible than other species in its twisting and lashing motions. Unlike other spirochetes, species of *Borrelia* can be stained with bacteriologic dyes, such as methylene blue,

Giemsa's and Wright's stains, and the safranin of the Gram stain (they are Gram-negative).

Borrelia can be cultivated in liquid media enriched with blood or serum, or in chick embryos, mice, and rats.

II. Identification of Patient's Serum Antibodies. Agglutinating and complement-fixing antibodies arise during the course of infection, but their identification is difficult because cultivated spirochetes used to identify them possess unstable antigenic components. These organisms also appear to undergo antigenic variation during the course of human infection, possibly as a result of interactions with antibody produced in vivo. The multiplication of new variants may account for the relapsing character of the infection, remissions occurring as specific antibodies for each variant reach a neutralizing level.

III. Specimens for Diagnosis. Blood samples should be collected repeatedly during the febrile periods for examination by stained smear, dark-field microscopy, culture, and animal inoculation. Serologic tests with spirochetal antigens may be inconclusive for reasons outlined in II above.

Epidemiology

I. Communicability of Infection. This disease has two epidemiologic patterns of spread. (1) Human epidemics may arise because man and one of his common ectoparasites, the body louse, may become reservoirs for the organism. In this situation the louse transmits the disease from one person to another, the rapidity of spread being favored by overcrowded conditions among people who are unable to maintain hygienic standards or adequate nutrition. Wars, famines, floods, and other major disasters favor the louse-borne epidemic type of spread of this infection. (2) Under natural circumstances, this infection has a reservoir in wild rodents (squirrels, prairie dogs, and others) and is transmitted among them, or to man, by ticks. The endemic, tick-borne disease occurs sporadically in man in many parts of the world, including the western part of the United States, Mediterranean Europe and Africa, the Near East, and South America. Epidemic louse-

borne relapsing fever is now restricted to parts of Asia, Africa, and South America.

The *incubation period* following the bite of a tick or a louse varies from three days to about two weeks, with an average time of one week.

The disease is *not communicable* from man to man. Ticks may remain infective throughout their lifetime of many years. Lice become infective within a few days of ingestion of blood from infected persons and remain so within their short lifespan of five to six weeks.

Immunity following an attack of relapsing fever does not persist for more than one or two years. Acquired immunity constitutes the only form of human resistance to this infection.

II. Control and Prevention. Patients with active infection do not require isolation provided they are free of insect parasites. The control of this disease depends on the elimination of lice as the source of epidemic infection or the suppression of ticks in areas where the disease is endemic among native rodents. Human infection can be successfully treated with penicillin and other antibiotics, or with arsenical compounds.

Bartonellosis (Oroya Fever and Verruga Peruana)

The arthropod vector of this human infection is restricted to the mountainous areas of northwestern South America, and the disease provides an excellent example of a geographically limited bacteriologic infection. The organism (*Bartonella bacilliformis*) is a Gram-negative, small but highly pleomorphic, motile bacterium (classified with the rickettsiae) and is itself restricted to the human reservoir. It parasitizes red blood cells, producing an acute febrile disease marked by a severe, sometimes fatal anemia (*Oroya fever*). After a period of quiescence, an eruptive stage (*verruga peruana*) develops and runs a prolonged course. The lesions are granulomatous nodules that are highly vascular and resemble hemangiomas. The organisms within the nodules parasitize the endothelial cells of the blood vessels. The disease responds to antibiotic therapy, although the organisms are

not completely eliminated. Specific immunity prevents the recurrence of Oroya fever, but the verrugous disease may continue.

Bartonella infection is important in areas of Peru, Ecuador, and Colombia where the sandfly vector is active. Its control requires suppression of the vector with insecticides such as DDT applied to breeding places and to human living quarters.

Tularemia

This bacterial disease of rabbits and other wild animals may be transmitted directly to man, through a number of entry routes, as previously discussed (Chaps. 14, 19, and 24). In nature it is transmitted among animals hosts by several biting arthropods, such as deerflies, wood ticks, and rabbit ticks, and these insects may also transmit the disease to human beings. Man is an accidental host for the infectious organism, and does not transmit it to others. The disease and its epidemiology are described in Chapter 24 (pp. 536 to 537) with other diseases acquired through animal contacts.

Rickettsial Diseases Transmitted by Arthropods

General Epidemiology

The rickettsiae were described in Chapter 2 (pp. 32 to 33) as coccobacillary, nonmotile forms, smaller than the bacteria, but larger than viruses. They are obligate intracellular organisms that parasitize arthropods, notably ticks and mites, lice and fleas. These insects in turn parasitize animals, such as rodents, rabbits, dogs, and others, and together the insect and animal hosts maintain the reservoir and a natural cycle of rickettsial infection. In most instances, man is an occasional, accidental victim of infection transmitted to him by an infective arthropod. The most outstanding exception to this general epidemiologic pattern is the form of typhus fever known as *epidemic typhus*. In this case, man him-

self is the only known reservoir for the rickettsial agent. When infected human beings are parasitized by lice, these insects acquire the infection and transmit it from person to person. A rapid epidemic spread of this disease may occur when masses of people live in overcrowded, unhygienic conditions.

Another exception to the usual route of transfer of rickettsial infection occurs in the human disease known as Q fever. The infective agent, *Coxiella burnetii*, is thought to be a rickettsia but displays certain biologic differences from other organisms of the group. It is maintained in nature by ticks, which transmit it to domestic animals. The human disease, however, is acquired as a respiratory infection transmitted on air-borne routes from sources associated with infected animals. Q fever is discussed in Chapter 16 (pp. 387 to 388) as a disease of respiratory entry, the only one of the human rickettsioses that is not transferred by an infective arthropod.

Clinical Rickettsiosis

The arthropod-borne rickettsial infections have many clinical as well as epidemiologic features in common. In the human body these organisms parasitize the endothelial cells and smooth-muscle fibers of small blood vessels. Following their introduction into the skin, they may be disseminated through the blood stream, localizing in many peripheral vessels, as well as those of the heart or the brain. The incubation period ranges from a few days to about three weeks, with an average time of two weeks. The clinical symptoms include fever, headache, and a typical skin rash. Depending on the virulence of the organism, or the severity of infection, there may be prostration, delirium or stupor, myocarditis, or peripheral vascular collapse. These diseases respond well to antibiotic therapy, although antimicrobial drugs merely suppress the organisms and do not eliminate them from the body. Antibodies arise during the course of infection, however, and the immune response leads to final recovery, usually without residual tissue damage. The rickettsial agent re-

sponsible for epidemic typhus sometimes persists in its human reservoir for many years following recovery from the initial disease. These infected persons display no symptoms until some change in individual resistance permits a recrudescence of infection. This recurring form of typhus is called *Brill's disease* and is discussed further below.

The rickettsial diseases are associated with particular types of arthropod vectors. They can be classified in three groups on the basis of insect transmission and of certain clinical features, as shown in Table 27–1.

The individual features of these diseases are described briefly below.

The Typhus Fever Group

Epidemic typhus fever is a severe disease with a high mortality rate (6 to 30 per cent). It was known in Europe throughout the Middle Ages as a disease that could sweep in epidemic form through armies and the huddled, refugee victims of wars. The louse is an ectoparasite of man that thrives when human conditions are at their worst. Unsanitary, crowded, malnourished people living in concentration camps, prisons, poorhouses, or slums are the usual hosts for body and head lice. In central and eastern Europe, and in some other parts of the world as well (Africa, Asia, Mexico, and South America), these same human beings also became endemic reservoirs for the rickettsial parasite, transmitting it to each other by way of their lice. The infected louse excretes the organism in its feces, defecating on the skin at the time it bites. When the bite is scratched, the organisms are rubbed into the minor wound, penetrating to the tissues below the skin. It is small comfort to the human victim that the louse also dies of this infection.

Special features of the control of active typhus infection center on early treatment of the patient; delousing him, his clothing, surroundings, and contacts; and protecting the medical personnel who care for him. Isolation of the patient is not necessary provided he is protected from further infestation by lice. In epidemic areas, vaccines

Table 27–1. Classification of the Arthropod-Borne Rickettsial Diseases

Diseases	Insect Vector	Animal Host	Causative Organism
The Typhus Fever Group (Flea- and Louse-Borne)			
Epidemic typhus	Louse	Man only	*Rickettsia prowazeki*
Endemic typhus (also called murine typhus)	Flea	Rat	*R. typhi*
The Spotted Fever Group (Tick-Borne)			
Rocky Mountain spotted fever	Ticks	Rabbits Field mice Dogs (and ticks)	*R. rickettsii*
Boutonneuse fever	Ticks	Rabbits Field mice Dogs (and ticks)	*R. conorii*
The Mite-Borne Rickettsial Diseases			
Scrub typhus (tsutsugamushi fever)	Mite	Wild rodents	*R. tsutsugamushi*
Rickettsialpox	Mite	House mouse	*R. akari*

and sometimes antimicrobial drugs are used prophylactically for those who run a high risk of infection, and vigorous efforts are concentrated on eliminating the louse from the resident population. DDT dusting is highly effective and can be used to delouse the skin and clothing, as well as bedding. Other insecticides, such as lindane and malathion may also be used.

Lice breed on their human hosts, leaving eggs (nits) on the skin or in the hair, and these deposits also must be carefully removed. Bathing, shampooing, and frequent washing of clothes are highly effective in discouraging louse infestation.

Typhus *vaccines* have proved to be of great value in the *prevention* of this disease. They are recommended for medical personnel in areas of risk, as well as for travelers or military units entering such regions. During World War II, the vaccination of American troops was completely successful in protecting them from severe infection, and there were no fatalities among those who did contract the disease. This was in contrast to a 30 per cent mortality rate seen among non-immunized British troops in the Mediterranean area during an epidemic that also took the lives of many in the civilian population of southern

Italy and North Africa. A vigorous campaign of DDT dusting helped to control the spread of the disease among civilians.

Brill's Disease is a modified form of typhus fever that may occur in an individual who has recovered from a previous attack of the disease. Following recovery, the organisms may remain latent for many years, the disease recrudescing only when some condition of stress shifts the patient's balance of resistance. If this happens in an area where human louse infestation is widespread, the recrudescing case may be the starting point of a new epidemic of unmodified typhus.

Endemic typhus fever, or murine typhus as it is often called, is a sporadic disease occurring in many parts of the world where people are exposed to infected rats and their fleas. It was once an urban disease associated with granaries and other areas in cities or seaports where rats breed and congregate. In the United States, continuing campaigns to eradicate rats and prevent their breeding has decreased the incidence of this disease to less than one hundred cases per year. Murine typhus is clinically milder than epidemic typhus but runs a similar course, conferring active immunity on those who recover. The fatality rate is about 2 per cent.

The Spotted Fever Group

Rocky Mountain spotted fever was given this name when it was first recognized in patients who acquired their infection in the Rocky Mountain area. Since that time the disease has been reported in most of the states in this country and is also known to occur in Canada, Mexico, and South America. The tick reservoir and vector species differ in various regions. The dog tick (*Dermacentor variabilis*) maintains the infection in the eastern states; the wood tick (*Dermacentor andersoni*), in northwestern sections. Rabbits, field mice, dogs, or other animals parasitized by ticks help to maintain the infection in nature, but ticks themselves are an important reservoir, because they pass the organism along, transovarially, to the eggs of succeeding generations.

Special features in the control of rickettsial spotted fever include antibiotic therapy of the patient and the prompt removal and destruction of ticks from his body, if any remain at the time he becomes ill. Isolation and other special precautions are not necessary. The prevention of this disease is primarily a matter of the protection of individuals who may be exposed to ticks in endemic areas (hunters and campers, sheep herders, people engaged in land clearance or forest protection work). Vaccines reduce the chance of infection or modify disease. Protective clothing is important also, but persons at risk learn to examine themselves closely for ticks and to remove them promptly. Dogs should also be examined frequently and carefully, so that ticks can be removed before they have embedded their biting mouthparts in the skin and settled down to a long blood meal. It is generally not practical to attempt the eradication of ticks, except in limited areas where the land has been cleared. Various insecticides, such as DDT, chlordane, lindane, and others, control the vectors well under these circumstances.

Boutonneuse fever is a rickettsial spotted fever that is endemic in the Mediterranean countries, and similar diseases occur in other parts of the world, notably Australia, India, and Siberia. Each of these is associated with its own tick reservoir, as well as the animal hosts parasitized by the arthropod.

The Mite-Borne Rickettsial Diseases

Scrub typhus (tsutsugamushi fever) is a rickettsial infection limited to the eastern part of the world. The mites and wild rodents that maintain the natural infection are found in southeast Asia, Australia, many of the Pacific islands, and some sections of China, Japan, and Korea. There are numerous antigenic types of the rickettsial species, and the immunity resulting from disease is not cross-protective, so that second and third attacks are not uncommon in resident populations. Military operations in these regions during the last two or three decades have been marked by epidemics occurring among susceptible men newly exposed to mite infestation.

Scrub typhus and other mite-borne rickettsial infections are characterized by a primary lesion, or "eschar," that forms at the skin site where an infective mite attached and inoculated the organisms. Fever, headache, and rash follow, persisting for about two weeks unless treated with antibiotics. The control of scrub typhus depends on protection against mites, together with chemoprophylaxis or vaccines that prevent disease even though infection may occur. Military measures include the stripping of vegetation from camp sites, insecticide spraying, rodent controls, the impregnation of clothing and bedding with miticidal chemicals, and the use of insect repellents on the skin.

Rickettsialpox is a disease that so far appears to be limited to some of the cities of Russia and of the eastern and central areas of the United States (New York, Boston, Hartford, Philadelphia, and Cleveland). This is a mild disease and perhaps goes undiagnosed on many occasions. It is carried by a mite that shares the infection with mice under natural circumstances. The human disease begins with an eschar at the site of the mite's attachment to the skin and proceeds as a febrile illness with a rash that lasts about a week. Rickettsialpox commonly appears as a small out-

break involving people in apartment houses or tenements infested with mice that carry the infection and maintain it with mites, the latter also parasitizing the human tenants. (One might call this a "mitey-mouse" infection!) Control is readily accomplished by clearing basements and incinerator closets of trash that encourages mouse breeding. The use of insecticides is also helpful.

Laboratory Diagnosis

I. Identification of Organisms. The microscopic and cultural identification of rickettsiae is technically difficult, and also hazardous for the laboratory worker. Biopsies of skin lesions may be stained by special techniques to reveal the organisms in endothelial cells (see Fig. 27–2), and specimens of whole blood (or macerated blood clots) can be inoculated into embryonated chick eggs, guinea pigs, or mice, to propagate the infectious agents, but these techniques are usually available only in public health reference laboratories.

II. Identification of Patient's Serum Antibodies. Specific antibodies arise during the course of rickettsial infections. These can be identified by complement-fixing or agglutination techniques using rickettsial antigens, but the latter are difficult to prepare and expensive to buy. These tests are usually deferred, therefore, until cross-reacting bacterial antigens have been tried.

Certain strains of *Proteus* bacilli (these are Gram-negative enteric bacteria) have been found to possess antigens in common with many rickettsiae, and therefore rickettsial antibodies in patients' serums are capable of agglutinating these related *Proteus* species. This circumstance forms the basis for the *Weil-Felix test.* The rise in antibody titer that occurs during infection can be detected with *Proteus* agglutination, three strains being used to differentiate the different kinds of rickettsial disease.

III. Specimens for Diagnosis. The patient's serum can be submitted to the routine microbiology or serology laboratory for the Weil-Felix test. At least two samples should be collected, one in the early stages of illness and another in about ten days to two weeks, to detect a rising level of antibody. It should be noted, however, that if antibiotic therapy is given early in the disease there may be little stimulus for the production of antibody, and titers may be low and inconclusive.

If isolation and identification of the rickettsiae are deemed necessary and desirable, two specimens of blood should be collected as soon as possible after the onset of symptoms. The blood should be taken by aseptic technique and divided between two sterile tubes. One sample should be defibrinated, the other allowed to clot. The tubes can then be packed in an unbreakable container, which is placed in turn in an insulated shipping box containing ice to keep the blood cool, and forwarded to a reference laboratory equipped for rickettsial work.

Control and Prevention

I. Isolation. As pointed out above, these diseases are not directly communicable from man to man. The first step required in the management of cases is the removal and destruction of insects

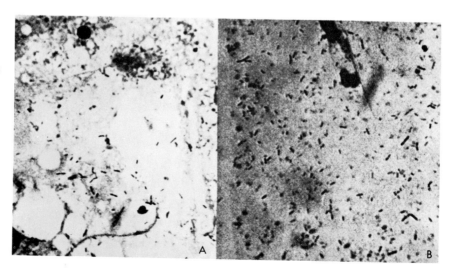

Fig. 27–2. Photomicrograph of rickettsiae of the typhus fever group (1000 ✕). (Reproduced from Plotz, Harry; Smadel, Joseph E.; Anderson, Thomas F.; and Chambers, Leslie A.: Morphological Structure of Rickettsiae, *J. Exp. Med.,* **77**:355–58, 1943.)

on the patient's body. Continuing measures must be taken to protect patients and personnel from insect infestation, particularly in the case of louse-borne typhus. When this is assured, isolation of the patient is not necessary.

II. Precautions.   The blood of patients suffering with rickettsial diseases may be infectious. Syringes and needles used for blood collection should be handled with caution and sterilized promptly.

III. Treatment.   The tetracycline antibiotics and chloramphenicol are the drugs used in rickettsial infections. Because drugs suppress the organisms but do not eliminate them, the patient's immune mechanism is important to full recovery. Antibodies may fail to rise to protective levels when antimicrobial drugs are given early in the disease, and when the drugs are withdrawn, relapses may occur. To prevent this, a second course of antibiotic is started a week after the end of the first course.

IV. Chemoprophylaxis.   Chloramphenicol has been used prophylactically in the control of scrub typhus in endemic areas. It does not avert infection, but it does prevent the development of disease if continued for a month after infection is acquired.

V. Immunity.   An attack of rickettsial disease usually confers permanent immunity against the specific infecting strain. This depends somewhat on the judicious use of antibiotics, as pointed out above.

VI. Immunization.   Formalinized vaccines are available containing rickettsiae that were cultivated in chick embryos. They induce an immunity that remains effective for a few months to a year. Persons exposed to risk of infection should receive booster doses at regular intervals as indiated by the demands of the local situation.

VII. Other Preventive Measures.   Control of the rickettsial diseases depends also on breaking the chain of natural infection or of its transmis-

sion to man. The eradication of rodent hosts is an important feature of the prevention of some of these infections, but human protection from arthropod infestation is essential in each case.

Viral Diseases Transmitted by Arthropods

The arthropod-borne viruses are often called *arboviruses* to distinguish them from others that are directly transmissible from man to man. The arboviruses characteristically require arthropod hosts, multiply in these insects without damaging them, and are transmitted by their bites to man or other animals, including birds and even reptiles. In some instances, the arthropod is itself a reservoir for a particular virus, passing it along to its own succeeding generations, as in the case of some rickettsial infections. Some arboviruses, however, must cycle sequentially between mammalian reservoirs and the insect host.

The arbovirus group includes a very large number of viruses, usually classified in several groups on the basis of their antigenic relationships. They are also sometimes grouped according to their insect vectors. Mosquitoes, biting flies, ticks, and mites are the major types of arthropods that play host to viruses, and, as usual, the biologic requirements of an insect species may sharply limit the geographic distribution of the virus or the human disease associated with it. For purposes of convenience, we shall present the arbovirus diseases in two groups based on clinical distinctions: (1) those that are systemic infections, the viruses being *viscerotropic* (they have a predilection for cells of the visceral organs), and (2) those that are *primary* infections of the brain and spinal cord, the viruses being *neurotropic* (they have an affinity for neural cells). *Encephalitis* is the characteristic clinical syndrome of the latter group of diseases (encephalitides, in the plural). (The student should distinguish between the primary encephalitis caused by neurotropic arbovirus infection and those viral infections of the CNS that may occur as secondary extensions of systemic diseases such as measles, mumps, smallpox, herpesvirus invasions, and others. The term

"postinfectious encephalitides" differentiates this group.)

Systemic Arbovirus Diseases

Yellow Fever

The Clinical Disease. Yellow fever is an acute infectious disease with symptoms that may be quite mild or extremely severe. The fatality rate is low (less than 5 per cent) among people who live in tropical areas where the disease is endemic, but it may be as high as 30 to 40 per cent among susceptible people who have not been previously exposed to this infection. At one time epidemic yellow fever was one of the great plagues of the urban areas of South America, the Caribbean, the seaport cities of the Atlantic and Gulf coasts in the United States, and also those of Western Europe that were connected by trade vessels with the American focus of yellow fever. The epidemic disease came under control in 1900 when the Yellow Fever Commission under Dr. Walter Reed studied the disease in Cuba and demonstrated the causative filterable agent in the blood of patients and in a mosquito vector (species *Aedes aegypti*). Mosquito eradication programs promptly eliminated the disease from the large *urban* centers in the Americas. A few years later it became apparent, however, that a sylvatic or *jungle* form of yellow fever is entrenched in mosquito vectors of the tropical rain forests of South America and Africa. In these areas, forest mosquitoes transmit the virus to animals and to human beings, the native populations displaying mild or inapparent infections. When infected human beings bring the virus into an area where the *Aedes* mosquito is abundant, this species may quickly pick up the infection and pass it along to the resident human population. If the latter contains many susceptible people who have never before been exposed to the virus, the result may be a devastating epidemic. This means that continuous control of the disease depends not only on vigilant efforts to keep the *Aedes* vector suppressed but also on active immunization of persons entering, residing in, or leaving areas where

jungle yellow fever is endemic. Fortunately effective vaccines are available to assist in this control, as we shall see.

When yellow fever virus is injected into human skin through the bite of an infective mosquito, the organism spreads to the lymph nodes, enters the blood stream, and localizes in the liver, spleen, kidney, and bone marrow. After a few days, symptoms begin with fever, chills, headache, and malaise. The foci of virus multiplication in the viscera become necrotic. The liver parenchyma is often the hardest hit, the symptoms of jaundice being prominent (hence *yellow* fever). In severe cases the gastric mucosa may be involved, hemorrhage from the stomach producing black vomitus. Death may result if the hepatic and renal damage is excessive. Patients who recover do so completely, without residual damage.

Laboratory Diagnosis. The virus is present in the blood stream during the first three to five days of illness. It can be recovered and identified by inoculating mice with serum collected from a suspected case.

As the disease progresses, neutralizing antibodies appear in the patient's serum in a rising titer. They are identified by their specific capacity to neutralize the infectivity for mice of known virulent yellow fever strains. It is essential to demonstrate the increasing level of antibody that characterizes the course of active disease by comparing the titer of serum collected during the acute phase with that of a sample drawn after a week or ten days of illness.

Epidemiology

I. COMMUNICABILITY OF INFECTION

A. Reservoirs, Sources, and Transmission Routes. In urban areas, man and the *Aedes aegypti* mosquito are both reservoirs for yellow fever virus.

In jungle areas, mosquitoes maintain the natural infection with animals, transmitting it to man also if he enters the circle.

B. Incubation Period. Less than a week; as a rule three to six days.

C. Communicable Period. Virus is present in the blood stream just before symptoms begin and

for the next few days. During this time man is infective for the mosquito. Following the mosquito's blood meal, the virus requires about 10 to 12 days to develop and multiply before the mosquito becomes infectious. Mosquitoes remain infected while they live but do not pass the virus along to their progeny.

D. Immunity. During infection antibodies are produced rather rapidly, and following recovery they provide a permanent immunity. Repeated exposure to virus in an endemic area provides a protective immunity, as evidenced by a high incidence of inapparent infections. Congenital immunity is passively transferred to the infants of immune mothers and is protective for the first few months of life.

II. CONTROL OF ACTIVE INFECTION

A. Isolation. It is not necessary to isolate patients from other persons, but it is essential that they be screened from mosquitoes, especially during the first few days of illness and viremia.

B. Precautions. Special nursing precautions are not indicated, but the patient's living quarters and all those nearby are immediately sprayed with insecticides.

C. There is no specific antimicrobial therapy for yellow fever.

D. Control of Contacts. Nonimmune persons in the immediate vicinity of a new case of yellow fever are vaccinated promptly, to prevent their possible infection by local mosquitoes that may have newly acquired the virus from the patient. A search is made for the origin of each new case, and a campaign is conducted, particularly in and around houses, against mosquito species that might carry and transfer the infection.

E. Epidemic Controls. Yellow fever is a matter of international concern, and all governments work through the World Health Organization to report the disease and control it.

Urban yellow fever is fought by attacking the mosquito on a communitywide basis, using residual insecticide sprays. *Aedes aegypti* breeding places are searched out and treated with compounds that kill mosquito larvae. At the same time, yellow fever vaccine is given to all who live within the area ranged by the infective species.

Jungle yellow fever cannot be controlled by an attack on the vector, because its breeding places are too numerous and inaccessible. Vaccination is the principal line of defense for those who live in endemic areas or travel into them. Public health authorities maintain surveillance programs in these regions, investigating fatal cases of human illness, searching the forests for monkeys that might have died of the disease, and conducting immunologic surveys of captured animals (especially primates) to determine the range of virus infection in the area.

International control of yellow fever includes the quarantining of animals shipped from endemic regions, the inspection and spraying of aircraft or other vessels arriving from infected areas, and requirements for the vaccination of travelers. Vaccination certificates are valid for six years. Persons without evidence of vaccination who have come from or passed through endemic zones are quarantined on their arrival in countries where the *Aedes* vector exists and might become infected from a human case. Quarantine periods are based on the expectation that persons incubating yellow fever should develop symptoms within 10 to 12 days of their last exposure to infective vectors.

III. PREVENTION

A. Immunization. A live attenuated strain of yellow fever virus is used for artificial active immunization. This variant, called the 17D strain, is highly antigenic but nonpathogenic for man. A single subcutaneous injection stimulates good levels of antibodies within a week to ten days, and provides a solid immunity for several years. Routine use of the vaccine is desirable for persons exposed to the jungle type of endemic disease. In other areas, vaccine is administered only when the threat arises of an *Aedes*-carried urban epidemic.

B. Continuing control and surveillance programs, as outlined above, are necessary to prevent the recurrence of yellow fever as an epidemic disease.

Other Arbovirus Fevers. Many other systemic virus infections are carried by arthropods in dif-

ferent parts of the world. Some are mosquito-borne, others are carried by ticks or mites. A group of these diseases is characterized, like yellow fever, by hemorrhagic lesions in mucosal areas (enanthems), but petechial or purpuric skin lesions also occur (exanthems). These hemorrhagic fevers, as they are called, occur in scattered areas (Crimea, southeast Asia and the Pacific Islands, Russia and Siberia, South America), usually limited by the range of the arthropod host harboring the virus.

Some arboviruses do not produce hemorrhagic injury, but characteristically elicit a maculopapular rash much like that of measles. The fever lasts for a few days and is often accompanied by lymph node involvement, joint and muscle pains, pain in the eyes, and conjunctivitis. The viruses of this group do not localize in the liver or other vital organs, as a rule, and these fevers are rarely, if ever, fatal. They are also distributed geographically according to the range of their vectors or the introduction of virus to new arthropod hosts able to accommodate them. In the Americas, perhaps the best-known example of a recently introduced arbovirus is the agent of *dengue fever* (also called "breakbone fever" because of the severe muscle and joint pain experienced by many patients). This disease is endemic in southeast Asia and the southwest Pacific, but was introduced into the Carribean area, where several large outbreaks occurred in 1963, transmitted by *Aedes* mosquitoes. *Colorado tick fever* is a similar disease seen in the western areas of the United States, and *sandfly fever* is another one, its vector being distributed in Central and South America as well as the hot, dry sectors of Europe, Africa, and Asia.

The Arbovirus Encephalitides

There is a rather large group of encephalitides associated with arboviruses. Most of them are carried by mosquitoes, but there is also a small group transmitted by ticks. Birds and possibly many other animals (rodents, bats, reptiles, and domestic animals such as horses and sheep) ap-

pear to play a role in the maintenance of these infections in nature, possibly with the assistance of their ectoparasites, notably ticks and mites.

In the United States only the mosquito-borne encephalitides are known, the tick-borne variety being restricted to spotty areas of northern and central Europe and Russia. The clinical diseases recognized in the United States and other parts of this hemisphere are *Eastern equine encephalitis* (EEE), *Western equine encephalitis* (WEE), and *St. Louis encephalitis* (SLE). (In the Far East, Japanese B and Murray Valley encephalitis are arbovirus infections carried by mosquitoes.)

Eastern Equine, Western Equine, and St. Louis Encephalitis

The Clinical Disease. These are acute, self-limited diseases characterized by inflammation of the brain, spinal cord, and meninges. They may occur as mild cases of aseptic meningitis, or they may be quite severe, with a sudden onset of high fever, chills, nausea, and malaise with localizing symptoms of meningitis and encephalitis occurring within the next day or two. Pain and stiffness of the neck, drowsiness or stupor, and disorientation are frequent. In severe cases, there may be aphasia, convulsions, and coma. Spastic paralysis may occur. There may be sequelae, such as impaired mental function, blindness, deafness, or epilepsy, and paralysis may also be residual. The severity and mortality rate of these "American" encephalitides are not so great as those seen in Japanese B encephalitis, but they take their worst toll among infants and young children.

Laboratory Diagnosis. The viruses of these diseases can seldom be isolated from the blood of patients, because viremia usually occurs before the onset of symptoms. By the time the illness becomes apparent, virus is localized within the central nervous system. It is seldom identified except in brain tissue taken at autopsy. These viruses can be cultivated in mice and embryonated eggs, then identified by neutralizing or complement-fixing antibodies.

A serologic diagnosis can be obtained by identifying the patient's serum antibodies. It is important, however, that a rising titer of antibody be demonstrated, by comparing a sample of serum collected in the acute stage of illness with another one taken about three to four weeks later.

When outbreaks of these encephalitides occur, public health epidemiologists search for mosquito and animal reservoirs. The virus may be isolated from these sources and tested with patient's serum as well as with known antisera.

Epidemiology

I. COMMUNICABILITY OF INFECTION

A. Reservoir, Sources, and Transmission Routes. The identity of the year-round reservoirs for these viruses is not yet known, but wild birds as well as rodents and reptiles (and their ticks and mites) are thought to be important in the annual cycle. During the summer mosquito season, birds are the source of infection for mosquitoes, and the latter transfer it to man. The two equine viruses are also transferred to horses, and large epizootics may occur among these animals. Neither horses nor man is a likely source of infection for mosquitoes, because the viremic stage is brief, and virus is not heavily concentrated in the blood. The virus of St. Louis encephalitis is not known to infect horses. A number of mosquito vectors may be involved, but the most important of them belong to the genus *Culex.*

B. Incubation Period. Varies from four or five days to three weeks, with an average time of 10 to 15 days.

C. Communicable Period. These diseases are not transmissible from person to person, and man probably does not infect the mosquito. Viremia persists in birds for several days, and the mosquito remains infective throughout its life.

D. Immunity. In areas where these diseases occur frequently, most adults are immune because of frequent inapparent infection. Active disease results in a solid immunity against the infecting virus strain. Infants, young children, and aging people are among the most susceptible because their immunity is incomplete or waning. WEE is distributed in the western states and

Canada, with a few foci on the East Coast of the United States, and in South America. EEE occurs in the eastern and north central states of the United States, as well as Canada, and also in Central and South America and the Caribbean. St. Louis encephalitis may be seen in most of the country except the northeast and has also been identified in the West Indies and in Brazil.

II. CONTROL OF ACTIVE INFECTION. Isolation and special precautions are not indicated for patients with these encephalitides. However, they must be clinically differentiated from other syndromes that may represent extension of systemic infection with a communicable disease (poliomyelitis, mumps, rabies, postinfectious viral encephalitides, as well as those of bacterial or mycotic origin). There is no specific treatment.

The control and prevention of these infections depend on the recognition of human cases, as well as related disease in horses or birds, and elimination of the vector mosquitoes.

Formalinized vaccines are available for the protection of those who run unusually high risks of infection (such as laboratory and field workers), and these may also be passively protected, following known exposure, with specific immune serum from humans or animals.

Parasitic Diseases Transmitted by Arthropods

Most of the arthropod-borne parasitic diseases are caused by protozoan species. There are three important genera of protozoa that are transmitted by arthropods to man and animals, each genus containing several species: *Plasmodium*, the causative agent of malaria; *Leishmania*, which is associated with three types of clinical disease; and *Trypanosoma*, the cause of African sleeping sickness and of a South American infection called Chagas' disease.

In addition, there is a family of nematodes, often referred to as *filarial* worms (filaria meaning "thread"), whose adult forms live in man's tissues or body cavities. Mosquitoes are intermediate hosts for these parasites.

All the organisms of this group display the third type of life cycle previously described for the animal parasites in Chapter 9 (pp. 194 to 195), definitive and intermediate hosts playing alternate roles in maintaining the natural infection. The life cycles and the characteristic human diseases produced by these parasites are presented below in semioutline form highlighting their developmental patterns, the clinical syndromes, and their control.

Malaria

Organisms. *Plasmodium vivax, Plasmodium malariae, Plasmodium falciparum, Plasmodium ovale, Plasmodium knowlesi* (members of the protozoan class Sporozoa).

These organisms parasitize man's red blood cells, and in the process they go through several stages of asexual division and development. Precursors of sexual cells (gametocytes) are also formed. When the latter are taken up by a mosquito they proceed through stages of sexual division in the arthropod host.

Life Cycle (Type 2)

I. Definitive Host. Mosquitoes of the genus *Anopheles.*

II. Intermediate Host. Man (a number of animals may be hosts for *Plasmodium* species that are not infective for man).

III. Human Infestation

A. SOURCE OF INFECTION. The bite of an infective female anopheline mosquito.

B. INFECTIVE FORM. *Sporozoites* congregated in the salivary gland of the mosquito, injected into the skin when she bites.

C. LOCALIZATION AND DEVELOPMENT. Sporozoites are first carried by way of the blood stream to a localizing point in the liver. They undergo several cycles of asexual multiplication in the liver during the following week or two. The basic unit capable of initiating the asexual cycle is called a *merozoite*. These units begin to emerge

from the liver and invade the red blood cells. Within the erythrocyte the invading merozoite (there may be more than one in a cell in some types of infection) repeats the asexual cycle of division and development, in stages successively called: (1) the *ring* stage (this is a young trophozoite, see Fig. 2–4, p. 20); (2) an amoeboid *trophozoite;* (3) a *schizont* (the nuclear material divides and redivides forming many segments); (4) a *mature schizont*, which ruptures the erythrocyte scattering its segments, now called merozoites again. These enter new cells and the cycle repeats with a growing density of parasites. This process is called *schizogony.*

In time, some of the parasites develop into specialized precursors of gametes, or sex cells. The precursors are called *microgametocytes* and *macrogametocytes*. These do not enter into sexual combinations in the human body, but must wait for the conditions provided by the mosquito host.

D. EXIT FROM HUMAN BODY. The female anopheline mosquito must take a blood meal from an infected person, and the blood removed must contain both micro- and macrogametocytes. The asexual forms do not develop further in the insect.

IV. Cyclic Development in the Mosquito Host. The microgametocyte fertilizes the macrogametocyte, and a *zygote* is formed. The latter enters the wall of the mosquito's stomach, forms an *oocyst*, and the *sporozoites* develop within the latter structure. This process is known as *sporogony* and culminates with the liberation of hundreds of sporozoites into the mosquito's body cavity. Most of them migrate to the salivary or other glands of the insect, where they can develop no further until injected into a human host. The life cycle of the malaria parasite is shown diagrammatically in Figure 27–3.

Characteristics of Human Malaria. Malaria is an old disease of mankind that has killed many millions of people since the ancient Chinese, Assyrians, and Egyptians first made note of it. It has often been spread in epidemic form when infected persons have introduced the parasite to new vectors in areas where the human population

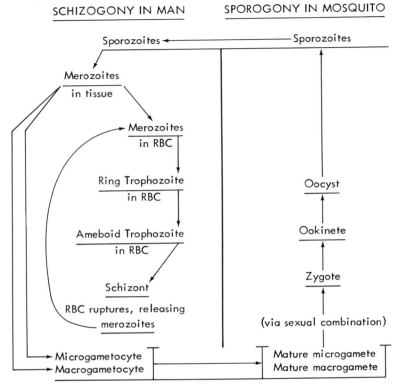

SCHIZOGONY IN MAN   SPOROGONY IN MOSQUITO

Fig. 27–3. Diagrammatic scheme of the life cycle of the malaria parasite.

has not previously experienced the disease. Human susceptibility is fairly universal, however. True immunity does not develop and resistance to the effects of the parasite builds up very slowly in those regions where the infection has occurred continuously over a period of many years. For this reason, the establishment of a new vector can be disastrous in previously uninfected areas.

Malaria is a chronic disease that produces invalids. It is directly responsible for deaths in only about 1 to 2 per cent of adult cases, but the rate may be much higher than this among infants. It is a debilitating disease that retards physical and mental development, sometimes on a scale large enough to be felt in every social and national effort of an afflicted people. Endemic malaria has been controlled and virtually eliminated from many countries where it was once a problem, but

it is estimated that 1100 million people throughout the world still live under the shadow of this infection, that 350 million people acquire it each year, and that 3.5 million die of its direct or indirect results. It remains a serious public health problem in many of the countries of Central and South America, Africa, the Near and Far East, Southeast Asia (including Vietnam), and the Southwest Pacific. The concerted efforts of local governments and the World Health Organization have resulted in the eradication of malaria from many endemic zones, but much remains to be done.

Man is the only known host for the five species of malaria listed at the beginning of this section, although other species of the *Plasmodium* have been recognized in animal infections. The most common species of the human parasites are *P. vivax* and *P. falciparum*, the latter producing a

clinical disease more virulent than that associated with any of the others. *P. malariae* has a wide distribution but the incidence of infection is low. *P. ovale* causes a relatively mild human disease seen only in West Africa. *P. knowlesi* has recently been demonstrated as a cause of human disease in Malaya. Throughout the "malaria belt" that stretches across the tropical and subtropical areas of the globe, the female *Anopheles* mosquito is the responsible vector. Her species varies in different regions, but she restricts the spread of human malaria chiefly by her requirement for warm, moist climates in altitudes of less than 6000 ft. The availability of human populations within the range of this mosquito assures the perpetuation of the parasite until the vector is eradicated.

The asexual maturations and divisions of malarial parasites in the peripheral blood cells are responsible for many of the clinical symptoms of this disease, and especially for their cyclic recurrence. When large numbers of maturing schizonts simultaneously reach the stage of erythrocyte rupture, with the liberation of new merozoites, the event is marked by a paroxysmal fever, with shaking chills that rack the patient. These symptoms may endure for a few minutes to an hour and are often accompanied by nausea, vomiting, and severe headache. The fever may persist for several hours as parasitemia continues, and the liberated merozoites circulate before invading new red blood cells. The episode is finally concluded with a drenching sweat that leaves the patient afebrile and exhausted, but able to rest and sleep. For the next two or three days the patient feels reasonably well, until another cycle of parasite maturation overtakes him and he enters a new paroxysmal stage. These episodes of fever and chills are at first quite irregular, but later develop a rhythm that is sometimes characteristic for the parasite species. *Falciparum* and *vivax* malaria are usually *tertian;* that is, cyclic fever and chills recur every third day (at 48-hour intervals); while the cycle is *quartan* for *P. malariae*, with paroxysms recurring every fourth day (72 hours).

Malaria may eventually burn itself out, if mosquito-borne infection is not renewed, but not before damage has been done to the hema-topoietic system. There are hepatomegaly, splenomegaly, anemia, and, sometimes in the case of *falciparum* malaria, hemorrhagic damage to kidneys and liver ("blackwater fever," marked by hematuria and jaundice as signs of glomerular nephritis and hepatic necrosis). "Cerebral malaria" is another possible consequence of *falciparum* infections, resulting in excessive fever, delirium, or coma and death when the vascular supply to the brain is seriously compromised by parasitic occlusions of cerebral blood vessels.

Diagnostic Methods.   Blood smears are examined microscopically. *Thin* blood smears are made by the technique usual for the differentiation of white blood cells. *Thick* smears are also important because the organisms may be scarce and hard to find. A thick smear is made by allowing several drops of the patient's fingertip blood to puddle in the center of a glass slide. A wooden applicator is used to stir this puddle to defibrinate it. Fibrin threads are wrapped on the end of the stick and removed. In the laboratory thin smears are stained to visualize the parasites within the red blood cells. Thick smears are first treated so that the erythrocytes are lysed, freeing their parasites. When properly stained, the organisms can be seen lying among the white blood cells and platelets left on the slide (see Fig. 27–4).

When blood smears are reported to be nega-

Fig. 27–4.   A photomicrograph of a thick human blood smear showing many malaria parasites freed from the lysed red blood cells. The large cells are blood leukocytes (1000 ×).

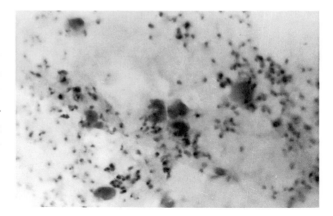

Fig. 27–5. Gentle persuasion can be a mighty weapon in malaria eradication campaigns. Here a World Health Organization advisor is explaining to a housewife that mosquito spraying is necessary even though no one in her family is suffering from malaria at this time. (Courtesy of WHO, Geneva, Switzerland.)

tive for malarial parasites, but the clinical picture and history of exposure are suggestive, it is important to take additional smears on repeated occasions. Maturing organisms are present in the blood during the few hours preceding the paroxysms of fever and chills. When the latter can be predicted, smears should be taken during the day before they are expected, while the fever is rising, and during the first chills. Later in the episode one is not likely to find intracellular organisms

unless alternate generations of trophozoites are maturing.

Differentiation of the various species of malarial parasites sometimes depends on finding the organisms in varying stages of maturity. The morphologic distinctions between species are not obvious and require an expert eye. The physician must often correlate the laboratory's findings with the clinical developments, steering the collection of smears judiciously so that full species diagnosis can be obtained.

Special Features of Control

Treatment. Malaria was treated with extracts of the bark of the cinchona tree long before its etiologic agent was known. (The parasite was discovered in 1880 by Charles Louis Alphonse Laveran, a French Army doctor.) The active ingredient of cinchona bark is quinine, which was the standard drug until more effective synthetic compounds were developed during World War II. The first of these was *atabrine*, or quinacrine. This drug has been largely supplanted by newer ones with greater antimalarial activity and less toxicity, notably *chloroquine* and *amodiaquine*. Other compounds that may be used in combination with these drugs are *proguanil* and *pyrimethamine*.

Drug therapy in malaria has several goals, which usually cannot be accomplished by the use of a single compound. Not only must the clinical attack be treated, but there must also be a cidal effect on parasitic stages developing in the liver, or elsewhere outside of the red blood cells, so that relapses will not occur. Furthermore, it is important to kill the gametocytes that perpetuate the parasite's life cycle (see Fig. 27–3) when they are transmitted to mosquito vectors, particularly if the patient remains in an endemic area and is being treated there. The prophylactic or *suppressive* use of these drugs has great value in preventing infection or in suppressing the development of the parasites, so that clinical symptoms do not occur. Persons on suppressive treatment who

leave endemic areas must continue the drug for about a month to avoid later clinical attack, and to reduce the risk of transmitting infection to new *Anopheles* vectors.

The control of malaria depends on coordinated efforts to treat and cure active cases of human malaria, thus eliminating the intermediate reservoir, and to eradicate the mosquito host as well. Patients with malaria should be carefully screened from mosquitoes until they are under drug control. The attack on the insect includes the community application of residual insecticides in and around dwellings (see Fig. 27–5), but the most effective control is achieved when mosquito breeding places are eliminated, by the draining and filling of stagnant swamps and water holes, or by the use of chemicals that kill larvae (see Fig. 27–6).

Leishmaniasis

Organisms. *Leishmania donovani, Leishmania tropica, Leishmania braziliensis* (members of the protozoan class Flagellata, also called Mastigophora).

These organisms, like the trypanosomes discussed in the next section, are frequently referred to as *hemoflagellates* to distinguish them from the intestinal flagellates such as *Trichomonas* and *Giardia*. The hemoflagellates live in man's blood stream or parasitize his tissues.

The leishmanias are intracellular parasites in their human hosts, occurring as nonmotile round forms within tissue cells (see Fig. 27–7). The three species listed have affinities for reticuloendothelial cells in different tissues and therefore produce different clinical syndromes. Each re-

Fig. 27–6. In India, insecticide teams engaged in malaria eradication may be obliged to walk for hours through deep forests and across many streams to reach isolated villages. A nationwide campaign against malaria was launched by the government of India in 1958, with the assistance of the World Health Organization. (WHO photo by P. N. Sharma.)

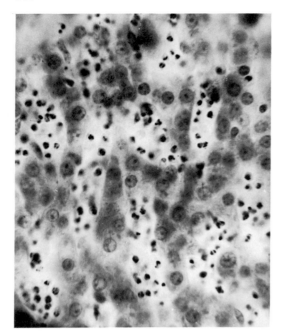

Fig. 27–7. A photomicrograph of human liver cells containing nonmotile forms of *Leishmania donovani* (1000 ×). (Courtesy of Dr. Kenneth Phifer, Rockville, Md.)

quires an insect host to complete its life cycle, the parasite assuming a flagellated motile form within the body of the arthropod. Infective insects transmit the parasites to animals as well as to man, both constituting the natural reservoir of these infections.

Life Cycle (Type 3)

I. Definitive Host. Sandflies (motile forms of the parasite develop).

II. Intermediate Host. Man and animals (nonmotile intracellular forms in tissues).

III. Human Infestation
A. SOURCE OF INFECTION. Bite of infective sandfly.
B. INFECTIVE FORM. Flagellated stage called a *leptomonad*.
C. LOCALIZATION AND DEVELOPMENT. *L. don-*

ovani establishes a *visceral* infection called *kala-azar*. Following their entry into the skin, the organisms are engulfed by wandering macrophages of the RE system and are carried by these through the blood stream to various organ sites. They are found in the endothelial cells of the liver, spleen, bone marrow, lymph nodes, and sometimes many other organs as well. They may be present in the intestinal wall, the kidneys, or the meninges and are found, correspondingly, in the feces, urine, or spinal fluid. They are not transmissible by these routes, but must be transferred again to the sandfly host.

L. tropica establishes a *cutaneous* infection called *Oriental sore.* The organisms are found in the reticuloendothelial cells and the lymphoid tissue of the skin where they produce an ulcerating lesion. This infection may be acquired by *contact* with infected persons as well as from the insect vector. It may also be spread on the infected individual's own skin, producing multiple sores.

L. braziliensis parasitizes the cells of the skin and mucosa of the mouth, nose, and pharynx. The disease is called by several names, such as *American leishmaniasis* (it occurs in Central and South America), *mucocutaneous leishmaniasis*, *espundia*, or *uta.* This disease may also be transmitted from person to person by direct contact or by autoinoculation, with secondary lesions in various skin sites.

IV. Cyclic Development in the Insect Host. When the nonmotile leishmania forms are ingested in the blood meal of the sandfly they develop into leptomonad forms that have a single polar flagellum and divide by longitudinal fission. Very large numbers of leptomonads are produced in the insect's intestine and are later found in the pharynx and buccal cavity.

The leptomonad form can also be propagated on artificial culture media in the laboratory.

Characteristics of Human Disease; Diagnosis and Control. *Kala-azar (L. donovani)* is a disease of the tropical and semitropical countries of the world. It is found in both hemispheres, in scattered areas reflecting the incidence of infective

sandflies, and occurs chiefly during the first two decades of life. Kala-azar is a chronic systemic disease, progressive and fatal when it is untreated. Antimony compounds provide effective therapy.

> *The disease is diagnosed* by demonstration of the intracellular bodies in biopsies of spleen or liver, or in aspirated bone marrow or blood. Clinical material can be inoculated into culture media or into hamsters for propagation of the causative organisms.

Visceral leishmaniasis is not directly transmitted from person to person. Effective control is achieved when human cases are diagnosed and placed under treatment while concurrent application of insecticides is aimed at elimination of the infective vector.

Cutaneous leishmaniasis is divided in distribution between the two hemispheres. *Oriental sore* (*L. tropica*) is found in the tropical and semitropical areas of the Old World: the Mediterranean countries, Africa, the Near and Far East, and southeast Asia. *American leishmaniasis* (*L. braziliensis*) occurs in the southern countries of our own hemisphere.

> These infections are diagnosed by demonstrating the intracellular *Leishmania* bodies in the cells of skin scrapings taken from the edges of exposed lesions, or by cultivating the leptomonad form.

Like kala-azar, the cutaneous diseases respond to treatment with antimony compounds. Their control is made more difficult by the fact that they can be transmitted directly by infected persons, so that mass treatment campaigns, as well as vector controls, are necessary to prevent continuing spread.

Trypanosomiasis

Organisms. *Trypanosoma gambiense, Trypanosoma rhodesiense* (agents of African trypanosomiasis or "African sleeping sickness"), and *Trypanosoma cruzi*, the agent of American trypanosomiasis (members of the protozoan class *Flagellata*, also called *Mastigophora*).

Mature trypanosomes are flagellated protozoans that characteristically possess an undulating membrane. The African species appear in this form in the blood of their human hosts (see Fig. 27–8), but assume a slightly different morphology in the insect host. The American species may be found in the trypanosomal form in human blood, but also in an intracellular leishmanial stage in the RE cells of many organs. The insect stages of *T. cruzi* are like those of the African species.

Life Cycle (Type 3)

I. Definitive Host. African species: the tsetse fly. American species: the "kissing" bug (reduviid bug). (Trypanosomal and crithidial stages occur in the insect host.)

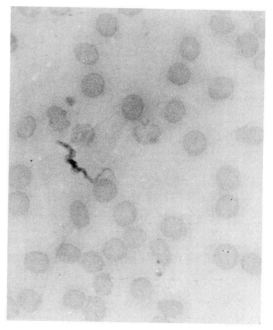

Fig. 27–8.   *Trypanosoma gambiense* in a blood smear. The round objects are red blood cells. Note the terminal flagellum and the undulating membrane that extends along the body of this organism.

II. Intermediate Host. Man and animals. African species: Trypanosomes in blood, lymph, and spinal fluid. American species: Trypanosomes in blood; intracellular leishmanial forms in lymphoid tissue.

III. Human Infestation and Epidemiology

A. AFRICAN TRYPANOSOMIASIS. The source of infection is the bite of an infective tsetse fly (genus *Glossina*). The infective form is a mature trypanosome that first multiplies at the site of inoculation into the skin, producing a primary lesion. The organisms multiply extracellularly and eventually are distributed through the body. The most serious effects of localization occur in the heart muscle, and in the central nervous system. In the acute stages there are fever, lymphadenopathy, severe headache, and anemia. The disease progresses in chronic fashion and leads to emaciation, as well as symptoms of mental apathy, sleepiness, and neuromuscular disorders.

Diagnosis is made by demonstrating the organisms in smears of the peripheral blood or aspirated lymph. During the stages of CNS involvement it may be seen in the spinal fluid.

The disease is not transmitted from person to person, but man, cattle, and a few wild game animals are reservoirs of infection for the fly host. The organism develops from trypanosomal to crithidial stages in the insect and is transformed again into an infective trypanosome form, this process requiring about three weeks. The fly remains infective throughout its life-span of three months, but does not pass the organism to its progeny.

Treatment is with arsenical compounds or drugs of the diamidine group, but the prognosis is poor when the patient reaches the somnolent stage. The Rhodesian type of disease is more virulent and difficult to cure than the Gambian variety.

Control and prevention of trypanosomiasis are difficult because the breeding places of the insect host are sometimes inaccessible, an animal reservoir contributes to the parasite's cycle, and the

human disease does not yield readily to treatment. The Gambian variety is found in some of the countries of west central Africa (Gambia, Liberia, Ghana, the Congo, Sudan, and others); the Rhodesian type in the dryer areas to the southeast (Rhodesia, Tanganyika, Mozambique, and Malawi). Control measures include intensive efforts to clear the fly away from villages, while conducting mass treatment campaigns in the local populations.

B. AMERICAN TRYPANOSOMIASIS. This infection, often called *Chagas' disease*, is found in Central and South America. It is transmitted to man by blood-sucking, cone-nosed bugs of the reduviid family. They are often called "kissing bugs" because of their tendency to bite at the mucocutaneous junction of the lips. The infective organisms are not transmitted by the insect's bite, however, but from its fecal deposits, which are rubbed into the conjunctivae, other mucous membranes, or a skin abrasion. The parasite's development in the insect is similar to that described for the African species. At the site of inoculation, the mature trypanosomes derived from the insect progress locally through leishmanial, leptomonad, and crithidial stages, producing a swollen lesion called a "chagoma." Acute systemic disease occurs at the same time, with fever, malaise, and localization of the organisms in the RE cells of the spleen, liver, and myocardium. Conjunctival entry is common in children, who display unilateral edema of the eyelids and face, with inflammatory involvement of the lacrimal glands. In adults the disease may be mild or asymptomatic, but it is often fatal for children. It may end with chronic progression to the central nervous system, or with myocardial failure.

Diagnosis is made by demonstrating trypanosomal forms in the circulating blood, or intracellular leishmanial forms in biopsies of lymph nodes or involved tissues.

Treatment is difficult, and generally unsuccessful, particularly when the chronic, leishmanial stage of disease has been reached. A group of drugs known as aminoquinolines is effective in

clearing the blood of the majority of trypanosomal forms, so that tissue localizations are controlled and reduced if the disease is recognized and treated early.

Control measures are similar to those described for African trypanosomiasis, except that the insect host may be attacked with greater effect in endemic areas. Infected domestic animals must be destroyed, houses disinfested of the vector, and bed nets used where the insect remains prevalent.

Filariasis

Organisms. A number of species of filarial roundworms may parasitize the tissues of man and sometimes other animal hosts. Man appears to be the principal reservoir, however, for those species most commonly associated with human disease:

Wuchereria bancrofti   } adults live in lymphatic *Brugia malayi*   } vessels

Onchocera volvulus   } adults live in skin and *Loa loa*   } subcutaneous tissues

Life Cycle (Type 3)

I. Definitive Host. Man.

II. Intermediate Host. *Wuchereria* and *Brugia* species: *mosquitoes. Onchocerca:* a *blackfly* species (*Simulium damnosum*). *Loa loa:* a *deerfly* or mango fly (genus *Chrysops*).

The cyclic development of the filarial parasites requires both the human and the insect host. The bisexual adults mature in human tissues, copulate, and produce immature larvae called "microfilariae." These usually find their way into the circulating blood stream, except in the case of the subcutaneous worm *Onchocerca.* The

Table 27–2. Human Infestation

Organism	Source of Infection	Infective Form	Adult Localization	Transmission	Geographic Distribution
W. bancrofti	Culex Aedes Anopheles mosquitoes	Larvae matured in mosquito	Large lymph vessels, especially in the pelvis	Larvae called "microfilariae" circulate in blood, especially at night; these transferred to mosquito	West Indies Central and South America Arabia S.E. Asia Far East Australia and Pacific Islands
B. malayi	Mansonia Anopheles mosquitoes	Larvae matured in mosquito	As above	As above	Southeast Asia India China
O. volvulus	Blackfly	Larvae matured in fly	Subcutaneous tissues, especially those of head and shoulders, lower trunk, and legs	Microfilariae remain in skin and lymphatics adjacent to adult and are picked up by biting fly	Guatemala So. Mexico Venezuela West Africa
Loa loa	Deerfly	Larvae matured in fly	Adult migrates through subcutaneous tissues	Microfilariae in circulating blood are picked up by biting fly	West and Central Africa

Table 27–3. Summary : Infectious Diseases Acquired from Arthropod Vectors

Clinical Disease	Causative Organisms	Other Possible Entry Routes	Incubation Period	Communicable Period
I. Bacterial Diseases Transmitted by Arthropods				
Plague	*Pasteurella pestis*	Respiratory	2–6 days	Not transmissible from man to man except when plague pneumonia develops then communicable during time sputum bacteriologically positive
Relapsing fever	*Borrelia recurrentis*		3 days to 2 weeks	Not communicable from man to man
Bartonellosis (Oroya fever and verruga peruana)	*Bartonella bacilliformis*		16–22 days ; may be as long as 3–4 months	Not communicable from man to man
II. Rickettsial Diseases Transmitted by Arthropods				
Epidemic typhus fever, Brill's disease	*Rickettsia prowazeki* louse men		6–15 days, usually about 12 days	Not communicable from man to man
Endemic typhus fever	*Rickettsia typhi* flea rat		Same as above	Same as above
Rocky Mountain spotted fever	*Rickettsia rickettsii* Tick		3–10 days	Same as above
Boutonneuse fever	*Rickettsia conorii*		5–7 days	Same as above
Scrub typhus (tsutsugamushi fever)	*Rickettsia tsutsugamushi* mite		6–21 days	Same as above

ecimens equired	Laboratory Diagnosis	Immunization	Treatment	Nursing Management
spirated buboes, centesis s, spinal	Culture Smear and culture	Killed vaccines	Sulfonamides Streptomycin Tetracyclines	Isolation until danger of pneumonic form has passed; strictest isolation for pneumonic plague including hoods, face mask with goggles, gloves and over-all protective clothing
m and valescent m	Rising titer of antibodies			Concurrent disinfection of discharges and excretions; terminal disinfection-cleaning must be thorough
	Smear and culture Dark-field examination Animal inoculation	None	Penicillin Arsenicals	Isolation not required if patient free of insect parasites
	Smear and culture	None	Penicillin Streptomycin Tetracyclines	Isolation not required; protect patient from vector
and valescent m	Isolation of rickettsiae Weil-Felix titer	Killed vaccines	Tetracyclines Chloramphenicol	Isolation not necessary if patient is *thoroughly* devectored
and concent serum	Weil-Felix titer		Same as above	Same as above
as above	Same as above	Same as above	Same as above	Same as above
as above	Same as above		Same as above	Same as above
as above	Same as above	Same as above	Same as above	Same as above

Table 27–3. (*Cont.*)

Clinical Disease	Causative Organisms	Other Possible Entry Routes	Incubation Period	Communicab Period
Rickettsialpox	*Rickettsia akari*		Probably 10–24 days	Same as above
III. Viral Diseases Transmitted by Arthropods				
Yellow fever	Yellow fever virus		Less than a week, as a rule 3–6 days	Not transmissible from person to pe
Eastern equine, Western equine, and St. Louis encephalitis	Arboviruses		4–5 days to 3 weeks, average 10–15 days	Not transmissible from person to pe
IV. Parasitic Diseases Transmitted by Arthropods				
Malaria	*Plasmodium* species		12–30 days, depends on species	When gametocytes circulate in blood
Leishmaniasis	*Leishmania* species		From a few days to 24 months, depends on species	While leishmaniae circulate in blood
Trypanosomiasis	*Trypanosoma* species		1–3 weeks, depends on species	While trypanosome circulate in blood
Filariasis	*Wuchereria bancrofti Brugia malayi Onchocerca volvulus Loa loa*		About 9 months before microfilariae are found in blood	While microfilariae circulate in blood

blood-sucking arthropod becomes infected during a blood meal (which must include some tissue fluid in the case of *Onchocerca*), and the microfilariae undergo a series of developmental changes requiring two to three weeks. Infective larvae are injected into the next human victim when the insect bites again.

Characteristics of Human Disease. *Filariasis* caused by *W. bancrofti* and the Malayan variety of worm is characterized by lymphadenopaphy, which may lead to obstruction of the lymph flow and "elephantiasis" of the region drained by the affected vessels. Localization of the adult worms occurs most commonly in the

cimens quired	Laboratory Diagnosis	Immunization	Treatment	Nursing Management
as above	Same as above Weil-Felix titer negative		Same as above	Same as above
and con- cent serum	Virus isolation in mouse Rising titer of antibodies	Live attenuated vaccine	None specific	Isolation is not necessary; patient must be screened from mosquitoes
and con- cent serum	Virus isolation Rising titer of antibodies	Killed vaccines	None specific	Isolation and special precautions not indicated
smears, and thin	Recognition of parasitic forms in red blood cells		Chloraquine Amodiaquine Proguanil Pyrimethamine	Same as above; screen patient from mosquitoes
es of spleen er, blood ted bone ow	Culture and microscopic recognition of intracellular forms		Antimony compounds	Isolation and special precautions not indicated; protect patient from vector
fluid ted lymph	Microscopic recognition of intracellular or extracellular forms		Arsenicals Diamidine group	Same as above
	Recognition of microfilariae		Diethylcarbamazine Naphuride sodium	Same as above

lymphatic vessels of the pelvis, with resulting orchitis, hydrocele, and elephantiasis of the genitalia or the lower limbs, or both. The infection may produce few or no clinical symptoms. Microfilariae may be found in the blood even in the absence of symptoms, or they may not be able to reach the blood stream in cases of lymphatic ob-struction. They are most frequently found in the peripheral blood during the night hours and for this reason are said to display "nocturnal periodicity." The explanation for this is not complete. It may have to do with anatomic factors related to the host's relaxation during sleep, with physiologic changes in the microfilariae that make them

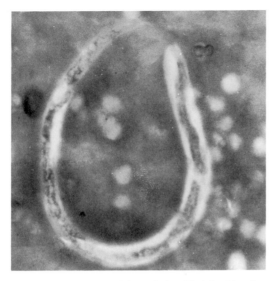

Fig. 27–9. The larval form (microfilaria) of *Loa loa* as it appears in a smear of peripheral blood (1000 ×).

more sluggish during the daytime hours, or with their adaptation to the feeding habits of the insect host. In this connection it is interesting to note that those filariae whose vectors are daytime feeders do not display periodicity, their micro-filariae being present in the blood by day or night.

Onchocerciasis is characterized by the appearance of firm nodules in the subcutaneous tissues, particularly of the head and shoulders or the lower part of the body. The microfilariae do not enter the blood stream but migrate through the tissues. They may drain or migrate from lesions on the head into the tissues of the eye, producing local tissue reaction, ocular disorders, and sometimes blindness.

Loiasis is also an infestation of the subcutaneous tissues, but in this case the *adult* worm migrates through the tissues, producing extensive reaction at each new site of localization. Nodules arise and may later be resolved when the worm moves on. These "fugitive" or "calabar" swellings are characteristic of the disease. This worm may also reach the eye and wander through the conjunctival membrane across the ball of the eye, producing intense pain and swelling. Microfilariae circulate in the peripheral blood stream, where they may be found during the day as well as at night (see Figs. 27–9 and 27–10).

Allergic reactions are often prominent features of these infestations, particularly as time goes on. Urticarial rashes, fever, and local tissue inflam-

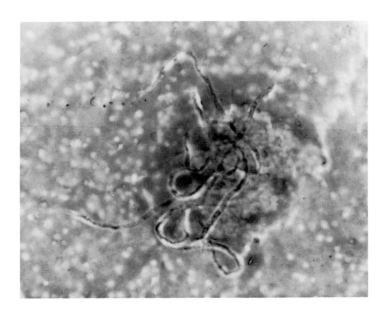

Fig. 27–10. A tangle of microfilariae (*Loa loa*) in a thick smear of blood (300 ×).

mation may occur, especially in those diseases in which lymphatic blockade occurs.

Diagnosis is made in the laboratory by the demonstration of viable microfilariae in wet-mount preparations of blood, or by staining them in dried smears of blood. Anticoagulated whole blood may be submitted for examination, or a small blood sample may be placed in a tube containing water or formalin. Either of the latter agents will lyse the red blood cells when the tube is gently rotated. The tube can then be centrifuged to concentrate the microfilariae in the sediment. If water has been used, the larvae will be alive and motile and can be found easily. They are not readily identified as to species, however, when they are actively lashing under the cover slip. The sediment of formalinized blood will reveal dead microfilariae, which can then be stained and examined for the microscopic details by which the various species are recognized.

Onchocerciasis must be diagnosed in tissue obtained by biopsy or by surgical removal of a nodule. Microfilariae can be demonstrated in wet preparations of the tissue fluid, or the adult worms may be found in the nodule.

Treatment. Diethylcarbamazine is used in these infestations to kill the microfilariae, but it does not affect the adult worm. Naphuride sodium is the drug generally used for the latter purpose, particularly if the worm is in an inoperable position. Surgical removal of the adult worms may offer the most feasible cure of onchocerciasis or loiasis.

Control and prevention require concomitant efforts to suppress the insect vector and to treat all infected human hosts who may perpetuate the parasites' cycles.

Questions

1. What two kinds of illness does the plague bacillus produce?
2. What organism causes the disease bubonic plague?
3. What is the vector for the plague bacillus?
4. What specimens are used for diagnosis?
5. What is the primary reservoir for the plague bacillus?
6. What nursing precautions are required while caring for a patient with bubonic plague?
7. What organism causes relapsing fever?
8. What arthropods transmit relapsing fever?
9. What vectors transmit the typhus fevers?
10. Describe the organisms responsible for the rickettsial diseases.
11. What steps are necessary to control active typhus infection?
12. What is Brill's disease?
13. What is the Weil-Felix test?
14. What are the arboviruses?
15. What is the reservoir for yellow fever virus?
16. What vector transmits yellow fever?
17. How can yellow fever be prevented?
18. What are the vectors of the encephalitides?
19. What are the three most common mosquito-borne encephalitides?
20. How is a diagnosis of encephalitis made?
21. What methods are used for control and prevention of the encephalitides?
22. Name the three important genera of protozoa that are transmitted by arthropods to man and animals?

23. What is the definitive host for the *Plasmodium* species? The intermediate host?
24. What is the vector for malaria?
25. What causes the symptoms of malaria?
26. What is a hemoflagellate?
27. What is the vector for leishmaniasis?
28. What is kala-azar?
29. What is the vector for African trypanosomiasis?
30. What is the reservoir of infection for trypanosomiasis?
31. Name the filarial roundworms that live in the skin and subcutaneous tissue.
32. How is the diagnosis of the filarial infection made?
33. How are these diseases controlled and prevented?

28 Infectious Diseases Acquired Through Accidental Injuries

The infectious diseases discussed in this chapter include those that are characteristically acquired through particular sources of injury to the skin, such as *animal bites*, "*street wounds*," or *burns*. Animals sometimes transmit their own infectious diseases through injuries they inflict on man, the most notable example of such infections being rabies, a viral disease that is fatal for both animals and man. In more usual instances, however, animals transmit viral or bacterial agents they happen to be harboring in inapparent infections at the time they bite or scratch people, inflicting injury to the skin and inoculating commensalistic organisms into the subcutaneous tissues at the same time. The microbial species involved may induce severe local infections and sometimes spread systemically as well. Similar problems may arise as a result of human bites.

For practical purposes, the term "street wound" is used here to distinguish those injuries that are incurred accidentally and are exposed to environmental sources of infection from those that are inflicted by animals, burns, or surgery. (The latter are discussed in Chap. 29.) Animals are likely to transmit microorganisms

adapted to a parasitic or commensalistic life, whereas environmental reservoirs teem with saprophytic bacteria and fungi, many of which are not capable of establishing themselves in human tissue. The most serious diseases acquired through the exposure of injured tissues to environmental sources of infection are those of clostridial origin (tetanus and gas gangrene) and those caused by fungi. It should be noted, however, that the clostridia responsible for these diseases of injury are derived from the intestinal tract of man and animals and survive in the environment only because they can form resistant spores, while the fungi that can infect man normally live in the soil as saprophytes.

Traumatized human skin offers entry to a great variety of microorganisms. These may be derived from the surfaces of the injurious agent (animal teeth or claws, a splinter, a bullet or knife, a rusty nail, or a crushing object), from endogenous sources on the injured skin or membrane, or from the external environment to which the wound is subsequently exposed. In many instances, the nature of bacterial infections established in bite wounds, "street" injuries, burns, or even surgical wounds is very similar, because the microbial agents involved may be drawn from common sources. The organisms most capable of establishment in injured soft tissue are species of streptococci, staphylococci, and Gram-negative enteric bacteria. In the latter group, the species *Pseudomonas aeruginosa* is a notorious troublemaker in wounds, and particularly in burns. Clostridia and other anaerobes, including species of *Actinomyces* (from the group of "higher" bacteria), may infect soft tissues if local conditions meet their requirements for anaerobic growth. These organisms are all normally associated with man or animals, and many of them are also capable of establishing themselves in environmental reservoirs, so that their opportunistic invasion of wounds does not necessarily reflect the origin of the injury. The principal determining factors in the development and severity of wound infections are related to conditions within the traumatized tissues and the degree of their exposure to various sources of microorganisms having a pathogenic potential.

Infectious Diseases Acquired Through Animal Bites

Rabies

The Clinical Disease. Rabies is probably the only infectious disease that is invariably fatal for man. It is a zoonosis that is occasionally transmitted to man, chiefly by the bite of an infected, rabid animal. Saliva of the infectious animal contains the organism. When introduced into the tissues, the virus is thought to travel along the sensory nerves to the brain, where it multiplies. From the CNS it may spread along peripheral nerves to other tissues, including the salivary glands. The disease is an acute encephalitis characterized by both physical and psychologic symptoms of deranged cerebral function. Fever and headache are followed by sensory disturbances, particularly at the site of the bite wound, spasms in the muscles required for swallowing, convulsive seizures, and respiratory paralysis. The mental suffering of the patient is associated with his fear of swallowing because of painful throat spasms. (This disease has, for centuries, been called *hydrophobia* because the patient is afraid to swallow water, or anything else for that matter.) He may become more and more apprehensive, nervous, excitable, and finally delirious. Death usually occurs within six days.

Laboratory Diagnosis

I. Identification of the Organism. The virus of rabies forms inclusion bodies within the nucleus or cytoplasm of the affected cells of the brain. These characteristic inclusions, called *Negri bodies*, can be readily visualized under the light microscope in stained impression smears or sections of brain tissue. The virus can be cultivated in mice and other laboratory animals, or in embryonated chicken and duck eggs. It is identified serologically by known antiserum that specifically neutralizes its infectivity for animals or combines with the virus to fix complement. Fluorescein-tagged antiserum also readily identifies the virus within the cells of infected tissue.

Identification of the human patient's serum antibodies is of very little diagnostic value, since patients do not recover.

II. Specimens for Diagnosis. During life, the patient's saliva may be a source of the causative virus. Specimens collected from beneath the tongue, near the opening of the submaxillary salivary gland, may be examined by stained smear, by the fluorescent antibody technique, and also by inoculation into mice. These animals die of rabies infection in a few days. Their brains are examined for Negri bodies, and harvested virus is identified serologically as well.

At autopsy, the patient's brain is examined histologically for evidence of rabies. Negri bodies are most likely to be found in the medulla and thalamus. Virus isolation and serologic testing as outlined above confirm the diagnosis.

When a dog or other animal has bitten a human being, it is of immediate importance to restrain and isolate the animal if possible. Even an apparently healthy animal should be observed for at least one week for signs of developing illness. Whether or not the suspect biting animal appears to be sick, it should not be destroyed until it has been examined by a veterinarian or a physician who is competent to make the diagnosis of rabies. If it is decided that the animal must be killed, it is essential that the head not be destroyed in the process, because only the brain or salivary secretions can provide conclusive histologic or virologic evidence of rabies. Animals that appear to be rabid should be killed and examined without delay. Speed of diagnosis of the animal infection is of vital importance to the human victim of an animal bite because the prolonged incubation period of rabies affords some limited time to provide him with the protection of active vaccination, if the exposure is confirmed or reasonably certain. If the biting animal cannot be properly diagnosed (because it has escaped, was killed too soon, destroyed in such a way that the head cannot be examined; or because the brain was not properly preserved), the decisions that must be made concerning the prophylactic treatment of the human patient may become very difficult.

Epidemiology

I. Communicability of Infection

A. RESERVOIR, SOURCES AND TRANSMISSION ROUTES. The largest reservoir for rabies is among wild animals, particularly wolves, coyotes, foxes, wildcats, skunks, racoons and other carnivores. At least three varieties of bats are known to carry rabies. Insect-eating types are known to be involved in this country, Canada, and Europe, while fruit-eating as well as vampire bats are infected in Central and South America. Domestic dogs are infected from these wild sources and are the most usual source of rabies in man. It is possible, but not usual, for man to acquire the infection without being bitten, if he has scratches or other skin wounds that are exposed to infectious saliva. Great care must be exercised by those who handle sick or dead animals to protect their skin from such exposures. It is also possible that the disease may be acquired through exposure to the dust of caves contaminated with the excreta of bats harboring rabies virus. Man-to-man transmission has not been documented but is possible, since human saliva also becomes infectious during the course of the disease.

B. INCUBATION PERIOD. The average time is four to six weeks, but it is sometimes as prolonged as two or three months. The length of the incubation period is influenced to some extent by the length of the path the virus must travel from the site of inoculation to the brain. Bites inflicted on the face or neck may result in infection with an onset of symptoms in one or two weeks. The amount of virus inoculated, as well as the type and distribution of the local nerve supply, also affect the duration of the incubation period.

C. COMMUNICABLE PERIOD. The virus is present in the salivary secretions of biting animals for several days before their symptoms appear and throughout the course of their illness. Vampire bats (the only animals that can carry the rabies virus without dying of infection) have been proved capable of transmitting the disease through their salivary secretions for a period of at least five months.

D. IMMUNITY. Natural immunity to rabies

virus does not exist among human beings or animals, but antibody production can be stimulated by virus vaccines.

1. *Active Immunization.* There is only one antigenic type of rabies virus, but there are several biologic variants that display differences in their affinities for neural or extraneural tissues:

   a. "Street" virus is the term used for the rabies agent freshly isolated from animal or human cases. This virus produces disease in laboratory animals, invading both neural tissue in the CNS and the cells of the salivary glands, forming intracytoplasmic inclusion bodies.

   b. "Fixed" virus is a variant that arises when serial passages are made in rabbits inoculated intracerebrally. After several passages, the variant multiplies rapidly in rabbit neural tissue, but inclusion bodies are seldom formed, and it is incapable of reproducing in extraneural cells. When the virus has become fully adapted to rabbits, it consistently kills them within five to six days of inoculation. At this point the virulence of the organism for rabbits is "fixed" and cannot be increased by further passages in these animals, but its virulence for man is decreased.

   c. "Avianized" virus has been adapted to multiply in chicken or duck embryos. The *Flury strain* of this variant does not produce disease in animals when it is injected in extraneural sites.

   d. The virus has recently been propagated in tissue cultures prepared from mouse or chick embryos. The adapted virus is not pathogenic for monkeys, and when it is inactivated it remains highly antigenic when tested in animals.

The original vaccine prepared by Pasteur contained "fixed" virus that he had passed through rabbits. The spinal cords of these animals were dried to reduce the virulence of the organisms for man still further. Later, the *Semple vaccine* was developed, using phenol-inactivated preparations of infective rabbit brain tissue. The use of this material for human beings carries the risk of provoking hypersensitive reactions to the foreign brain protein. This hypersensitivity is usually expressed as an allergic encephalitis, sometimes with paralysis. Such responses may occur in about 0.1 per cent of persons vaccinated.

Other methods of preparing fixed virus vaccines differ in the method of inactivating the virus. The UV vaccine is prepared by exposing virus to ultraviolet irradiation and further inactivating with Merthiolate or phenol.

The avianized virus is inactivated with beta-propriolactone for use as a human vaccine, but the attenuated Flury strain is used for dog immunization without inactivation. The tissue culture vaccines have not yet been put to human trial.

Human vaccination is performed only after injury has been inflicted by an animal known or suspected to be rabid. The procedure requires a series of daily subcutaneous injections throughout a 14-to-21-day period. Dogs are immunized by a single intramuscular injection of live-virus vaccine, repeated once yearly.

2. *Passive Immunization.* Hyperimmune antirabies horse or sheep serum also provides effective protection against this virus. It is used in conjunction with active immunization. Hyperimmune serum is given in a single dose immediately after a bite exposure to rabies and is followed 24 hours later by the first of the vaccine injections. This delay is necessary to avoid immediate neutralization of the vaccine antigen by passively acquired antibody.

II. Control of Active Infection

A. ISOLATION. The patient should be hospitalized and kept in private-room isolation throughout the course of the illness.

B. PRECAUTIONS. The patient's saliva should be considered infectious, and all items contaminated with it should be disinfected. The nursing care of these patients is difficult because of their apprehension, excitability, and disorientation. Particular caution must be exercised by those in close attendance to protect their own skin and clothing from salivary contamination, and to avoid injury to their hands from the patient's teeth when mouth care is given.

C. TREATMENT. There is no specific treatment for rabies after symptoms have started and the disease is established. However, immediate attention should be given to the bite wound. It should be thoroughly cleaned by irrigating and washing with soap or detergents. Puncture wounds are sometimes cauterized with nitric acid. Open wounds are first washed and then treated by the instillation of hyperimmune antirabies serum. The muscle tissue beneath the wound is also infiltrated with antiserum. When immune serum is used, vaccination treatment is not instituted until the following day.

D. CONTROL OF CONTACTS. The human contacts of a rabies patient require no protective control measures, but a search is made for the rabid animal source of the case, if it is not already in custody, and for other persons or animals that may have been bitten.

III. Prevention. The control and prevention of rabies require its suppression in the animal population. The immunization of dogs, as well as enforced restrictions on stray animals, is an essential feature of control and is a requirement of most local or state governments. The control of rabies in wild animals is the responsibility of state and federal wildlife conservation agencies, who work in cooperation with public health authorities when the threat of rabies exists. This aspect of prevention is discussed also in Chapter 11 (pp. 278 to 279).

The decision to vaccinate the human victims of biting animals must be based on their risk of contracting a fatal infection, balanced against the small chance (1 in 1000 to 10,000) of a postvaccinal allergic encephalitis. If the animal is in custody and appears to be healthy, vaccination can be postponed until it displays signs of developing rabies. If none appear within ten days, vaccine is not given to the patient. When there is doubt as to the animal's condition, if rabies is known to be present in the animal population, or if the victim has been bitten about the face and neck, the vaccination treatment is instituted without delay. This may also be the decision when the biting animal cannot be found but the disease

has been noted in other wild or domestic animals of the region.

Apparently healthy dogs that have bitten people should not be destroyed hastily. If they are incubating and transmitting rabies, this fact can be discovered by awaiting the onset of their own disease, then destroying them and examining the brain tissue. There may be no signs of Negri bodies in the brain during the incubation period, and laboratory attempts to cultivate the virus from dogs that have been killed too soon may require more time than would the development of the disease in the suspect animals.

The widespread incidence of rabies in the bat population of the United States appears to justify the vaccination treatment of all persons bitten by bats. The necessity for treatment is often underscored by the fact that the offending bat may not be captured and hence is unavailable for examination. Furthermore, it is often difficult to demonstrate the virus in bats by rapid smear examination, and the time required for virus cultivation may be more than the patient can safely afford.

Cat Scratch Fever

The Clinical Disease. Cat scratch fever is a clinical syndrome characterized by a regional lymphadenopathy associated with a scratch wound usually (but not necessarily) inflicted by a cat. There is an initial mild inflammatory reaction at the site of the wound, sometimes with induration or minor ulceration. The nodes that drain the area then become swollen with a thick, gray, bacteriologically sterile pus, and they may eventually suppurate. This reaction requires at least two or three weeks to subside, but may persist for months. There is often a recurring fever, sometimes with chills and general malaise. Involvement of the eye sometimes occurs and takes the form of the "oculoglandular" syndrome that may be seen in tularemia infections (see Chap. 24, p. 536). Recovery is always complete but requires variable periods of time.

Laboratory Diagnosis

I. Identification of the Organism. The organism is a filterable agent that has not been identified with certainty. It is thought to belong to the *Bedsonia* group of "large viruses," because the convalescent serums from patients with this infection cross-react in complement-fixation tests with agents of the psittacosis-lymphogranuloma-trachoma group (see Chap. 16, p. 389). Also, large cellular inclusions can be seen in stained sections of infected lymph nodes. Recently, however, it has been reported that a virus antigenically related to herpesvirus has been isolated from lymph node pus in cat scratch fever.

II. Identification of Patient's Immune Response. Serologic testing of the patient's serum is inconclusive, except for the response to *Bedsonia* antigens mentioned above.

A skin-testing antigen may be diagnostically useful. It is prepared from cellular suspensions of infected lymph nodes or pus and inactivated by heat. This antigen produces the delayed type of erythematous skin reaction when injected intradermally into patients with cat scratch fever.

III. Specimens for Diagnosis. Pus aspirated from suppurating lymph nodes should be submitted for bacteriologic smear and culture, to rule out the possibility of bacterial infections.

Serum specimens taken early and late in the course of infection may be useful in establishing the character of this infection.

Epidemiology

I. Communicability of Infection. The reservoir and sources of this infection will not be fully understood until the agent has been identified with certainty. It appears that cats, possibly other animals, insects, or even thorny plants or splintered wood may inflict the initial injury that leads to development of this syndrome. Cat scratches have been associated with the disease most frequently. It is thought that cats either transmit the organism mechanically from some natural source or they themselves have an inapparent infection.

The incubation period is usually one or two weeks from the time of the initial injury, but it may be shorter. Communicability has not been clarified, but infection is not directly transmissible from person to person.

This is a sporadic human infection that may occur in any part of the world, but is seen most often in children and young adults, possibly because of more frequent exposure to infection as well as a susceptibility that later decreases through repeated encounters with the infectious agent.

II. Control and Prevention. *Treatment* with the broad-spectrum antibiotics may relieve symptoms and shorten the course of disease, but it does not necessarily eliminate the infection. Measures to prevent cat scratch fever cannot be outlined until the agent and its epidemiology have been defined. In the meantime, the best control probably can be obtained by the careful, hygienic cleansing and management of skin wounds, particularly those inflicted by cats.

Bacterial Infections of Bite Wounds

The resident bacteria of the mouths of animals (or humans) may produce serious local or even systemic infections and tissue reactions when they are introduced deeply into the tissues by biting teeth. The normal flora of the human mouth includes both aerobic and anaerobic microorganisms, as we know (see Chap. 5, p. 93). This is also true for animals, although there are some differences in bacterial species because the anatomy and physiology of animal mucous membranes differ in many respects from those of the human mucosa and therefore provide different conditions for commensalistic microorganisms. Furthermore, the mouths of animals often harbor many transient microbial species from the soil, from feces, from their own hair or fur, or from other sources, depending on their nature and habits (see Chap. 6, p. 111).

The development of infection in a bite wound is greatly influenced by the nature of the injury. For example, an open tear or laceration inflicted by teeth can be easily cleansed and kept aerated while healing proceeds, so that microorganisms have little opportunity to establish themselves.

Puncture wounds, however, may implant bacteria more deeply in positions that are inaccessible unless the wound is laid open by surgical incision. Infected bites often contain a mixed flora, but sometimes a particular species may predominate or take over entirely if it possesses more of the properties required for establishment and growth in human tissues. The process may be promoted still further if the defensive mechanisms of the tissue are handicapped by injury to the blood supply, with local hemorrhage, clotting, and devitalization of surrounding cells. This not only interferes with the marshaling of phagocytes and of antibacterial components of blood plasma, but it also prevents adequate oxygenation of the local area, which becomes progressively anaerobic. It should be remembered that many of the bacteria that live aerobically on mucous membranes, or on culture media in the laboratory, are in reality "facultative" anaerobes, capable of growth and multiplication even under conditions of reduced oxygen tension or of anaerobiasis (Chap. 3, pp. 46 to 47). The facultative anaerobes of the resident oral flora include species of staphylococci and streptococci. In addition, there are microaerophilic organisms, such as species of *Hemophilus* (these are rarely capable of establishing themselves in soft tissue, however) and obligate anaerobes of the *Actinomyces* and *Bacteroides* genera (see Chaps. 12 and 30).

The character of the infectious process in a bite wound reflects both the nature and the properties of the multiplying organism and the tissue response to it. Staphylococci characteristically induce the formation of localizing abscesses, or suppuration (Chap. 23, p. 512), while streptococci are often more invasive because their enzymes and toxins are destructive for cells and components of connective tissue (Chap. 14, p. 327). *Cellulitis*, which is an advancing inflammatory involvement of subcutaneous and connective tissues, is frequently induced by streptococcal infection. Some other invasive organisms may also cause this type of infection (see the discussion of clostridial gas gangrene in the following section). *Bacteroides* species are Gram-negative, nonsporing, anaerobic rods normally found in the mouth or alimentary tract (Chap. 5, pp. 93 to

95), but they are capable of causing suppurative, inflammatory reactions in soft tissues. Actinomycotic infections are also characterized by suppuration. If they become chronic there may be multiple granulomatous abscesses that progress and coalesce to form sinuses and sinus tracts (Chap. 17, p. 405, and Chap. 30).

If the local tissue reaction fails to contain these infections, or if prompt medical or surgical treatment is not obtained, the threat of dissemination through draining lymph channels or the blood stream may ensue. The spread of infection from a wound on an extremity is often marked by red streaks extending proximally. This is a sign of *lymphangitis*, or inflammation of the lymph vessels draining the affected part and leading to the proximal nodes, which may also become involved. The reactivity of lymph nodes, with swelling and tenderness, is referred to as *lymphadenopathy*. Immediate treatment is indicated at this stage to prevent further advance, with resulting bacteremia or septicemia.

The infectious organisms mentioned above are the usual types to be anticipated in animal or human bite wounds. Animal bites, however, present the additional and more dangerous hazard of *clostridial* infection. The mouths of animals may be transiently contaminated with the spores of clostridial species picked up from the soil, or with vegetative bacilli derived from fecal sources. It will be remembered that the *Clostridium* genus contains Gram-positive, sporeforming bacilli, which are obligate anaerobes normally residing in the human or animal intestinal tract (Chap. 5, pp. 94 to 95), and that they are dangerous contaminants of wounds, because if they can establish a foothold and multiply anaerobically in soft tissues they produce substances that are highly toxic for human cells (Chap. 6, pp. 114 to 115). Tetanus and gas gangrene, the two serious clostridial diseases acquired through the infection of injured soft tissues, are described in the following section of this chapter. They are most commonly incurred through accidental injuries of many other types, but must be considered as a possibility when animal bite wounds are inflicted.

Two other types of bacterial infections are associated with rat bites. The term "rat bite fever"

refers to two diseases, each associated with a different bacterial agent. In the United States, this type of infection is associated with an unusual Gram-negative bacillus that is very pleomorphic and displays branching. This organism is *Streptobacillus moniliformis* (interesting also because of its ability to enter into a stage of growth similar to that of the PPLO group described in Chap. 16, pp. 385 to 386). The bacillus frequently infects rodents, which transmit it to man by biting. After an incubation period of three to ten days, the organism progresses from the primary lesion to the regional lymph nodes and then to the blood stream, producing lymphadenitis, a petechial skin rash, joint involvement (arthritis), and attacks of recurring fever. The disease is diagnosed on the basis of a history of rat bite, as well as by the bacteriologic demonstration of the organism in pus from the skin lesion or lymph nodes, in joint fluid, and in blood. Penicillin or the tetracycline drugs are effective in the treatment of this infection. Control depends on the eradication of rats, especially from buildings where people live or work. It should be noted that this disease can also be transferred through unpasteurized or contaminated milk. The source of infection in milk has not been determined, but a few epidemics have been related to such an origin. One of these occurred in the town of Haverhill, Massachusetts, and the milk-borne disease came to be known as *Haverhill fever*.

Another type of rat bite fever is caused by a spiral-shaped bacterium called *Spirillum minus*. This is a Gram-negative, motile organism, spiraled in two or three short, rigid coils. It produces a clinical disease similar to that caused by *Streptobacillus*, except that the joints are seldom involved in infection. This form of rat bite fever occurs more frequently in the Far East (where it is called *sodoku*) than in the United States. The organism does not grow on ordinary laboratory culture media, but it can sometimes be demonstrated in the blood of infected patients or by inoculating blood into mice or guinea pigs. Penicillin is the drug of choice for *Spirillum minus* infection. As in the case of *Streptobacillus* rat bite fever, the

prevention of this disease depends on the control or eradication of rats.

The treatment and control of bite wound infections should begin with prompt surgical cleansing and debridement, to clear away contaminating organisms, to aerate the tissues, and to ensure an adequate blood supply so that healing can proceed normally. Antibiotics are sometimes given prophylactically if the wound is severe or if deep punctures provide the possibility that infecting bacteria might have penetrated beyond reach. Closed wounds that become infected are treated with continuous hot soaks to maintain a rich blood supply, and the affected part is kept elevated to assure good venous and lymphatic drainage from the area. Surgical incision and drainage may be indicated as well, together with antibiotics chosen on the basis of laboratory tests of the isolated organism(s). The prevention of tetanus, or of the establishment of clostridial strains associated with gas gangrene, is discussed in the next section.

Diseases Acquired Through the Infection of "Street Wounds"

Tetanus (Lockjaw)

The Clinical Disease.   Tetanus is an acute disease caused by the neurotoxin of *Clostridium tetani*. This organism is not invasive and remains localized in the area where its spores were introduced into the body. If anaerobic conditions prevail in the tissues at the site of entry, the spores germinate, and the vegetative bacterial cells multiply, proliferating toxin. The local infection is often quite insignificant, producing little tissue damage, but the exotoxin is absorbed from the area and extends along peripheral motor nerve trunks to the spinal cord. Within the cord, the toxin causes increased reflex excitability, while its action on peripheral nerves interferes with the normal transmission of nerve impulses to muscles. Severe muscle spasms occur first at the area of infection and toxin production, then along the route of nerve trunk involvement. The muscles of the jaw

and neck contract convulsively and remain "locked" so that the mouth cannot be opened and swallowing is very difficult. Other voluntary muscles also become involved, but respiratory paralysis is the most serious complication and may be fatal. The toxin does not inflict permanent damage, and those who recover do so completely but slowly. Tetanus fatalities are related to the time lapse between the dissemination of toxin and the institution of antitoxin and other therapy, as well as the age and general condition of the patient, the average mortality rate being about 35 per cent.

Laboratory Diagnosis

I. Identification of the Organism (*Clostridium tetani*)

A. MICROSCOPIC CHARACTERISTICS. The tetanus bacillus is a Gram-positive, anaerobic, spore-forming bacillus (see Fig. 28–1). The spore is characteristically wider than the diameter of the bacillus and forms at one end so that the rod has a drumstick appearance. Vegetative tetanus bacilli have an even diameter and are motile.

B. CULTURE CHARACTERISTICS. *Cl. tetani* is a strict anaerobe. It grows on blood agar plates incubated at 37° C in an airtight jar or incubator from which air has been evacuated and replaced by an inert gas. A mixture of nitrogen with 10 per cent CO_2 is commonly used to provide the necessary atmospheric conditions. The organism can also be cultivated in fluid media having a low oxidation-reduction potential. Broth containing a reducing agent such as thioglycollate and enough agar to provide viscosity (about 0.1 per cent) will support the organism and can be incubated in an ordinary atmosphere. A liquid medium containing fresh chopped animal meat can also be used because reducing enzymes are released from the tissue. Fluid media must be tubed in deep columns, however, to assure an oxygen-free environment below the surface level where atmospheric oxygen may be dissolved. Because many different anaerobic and facultative bacteria grow well in these media, they cannot be relied on to *isolate Cl. tetani* or other anaerobes in pure culture.

On the surface of blood agar, *Cl. tetani* colonies have a filamentous periphery marking an area of swarming growth, and they are usually hemolytic. The clostridial species are distinguished from each other by the patterns of their carbohydrate fermentations and their proteolytic activities. Some can digest gelatin and milk proteins; others have only a weak action on proteins, or none at all. The tetanus bacillus does not ferment carbohydrates and is weakly proteolytic.

C. SEROLOGIC METHODS OF IDENTIFICATION. The final differentiation of clostridial species can be made with specific antisera. When labeled with fluorescent dyes sera can be valuable in providing a means of rapid identification of clostridia in smears of clinical specimens or in materials suspected as a source of infection.

D. TOXIN PRODUCTION. Definitive identification of *Cl. tetani* is also obtained by demonstrating its capacity for toxin production, the pathogenic effect of the toxin for laboratory animals, and the specific neutralization of this effect by tetanus antitoxin.

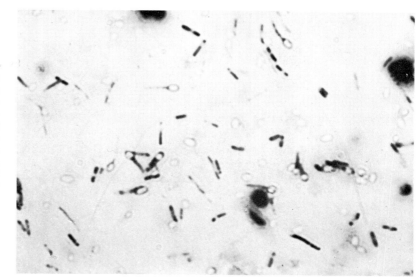

Fig. 28–1. A photomicrograph of *Clostridium tetani* (2400 ×), a Gram-positive, anaerobic, spore-forming rod. Note the large, unstained terminal endospores that give this organism a characteristic "drumstick" appearance. (Reproduced from Schneierson, S. Stanley: *Atlas of Diagnostic Microbiology.* Abbott Laboratories, North Chicago, 1965.)

II. Identification of Patient's Serum Antibodies. This procedure has no diagnostic meaning in tetanus for the obvious reason that the patient who develops tetanus as a result of infection does so because he has no protective antitoxin in his blood stream.

III. Specimens for Diagnosis. The diagnosis of tetanus is generally based on the clinical picture. The site of injury and infection may be insignificant, or the wound may be closed and the area of clostridial growth inapparent. When feasible, pus or tissue from the wound should be submitted for smear and anaerobic culture, but neither the diagnosis nor the institution of therapy can safely wait for laboratory findings, nor can negative findings be considered conclusive.

Epidemiology

I. Communicability of Infection

A. RESERVOIR, SOURCES, AND TRANSMISSION ROUTES. The normal habitat of the tetanus bacillus is the intestinal tract of man and animals (see Fig. 28–2), horses and cows being particularly notable reservoirs. Animals, and sometimes humans also, disseminate the organism widely in nature, so that it is commonly present in the dust of the streets as well as in soil. The spores can also be found frequently in the dust of soiled bed linens or clothing. Tetanus spores are generally introduced into the body through wounds of various kinds, not all of which may appear important at the time. Puncture or crushing wounds; injuries caused by bullets, knives, or clubs; obstetric wounds or those incurred when abortion is performed or attempted; an unhealed umbilical stump (tetanus neonatorum); burns; and surgical wounds — all may offer an entry point for the organisms. In many instances, the spores are introduced by the object that inflicts the injury (a rusty nail, a thrown or falling object, a knitting needle that attempts abortion, an unsterilized surgical knife); in others, infections result from subsequent exposure of the wound to an environmental source. Wounded soldiers or automobile accident cases may lie on the ground or be ex-

posed to other sources arising from attempts to treat wounds under field conditions. Surgical wounds sometimes are contaminated by inadequately sterilized instruments, sutures, or dressings; and orthopedic surgery is confronted with the occasional hazard of tetanus-contaminated plaster materials used for casts. Surgical wounds are also threatened by subsequent exposure to endogenous fecal sources of infection during the patient's postoperative course, but tetanus is not likely to occur in this situation unless the wound provides the necessary anaerobic conditions for growth of this noninvasive organism. Good surgical technique and nursing care play a large role in preventing this type of infection.

B. INCUBATION PERIOD. The nature, extent, and location of the wound, as well as the numbers of infecting organisms, influence the incubation period. If the tetanus bacilli can begin to grow immediately and to multiply rapidly, the production of toxin may begin within a few days (two to six, with an average of four); but incubation sometimes requires two or three weeks, or even longer.

C. COMMUNICABLE PERIOD. Tetanus is not directly communicable from person to person.

D. IMMUNITY. Specific protection is provided by antibodies directed against tetanus toxin. Antitoxin may arise naturally as a result of tetanus infection and toxin dissemination, but immunity acquired in this way is not necessarily durable. Artificial active immunization with tetanus toxoid provides the most solid protection, but passive immunization may be necessary when the threat of infection arises in nonimmune persons. Susceptibility to tetanus infection is universal, and the threat of resulting toxic disease is removed only by antitoxin immunity.

II. Control of Active Infection

A. ISOLATION. Not indicated.

B. PRECAUTIONS. Unnecessary.

C. TREATMENT. *Tetanus antitoxin* can neutralize the toxin *before* it becomes attached to nerve tissue but not afterward. For this reason, antitoxin is administered immediately when non-

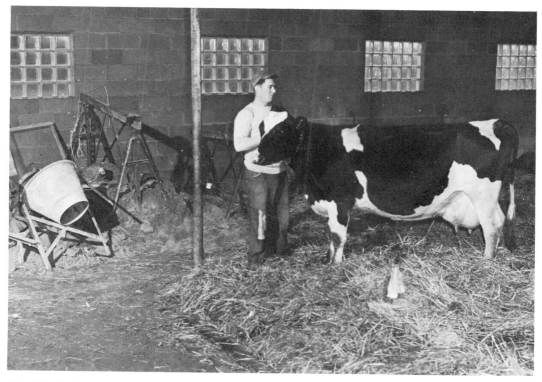

Fig. 28–2. A favorite breeding ground for the tetanus bacillus is the intestinal tract of domestic animals such as cattle. Thus, soil containing animal fertilizer usually contains enormous numbers of *Cl. tetani.* (Reproduced from *Health News,* April, 1965. Courtesy of New York State Department of Health, Albany, N.Y.)

immune persons sustain traumatic injuries. The decision to give antitoxin is supported by a negative history pertaining to recent active immunization. Antitoxin is administered in a single large intramuscular dose, preferably in *human* hyperimmune serum to avoid hypersensitive reactions to foreign proteins in animal antiserums. Administration of an animal antiserum must be preceded by skin testing to determine whether or not hypersensitivity exists and anaphylactic reactions are a risk (see Chap. 7, pp. 146 to 153). Not only are reactions to previously encountered foreign proteins dangerous, but animal serum proteins may be promptly destroyed by hypersensitive tissues, so that the toxin-neutralizing

effect of passively administered antitoxin can be very short-lived and possibly ineffective. Human antitoxin is given in a dose of 250 to 500 units and should be protective for about a month. When human antiserum is not available, horse or other animal antitoxins are used in a dose of 1500 units or more, depending on the clinical situation and the manufacturer's specifications of unit strength. Larger doses may be given to patients who have already developed symptoms of tetanus toxicity, so that newly produced, unbound toxin may be neutralized before it can cause further nerve damage.

Antibiotics are given to control simultaneous mixed infections that may encourage the an-

aerobic conditions required for the growth of the tetanus bacillus. The latter is specifically inhibited by penicillin, and this is the drug of choice to prohibit further growth and toxin production by the causative organism.

Surgical débridement of a wound with obviously active infection is essential to remove dead tissue and to provide aeration so that tetanus bacilli cannot continue to multiply locally and produce toxin.

Tetanus toxoid is given to stimulate active immunity when a potentially dangerous wound is sustained, whether or not the individual has been previously immunized with this material. If he gives a reliable history of artificial active immunization, a booster shot of toxoid together with an immediately protective dose of passive antibody may prevent the disease. If he has not been actively immunized within recent years, the first of a series of toxoid injections (see Prevention) should be given shortly after antitoxin prophylaxis is instituted.

D. CONTROL OF CONTACTS. The chief problem in obstetric, pediatric, and surgical situations is to locate the possible source of infection so that further cases may be prevented, and for this reason case reports are mandatory in most states and countries. If the source is associated with inadequate techniques of surgery or sterilization, these can be identified and controlled before they lead to serious outbreaks in hospital or midwife practice. Sporadic cases acquired from environmental sources of infection require only individual control, as outlined in C above, but the prevention of such cases can be achieved by adequate programs of immunization, as described in the following section.

III. Prevention by Immunization. Active immunization with tetanus toxoid provides certain and durable protection and should be initiated during infancy or early childhood. The preferred program is the immunization of infants at three to four months of age with triple vaccine containing diphtheria and tetanus toxoids and pertussis vaccine (DTP), as previously outlined for the prevention of diphtheria (Chap. 14, p. 339).

Booster doses at regular intervals reinforce the immunity during childhood and adolescence.

Adult immunization with tetanus toxoid is universally advised as the safest method for preventing the serious consequences of infection with this ubiquitous organism. Alum-precipitated toxoid is used for adults in two doses separated by a four-week interval and a reinforcing dose given about one year later. Boosters at ten-year intervals thereafter maintain a safe level of immunity, but if an injury is sustained a single injection of toxoid is given immediately. The need for passive protection with antitoxin (and its attendant risks) is obviated for the individual with a history of scheduled toxoid immunization, the single booster providing a prompt increase in protective antitoxin and an assurance of safety from a minor infection that might be overlooked. Tetanus toxoid is particularly recommended for all persons who run unusual risks of accidental injuries (farmers, veterinarians, military personnel, policemen, firemen, laboratory personnel who work with animals, and others) (see Fig. 28–3). It is also wise for pregnant women to acquire active immunity because the congenital transfer of antitoxin protects the newborn infant against tetanus acquired through infection of the umbilical stump.

When nonimmune persons sustain traumatic injuries the use of antitoxin becomes imperative. Adequate passive immunization can prevent the development of tetanus if it is given *before* toxin elaborated by the infecting organism reaches nerve tissues and becomes attached. When symptoms of tetanus toxicity have begun, the use of antitoxin can only prevent the attachment of still unbound toxin, as stated above under Treatment. Passively acquired antibody in animal serums is protective for about ten days. Its use should be accompanied by the administration of toxoid to provide a continuing level of actively produced antibody, not only as protection in the current emergency but to prevent a similar crisis in the future. When animal serums have been used, there is a strong possibility that hypersensitive reactions to them will occur if they must be used again in the future, and for this reason the con-

tinuation of artificial active immunization is of even greater importance. The use of human serum in passive immunization avoids this difficulty also.

Gas Gangrene

The Clinical Disease. Clostridial gas gangrene is a fulminating infection that can arise in necrotic tissue and spread rapidly. When the organisms are introduced into tissues where conditions permit their anaerobic multiplication, they utilize carbohydrates freed from dead or dying cells, producing gas that distends the tissues and interferes with their bood supply and oxygenation. As their multiplication proceeds, the clostridia secrete enzymes such as lecithinase, collagenase, and hyaluronidase (see Chap. 6, pp. 114 to 115) which are destructive to adjacent normal tissues and also to red blood cells, so that the area of necrosis is extended. Bacterial growth accelerates and advances under these accumulative conditions, threatening severe anemia and toxemia. Gas production in the tissues produces crepitation, which is one of the diagnostic criteria of the nature of this destructive infection. Muscle tissue is characteristically involved (*clostridial myositis*) and is rapidly invaded because of its rich content of carbohydrate. The organisms may also advance through connective and subcutaneous tissues, however, producing a progressive anaerobic *cellulitis* (see p. 597). Acute toxemia may result in shock and rapid death, depending on the speed and efficacy of therapeutic intervention, the location of the infection, and the general condition of the patient.

The clostridial species that are capable of tissue invasion are often present in the normal human intestinal tract. They may sometimes induce gangrenous infections of the intestinal wall and the peritoneum in patients with bowel obstructions. The risk of clostridial infection from endogenous sources is constantly present in abdominal surgery, or during the postoperative course, if segments of bowel become ischemic (lacking in adequate blood supply) or nonviable for any reason, this being the underlying hazard of mechanical obstruction also.

Clostridial species may also occur as members of the genital flora in about 5 per cent of normal women. Organisms derived from genital, or even from intestinal, sources may induce severe uterine infections as a result of septic instrumental abortion.

Some strains of clostridia can be responsible for acute food poisoning if they are introduced into food and have an opportunity to multiply there before it is eaten. Meat provides the best medium for clostridial growth, particularly if it has been previously cooked in a stew or meat pie. Contaminated leftover meat dishes that are not thoroughly reheated before eating are the usual source of clostridial enteritis, which is seldom a serious or fatal disease.

Fig. 28–3. Tetanus is a disease that can be prevented by active immunization with tetanus toxoid. During World War II only four cases of tetanus were reported among nearly 2,800,000 wounded American soldiers who had been immunized and had received a booster shot at the time of the injury. (Courtesy of the Office of the Surgeon General, Department of the Army, Washington, D.C.)

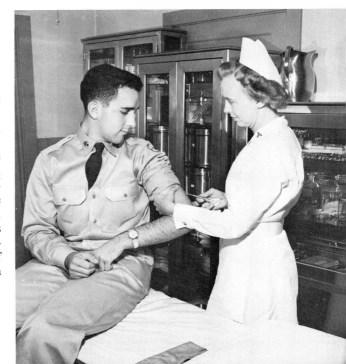

Laboratory Diagnosis

I. Identification of the Organism. Clostridium perfringens (the Welch bacillus), *Clostridium novyi, Clostridium septicum, Clostridium histolyticum.*

The organisms listed above are the species most commonly associated with infections of the gas gangrene type. This disease is often a mixed infection, which is not surprising considering the usual exposure of traumatized tissues to environmental or endogenous reservoirs of bacterial contamination or growth. In gas gangrene there may be more than one clostridial species present, as well as streptococci or staphylococci and Gram-negative enteric bacteria.

It must also be emphasized that the diagnosis of gas gangrene is primarily made on clinical grounds, and that the mere finding of clostridia in wounds does not necessarily incriminate them as the cause of infection. The spores of these organisms may be found as transient contaminants of surface tissues in wounds where they are unable to vegetate and multiply in the absence of necrotic tissue and anaerobic conditions. On the other hand, their isolation in relatively large numbers from exudates or tissues obtained from gangrenous, crepitant lesions confirms the bacterial nature of the clinical disease.

A. MICROSCOPIC AND CULTURE CHARACTERISTICS. Like the tetanus bacillus, other members of the *Clostridium* genus are anaerobic, sporeforming bacilli. They differ microscopically from *Cl. tetani* in that their spores usually are placed in central or subterminal positions. They are isolated and identified by the methods described in the section on the laboratory diagnosis of tetanus, pages 599 to 600. Most of these strains actively attack carbohydrates and they are strongly proteolytic. Their final identification rests with the demonstration of toxin production and its neutralization with specific antisera.

II. Identification of Patient's Serum Antibodies. Serologic diagnosis is of no value in clostridial infections.

III. Specimens for Diagnosis. Exudates and tissue from infected wounds are submitted for smears and culture. Care should be taken to collect this material from the active depths of the wound, so that misleading surface contaminants may be avoided.

Epidemiology

I. Communicability of Infection

A. RESERVOIR, SOURCES, AND TRANSMISSION ROUTES. See the corresponding discussion in the section on tetanus (p. 600).

B. INCUBATION PERIOD. This is usually very short, infection arising in from one to three days following wound contamination.

C. COMMUNICABLE PERIOD. Clostridial infections are ordinarily not transmissible from man to man. In the hospital surgical service, however, the infected patient may be a rich source of the organism, in the operating room or on the surgical ward. Every precaution must be taken to prevent the transfer of clostridial infection to other surgical patients by direct or indirect routes.

D. IMMUNITY. Susceptibility to clostridial infection is general. Antitoxin immunity may arise as a result of infection, but its durability and protective value are questionable. Passively administered antitoxin is often used in the treatment of active infection, as discussed below.

II. Control of Active Infection

A. ISOLATION. Patients with gas gangrene should be isolated to prevent the transfer of pathogenic clostridia and other infecting organisms, particularly to other surgical cases. There is no danger of transmission except to persons with surgical or traumatic wounds, which may offer suitable conditions for clostridial multiplication.

B. PRECAUTIONS. The attendant surgical and nursing staff must take suitable precautions to prevent their own transmission of the infection from an active case to other patients. Gowns and gloves should be worn by those who treat the wound or attend the patient closely, and handwashing is an urgent necessity. Individualized instruments and equipment should be used, and these should be sterilized by autoclaving. Boiling and chemical disinfection are of dubious value since these methods do not kill resistant clostridial spores. Concurrent and terminal disinfection pose a problem for this reason. Probably the most satisfactory program is one that aims at the destruction of the richest sources of the organism (dressings should be burned, bed linens auto-

claved before being laundered, unprotected mattresses and pillows sterilized in an ethylene oxide chamber) and the removal of environmental contamination by thorough disinfection-cleaning of the patient's unit. Good disinfection will kill the vegetative bacilli, and careful cleaning removes spores mechanically. Beyond this, it is not practical to attempt the removal of the last clostridial spores, because they are constant contaminants of the environment in any case.

In the operating room the same principles apply. Washer-sterilizers have particular value in the care of instruments contaminated during surgical treatment of clostridial gangrene. All linens associated with the case, including personnel gowns, should be autoclaved before they are laundered; disposable items are incinerated; heat-sensitive equipment is subjected to gas sterilization and the rest is autoclaved. The room and all of its permanent equipment are then thoroughly scrubbed down with an effective cleansing agent.

When the epidemiology of a hospital case of gas gangrene suggests that its source arose from cross-infection or contamination, immediate steps must be taken to prevent additional cases. Clostridial organisms may display marked increases in their virulence as a result of human passage, which constitutes another reason for the isolation of patients and the destruction of sources of the infecting strain. Operating-room and surgical service supplies should be resterilized, sterilizing methods should be reviewed, bacteriologic checks on the efficacy of these procedures should be performed, environmental sources of the organism should be sought in the operating room, and technical errors should be identified when this is possible in retrospective review.

C. TREATMENT. The most urgently important treatment is the surgical débridement of the involved area, with removal of necrotic tissue and aeration of the wound. Antibiotic therapy is instituted promptly, penicillin being the drug of choice for its bactericidal action on clostridial species. Polyvalent antitoxin, containing antibodies against the major toxins produced by the clostridial strains usually associated with gas gangrene, is also given but this is probably less important than surgical cleansing of the wound

and the use of antimicrobial drugs to control infection.

In recent years the application of oxygen under pressure has proved useful in the management of clostridial myositis or cellulitis. The patient is placed in a room called a *hyperbaric chamber*, which contains oxygen at a concentration and pressure greatly in excess of that of the normal atmosphere, so that the blood stream and tissues are saturated for a time with oxygen.

D. CONTROL AND PREVENTION. As pointed out above, sporadic cases of clostridial disease may arise from endogenous or environmental sources when tissues are devitalized by trauma or other mechanisms. It is important to identify and control these sources when they appear to involve more than one case in hospital cross-infections. Strict adherence to the principles of surgical asepsis (see Chap. 10, pp. 239 to 240) and controlled techniques for the sterilization of surgical supplies offer the best means of control and prevention of these infections in hospitals.

Other Bacterial Infections of "Street Wounds"

Soft tissues subjected to traumatic injury may be infected with any of a variety of bacteria derived from the environment or from the patient's own skin. The most common of these were mentioned in the preceding discussion of the laboratory diagnosis of gas gangrene (p. 604) as well as in the section of this chapter dealing with the infection of bite wounds (pp. 596 to 598). Another organism frequently associated with traumatic injuries, and also with burns, is *Pseudomonas aeruginosa*, a Gram-negative, aerobic bacillus that may be found in the normal intestinal tract as well as in the environment. This organism induces suppurative lesions in soft tissues and is characterized by its production of a blue-green pigment (*pyocyanin*) that imparts its color and sickly sweet odor to pus. (See also p. 292.)

Traumatic wounds are most frequently infected with a mixed flora, containing both Gram-positive cocci and Gram-negative bacilli. Deep wounds often support anaerobic bacteria, such as species

**Table 28–1. Summary: Infectious Diseases Acquired Through
Accidental Injuries**

Clinical Disease	Causative Organisms	Other Possible Entry Routes	Incubation Period	Communicable Period
I. Infectious Diseases Acquired Through Animal Bites				
Rabies	The rabies virus		4–6 weeks, sometimes as prolonged as 2–3 months	Virus is present in biti͏ animals for several c before their sympto͏ appear and througho the course of their illness; vampire bats transmit disease for least 5 months
Cat scratch fever	Unknown, possibly a "large virus" of the *Bedsonia* group or a herpesiurus		1 or 2 weeks from initial injury, may be shorter	Has not been clarifie͏ but infection is not directly transmissible from person to perse
II. Diseases Acquired Through the Infection of "Street Wounds"				
Tetanus	*Clostridium tetani*		2–6 days, average 4; sometimes 2 or 3 weeks or longer	Not communicable from man to man
Gas gangrene	*Clostridium perfringens*		1–3 days	In the hospital surgica͏ service, infected pat͏ may be a rich source organisms in the operating room or o͏ the surgical ward
III. Burn Wound Infections				
Local infection, superficial or deep; sepsis	*Pseudomonas aeruginosa* Streptococci Staphylococci *Cl. tetani* *Bacteroides* species Gram-negative enteric bacilli		1 to several days	Infected patient may k͏ a source of infection͏ for others with open wounds

ecimens equired	Laboratory Diagnosis	Immunization	Treatment	Nursing Management
a (from ieath gue near ening of maxillary vary nd)	Stained smear Fluorescent antibody technique Negri bodies in brain of inoculated mice	Inactivated virus (administered after exposure is confirmed or reasonably certain)	Active vaccination and immune serum	Private-room isolation; saliva and articles contaminated thereby considered infectious; protect skin, clothing from saliva; avoid injury to hands from patient's teeth during mouth care
from purating iph node test	Smear and culture (rule out bacterial infection) Positive response		None specific, chloramphenicol and tetracyclines may be helpful	Isolation not necessary; concurrent disinfection of pus from suppurating lesion or lymph node
or tissue m wound, easible	Smear and anaerobic culture	Toxoid for active immunization; antitoxin for passive immunization after injury has occurred	Antitoxin Penicillin	Isolation and special precautions not necessary
dates and sue from und	Smears and culture	Antitoxin	Penicillin Antitoxin	Isolation to protect other patients with surgical wounds; gowns and gloves when changing dressings; autoclave all equipment; burn dressings; *hand-washing*
dates and sue from unds; od	Smears and culture		Polymyxin or sulfonamide burn cream (especially for *Pseudomonas* infection); other antibiotics as indicated by laboratory studies of organisms	Private-room isolation if burns extensive; reverse aseptic precautions; "germ-free isolator" if available; *hand-washing*

of *Bacteroides* or streptococci, as well as clostridia. These organisms should always be sought by probing deeply into the wound for material to be submitted to the laboratory for anaerobic culture. Aerobic organisms recovered from the surfaces of such wounds may be mere contaminants that are not necessarily multiplying actively or injuring the tissue.

Reference should be made to the earlier section of this chapter describing the character of the infectious process in bite wounds as well as their treatment and control, for these considerations also apply to street wounds.

The Systemic Mycoses

A number of fungi capable of causing serious systemic diseases in man may gain entry to the body through injured skin or mucosal surfaces. These organisms and the mycotic infections they induce are discussed in Chapter 17, together with other mycoses of respiratory or endogenous origin. This arrangement was planned to provide the reader an opportunity to become acquainted with all the important systemic fungous infections, their usual routes of entry, and their common epidemiologic implications. From the nursing point of view, the important generalities that apply to this group of diseases are: (1) the causative fungi have a natural reservoir in the soil, but two types are known as commensals of human mucosa, (2) they are rarely if ever transmitted directly from man to man, and (3) isolation of the patient is generally not necessary, but barrier techniques should include the disinfection of discharges from open lesions (see especially pp. 396 to 397).

Burn Wound Infections

Burns represent one of the most difficult problems in medical and nursing management, particularly because the nature of the injury predisposes the exposed surface tissues to infection.

In severe burns, infection is the chief cause of death in patients who have survived the first three or four days of massive injury, surface fluid loss, pulmonary edema, or shock. The devitalized surface tissue offers suitable conditions for the growth of many opportunistic organisms, notably streptococci, staphylococci, Gram-negative enteric bacteria, and even anaerobes, including the tetanus bacillus and other clostridia, or *Bacteroides*. The complications of tetanus or clostridial cellulitis are usually fatal when superimposed on the many physiologic problems created by burns.

The organism most frequently encountered in burn wound infections, however, is *Pseudomonas aeruginosa* (see p. 605, above). *Pseudomonas* infections present very difficult problems because the organism is generally resistant to many of the clinically useful antibiotics, responding as a rule only to drugs of the polymyxin group. The polymyxins are basic polypeptides of large molecular size (they are derived from a species of the aerobic, sporeforming genus *Bacillus*). They have some toxicity for the central nervous system, but this is reversible and relatively harmless. Their renal toxicity is more important, particularly in patients, including those with burns, who may suffer an existing inadequacy of renal function.

When efforts to control *Pseudomonas* or other infections of burns fail, septicemia is the usual consequence and most often the cause of death. The wound itself becomes overwhelmed with colonizing bacteria, and systemic invasion may induce fatal shock. In recent years many efforts have been made to develop methods that would prevent the complication of "burn wound sepsis." These have included the provision of closed hospital areas in which strict aseptic control can be maintained against air-borne infection. The patient is kept in a room ventilated by bacteria-free filtered air delivered under positive pressure so that air currents move away from his wounds and also prevent the entry of air from outside contaminated areas when the door is opened. The room walls, floor, and furniture are treated with disinfectants having a residual action (see Chap. 10), and all of the patient's attendants practice reverse aseptic precautions, putting on sterile clothing (gowns, masks, hair covering,

and gloves) before they enter the room. Access to the room is generally available only through an antechamber or closed corridor where clothes can be changed. The use of ultraviolet lamps at the entrance to the room also assists in maintaining an aseptic room environment. This type of closed unit is used for the treatment and care of patients other than burn victims who may also be extremely susceptible to infection that could easily prove fatal. Such patients might include premature infants, persons who have required extensive surgery, those with renal disfunctions who are maintained by an "artificial kidney" apparatus, and those who are undergoing surgical efforts to achieve tissue or organ transplants. Recently, the use of presterilized, individual, plastic enclosures ("germ-free isolators") has proved feasible and is being advocated for the protective isolation of burn patients and others for whom the risk of superimposed infection may be grave.

Success has also been reported in recent years in the development of a method for treating burns that prevents or controls infection through the topical application of an antibacterial "burn cream." The buttery cream base contains a sulfonamide formulation that suppresses bacterial growth in the burned tissue and permits the regeneration of surviving epithelium that might otherwise be lost to infection. This material has been reported* to reduce significantly the incidence of infection in burns, as well as the development of burn wound sepsis, and to lower the mortality rate in burns that involve up to 60 per cent of the body surface. This form of treatment appears to offer a great deal of hope that the control of infections in burns can be achieved when therapy is instituted promptly.

Questions

1. What is the reservoir for rabies?
2. What is the incubation period for rabies?
3. When is active immunization indicated for rabies?
4. What nursing precautions are considered necessary for the patient with rabies?
5. What do the control and prevention of rabies require?
6. What organism is believed to cause cat scratch fever?
7. Why do dog and human bites often produce serious local or even systemic infections?
8. What does the character of the infectious process in a bite wound reflect?
9. Why do animal bites present the additional and more dangerous hazard of clostridial infection?
10. What do the treatment and control of bite wound infections entail?

* "Control of Bacterial Infection in Severe Burns with a Topical Sulfonamide Burn Cream," by R. B. Lindberg, J. A. Moncrief, W. E. Switzer, and A. D. Mason, Jr. U.S. Army Surgical Research Unit, Fort Sam Houston, Texas, *Antimicrobial Agents and Chemotherapy*, pp. 708–16, 1964.

29 Infections Acquired Through Medical and Surgical Procedures

Hospitalized patients constitute a group whose susceptibility to infection is often increased simply because they are ill and therefore physiologically less capable of resisting the inroads of virulent, or even opportunistic, microorganisms they may encounter. The problem is frequently compounded for such patients by the institutional conditions of hospital living, or by the added risks inherent in some of the procedures of medical, surgical, and nursing practice. The opportunities for exposure are multiple and may arise from a number of directions and sources (see Fig. 29–1). In his personal contacts, direct or indirect, the hospital patient may be exposed to the infections of neighboring patients, visitors, or personnel. This is one of the most important reasons for isolating patients with infectious diseases, as repeatedly stressed in previous chapters of this book. It has also been pointed out, however, that infection may be transferred before its active source in patients or their contacts is recognized, a problem that requires extra vigilance in hospitals but unfortunately lacks an easy solution.

The Infectious Risks of Medical and Surgical Procedures

In this chapter we shall be concerned with some of the infections that can be introduced parenterally into patients undergoing certain types of

procedures during the course of their medical or surgical treatment for many kinds of illnesses. The procedures involving the greatest risks of superimposed infection fall into four major categories: (1) surgery, (2) instrumentation through mucosal orifices, (3) catheterization of blood vessels or urinary passages, and (4) the insertion of hypodermic needles for the injection or the withdrawal of fluids. The nature and sources of infections that may be acquired through these routes are reviewed, and some diseases that are characteristically associated with hospital or other medical practice are discussed. The latter include puerperal fever, urinary tract infections,

and viral hepatitis. Methods for the control of hospital infections are discussed in detail in Chapter 10 and should be reviewed, with particular reference to pages 233 to 247. The Appendix may also be consulted for some recommended techniques of infection control.

Surgical Infections

One of the most obvious risks of surgery lies in the exposure of tissues to exogenous sources of infection, or in the activation of endogenous microorganisms. The major sources of *exogenous*

THE EPIDEMIOLOGY OF STAPHYLOCOCCUS

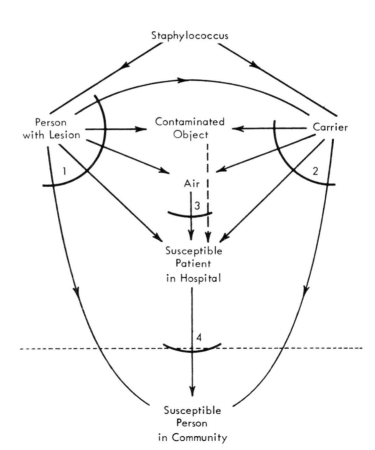

Fig. 29–1. Routes of transmission of *Staphylococcus* infections within a hospital and from the hospital to the community. (Reproduced from Godwin, John T., and Nahmias, Andre J.: What Can Be Done About the Staphylococcal Disease Problem, *J. Med. Assoc. Georgia*, **48**:209, May, 1959.)

infection are the skin and respiratory secretions of the operating team and environmental contamination from objects in intimate contact with surgically exposed tissues (instruments, sponges, sutures, linen drapes, irrigating solutions, etc.). Contaminated air may also play a role in surgical infections. *Endogenous* infections may arise when microorganisms are disseminated into adjacent tissues or the blood stream from their usual sites of commensalism on the patient's skin or mucous membranes, such as the lumen of the intestinal tract, the genitourinary membranes, the oral mucosa, and other surface areas having a normal microbial flora.

Surgical patients are often subjected to a variety of procedural risks in addition to those inherent in surgery itself. They may require intubation (the insertion of an airway into the larynx) while under anesthesia; the administration of intravenous fluids; urinary catheterization; or other techniques of management that can open the door to infection. Inhalation anesthesia also leaves them more vulnerable to the chance of respiratory infection.

The degree of trauma suffered by tissues exposed to surgery, or to the ancillary procedures mentioned above, is an important determining factor in the development of wound infections. Excessive or rough handling can be a threat to the architectural integrity of tissues. It may inter-fere with their vascular structures, leaving areas of devitalization. Also, continued bleeding from severed vessels may lead to the formation of hematomas in which bacteria can grow without opposition, as they may also do in devitalized, necrotizing tissues. Speed, skill, manual dexterity, and delicacy are essential factors in the control and prevention of surgical wound infections.

The nature and source of infecting microorganisms both may vary somewhat with the type of surgery performed and the region of the body involved. Table 29–1 shows some of the infectious complications that may result from surgery and indicates their possible origins. The sources of surgical infection are often difficult to prove conclusively, but it should be noted that the microorganisms involved are those that are commonly associated with human surface tissues. The route of their access to the surgical wound or to systemic localizations may reflect the quantity and quality of the patient's own regional flora, the health and physiologic resistance of local tissues, or an exogenous source. Usually the best evidence that surgical personnel, techniques, or supplies must be incriminated lies in the demonstration of a continuing incidence of wound infections or other complications among all surgical patients or those of a given service, especially if the same etiologic agents are involved in most or all of these infections.

Table 29–1. Infectious Complications That May Result from Surgery

Surgical Area	Types of Infection and Their Possible Origins		Some Sources of Exogenous Infections
	Endogenous	Exogenous	
Mouth, nose, or throat	Infections of local soft tissues Regional lymphadenopathies Bacteremia and systemic infection		
	Organisms from upper respiratory tract, or buccal mucosa: streptococci (*Str. viridans* or *Str. faecalis* may induce subacute bacterial endocarditis)	Streptococci (especially beta-hemolytic strains) Staphylococci (especially *S. aureus*)	Infected personnel Unsterile instruments, wound packing, sponges, irrigating solutions

Table 29–1. (*Cont.*)

Staphylococci
Actinomyces israeli
   (cervicofacial or thoracic
   actinomycosis)

Poliomyelitis virus (patient may have inapparent naso-pharyngeal colonization, especially in seasons of high community incidence)	Poliomyelitis virus	Previous infected contacts or infected surgical personnel

Chest
(including
cardiac
surgery)

Wound infections
Pulmonary infection
Systemic infection

Organisms from upper respiratory tract or skin: Streptococci Staphylococci (coagulase-negative as well as -positive strains sometimes involved in endocarditis following cardiac surgery) *Actinomyces israeli* Gram-negative enteric bacilli: *E. coli* *Klebsiella* species *Proteus* species *Pseudomonas aeruginosa*	As in the endogenous column on left, except actinomycotic disease is not derived from exogenous sources	Infected personnel Hands in punctured or torn gloves Contaminated gowns Contaminated instru-ments, sutures, solutions Contaminated fluids or blood for transfusion Contamination in heart-lung machine

Intestinal
tract

Wound infections
Infection of bowel wall
Peritonitis
Systemic infections (including endocarditis)

Organisms from intestinal tract or skin: Streptococci Staphylococci (usually *S. aureus* Gram-negative enteric bacilli: *E. coli* *Klebsiella* species *Proteus* species *Ps. aeruginosa* *Salmonella* species (may be spread from in-apparent bowel infection, inducing *Salmonella* septicemia	As in the endogenous column on left, except salmonellosis is rarely derived from exogenous sources during surgery	Infected personnel Hands in punctured or torn gloves Contaminated gowns Contaminated instru-ments, sutures, solutions Contaminated blood or fluids given intravenously

TABLE 29–1. (*Cont.*)

Surgical Area	Types of Infection and Their Possible Origins		Some Sources of Exogenous Infections
	Endogenous	Exogenous	
	Anaerobic organisms: *Clostridium tetani* *Clostridium perfringens* and others of gas gangrene group *Bacteroides* species Streptococci		
Orthopedic surgery	Wound infections Osteomyelitis Systemic infection		
	Organisms from skin or intestinal tract: Streptococci (usually beta-hemolytic) Staphylococci (usually *S. aureus*) *Clostridium tetani* *Clostridium perfringens* and others of gas gangrene group Anaerobic streptococci *Bacteroides* species Gram-negative enteric bacilli, especially *Ps. aeruginosa*	As in the endogenous column on the left	Infected personnel Hands in punctured or torn gloves Contaminated gowns Contaminated instruments, sutures, solutions Contaminated blood or fluids given intravenously Contaminated prosthetic devices implanted in tissues Plaster dust
Ophthalmic surgery	Conjunctivitis Bulbar infections		
	Organisms from conjunctiva or skin: Pneumococci Streptococci Staphylococci *Hemophilus* species Herpesvirus	The bacterial species listed in the endogenous column on the left plus: Fungi (various species, e.g., *Aspergillus, Mucor*) The viral agent of inclusion conjunctivitis	Infected personnel Contaminated hands or gowns Contaminated instruments Contaminated eyedrops or anesthetizing solutions
Plastic surgery	Wound infections Infectious disruption of grafts		
	Organisms from skin or mucosa: Streptococci Staphylococci Gram-negative enteric bacilli, especially *Ps. aeruginosa*	As in the endogenous column on the left	Infected personnel Hands in punctured or torn gloves Contaminated gowns Contaminated instruments, sutures, solutions

TABLE 29–1. (*Cont.*)

Gynecologic and obstetric surgery	Puerperal fever Urinary tract infections (cystitis, pyelonephritis)		
	Organisms from genital or intestinal tract mucosa: Streptococci Staphylococci Gram-negative enteric bacilli Anaerobic organisms: *Clostridium perfringens* and others of the gas gangrene group *Bacteroides* species	As in the endogenous column on the left Streptococci and staphylococci most commonly associated with puerperal sepsis; beta-hemolytic strep or *S. aureus* strains usually derived from obstetric personnel	Infected personnel Hands in punctured or torn gloves Contaminated gowns Contaminated instruments, solutions Contaminated catheters

The Infectious Risks of Instrumentation Through Mucosal Orifices

Lensed instruments are frequently used for the examination of mucosal passageways and deep surfaces (endoscopy). These instruments consist, essentially, of a metal tube equipped with magnifying lenses, a light source at the inserted end, and a series of prisms that direct light to the observer's eye, permitting visualization of the depths of the passageway. They are constructed for specific use on various anatomic structures and are named accordingly, each term having the suffix "-scope" to indicate a viewing instrument. Some examples are listed at the foot of the page.

These instruments present the risk of infection for two reasons: (1) they are difficult to sterilize because of their construction and the fact that their lenses, lighting system, and prisms are mounted in cementing substances that may be dissolved by moist heat or chemical solvents; and (2) they must be large enough in diameter to permit an adequate view of the passageway, which means that they can be disruptive to delicate mucosal linings. If they are not properly disinfected endoscopes may introduce extraneous microorganisms, including those derived from patients previously examined, and if they are not carefully inserted, they may irritate or break the mucosal barrier, permitting entry of local or exogenous organisms to deeper tissues.

Recommended methods for the disinfection of endoscopes can be found in Appendix VII (p. 658).

Catheterization of Blood Vessels or Urinary Passages

The insertion of catheters into blood vessels or into the long narrow passages of the urinary tract (ureters or the urethra) is frequently done for diagnostic or therapeutic purposes. The cath-

Nasopharyngoscope	used for examination of the nasopharynx
Laryngoscope	used for examination of the larynx
Bronchoscope	used for examination of the trachea and bronchial tree
Gastroscope	used for examination of the esophagus and stomach
Sigmoidoscope	used for examination of the sigmoid and rectum
Cystoscope	used for examination of the urethra and bladder
Endoscope	a collective term for such instruments

eters themselves may be a source of infection if not properly sterilized, and the technique of insertion requires strict aseptic precautions.

Vascular catheters may introduce microorganisms directly into the blood stream. Organisms of low pathogenicity may be removed by the phagocytes and antibacterial components of the blood, but it is always possible that some may localize and multiply, particularly in sites where the vascular or endocardial endothelium is defective or injured, or where a thrombus or embolus exists. These clinical problems usually provide the necessity for catheterization and at the same time increase the risks inherent in the introduction of even "avirulent" organisms. These may be able to establish themselves with little opposition in a blood clot, or on a defective heart valve, producing local injury and recurrent bacteremia. Coagulase-negative strains of staphylococci (*S. epidermidis*) not infrequently are responsible for these infections, which complicate the patient's postcatheterization course. *Streptococcus viridans* and *Str. faecalis* are other frequent offenders, while *S. aureus* (coagulase-positive) may induce a fulminating septicemia as well as local injury at its sites of colonization. The source of these infections may be the skin or respiratory membranes either of the patient or of a member of the operating team. Environmental contamination of catheters or instruments is also very possible because these procedures frequently are carried out in x-ray rooms or other areas where radiologic visualization of catheter placement can be obtained, and where strict asepsis is difficult to maintain.

Urinary tract catheterizations may be responsible for cystitis, pyelonephritis, or even more disseminated systemic infections. The procedures most frequently associated with complicating urinary infections are urethral or ureteral catheterization, the use of indwelling catheters for continuous bladder drainage, cystoscopy, and prostate or bladder surgery. These infections may have an endogenous source in the microbial flora of the patient's genital, perineal, or perianal mucosa, or they may be introduced from exogenous sources. The technique of catheterization should be conducted with strict asepsis and with great care to avoid injuring delicate mucosal linings with the catheter itself. Urinary tract infections and their control are discussed in more detail in a later section of this chapter.

Hypodermic Needles, Syringes, and Injectable Solutions

Among the many tools of medical practice that may be responsible for the parenteral introduction of infection, the hypodermic needle is the most frequently employed and therefore sometimes the most carelessly used. It can be directly or indirectly responsible for infection for one or more of the following reasons:

1. The needle itself is contaminated.

2. The syringe or other vessel containing fluid to be injected is contaminated.

3. The patient's skin is inadequately disinfected.

4. The patient's skin is contaminated with microorganisms growing in *inactive* disinfectants used to prepare the injection site.

5. The injected fluid contains contaminating or multiplying organisms.

Sources of Infection by the Hypodermic Route. The sources of contamination for needles, syringes, or injectable solutions are quite varied, but the most obvious of these and their serious implications are discussed below:

1. Pathogenic microorganisms may be derived from the blood, tissues, or skin of infectious patients for whom the needle or syringe was previously used. This of course implies that reused instruments were inadequately cleaned and sterilized. The infectious agents most frequently involved in this kind of mishap are the *viruses of infectious hepatitis and serum hepatitis*. These viruses are not only quite resistant to physical and chemical agents of disinfection, but they are also virulent for man and capable of establishing infection in nonimmune susceptible persons even when they are introduced into the blood or tissues in small numbers. Heat sterilization of reusable needles or syringes or the use and discard of disposable presterilized hypodermic equipment afford the only guarantee of

prevention of the spread of viral hepatitis by this route (see Appendix, p. 654). Viral hepatitis is discussed in the next section of this chapter (see also Chap. 20, p. 458).

2. Faulty techniques of the operator may result in the contamination of needles or syringes subsequent to their sterilization. Microorganisms from the hands or respiratory secretions of the nurse, physician, or laboratory worker, or from environmental sources, may reach the shaft of the needle, the inner surfaces of a disassembled syringe, or its tip if these items are not handled correctly. They must be packaged for sterilization in such a way that they can later be removed from wrappings or envelopes without being touched on surfaces that will be in contact with the patient's tissues or with the material to be injected. The shaft of a sterile needle must also be continuously protected from contamination from the air, from the table or bench top where it is laid pending final preparation of the patient's skin, or from the operator's hands. A needle known to have touched any of these surfaces should be immediately discarded, before it is used, and replaced with a sterile one. Disposable needles are packaged in plastic protectors, which should be left in place until the moment comes to charge the syringe with the material to be injected or to introduce the needle through the patient's skin. If a loaded syringe and needle must be momentarily set aside before an injection is finally given, the plastic needle protector should be replaced for the interim period. Reusable needles are usually sterilized in glass tubes that can be retained for protection of sterility while a hypodermic assembly is awaiting final use. If plastic or glass protectors are not available, sterile dry gauze pads may be used to guard the hypodermic needle from environmental sources of contamination.

3. Inadequate disinfection of the patient's skin prior to the introduction of hypodermic needles may also lead to infection. The organisms usually introduced from this or from environmental sources may include strains of streptococci, staphylococci, Gram-negative enteric bacteria, and occasionally the spores of aerobic or anaerobic bacilli. As a general rule, the casual introduction of a few organisms from such sources leads to

serious disease only if the microbial species involved possess truly virulent properties, or the patient is unusually susceptible for some reason. The route of introduction of contaminated materials also influences the outcome. Microorganisms injected into intradermal or subcutaneous tissues meet a great deal of opposition from local phagocytes as well as from the components of blood supplied to well-vascularized tissues. In intramuscular positions, contaminating organisms may have more opportunity to establish themselves because muscle tissue contains fewer fixed phagocytes, but the blood supply soon brings defensive white blood cells and plasma components that resist infection. Intravenous injections or venipuncture for the collection of blood samples affords the greatest risk of introduction and wide dissemination of contaminating microorganisms. Here again, the degree of risk depends on the numbers of organisms injected, their virulent properties, or the toxicity of their preformed products if they have been multiplying in exogenous sources. Small numbers of "avirulent" organisms from the skin may be easily removed from the blood stream by phagocytes, or inactivated by opsonins or antibodies, but the properties of virulent organisms (e.g., hemolytic streptococci or coagulase-positive staphylococci) provide them with greater resistance to the body's defenses, and even a few such bacterial cells are dangerous if introduced directly into blood or tissues.

4. Another dangerous possibility of systemic bacterial infection arises when the hypodermic technique introduces materials in which microbial multiplication has occurred prior to injection. One of the ways in which this can happen involves the use of inactive skin antiseptics in which bacteria have been growing. When the patient's skin is prepared for injection by applying the "disinfectant," large numbers of contaminating organisms may be wiped on to the skin surface and later pushed through to the tissues below, or into a vein, by the injected needle as it passes through this teeming culture. Antiseptics and other chemical disinfectants may be inactivated in a number of ways, depending on their structure and their exposure to proteins or other substances that

bind the active portions of their molecules (see Chap. 10, pp. 219–20, and 223–24). Fresh working solutions should be prepared frequently and kept in clean, closed containers, protected from chemical or excessive microbial contamination. The practice of setting up jars of cotton or gauze pads soaked in antiseptic solution, and ready to use for the preparation of patient's skin for injection, is particularly dangerous because cellulose fibers may bind with the antiseptic molecule and inactivate it. Bacteria are constantly introduced into these jars from the fingers of personnel who reach in for a new pad, and in a short time the jar may contain a rich culture of organisms growing in a solution that can no longer suppress them. Staphylococci and Gram-negative enteric bacteria are particularly capable of surviving and multiplying in these situations. *Pseudomonas aeruginosa* is a frequent contaminant of aqueous solutions that have been made from unsterile tap water. This organism can live and grow on the surfaces of water taps, and in other moist areas where a minimum of organic nutrient is available (soiled sinks and basins, humidity chambers, oxygen tents, resuscitators). It may multiply extensively in inactive aqueous germicides and induce serious systemic infection if introduced into the body from skin or mucosal surfaces that have been "cleansed" with such solutions prior to the introduction of a needle, catheter, or other instrument.

5. Fluids injected by the hypodermic technique may themselves be the most dangerous source of infecting microorganisms, particularly if the latter have had a preliminary opportunity to multiply and to produce substances that may be toxic to the human body. The patient who receives such material not only runs the risk of generalized systemic infection but may suffer a severe febrile reaction to the injected pyrogenic microbial byproducts (see Chap. 8, p. 158). If he is also hypersensitive to the bacterial antigens suddenly introduced into his tissues, he may experience an immediate reaction ranging in severity from anaphylaxis and shock to that of the "serum sickness" type (see Chap. 7, pp. 146 to 153).

Any type of injectable solution may be involved in this type of accident, sometimes with disastrous results for the patient. Fluids given intravenously; vitamins; vaccines; antisera; anesthetizing solutions used to induce local skin or mucosal anesthesia in dental, ophthalmic, or other surgery or for such procedures as lumbar puncture, biopsies, or bone marrow aspiration — all these and many others may be the source of contaminating organisms capable of establishing infection. Continuing vigilance is essential to the prevention of these problems. Careful visual inspection of each ampule, vial, or bottle immediately prior to its use is helpful only if the material to be injected is in clear solution and is not hidden by a label or by markings pressed into the glass or plastic container. Cracked or otherwise damaged vessels containing injectable material should never be used, under any circumstances. The use of vials containing multiple doses of fluids for injection should be discouraged also, because each entry into such a container affords a new opportunity for its contamination. These vials are generally sealed with a cap containing a rubber diaphragm through which the hypodermic needle is inserted for withdrawal of a dose of material to be administered to a patient. The hole made by the needle as it passes through the rubber may be enlarged every time the vial is used, threatening contamination of the vial's contents by this route. The needle itself may also introduce a few organisms. If the contaminating bacteria then have an opportunity to multiply in the vial before it is used again, the next patient receiving a dose of its contents may suffer the consequences of superimposed infection. Vials or bottles containing cloudy material that originally was clear should be discarded immediately. Those containing fluids that are not clear to begin with (e.g., microbial vaccines) present a more difficult problem. The manufacturer's label should be carefully read for information concerning the presence of an antibacterial preservative, the date of preparation and sterilization, an expiration date, and any instructions concerning the handling, administration, and storage temperature of the material. Whenever possible, however, injectable solutions should be prepared or purchased in containers sufficient for a single, individual use and discarded thereafter.

Blood for transfusion requires special emphasis in this connection. Not only is it subject to contamination from extraneous sources, but it may transfer active infection from the donor to the recipient. Under well-controlled circumstances, most problems of this variety are avoided by the legal requirements for the operation of blood banks, which stipulate that blood donors must be examined for evidence of current active infection and for a history of acute or chronic disease transmissible by blood. Unfortunately, however, there are a few diseases of this type that may exist in latent, asymptomatic form. Would-be donors may themselves be unaware of their infection, or they may give an inaccurate history of past disease, unintentionally or willfully. The diseases most readily transmissible from "silent" donors are syphilis, malaria, infectious hepatitis, and serum hepatitis. In the case of syphilis, routine physical and serologic examination is generally successful in screening infectious donors (see Chap. 23, pp. 498 to 499). Malaria and infectious hepatitis are not readily diagnosed in their inapparent stages, but a well-taken history can provide evidence of clinically characteristic disease experienced in the past (see Chap. 27, pp. 575–579; and Chap. 20, pp. 458–62, respectively). Serum hepatitis is the most difficult problem of this type, because a fair number of people may carry the viral agent of this disease without ever showing any evidence of clinical illness (in the United States, the carrier rate has been estimated to range from 2 to 4 per cent). This disease is discussed more fully in the next section of this chapter.

Some Important Infectious Diseases Associated with Medical and Surgical Procedures

Puerperal Fever

The Clinical Disease. Puerperal fever is an acute bacterial disease associated with infection incurred during childbirth or abortion. It begins with local symptoms of bacterial invasion of the genital tract, including the uterus and the fallo-pian tubes. If the infection is not treated promptly or adequately, it may extend as a peritonitis, usually with bacteremia or septicemia.

Laboratory Diagnosis

I. Identification of the Organisms. Puerperal fever may be caused by a number of different bacterial agents. Hemolytic streptococci of group A are the most frequent cause of postpartum infections, but a variety of organisms have been recognized in postabortion sepsis. Anaerobic bacteria, such as *Bacteroides* species, *Clostridium perfringens*, and streptococci, may be involved, and the aerobic Gram-negative enteric bacilli (*E. coli*, *Klebsiella* species, or *Pseudomonas aeruginosa*) and *Staphylococcus aureus* are not infrequent agents. Mixed infections with two or more of these organisms are sometimes seen in septic abortions.

The microscopic and cultural characteristics of these organisms have been described in previous chapters. (See Chap. 14, pp. 328–29, and Chap. 23, pp. 512–13, for discussion of the hemolytic streptococci and staphylococci, respectively.) The other strains mentioned may be found by reference to the Index.

II. Identification of Patient's Serum Antibodies. In puerperal fever caused by hemolytic streptococci the serum antistreptolysin titer rises between the onset of acute symptoms and the convalescent stage. Serologic diagnosis has no value when other types of infection induce this syndrome.

III. Specimens for Diagnosis. Vaginal discharges and pus from the cervix or uterus are appropriate for smear and culture (aerobic and anaerobic).

Repeated blood cultures may be useful if the disease advances to a bacteremic or septicemic stage.

When streptococcal infection is suspected, two samples of blood should be submitted for antistreptolysin titers. The first should be collected as soon as possible after the onset of symptoms, the second in about ten days to two weeks.

Epidemiology

I. Communicability of Infection

A. Reservoir, Sources and Transmission Routes. The human reservoir supplies the or-

ganisms encountered in puerperal sepsis. They are found on the skin and mucosa of normal persons, as well as in the lesions of infected patients or personnel. The chief source of *hemolytic streptococcal* postpartum infections is rarely the patient herself, however, for these strains are not normal to the female genital tract. They are transmitted to her from the nose, throat, or hands of obstetricians, midwives, nurses, or other attendants, or from instruments contaminated by these sources. Before the mid-1860's, when Joseph Lister first applied Pasteur's concepts of infectious disease to surgery (see Chap. 10, p. 219), puerperal fever was a frequent complication of childbirth, and a dreaded one because of its high mortality rate. It was seen most often in the maternity wards of hospitals, but mothers who delivered at home were not safe either, because their physicians or midwives brought the infection to them from other cases they had attended. Wiping their contaminated hands on lapels or aprons, these attendants would set to work, full of confidence, to deliver a new baby and to institute a new infection.

Fully two decades before Lister's aseptic approach to surgery began to impress his surgical colleagues with its success in preventing infection, the first important epidemiologic study of puerperal fever had been reported by an American physician, Oliver Wendell Holmes. In 1843 he presented a paper on "The Contagiousness of Puerperal Fever" to the Boston Society for Medical Improvement. This report created a furor of opposition among the leading obstetricians of the day because Holmes dared to present the thesis that puerperal fever was due largely to "the carelessness, ignorance, and negligence of the obstetrician and midwife."* A similar conclusion was being reached independently at about the same time by an Austrian physician whose name

was Ignaz Semmelweis. Holmes and Semmelweis did not know each other but they had much more in common than a faculty for accurate observation. In their own obstetric practices they instituted rules of cleanliness, which included hand-washing as well as other careful precautions regarding changes of clothing between infectious cases or after attending autopsies of patients who had died of puerperal sepsis. They managed to keep their own patients relatively free of infection, but they were both subjected to a great deal of ridicule and abuse from their medical colleagues. Semmelweis suffered more from this than Holmes, and in the end was so disturbed (by his failure to persuade other physicians to accept the methods he had used effectively to save women in childbirth from fatal infections) that his sanity was affected, and he died in a mental hospital (of sepsis from a wound on his hand!). Holmes's reactions were different. He said, "No man makes a quarrel with me over the counterpane that covers a mother, with her new-born infant at her breast!"† "Where facts are numerous, and unquestionable, and unequivocal in their significance, theory must follow them as best it may, keeping time with their step, and not go before them, marching to the sound of its own drum and trumpet."‡ Having laid down some simple rules he had found reliable in the prevention of the transmission of puerperal fever, Holmes wrote also, "Whatever indulgence may be granted to those who have heretofore been the ignorant causes of so much misery, the time has come when the existence of a *private pestilence* in the sphere of a single physician should be looked upon not as a misfortune but a crime; and in the knowledge of such occurrences, the duties of the practitioner to his profession, should give way to his paramount obligations to society." § These words remain even more pointed today when

* Smillie, Wilson G.: *Public Health, Its Promise For the Future*. The Macmillan Co., New York, 1955, p. 156.
† Holmes, Oliver Wendell: Puerperal Fever as a Private Pestilence, *Medical Classics*, **1**:252, Nov., 1936, originally published in Boston by Ticknor and Fields, 1855.
‡ *Ibid.*, p. 249.
§ Holmes, Oliver Wendell: The Contagiousness of Puerperal Fever, *Medical Classics*, **1**:243, Nov., 1936 (from *New England Quarterly Journal, Medicine & Surgery*, **1**, 1843, published in Boston by D. Clapp, Jr.)

the causes of infectious disease are so well understood and yet sometimes ignored or underestimated even now.

When illegal abortion is attempted by the individual or performed by others working under circumstances that do not permit asepsis (ignorance plays its part again, together with legal and social pressures), the probabilities of infection are even greater than in normal childbirth, and a wider range of sources and species of microorganisms may be involved. In many instances, however, these infections probably arise from endogenous sources, species such as anaerobic streptococci, *Bacteroides*, *Clostridium*, or coliform bacilli being derived from the intestinal tract or the regional surface mucosa. Today, this type of problem is much more frequent than postpartum sepsis, primarily because of the difference in the aseptic and antiseptic control of normal childbirth (or of medically justified abortion) as compared with that applied to abortions performed under the pressures of expediency.

B. INCUBATION PERIOD.   Usually between one and three days.

C. COMMUNICABLE PERIOD.   While purulent discharges continue. When treatment is prompt and adequate, control of communicability can be achieved within a day or two, but untreated patients may remain infectious for days or weeks.

D. IMMUNITY.   Antibacterial and antistreptolysin immunity may develop against group A *Streptococcus* types if one of these is the cause of the infectious disease, but susceptibility to other kinds of infection remains general.

II. *Control of Active Infection*

A. ISOLATION.   The hospital maternity service must be rigidly protected from transmissible infections. New patients who have developed sepsis following abortion or delivery outside of the hospital are not admitted to the maternity service but are placed in private-room isolation elsewhere in the hospital (usually on the medical or surgical service). Women who develop puerperal fever in the hospital are transferred immediately from clean postpartum areas to a separated area where they can be isolated. Appropriate and adequate antibiotic therapy shortens the period of communicability and relieves the necessity for isolation, but the time required must be decided on an individual basis, preferably with bacteriologic evidence that vaginal discharges are no longer infectious.

B. PRECAUTIONS.   Careful concurrent disinfection is required for vaginal discharges and all equipment soiled by them (bedpans, items required for perineal care, specula, etc.). Infectious patients should not be permitted to share bathroom facilities with others. Soiled clothing and bed linens are placed in individual bags, marked for special handling in their transport to the laundry. When sporebearing bacteria (e.g., *Clostridium* species) have been demonstrated as the causative agents of puerperal sepsis, all equipment (including linens) must be bagged and autoclaved before it is cleaned. Disposable items are placed in closed containers and incinerated; heat-sensitive items may be soaked in strong sporidical disinfectants (see Appendix, p. 658) or subjected to gas sterilization (ethylene oxide). Regardless of the nature of the infection, a clean gown must be worn by each person who attends or examines the patient, and careful hand-washing technique must be observed. Terminal disinfection-cleaning of the patient's unit is necessary.

C. TREATMENT.   Penicillin is the antibiotic drug of choice in cases of hemolytic streptococcal infection. Erythromycin, chloramphenicol, the tetracyclines, or others may be effective for patients who are hypersensitive to penicillin. The therapy of other kinds of bacterial infection is adjusted on the basis of laboratory studies of the antibiotic susceptibility of isolated organisms suspected to be responsible for the patient's disease.

D. CONTROL OF CONTACTS.   Obstetricians, midwives, nurses, and other persons who attend abortions or deliveries should be examined if they have been associated with cases developing puerperal sepsis. Cultures of the nose, throat, skin, or active lesions should be taken to establish the possible source of hemolytic streptococci. Individuals harboring group A streptococci, and those with other acute or chronic infections, should be removed from obstetric duties and treated specifically. Delivery techniques should

be carefully reviewed and environmental sources of infection should also be sought, with particular attention to the sterility of instruments or other equipment involved. These investigations are of particularly urgent concern when an unusual incidence of cases occurs within an individual hospital service or practice.

III. Prevention. The prevention of puerperal fever depends entirely on the maintenance of strict asepsis in obstetric techniques and procedures, and on protection of the patient from possible sources of infection in the nose, throat, hands, or infectious lesions of those who attend or visit her, or of other patients who have communicable diseases.

Urinary Tract Infections

Clinical Diseases. Urinary tract infections frequently occur as a result of urologic procedures carried out in medical offices or in the hospital. The procedures most commonly involved include operations on the bladder, transurethral resection of the prostate, cystoscopy, urethral or ureteral catheterizations, and the use of indwelling catheters for continuous bladder drainage. These infections may involve colonization and inflammation of the urethra (*urethritis*), the bladder (*cystitis*), the ureters (usually an ascending *ureteritis*), the pelvis of the kidney, or the renal parenchyma (*pyelonephritis*). Infections of the lower urinary tract may be mild, transient, and insignificant, but they may also lead to acute or chronic kidney disease, sometimes with permanent damage to renal function. In some instances infectious disease may arise from endogenous sources, but even then it may be superimposed in the sense that procedural damage inflicted on the epithelial lining of the tract provides an opportunity for entry and establishment of commensal organisms from the genitourinary mucosal surfaces. In many cases, however, infection is introduced by faulty technique, by inadequately sterilized or disinfected equipment, or by unwashed hands.

Urinary tract infections are not by any means associated exclusively with such procedures. Kidney infection, for example, may be a complication of the systemic dissemination of microorganisms from any other entry route. Other types of disease or anatomic problems may also predispose to infection of the urinary system. Stones or tumors may be important centers of bacterial localization. The frequency with which urinary tract infection occurs in females may have several explanations. The shortness of the female urethra may be a factor, and with little girls the problem may be related to their tendency to retain urine until the bladder becomes quite distended. In adults, tumors sometimes cause urinary retention also (fibroid tumors of the uterus, in women; prostatic tumors, in men; bladder tumors), and the resulting distention strongly predisposes to cystitis. Pregnant women may have a similar problem as the developing fetus places increasing pressure on the surrounding pelvic structures. During labor, urinary retention is common, and when catheterization is necessary another risk of infection is added to the pre-existing possibilities.

Laboratory Diagnosis
I. Identification of the Organisms. The most common agents of urinary tract infections include many species of the commensalistic Gram-negative enteric bacilli (*Escherichia coli*, *Klebsiella* and *Proteus* species, and *Pseudomonas aeruginosa*); *Staphylococcus aureus*, and sometimes coagulase-negative staphylococci as well; and *Streptococcus faecalis*. *Candida albicans* is sometimes involved, particularly in the infections of older or debilitated persons. Infections of the lower urinary tract are not infrequently mixed, two or more bacterial strains being synergistically active.

A number of pathogenic organisms associated with systemic disease may cause primary or secondary lesions in the kidney, and these organisms may also be identified in the urine. They include the following:

Mycobacterium tuberculosis (see Chap. 14)
Salmonella species (including *S. typhosa*) (see Chap. 19)
Leptospira icterohemorrhagica (and other species) (see Chap. 25)

In addition, the blood fluke *Schistosoma haematobium* characteristically lodges in pelvic veins,

producing ova that migrate through the bladder wall and are excreted in urine.

II. Identification of Patient's Serum Antibodies. Serologic diagnosis generally has no value in infections of the lower urinary tract. The immunology of systemic diseases involving the kidney has been discussed in chapters describing specific infections.

III. Specimens for Diagnosis. Urine specimens for microscopic examination and quantitative culture. (See IV below.)

The practice of collecting catheterized urine specimens for bacteriologic studies has been largely abandoned because of the risk of superimposed infection inherent in the technique. This procedure should be reserved for those cases in which a conclusive demonstration of infection is difficult to obtain with voided specimens.

Clean, midstream urine collections are satisfactory for routine culture. When quantitative results are desired, the urine should be delivered to the laboratory within 30 minutes or refrigerated until transport can be arranged. If specimens are permitted to remain at room temperature for periods longer than one-half hour, contaminating organisms from the external genitourinary mucosa may multiply freely, providing quantitative results that are open to misinterpretation.

Satisfactory specimens can be collected after careful cleaning of the meatus and external mucosa, using an antiseptic solution, such as a quaternary ammonium compound, a 1 to 2 per cent dilution of a synthetic phenol, or a bisphenol. The first and last portions of urine voided should be discarded, only the midstream portion being collected in a *sterile* container possessing a cover. Male collections offer little difficulty, but when urine samples are collected from women, care must be taken not to permit contamination of the open lip of the vessel by surrounding unsterile surfaces. The labia should first be carefully cleansed, the first passage of urine is discarded, and then the collecting vessel is held close to, but not touching, the meatus, the patient being positioned so that a vertical stream can be delivered directly into the container.

IV. Special Laboratory Tests. *Qualitative techniques* for examination or culture of urine are adequate when pathogenic species such as the tubercle bacillus or *Salmonella* are suspected, because these organisms are of diagnostic significance regardless of their numbers in a given specimen.

Quantitative culture techniques are used to establish the significance of staphylococci, streptococci, or Gram-negative enteric bacilli in urine. These techniques and their interpretation are discussed in detail in Chapter 4 (pp. 74 to 76) and should be carefully reviewed at this point.

Antibiotic susceptibility testing is of value only when it is performed on pure cultures of isolated organisms present in significant numbers in clean urine specimens.

Epidemiology

I. Communicability of Infection

A. RESERVOIR, SOURCES, AND TRANSMISSION ROUTES. See the initial discussion of urinary tract infections.

B. INCUBATION PERIOD. Generally short (one to five days).

C. COMMUNICABLE PERIOD. Continues for as long as the urine contains infectious microorganisms in significant numbers.

D. IMMUNITY. Susceptibility is general, and immunity does not usually develop.

II. Control of Active Infection

A. ISOLATION. It is usually not necessary to isolate patients with urinary tract infections. However, patients being treated at home should be carefully instructed as to the necessity for personal hygiene in shared bathroom facilities. Hospitalized patients should not be permitted to share bathrooms with other patients until antibiotic therapy has significantly reduced the numbers of organisms shed in the urine. This is particularly important in the case of renal tuberculosis and in salmonellosis.

B. PRECAUTIONS. Concurrent disinfection or sterilization procedures should be carried out for all instruments or equipment used for urologic examination or treatment. This includes bedpans, catheters, cystoscopes, and items used for perineal nursing care. (See Appendix, p. 652, for recommended methods.) Gowns should be worn by personnel performing catheterizations or other urologic procedures, and careful hand-washing

should be practiced before and after these techniques. Soiled bed linens and clothing should be placed in individual bags marked for special handling in their transport to the laundry. Terminal cleaning of the patient's unit may be routine, but bathrooms should receive special attention and be cleaned with disinfectant cleansers.

C. TREATMENT. The choice of antibiotic therapy depends on the results of laboratory studies identifying the significant organism(s) and testing their susceptibility to antimicrobial drugs. Supportive measures often include the use of antiseptic solutions as bladder irrigants and drugs that maintain the pH of the urine at alkaline levels that are suppressive for most bacteria.

D. CONTROL OF CONTACTS. The source of possible contamination of the urinary tract should be sought, particularly when the incidence of cases suggests extraneous reservoirs persisting within a urologic service or practice. Techniques should be carefully reviewed with all personnel and corrective procedures instituted as indicated. Sterilization and disinfection methods should be tested for efficacy by bacteriologic techniques.

III. Prevention. The prevention of urinary tract infections associated with urologic procedures is dependent on adequate sterilization or disinfection of equipment, especially catheters and cystoscopes, and on the careful maintenance of aseptic technique.

A. STERILIZATION OR DISINFECTION OF EQUIPMENT

1. *Cystoscopes.* These instruments cannot be sterilized by the use of heat in autoclaves or ovens, because their delicate lens and prism systems are quickly damaged beyond repair by such methods. They can be sterilized by ethylene oxide gas, however, and this is the method of choice when gas sterilizing equipment is available. The method is expensive and time-consuming, requiring an adequate supply of instruments to outlast the four-hour period of sterilization and a matching period for the dissipation of the toxic gas from instrument packs (see Chap. 10, pp. 231 to 232). Gas sterilization is not destructive to cystoscopes, however, and this advantage must be weighed,

together with safety factors, against the expense and inconvenience of the method.

The disinfection of cystoscopes is also possible, but it requires meticulous attention to detail, including preliminary cleansing and the proper application of effective germicides. The latter should always be chosen with the possibility in mind that tuberculous infection may be present though unsuspected (see Appendix, p. 658) for suggested methods of disinfection of lensed instruments).

2. *Catheters.* Most urethral and ureteral catheters can be successfully sterilized in the autoclave (20 minutes at 121° C, or 250° F). This is particularly true of soft rubber, latex, and woven-base catheters (see Appendix, p. 656). Hard rubber, "shellac," and "web" catheters may be chemically disinfected, but again the choice of a routine should take into consideration the possibility of unsuspected tuberculous infection (see Appendix, pp. 658 to 660).

The problem of sterilization and disinfection of catheters can also be solved today by the purchase and use of presterilized disposable polyethylene catheterizing equipment. Its expense must be weighed against the cost of superimposed infection. For the patient this can mean many days or weeks of physical discomfort and financial loss. In hospital and medical practice, the added price of avoidable infection is incalculable.

B. ASEPTIC TECHNIQUE IN UROLOGIC NURSING PRACTICE. *The technique of catheterization* is frequently the responsibility of nurses or of orderlies working under nursing supervision. They must carefully apply the principles of asepsis in their practice of this technique if the chain of procedures involved in the sterilization or disinfection of equipment is to have final value for the patient. The precautions taken should be of the same order as those required for a surgical dressing. Before initiating the procedure, the nurse removes the necessary equipment from a supply cart (to which she does not return lest she contaminate its remaining supplies), positions the patient with proper illumination, and places the equipment within convenient reach. After thoroughly washing her hands and donning

sterile gloves, she cleans the urinary meatus and surrounding mucosal surfaces, then proceeds to insert the catheter with maximum care to avoid contaminating it by contact with the patient's skin or nearby objects. A skillful touch must be developed for this procedure, so that the risk of damage to delicate mucosal surfaces is minimized. When the procedure is completed, used materials are discarded into a container that can be closed for transport to an incinerator or an autoclave, and the nurse carefully washes her hands once more before continuing to the next patient or to other duties.

Indwelling catheters are often an infectious hazard because bacterial infection may spread in retrograde fashion from contaminated drainage bottles, backward along the course of the tubing. This hazard can be reduced by using a closed system that does not permit air contamination of the contents of the drainage container, or contact between the catheter and the vessel's contents. Presterilized plastic bags and catheter tubing are currently available as a solution to the problem, but they must be given frequent attention to assure that the tubing remains in proper position within the patient's bladder and also at the upper end of the collecting bag. The catheter tubing should never be allowed to come loose from the collecting vessel and hang free at its distal end where it can be contaminated from the air or by any surface it touches in its random swinging. Also, the bag should not be permitted to fill to the point of contact with the delivery end of the tubing, so that retrograde contamination of the bladder becomes possible for this reason.

The maintenance of asepsis is the province of all who are responsible for the care and treatment of patients with urologic problems. Many of the techniques are applied by physicians, but the attendant nurse must remain the epidemiologic guardian against infection, supplying safe materials and equipment and establishing an aseptic area in which the urologist can work with final concern only for his own contribution to the patient's welfare. From the moment of his participation in any urologic procedure, however, the physician assumes the responsibility and liability for his patient.

Viral Hepatitis (Serum Hepatitis and Infectious Hepatitis)

The Clinical Diseases. Viral hepatitis may be caused by one of two types of viruses, which display certain differences in their physical properties and epidemiologic patterns but induce the same clinical syndrome of liver disease with jaundice. In clinical practice, recognition of the specific causative agent of hepatitis is based on differences in the incubation period, the character of symptoms at the onset, and the patient's history of exposure to the different sources of the two viruses. A diagnosis of *infectious hepatitis*, or *viral hepatitis A*, is made in cases that have an abrupt onset of fever and chills and a history of natural exposure, via intestinal or possibly respiratory entry, not more than six weeks previously. (The average incubation period for virus A is about three weeks.) A diagnosis of *serum hepatitis*, or *viral hepatitis B*, is made when the disease has a slow, insidious onset, jaundice beginning after a period of only slight malaise with little or no fever; there is no history of natural exposure, but not less than seven weeks previously there was an opportunity for parenteral transfer of virus B from an infected human source. (The average incubation period for virus B is 12 to 14 weeks, but it may be as long as 25 weeks.) The only known source of serum hepatitis virus is the blood of infected persons, but the transfer can be made not only by the injection of a volume of blood or blood products (serum, plasma, thrombin) but also by the introduction of a mere trace of infectious material on a contaminated needle, stylet, or other penetrating instrument.

Infectious hepatitis (virus A, or I.H. virus) is discussed in Chapter 20 (pp. 458 to 462) together with other viral diseases of enteric origin which have an intestinal route of entry and initial localization. It should be noted, however, that

Table 29–2. Differences in the Properties of Infectious Hepatitis and Serum Hepatitis Viruses

	Virus A Infectious Hepatitis	Virus B Serum Hepatitis
Transmission	Via gastrointestinal or parenteral routes (possibly respiratory)	Parenteral route the only one known
Source of virus	Feces, urine, blood (contaminated water, milk, food, shellfish, needles, syringes, stylets)	Blood only (contaminated needles, syringes, stylets)
Incubation period	10–40 days, average 3 weeks	60–175 days, average 12–14 weeks
Onset of symptoms	Abrupt, fever, chill	Insidious, fever less than 100° F, chill rare
Immunization (passive prophylaxis)	Gamma globulin	Questionable value
Natural active acquired immunity	For virus A only	For virus B only
Isolation	At least for the first week of illness	None required
Resistance of virus to heat*	Resists 56° C for 30 min	Resists 56° C for 30 min Resists 60° C for 4 hr Destroyed at 60° C in 10 hr (in albumin)
Resistance of virus to: Merthiolate (1:2000)* Chlorine, 1 ppm*	 Not known Resistant	 Resistant Not known

* Data from: *Progress in Medical Virology*. Hafner Publishing Co., New York, 1962, Vol. 4, p. 91.

the virus of this disease is present in the blood stream as well as in feces, and that it can be transmitted by the transfusion of blood or by needles and syringes contaminated after use for an infectious patient, as well as by the fecal-oral route. Clinically, the two viral agents display no differences in their capacity to induce serious liver damage. The mortality rates for serum hepatitis are often higher, however (the range is from 6 to 12 per cent), because of the nature of its transmission and the fact that it so often occurs in persons who have an underlying illness or debility.

Laboratory Diagnosis of Serum Hepatitis

I. Identification of the Organism. This virus, like that of infectious hepatitis, has not yet been successfully isolated and identified. Its properties have been studied in human volunteers and compared with those of virus A. Serum hepatitis virus B (S.H. virus) is more resistant to heat than is the I.H. virus, and differences have been noted in the response of the two viruses to disinfectants. Table 29–2 presents a summary of the differences in the properties of the viral hepatitis agents.

II. Identification of Patient's Serum Antibodies. Circulating antibodies appear during the course of the disease and appear to confer protection

against the specific virus agent but not against other hepatitis viruses. Thus, patients who have had infectious hepatitis remain susceptible to serum hepatitis but not to virus A, and vice versa. It is possible, however, that there are several strains of serum hepatitis virus B, and that these do not confer cross-immunity. The evidence for this is the fact that persons who are frequently exposed to the risk of serum hepatitis, notably narcotic addicts, have experienced multiple attacks of the disease.

Adequate methods for the in vitro recognition of serum antibodies must await the development of methods to isolate and propagate the virus.

III. Specimens for Diagnosis.   Laboratory tests are not available. The diagnosis is made on clinical grounds, supported by tests for abnormal liver function.

Epidemiology of Serum Hepatitis

I. Communicability of Infection

A. Reservoir, Sources, and Transmission Routes.   The human reservoir is the only one known for the viruses of hepatitis. In the case of serum hepatitis it has been estimated that approximately 2 to 4 per cent of persons (in the United States) carry the virus in the blood without evidence of clinical disease. These infected individuals, as well as those with a history of active infection, constitute the principal sources. Narcotics addicts provide a large reservoir for this infection and are a particular problem because of the frequency with which they offer themselves as paid blood donors. Blood banks that purchase blood are under a particular obligation to screen such donors with meticulous care.

The virus may be transferred by any route of parenteral inoculation (subcutaneous, intramuscular, or intravenous) of traces or large volumes of blood, serum, or plasma from an infected person. Contaminated syringes and needles are commonly involved as transmitting agents, but other items have also been incriminated, such as improperly sterilized stylets, lancets, and tattooing needles.

B. Incubation Period.   60 to 175 days, usually 12 to 14 weeks.

C. Communicable Period.   In experiments with human volunteers, blood taken from infected persons 12 to 13 weeks before the onset of symptoms and up to eight days following the appearance of jaundice has produced serum hepatitis. Infected persons who have served as blood donors have been demonstrated to be capable of transmitting infection for many years.

D. Immunity.   See part II under Laboratory Diagnosis of Serum Hepatitis (p. 626).

II. Control of Active Infection

A. Isolation.   Not necessary, provided the disease has been clinically distinguished from infectious hepatitis.

B. Precautions.   Syringes, needles, and any other equipment contaminated with the patient's blood must be carefully sterilized before reuse or discarded for incineration. Suitable sterilization techniques* are:

1. Autoclaving for 30 minutes at 121° C (250° F)
2. Dry heat for one hour at 180° C (356° F) or two hours at 170° C (338° F)
3. Boiling in water for 30 minutes (*only* if other sterilizing methods are not available)

C. Treatment.   There is no specific antimicrobial therapy for serum hepatitis.

D. Control of Contacts.   A search is made for the source of infection, particularly if such source is associated with blood banks, clinics, medical offices, or hospitals where large numbers of people are bled as donors, treated with parenterally administered medications, or given blood transfusions. Case reports are helpful in determining the incidence of the problem and the techniques required to control it.

III. Prevention

A. Control of Blood Donors.   Persons who have themselves received a blood transfusion

---

* See "Guide to Control of Infections in Hospitals," New York State Department of Health, N. Y., p. 36.

within the past six months are not accepted as donors. Persons who give a history of clinical hepatitis at any time in the past are rejected as are those known or suspected to be addicted to narcotics.

The names of patients developing posttransfusion hepatitis are reported to local health agencies, together with the identification numbers of donors who supplied blood in each case. The health agency then circulates to all blood banks a current list of patients and donors involved so that the banks can check all future donors against this record.

B. CONTROL OF BLOOD OR BLOOD PRODUCTS. The transfusion of whole blood is limited to those for whom it represents a therapeutic necessity. The use of pooled blood products should be particularly limited, because the statistical chance of virus infection is increased by pooling.

Plasma and plasma pools should be stored for a six-month period at a warm temperature (32° C, or 90° F, is recommended*) before being used.

C. CONTROL OF EQUIPMENT. Disposable, presterilized needles, syringes, lancets, tubing, and blood bottles should be used when possible.

Heat sterilization of nondisposable items must be carried out with accuracy (see II, B under Epidemiology of Serum Hepatitis).

Every injection or finger puncture must be performed with fresh sterile equipment.

D. PROPHYLAXIS. The use of gamma globulin as prophylactic therapy for persons who have received blood transfusions is of questionable value, and usually impractical.

Questions

1. Why are hospital patients more susceptible to infection?
2. List the sources of exogenous infection following chest surgery; orthopedic surgery; gynecologic and obstetric surgery.
3. Why does instrumentation through mucosal surfaces present the risk of infection?
4. What procedures are most frequently associated with complicating urinary infections?
5. List five reasons that account for the hypodermic needle being directly or indirectly responsible for infection.
6. What is puerperal fever? What organisms frequently cause this disease?
7. Why are the names Semmelweis and Holmes associated with puerperal fever?
8. What nursing management is required in puerperal fever?
9. What other types of disease or anatomic problems may predispose to infection of the urinary tract?
10. What are the nurse's responsibilities in the use of indwelling catheters?
11. List the differences in the properties of infectious and serum hepatitis.

---

* Allen, J. G.: Serum Hepatitis: A Study in Retrospect, *Stanford Med. Bull.*, **18**: 40–46, 1960.

30 Infections of Endogenous Origin

This chapter recapitulates some of the infectious diseases of man that are most probably derived from endogenous sources and arise because of deficiencies in the normal mechanisms of resistance. These deficiencies may be the temporary result of minor or major traumatic injury, or they may be due to disturbances in the normal physiologic responses of the body because of underlying disease. The infections are summarized in the first part of the chapter according to the area of the body involved. The normal microbial flora of each area is reviewed (see Chap. 5 also), and the common infectious problems associated with the region are listed. A few infections that have not been discussed previously in other contexts are described in more detail.

In the second part of the chapter, the infectious diseases of infants are summarized. These include infections acquired during intrauterine life or at the time of birth and the "nursery" diseases that may be severe problems during the first days of postnatal life. As we have seen (Chap. 19, pp. 435 to 439, and Chap. 23, pp. 507 to 508), these diseases of infants are caused by microorganisms transferred to them by adults, the causative species being in many instances indigenous commensals of adult skin or mucosal surfaces. (The outstanding exceptions to this are the agents

of rubella, syphilis, and gonorrhea, which are pathogenic for adults and are transmitted to infants either in utero [rubella and syphilis] or at the time of birth [gonococcal ophthalmia neonatorum]). In a sense, therefore, the common infections of infants have an "endogenous" origin among the adults with whom they have intimate contact, an important point for nurses and mothers alike to remember. Babies are susceptible to these infections because their mechanisms for resistance are relatively undeveloped at the time of birth, their surface tissues are delicate and easily penetrated, and their physiologic adjust-

ment to commensalistic microorganisms is slow when they first emerge from the uterus to meet the outside world and its microbial life.

The final discussion of this chapter deals with a common infectious disease of unknown origin, whose agent has not been identified. This is *infectious mononucleosis*, long presumed to be a viral disease having an oral-respiratory entry route. Because the agent of this clinical syndrome has not been identified and its transmissibility has not been clearly demonstrated, even with human volunteers, it has been left in an unclassified position in this text.

Summary of Regional Endogenous Infections*

Skin and Nails

Normal Flora: Corynebacteria (diphtheroid bacilli)
Staphylococcus epidermidis (sometimes *S. aureus* also)
Bacillus species (aerobic sporeformers)
Streptococcus viridans
Nonhemolytic streptococci
Streptococcus faecalis
Gram-negative enteric bacilli (coliform type) (especially on the skin of the groin and buttocks)
Yeasts and fungi (especially in the axillae and groin or under the nails)
Nonpathogenic mycobacteria (especially on the genitalia or in the external ear canal where sebaceous secretions are abundant)

Common Endogenous Infections of Skin and Nails

Acne
Pimples   } *Staphylococcus aureus*
Furuncles   (see Chap. 23, pp. 511 to 517)
Carbuncles

Decubitus ulcers } Infection often mixed: Staphylococci, streptococci, and aerobic
Varicose ulcers   Gram-negative enteric bacilli (coliforms and *Pseudomonas*)
                   (see Chap. 5, pp. 94 to 95, Chap. 12, pp. 292 to 295, and
                   Chap. 23, pp. 511 to 517)

Pilonidal Abscesses. A *pilonidal cyst* is formed by an abnormally diverted growth of hair in a subcutaneous position, usually in a nest formation. This type of lesion is seen most often in the skin of the buttocks adjacent to the rectum, sometimes

* Diseases that have not been described previously are placed in box outline.

with the formation of a rectal fistula or sinus tract. Such cysts are extremely subject to infection, usually with the development of a suppurative abscess. Aerobic and anaerobic intestinal organisms, as well as staphylococci from the skin, are frequently found in mixed infections in pilonidal abscesses.

Species that may be involved include anaerobic streptococci and *Bacteroides;* coliform bacilli, *Proteus* species, *Streptococcus faecalis* (enterococcus), and *S. aureus.*

These infections are usually treated by surgical incision and drainage, sometimes with added antibiotic therapy. Nursing precautions would be the same as for any draining lesion, with concurrent disinfection of discharges and careful attention to the bagging and transport of contaminated bed linen or clothing. The patient should be isolated if he is on a surgical service or placed in partial isolation in other hospital areas, until the drainage is no longer infectious.

Paronychia	*Candida albicans* (Chap. 17, pp. 406 to 410), *S. aureus* (Chap. 23, pp. 511 to 517). Sometimes other skin organisms
Onychia	*Candida albicans* (Chap. 17, pp. 406 to 410). Other fungi, usually the pathogenic dermatophytes (Chap. 23, pp. 521 to 530)

Eyelids and Conjunctiva

Normal Flora: Corynebacteria (diphtheroid bacilli)
Staphylococcus epidermidis (*S. aureus*, on skin)
Nonhemolytic streptococci
Neisseria species
Moraxella species

Common Endogenous Infections of Eyelids and Conjunctiva

Conjunctivitis   *Moraxella* species (see Chap. 23, p. 509)
Staphylococci (usually *S. aureus*) (see Chap. 23, p. 509)
Streptococci (see Chap. 23, p. 509)
(Pneumococcal and *Hemophilus* species from the upper respiratory tract are frequent agents also)

Sties.   A sty is a small abscess of a sebaceous crypt or hair follicle (usually that of an eyelash) at the edge of an eyelid. Like pimples and boils, this type of abscess is generally caused by *S. aureus* infection.

Sties are best treated by the application of hot compresses to hasten suppuration and drainage to the surface. Care must be taken to prevent extension of the infection to the conjunctiva. Mild antiseptic solutions formulated for use on this delicate tissue are applied as conjunctival irrigants.

The patient should be instructed to avoid possible spread of the infection by keeping his hands scrupulously clean before and after he applies self-treatment, and by refraining from touching or rubbing the eye at other times.

Oral and Upper Respiratory Mucosa

Normal Flora: Corynebacteria (diphtheroid bacilli)
Streptococcus viridans
Streptococcus salivarius
Nonhemolytic streptococci
Staphylococci (including *S. aureus*)
Pneumococci
Neisseria species (sometimes including the meningococcus)
Hemophilus species
Lactobacilli   ⎫
Vibrio species (anaerobic)   ⎪
Bacteroides species (anaerobic)   ⎪   Usually found in the
Fusobacterium fusiforme (anaerobic)   ⎬   mouth, especially the
Actinomyces species (anaerobic)   ⎪   gingival tissues
Spirochetes (*Treponema* and *Borrelia* species)   ⎪
Yeasts (including *Candida albicans*)   ⎪
Mycoplasma species and PPLO   ⎪
Herpesvirus (simplex)   ⎭

Common Endogenous Infections of the Mouth or Upper Respiratory Tract

Pharyngitis   ⎫
Laryngitis   ⎪   When these infections are of *endogenous* origin, the organisms most
Sinusitis   ⎬   usually involved are *S. aureus*, streptococci (other than those of
Otitis media ⎪   hemolytic group A), pneumococci, and *Hemophilus* species (see
Tonsillitis   ⎪   Chap. 14, pp. 312, 315, and 319)
Adenoiditis   ⎭

Trench Mouth (*Vincent's Angina*).   This is a painful infection of the oral and pharyngeal mucosa (extension to the lower respiratory tract may sometimes occur as well). It is a mixed synergistic infection involving anaerobic fusiform bacilli and spirochetes of the *Borrelia* genus as the major offenders. Anaerobic vibrios and streptococci may also play a role. These organisms are all normally present in the deep recesses of gingival tissue. When the latter become debilitated or chronically ischemic for any reason (dietary factors, neglected teeth, and poor mouth care may play a role in this), these organisms may have an opportunity to overgrow, forming localized or extending lesions, often characterized by the formation of a pseudomembrane.

Fusobacterium fusiforme (see Chap. 12, p. 293) is a Gram-negative, straight or slightly curved, nonmotile, anaerobic bacillus. *Borrelia vincentii* is a spirochete having loose, coarse, irregular spirals. (See Chap. 12, p. 296.) Both can be seen in Gram-stained smears of the lesions (the spirochete is also Gram-negative), usually in enormously larger numbers than may be seen in smears taken from the normal mouth or gums.

Trench mouth is directly transmissible to others, particularly those who may have areas of local injury in their mouths where the transmitted organisms can gain a foothold. Usually intimate contact is necessary, as in kissing or by immediate

oral transfer from contaminated dishes, eating utensils, or other articles carried to the mouth.

The infection is treated with penicillin or other antibiotic drugs, sometimes with arsenical compounds.

Prevention and control depend on adequate oral hygiene and dietary habits that support the health of oral tissues. Nursing precautions include the concurrent disinfection of oral secretions and of objects contaminated by them.

Thrush   *Candida albicans* (see Chap. 17, pp. 406 to 410)
Actinomycosis, cervicofacial   *Actinomyces israeli* (see Chap. 17, p. 405)

Parenteral Infections Derived from Commensal Organisms in the Mouth or Throat

Secondary bacterial pneumonia	Streptococci Staphylococci *Hemophilus* species *Klebsiella* species	(Chap. 14, pp. 318 to 320)
Secondary bacterial meningitis	*Hemophilus influenzae* Pneumococci Streptococci Staphylococci Enteric bacilli	(Chap. 14, pp. 325 to 326)
Actinomycosis, thoracic or abdominal	*Actinomyces israeli* (Chap. 17, p. 405)	
Subacute bacterial endocarditis	*Strep. viridans* *Strep. faecalis* *Candida albicans* Enteric bacilli	(Chap. 14, pp. 331 to 333)

The Gastrointestinal Tract

Normal Flora: *Streptococcus faecalis*
Streptococcus viridans
Anaerobic streptococci
Staphylococci
Lactobacilli
Escherichia coli (aerobic)
Klebsiella species (aerobic)
Aerobacter species (aerobic)
Proteus species (aerobic)
Pseudomonas species (aerobic)
Citrobacter species (intermediate coliforms)
Bacteroides species (anaerobic)
Clostridium species (anaerobic)
Yeasts (including *Candida albicans*)
ECHO viruses
Coxsackie viruses

Common Endogenous Infections of the Gastrointestinal Tract

Pseudomembranous colitis   *S. aureus*
                                           Pseudomonas aeruginosa $\Big\}$ (Chap. 5, pp. 94 to 95)
                                           Proteus species

Candidiasis   *Candida albicans* (Chap. 17, pp. 406 to 410)

Parenteral Infections Derived from Commensal Organisms in the Intestinal Tract

Subacute bacterial endocarditis *Strep. faecalis*
                                             Strep. viridans $\Bigg\}$ (Chap. 14, pp. 331 to 333)
                                             Candida albicans
                                             Enteric bacilli

Wound infections,
    following abdominal surgery *S. aureus*
                                             Anaerobic streptococci
                                             Strep. faecalis
                                             Strep. viridans $\Bigg\}$ (Chap. 29)
                                             Aerobic enteric bacilli
                                             Bacteroides species
                                             Clostridium species
                                             Candida albicans

The Genitourinary Tract

Normal Flora: *External genitalia, both sexes:*
    Staphylococci
    Streptococcus faecalis
    Nonhemolytic streptococci
    Streptococcus viridans
    Gram-negative enteric bacilli (aerobic coliform type)
    Mycoplasma species and PPLO
    Treponema species (other than *T. pallidum*)
    Leptospira species (other than *L. icterohemorrhagica*)
    Borrelia species
    Yeasts (including *Candida albicans*)
    Trichomonas vaginalis (especially normal male genitalia)
    Herpesvirus (simplex)
The vagina:
    Lactobacilli
    Streptococci (aerobic and anaerobic)
    Staphylococci
    Gram-negative enteric bacilli (aerobic coliform type)
    Clostridium species
    Bacteroides species
    Listeria monocytogenes
    Yeasts (including *Candida albicans*)

Common Endogenous Infections of the Genitourinary Tract

Urinary tract infections   Gram-negative enteric bacilli ⎫
                                Streptococcus faecalis   ⎪
                                Nonhemolytic streptococci   ⎬ (Chap. 29, pp. 622 to 625)
                                Staphylococci   ⎪
                                Candida albicans   ⎭

                                Mycoplasma species (Chap. 16, pp. 384 to 387)

                   Vaginitis ⎫ *Trichomonas vaginalis* (Chap. 23, p. 506)
                   Prostatitis ⎬ *Candida albicans* (Chap. 17, pp. 406 to 410)
                   Cervicitis ⎭ Various bacteria (Chap. 5, p. 93)
                                  Mycoplasma species (Chap. 16, p. 384)

Parenteral Infections Derived from Commensal Organisms in the Genitourinary Tract

Puerperal fever   ⎧ Normal flora
                                   ⎨   (and hemolytic *Streptococcus*, group A)
                                   ⎩   (Chap. 29, pp. 619 to 622)

Listeriosis   *Listeria monocytogenes* (Chap. 14, pp. 323 to 325)
    (meningitis in adults, granulo-
    matosis infantiseptica in infants)

Subacute bacterial endocarditis   ⎰ *Strep. faecalis* ⎱ (Chap. 14, pp. 331 to 333)
                                     ⎱ *Strep. viridans* ⎰

Joint infections, and   *Mycoplasma* species (Chap. 16, p. 384)
    deep tissue abscesses

Summary of the Infectious Diseases of Infants

Congenital Infections

Syphilis   *Treponema pallidum* (Chap. 23, p. 497)
Listeriosis   *Listeria monocytogenes* (Chap. 14, pp. 323 to 325)
    (granulomatosis
    infantiseptica)
Rubella syndrome   Rubella virus (German measles) (Chap. 15, pp. 369 to 370)

Toxoplasmosis. This is a disease caused by a protozoan organism, *Toxoplasma gondii*, which has a worldwide distribution among adult human beings (and animals). In postnatal life *Toxoplasma* infections are generally either inapparent or mild and localized to lymph nodes. Chorioretinitis, muscle involvements, and cerebral infections are sometimes seen in adults, but severe disease occurs more frequently during prenatal development of the fetus as a result of inapparent maternal infection. The organism localizes in the parenchymal cells of developing organs, or in the RE system, resulting in liver disease, splenomegaly, or brain damage. Intrauterine infections may be fatal, or infants may be born with severe

disease, displaying symptoms such as hydrocephaly or microcephaly, psychomotor disturbances, or jaundice.

The organism can sometimes be demonstrated in body fluids or tissues as a crescent-shaped body with a centrally placed nucleus, about the size of a trypanosome but without an undulating membrane or a flagellum ($6 \times 3\mu$). It is classified with the Sporozoa (Chap. 12, p. 300). In body fluids it is usually found in extracellular positions, but in tissues numerous organisms may be seen clustered together within parenchymal cells or in cyst formations. The laboratory diagnosis is made by visualization of the organism in stained smears, by fluorescent antibody techniques, or by the "Sabin dye test." The latter identifies the patient's serum antibodies, which inhibit the uptake of a vital stain (methylene blue) by living *Toxoplasma* cells.

Numerous animal species (cats, dogs, rodents, farm animals, and birds) appear to form the reservoir for this organism. The source of human infection is not known, and the transmission route of postnatal infection has not been identified. Infant infections are acquired transplacentally or at birth from mothers in an early stage of infection; otherwise the disease is not directly communicable from person to person.

Adult patients with mild acquired toxoplasmosis do not require isolation. In view of the paucity of information of the transmission routes, however, it is recommended that infants with acute congenital infections or adults with severe disease be isolated, and that nursing precautions be centered on the possibility of respiratory or conjunctival spread.

The efficacy of specific therapy has not been proved. Sulfonamides combined with pyrimethamine are in current use, but these have little value in severe congenital infections.

The prevention or control of this disease remains a matter of trial and error until its source and transmission route have been better defined. An unusual incidence of cases may suggest an animal or avian source, or an arthropod vector, and point to a reservoir that can be eradicated or avoided.

Infections Acquired at Birth

Gonococcal ophthalmia neonatorum	*Neisseria gonorrhoeae* (Chap. 23, pp. 501 to 506)
Herpesvirus infections	Herpes simplex virus (Chap. 23, pp. 511 and 520)
Inclusion conjunctivitis	A "*Bedsonia*" agent (Chap. 23, p. 510)
Coxsackie infections	Coxsackie viruses (Chaps. 15 and 20)

Pneumocystis carinii **Infection.**   This is a protozoan disease caused by a member of the subphylum Sporozoa (Chap. 12, p. 300). It produces an interstitial pneumonia in man and has been identified most frequently in newborn infants, particularly

those under stress of premature birth, malnutrition, or toxic medication (steroids, antitumor drugs, or prolonged dosage with antibiotics).

Diagnosis must be made by recognition of the organisms, packed into the mononuclear and polymorphonuclear cells of alveolar exudates or in the foamy exudate itself. Sputum, pulmonary biopsy, or lung tissue obtained at autopsy has been the source of laboratory information.

This organism is thought to have a reservoir among domestic animals and rodents, but its sources and transmission routes are not known. Inapparent adult infections are probably the source for newborn infants (mothers or nursery attendants).

Specific therapy has not been developed, but antiprotozoal drugs (quinine and its derivatives, or emetine) may be effective.

Prevention and control measures must await definition of the route of transmission, sources, and reservoirs of infection.

Neonatal Infections

	Pathogenic serotypes of *E. coli*	(Chap. 19, pp. 435 to 439)
	Proteus species	
	Pseudomonas species	
Diarrhea (epidemic)	*Strep. faecalis*	
	Staphylococci	
	Clostridium species	
	ECHO viruses	(Chap. 20, pp. 456 to 458)
	Coxsackie viruses	

Myocarditis
Encephalomyocarditis
Skin infections (pemphigus neonatorum)
Pneumonia
Septicemia

Coxsackie virus (Chap. 20, pp. 456 to 458)
Staphylococcus aureus (Chap. 23, pp. 511 to 517)

Infectious Mononucleosis: A Disease of Unknown Origin

The Clinical Disease. This is an acute disease, apparently infectious, that is characterized by fever, pharyngitis, tonsillitis, cervical lymphadenopathy, and in some instances disease of the spleen and liver (with jaundice). It is rarely fatal, but death has been associated with rupture of the spleen.

Laboratory Diagnosis

I. Identification of the Organism. The agent of this disease has not been identified but is thought to be a virus. Experiments with human volunteers have not resulted in a clear demonstration of the transmissibility of this syndrome.

II. Identification of Patient's Serum Antibodies. "Heterophil" antibodies, capable of agglutinating sheep red blood cells, develop during the course of this disease and rise to high titer. Merely finding these agglutinins in the patient's serum does not diagnose infectious mononucleosis with certainty, however, because serum from normal persons may also agglutinate sheep erythrocytes. Fortunately, agglutinin absorption will distinguish these two types of heterophil antibody. *Normal* heterophil antibody is removed (absorbed) when the serum is mixed with guinea pig tissue cells, but not when

the serum is mixed with beef erythrocytes. The heterophil antibody of *infectious mononucleosis* is absorbed by beef erythrocytes but not to any appreciable extent by guinea pig tissues. Thus, two serum samples giving the same heterophil titer can be differentiated as in the following examples:

Heterophil Titer Before Absorption	Titer After Absorption with		Diagnosis
	Beef RBC	Guinea Pig Tissue Cells	
1:224	1:224	0	Normal serum
1:224	0	1:112	Infectious mononucleosis

III. Specimens for Diagnosis.   Serum samples for heterophil agglutination.

Blood counts show marked lymphocytosis with many abnormal lymphocytes.

Chemical analysis of blood reveals dysfunction of liver parenchyma.

Epidemiology

I. Communicability of Infection.   Man appears to be the reservoir of this disease and to transmit it through respiratory secretions. Contact must generally be intimate (infectious mononucleosis is sometimes called the "kissing disease" because it appears so frequently among young adults who have been in direct contact).

The incubation period among contacts appears to require two to six weeks, with a communicable period beginning before symptoms appear and extending for the duration of clinical signs of infection in the oral and pharyngeal mucosa.

This disease is most common among children and young adults. Immunity may develop in childhood and persist thereafter, accounting for the fact that infection seldom occurs in persons who have passed their middle twenties.

II. Control of Active Infection.   It is not necessary to isolate cases of infectious mononucleosis, but nursing precautions should include the concurrent disinfection of oral and respiratory discharges, or articles soiled by them.

There is no specific therapy for this disease, and its epidemiologic control or prevention still awaits scientific demonstration of the agent, its sources, and transmission routes.

Questions

1. What is a pilonidal cyst?
2. What is a sty?
3. What organisms cause Vincent's angina?
4. List several congenital infections.
5. List several infections acquired at birth.
6. List several neonatal infections.
7. How is infectious mononucleosis diagnosed?

Questions for Discussion — Section VII

Mr. Woodrow, aged 69, has poor peripheral circulation. He is now hospitalized with a large recurrent infected leg ulcer.

1. What makes Mr. Woodrow a likely candidate for infection?

2. Basic techniques of asepsis are followed by the nurse in dressing Mr. Woodrow's leg. Explain the reason for the measures.

3. Bandage scissors are a traditional and much-used part of the nurse's uniform and equipment. What hazards do you see in this practice?

References — Section VII

Textbooks

Conant, Norman F., Smith, D. T., Baker, R. D., Callaway, J. L., and Martin, D. S.: *Manual of Clinical Mycology*. W. B. Saunders, Philadelphia and London, 1954.

Dubos, René J., and Hirsch, James G. (eds.): *Bacterial and Mycotic Infections of Man*, 4th ed. J., B. Lippincott, Philadelphia, 1965.

Faust, Ernest, and Russell, Paul Farr: *Craig and Faust's Clinical Parasitology*, 7th ed. Lea & Febiger, Philadelphia, 1965.

Horsfall, Frank L., Jr., and Tamm, Igor (eds.): *Viral and Rickettsial Infections of Man*, 4th ed. J. B. Lippincott, Philadelphia, 1965.

Hunter, George W., Frye, William W., and Swartzwelder, J. Clyde: *A Manual of Tropical Medicine*, 4th ed. W. B. Saunders, Philadelphia and London, 1966.

Jawetz, Ernest, Melnick, J. L., and Adelberg, E. A.: *Review of Medical Microbiology*, 7th ed. Lange Medical Publications, Los Altos, Calif., 1966.

Perkins, J. J.: *Principles and Methods of Sterilization*. Charles C Thomas, Springfield, Ill., 1956.

Pertinent References

GENERAL — ARTHROPOD VECTORS

Pictorial Keys to Some Arthropods and Mammals of Public Health Importance. U.S. Dept. HEW, CDC Atlanta, Ga., 1964.

Pratt, Harry D., Littig, Kent S., and Marshall, Clarence W.: *Introduction to Arthropods of Public Health Importance*. U.S. Dept. HEW, CDC, Atlanta, Ga., 1960.

Schliessman, Donald J.: *Aedes aegypti* Eradication Program of the United States, Progress Report, 1965, *Amer. J. Public Health*, **57**:460, March, 1967.

BUBONIC PLAGUE

Defoe, Daniel: *A Journal of the Plague Year*. New American Library, New York, 1960.

Kartman, Leo, Goldenberg, Martin I., and Hubbert, William T.: Recent Observations on the Epidemiology of Plague in the United States, *Amer. J. Public Health*, **56**:1554, Sept., 1966.

Langer, William L.: The Black Death, *Sci. Amer.*, **210**:114, Feb., 1964.

Leasor, James: *The Plague and the Fire*. McGraw-Hill Book Co., New York, 1961.

Nohl, Johannes: *The Black Death*. Ballantine Books, New York, 1960.

Slaughter, Frank G.: *Epidemic!* Permabook, New York, 1962.

Styler, Herman: Pale Horseman, in *Plague Fighters*. Chilton Co., Philadelphia and New York, 1960.

Wedgewood, C. V.: When Black Death Stalked in London, *The New York Times Magazine*, Sept. 12, 1965.

RICKETTSIAL DISEASES

Roueché, Berton: Alerting Mr. Pomerantz, in *Eleven Blue Men*. Berkeley Medallion, New York, 1965.

Styler, Herman: Destiny Takes a Hand, in *Plague Fighters*. Chilton Co., Philadelphia and New York, 1960.

Woodham-Smith, Cecil: *The Great Hunger*, Chap 10. Harper & Row, New York, 1962.

Wisseman, Charles L., Jr. (ed.): Symposium on the Spotted Fever Group of Rickettsiae, by
  Commission on Rickettsial Diseases Armed Forces Epidemiological Board, *Medical Science
  Publication* #7, 1960.

YELLOW FEVER
Carey, Mathew: A Short Account of the Malignant Fever Lately Prevalent in Philadelphia,
  in Roueché, Berton: *Curiosities of Medicine*. Berkeley Medallion, New York, 1964.
Powell, J. H.: *Bring Out Your Dead*. University of Pennsylvania Press, Philadelphia, 1949.
Styler, Herman: Tropic Graveyard, in *Plague Fighters*. Chilton Co., Philadelphia and New
  York, 1960.

ARBOVIRUS ENCEPHALITIDES
DiSandro, Edith H.: Eastern Viral Encephalitis, *Amer. J. Nurs.*, **60**:507, April, 1960.
Dougherty, William J.: Epidemiology, *Amer. J. Nurs.*, **60**:508, April, 1960.
Editorial: Migratory Birds May Carry Encephalitis Virus, *Amer. J. Nurs.*, **59**:1118, Aug., 1959.

MALARIA
Alvarado, Carlos A., and Bruce-Chwatt, L. J.: Malaria, *Sci. Amer.*, **206**:86, May, 1962.
Bowery Blood? *Time*, April 19, 1963.
Gilmore, C. P.: Malaria Wins Round Two, *The New York Times Magazine*, Sept. 25, 1966.
Malaria in Ethiopia, *World Health*, **13**:39, May/June, 1960.
Styler, Herman: A Vicious Female and He Brought Back Quinine, in *Plague Fighters*. Chilton
  Co., Philadelphia and New York, 1960.
The World Against Malaria, *World Health*, Extra Issue, Undated.
The World Health Organization Program to Rid the World of Malaria, *Amer. J. Nurs.*,
  59:1402, Oct., 1959.

RABIES
Creighton, Helen, and Armington, Sister Catherine: The Bite of a Stray Dog, *Amer. J. Nurs.*,
  7:121, July, 1964.
Humphrey, George, *et al.*: A Fatal Case of Rabies in a Woman Bitten by an Insectivorous Bat,
  Public Health Rep., **75**:317, April, 1960.
Lester, Mary: Rabies in Man, *Amer. J. Nurs.*, **58**:534, April, 1958.
Roueché, Berton: *The Incurable Wound*. B. Berkeley Medallion, New York, 1957.
Steele, James H.: Rabies and Rabies Control, *Amer. J. Nurs.*, **58**:531, April, 1958.

CAT SCRATCH FEVER
Snyder, John N.: Family Outbreak of Cat Scratch Fever, *J.A.M.A.*, **180**:780, June 2, 1962.

TETANUS
Albrecht, Robert M.: Tetanus — The Hidden Hazard, *Health News*, **42**:12, April, 1965.
Braley, Naomi L.: Nurse at Work — The Progress of Plant Wide Tetanus Immunization
  Program, *Amer. Assoc. Industr. Nurses J.*, May, 1965.
Bruton, Mary R.: When Tetanus Struck, *Amer. J. Nurs.*, **65**:107, Oct., 1965.
Cirksena, William J.: Tetanus, *Amer. J. Nurs.*, **62**:65, April, 1962.
Dull, H. Bruce, and Rakich, Jennie: Tetanus Today, *Nurs. Outlook*, **7**:464, Aug., 1959.
Houston, R., and Faust, E.: The Tetanus Problem in the South, *Amer. Assoc. Industr. Nurses J.*,
  8:25, March, 1960.
Roueché, Berton: Pinch of Dust, in *Eleven Blue Men*. Berkeley Medallion, New York, 1965.

GAS GANGRENE
Adams, John G.: Hyperbaric Oxygen Therapy, *Amer. J. Nurs.*, **64**:76, June, 1964.
Brewster: Gas Gangrene Following an IM Injection of Concentrated Liver Extract, *J.A.M.A.*,
  181:10, Sept. 8, 1962.
Eickhoff, Theodore C.: An Outbreak of Surgical Wound Infections Due to *Clostridium
  perfringens*, *Surg. Gynec. Obstet.*, **114**:102, 1962.

Neelon, Virginia J.: Hyperbaric Oxygenation Benefits and Hazards, *Amer. J. Nurs.*, **64**:72, Oct., 1964.

Tolchin, Martin: Patient Rushed to Oxygen Chamber, *The New York Times*, July 28, 1967.

Wound Infections

Hanson, Daniel J.: Intramuscular Injection Injuries and Complications, *Amer. J. Nurs.*, **63**:99, April, 1963.

Streeter, Shirley, Dunn, Helen, and Lepper, Mark: Hospital Infection — A Necessary Risk? *Amer. J. Nurs.*, **67**:526, March, 1967.

Teplitz, C., Davis, D., Mason, A. D., Jr., and Moncrief, J. A.: Pseudomonas Burn Wound Sepsis. I. Pathogenesis of Experimental Pseudomonas Burn Wound Sepsis, *J. Surg. Res.*, **4**:200–16, 1963.

Walker, H. L., Mason, A. D., Jr., and Raulston, C. L.: Surface Infection with *Pseudomonas aeruginosa*, *Ann. Surg.*, **160**:297, 1964.

Prevention and Control of Wound Infections

Cavanagh, Max: Housekeeping and the Operating Room, *Amer. J. Nurs.*, **60**:686, May, 1960.

Colbeck, J. C.: Control of Infections Among Surgical Patients, Chap. 29, *Control of Infections in Hospitals*. American Hospital Association, Chicago, Hospital Monograph Series #12, 1962.

Fitzwater, Janet: Bacteriological Effect of Ultraviolet Light on a Surgical Instrument Table, *Amer. J. Nurs.*, **61**:71, March, 1961.

Garrett, Ellen G.: The Dressing Nurse, *Amer. J. Nurs.*, **61**:57, Jan., 1961.

Kleine, Patricia A.: Isolating Patients with Staphylococcal Infections, *Amer. J. Nurs.*, **65**:102, Jan., 1965.

Laduke, Marjorie Morrill, Hrynus, G. W., Johnston, M. A., Alpert, S., and Levenson, S. M.: Germfree Isolators, *Amer. J. Nurs.*, **67**:72, Jan., 1967.

Operating Room Nursing — Is It Professional Nursing? *Amer. J. Nurs.*, **65**:58, Aug., 1965.

Voda, Anna M., and Withers, Jane E.: Laminar Airflow in the O.R., *Amer. J. Nurs.*, **66**:2454, Nov., 1966.

Wolf, Harold W., Harris, Marvin M., and Hall, Lawrence B.: Open Operating Room Doors and Staphylococcus Aureus, *Hospitals*, **35**:57, March 16, 1961.

General: Maternity and Neonatal Units

Colbeck, J. C.: Control of Infection in Maternity and Neonatal Units, Chap. 5 in *Control of Infection in Hospitals*. American Hospital Association, Chicago, Hospital Monograph Series #12, 1962.

Thomas, Margaret W.: *Aseptic Nursing Techniques, A Survey of Maternity Departments in Thirteen Medical Centers*. U.S. Dept. HEW, Public Health Service, CDC, Atlanta, Ga., 1960.

Puerperal Fever

Holmes, Oliver Wendell: The Contagiousness of Puerperal Fever, in Clendening, Logan: *Source Book of Medical History*. Dover Publications, Inc., New York, 1960.

Semmelweis, Ignaz Philip: The Concept of Childbed Fever, in Clendening, Logan: *Source Book of Medical History*. Dover Publications, Inc., New York, 1960.

Serum Hepatitis

Dull, J. C.: Syringe Transmitted Hepatitis, *J.A.M.A.*, **176**:413, May 6, 1961.

Finlayson, Eleanor: Operation Big Switch, *Nurs. Outlook*, **9**:680, Nov., 1961.

Urinary Tract Infections

MacKinnon, Harold A.: Urinary Drainage: The Problem of Asepsis, *Amer. J. Nurs.*, **65**:112, Aug., 1965.

Santora, Delores: Preventing Hospital-Acquired Urinary Infections, *Amer. J. Nurs.*, **66**: 790, April, 1966.

INFANT DISEASES

Canice, Sister M.: Rotation Plan in the Nurseries, *Amer. J. Nurs.*, **61**:96, Nov., 1961.

Fierer, Joshua, Taylor, Paul M., and Gezon, Horace M.: *Pseudomonas aeroginosa* Epidemic Traced to Delivery Room Resuscitators, *New Eng. J. Med.*, **276**:991, May 4, 1967.

Shaker, Yehia, Aziz, Rauouf, and El Naga, Amal Abu: A Preliminary Study of Infantile Diarrhea in Kuwait, *Amer. J. Public Health*, **56**:1580, Sept., 1966.

Thompson, LaVerne: Nursery Infections: Apparent and Inapparent, *Amer. J. Nurs.*, **65**:80, Nov., 1965.

Wilson, Miriam G., Nelson, R. C., Phillips, L. H., and Boak, R. A.: New Source of *Pseudomonas aeruginosa* in a Nursery, *J.A.M.A.*, **175**:1146, April 1, 1961.

INFECTIOUS MONONUCLEOSIS

Hoagland, Robert J.: Infectious Mononucleosis, *Amer. J. Nurs.*, **64**:125, Oct., 1964.

Appendixes

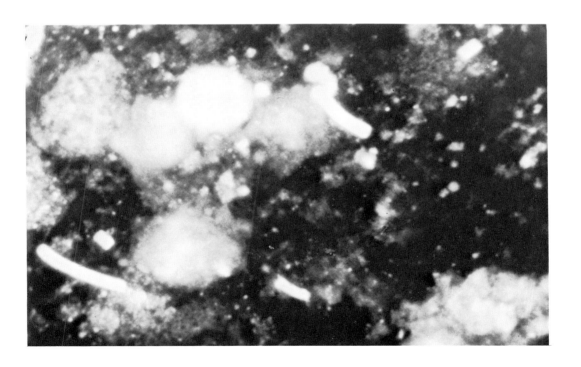

Appendix I

The Pathogenic and Commensalistic Flora of Clinical Specimens

Blood	Wounds	Throat	Feces	Urine
Bacteria	**Bacteria**	**Bacteria**	**Bacteria**	**Bacteria**
Brucella species	*Bacteroides* species	*Bordetella*	*Bacteroides* species	*Escherichia coli*
Diplococcus	*Clostridium*	*pertussis*	*Clostridium* species	and other Gram-
pneumoniae	*perfringens* and	*Corynebacterium*	*Escherichia coli*	negative enteric
Escherichia coli	other species	*diphtheriae* and	and other Gram-	bacilli
and other Gram-	*Escherichia coli*	diphtheroids	negative enteric	*Herellea* species
negative enteric	and other Gram-	*Diplococcus*	bacilli	*Pseudomonas*
bacilli	negative enteric	*pneumoniae*	*Salmonella* species	*aeruginosa*
Francisella	bacilli	*Escherichia coli*	*Shigella* species	*Salmonella* spec
tularensis	*Pseudomonas*	and other Gram-	*Staphylococcus*	*Staphylococcus*
Listeria	species	negative enteric	species	*aureus*
monocytogenes	*Staphylococcus*	bacilli	*Streptococcus*	*Staphylococcus*
Neisseria	*aureus*	*Hemophilus*	*faecalis*	*epidermidis*
meningitidis	*Staphylococcus*	influenzae	*Vibrio comma* Cholerie	*Streptococcus*
Pasteurella pestis	*epidermidis*	*Neisseria*		*faecalis*
and other species	*Streptococcus*	*meningitidis* and	**Higher Bacteria**	*Streptococcus*
Spirillum minus	*faecalis*	other species	*Mycobacterium*	*pyogenes*
Salmonella species	*Streptococcus*	*Staphylococcus*	species	*Streptococcus*
Staphylococcus	*pyogenes*	*aureus*		*viridans*
aureus		*Staphylococcus*	**Fungi**	
Staphylococcus	**Higher Bacteria**	*epidermidis*	*Candida albicans*	**Higher Bacteri**
epidermidis	*Actinomyces*	*Streptococcus*		*Mycobacterium*
Streptobacillus	species	*faecalis*	**Parasites**	species
moniliformis	*Mycobacterium*	*Streptococcus*	Protozoan cysts	
Streptococcus	species	*pyogenes*	or trophozoites	
faecalis	*Nocardia* species	*Streptococcus*	Roundworm adults,	
Streptococcus		*viridans*	larvae, or ova	
pyogenes			Tapeworm strobila,	
Streptococcus		**Higher Bacteria**	scolex, proglottids,	
viridans		*Actinomyces*	or ova	
Vibrio fetus		species	Trematode ova	
Parasites		**Fungi**	**Viruses**	
Microfilariae		*Candida albicans*	Coxsackie viruses	
Plasmodium species			ECHO viruses	
Trypanosoma		**Viruses**	Poliomyelitis virus	
species		Adenoviruses	Infectious hepatitis	
		Coxsackie viruses	virus	
		ECHO viruses		
		Influenza virus		
		Poliomyelitis virus		

ital Tract	**Spinal Fluid**	**Eye**	**Ear**

ria
richia coli
  other Gram-
  tive enteric
li
philus
eyi and
  species
bacillus
ies
eria GC
rrhoeae
ylococcus
us
ylococcus
ermidis
ococcus
ilis
ococcus
enes
ococcus
ans
nema
lum Sophiles

r Bacteria
bacterium
ies

da albicans

ites
monas
nalis

es
nogranuloma
reum

Spinal Fluid

Bacteria
Bacteroides species
Diplococcus
  pneumoniae
Escherichia coli
  and other Gram-
  negative enteric
  bacilli
Hemophilus
  influenzae
Leptospira species
Listeria
  monocytogenes
Neisseria
  meningitidis
Staphylococcus
  aureus
Streptococcus
  pyogenes
Treponema
  pallidum

Higher Bacteria
Mycobacterium
  tuberculosis

Fungi
Cryptococcus
  neoformans

Parasites
Toxoplasma gondii

Viruses
Equine
  encephalitis
  viruses
Poliomyelitis virus

Eye

Bacteria
Corynebacterium
  species
Hemophilus species
Moraxella species
Neisseria
  gonorrhoeae
Pseudomonas
  species
Staphylococcus
  aureus
Staphylococcus
  epidermidis
Streptococcus
  pyogenes
Streptococcus
  viridans

Viruses
Inclusion
  conjunctivitis
  virus
Trachoma virus

Ear

Bacteria
Escherichia coli
  and other Gram-
  negative enteric
  bacilli
Pseudomonas
  aeruginosa
Staphylococcus
  aureus
Staphylococcus
  epidermidis
Streptococcus
  faecalis
Streptococcus
  pyogenes
Streptococcus
  viridans

Fungi
Aspergillus species
  and other molds
Candida albicans
  and other yeasts

Appendix II

Serologic Tests of Diagnostic Value*

Diseases	Antigens	Tests
Bacterial Diseases		
Brucellosis	Heat-killed smooth *Brucella* organisms	Precipitation or agglutination tests
Leptospirosis	Cultured leptospira	Agglutination test
Plague	*Pasteurella pestis* organism	Agglutination test
Primary atypical pneumonia (*Mycoplasma pneumoniae*)	{ Human group O cells { *Mycoplasma* antigen	{ Cold agglutination test { Fluorescent antibody technique or complement-fixation test
Streptococcal infections	Streptolysin O	Anti-streptolysin O titer
Syphilis	{ Cardiolipid extracts	{ Flocculation tests: VDRL, Kline, Kahn, Mazzini { Complement-fixation tests: Kolmer, Wassermann
	Living spirochetes (*Treponema pallidum* strains)	{ TPI, fluorescent antibody techniques (FTA) { Reiter's complement-fixation test
Tularemia	*Franciscella tularensis* organism	Agglutination test
Typhoid fever, paratyphoid fever, and other *Salmonella* infections	H and O antigens obtained from *Salmonella* species	Agglutination test (Widal)
Rickettsial Diseases		
Q fever Rickettsialpox Scrub typhus Spotted fever Typhus fever (epidemic and endemic)	*Proteus* strains	Agglutination test (Weil-Felix)
Viral Diseases		
Viral infections including: Lymphogranuloma venereum Ornithosis Poliomyelitis Psittacosis	Specific virus	Complement-fixation and/or neutralization tests Fluorescent antibody technique
Infectious mononucleosis	Fresh washed sheep red blood cells	Heterophil agglutination test

* Titers are measured in two samples of sera taken during the acute and convalescent stages of the disease, respectively. Diagnosis depends on demonstrating at least a fourfold rise in titer between the first and the later stages of the disease.

Serologic Tests of Diagnostic Value (*Cont.*)

Mycotic Diseases

Blastomycosis	Obtained from the organism *Blastomyces*	Complement-fixation test
Coccidioidomycosis	Obtained from the organism *Coccidioides immitis*	Complement-fixation test
Histoplasmosis	Obtained from the organism *Histoplasma capsulatum*	Complement-fixation test

Parasitic Diseases

Cysticercosis Echinococcosis Trichinosis	Extracts of the parasites	Complement-fixation and/or precipitation tests

Appendix III

Skin Tests of Diagnostic Value

Diseases	Antigen Skin Test	Interpretation
Bacterial Diseases		
Brucellosis	Sterile broth culture filtrate Extract of bacterial nucleoproteins	Careful interpretation is required; serologic test is more specific
Chancroid (Ducrey test)	Treated suspension of *Hemophilus ducreyi*	Positive test indicates previous or current infection
Diphtheria (Schick test)	Active diphtheria toxin and heated toxin for control	Positive test indicates absence of antitoxin and therefore susceptibility
Scarlet fever (Dick test)	Diluted erythrogenic toxin and heated toxin for control	Positive test indicates absence of anti-toxin and therefore susceptibility
Tuberculosis (Tuberculin tests)	Purified protein derivative (PPD)	Positive test indicates previous or current infection.

Heaf
  Mantoux
  Tine
  Vollmer
	Old tuberculin (OT)	Same as above

Viral Diseases		
Cat scratch fever	Treated pus from another active infection	May confirm clinical diagnosis
Herpes simplex	Soluble antigen from growing virus	Positive result indicates previous or current infection
Lymphogranuloma Frei test	Virus suspension	Positive result indicates previous or current infection of LGV-trachoma group viruses
Mumps	Mumps vaccine	Negative test identifies susceptible individual
Mycotic Diseases		
Blastomycosis	Concentrate of broth culture filtrates	Cross-reactions frequently occur with these fungal antigens in systemic mycotic disease; positive skin tests may be obtained in persons who have had previous subclinical or clinical infections, or who have current active disease
Coccidioidomycosis	Same as above	
Histoplasmosis	Same as above	
Parasitic Diseases		
Echinococcosis	Inactivated hydatid fluid	Positive skin test indicates infection
Toxoplasmosis	Suspension of killed organisms	Positive test indicates previous or current infection
Trichinosis	Antigens extracted from parasite	Positive test indicates previous or current infection

Appendix IV

Transmission and Tissue Localization of Important Parasites of Man

Type I. Cycle Is Maintained Without Intermediate or Alternate Hosts

Transmission	Parasite	Infective Stage for Man	Entry Portal for Man	Location of Adult in Man	Location of Intermediate Stage (Larvae) in Man
A. Protozoa					
1. Via *fecally* contaminated water and food	*Endamoeba histolytica*	Amoebic cyst	Mouth	Large intestines	Large intestine
B. Roundworms					
1. Via *fecal* contamination of fingers, toys, clothes	*Enterobius vermicularis*	Helminth egg	Mouth	Large intestines	Perianal skin
2. Via *soil* contamination of fingers, foods, toys, clothes	*Trichuris trichiura*	Helminth egg	Mouth	Intestines	
3. Via *soil* contamination	*Ascaris lumbricoides*	Helminth egg	Mouth	Large intestines	Lungs
4. Penetration of skin by larvae in *soil*	*Necator americanus* and other hookworms	Helminth larvae	Skin	Small intestines	Lungs

Type II. Cycle Is Maintained by Alternate Hosts

Transmission	Parasite	Infective Stage for Man	Entry Portal for Man	Location of Adult in Man	Location of Intermediate Stage (Larvae) in Man
A. Via larvae-infected pork meat inadequately cooked	*Trichinella spiralis*	Larvae encysted in pork muscle	Mouth	Intestinal mucosa	Muscle fibers

649

Transmission and Tissue Localization of Important Parasites of Man (Cont.)

Transmission	Parasite	Infective Stage for Man	Entry Portal for Man	Location of Adult in Man	Location of Intermediate Stage (Larvae) in Man
Type III. Cycle Is Maintained by Biting or Blood-Sucking Insects (Adult and Intermediate Stages of Parasites Develop Sequentially in Insect and Animal Hosts)					
A. Protozoa					
1. Mosquito (definitive host) bites man (intermediate host)	*Plasmodium vivax* and other species	Sporozoite (developed in mosquito)	Skin	Not in man Sexual stage in mosquito host (salivary glands)	Asexual stage in red blood cells of man
2. Bite of tsetse fly	*Trypanosoma*	Trypanosomes	Skin	Blood and tissues (especially CNS)	Not in man; occurs in tsetse fly
3. Bite of sandfly	*Leishmania*	Flagellated forms	Skin	Not in man; flagellates develop in insect vector	Nonmotile intracellular forms in reticulo-endothelial cells
B. Tissue worms					
1. Mosquito (intermediate host) bites man (definitive host)	*Wuchereria bancrofti* (filarial roundworm)	Mature larvae	Skin	Lymphatics	Microfilarias in circulating blood
Type IV. Cycle Is Maintained by One Definitive Host and One or More Intermediate Hosts					
A. Tapeworms					
1. Ingestion of larvae-infected pork (intermediate host)	*Taenia solium*	Larvae	Mouth	Intestines (man a definitive host)	Not in man; occurs in skeletal muscle of pigs
2. Ingestion of larvae-infected beef	*Taenia saginata*	Larvae	Mouth	Intestines (man a definitive host)	Not in man; occurs in skeletal muscle of beef

650

...infected fish (intermediate host)	...*latum*				...second intermediate hosts are the "water flea" (or copepod) and fish, respectively
4. Man (or sheep) ingests eggs derived from adult worm in intestines of dog (dog eats larvae in infected sheep tissues)	*Echinococcus granulosis*	Egg	Mouth	Not in man; occurs in intestines of dog	In man and sheep, capillary filter beds of various organs, especially liver
B. Blood flukes					
Man (definitive host) swimming or washing in waters infested with cercariae	*Schistosoma japonicum S. mansoni S. haematobium*	Cercariae (larval stage) free swimming in water re-leased from intermediate snail host	Skin or mucosa	Mesenteric vein in large intestines, liver, pelvis	Not in man; occurs in snail
Man (definitive host) ingests marine animals, fish, or plants containing encysted larvae	*Clonorchis sinensis*	Larvae	Mouth	Liver and bile ducts	Not in man; occurs in aquatic animals: Snail and fishes
	Fasciolopsis buski	Larvae	Mouth	Intestinal wall	Snail and water plants
	Paragonimus westermani	Larvae	Mouth	Lung	Snail and crayfish

651

Appendix V

Clean areas	Hospital areas that must be kept free of contamination include nurses' stations, treatment rooms, hallways, closets, kitchens
Contaminated areas	Contaminated areas include patient's units and their contents, floors, sinks, hoppers, toilets, waste containers, and utility rooms or areas where contaminated articles are cleaned prior to sterilization or disinfection
Hands	The basic technique of hand-washing should be performed whenever hands have been soiled or contaminated; soap, water, and friction applied to dorsal and palmar surfaces of hands and interdigital spaces remove transient microorganisms
Gowns	An ample supply of gowns should be available so that each gown can be discarded after a single use
Masks	Recommended in highly communicable diseases such as tuberculosis, smallpox, staphylococcal pneumonia, pneumonic plague, measles, and chickenpox, and in special areas such as the operating room and the delivery room
Waste materials	Refuse containers with plastic bag liners provide a safe place for contaminated articles such as soiled dressings and paper tissues; when collected they are secured at the top to avoid spillage and the distribution of microbes in the air; these plastic bags are easily transported to the incinerator, but care must be taken to avoid ripping or penetrating them by rough handling or sharp objects within them (needles)
Body wastes	Where adequate sewage systems are available, body wastes can be disposed of without special treatment; if sewage systems are not available, chemical disinfection with 3–5% Lysol for 1 hour is necessary
Oral and nasal secretions	Paper tissues, paper bags, and covered sputum cups should be provided for patients with instructions in their use and disposal; these articles should be collected frequently and placed in a covered refuse container; the contents of these containers should be burned
Dressings	Contaminated wound and surgical dressings should be handled carefully and placed in waxed bags for disposal and burning
Linen	Careful removal and placing of soiled linen into linen hampers near the patient's bed will reduce air contamination; linen from infectious patients should be bagged and tagged for precaution technique before sending to laundry to protect laundry workers; linen from patients with gas gangrene or anthrax is autoclaved for 45 minutes at 121° C to kill spores before being sent to the laundry
Dishes	Dishes from all patients are washed in mechanical dishwashers with hot water at 120°–140° F, rinsed at 170° F and air-dried; dishes from infectious patients are placed in paper bags, scraped in the utility room, and washed as described

Aseptic Nursing Precautions (*Cont.*)

Water and ice supplies	The patient's carafe is washed and sanitized at least once daily with boiling water or steam for $\frac{1}{2}$ minute or hot water at 170° F for 2 minutes; marking the patient's carafe with a wax pencil will ensure its return to the proper patient when fresh water is again distributed; the ice scoop and ice bucket are also sanitized daily; periodic bacteriologic testing of the ice-making machine and ice containers is necessary to ascertain their cleanliness and safety
Utensils	Bedpans, emesis basins, washbasins, cups, and soap dishes are washed with hot soapy water, rinsed, and autoclaved for 15 minutes unwrapped
Thermometers	See Appendix VII
Furniture	Detergent, water, and disinfectant should be used for concurrent and terminal disinfection (see Chap. 10, p. 205)
Walls and floors	Rooms are aired as long as possible after discharge of the patient; walls and floors are cleaned using disinfectants (see Appendix VII)

Appendix VI

Sterilization Methods

Article	Autoclave		Hot Air	Chemicals
Temperature	121° C 250° F	132° C 270° F	160° C 320° F	
Pressure	15 lb	30 lb		
	Minutes	Minutes	Minutes	
Anesthesia equipment				
Airways, plastic				x
GOE masks				x
Intratracheal catheters				x
Accordian tubings				x
Bags				x
Laryngoscopes				x
Bottles, formula, inverted unwrapped	15			
Brushes, in dispensers, in cans or individually wrapped	30	10		
Catheters, shellac, web, and hard rubber				x
Cystoscopes				x
Diapers	30	10		
Dressings, wrapped in paper or muslin	30	10		
Dressings, in canisters (on sides)	30	10		
Endoscopes				x

Flasked solutions   75–250 ml.
                   500–1000 ml.
                   1500–2000 ml.
	20
	30
	45			

Instruments, cutting edge			60	
Instruments, metal only	15	3	60	
Instruments, metal combined with other material	15			
Instruments, metal only in covered and/or padded tray	15	3		
Instruments, metal combined with other material in covered and/or padded tray	20	10		
Instruments wrapped in double-thickness muslin	20	10		
Laryngoscopes				x
Linen packs, 12 × 12 × 20" or less	30			

Appendix VII

Appendix VII

Appendix VII

e packs on side in autoclave

e cover open at lower edge to permit drainage of air from canister and replacement by steam

Appendix VII

slow exhaust to avoid ebullition of liquid

uments must be clean and free of oil and grease; avoid dense packing

e as above

e as above

e as above

e as above

Appendix VII

s should not be larger than $12 \times 12 \times 20''$ and should not be tightly packed; steam cannot penetrate
se packages; place pack on side

Sterilization Methods (*Cont.*)

Article	Autoclave		Hot Air	Chemicals
Temperature	121° C 250° F	132° C 270° F	160° C 320° F	
Pressure	15 lb	30 lb		
	Minutes	Minutes	Minutes	
Maternity packs	30			
Needles, Luer, individually packaged in glass tubes or paper (lumen moist)	30	10	120	
Needles, unwrapped (lumen moist)	15	3		
Needles, suture			60	
Oils, various (1-oz quantity)			120	
Plastic materials	See manufacturers' instructions			
Rubber gloves, wrapped in muslin or paper	20			
Rubber catheters, tubing drains, individually packaged in paper or muslin	20			
Rubber catheters, drains, etc., unwrapped	20	10		
Scalpel blades	30	10		
Sigmoidoscopes				x
Surgical packs	30			
Syringes, unassembled, individually packaged in muslin or paper	30	10	60	
Syringes, unassembled, unwrapped	15	3	60	
Treatment trays, wrapped in muslin or paper	30	10		
Utensils, unwrapped	15	3		

Special Considerations

pack on side in autoclave

thoroughly; rinse with distilled water so lumen remains moist at time of sterilization

as above

plastics can be autoclaved; chemicals can be used on others

gloves loosely; sterilize alone, not with other bulky objects; place packs on edge in autoclave

by syringing with water so lumen remains moist at time of sterilization

ppendix VII

pack on side in autoclave

e assembled in hot-air sterilizers

as above

on side in autoclave; do not use high temperature if rubber goods are included in pack

t nest together; separate with layer of muslin

Appendix VII

Recommendations for Chemical Disinfection of Medical and Surgical Materials[*][†]

Earle H. Spaulding, Ph.D.

Professor and Chairman,
Department of Microbiology
Temple University Medical Center, Philadelphia

We have evaluated only a small proportion of the total number of proprietary and nonproprietary liquid germicides available. The ones named here gave the best results in laboratory and/or hospital tests. Many others may be satisfactory for certain purposes.

Which germicidal solution to use and how to use it is influenced both by the types of microorganisms to be destroyed and the nature of the material to be disinfected. For the purposes of disinfection bacteria fall into three types: (a) ordinary (vegetative) bacteria such as staphylococci; (b) tubercle bacilli; and (c) spores. *Provided prior cleansing is thorough*, satisfactory disinfection can be obtained as follows:

I. Vegetative Bacteria and Fungi

A. General Comment. Many germicides are satisfactory. Some of them are

    1. 80 to 90% *ethyl* or *isopropyl alcohol*

* Updated version of material appearing in *J. Hosp. Res.*, **3**:20, 1965. Courtesy of Dr. Earle H. Spaulding and American Sterilizer Company (Erie, Pa.).

† The large number of tests upon which these recommendations are based were carried out by several assistants, especially Mrs. Eilen Emmons. I also acknowledge the valuable assistance of Mildred L. Guzara, R.N., B.S., Supervisor of Operating Rooms, Temple University Medical Center; and of (Mrs.) Vernita Cantlin, R.N., M.S.

2. strong *formaldehyde-alcohol solutions* of the Bard-Parker Germicide type

3. cationic quaternary ammonium solutions such as *Zephiran*, 1 : 500 aqueous

4. 1% phenolic germicides or germicide-detergents such as **Amphyl**, Tergisyl, O-syl, San Pheno X, and Staphene, or

5. 2% Di-crobe, and Vesphene

6. iodophors such as *Hi-Sine*, *Ioclide*, *Virac*, and Wescodyne, 75 ppm available iodine

7. 2% activated glutaraldehyde, aqueous (Cidex)

B. Smooth, Hard-Surfaced Objects. 5 minutes' exposure to any of the solutions in I, A. If the object is metal, add 0.2% sodium nitrite to solutions in italics, and 0.5% sodium bicarbonate to solutions in boldface to prevent rusting.

C. Rubber Tubing, "Shellac," and "Web" Catheters. Flush by syringing with solution I, A, 3, 4, 6, or 7, and immerse in the same solution for 10 minutes. Follow by a sterile water flush and rinse.

D. Polyethylene Tubing. Same as I, C. Solutions I, A, 1 and 2 are very satisfactory if tubing is clean.

E. Lensed Instruments. Cleanse and immerse for 5 minutes in I, A, 7. Rinse with sterile water.

F. Hypodermic Needles and Syringes. Until more is known about the chemical resistance of the hepatitis viruses the only safe method is heat sterilization.

G. Hinged Instruments. Cleansing must be particularly thorough. Then immerse for 20 minutes in any of the solutions in I, A, except 5. See I, B, for comment on rust prevention.

H. Floors and Walls. A disinfectant is no substitute for soap and water. Use one of the phenolic germicide-cleansers in I, A, 5 or a good detergent scrub followed by a I, A, 4 solution.

I. Furniture and Plastic Bedding Covers. Use one of the solutions in I, A, 4 or 6.

II. Organisms in I, Plus Tubercle Bacillus

A. General Comment. The "quats" should not be used; and the concentration of phenolic or iodophor is increased:

1. 80 to 90% ethyl or isopropyl alcohol

2. strong formaldehyde-alcohol solutions of the Bard-Parker Germicide type

3. the phenolic germicides in I, A, 4, in 2% final concentration

4. the phenolics in I, A, 5, in 3% final concentration

5. a strong concentration (450 ppm of available iodine) of one of the iodophors in I, A, 6

6. 2% activated glutaraldehyde

B. Smooth, Hard-Surfaced Objects. 2 minutes' exposure to II, A, 1 or 2; 5 minutes' to II, A, 6; 10 minutes' for the other solutions in II, A.

C. Rubber Tubing, "Shellac," and "Web" Catheters. Flush by syringing with II, A, 3, 5, or 6. Then immerse in same solution for 5 minutes (6) or for 10 minutes (3 or 5). Rinse and flush thoroughly with sterile water.

D. Polyethylene Tubing. Use II, A, 6, as in II, C. OR flush by syringing with II, A, 3, or 5 and then with water; follow with a II, A, 1, or 2 flush and immerse for 2 minutes.

E. Lensed Instruments. Cleanse and immerse in II, A, 6.

F. Hypodermic Needles and Syringes. See I, F.

G. Hinged Instruments. Cleansing must be particularly thorough. Then immerse for 20 minutes in II, A, 1, 2, 3, 5, or 6. See I, B, for comment on rust prevention.

H. Floors and Walls. Thorough cleansing with II, A, 4.

I. Furniture and Plastic Bedding Covers. Use II, A, 3 or 5.

III. Organisms in I and II Plus Spores

A. General Comment. The following germicides qualify as useful sporicides
1. strong formalin-alcohol solutions of the Bard-Parker Germicide type
2. 2% activated glutaraldehyde (Cidex)
3. boiling 3% O-syl, San Pheno X or Staphene

B. Smooth, Hard-Surfaced Objects. At least 3 hours' exposure to III, A, 1 or 2.

C. Rubber Tubing, "Shellac," and "Web" Catheters. Flush with and immerse in solution III, A, 2, for at least 3 hours.

D. Polyethylene Tubing. Same as II, D, except for immersion of at least 3 hours.

E. Lensed Instruments. Use III, A, 2, for 3 hours.

F. Hypodermic Needles and Syringes. See I, F.

G. Hinged Instruments. Cleansing must be particularly thorough. Then immerse in III, A, 1 or 2. See I, B, for comment on rust prevention.

H. Floors, Walls, Furniture, etc. The sporicides in III, A, are not applicable. Therefore, spores must be removed mechanically by thorough cleansing.

Viruses*

Use 10 minutes' exposure to 80 to 90 per cent by volume ethyl alcohol, formaldehyde-alcohol solution of the Bard-Parker Germicide type, 2% glutaraldehyde (Cidex), or an iodophor at 150 ppm or more available iodine. *Note:* All articles which may carry hepatitis virus should be heat sterilized. The resistance of the human hepatitis viruses to chemical disinfection is not known.

Supplementary Recommendations

Transfer Forceps.   Solution I, A, 2 or 7.

Contaminated Cases

Instruments.   Soak in a solution in I, A, 3, 4, 5, 6, or 7 for 10 minutes. Cleanse sharps and follow procedure in III, B. Autoclave everything else that can be sterilized this way.

Furniture, Floors, etc.   See I, H.

Oral Thermometers.   Wash with soap and water; wipe dry and store in 80 to 90% ethyl alcohol containing 0.2% iodine.

Anesthesia Apparatus.   Immerse in or wipe with solution I, A, 1 or 7.

Complex Heat-Labile Items (e.g., Heart-lung Oxygenator Parts). Ethylene oxide, 850 mg/liter, for at least 8 hours.

---

* Based upon the tests and opinions of Dr. Morton Klein, Department of Microbiology, Temple University Health Sciences Center, Philadelphia.

Appendix VIII

The Bacteriologic Control
of Sterilizing Equipment

Purpose

It is essential that all sterilizing equipment (autoclave, gas and oven sterilizers) be operated correctly, maintained in good working order, and checked regularly, at *monthly intervals*, for bacteriologic safety.

Review of Principles of Sterilization by Heat or Gas

Sterilization by *steam* under pressure in an autoclave, by *hot air* in an oven, or by *gas* such as ethylene oxide is a function of the *agent* in use operating, under proper conditions for its action, for a period of *time* sufficient to kill all forms of microbial life, including spores.

The Sterilizing Agent and Time

Within the sterilizer, the agent (whether it is steam, hot air, or gas) must be fully effective at every point, for every item, for the necessary time, if the entire load is to be sterilized. This means that:

1. In an *autoclave*, steam at the correct temperature and pressure must replace *all* air and penetrate every pack or item. Under most circumstances autoclaving is done at 250° F (121° C)

and 15 to 18 lb pressure. In operating rooms where fast sterilization of instruments is required, autoclaves are often set for 270° F (132° C) and 27 to 30 lb pressure. The time for which the temperature and pressure must be maintained depends on the size, nature, and arrangement of the largest, thickest items in the load as well as on the size and contents of the whole load. At 250° F sterilization may require from 15 minutes (minimum for *any* load) to 45 minutes. At 270° F sterilization can be achieved in from three to ten minutes depending on the load, wrapping methods, and so forth.

2. In an *oven*, hot air at a sterilizing temperature must circulate freely, so that all surfaces of every item will be heated evenly to this temperature. The heat stability of items in the load, as well as practical considerations of the time involved, are factors in choosing the temperature. The lower the temperature, the longer the time required for sterilization, provided the load does not overcrowd the oven. The two methods most commonly used for oven sterilization are: 320° F (160° C) for two hours, or 356° F (180° C) for one hour. At temperatures below 320° F the longer time required is usually impractical, while temperatures above 356° F become destructive to materials to be sterilized.

3. In a *gas* sterilizer, air is replaced by gas, which must be provided in adequate concentration at a temperature and pressure required for full penetration of every item in the load. The time under these conditions then depends on the nature of the load. When clean materials, relatively free from contamination, are sterilized in this way, a uniform method can be used for each load, arranged in a standard way. The gas is applied at 46° to 54° F (115° to 130° C), 25 to 28 lb pressure, for a period of four hours.

The Load

Uniform and standard methods should be applied to the preparation of each item to be sterilized, in any type of equipment, and to its final position in the total load.

1. Individual packs of any kind should not be made so large, thick, or bulky that the sterilizing agent cannot penetrate them easily.

2. When an autoclave or gas sterilizer is used, each item (particularly *vessels* of any kind including syringe barrels) must be wrapped and placed in such a way as to permit the free replacement of air within the pack (or the vessel) by the sterilizing agent (steam or gas).

3. Items loaded together into the sterilizer must be placed in relation to each other, in such a way as to permit the sterilizing agent to do its work. In an autoclave, air must be able to pass down freely between each item (no trapped air pockets!) and out the air discharge line at the bottom front, and steam must be able to penetrate each item fully. In an oven, hot air freely circulating among and between all items of the load is essential. In a gas sterilizer, air replacement and gas penetration are required.

4. The nature and size of the load must determine the sterilizing agent to use and the total time required. Time is particularly critical when an autoclave is used, as pointed out above.

The Sterilizer and the Operator

The mechanical efficiency of the sterilizer, including any automatic controls it may have, is an obvious factor in the success of sterilizing procedures. The operator in charge, however, bears the final responsibility for the outcome, and this person should be familiar with the mechanical functions of the equipment, as well as with the principles and methods discussed above, particularly so that failures can be recognized immediately. Prompt recognition of trouble depends on the alertness of those operating the equipment.

In the case of autoclaves with automatic controls, the following points are of particular importance:

1. The timer is a clock, and, therefore, its ability to keep accurate time (assuring a full period at *sterilizing* temperature) should be checked frequently by visual observation with reference to another reliable clock.

2. The timer is set in motion by a thermostatic valve, which should respond only when the temperature has reached a sterilizing level, not before. This can and should be checked frequently by observing the thermometer reading at the moment the timer begins to operate. *Timing should not begin until the temperature has reached at least 248° F (120° C).*

3. The air discharge line, located just inside the door at the bottom front, *must never be occluded*, either by an item in the load or by accumulated lint and debris. The strainer placed in the opening of this line can easily be examined, and removed, if necessary, by unscrewing its holder. It should be kept *clean and free of obstruction* at all times.

4. Any unusual lag in the time required for steam pressure to build, and sterilizing temperature (350° F) to be reached, or for the timer to begin, should be reported promptly to the maintenance department, as should any other irregularities in performance of the autoclave or its automatic controls.

Bacteriologic Testing of Sterilizing Equipment

It must be remembered that the results of a bacteriologic test reflect only the particular conditions existing in the sterilizer *at the time the test was made.* A test may indicate that sterilization was accomplished for *that* load, under the conditions provided, but it does not, and *cannot*, provide security for any other load at any other time. Such security depends on the careful standardization of all techniques involved in sterilization and the maintenance of these standards by constant supervision of, and attention to, every necessary detail.

Monthly bacteriologic controls should be used in such a way as to provide a check on each of the various factors involved in sterilization, i.e.,

Methods of packing or wrapping individual items

Methods of loading items together in the sterilizer

The time and temperature used for the load

The mechanical efficiency of the sterilizer

When properly performed, bacteriologic testing provides information about each of these factors *but only in regard to the specific load tested, and no other load.*

Test Material

One satisfactory test material for *autoclaves* is a living suspension of heat-resistant bacterial spores (*B. stearothermophilus*), contained in a sealed glass ampule (Baltimore Biological Laboratory, "Kilit Autoclave Control"). Each ampule may be placed in a glass tube with a cotton pad in the bottom and a cotton plug in the mouth, or in a paper envelope, to provide space for labeling. A label on the tube or envelope provides space for recording the necessary identification of each ampule according to its position in the autoclave.

From one to four ampules may be required to test one autoclave, depending on the capacity of the autoclave, as follows:

Small table model	One ampule
Floor models with one tray	Three ampules
Floor or wall models with two trays	Four ampules

Gas and *electric oven* sterilizers, as well as *autoclaves*, can be tested with living spores dried on paper strips (American Sterilizer Company, "Spordex" strips). These dry strips are sealed in glassine envelopes, packaged in a larger envelope on which the manufacturer has printed instructions for their use. Each envelope must be carefully labeled and identified when the strips are used for sterilizer testing.

Method for Using the Test Material

The purpose of using living bacterial spores of high heat resistance is to determine whether enough heat is provided, for a sufficient period of time, to kill them under the conditions prevailing within the sterilizer at the time of the test. The following rules apply to the use of test ampules or strips:

1. Do *not keep* ampules containing suspensions at room temperature for more than one hour.

2. While items for the load to be tested are being prepared for sterilization, select one for each of the ampules or strips to be included in the test. (See rule 13 below for very small or unwrapped items.) Make these selections representative of different items and different types of wrapping or packing methods, whenever possible. Change these selections, if possible, from month to month so that in time all wrapping methods can be checked. Make a point of including an ampule in at least one of the largest, thickest, or tightest packs.

3. Place the tube containing the ampule or strip *on its side* with the item or items to be wrapped in the chosen pack.

4. If a tube has been used, REMOVE ITS COTTON PLUG.

5. Write heavily on the label the following information, using a no. 2 lead pencil: (a) sterilizer number, (b) type of pack in which test material was wrapped, (c) its final position in the sterilizer.

6. Complete the wrapping of the package in the normal way.

7. Position the packs containing the test material in the load so that different areas within the sterilizer will be tested. If a tube is used, REMEMBER TO PLACE THE PACK SO THAT THE TUBE REMAINS IN A HORIZONTAL POSITION.

8. For AUTOCLAVE testing, one of the test packs MUST be positioned in the bottom front, as close as the tray permits to the air discharge line. (This is the coolest part of the chamber.) Other test packs should be placed to check the middle of the load, the back, or the top, depending on the total size of the load or the capacity of the autoclave.

9. Make a note for each *ampule* or *strip* of its final position in the load.

10. Run the sterilizer by the method normally used for the load being tested.

11. When the load is removed from the sterilizer, remove the tubes from the test packs (these will have to be resterilized before use, of course), and replace the cotton plug in the mouth of the tube.

12. Return the tubes as promptly as possible to the laboratory.

13. If unwrapped instruments or small items are being autoclaved, the tube or envelope containing the ampule may be laid on its side (REMOVE THE COTTON PLUG) among them without wrapping. Place one ampule at the front of the bottom tray, others at different locations as described above. For small table-model autoclaves one ampule placed in the front is sufficient for testing.

Labeling

The labeling should clearly indicate the position of the test material in the pack and in the autoclave, so results can be interpreted intelligently.

Results of Bacteriologic Testing

Not only does *B. stearothermophilus* produce heat-resistant spores that provide a critical test of sterilizing conditions, it is also a *thermophilic* organism, requiring a higher temperature of incubation for its growth than do most commensalistic or pathogenic bacteria. Incubation at 56° C must be provided, either in a water bath or an incubator.

If the test material is contained in a sealed glass ampule, the latter may be placed in a 56° C environment and observed daily for evidence of growth of the organisms, as shown by a developing turbidity and a change in the color of the indicator incorporated in the suspension. A positive result may be reported without the necessity of opening the ampule.

If the test material is contained on a paper strip, the glassine envelope that protects the strip from extraneous contamination must be opened in the laboratory with strict aseptic technique. The strip is removed from its envelope, placed in a tube of appropriate growth medium, and in-

cubated at 56° C. If the tube shows evidence of growth, smears must be made to determine whether the culture contains organisms resembling those impregnated on the strip and to rule out the possibility of irrelevant contamination. Culture confirmation of a positive result may also be necessary when doubt exists.

A *negative* culture result reported by the laboratory (cultures are incubated for seven days), with a positive unheated control noted, indicates that the test spores were killed in the sterilizer. If all ampules or strips used in the test are negative, it is reasonable to assume that all other organisms present in the load were also killed and that the test provided the conditions necessary for sterilization.

A *positive* result indicates that the test spores were *not* killed, and one or more of the following possibilities exist:

1. The glass tube with the test material was not placed in the sterilizer correctly.

2. The packaged item containing the test material was not wrapped or placed correctly in the sterilizer.

3. The total load in the sterilizer was incorrectly arranged.

4. If the sterilizer is an autoclave, the air discharge line (just inside the door, bottom front) may be occluded so that air in the autoclave cannot be fully replaced by steam under pressure. Check the strainer in this line for lint and debris.

5. A functional defect in the sterilizer exists that prevents the development and/or the maintenance of the proper temperature for the full period required for sterilization.

When a positive result is reported, items 1 through 4 above should first be checked by the nurse in charge, with consultation and repeat testing furnished by the microbiology laboratory. If a functional defect is suspected, the maintenance department should be called upon at once to correct it. Negative culture results must be obtained on a recheck before the sterilizer can be used again.

Index

Page numbers in **boldface** refer to illustrations.

Abscess formation, 129
Acari, 302
Acetobacter, 48
Acetone as a preservative, 233, 378
Acid-fast bacilli. *See Mycobacterium tuberculosis*, morphology and staining
Acid-fast stain. *See* Microscopic examination techniques
Acne, 512, 630
Actinomyces, antibiotics effective for, 250, 411
  bite wound infections, 597
  diseases caused by. *See* Actinomycosis
  species indigenous to the human body, 96, 395, 406, 632
  species of medical importance, *bovis*, 296, 394, 406, 410–11
    israeli, 296, 406, 410–11, 613
  sulphur granule, **406**
  surgical wound infections, 613
Actinomycetaceae, 296
Actinomycetales, 290, 295–96, 394
Actinomycosis, 182, 250, 296, 394, 397, **406**, 410–11, 613, 633
Acute infectious disease — stages, 157–60
  acute phase, 158–59
  convalescent phase, 159–60
  incubation period, 157
  prodromal period, 157
Adenoviruses. *See* Virus(es), species of medical importance
Adrenal hormones, suppressive effect on resistance mechanisms, 130
Aedes mosquito as vector, dengue fever, 573
  yellow fever, 571
Aeration, in purification of water, 265
Aerobacter aerogenes, 250, 292
Aerobic bacteria, 46
Aerosol disinfection, 231
African sleeping sickness. *See* Trypanosomiasis
African trypanosomiasis. *See* Trypanosomiasis
Agar media, 68–69. *See also* Culture media
Age in resistance to infection, 129–30
Agglutination reaction, principle, 137
Air as a reservoir of infectious disease, 175–76

Air-borne infection, limiting factors, 175
Alastrim. *See* Smallpox
Alcohols, disinfectants, 226–27, 234, 658–60
  microbial production from glucose, 43, **44**
  skin degermation, 224
Algae, 24, 290
Allergens, 147, 151
Allergy. *See* Hypersensitivity
Altered reactivity. *See* Hypersensitivity
Amebiasis, 467–69
  causative organism, **8**, 18–**19**, 300, 467, **468**, 484
  clinical characteristics, 468
    amebic abscesses, 468
  diagnostic methods, 468, 485
  epidemiology, 467–68
    control and prevention, 273, 468–69
    reservoirs, sources, and transmission, 175, 178–79, 180, 182, 467
    treatment, 468–69, 485
  pathogenesis, 104, 105, 468
  summary, 484–85
Amebic abscesses, 468
Amebic dysentery, 468
American leishmaniasis. *See* Leishmaniasis
American Public Health Association, 261, 267
American Red Cross, 261
American trypanosomiasis. *See* Trypanosomiasis
Aminoquinolines, treatment, trypanosomiasis, 582–83
Amodiaquine, treatment, malaria, 578, 587
Amoebae. *See* Protozoa
Amphotericin, treatment, systemic mycoses, 397, 409, 411
Amphyl, 227, 236, 658–60
Ampicillin, **249**, 250, 251
  specified infectious diseases, 250, 251
  formula, **249**
Anaerobic bacteria, 46–47, 71
  cultivation, 71
  facultative, 47
  indigenous to the human body, 93, 94–95, 96, 97
  obligate, 47
Anamnestic response, 143
Anaphylaxis, 149
Ancylostoma braziliense, agent of "creeping eruption," 543, 545. *See also* Hookworm disease